W9-DHT-151

W77-1002

the science of biology

paul b. weisz
professor of biology, brown university

the science of biology

fourth edition

mc graw-hill book company
new york st. louis san francisco düsseldorf johannesburg kuala lumpur london mexico montreal new delhi panama rio de janeiro singapore sydney toronto

the science of biology

Copyright © 1959, 1963, 1967, 1971 by McGraw-Hill, Inc. All rights reserved. Printed in the United States of America. No part of this publication may be reproduced, stored in a retrieval system, or transmitted, in any form or by any means, electronic, mechanical, photocopying, recording, or otherwise, without the prior written permission of the publisher.

Library of Congress Catalog Card Number 74-150467

07-069132-0

6 7 8 9 0 1 2 3 4 5 VHVH 8 5 4 3 2 1 0 7 9 8 7 6

This book was set in Galaxy by York Graphic Services, Inc., and printed and bound by Von Hoffmann Press, Inc.
The designer was Elliot Epstein; the drawings were done by BMA Associates, Inc. The editors were Thomas Adams, Sally Anderson, and Andrea Stryker-Rodda. John F. Harte supervised production.

color photo credits

1. *B,* M. C. Noailles.
2. General Biological Supply House, Inc.
4. R. H. Noailles.
5. *A,* D. P. Wilson. *B,* Dr. Boris Gueft.
7. M. C. Noailles.
10. *A, C,* R. H. Noailles.
11. Eric V. Gravé.
12. General Biological Supply House, Inc.
13. D. P. Wilson.
14. R. H. Noailles.
15. D. P. Wilson.
16. General Biological Supply House, Inc.
17. *A,* D. P. Wilson.
18. *B,* D. P. Wilson. *C,* R. H. Noailles.
19. *A,* R. H. Noailles. *B,* General Biological Supply House, Inc.
20. *B,* Dr. Jonathan Green, Brown University.
22. *A,* D. P. Wilson. *B, D,* Ward's Natural Science Establishment, Inc. *C,* Dr. Jonathan Green, Brown University. *E,* General Biological Supply House, Inc.
26. *A,* R. H. Noailles.
27. R. H. Noailles.
28. R. H. Noailles.
29. General Biological Supply House, Inc.
30. General Biological Supply House, Inc.
31. General Biological Supply House, Inc.
32. General Biological Supply House, Inc.
33. General Biological Supply House, Inc.
34. General Biological Supply House, Inc.

chapter photo credits

2.3 Dr. Norman E. Williams, University of Iowa.
2.4 *A,* American Museum of Natural History; *B,* R. H. Noailles.
2.6 Carolina Biological Supply Company.
2.7 © Walt Disney Productions.

5.1 *A,* Dr. Melvin S. Fuller, University of Georgia; *B,* Eric V. Gravé.
5.2 *A,* Dr. Keith R. Porter, Harvard University; *B,* Drs. D. F. Poulson and C. W. Metz, from fig. 1, *J. Morph.,* vol. 63, p. 366.
5.3 Dr. Keith R. Porter, Harvard University.
5.5 Dr. Robert M. Brenner, Oregon Primate Research Center.
5.6 *A,* Dr. Keith R. Porter, Harvard University; *B,* Dr. H. Fernandez-Moran, University of Chicago, and *J. Cell Biol.,* vol. 22, 1964.
5.7 *A,* Dr. W. G. Whaley, University of Texas; *B,* Dr. Luis Biempica, Albert Einstein College of Medicine, New York.
5.8 Dr. A. J. Hodge, California Institute of Technology, and *J. Biophys. Biochem. Cytol.,* vol. 1, p. 605.
5.9 *A,* Dr. Robert M. Brenner, Oregon Primate Research Center, and *J. Fertility Sterility,* vol. 20, pp. 599–611, 1969; *B,* Dr. Robert M. Brenner.
5.10 *B,* Dr. Melvin S. Fuller, University of Georgia.
5.12 *A,* Dr. Norman E. Williams, University of Iowa; *B,* General Biological Supply House, Inc.
5.13 *B,* Dr. Robert M. Brenner, Oregon Primate Research Center; *C,* Dr. Dorothy R. Pitelka, University of California, Berkeley; *D,* Dr. Norman E. Williams, University of Iowa.
5.14 *A,* Ripon Microslides, Inc.; *B,* Carolina Biological Supply Company.
5.15 *A,* Ward's Natural Science Establishment, Inc.; *B,* Dr. Melvin S. Fuller, University of Georgia.
5.16 Dr. Melvin S. Fuller, University of Georgia.
5.18 *B, C,* Dr. C. J. Hillson, Pennsylvania State University.
5.19 Dr. Melvin S. Fuller, University of Georgia.
5.20 *B, C,* Dr. C. J. Hillson, Pennsylvania State University.
5.21 *C,* General Biological Supply House, Inc.
5.22 *B, C,* Dr. C. J. Hillson, Pennsylvania State University.
5.23 General Biological Supply House, Inc.
5.24 *B,* Eric V. Gravé.
5.25 *A,* General Biological Supply House, Inc.; *B, C,* Dr. B. J. Serber; *D,* Carolina Supply Company.
5.26 *A,* General Biological Supply House, Inc.; *B,* Ward's Natural Science Establishment, Inc.
5.27 *C,* M. C. Noailles.
5.28 *A,* Ward's Natural Science Establishment, Inc.; *B, C,* Carolina Biological Supply Company.
5.29 *A,* Dr. Mac E. Hadley, University of Arizona; *B,* R. H. Noailles; *C,* M. C. Noailles.
5.30 Ward's Natural Science Establishment, Inc.
5.31 M. C. Noailles.
5.32 *B,* Ward's Natural Science Establishment, Inc.

6.2 New York Zoological Society.
6.3 American Museum of Natural History.
6.4 *A,* Standard Oil Company, New Jersey; *B,* Jeanne White, from National Audubon Society.
6.5 *A,* American Museum of Natural History; *B,* Ward's Natural Science Establishment, Inc.; *C,* U.S. Fish and Wildlife Service.
6.14 *A,* S. Dalton, Natural History Photographic Agency; *B,* U.S. Department of Agriculture; *C,* Paul Popper, Ltd.
6.15 R. H. Noailles.
6.16 *A,* Paul Popper, Ltd.; *B,* American Museum of Natural History.
6.17 *A,* Drs. R. M. Herriott and J. L. Barlow, and *J. Gen. Physiol.,* vol. 36, p. 17; *B, C,* Dr. R. W. G. Wyckoff, from "Electron Microscopy," Interscience Publishers, Inc., 1949.
6.18 *A,* Leonard L. Rue; *B,* Armed Forces Institute of Pathology.
6.19 U.S. Department of Agriculture.

7.2 General Biological Supply House, Inc.
7.4 *A, B,* Jean Carel and Larousse Publishing Company; *C, D,* Douglas P. Wilson.
7.5 American Museum of Natural History.
7.6 *A,* U.S. Fish and Wildlife Service; *B, D,* R. H. Noailles; *C,* Clay-Adams Company, Inc.
7.7 *A,* U.S. Department of Agriculture; *B,* © Walt Disney Productions.
7.8 *A,* U.S. Forest Service; *B,* South African Tourist Corporation.
7.9 *A,* U.S. Forest Service; *B,* National Park Service.
7.10 *A,* U.S. Forest Service; *B,* © Walt Disney Productions.
7.11 *A,* U.S. Forest Service; *B,* Leonard L. Rue.
7.12 *A,* U.S. Fish and Wildlife Service; *B,* W. Suschitzky.
7.16 U.S. Department of Agriculture.
7.19 U.S. Department of Agriculture.
7.20 Soil Conservation Service.
7.21 Soil Conservation Service.
7.26 Kit and Max Hunn, John H. Gerard, Maurice E. Landre, from National Audubon Society.
7.27 World Health Organization, United Nations.

8.9 *A,* Society of American Bacteriologists; *B,* Drs. C. F. Robinow and J. Hillier, and Society of American Bacteriologists.
8.10 General Biological Supply House, Inc.
8.11 *A,* Dr. C. F. Robinow, from "The Cell," Academic Press, vol. 4; *B,* Drs. G. Knaysi, R. F. Baker, and J. Hillier, *J. Bacteriol.,* vol. 53, 1947, and Society of American Bacteriologists.
8.13 Dr. Melvin S. Fuller, University of Georgia.

9.6 *A, C,* Dr. Melvin S. Fuller, University of Georgia; *B,* General Biological Supply House, Inc.
9.7 *A, C, D,* Dr. Melvin S. Fuller, University of Georgia; *B,* General Biological Supply House, Inc.
9.8 *A,* Dr. Melvin S. Fuller, University of Georgia; *C,* General Biological Supply House, Inc.
9.9 *B, C,* Dr. Melvin S. Fuller, University of Georgia; *D,* Clay-Adams Company, Inc.
9.10 *B,* Dr. Melvin S. Fuller, University of Georgia.
9.11 *B,* M. Woodbridge Williams.
9.12 *A, C, E,* General Biological Supply House, Inc.; *B,* Jean Carel and Larousse Publishing Company; *D,* Dr. Melvin S. Fuller, University of Georgia.
9.13 *A,* Dr. Melvin S. Fuller, University of Georgia; *B,* Drs. A. J. Shatkin and E. L. Tatum, Rockefeller Institute, and *J. Biophys. Biochem. Cytol.,* vol. 6, p. 423.
9.14 *A, B,* Dr. R. Emerson, University of California, Berkeley, and *Mycologia,* vol. 50, p. 589; *C,* Dr. Charles L. Curry, Pennsylvania State University.
9.15 *A, B,* General Biological Supply House, Inc.; *C, D,* Dr. C. L. Fergus, Pennsylvania State University.
9.16 *A,* Jean Carel; *B,* Dr. Melvin S. Fuller, University of Georgia.
9.17 *A, C,* Dr. Melvin S. Fuller, University of Georgia; *B,* Dr. C. M. Christensen, University of Minnesota, and University of Minnesota Press.
9.18 Dr. Melvin S. Fuller, University of Georgia.
9.20 *C,* Natural History Photographic Agency.
9.21 *B,* Carolina Biological Supply Company; *C,* R. H. Noailles.
9.23 *B,* General Biological Supply House, Inc.; *C,* Eric V. Gravé.
9.24 *B,* Eric V. Gravé.
9.25 *A,* Carolina Biological Supply Company; *B,* Dr. Roman Vishniac.
9.27 *A,* Carolina Biological Supply Company; *B,* Dr. Maria A. Rudzinska, and *J. Gerontol.,* vol. 16, p. 213, 1961.

10.1 *B,* Dr. Melvin S. Fuller, University of Georgia.
10.4 *A,* Dr. C. J. Hillson, Pennsylvania State University.

10.5 Dr. Melvin S. Fuller, University of Georgia.
10.6 *A, B,* U.S. Department of Agriculture; *C,* Brooklyn Botanical Garden.
10.7 Dr. Melvin S. Fuller, University of Georgia.
10.9 Dr. Melvin S. Fuller, University of Georgia.
10.11 *A,* General Biological Supply House, Inc.; *B,* Dr. Melvin S. Fuller, University of Georgia.
10.12 *B,* Dr. Melvin S. Fuller, University of Georgia; *C,* Dr. C. L. Curry, Pennsylvania State University.
10.13 *B,* G. H. Conant, Triarch Products, Inc.; *C,* J. Limbach, Ripon Microslides, Inc.
10.14 *A,* Dr. Melvin S. Fuller, University of Georgia.
10.16 General Biological Supply House, Inc.
10.17 *B,* Brooklyn Botanical Garden.
10.19 Dr. Melvin S. Fuller, University of Georgia.
10.20 J. Limbach, Ripon Microslides, Inc.
10.23 General Biological Supply House, Inc.
10.25 *B,* Dr. Melvin S. Fuller, University of Georgia.
10.26 *A,* Dr. Melvin S. Fuller, University of Georgia; *B,* J. Limbach, Ripon Microslides, Inc.
10.27 *A,* U.S. Forest Service; *B,* General Biological Supply House, Inc.
10.28 Dr. Melvin S. Fuller, University of Georgia.
10.29 *A,* Dr. Melvin S. Fuller, University of Georgia; *B,* Jean Carel and Larousse Publishing Company; *C,* Dr. R. H. Mohlenbrock, University of Southern Illinois, and *Amer. Fern J.,* vol. 50, p. 181.
10.30 *A,* Jean Carel and Larousse Publishing Company; *B,* Dr. Melvin S. Fuller, University of Georgia.
10.31 *A,* Walter H. Hodge; *B,* Dr. Melvin S. Fuller, University of Georgia.
10.32 *A,* Walter H. Hodge; *B,* New York Botanical Garden.
10.33 J. Limbach, Ripon Microslides, Inc.
10.34 *B,* Stan Menscher, McGraw-Hill Book Company. *C,* General Biological Supply House, Inc.
10.35 *A, B,* J. Limbach, Ripon Microslides, Inc.; *C,* General Biological Supply House, Inc.

11.2 *A,* American Museum of Natural History; *B,* U.S. Department of Agriculture; *C,* Ward's Natural Science Establishment, Inc.
11.11 *E,* Carolina Biological Supply Company.
11.12 *A,* M. Woodbridge Williams; *B, C,* American Museum of Natural History.
11.13 Douglas P. Wilson.
11.16 *B,* M. C. Noailles.
11.17 *A, D,* Douglas P. Wilson; *B,* American Museum of Natural History; *C,* Dr. Roman Vishniac.
11.18 *A,* Douglas P. Wilson; *B,* Carolina Biological Supply Company.
11.20 Douglas P. Wilson.
11.22 *A,* General Biological Supply House, Inc.
11.23 *B,* Ward's Natural Science Establishment, Inc.
11.24 General Biological Supply House, Inc.
11.25 *A,* M. C. Noailles.
11.27 *A,* Dr. W. F. Mai, Cornell University; *B,* Carolina Biological Supply Company.
11.28 *A,* Ward's Natural Science Establishment, Inc.; *B,* United Nations.
11.29 *A,* Carolina Biological Supply Company.

12.2 *B,* R. H. Noailles; *C,* General Biological Supply House, Inc.
12.3 *A,* General Biological Supply House, Inc.
12.4 *B,* Douglas P. Wilson.
12.5 *A,* Carolina Biological Supply Company; *C,* Australian News and Information Bureau.
12.7 *A,* American Museum of Natural History.
12.8 *B,* Douglas P. Wilson.
12.10 *A, B,* R. H. Noailles; *C,* Douglas P. Wilson.
12.13 *A,* Carolina Biological Supply Company; *B,* R. H. Noailles; *C,* Paul Popper, Ltd.
12.14 *B,* American Museum of Natural History.
12.16 *A,* R. H. Noailles; *B,* American Museum of Natural History.
12.17 *B,* Douglas P. Wilson.
12.18 *A,* R. H. Noailles.
12.20 American Museum of Natural History.
12.21 *B,* Ward's Natural Science Establishment, Inc.
12.22 *A,* Lynwood M. Chace; *B,* General Biological Supply House, Inc.; *C, D,* Carolina Biological Supply Company.
12.23 U.S. Department of Agriculture.
12.24 *C,* Paul Popper, Ltd.
12.26 *A,* Leonard L. Rue; *B, D,* R. H. Noailles; *C,* Ward's Natural Science Establishment, Inc.; *E,* General Biological Supply House, Inc.; *F,* Lynwood M. Chace.
12.28 *B,* American Museum of Natural History.
12.29 *A,* M. C. Noailles; *B,* Douglas P. Wilson; *C,* R. H. Noailles.
12.30 *A,* E. Leitz, Inc.; *B,* Eric V. Gravé; *C,* American Museum of Natural History; *D,* U.S. Department of Agriculture; *E,* R. H. Noailles; *F,* U.S. Fish and Wildlife Service.
12.31 Carolina Biological Supply Company.
12.32 U.S. Department of Agriculture.
12.33 *A,* Carolina Biological Supply Company; *B,* Eric V. Gravé; *C, F,* Leonard L. Rue and J. Focht; *D,* R. H. Noailles; *E,* U.S. Department of Agriculture.
12.34 *A,* M. C. Noailles; *B,* Lynwood M. Chace; *C, D,* R. H. Noailles; *E,* U.S. Department of Agriculture; *F,* Natural History Photographic Agency.
12.35 *C,* John L. Schumacher; *D,* R. H. Noailles; *E, F,* Carolina Biological Supply Company.
12.36 *A,* Lynwood M. Chace.
12.37 *C,* Ward's Natural Science Establishment, Inc.
12.39 U.S. Department of Agriculture.
12.40 *A,* U.S. Department of Agriculture; *B,* Lynwood M. Chace; *C, D,* R. H. Noailles.

13.1 *A,* Douglas P. Wilson; *C,* American Museum of Natural History.
13.4 *A, B,* Carolina Biological Supply Company; *C,* U.S. Fish and Wildlife Service; *D,* M. Woodbridge Williams.
13.7 Douglas P. Wilson.
13.8 Carolina Biological Supply Company.
13.9 *A,* American Museum of Natural History; *B,* R. H. Noailles.
13.10 *A,* American Museum of Natural History; *B,* Paul A. Knipping; *C,* G. Cripps and Harold V. Green.
13.12 *B,* General Biological Supply House, Inc.; *C,* American Museum of Natural History.
13.13 *A,* Douglas P. Wilson; *B,* Natural History Photographic Agency.
13.14 Douglas P. Wilson.
13.15 Carolina Biological Supply Company.
13.17 Dr. William Montagna, Oregon Regional Primate Research Center.
13.19 Carolina Biological Supply Company.
13.20 *A,* R. H. Noailles; *B,* General Biological Supply House, Inc.
13.21 American Museum of Natural History.
13.22 *A,* R. H. Noailles; *B,* Natural History Photographic Agency.
13.24 *B, C,* Carolina Biological Supply Company.
13.25 *A, B,* Carolina Biological Supply Company; *C,* Dr. Roberts Rugh and Burgess Publishing Company; *D,* Lynwood M. Chace.
13.26 *A,* Carolina Biological Supply Company; *B,* Ward's Natural Science Establishment, Inc.
13.27 *A,* American Museum of Natural History; *B,* Paul Popper, Ltd.
13.28 *A, B,* Australian News and Information Bureau; *C,* Lynwood M. Chace.
13.29 Australian News and Information Bureau.
13.30 American Museum of Natural History.
13.32 *A,* W. Suschitzky; *B,* R. H. Noailles; *C,* Paul Popper, Ltd.

14.7 Dr. K. Esau, from "Plant Anatomy," J. Wiley & Sons, Inc., 1953.
14.12 *A, D,* Dr. B. J. Serber; *B, C,* M. C. Noailles; *E,* General Biological Supply House, Inc.; *F,* Carolina Biological Supply Company.
14.13 Ward's Natural Science Establishment, Inc., from model by Dr. J. F. Mueller.
14.15 Rhode Island Hospital Photographic Department.

17.4 Dr. W. Beerman.
17.9 *A,* Ward's Natural Science Establishment, Inc.; *B,* Dr. Keith R. Porter, Harvard University.
17.14 *B,* Carolina Biological Supply Company.
17.16 *A, B,* Dr. Melvin S. Fuller, University of Georgia; *C,* Dr. William Montagna, Oregon Regional Primate Research Center; *D,* Carolina Biological Supply Company.

18.14 Bureau of Human Nutrition and Home Economics.

19.2 *B,* J. B. Hill, H. W. Popp, and A. R. Grove, Jr., from "Botany," 4th ed., McGraw-Hill Book Company, 1967.
19.3 Drs. S. H. Wittwer and M. J. Bukovac, Michigan State University, and *Econ. Botany,* vol. 12, p. 213.
19.5 Boyce Thompson Institute for Plant Research.
19.9 Dr. Melvin S. Fuller, University of Georgia.
19.10 *A,* Carolina Biological Supply Company; *B, C,* General Biological Supply House, Inc.
19.12 Dr. A. Braun, Rockefeller University.
19.13 *A,* Dr. K. Esau, from "Plant Anatomy," J. Wiley & Sons, Inc., 1953.
19.14 Boyce Thompson Institute for Plant Research.
19.15 Monsanto Chemical Company.
19.19 U.S. Department of Agriculture.
19.21 *A,* Ward's Natural Science Establishment, Inc.
19.22 Ward's Natural Science Establishment, Inc.
19.23 Dr. Robert Brenner, Oregon Regional Primate Research Center.

20.2 General Biological Supply House, Inc.
20.3 Dr. Robert Brenner, Oregon Regional Primate Research Center.
20.4 Dr. Boris Gueft.
20.6 *B*, Dr. B. J. Serber; *C*, General Biological Supply House, Inc.
20.7 *A*, Rhode Island Hospital Photographic Department; *B*, Dr. Boris Gueft.
20.13 Bell Telephone Laboratories, Inc.

21.1 *B*, Ward's Natural Science Establishment, Inc.; *D*, Dr. Jan Cammermeyer, National Institutes of Health, Bethesda, Md., and *Z. Anat. Entwickl.* vol. 124, pp. 543–561, 1965.
21.2 *B*, General Biological Supply House, Inc.
21.3 *C*, Ward's Natural Science Establishment, Inc.
21.4 *C, D*, Rhode Island Hospital Photographic Department.
21.13 Ward's Natural Science Establishment, Inc.
21.14 *A*, General Biological Supply House, Inc.
21.15 *A*, Carolina Biological Supply Company; *B*, Dr. William Montagna, Oregon Regional Primate Research Center.
21.21 *B*, Ward's Natural Science Establishment.
21.27 Ward's Natural Science Establishment.

22.1 Dr. N. Tinbergen.
22.2 Ron Church, Photo Researchers, Inc.
22.3 Ringling Bros. and Barnum & Bailey Circus photo.
22.4 Ringling Bros. and Barnum & Bailey Circus photo.
22.5 Wisconsin Regional Primate Research Center.
22.7 Leonard L. Rue, from the National Audubon Society.
22.10 Stan Mensher, McGraw-Hill, Inc.
22.13 Australian News and Information Bureau.

23.1 U.S. Department of Agriculture.
23.2 U.S. Department of Agriculture.
23.3 © Walt Disney Productions.
23.4 *A, B, C*, U.S. Department of Agriculture; *D*, Buffalo Museum of Science.
23.5 *A*, American Museum of Natural History; *B*, R. H. Noailles.
23.6 *D*, Dr. Phyllis J. Dolhinow, University of California, Berkeley.
23.7 Irven DeVore.
23.8 U.S. Department of Agriculture.
23.9 Jeanne White, from National Audubon Society.
23.10 U.S. Fish and Wildlife Service.
23.11 Dr. N. Tinbergen.

24.2 General Biological Supply House, Inc.
24.3 General Biological Supply House, Inc.
24.5 Dr. Clifford Grobstein, and 13th Growth Symposium, Princeton University Press, 1954.
24.6 *A*, Dr. Melvin S. Fuller, University of Georgia; *B, C*, Douglas P. Wilson.
24.13 General Biological Supply House, Inc.
24.14 *B*, R. H. Noailles.
24.22 *A, B*, General Biological Supply House, Inc.; *C*, © Walt Disney Productions.
24.23 Carolina Biological Supply Company.
24.24 Dr. Clifford Grobstein, and 13th Growth Symposium, Princeton University Press, 1954.
24.25 *A, C*, Dr. Charles Thornton, Michigan State University; *B*, Dr. Richard Goss, Brown University.

25.1 *A*, Dr. C. F. Robinow and Society of American Bacteriologists; *B*, Drs. E. A. Duchow and H. C. Douglas, University of Washington, and *J. Bacteriol.*, vol. 58, p. 411.
25.9 Dr. Melvin S. Fuller, University of Georgia.
25.13 *B*, Dr. John T. Bonner, and *J. Exp. Zool.*, vol. 106, p. 7.
25.14 *B*, Carolina Biological Supply Company.
25.15 *B*, Ward's Natural Science Establishment, Inc.
25.17 *A, B*, Carolina Biological Supply Company; *C, D*, General Biological Supply House, Inc.
25.18 *B*, General Biological Supply House, Inc.
25.20 *B*, Dr. Melvin S. Fuller, University of Georgia.
25.21 *B, C*, Dr. Melvin S. Fuller, University of Georgia; *D, E*, Carolina Biological Supply Company.
25.22 *A*, Carolina Biological Supply Company; *B*, Dr. Melvin S. Fuller, University of Georgia.
25.25 Dr. Melvin S. Fuller, University of Georgia.
25.26 General Biological Supply House, Inc.
25.27 *B*, R. H. Noailles.
25.30 *A*, Dr. Melvin S. Fuller, University of Georgia; *C*, Ward's Natural Science Establishment, Inc.
25.31 *A*, Dr. Melvin S. Fuller, University of Georgia.
25.32 *B*, Dr. Melvin S. Fuller, University of Georgia.
25.34 R. H. Noailles.
25.35 *A*, Ward's Natural Science Establishment, Inc.
25.36 *A*, Ward's Natural Science Establishment, Inc.
25.38 *A*, Dr. Melvin S. Fuller, University of Georgia; *B*, J. Limbach, Ripon Microslides, Inc.
25.39 Dr. Melvin S. Fuller, University of Georgia.
25.40 Sid Karson, McGraw-Hill Book Company.

26.1 *B, C*, General Biological Supply House, Inc.
26.2 *A*, Carolina Biological Supply Company.
26.3 *A*, Ruda Zukal, TFH Photo; *B*, Lynwood M. Chace; *C*, Dr. David Rentz, Academy of Natural Sciences, Philadelphia.
26.6 *A*, Ward's Natural Science Establishment, Inc.
26.7 *A*, Ward's Natural Science Establishment, Inc.
26.9 *A*, J. VanWormer; *B*, Jane Burton.
26.10 Gerhard Marcuse.
26.15 *A*, Dr. Roberts Rugh and Burgess Publishing Company.
26.18 *B*, General Biological Supply House, Inc.
26.20 *A*, Dr. Roberts Rugh, from "Experimental Embryology," Harcourt, Brace & World, Inc.
26.21 Dr. Dietrich Bodenstein, from figs. 2 and 3, *J. Exp. Zool.*, vol. 108, pp. 96, 97.
26.22 Drs. S. R. Detwiler and R. H. Van Dyke. from fig. 16, *J. Exp. Zool.*, vol. 69, p. 157.
26.23 L. E. Perkins, Natural History Photographic Agency.
26.25 Carnegie Institution of Washington.
26.27 Dr. A. Gesell, from fig. 10; "The Embryology of Behavior," Harper & Brothers.
26.29 Dr. G. W. Corner, and Carnegie Institution of Washington.

27.1 *B, C*, R. H. Noailles.
27.14 Dr. W. Beerman.
27.17 *B, C*, Carolina Biological Supply Company.

28.5 New York Zoological Society.
28.6 *A*, New York Zoological Society; *B*, Dr. W. C. Galinat, University of Massachusetts, and Massachusetts Agricultural Experiment Station Bulletin 577, 1969.
28.7 *A*, Chicago Natural History Museum; *B*, U.S. Department of Agriculture.
28.8 *A, B, C*, American Museum of Natural History; *D*, Chicago Natural History Museum.

29.1 American Museum of Natural History.
29.4 Chicago Natural History Museum.
29.7 *C*, Chicago Natural History Museum.
29.8 Chicago Natural History Museum.
29.13 *A*, American Museum of Natural History; *B*, Chicago Natural History Museum.
29.14 *A, B*, Chicago Natural History Museum; *C*, American Museum of Natural History.
29.15 American Museum of Natural History.
29.17 American Museum of Natural History.
29.18 American Museum of Natural History.
29.19 *A*, American Museum of Natural History; *B*, Chicago Natural History Museum.
29.21 American Museum of Natural History.
29.22 Chicago Natural History Museum.
29.23 American Museum of Natural History.
29.24 American Museum of Natural History.
29.25 American Museum of Natural History.
29.27 American Museum of Natural History.
29.28 *A*, Paul Popper, Ltd.; *B*, Lynwood M. Chace.
29.29 *A*, W. Suschitzky; *B*, American Museum of Natural History.

30.2 *A*, adapted from painting by Peter Bianchi, © National Geographic Society, 1961; *B*, American Museum of Natural History.
30.3 American Museum of Natural History.
30.4 American Museum of Natural History.
30.5 *A*, American Museum of Natural History; *B*, Chicago Natural History Museum.
30.8 American Museum of Natural History.

unit 1
the organization of life

part 1
the study of life

chapter 1
the scientific background
page 5

methods of science
- *observation, problem, hypothesis*
- *experiment, theory*

limitations of science
- *aims and values*
- *scientific philosophy*

the voice of science

chapter 2
the biological background
page 15

life and function
- *metabolism, self-perpetuation*
- *living matter*

organism and structure
- *levels of organization*
- *specialization*

living organisms
- *classification: the main groups*
- *classification: the subgroups*

chapter 3
the chemical background
page 31

chemical substances
- *atoms*
- *ions*
- *molecules*
- *dissociation*

chemical changes
- *reactions*
- *energetics*
- *pressure, temperature, concentration*
- *catalysis*

part 2
the levels of life

chapter 4
molecule and cell
page 49

chemical organization
- *elements and compounds*
- *carbohydrates*
- *lipids*
- *proteins*
- *nucleotides*

physical organization
- *colloids*
- *membranes*
- *osmosis*

chapter 5
cell and organism
page 67

cells
- *nucleus and cytoplasm*
- *cell surfaces*

tissues, organs, systems
- *the plant pattern*
- *the animal pattern*

chapter 6
species and ecosystem
page 93

the species
- *structures and functions*
- *development and geography*
- *population*

the ecosystem
- *structure and growth*
- *links and balances*

symbiosis
- *mutualism and commensalism*
- *parasitism*

contents

color photo credits, *v*
chapter photo credits, *v*
preface, *xiii*

part 2
the levels of life (*cont.*)

chapter 7
habitat and biosphere
page 111

habitats
- *the sea*
- *the fresh water*
- *the land*

the biosphere
- *the hydrosphere*
- *the lithosphere*
- *the atmosphere*

the ecological crisis

chapter 8
the earliest organisms
page 137

origins of life
- *chemical evolution: cells*
- *biological evolution: premonera*

monera
- *bacteria*
- *blue-green algae*

part 3
the world of life: nonanimal organisms

chapter 9
protists
page 151

general characteristics
algae
- *green algae*
- *stoneworts*
- *euglenoids*
- *golden-brown algae*
- *fire algae*
- *brown algae*
- *red algae*

colorless protists
- *fungi*
- *slime molds*
- *protozoans*

chapter 10
plants
page 175

general characteristics
bryophytes
tracheophytes
- *patterns of life*
- *growth and structure*

tracheophytes: the main groups
- *psilopsids*
- *lycopsids*
- *sphenopsids*
- *pteropsids*

part 4
the world of life: animal organisms

chapter 11
animal nature and noncoelomates
page 203

patterns of life
growth and structure
the main groups
- *sponges*
- *radiates*
- *bilateral forms*

chapter 12
coelomate groups: protostomes
page 225

lophophorates
schizocoelomates
- *mollusks*
- *annelids*
- *arthropods*

chapter 13
coelomate groups: deuterostomes
page 259

enterocoelomates
- *echinoderms*
- *chordates*

vertebrates
- *general characteristics*
- *the main groups*

unit 2 the operations of life

part 5 metabolism

chapter 14 nutrition *page 289*

patterns
- *forms of nutrition*
- *processes of nutrition*

plants: absorption, conduction
- *roots, leaves, and xylem*
- *leaves, stems, and phloem*

animals: alimentation, circulation
- *nutrients and ingestion*
- *digestion and egestion*
- *absorption and distribution*

chapter 15 respiration *page 307*

the pattern
- *decomposition: oxidation*
- *energy transfer*
- *hydrogen transfer*
- *aerobic and anaerobic transfer*

the process
- *formation of CO_2*
- *carbohydrate respiration*
- *lipid respiration*
- *amino acid respiration*

chapter 16 synthesis *page 323*

photosynthesis
- *the pattern*
- *photolysis*
- *CO_2 fixation*
- *the endproduct*

synthesis metabolism
- *carbohydrates*
- *lipids*
- *amino acids*

chapter 17 genetic codes, physical functions *page 339*

genes and protein synthesis
- *the pattern*
- *code transcription: DNA → protein*
- *code transcription: DNA → DNA*

biophysical metabolism
- *movement*
- *heat, light, electricity*
- *metabolic maintenance*

part 6 steady states

chapter 18 cellular control *page 357*

the pattern
- *control operations*
- *control systems*

control in cells
- *DNA and operons*
- *enzymes and growth factors*
- *minerals and vitamins*

chapter 19 hormonal control *page 371*

plant behavior
- *motion responses*
- *developmental responses: auxin effects*
- *developmental responses: light effects*
- *developmental responses: temperature and other effects*

endocrine secretions
- *pituitary hormones*
- *thyroid hormones*
- *parathyroid hormones*
- *adrenal hormones*
- *other hormones*

part 6
steady states (*cont.*)

chapter 20
intercellular control
page 391

blood and lymph
- *plasma*
- *blood cells*

circulation
- *vessels and heartbeat*
- *heart rate and blood pressure*

breathing
- *the apparatus*
- *the process*

excretion

chapter 21
nervous control
page 407

neural pathways
neural impulses
neural centers
neural receptors
- *chemoreceptors*
- *mechanoreceptors*
- *statoreceptors*
- *phonoreceptors*
- *photoreceptors*
- *other receptors*

chapter 22
behavioral control: the individual
page 427

forms of behavior
- *behavior processes*
- *behavior patterns*

systems of behavior
- *stimulus and response*
- *time orientation: biological clocks*
- *space orientation: directional motion*

chapter 23
behavioral control: the society
page 443

social groupings
- *insect societies*
- *vertebrate societies*

aggression
social constraints

part 7
reproduction

chapter 24
patterns of propagation
page 459

reproductive processes: cells
- *molecular reproduction*
- *mitosis and division*

reproductive processes: organisms
sexual processes
- *forms of sexuality*
- *meiosis and life cycles*

developmental processes

chapter 25
reproduction: nonanimal organisms
page 477

moneran reproduction
protistan reproduction
- *algae*
- *slime molds, protozoa*
- *fungi*

plant reproduction
- *bryophytes*
- *tracheophytes: the primitive pattern*
- *tracheophytes: the seed-forming pattern*

part 7
reproduction (*cont.*)

chapter 26
reproduction: animals
page 499

patterns
- *reproductive cells*
- *reproductive systems*
- *reproductive behavior*
- *reproductive mechanisms*

the embryo
- *cleavage and blastula*
- *gastrula and induction*

larvae and pregnancy

chapter 27
heredity
page 521

mendelian inheritance
- *the chromosome theory*
- *segregation*
- *independent assortment*
- *linkage*

non-mendelian inheritance
- *mutation*
- *sex determination*
- *genetic systems*

part 8
adaptation

chapter 28
evolution
page 537

background
forces of evolution
- *the evolutionary process*
- *the genetic basis*

effects of evolution
- *speciation*
- *diversification*

chapter 29
change with time
page 551

the fossil record
plant evolution
- *the paleozoic*
- *the mesozoic and cenozoic*

animal evolution
- *early history*
- *the paleozoic*
- *the mesozoic*
- *the cenozoic*

chapter 30
the history and races of man
page 575

prehistoric man
modern man
- *the human animal*
- *the human society*

races of man
- *the concept of race*
- *the meaning of race*

glossary, *593*
index, *631*

preface

The potential scope of introductory biology courses continues to enlarge unabated. A decade or so ago new curricular time had to be found for biochemical genetics and ''molecular'' biology; now new time must be found for behavioral biology, studies on the environmental crisis, and the genetics of population and human races. The emergence of new subjects of current relevance also tends to raise questions as to whether or not yesterday's ''new'' topics still ought to be given classroom time at all. Is it justifiable to burden today's freshman with the fine details of, for example, the Krebs cycle, when the time might be spent on the biology of pollution?

New knowledge evolves from old, and at least a distillate of earlier knowledge probably will always be required for an appreciation of the new. Thus, notwithstanding the present valid need for relevance, a ''topical'' course that is not based on established insights is likely to amount to little more than a series of shallow talk sessions; it probably cannot achieve the desired objective of fostering a significant, analytic understanding of the scientific and social realities of the day. Conversely, however, it would be indefensible—and indeed almost impossible—simply to ignore biological topics currently of great importance and interest.

The proper answer seems to lie in a new balance, a readjustment of course content, between established and new subject matter. As a case in point, the fine details of the Krebs cycle can well be left for study after the first year, but the introductory course nevertheless ought to concern itself with the existence and significance of this cycle. At the same time, a topic such as human races should receive far more attention today than the traditional cursory (and usually outdated) mention; the subject clearly demands an even more thorough examination than Krebs-cycle details did earlier.

A beginning toward a new balance of this sort has been made in the present edition. First, although emphasis on principles and the ''molecular'' outlook have been retained as necessary foundations for a presentation of modern biology, the chemical and biochemical subject matter has been curtailed and simplified greatly. Second, the elbow room so gained has been used for an introduction of new topics: the problem of environmental decay; animal behavior, both individual and social; and the evolutionary history and status of man, both social and racial. And third, other portions of the book have been rewritten, reorganized, and updated, so that little of the previous edition now remains the same; most chapters differ in scope and content from those of the third edition.

However, the various changes are well accommodated in the same broad conceptual framework that has characterized the text before: the basic sequence of topics is relatively unaltered, and the material is again divided into two large units, one on the organization and one on the operation of living matter. Of the four parts in Unit 1, the first provides a scientific, biological, and chemical background. The chemical introduction is now presented far more concisely than previously, in a single chapter, and it suffices for the amount of biochemistry that follows later. Part 2 represents a level-by-level examination of the living organization from molecule to ecosystem. The concluding chapter here contains accounts on the various aspects of the current ecological crisis. Parts 3 and 4 deal with the biology and morphology of living types. These chapters too have been reorganized, but the running theme again is historical and phylogenetic.

In the second unit, Part 5 on metabolism has been revised, with a simplified biochemical treatment. Control operations and steady states are considered in Part 6, which has been expanded by two new chapters, on behavior. Part 7 again analyzes the processes of reproduction, and in Part 8, on adaptation, the new last chapter focuses attention specifically on man; it contains a discussion of human biological and social prehistory as well as a reasonably detailed introduction to the biology and genetics of race.

Practically all the diagrams and many of the photographs in this edition are new. Included as before are 32 full-color plates, and appended to each chapter are revised review questions and updated descriptive lists of collateral readings. A thorough two-part glossary is at the end of the book, as is an index. New editions of the Instructor's Manual and the Study Guide have been prepared in conjunction with the text and the Laboratory Manual, has been revised to conform with the new edition.

Notwithstanding its new or altered structure and content, this edition remains dedicated just as fully to the same teaching aims as the previous one: emphasis on depth, not simply breadth; on conceptual synthesis, not meaningless memorization; and on developing real comprehension, not cataloguing empty "facts." The hoped-for goal, thus, is not better "instruction" or information transfer, but better *education.*

Paul B. Weisz

unit 1
the organization of life

unit 1
the organization of life

part 1
the study of life

part 2
the levels of life

part 3
the world of life: nonanimal organisms

part 4
the world of life: animal organisms

Despite their numerous and often obvious differences, living creatures have far more in common than might at first be suspected. Most important, the events that maintain a ''living'' state turn out to be very similar in all creatures. In effect, the most fundamental traits are shared in common and the differences involve only the more or less superficial characteristics.

Such general similarities and specific differences are expressions of how living material is put together, from atoms to whole groups of interacting individuals. The first unit of this book is devoted to a study of this living organization. *The second unit deals with the living* operations, *the means by which the organization actually maintains itself in a living state.*

part 1
the study of life

part 1
the study of life

chapter 1
the scientific background

chapter 2
the biological background

chapter 3
the chemical background

The investigation of living things is the concern of the science of biology. As a science, biology is interrelated closely with all other natural sciences, chemistry in particular. Therefore, a study of biology appropriately can begin with three questions: (1) ''What is science?'' (2) ''What do we mean by 'living'?'' (3) ''What areas of chemistry and other natural sciences are important in understanding living things?'' Answers to these questions are outlined in the three chapters of this first part.

It is sometimes useful to distinguish two forms of science: basic research, or *pure* science, and technology, or *applied* science. Basic research promotes our understanding of how the universe and its parts operate, and technology puts the results of basic research to practical uses. However, every scientific activity actually has both pure and applied aspects. Every pure scientist depends on equipment produced by technology, and every technologist depends on the ideas and insights generated by basic research. The relative emphasis between pure and applied work can vary greatly, yet both kinds are always required in any science.

methods of science

Everything that is science is ultimately based on some *scientific method.* Taken singly, most of the steps of such a method involve commonplace procedures carried out daily by every person. Taken together, they amount to the most powerful tool man has devised for learning about nature and making natural processes serve human purposes.

observation, problem, hypothesis

Science generally begins with *observation,* the usual first step of scientific inquiry. This step immediately limits the scientific domain; something that cannot be observed, directly or indirectly, cannot be investigated by science. Furthermore, for reasons that will become clear presently, it is necessary that an observation be *repeatable,* actually or potentially. One-time events are outside science (the one-time origin of the universe possibly excepted).

Correct observation is a most difficult art, acquired only after long experience and many errors. Everyone observes, with eyes, ears, touch, and all other senses, but few observe correctly. The problem here is largely unsuspected bias. People forever see what they want to see or what they think they *ought* to see. It is extremely hard to rid oneself of such unconscious prejudice and to see just what is actually there, no more and no less. Past experience, "common knowledge," and often teachers can be subtle obstacles to correct observation, and even experienced scientists may not always avoid them. That is why a scientific observation is not taken at face value until several scientists have repeated it independently and have reported matching data. That is also a major reason why one-time, unrepeatable events generally cannot be investigated scientifically.

After an observation has been made, a second usual step of scientific procedure is to define a *problem;* one asks a question about the observation. "How does so-and-so come about?" "What is it that makes such-and-such happen in this or that fashion?" Question-asking again distinguishes the scientist from the layman; everyone makes observations, but not everyone has the curiosity to go further. Indeed, few become aware that a particular observation actually might pose a problem. For thousands of years, even curious people simply took it for granted that a detached, unsupported object falls to the ground. It took genius to ask "How come?" and not many problems have ever turned out to be more profound.

Thus, scientists take nothing for granted and they ask questions, even at the risk of irritating others. Question-askers are notorious for getting themselves into trouble, and so it has always been with scientists. But they have to continue to ask questions if they are to remain scientists, and society has to expect annoying questions if it wishes to have science.

Like good observing, good questioning is a high art. To be valuable scientifically, a question must be *relevant* as well as *testable.* Often it is difficult or impossible to tell in advance whether a question is relevant or irrelevant, testable or untestable. If a man collapses on the street and others want to help him, it may or may not be irrelevant to ask when the man had his last meal. Without experience one cannot decide on the relevance of this question, and a wrong procedure might be followed. As to testability, it is clear that proper testing techniques must be available. But this cannot always be guaranteed. For example, Einstein achieved fame for showing that it is impossible to tell whether or not the earth moves through an "ether," an assumption held for many decades. All questions about an ether therefore became untestable. Einstein reformulated such questions and came up with relativity, an idea that posed fully testable problems.

In general, science does best with "how" or "what" questions. "Why" questions are more troublesome. Some of them can be rephrased to ask "How?" or "What?" But others, such as "Why does the universe exist?," fall into the untestable category. These are outside the domain of science.

Once a proper question has been asked, the third step of scientific methodology usually involves the seemingly quite unscientific procedure of guessing what the answer to the question might conceivably be. Scientists refer to this as postulating a *hypothesis*. Hypothesizing distinguishes the scientist still further from the layman. For while many people observe and ask questions, most stop there. Some do wonder about likely answers, and scientists are among these.

Since a particular question usually has thousands of possible answers but in most cases only a single right one, chances are excellent that a random guess will be wrong. The scientist will not know if his guess was or was not correct until he has completed the fourth step of scientific inquiry, *experimentation*. It is the function of experiments to test the validity of scientific guesses. If experiments show that a first guess was wrong the scientist then must formulate a new or modified hypothesis and perform new experiments. Clearly, guessing and guess-testing could go on for years and a right answer might not be found. This happens.

But here artistry, genius, and knowledge of the field usually provide shortcuts. There are good guesses and bad ones, and the experienced scientist is generally able to decide at the outset that, of a multitude of possible answers, so-and-so many are unlikely answers. This is also the place where hunches, intuitions, and lucky accidents aid science enormously. The ideal situation the scientist will strive for is to reduce his problem to just two distinct alternative possibilities. Experimental tests should then answer one of these with a clear "yes," the other with a clear "no." It is exceedingly difficult to streamline problems in this way, and with many it cannot be done. Very often the answer obtained is "maybe." But if a clear yes or no does emerge, the result well might be a milestone in science.

experiment, theory

With the next general step in a scientific inquiry, *experimentation,* science and nonscience part company completely. Most people observe, ask questions, and also guess at answers. But the layman then stops: "My answer is so logical, so reasonable, and it sounds so 'right,' that it must be correct." The listener considers the argument, finds that it is indeed logical and reasonable, and is convinced. He goes out and in his turn converts others. Before long, the whole world rejoices that it has the answer.

Now the small, killjoy voice of the scientist is heard in the background: "Where is the evidence?" Under such conditions in history it has often been easier and more convenient to ignore the scientist than to change emotionally fixed public opinions. But disregarding the scientist does not alter the fact that answers without evidence are at best wishful thinking, at worst fanatical illusions. Experiments *can* provide the necessary evidence.

Experimenting is the hardest part of the scientific process. There are few rules, and each experiment must be tackled in its own particular way. The general nature of an experiment can be illustrated by the following example. Suppose that a chemical substance *X* has spilled accidentally into a culture dish full of certain disease-causing bacteria, and you observe that this chemical kills all the bacteria in the dish. Problem: can drug *X* be used to protect human beings against these disease-causing bacteria? Hypothesis: yes. Experiment: you find a patient with that bacterial disease and inject some of the drug into him. One possible result is that the patient gets well fairly quickly, in which case you would consider your hypothesis confirmed. Another possible result is that the patient remains ill or dies, and you would then conclude that your drug is worthless or dangerous.

However, in this example the so-called *experiment* was not really an experiment at all. First, no allowance was made for the possibility that different people might react differently to the same drug. Obviously, one would have to test the drug on many patients. Besides, one would make preliminary tests on mice or guinea pigs or monkeys. Second, the quantity of drug to be used was not determined. Clearly, a full range of dosages would have to be tested. Third, and most important, no account was taken of the possibility that your patient might have recovered (or died) even without your injecting the drug. What is needed here is *experimental control;* for every group of patients treated with the drug solution, a precisely equal group must be treated with a plain solution that does not contain the drug. Then, by comparing the control and the experimental groups, one can determine to what extent the results are actually attributable to the drug.

Every experiment thus requires at least two parallel sets of tests identical in all respects except one. One set is the control series that provides a standard of reference for assessing the results of the experimental series. In drug experiments on people, up to 100,000 to 200,000 tests, half of them controls, half of them experimentals, must sometimes be performed. Such a drug-testing program is laborious, expensive, and time-consuming, but the design of the experiment is nevertheless extremely simple. There are few steps to be gone through, and it is fairly clear what these steps must be. By contrast, experiments in many cases do not take more than an hour or two, whereas thinking up appropriate, foolproof plans for the tests can take several years.

And despite a most ingenious design and a most careful execution, the result still may not be a clear yes or no. In a drug-testing experiment, for example, it is virtually certain that some patients in the experimental group will not recover and that some of the untreated control patients will get better. The actual results might be something like 70 percent recovery in the experimentals and perhaps 20 percent recovery in the controls. In other words, 30 percent of the experimentals do not recover despite treatment, and 20 percent of the controls get well even without treatment. The drug is therefore effective in only 70 minus 20, or 50 percent, of the cases.

Such a result can be a major medical accomplishment, for having the drug is obviously better than not having it. Scientifically, however, one is confronted with an equivocal "maybe" result. It will probably lead to research based on the new observation that some people respond to the drug and some do not, and to the new problem of why and what can be done about it.

The result of any experiment represents *evidence;* the original guess about the answer to a problem is confirmed as correct or is invalidated. If it is invalidated, a new hypothesis and new experiments must be thought up. This process must be repeated until a hypothesis is hit upon that can be supported with confirmatory experimental evidence.

As with legal evidence, scientific evidence can be strong and convincing, or merely suggestive, or poor. In any case nothing has been "proved." Depending on the strength of the evidence, one merely obtains a basis for regarding the original hypothesis with a certain degree of confidence. Our new drug, for example, may be just what we claim it to be when we use it in this country. In another part of the world it might not work at all or it might work better. All we can confidently say is that our evidence is based on so-and-so many local experiments, and that we have shown the drug to have an effectiveness of 50 percent. Experimental results are never better or broader than the experiments themselves.

This is where many who have been properly scientific up to this point become unscientific. Their claims exceed the evidence; they mistake their partial answer for the whole answer; they contend that they have "proof" for a "fact," while all they actually have is some evidence for a hypothesis. There is always room for more and better evidence, or for new contradictory evidence, or indeed for better hypotheses.

Experimental evidence is the basis for a fifth general step in scientific procedure, the formulation of a *theory.* In our drug example, a simple theory would be the statement that "against such-and-such a bacterial disease, drug *X* is effective in 50 percent of the cases." To be sure, this statement cannot be regarded as a particularly significant or far-reaching theory. Nevertheless, it implies, for example, that drug *X* will be 50 percent effective anywhere in the world, under any conditions, and can be used also for animals other than man. Direct evidence for these extended implications does not exist. But inasmuch as drug *X* is already known to work within certain limits, the theory expresses the belief, or *probability,* that it will also work within certain wider limits.

To that extent every good theory has *predictive* value; it forecasts certain results. In contrast to nonscientific predictions, scientific ones always have a substantial body of evidence to back them up. Moreover, a scientific forecast does not say that something will certainly happen, but says only that something is likely to happen with a stated degree of probability.

A few theories have proved to be so universally

valid and to have such a high degree of probability that they are spoken of as *natural laws.* For example, no exception has ever been found to the observation that an apple disconnected from a tree and not otherwise supported will fall to the ground. A law of gravitation is based on such observations. Yet even laws do not pronounce certainties. For all practical purposes it well might be irrational to assume that some day an apple will rise from a tree, but there simply is no evidence that can absolutely guarantee the future. Evidence can be used only to estimate probabilities.

Most theories have rather brief life spans. For example, if our drug *X* should be found to perform not with 50 percent but with 80 percent efficiency in chickens, then our original theory becomes untenable and obsolete. The exception to the theory now becomes a new observation, the start of a new cycle of scientific investigation. New research might show, for example, that chickens contain a substance in their blood that enhances the action of the drug substantially. This finding might lead to isolation, identification, and mass production of the booster substance, hence to worldwide improvement in curing the bacterial disease. And we would also have a new theory of drug action, based on the new evidence.

Thus, science is never finished. One theory predicts, holds up well for a time, exceptions are found, and a new, more inclusive theory takes over—for a while. Science is steady progression, not sudden revolution. Clearly, knowledge of scientific methodology does not by itself make a good scientist, any more than knowledge of English grammar alone makes a Shakespeare. At the same time, the demands of scientific inquiry should make it evident that scientists cannot be the cold, inhuman, precision machines they are so often and so erroneously pictured to be. Scientists are essentially artists who require a sensitivity of eye and of mind as great as that of any master painter, and an imagination and keen inventiveness as powerful as that of any master poet.

limitations of science

Observing, problem-posing, hypothesizing, experimenting, and theorizing—these are the most common procedural steps in scientific investigations. To determine what science means in wider contexts, we must examine what scientific methodology implies and, more especially, what it does not imply.

aims and values

First, scientific investigation defines the domain of science. Anything that is amenable to scientific investigation, now or in the future, is or will be within the domain of science; anything that is not amenable to such investigation is not in the scientific domain.

An awareness of these limits can help us avoid many inappropriate controversies. For example, does the idea of God lend itself to scientific scrutiny? Suppose we wish to test the hypothesis that God is universal and exists everywhere and in everything. Being untested as yet, this hypothesis could be right or wrong. An experiment about God would then require experimental control, or two situations, one with God and one without, but otherwise identical.

If our hypothesis is correct, God would indeed exist everywhere. Hence He would be present in every test we could possibly make, and we would never be able to devise a situation in which God is not present. Yet we need such a situation for a controlled experiment. But if our hypothesis is wrong, He would not exist and would therefore be absent from any test we could possibly make. We would then never be able to devise a situation in which God *is* present. Yet we would need such a situation for a controlled experiment.

Right or wrong, our hypothesis is untestable, since we cannot run a controlled experiment. Therefore, we cannot carry out a scientific investigation. The point is that the concept of God falls outside the domain of science, and science cannot legitimately say anything about Him. It should be carefully noted that this is a far cry from saying "science disproves God," or "scientists must be godless; their method demands it." Nothing of the sort. Science specifically leaves anyone perfectly free to believe in any god whatsoever or in none. Many first-rate scientists are priests; many others are agnostics. Science commits you to nothing more and to nothing less than adherence to the ground rules of proper scientific inquiry.

It may be noted that such adherence is a matter of faith, just as belief in God or confidence in the telephone directory is a matter of faith. Whatever other faiths they may or may not hold, all scientists certainly have strong faith in scientific methodology. So do those laymen who feel that having electric lights and not having bubonic plague are good things.

A second consequence of scientific methodology is that it defines the aim and purpose of science. The objective of science is to make and to use theories. Many believe that the objective of science is to discover "truth," to find out "facts." We must be very careful here about the meaning of words. The word "truth" is popularly used in two senses. It can indicate a temporary correctness, as in saying, "It is true that my hair is brown." Or it can indicate an absolute, eternal correctness, as in saying, "In plane geometry, the sum of the angles of a triangle is 180°."

From the earlier discussion of the nature of scientific investigation, it should be clear that science cannot deal with truth of the absolute variety. Something absolute is finished, known completely once and for all, and nothing further needs to be found out. Science can only supply evidence for theories, and "theory" is simply another word for relative truth. Because the word "truth" is ambiguous if not laboriously qualified, scientists try not to use it at all. The words "fact" and "proof" have a similar drawback. Both can indicate either something absolute or something relative. If absolute they are not science; if relative, we actually deal with evidence. Thus, science is content to find evidence for theories, and it does not deal with truths, proofs, or facts.

A third important implication of scientific methodology is that it does not make value judgments or moral decisions. Very often, of course, we do place valuations on scientific results, but such assessments are human valuations and different people frequently assess the same results quite differently. Scientific results by themselves do not contain any built-in values, and nowhere in scientific inquiry is there a value-revealing step.

Thus the science that produces weapons for healing and creating and weapons for destroying and killing cannot of itself determine if such tools are good or bad. The decision in each case rests on the moral opinions of humanity, those of scientists included. Similarly, beauty, love, evil, happiness, virtue, justice, liberty, financial worth—all these are human values about which science as such is silent and noncommittal. For the same reason, it would also be folly to strive for a strictly "scientific" way of life or to expect strictly "scientific" government. To be sure, the role of science well might be enlarged in areas of personal and public life where science can make a legitimate contribution. But a civilization that adhered exclusively to the rules of scientific methods could never tell, for example, whether it is right or wrong to commit murder or whether it is good or bad to love one's neighbor. Science cannot and does not give such answers. This circumstance does not mean, however, that science does away with morals. The implication merely is that science cannot determine if one ought to have moral standards, or what particular set of moral standards one ought to live by.

scientific philosophy

A fourth and most important consequence of scientific methodology is that it determines the philosophical foundation on which scientific pursuits must be based.

Since the domain of science is the whole material universe, science must inquire into the nature of the forces that govern the universe and all happenings in it. What makes given events in the universe take place? What determines which event out of many possible ones will occur? And what controls or guides the course of any event to a particular conclusion?

We already know the framework in which the scientific answers to such questions must be given. If certain answers can be verified wholly or even partly through experimental analysis, they will be valuable scientifically. But answers that cannot be so verified will be without value in science, even though they well may be valuable in other human concerns.

vitalism versus mechanism

In the course of history two major types of answer have been proposed about the governing forces of the universe. They are incorporated in two systems of philosophy called *vitalism* and *mechanism.*

Vitalism is a doctrine of the supernatural. It holds, essentially, that the universe, and particularly its living components, are controlled by supernatural powers. Such powers have been variously called gods, spirits, or simply "vital forces." Their influence is held to guide the behavior of atoms, planets, stars, living things, and indeed of all components of the universe. Most religious philosophies are vitalistic ones.

Whatever value a vitalistic philosophy might have elsewhere, it cannot have value in science because the supernatural is by definition beyond reach of the natural. Inasmuch as scientific inquiry deals with the natural world, it cannot be used to investigate the supernatural. As already noted, for example, science cannot prove or disprove anything about God. Any other vitalistic concept is similarly untestable by experiment and is therfore unusable as a *scientific* philosophy of nature.

A philosophy that *is* usable in science is the idea of mechanism. According to this view the universe is governed by a set of natural laws, the laws of physics and chemistry man has discovered by experimental analysis. The mechanistic philosophy holds that if all physical and chemical events in the universe can be accounted for, no other events will remain. Therefore, life too must be a result of physical and chemical processes *only,* and the course of life must be determined automatically by the physical and chemical occurrences in living matter.

These differences between vitalism and mechanism clearly point up a conceptual conflict between religion and science. However, this conflict is not necessarily irreconcilable. To bridge the conceptual gap, one might ask how the natural laws of the universe came into being to begin with. A possible answer is that they were created by God. On this view, it could be argued that the universe ran vitalistically up to the time that natural laws were created and ran mechanistically thereafter. The mechanist would then have to admit the existence of a supernatural Creator at the beginning of time (even though he has no *scientific* basis for either affirming or denying this; mechanism cannot, by definition, tell anything about a time at which natural laws might not have been in operation). Correspondingly, the vitalist would have to admit that, so long as the natural laws continue to operate without change, supernatural control would not be demonstrable.

Thus it is not necessarily illogical to accept both scientific and religious philosophies at the same time. However, it is decidedly illogical to try to use religious ideas as explanations of scientific problems or scientific ideas as explanations of religious problems. Correct science does demand that supernatural concepts be kept out of those natural events that can be investigated scientifically. However much a vitalist he might be in his nonscientific thinking, man in his scientific thinking must be a mechanist. And if he is not he ceases to be scientific.

Many people, some scientists included, actually find it exceedingly difficult to keep vitalism out of science. Biological events, undoubtedly the most complex of all known events in the universe, have in the past been particularly subject to attempts at vitalistic interpretation. How, it has been asked, can the beauty of a flower ever be understood simply as a series of physical and chemical events? How can an egg, transforming itself into a baby, be nothing more than a "mechanism" like a clock? And how can a man who thinks and who experiences visions of God conceivably be regarded as nothing more than a piece of "machinery"? Mechanism *must* be inadequate as an explanation of life, it has been argued, and only something supernatural superimposed on the machine, some vital force, is likely to account for the fire of life.

In such replacements of mechanistic with mystical thought, the connotations of words often play a supporting role. For example, the words "mechanism" and "machine" usually bring to mind images of crude iron engines or clockworks. Such analogies tend to reinforce the suspicion of vitalists that those who regard living things as mere machinery must be simple-minded indeed. Consider, however, that the machines of today also include electronic computers that can learn, translate languages, compose music, play chess, make decisions, and improve their performance of such activities as they gather experience. In addition, theoretical knowledge now available would permit us to build a machine that could heal itself when injured and that could feed, sense, reproduce, and even evolve. Thus the term "mechanism" is not at all limited to crude, stupidly "mechanical" engines. And there is certainly nothing inherently simple-minded or reprehensible in the idea that living things are exquisitely complex chemical mechanisms, some of which even have the capacity to think and to have visions of God.

On the contrary, if it could be shown that such a mechanistic view is at all justified, it would represent an enormous advance in our understanding of nature. In all the centuries of recorded history, vitalism in its various forms has hardly progressed beyond its original assertion that living things are animated by supernatural forces. Just how such forces are supposed to do the animating has not been explained, nor have programs of inquiry been offered to find explanations. Such inquiries actually are ruled out by definition, since natural man can never hope to fathom the supernatural. In the face of this closed door, mechanism provides the only way out for the curious. But is it justifiable to regard living things as pure mechanisms, even complicated chemical ones?

A mechanistic interpretation of life turns out to be entirely justifiable, and interjection of touches of vitalism is entirely unjustifiable. Science today can account for many living properties in purely mechanistic terms. Moreover, biologists are well on their way to being able to create a truly living entity "in the test tube," solely by means of physical and chemical procedures obeying known natural laws. We shall discuss some of the requirements for such laboratory creation in the course of this book. Evidently, vitalistic "aids" to explain the mechanistic universe are unnecessary and, because they do not foster inquiry, also unjustifiable.

It may be noted in this connection that, historically, vitalism has tended to fill the gaps left by incomplete scientific knowledge. Early man was a complete vitalist, who for want of better knowledge regarded even inanimate objects as "animated" by supernatural spirits. As scientific insight later increased, progressively more of the universe was reclaimed from the domain of the supernatural. Thus it happened repeatedly that events originally thought to be supernatural, many living events included, were later shown to be explicable naturally. And those today who may still be prompted to fill gaps in scientific knowledge with vitalism must be prepared to have red faces tomorrow. We conclude that a mechanistic view of nature is one philosophic attitude required in science. A second may now be considered.

teleology versus causalism

Even a casual observer must be impressed by the apparent nonrandomness of natural events. Every part of nature seems to follow a plan, and there is a definite directedness to any given process. In living processes, for example, developing eggs behave as *if* they knew exactly what the plan of the adult is to be. A chicken soon produces two wings and two legs, as *if* it knew that these appendages were to be part of the adult. All known natural processes, living or otherwise, similarly start at given beginnings and proceed to particular endpoints. This observation poses a philosophical problem: how is a starting condition directed toward a specific terminal condition; how does a starting point appear to "know" what the endpoint is to be?

Such questions have to do with a detailed aspect of the more general problem of the controlling forces of the universe. We should expect, therefore, that two sets of answers would be available, one vitalistic and the other mechanistic. This is the case. According to vitalistic doctrines, natural events *appear* to be planned because they actually are planned. A supernatural "divine plan" is held to fix the fate of every part of the universe, and all events in nature, past, present, and future, are programmed in this plan. All nature is therefore directed toward a preordained goal, the fulfillment of the divine plan. As a consequence, nothing happens by chance but everything happens on purpose.

Being a vitalistic, experimentally untestable concept, the notion of purpose in natural events has no place in science. Does the universe exist for a purpose? Does man live for a purpose? You cannot hope for an answer from science, for science is not designed to tackle such questions. Moreover, if you already hold certain beliefs in these areas, you cannot expect science either to prove or to disprove them for you.

Yet many arguments have been attempted to show purpose from science. For example, it has been maintained by some that the whole purpose of the evolution of living things was to produce man—the predetermined goal from the very beginning. This conceit implies not only that man is the finest product of creation, but also that nothing could ever come after man, for he is supposed to be the last word in living magnificence. As a matter of record, man is sorely plagued by an army of parasites that cannot live anywhere except inside people. And it is clear that you cannot have a man-requiring parasite before you have a man.

Many human parasites did evolve after man. Thus, the purpose argument at best would show that the whole purpose of evolution was to produce living organisms causing influenza, diphtheria, gonorrhea, and syphilis. Even the most ardent purpose arguer would probably not care to maintain such a conclusion. If one is so inclined, he is of course perfectly free to believe that man is the pinnacle of it all. But one cannot maintain that such beliefs are justified by evidence from science. The essential point is that a statement that such-and-such is the purpose or goal of any material thing or event is to state a belief, not evidence obtained by scientific inquiry. Nowhere in such inquiries is there a purpose-revealing step.

The form of argumentation that has recourse to purposes and supernatural planning is generally called *teleology.* In one system of teleology, the preordained plan exists outside natural objects, in an external Deity, for example. In another system, the plan resides within objects themselves. According to this view, a starting condition of an event proceeds toward a particular end condition because the starting object has built into it supernatural foreknowledge of the end condition. For example, an egg develops toward the goal of the adult because the egg is endowed with information about the precise nature of the adult state. Clearly, this and all other forms of teleology "explain" an end state by simply asserting it to be already mapped out at the beginning. And in thereby putting the future in the past, the effect before the cause, teleology negates time.

The scientifically useful alternative to teleology is *causalism,* a form of thought based on mechanistic philosophy. Causalism denies foreknowledge of terminal states, preordination, purposes, goals, and fixed fates. It holds instead that natural events take place stepwise, each one conditioned by and dependent on earlier ones. Events occur only as previous events *permit* them to occur, not as preordained goals or purposes make them occur. End states are consequences, not foregone conclusions, of beginning states. A headless earthworm regenerates a new head because conditions in the headless worm are such that only a head—*one* head—can develop. It becomes the task of the biologist to find out what these conditions are and to see if, by changing the conditions, two heads or another tail could be produced. Because scientists actually can obtain different end states by changing the conditions of initial states, the idea of predetermined goals loses all validity in scientific thought.

Care must therefore be taken in scientific endeavors not to fall unwittingly into the teleological trap. Consider often-heard statements such as: "the *purpose* of the heart is to pump blood"; "the ancestors of birds evolved wings *so that* they could fly"; "eggs have yolk *in order to* provide food for developement." The last statement, for example, implies that eggs can "foresee" that food will be required in development and they therefore store up some. In effect, eggs are given human mentality. The teleologist is always anthropocentric, that is, he implies that the natural events he discusses are governed by minds like his. In making biological statements some of the teleological implications can be avoided by replacing every "purpose" with "function," every "so that" or "in order to " with "and."

Clearly then, science in its present state of development must operate within carefully specified, self-imposed limits. The basic philosophic attitude must be mechanistic and causalistic, and we note that the results obtained through science are inherently without truth, without value, and without purpose. But it is precisely because science is limited in this fashion that it advances. Truth is as subjective as ever, values change with time and place, and purposes basically express little more than man's desire to make the universe behave according to his own very primitive understanding. It has therefore proved difficult to build a knowledge of nature on the shifting foundations of values and truths or on the dogma of purpose. What little of nature we really know and are likely to know in the foreseeable future stands on the bedrock of science.

the voice of science

Fundamentally science is a *language,* a system of communication comparable to the systems of religion, art, politics, English, or French. Like the latter, science enables man to travel in new countries of the mind, and to understand and be understood in such countries. Like other languages, moreover, science has its grammar—the methods of scientific inquiry; its authors and its literature—the scientists and their written work; and its various dialects or forms of expression—physics, chemistry, and biology, for example.

Indeed, science is one of the few truly universal languages, understood all over the globe. Art, religion, and politics are also universal. But each of these has several forms, with the result that Baptists and Hindus, for example, have little in common—religiously, artistically, or politically. By contrast, science has the same single form everywhere, and Baptists and Hindus do speak the same scientific language.

None of these systems of communication is "truer" or "righter" than any other. They are only *different* systems, each serving its function in its own domain. Many an idea is an idiom of a specific language and is best expressed in that language. For example, one cannot discuss morality in the language of science, thermodynamics in the language of religion, or artistic beauty in the language of politics. To the extent that each system of communication has its own idioms, there is no overlap or interchangeability among the systems.

But many ideas can be expressed equally well in several languages. The English "water," the Latin "aqua," and the scientific "H_2O" are entirely equivalent, and no one of these is truer or more correct than the others. They are merely different. Similarly, in one language man was created by God, in another he is a result of chance reactions among chemicals and of evolution. Again, neither the scientific nor the religious interpretation is the truer. The theologian might argue that everything was made by God, including scientists who think that man is the result of chance chemical reactions. The scientist will then argue back that chance chemical reactions created men with brains, including those theological brains that can conceive of a god who made everything. The impasse is permanent, and within their own systems of communication the scientist and the theologian are equally right. Many, of course, assume without warrant that it is the compelling duty of science to prove or disprove religious beliefs and of religion, to prove or to disprove scientific theories.

The point is that there is no single "correct" formulation of any idea that spans various languages. There are only different formulations, and in given circumstances one or the other may be more useful, more satisfying, or more effective. Clearly, anyone who is adept in more than one language will be able to travel that much more widely, and he will be able to feel at ease in the company of more than one set of ideas.

We are, it appears, forever committed to multiple standards, according to the different systems of communication we use. But to be multilingual in his interpretation of the world has been the unique heritage of man from the beginning. Though different proportions of the various languages are usually mixed in the outlook of different individuals, science, religion, art, politics, spoken language, all these and many more are always needed to make a full life.

In the language of science as a whole, one important dialect is *biology,* the domain of *living things.* Man probably was a biologist before he was anything else. His own body in health and illness; the phenomena of birth, growth, and death; and the plants and other animals that gave him food, shelter, and clothing undoubtedly were matters of serious concern to even the first of his kind. The motives were sheer necessity and the requirements of survival. These same motives still prompt the same biological studies today; agriculture, medicine, and fields allied to them are the most important branches of modern applied biology. In addition biology today is strongly experimental, and pure research is done extensively all over the world. Some of this research promotes biological technology; all of it increases our understanding of how living things are constructed and how they operate.

Over the decades the frontiers of biological investigation have been extended to smaller and smaller realms. Some 100 to 150 years ago, when modern biology began, the chief interest was the whole plant or the whole animal, how it lived, where it could be found, and how it was related to other whole living things. Such studies have been carried on ever since. In addition, techniques have gradually become available for the investigation of progressively smaller parts of the whole, their structures, their functions, and their interrelations. As a result, the frontiers of biology have been extended down to the chemical level during the last few decades. And while research with larger living units continues as before, the newest biology attempts to interpret living operations in terms of the chemicals out of which living creatures are constructed. Biology today therefore attempts to show how chemicals are put together to form, on the one hand, something like a rock or a piece of metal and, on the other, something like a flower or a cat or a man.

This book is an outline of how successful the attempt has been thus far.

review questions

1 What are the aims and the limitations of science? Review fully. In what sense is science a language, and how does it differ from other languages?

2 Review the procedures commonly employed in scientific inquiries and discuss the nature of each such procedure. Define controlled experiment.

3 How would you show by controlled experiment whether or not (*a*) temperature affects the rate of growth of living things, (*b*) houseflies can perceive differently colored objects, (*c*) plants use up some of the soil they grow in?

4 Suppose it were found in the experiment described in question 3*a* that, at an environmental temperature of 28°C, fertilized frog eggs develop into tadpoles roughly twice as fast as at 18°C. What kinds of theories could such evidence suggest?

5 Which of the ideas you have previously held about science should you now, after studying this chapter, regard as popular misconceptions?

6 Can you think of observations or problems that have so far not been investigated scientifically? Try to determine in each case whether or not such investigation is inherently possible.

7 Describe the philosophic foundations of science. Define mechanism and causalism, and contrast these systems of thought with those of vitalism and teleology. Can conceptual conflicts between science and religion be reconciled?

8 Consider the legal questions "Do you swear to tell the truth, the whole truth, and nothing but the truth?" and "Is it not a fact that on the night of . . . ?" If questions of this sort were to be used in a strictly scientific context, how should they properly be formulated?

9 Biology is one of the so-called *natural sciences,* all of which deal with the composition, properties, and behavior of matter in the universe. What other sciences are customarily regarded as belonging to this category, and what distinguishes them from one another and from biology?

10 Do natural sciences differ procedurally from (*a*) social sciences, (*b*) mathematics? Explain.

collateral readings

Bronowski, J.: "Science and Human Values," Harper Torchbooks 505, Harper & Row, New York, 1959. A well-known paperback, containing a stimulating discussion of the role of science in modern society.

Butterfield, H.: The Scientific Revolution, *Sci. American,* Sept., 1960. A popularly written historical survey of the growth of science since the time of the Renaissance.

Conant, J. B.: "Modern Science and Modern Man," Columbia, New York, 1952.

———: "Science and Common Sense," Yale, New Haven, Conn., 1951.

———: "On Understanding Science," Yale, New Haven, Conn., 1947.

In these three works a noted educator discusses the scientific method, its application in research, and the role of science in society.

Russell, Bertrand: "The Scientific Outlook," Norton, New York, 1931. A famous philosopher writes most penetratingly on the philosophic and logical foundations of science and on the relation of science to religion.

Terman, L. M.: Are Scientists Different?, *Sci. American,* Jan., 1955. A psychologist examines the traits generally characteristic of scientists and compares them with those of nonscientists.

Wilson, E. Bright, Jr.: "An Introduction to Scientific Research," McGraw-Hill, New York, 1952. A good discussion of the nature of the scientific method and its application in scientific investigations.

chapter 2 the biological background

The properties of life are exhibited by individual living creatures, or *organisms.* What does "being alive" actually signify, and what is an "organism?"

Surely the most obvious difference between something living and something nonliving is that the first *does* certain things the second does not do. The essence of "living" evidently lies in particular activities, or processes, or *functions.*

"Nonliving" could mean either "dead" or "inanimate," terms that are not equivalent. If a chicken does not perform its living functions it is dead, but then it is still distinguishable readily from an inanimate object such as a stone. Chickens, either living or dead, are organisms; stones are not. All organisms are put together in such a way that the functions of life are or once were actually possible. Accordingly, the essence of "organism" lies in particular building materials and building patterns, or *structures.*

A "living organism," therefore, is what it is by virtue of its functions and structures; the functions endow it with the property of life, and the structures permit execution of the life-sustaining functions. What are these functions and structures?

life and function

metabolism, self-perpetuation

A main activity of organisms is *nutrition,* a process that provides raw materials for maintenance of life. All living matter depends unceasingly on such raw materials, for the very act of living continuously uses up two basic commodities, energy and matter. In this respect a living organism is like a mechanical engine or indeed like any other action-performing system in the universe. Energy is needed to power the system, to make the parts operate, to keep activity going—in short, to maintain function. And matter is needed to replace parts, to repair breakdowns, to continue the system intact and able to function—in short, to maintain structure. Therefore, by its very nature as an action-performing unit, a "living" organism can remain alive only if it continuously uses up energy and matter. Both must be replenished from the outside through nutrition.

The external raw materials used in this function are *nutrients.* One general class of nutrients includes water, salts, and other materials obtainable directly from the physical environment of the earth. Another class comprises *foods,* which are available in the biological environment. Foods are obtained in two main ways. One group of organisms, comprising the *autotrophic* types, manufactures its foods from the raw materials present in the physical world—the soil, water, and air in which organisms live. In the majority of autotrophs sunlight is used as an energy source in their food-manufacturing process, which is called *photosynthesis.* Such organisms include plants, algae, and others that contain the green pigment *chlorophyll,* an essential component in photosynthesis.

The second group of organisms, comprising the *heterotrophic* types, is unable to manufacture its own foods and must therefore depend on already existing supplies of them. In this category are animals, fungi, most bacteria, and generally all those organisms that must make use of ready-made foods available in other organisms, living or dead. Eating by animals is one familiar method of obtaining preexisting foods. Thus, whereas autotrophs can survive in a strictly physical, nonbiological environment, heterotrophs, which cannot make their own food, require a biological as well as a physical environment.

Nutrients of all kinds, foods included, are chemicals, and as such they contain chemical energy. All living matter is maintained on the chemical energy obtained from nutrients. Given nutrients become decomposed inside an organism, through a series of energy-yielding chemical reactions; and the energy made available by these reactions sustains living activities. In this respect living systems are in principle quite similar to many familiar machines. In a gasoline or steam engine, for example, fuel is decomposed by burning, and this process releases energy that drives the motor. In the living "motor," nutrients likewise function as fuels; indeed, foods and engine fuels belong to the same families of chemical substances. Moreover, foods are decomposed in a way that is actually a form of burning, and the energy so obtained then drives the living "machine."

In living organisms the process of obtaining energy through decomposition of foods is called *respiration.* This function is a second major activity of living matter; it is the basic power source that maintains *all* living processes—including nutrition and even respiration itself. Energy made available through previous nutrition and respiration is needed to make possible continued nutrition and respiration.

Nutrients play a second main role as construction materials. The whole structure of the living organism must be built from and kept intact with nutrient "bricks." In effect, the chemical stuff of living matter—the substance of your skin or your heart, for example—is fundamentally the same as that of nutrients. This consideration leads to an interesting inference. If nutrients and living matter are basically equivalent and if nutrients are also respiratory fuels, it follows that living matter should be able to use *itself* as fuel. This is indeed the case; all living matter is inherently self-decomposing and self-consuming. The living "motor" cannot tell the difference between external fuel and internal structural parts, because both are fundamentally the same. Organisms are therefore unstable structurally, but they counteract this instability with the aid of nutrients. Some of these substances are fashioned continually into new structural parts, and such new parts replace those that burn away.

Living matter thus changes from moment to moment. As wear and tear and reconstruction occur side by side, the substance of living matter always "turns over;" the structural pattern remains the same, but almost every bit of the building material is replaced sooner or later. Moreover, if new building materials are incorporated faster than old ones wear away, the living organism will grow. Growth is a characteristic outcome of the use of nutrients in the construction of living matter. The processes by which nutrients are formed into new structural parts can collectively be called *synthesis* activities. They represent a third basic function of all living things. Like other functions of life, synthesis requires energy, and respiration must provide it.

2.1 Metabolism. *The main processes of metabolism and their interrelations.*

2.2 Self-perpetuation. *The main processes of self-perpetuation and their interrelations.*

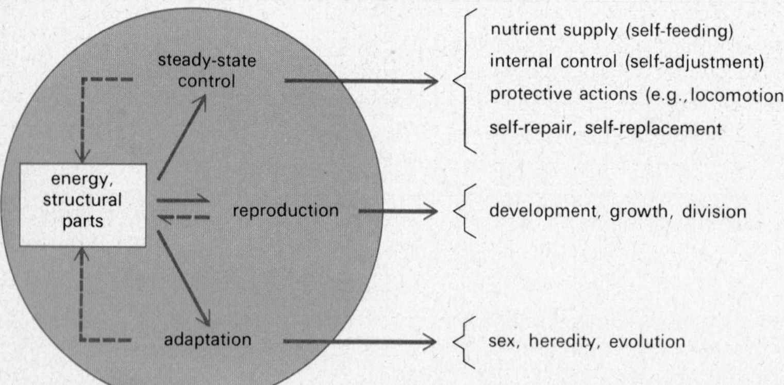

The three functions of nutrition, respiration, and synthesis together represent a broad living activity known as *metabolism.* Taken as a whole, metabolism is roughly equivalent to the operation of the living machinery. Metabolism also permits this machinery to continue in operation; a system that nourishes, respires, and synthesizes is capable of undertaking more nutrition, more respiration, and more synthesis (Fig. 2.1).

However, actual continuation of metabolism requires *control.* In this respect living matter is again like an engine. Continuous engine operation demands that the different parts of the engine act in harmony and that they become adjusted and readjusted in response to internal or external events that might change engine performance. In the same manner, continuation of metabolism in living matter depends on harmonized activity. Metabolizing as such is not equivalent to "living," but controlled metabolizing in a general sense is.

The necessary control is provided by *self-perpetuation,* a broadly inclusive set of processes. Self-perpetuation ensures that the metabolizing machinery continues to run indefinitely, and despite internal and external happenings that might otherwise alter or stop its operation (Fig. 2.2).

The most direct regulation of metabolism is brought about by the self-perpetuative function of *steady-state control.* Such control permits a living organism to receive *information* from within itself and from the external environment, and to act on this information in a usually self-preserving manner. The information is generally received in the form of *stimuli,* and the ensuing actions are *responses.* For example, a common stimulus is a decrease in the internal supply of nutrients, and the typical response is procurement of more nutrients from the environment. Or if the stimulus is produced by a situation of external danger, the response could be a protective activity such as movement away from danger. By thus making possible appropriate responses to given stimuli, the internal controls preserve *adequate operating conditions* in living matter; they make adjustments that result in a steady, living state in which an organism can remain intact and functioning.

But the span of existence of an organism is invariably limited. Death is a built-in attribute of living matter because the parts of the organism that maintain steady states are themselves subject to breakdown or destruction. When some of its controls become inoperative, the organism suffers *disease.* Diseases can be regarded generally as failures of steady-state controls, or as temporary *unsteady* states. Other, still intact controls may initiate self-repair, but in time so many controls break down simultaneously that too few remain intact to effect repairs. The organism is then in an irreversibly unsteady state and it must die.

However, before it dies it may have brought into play a second major self-perpetuative function, *reproduction.* With the help of energy and raw materials the living organism has enlarged, and such growth in size prepares the way for later growth in numbers. Reproduction in a sense anticipates and compensates for unavoidable individual death. By means of reproduction successive generations are produced and in this manner life can be carried on indefinitely (Fig. 2.3).

Reproduction implies a still poorly understood capacity of *rejuvenation.* The material out of which the offspring is made is part of the parent, hence is really just as old as the rest of the parent. Yet the one lives and the other dies. Evidently, there is a profound distinction between "old" and "aged." Reproduction also implies the capacity of *development,* for the offspring is almost always not only smaller than the parent but also less nearly complete in form and function.

As generation succeeds generation, long-term environmental changes are likely to have their effect on the living succession. In the course of thousands and millions of years, for example, climates may change profoundly; ice ages may come and go; mountains, oceans, vast tracts of land may appear and disappear. Moreover, living organisms themselves in time alter the nature of a locality in major ways. Consequently, two related organisms many generations apart could find themselves in greatly different environments. And whereas the steady-state controls of the ancestor may have coped effectively with the early environment, such controls could be overpowered rapidly by the new environment. In the course of many generations, therefore, organisms must change *with* the environment if they are to continue in existence. They actually do change, through *adaptation.* As will become apparent later, this self-perpetuative function itself consists of three subfunctions: *sex, heredity,* and *evolution* (Fig. 2.4 and see Fig. 2.2).

Self-perpetuation as a whole therefore comprises three basic kinds of activities. Steady-state controls maintain appropriate operating condi-

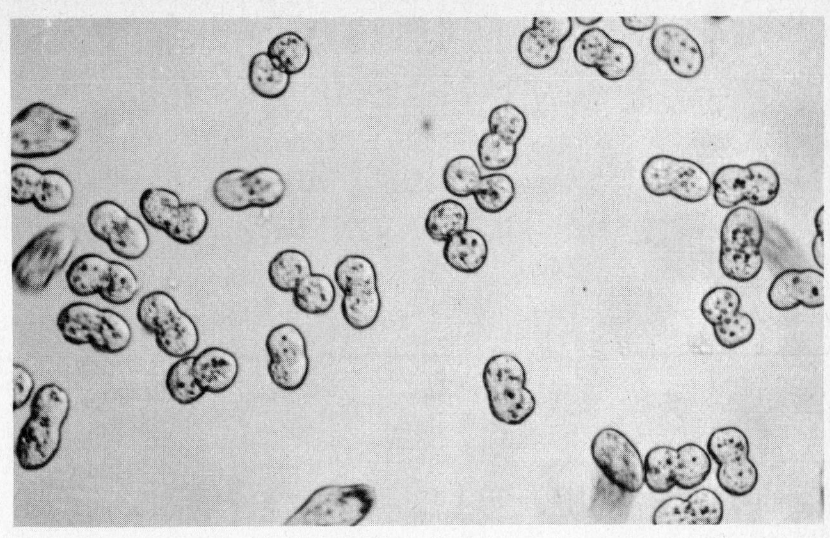

2.3 Reproduction: *growth in size followed by subdivision and growth in numbers. The living ciliate protozoa Tetrahymena shown here have grown in size for a period of time and are now in various stages of reproduction bv subdivision. Repeated at intervals, reproduction can maintain the living succession indefinitely* (approx. *X1,000*).

2.4 Adaptation: *change with the environment. The upper figure* (*A*) *is a drawing of a placoderm, a type of fish long extinct but very common some 300 million years ago. Fishes of this group were the ancestors of modern fish, of which one, a speckled brook trout, is shown in the lower figure* (*B*)*. Most of the differences between ancestor and descendant, here as in other cases, appear to be a result of adaptation to changes in the physical and biological environment.*

tions in individual organisms. Reproduction ensures a continuing succession of individual organisms. And adaptation molds and alters the members of this succession in step with the slowly changing nature of the environment. In effect, self-perpetuation adds the dimension of time to metabolism; regardless of how the environment might change in time, self-perpetuation virtually guarantees the continuation of metabolism. Metabolism in turn makes possible uninterrupted self-perpetuation, and the system so able to metabolize and to perpetuate itself can persist indefinitely; it becomes a ''living'' system.

living matter

The fundamental meaning of ''living'' can now be defined: *any structure that metabolizes and perpetuates itself is alive.* Moreover, the metabolic functions of nutrition, respiration, and synthesis make possible, and are themselves made possible by, the self-perpetuative functions of steady-state control, reproduction, and adaptation.

A first implication of this definition is that, by their very nature, living systems collectively are highly permanent kinds of matter, perhaps the most permanent in the universe. They are certainly the most enduring on earth. Every inanimate or dead object on earth sooner or later decomposes and crumbles to dust under the impact of the environment. But every living object metabolizes and perpetuates itself and consequently can avoid such a fate. Oceans, mountains, even whole continents have come and gone several times during the last 2 or 3 billion years, but living matter has continued indestructibly during that time and, indeed, has become progressively more abundant.

A second implication is that any structure that does not satisfy the above definition in every particular is either inanimate or dead. Life must cease if even one of the functions of metabolism or self-perpetuation ceases. This criterion of life offers an instructive contrast to the operation of modern machines, many of which perform some of the functions that also occur in living organisms. As noted, for example, a machine can take on ''nourishment'' in the form of fuel and raw materials. The fuel can be ''respired'' to provide operating energy, and, with it, the raw materials can then be ''synthesized'' into nuts, bolts, and other structural components out of which such a machine might be built. Evidently, machines can carry out activities fully equivalent to those of metabolism. Like living systems, moreover, many automated machines have ingenious steady-state controls built into them. For example, such controls could make a machine automatically self-feeding and self-adjusting.

But no machine is as yet self-protecting, self-repairing, or self-healing to any major extent, and no machine certainly is capable of growing. Furthermore, whereas living matter can reproduce before death, machines cannot. It is in this capacity of reproduction that living systems differ most critically from inanimate systems. However, the theoretical knowledge of how to build a self-reproducing machine now exists. A device of this kind would metabolize, maintain steady states, and eventually ''die'' but, before that, would produce ''offspring.'' It would be almost living. If it had the additional capacity of adaptation, it would be fully living. Here too the theoretical know-how is already available. On paper, machines have been designed that could carry out ''sexual'' processes of a sort, that could pass on heredity characteristics to their ''progeny,'' and that could ''evolve'' and change their properties in the course of many ''generations.'' If such machines should actually be built some day then the essential distinction between ''living'' and ''machine'' will have disappeared.

This consideration points up a third implication of the definition above: the property of life basically does not depend on a particular substance. *Any* substance of whatever composition will be ''living'' provided that it metabolizes and perpetuates itself. It happens that only one type of such a substance is now known. We call it ''living matter,'' or often also *protoplasm,* and it exists in the form of organisms. But if some day we should be able to build a fully metabolizing and self-perpetuating system out of nuts, bolts, and wires, then it too will have to be regarded as being truly alive. Similarly, if some day out in space we should encounter a metabolizing and self-perpetuating being made up in a hitherto completely unknown way, it too will have to be considered living. It will not be ''life as we know it,'' or life based on the earthly variety of protoplasm, but in any case it will be truly living if it metabolizes and self-perpetuates.

We conclude, then, that an object is defined as living or nonliving on the basis of its functional properties, not its structural ones. On the other hand, structural properties do determine whether an object is an "organism" or something inanimate. Linguistically as well as biologically, the root of "organism" is *organization:* a characteristic *structural order.*

organism and structure

levels of organization

The smallest structural units of matter, living matter included, are *subatomic particles*—mainly electrons, protons, and neutrons. The next larger units are *atoms,* each of which consists of subatomic particles. Atoms in turn form still more complex combinations called *chemical compounds;* and the latter are variously joined together as even more elaborate units, or *complexes of compounds.*

These units can be regarded as representing successively higher *levels of organization* of matter. They form a pyramid, or hierarchy, in which any given level contains all lower levels as components and is itself a component of all higher levels. For example, atoms contain subatomic particles as components, and atoms are themselves components of chemical compounds (Fig. 2.5).

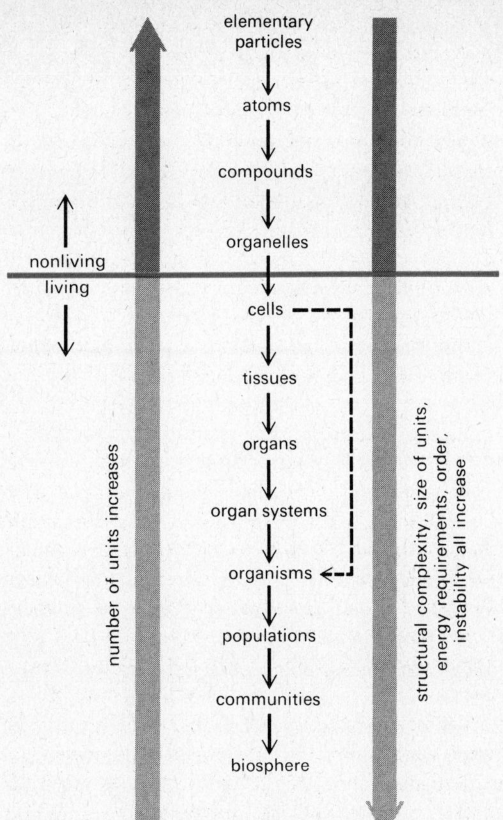

***2.5* Hierarchy of levels** *in the organization of matter. The biosphere represents the sum total of all living things on earth.*

All structural levels up to and including those of complexes of compounds are encountered in both the nonliving and the living world. For example, two familiar chemical compounds found in living as well as nonliving matter are water and table salt. Examples of complexes of compounds in the nonliving world are rocks, which are composed of several types of compounds (water and table salt among them). In living matter, complexes of compounds often occur as microscopic and submicroscopic bodies called *organelles.* But even in their most elaborate and complicated forms, organelles or complexes of compounds of any kind cannot qualify as living units. To reach the level of life, we must go to the next higher structure level, that of *cells.*

A cell is a specific combination of organelles, a usually microscopic bit of matter organized just complexly enough to contain all the necessary apparatus for the performance of metabolism and self-perpetuation. A cell in effect represents the least-elaborate known structure that can be fully alive. It follows that a living organism must consist of at least one cell. Indeed, *unicellular* organisms probably constitute the majority of living creatures on earth. All other organisms are *multicellular,* each composed of up to hundreds of trillions of joined cells.

Several distinct levels of organization can be distinguished within multicellular organisms. The simplest multicellular types contain comparatively small numbers of cells. If all such cells are more or less alike, the organism is often referred to as a cellular *colony.* If two or more different groups of cells are present, each such group usually forms a *tissue.* In structurally more complex organisms, not only are there several tissues, but some of the tissues are also joined further as one or more units called *organs.* The most complex organisms contain not only many tissues and organs, but also groups of organs united as one or more *organ systems.* Thus, living organisms exhibit at least five levels of structural complexity: the single-celled form, the colonial form, the organism with tissues, the type with organs, and the type with organ systems.

Several still higher levels of life can be distinguished beyond the organism level. A few individual organisms of one kind together sometimes make up a *family.* Groups of families of one kind often form a *society.* Groups of families, societies, or simply large numbers of organisms of a particular kind make up a geographically localized *population.* All populations of the same kind together form a *species.* Several different species are represented in a local *community.* And the sum of all local communities represents the whole living world.

This hierarchical organization of matter permits formulation of a structural definition of life and nonlife. Up to and including the level of the complex of compounds, matter is nonliving. At all higher levels matter can be living, provided that at each such level metabolic and self-perpetuative functions are carried out. For example, if a society is to be living it must metabolize and perpetuate itself on its own level as well as on every lower level down to that of the cell.

Moreover, as life is organized by levels, so is death. Structural death occurs when one level is disrupted or decomposed to the next lower. For example, if a tissue is disjoined into separate cells, the tissue ceases to exist. However, the lower levels need not necessarily be affected. Thus the separated cells of a tissue often carry on individually; or if a family is disrupted, the member organisms still can survive on their own. By contrast, death at a given level often does entail death at higher levels as well. If many or all of its tissues are destroyed, the whole organ will be destroyed; or if many or all of its families are dismembered, a society may cease to exist. In general, the situation is comparable to a pyramid of cards. Removal of a top card need not affect the rest of the pyramid, but removal of a bottom card usually topples the whole structure. Evidently, neither life nor death is a singular state but each is organized and structured by levels.

This hierarchy of levels provides a rough outline of the past history of matter. The universe as a whole is now believed to have begun in the form of subatomic particles. These then became joined as atoms and formed galaxies, stars, and planets. The atoms of planets later gave rise to chemical compounds and complexes of compounds. On earth, some of the complexes of compounds eventually produced living matter in the form of cells, and unicellular types were the ancestors of multicellular types. Among the latter, colonial types arose first, forms with organ systems last (see also Chap. 8). Considered historically, therefore, matter appears to have become organized progressively, level by level, and the presently existing hierarchy is the direct result.

Each level of organization includes fewer units than any lower level. There are fewer communities than species, fewer cells than organelles; and there is only one living world, but there are uncountable numbers of subatomic particles. Also, each level is structurally more complex than lower ones; a particular level combines the complexities of all lower levels and has an additional complexity of its own. For example, social complexity results from the characteristics of each member organism *as well as* from numerous special characteristics that arise out of the ways in which the members are organized as a society.

In any hierarchy of levels, moreover, a jump from one level to the next can often be achieved only at the expense of energy. It takes energy to build atoms into chemical compounds, and it took energy to create cells out of chemical complexes. Similarly, energy is needed to produce tissues out of cells or societies out of separate families. Indeed, once a higher living level has been created, energy expenditures must usually continue thereafter to maintain that level. For example, if the energy supply to the cell, the organ, or the organism is stopped, death and decomposition soon follow and reversion to lower levels occurs. Similarly, maintenance of a family or a society requires work over and above that needed to maintain the organization of subordinate units.

This requirement is an expression of the *second law of thermodynamics,* about which more will be said in the next chapter: if left to itself, any system tends toward a state of greatest stability. "Randomness," "disorder," and "probability" are equivalent to this meaning of stability. When a system includes high levels of organization, it also exhibits a high degree of order and it is correspondingly nonrandom and improbable. The second law tells us that such a system is unstable and that if we leave it to itself it will eventually become disordered, more random, more probable, and therefore more stable. Living systems are the most ordered, unstable, and improbable systems known. If they are to avoid the fate predicted by the second law, a price must be paid. That price is external energy—energy to maintain the order despite the continuous tendency toward disorder.

Such energy expenditures represent the price for the new properties obtained at higher levels. One of the new properties is united, integrated function: disunited structure means independent function and, by extension, *competition;* united structure means joint function and, by extension, *cooperation.* For example, if atoms remain structurally independent they can be in functional competition for other suitable atoms with which they might combine. Once they do unite as a compound, however, they have lost structural independence and must thereafter function jointly, as a single "cooperative" unit. Similarly, cells can remain independent structurally and can compete for space and raw materials. But if they form a multicellular unit they surrender their independence and become a cooperative, integrated system.

This generalization applies at every other organizational level as well. The results on the human level are very familiar. Men can be independent and competing, or they can give up a measure of independence, form families and societies, and begin cooperating. The sociological laws that govern the organizational groupings of men govern the organization of all matter, from atoms to the whole living world.

specialization

The fundamental advantage of cooperation is *operational efficiency;* the cooperating whole is more efficient in performing the functions of life than its lower-level components separately and competitively. For example, separate cells must expend more energy and materials for survival than if that same number of cells were integrated as a tissue. The situation is similar for all other organizational levels.

One underlying reason for this difference is that, in the integrated unit, duplication of effort can be avoided. In a set of separate cells, for example, every cell is exposed to the environment on all sides and must therefore expend energy and materials on all sides to cope with the impact of the environment. However, if the same cells are grouped together as a compact tissue only the outermost cells are in direct contact with the environment, and inner cells then need not channel their resources into protective activities.

Also, in addition to avoiding duplication of effort, cooperative groupings make possible continuity of effort. The general principle can be illustrated by contrasting unicellular and multicellular organisms, for example. A unicellular form must necessarily carry out all survival functions in its one cell. In many instances, however, the performance of even one of these functions requires most or all of the capacities of the cell. Thus the *entire* cell surface must often serve as gateway for entering nutrients and departing wastes. And *all* parts of the cell may have to participate directly in locomotion or in feeding, for example. Very often therefore, two such functions cannot be performed at the same time, for one function can preclude the simultaneous performance of the other. Mutual exclusion of some functions by others is a common occurrence in all unicellular organisms (Fig. 2.6).

In multicellular types, by contrast, continuity of a given effort becomes possible through *division of labor* among the cells. The total task of survival can be divided up into several subtasks, and each of these can become the continuous responsibility of particular cells only. Some cells might function in feeding, continuously so, and others in locomotion, again continuously. Frequently division of labor is actually so pronounced that many or most cells are permanently limited in functional capacity; they can perform only certain jobs and no others. For example, mature nerve cells can conduct nerve impulses only and are quite unable to reproduce or move. Mature muscle cells can move by contracting but they normally do not reproduce. Indeed, the majority of the cells of a multicellular organism is generally restricted in some ways in functional versatility. Such cells exhibit greater or lesser degrees of *specialization.*

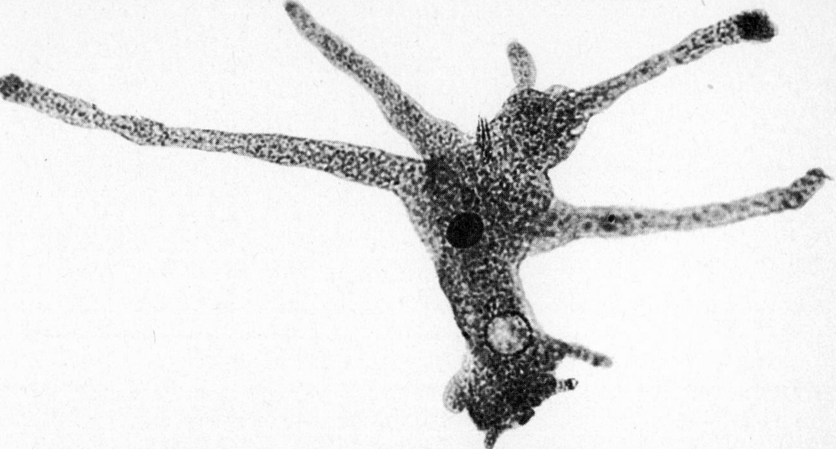

2.6 Amoeba *(approx. X5,000). Like all other unicellular organisms, this protozoon carries out all metabolic and self-perpetuative functions in a single cell. Often one of these functions—locomotion, for example—precludes a simultaneous execution of another—feeding, for example. Note nucleus (dark central body), excretory vacuole (light spherical body), and the pseudopodia, fingerlike extensions that serve in locomotion and feeding. (Courtesy Carolina Biological Supply Company.)*

An individual *specialized* cell therefore cannot perform all the functions necessary for survival. This is why, when some cells are removed from the whole organism, as in injury, for example, such cells usually die; the specialized cell has lost independence. The whole task of survival can be carried out only by the entire multicellular system with its many *differently* specialized cells.

Specialization makes possible not only division of labor but also increased effectiveness of labor. For example, all unicellular organisms are sensitive to environmental stimuli, but the degree of this relatively unspecialized sensitivity is quite modest. By contrast, many multicellular organisms have highly specialized sensory cells that are exceedingly sensitive and respond to even very weak stimuli. Moreover, several kinds of sensory cells are often present, some specialized specifically for light stimuli, others for sound stimuli, still others for mechanical stimuli, and so on. Thus both the degree and the range of sensitivity can become enormously greater in multicellular forms, in which the cells can become specialized. Similarly for all other functions.

We can now understand the fundamental advantage of higher organizational levels generally and of multicellularity specifically. First, a multicellular structure permits division of labor, through which duplication of effort can be avoided and several efforts can continue simultaneously and uninterruptedly. Second, division of labor leads to specialization, which permits any given effort to become highly effective. The overall result is an enormous saving of energy and materials, hence cheaper operation, and an enormous gain in efficiency. This is one reason why living history has produced multicellular organisms, equipped successively with tissues, organs, and organ systems, rather than only bigger and better unicellular organisms.

To be sure, loss of functional versatility in a specialized cell is never total. A cell cannot be so completely specialized that it performs just a single function. Certain irreducible "housekeeping" functions must be carried out by every living cell of a multicellular organism. Each such cell must absorb nutrients, must respire and synthesize, and must maintain steady states relative to its immediate environment. These metabolic and self-perpetuative functions cannot be specialized. Performed continuously and simultaneously in every cell, they are the bedrock of cellular survival. Specialization only affects additional functions, and the fewer of such additional functions a cell performs the more specialized it is. Conversely, a cell cannot be totally unspecialized and so versatile functionally that it could survive under any or all conditions. All cells, even the most independent, still depend on, for example, specific kinds of environments that are suitable for life. Cells therefore are only more or less highly specialized; and within limits the relative degree of functional versatility is an inverse measure of the relative degree of specialization.

The specializations at one level determine the specializations at higher levels. If the cells composing a tissue are specialized as muscle cells, then the whole tissue correspondingly will be specialized for contraction and movement. If the organs of an organ system include teeth, stomach, and intestine, then, since the organs perform nutritional functions, the whole organ system will be specialized for nutrition.

Every organism as a whole is therefore specialized in accordance with the specializations of its subordinate parts. For example, a plant is specialized as a stationary food-creating organism; an animal, as an organism that can move all or part of its body and thereby can obtain preexisting foods. Among plants, furthermore, some form seeds, others do not; some produce flowers, others develop cones; some become trees, others mature as shrubs or herbs. Among animals, some are *vertebrates,* with a skeleton containing a vertebral column, others are *invertebrates,* without such supports; some are wormlike, others have vastly different shapes. All such characteristics represent specializations in structure, function, or both, and they are based on the specializations of the parts that compose an organism.

As a general result, a given organism can live only in a very *particular* environment and can pursue only a very *particular* way of life. A tree cannot do without soil, a fish must lead an aquatic existence, and man too is specialized in his own way. He requires a terrestrial environment of certain properties, a social environment of variously specialized human beings, and he must live in a community that contains appropriate food organisms. And by being specialized, every organism in effect represents a necessarily cooperating unit of a higher living level: the population, the whole species, the community of several species. These higher-level units are specialized in their turn, according to the particular specializations of their individual members.

Thus, although all organisms are alike in their general characteristics, they differ in their detailed characteristics because of specialization. Functionally, all organisms pursue life identically through metabolism and self-perpetuation; structurally all organisms are composed of cells. But in each organism both the functions and the structures are in some respects specialized, and these specializations differ in different cases. Evidently there are many ways of making a living; and it is precisely because living matter is able to specialize that the problems of life can have different solutions in different cases.

What kinds of differently specialized organisms actually make up the living world?

living organisms

classification: the main groups

The classification of organisms on the basis of their specializations is the concern of the biological subscience of *taxonomy* (or *systematics*). The present method of classifying organisms was originated by Carolus Linnaeus, a Swedish naturalist of the early eighteenth century. This linnean system of taxonomy has since become greatly elaborated and is now in universal use. It is based on the proposition that if certain organisms can be shown to have similar body construction they can be regarded as members of the same classification group. Moreover, an evolutionary inference is also made: the more closely two organisms resemble each other, the more closely are they likely to be related. Thus, taxonomy deals with the structural makeup of organisms directly and with their evolutionary histories indirectly.

In a given classification group it is often possible to distinguish several subgroups, each containing organisms having even greater similarity of body structure and, by inference, evolutionary history. Such a subgroup can often be subdivided still further, and a whole hierarchy of classification groups can be established in this fashion. The progressively lower levels in this hierarchy represent *taxonomic ranks,* or *categories,* and each is named; in succession from highest, or most inclusive, to lowest, or least inclusive, the main categories are: *kingdom, phylum, class, order, family, genus,* and *species.* Intermediate ranks sometimes interpolated between two main levels are identified by the prefixes *sub-* or *super-;* for example, *subphylum, superclass, subgenus.* The actual organisms included in a given rank-category are referred to technically as *taxa.* For example, moss plants form a taxon of phylum rank; mammals are a taxon at the class rank.

In the hierarchy as a whole, progressively lower ranks consist of progressively more but smaller groups. The living world contains only some three dozen phyla but as many as $1\frac{1}{2}$ to 2 million or more species. Also, the groups at successively lower ranks have increasingly similar body forms and evolutionary histories. Thus the members of a class resemble each other to a great extent, but the members in one of the orders of that class resemble each other to an even greater extent. A corresponding relation holds for evolutionary histories (Fig. 2.7).

That taxonomy provides direct and inferential information about two kinds of data, body structure and evolutionary history, should be clearly kept in mind. Organisms have other characteristics as well, notably functions and ways of life. However, these play only a limited role in defining taxonomic types. Because metabolism and self-perpetuation are broadly the same in all organisms, such functions are not very useful as distinguishing traits. Moreover, both the ways of life and the detailed ways of performing functions can become modified greatly. Such characteristics therefore are usually less permanent than body architecture and evolutionary history.

Structural resemblances of presently living organisms can be studied readily, and indeed they are well known for the most part. But studies of evolutionary histories—through fossils, for example—represent an independent line of investigation, and the amount of information available here varies greatly. In general, evolutionary knowledge is less precise the higher the taxonomic rank. For many high rank-groups evolutionary information actually is quite incomplete or lacking altogether, and in such cases classification must be based almost wholly on studies of body structure. Conclusions regarding evolutionary histories are then correspondingly uncertain. In instances of this sort, classification is said to be artificial, or "unnatural," to greater or lesser degree.

The most unnatural grouping in the taxonomic hierarchy in effect is the kingdom. By tradition

A

B

C

2.7 Resemblance of related taxonomic groups. *The three members of the vertebrate class of mammals shown here are alike in, for example, having fur and nursing their young with milk. However, the snowshoe hare (*Lepus*) belongs to the order Lagomorpha, whereas both the jaguar (*Felis*) and the timber wolf (*Canis*) belong to the order Carnivora. The two orders resemble each other greatly, and they also have similar evolutionary histories. But they differ in, for example, tooth structure, eating habits, and locomotion. Of the two carnivores shown, the jaguar belongs to the cat family Felidae and the timber wolf to the dog family Canidae. The two resemble each other more in anatomy and evolutionary history than either resembles the hare.*

that goes back to Linnaeus and even to earlier times, all organisms have been classified into two kingdoms, the plant kingdom and the animal kingdom (Table 1). It is highly questionable whether this familiar, simple, and 250-year-old way of subdividing the living world is still justifiable or adequate today. For it is now clear that, in this linnean sense, plants and animals are ultimately indistinguishable by biological criteria. Every trait usually regarded as characteristic of one kingdom occurs also in the other. For example, plants are defined traditionally as organisms that photosynthesize and do not exhibit locomotion, and animals as organisms that exhibit heterotrophic nutrition as well as locomotion. On such a basis, however, many algae and all fungi and slime molds would have to be animals, for all these organisms are nongreen heterotrophs and a good many of them exhibit locomotion as well. Yet sponges, corals, barnacles, tunicates, and other groups could not be strictly labeled as animals since the adult forms are attached and without locomotion. Moreover, certain primitive algal types would be both plant and animal at once, since, as will be shown in Chap. 9, such organisms can be alternately photosynthetic and nonlocomotor or heterotrophic and locomotor.

Traits other than nutrition or locomotion fail similarly as distinguishing criteria. If animals are defined as organisms with nervous and muscular structures, or at least equivalent components, then many algae would have to be animals; and sponges, which lack such structures, would have to be plants. If plants are defined as organisms containing chemicals such as cellulose, then tunicates would have to be plants and a number of entire phyla to photosynthetic algae without cellulose would have to be animals. Actually there does not appear to be a single characteristic that would distinguish the traditional plant and animal kingdoms uniquely.

In effect, some organisms fit in neither the plant nor the animal category and several other groups fit in both. Traditional views notwithstanding, for example, bacteria really have very little in common with either plants or animals, and quite a number of unicellular algae and other types can be regarded equally well as plants *or* animals. To be sure, no one has much difficulty in deciding whether advanced organisms like cabbages and cats are plants or animals. But such a difficulty does exist with many organisms now known to be primitive, that is, organisms closely related to the

Table 1. The traditional classification of organisms: plant and animal kingdoms

Kingdom	Subkingdom	Members
Kingdom Plantae	Subkingdom Thallophyta	algae, fungi, bacteria, slime molds
	Subkingdom Embryophyta	moss plants, vascular plants
Kingdom Animalia	Subkingdom Protozoa	largely unicellular types
	Subkingdom Metazoa	multicellular types

ancestral types that gave rise to both cabbages and cats. As will be shown in Chap. 9, such ancestral types exhibited both plantlike and animal-like traits *simultaneously,* as is still true of some of their primitive descendants today. And if we go even farther back in time, the very first organisms on earth appear to have had neither plantlike nor animal-like traits at all.

The point is that plants and animals, clearly so recognizable, were not in existence right from the beginning. Instead, some of the early organisms *evolved* in plantlike or animal-like directions, slowly and gradually; and a definite, finalized ''plant'' status or ''animal'' status was attained only relatively late in evolutionary history. Therefore, a division of the living world merely into plant and animal kingdoms is too simple. It does not take into account the *gradual* evolution of distinct plant and animal groups, and it allows no place for those primitive organisms that even now are neither ''plant'' nor ''animal'' or that are both.

In view of this taxonomic difficulty, attempts have been made to establish alternative classifications that do reflect our present knowledge of evolution. One such alternative scheme recognizes not two but four largest groups of organisms. Each has a taxonomic rank roughly equivalent to a kingdom, although it is not desirable to use this designation as long as it is technically still reserved for ''plants'' and ''animals.'' These four highest taxa are the *Monera,* the *Protista,* the *Metaphyta,* and the *Metazoa.* The kinds of organisms included in each are listed in Table 2, and the probable evolutionary interrelations of the four are sketched in Fig. 2.8.

In this four-part classification every living creature has a proper place. Monera and Protista go back farthest in evolutionary history. Both groups are believed to be descended independently from the earliest organisms on earth (see also Chap. 8). Modern moneran representatives are the bacteria and the blue-green algae, all basically unicellular organisms and variously plantlike, animal-like, both, or neither. Protista today include unicellular as well as multicellular members. Some of the algae are both plantlike and animal-like simultaneously, but most of them have lost heterotrophic capacities and now have more or less plantlike traits. Conversely, the fungi, slime, molds, and protozoa have lost the plantlike modes of nutrition. Yet in other respects these three protistan groups again display certain plantlike and animal-like traits in combination. Fungi are rather more plantlike, protozoa, more nearly animal-like.

The other two large categories, Metaphyta and Metazoa, are both believed to have evolved from ancient protists, independently and at different times. Both groups are exclusively multicellular, and their structural complexity reaches the level of complicated organs and organ systems. Metaphyta are photosynthetic and without locomotion, and they are unmistakably ''plants.'' Metazoa are exclusively nonphotosynthetic and largely (but not always) capable of locomotion; they are unmistakably ''animals.''

Unlike the two linnean kingdoms, each of the four major categories above can be defined sharply and distinguished clearly from the others (see also Chaps. 8 and 9). Moreover, the four-part scheme has the important advantage that it is more nearly in line with the known evolutionary and structural characteristics of existing organisms. Throughout this book, therefore, any unqualified reference to plants or animals is restricted to mean Metaphyta or Metazoa, respectively. Also, an alga is not regarded as a plant nor a protozoon as an animal, but both organisms are identified as protists.

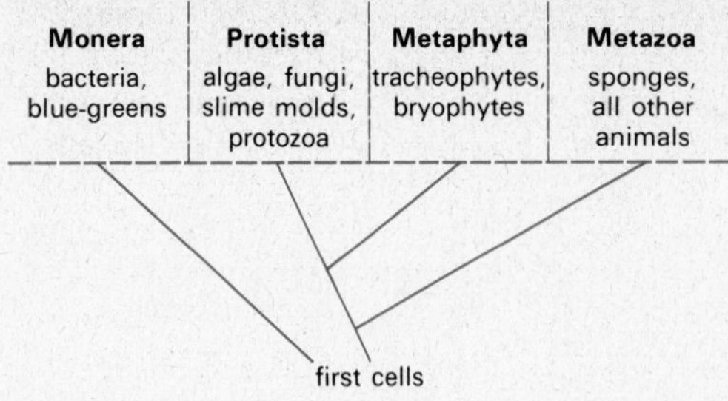

***2.8 The four main categories of organisms** and their probable evolutionary interrelations.*

Table 2. The main categories of living organisms

category	*representative phyla*	*representative membership*
Monera	Schizophyta	bacteria
	Cyanophyta	blue-green algae
Protista	Chlorophyta	green algae
	Chrysophyta	golden-brown algae
	Phaeophyta	brown algae
	Rhodophyta	red algae
	Mycophyta	fungi
	Myxophyta	slime molds
	Protozoa	protozoans
Metaphyta	Bryophyta	moss plants: mosses, liverworts
	Tracheophyta	vascular plants: ferns, coniferous seed plants, flowering seed plants
Metazoa	Porifera	sponges
	Cnidaria	coelenterates: hydras, jellyfishes, corals, sea anemones
	Platyhelminthes	flatworms: planarians, flukes, tapeworms
	Aschelminthes	sac worms: rotifers, roundworms
	Mollusca	mollusks: snails, clams, squids, octopuses
	Annelida	segmented worms: earthworms, leeches
	Arthropoda	arthropods: crustacea (barnacles, shrimps, crabs, lobsters, crayfishes), insects, scorpions, spiders, ticks, millipedes, centipedes
	Echinodermata	spiny-skinned animals: starfishes, sea urchins, sea cucumbers, brittle stars, sea lilies
	Chordata	notochord-possessing animals, or tunicates, amphioxus, and vertebrates; among vertebrates: jawless fishes (lampreys), bony fishes (herring, tuna, etc.), cartilage fishes (sharks), amphibia (salamanders, newts, toads, frogs), reptiles (turtles, lizards, snakes, alligators), birds, mammals

classification: the subgroups

In passing from the highest level to lower taxonomic ranks, classification tends to become progressively more "natural": evolutionary knowledge is more complete, and structural and evolutionary data come to dovetail more and more. At the lower levels, taxonomy thus tends to indicate an actual, real interrelation of organisms. For example, some notable exceptions notwithstanding, a phylum generally can be defined as the largest group of organisms for which a common ancestry has been demonstrated reasonably well and that is characterized by a common, basically unique body construction.

Table 2 indicates that most phyla represent more or less familiar categories of organisms, often named for one of their most distinctive anatomic features. For example, the phylum *Chordata* includes all animals that have an internal skeleton, the *notochord,* at least as embryos. This phylum contains a subphylum of *vertebrates,* identified by the presence of a vertebral column. In this subphylum one of the classes comprises the *mammals.* These animals share the possession of a vertebral column with all other vertebrate classes. But mammals are identified uniquely by hair and by their nursing young with milk. Every other class similarly has its own distinguishing traits.

In many cases the subgroups in a phylum differ greatly in their ways of life and their methods of executing functions, and a common body structure often is then not readily apparent. Consider, for example, the different appearance of three members of the phylum of vascular plants: a desert plant like a cactus, an aquatic plant like a water lily, and an underground plant like an onion bulb. Or consider the different appearance of a fish and a man, both members of the phylum Chordata. Nevertheless, all organisms in a phylum use the same kinds of structures in solving the different problems of their different environments. Thus the spines of a cactus, the surface float of a water lily, and the white, tear-producing layers inside an onion bulb all are structures of the same basic kind, namely, leaves. They all have evolved along different paths from one ancestral type of foliation. Similarly, the fins of a fish and the arms of a man are basically the same kind of structure, having evolved from one common ancestral type of body appendage.

Whenever body parts in an organism or in different organisms have evolved from a common ancestral starting point, as in the examples just cited, and whenever they also have the same structure at least at early developmental stages, then such components are said to be *homologous.* Homology thus indicates similarity of history and structure, without reference to function. Indeed, homologous structures may or may not function the same way. For example, fish fins and human arms are homologous but do not function in the same manner. Whenever two structures do function in like fashion, regardless of history or structure, they are *analogous.* Bird wings and bat wings are analogous. They also happen to be homologous, but analogous structures are not always homologous as well. For example, bird wings and insect wings are analogous inasmuch as both are used for flying, but they are not homologous (Fig. 2.9).

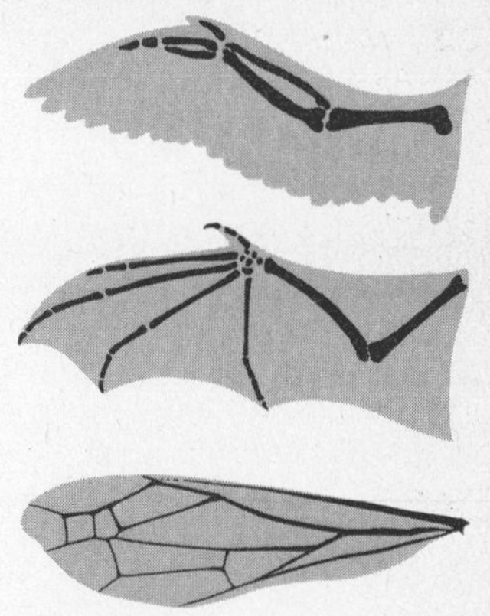

2.9 Homology and analogy. *The bird, bat, and insect wings diagrammed here are all analogous—they all serve the same function of flying. Bird and bat wings are also homologous, since they develop in similar fashion and have similar structure. But insect wings are not homologous to either of the other two.*

The homologies among and within groups provide the basic criteria for distinguishing classes in a phylum, orders in a class, families in an order, genera in a family, and species in a genus. The species, normally the lowest unit, is the most natural of all taxonomic categories. It is defined as an *interbreeding* group: the members of a species normally interbreed only with one another, not with members of a different species. A species thus encompasses all organisms of the same particular kind (see also Chap. 6). In this instance, therefore, classification is based on a characteristic that undoubtedly results from a very close structural and evolutionary similarity of the organisms in question. For example, all men now in existence are members of the same single species.

According to linnean tradition and internationally accepted rules, a species is always identified by *two* technical names, in Latin or latinized. For example, the species of grass frogs is known throughout the world as *Rana pipiens;* the species to which we belong is *Homo sapiens.* Such species names are always underlined or printed in italics, and the first name is capitalized. This first name always identifies the genus to which the species belongs. Thus the human species belongs to the genus *Homo,* but the genus *Rana* contains *Rana pipiens* and many other frog species as well.

A complete classification of an organism tells a great deal about the nature of that organism. For example, if we knew nothing else about corn plants and men except their taxonomic classifications, then we would know that the traits of these organisms are as outlined in Table 3. Such data already represent a substantial detailing of the body structure. We would also know by implication that the evolutionary history of corn plants traces back to the common ancestry of flowering plants, and that the history of men goes back to a common chordate ancestry.

In a number of cases the taxonomic ranks assigned today to certain groups of organisms are only tentative, and sometimes a particular group is placed at different rank-levels by different authorities. In general, taxonomic agreement among biologists increases with the lower, more natural rank-categories and decreases with the higher, less-natural ones. Indeed the higher categories are being reshuffled more or less continually. But this is as it should be, for as our knowledge of evolutionary histories improves, the rankings of the organisms must be adjusted accordingly.

On one point agreement is universal, however. Taxonomic studies clearly suggest, and evolutionary evidence fully confirms, that the interrelations among organisms have the pattern of a greatly branching *bush* (Fig. 2.10). All presently living organisms are *contemporaries,* appearing at the uppermost branch tips of the bush. Ancestral types, most of them long extinct, appear lower down, where branches join. Thus a particular common ancestor can give rise to *several* different types of descendants, each inheriting the characteristics of the common ancestor and evolving innovations of its own. And a particular descendant living today can become a common

Table 3. A partial classification of corn plants and men

taxonomic rank	***corn plant***	***man***
phylum	*Tracheophyta:* plants with vascular tissues	*Chordata:* animals with notochords
subphylum	*Pteropsida:* types with large leaves	*Vertebrata:* types with vertebral columns
superclass	*Spermatophyta:* seed producers	*Tetrapoda:* terrestrial; four limbs; bony skeletons
class	*Angiospermae:* flowering plants; seeds inside fruits	*Mammalia:* types with hair and milk glands
subclass	*Monocotyledonae:* parallel-veined leaves; single seed leaf; flower parts in threes or multiples	*Eutheria:* offspring develop in female parent, nourished by placenta
order	*Graminales:* grasses	*Primates:* fingers; flat nails
family	*Graminaceae:* leaves in two rows on round or flattened stem	*Hominidae:* upright posture; flat face; stereoscopic vision; large brain; hands and feet
genus	*Zea:* corn plants	*Homo:* double curved spine; long life span and long youth
species	*Zea mays:* cultivated, domesticated corn plants	*Homo sapiens:* with chin and high forehead; thin skull bones

ancestor of new and different types living tomorrow.

Evidently, contrary to an erroneous assumption in vogue several decades ago, it is no longer possible to speak of an evolutionary "ladder" or "scale" with "higher" and "lower" rung positions, implying a straight-line progression from one type of organism directly to the next. A scale simply does not exist, and only a bush pattern corresponds to the actual evidence (see also Chaps. 28 and 29). Moreover, we know that men, for example, did not descend "from amoebas" or some other "lower" type. Instead, men, amoebas, and all other organisms now living are modern contemporaries that have evolved coequally, and along entirely separate paths, from some ancient, long-extinct ancestors.

Thus there are also no "higher" and "lower" organisms, since all types now in existence occur at the same time level of the evolutionary bush, the present. There are only *different* organisms, with different specializations. Some of these organisms have longer evolutionary histories than others, and some are structurally more complex than others; yet each today stands only just as "high" (or just as "low") on the evolutionary bush as *every* other organism now living.

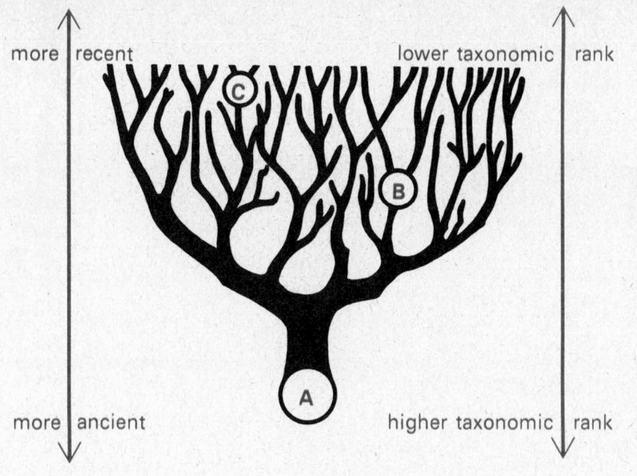

2.10 The bush pattern of evolution. *The uppermost tips of the branches represent currently living forms, all at the same time level, the present. Branches terminating below the top represent extinct forms. Fork points such as B and C are ancestral types. B is more ancient and of higher taxonomic rank than C. A represents the archancestor of all living types.*

review questions

1 What is metabolism? Self-perpetuation? What are the main subfunctions of each of these, and what specific roles do these subfunctions play in the maintenance of life?

2 What are the fundamental differences between inanimate, dead, and living systems? Discuss carefully and fully. Define living.

3 Review the hierarchy of levels in the organization of matter, and discuss how living matter is characterized in terms of levels.

4 Review the relation of levels of organization to energy, to numbers of units, to complexity, to competition and cooperation, and to operational efficiency.

5 Define cell (*a*) structurally and (*b*) functionally. Define organelle, tissue, organ, organ system, organism.

6 In terms of cellular specializations, how does a cell of a single-celled organism differ from a cell of a multicellular organism?

7 Cite examples of specialization at the organism, species, and community levels of organization. What are the functional advantages of specialization?

8 Review the structure of the linnean taxonomic system. What are the principal ranks? Name and define them, and cite groups of organisms of each. How is this system related to the size and the numbers of groups at each rank?

9 On what characteristics of organisms is the taxonomic system based? Why are other possible characteristics not used? Why are organisms not simply classified alphabetically or by some system equivalent to book-cataloguing in libraries?

10 What is meant by natural and unnatural taxonomic classifications? Give examples. What rules govern the naming of species? Review the taxonomic classification of a corn plant and man, with attention to the definition of each taxon.

11 Define homology, analogy. Give specific examples of each. Why are homologies more important in taxonomy than analogies?

12 Criticize and correct the following statement: "In the evolutionary scale, higher animals such as vertebrates have descended from lower animals such as protozoa."

collateral readings

Bonner, J. T.: Volvox, a Colony of Cells, *Sci. American,* May, 1950. A case study of living organization on the level of the cell colony.

Grobstein, C: "The Strategy of Life," Freeman, San Francisco, 1965. A thoughtful and stimulating paperback containing a section on levels of organization as well as discussions of other general phenomena of life.

Kemeny, J. G.: Man Viewed as a Machine, *Sci. American,* Apr., 1955. The article shows how computing machines can be built that can learn, and even reproduce, like living systems.

Mayr, E.: "Principles of Systematic Zoology," McGraw-Hill, New York, 1969. One of the important standard texts on taxonomy, well worth consulting for further information on this subscience of biology.

Minsky, M. L.: Artificial Intelligence, *Sci. American,* Sept., 1966. On the "thinking" processes a computer is capable of.

Penrose, L. S.: Self-reproducing Machines, *Sci. American,* July, 1959. Descriptions of models of self-duplicating mechanical systems that parallel the action of self-duplicating biological systems.

Schrödinger, E.: "What is Life?," Cambridge New York, 1944. A stimulating booklet by a noted physicist, discussing some of the basic characteristics of living material.

Sokal, R. R.: Numerical Taxonomy, *Sci. American,* Dec., 1966. Classification by means of computers is now becoming a feasible and useful technique.

Wald, G.: Innovation in Biology, *Sci. American,* Sept., 1958. The characteristics of living systems are interpreted in terms of our present knowledge in the physical sciences.

chapter 3 the chemical background

Regardless of what organism we examine, we ultimately find it to consist entirely of chemicals. And regardless of what particular function of an organism we examine, the function is ultimately always based on the properties and interactions of the chemicals present. Moreover, we now know that before the evolution of the first organisms there were only chemicals; living creatures originated out of chemicals. Basically, therefore, the story of life is a story of chemicals.

chemical substances

atoms

The material universe consists of roughly 100 fundamental kinds of substances called chemical *elements.* Iron, carbon, gold, oxygen, and aluminum are some familiar examples. Some others, most of them present also in living matter, are listed in Table 4. Each element exists in the form of exceedingly small units called *atoms.* Thus, a gold atom is the fundamental unit of the element gold.

Each element has a chemical symbol, often the first or the first two letters of its English or Latin name. For example, the symbol for hydrogen is H, that for carbon is C, and that for silicon is Si (see also Table 4). To represent a single atom of an element, one simply writes the appropriate symbol. For example, the letter H stands for one atom of hydrogen. If more than one atom is to be indicated, the appropriate number is put before the atomic symbol. For example, five separate hydrogen atoms are written as 5 H.

An atom is made up of *subatomic particles.* Two kinds of these, *neutrons* and *protons,* occur in varying numbers in the center of an atom, where they form an *atomic nucleus.* Neutrons are electrically neutral, protons carry one unit of positive charge. The atomic nucleus as a whole is therefore electrically positive. Orbiting around the nucleus are certain numbers of a third type of particle, *electrons.* Each of these carries one unit of negative electric charge, and an atom normally contains exactly as many electrons as there are protons in its nucleus. The electrons are maintained in orbit because they are attracted by the positively charged nucleus. Since the total positive charge equals the total negative charge, an atom as a whole is electrically neutral (Fig. 3.1).

Just as planetary orbits lie at various distances from the sun, so electron orbits are spaced out from the atomic nucleus at a number of fixed distances. The orbital paths at these distances form so-called electron "shells," one outside the other. The first shell, closest to the atomic nucleus, can hold a maximum of two electrons; the second shell, a maximum of eight. Known maximums also characterize all other shells. Electrons usually fill these shells from the innermost outward. Thus depending on the number of electrons in an atom, the outermost shell will be either complete and filled to capacity or incomplete to greater or lesser degree. Hydrogen, for example, has an incomplete outer shell since the single electron present does not fill the first shell to capacity. But helium, with two electrons, does fill this shell completely. In an oxygen atom, similarly, two of the total of eight electons fill the first shell and the remaining six occupy the second. Since this second shell can hold as many as eight electrons, oxygen has an incomplete outer shell (Fig. 3.2).

An atom is most stable when its electron shells are complete. Helium, for example, with a complete first shell, is stable and it is therefore usually also quite inert chemically; normally it does not react with other atoms. Similarly stable and chemically inactive are neon, with two complete

Table 4. Some common chemical elements

element	*symbol*	*common valences*	*common oxidation states in compounds*
hydrogen	H	1	+1
sodium	Na	1	+1
potassium	K	1	+1
chlorine	Cl	1	−1
iodine	I	1	−1
calcium	Ca	2	+2
magnesium	Mg	2	+2
sulfur	S	2	−2, +6
oxygen	O	2	−2
copper	Cu	1, 2	+1, +2
iron	Fe	2, 3	+2, +3
carbon	C	2, 4	+4, +2, −2, −4
silicon	Si	4	+4
aluminum	Al	3	+3
nitrogen	N	3, 5	−3, +3, +5
phosphorus	P	3, 5	−3, +5

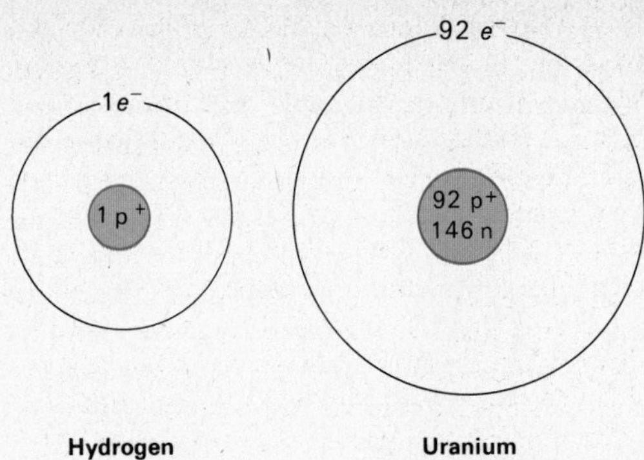

Hydrogen
atomic weight 1
atomic number 1

Uranium
atomic weight 238
atomic number 92

***3.1* Atomic structure:** *hydrogen and uranium. The atomic nucleus of hydrogen contains a single proton* (p^+)*; that of uranium, 92 protons and 146 neutrons* (n)*. The number of electrons orbiting around the nucleus equals the number of protons.*

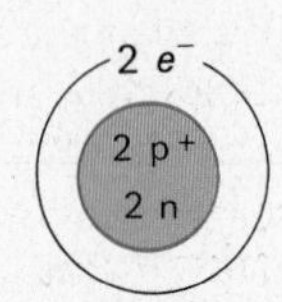

Helium
complete first shell

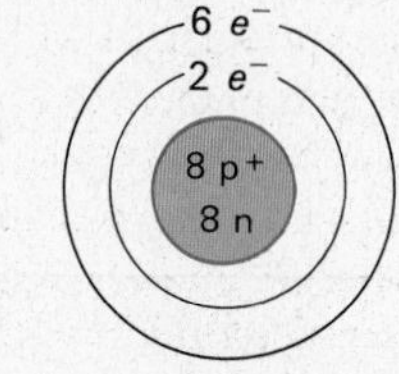

Oxygen
incomplete second shell

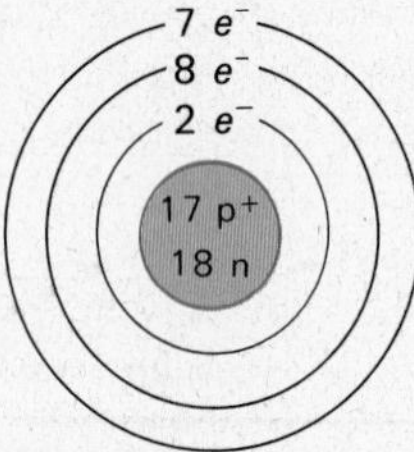

Chlorine
third shell incomplete
by one electron

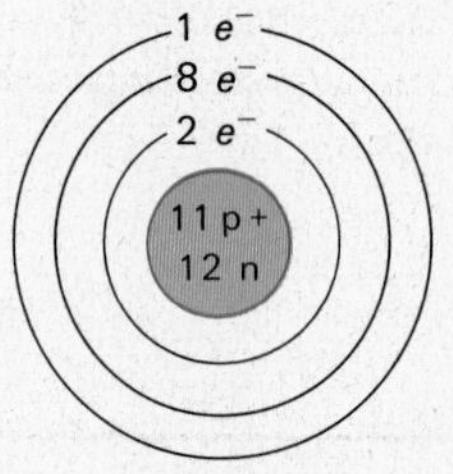

Sodium
third shell incomplete
by seven electrons

***3.2* Atomic electron shells.** *Helium has a complete (first) shell of two electrons. In oxygen the first shell is complete but the second shell is incomplete by two electrons. Chlorine has complete first and second shells and a nearly complete third shell. And sodium has a nearly empty third shell.*

shells, argon with three, krypton with four, xenon with five, and radon with six. These elements are the *inert gases.* In all other elements the outermost electron shells of the atoms are incomplete, and such atoms are more or less unstable. They reveal this comparative instability by their chemical reactivity; when two or more atoms come into contact, their incomplete outer shells can make them undergo chemical reactions. More specifically, atoms can become attached to one another through electric bonding forces, or *chemical bonds,* and the resulting atomic combinations are *compounds.* In effect, the chemical properties of atoms are determined by their outermost electron shells.

Each compound has a chemical name and a formula, both reflecting the kinds and numbers of atoms present. For example, table salt is technically the compound "sodium chloride," the name indicating the presence of sodium and chlorine. The formula NaCl also shows the quantitative ratio of these components: one sodium atom is linked to one chlorine atom. Water is technically the compound "hydrogen oxide," and the formula H_2O indicates the presence of two hydrogen atoms for every one of oxygen. The number of like atoms in a compound is customarily shown as a subscript. For example, iron oxide, Fe_2O_3, contains two iron atoms for every three oxygen atoms. A more complex compound is a calcium phosphate $Ca_3(PO_4)_2$. The formula here is a shorthand notation for the following combination of atoms: three calcium atoms are bonded to two subcombinations, each of which consists of one phosphorus and four oxygen atoms. Thus, thirteen atoms together form one unit of the compound calcium phosphate. If more than one unit of a compound is to be written in symbols, the appropriate number is put before the formula. For example, H_2O stands for one unit of the compound water and 5 H_2O stands for five such units.

Different kinds of atoms form bonds and compounds in different ways.

ions

Every atom has a tendency to complete its outer electron shell and thereby to become as stable as possible. How can an originally incomplete electron shell become complete? Consider an atom of chlorine. Of its 17 orbital electrons, 2 form a complete first shell, 8 a complete second shell, and the remaining 7 an incomplete third shell (see Fig. 3.2). Like the second shell, the third similarly can hold a maximum of 8 electrons. Evidently, the chlorine atom is just one electron short of having a complete outer shell. If the atom could in some way *gain* one more electron, it would satisfy its strong tendency for electronic completeness and greatest stability.

Consider now an atom of sodium. Of its 11 electrons, 2 form a complete first shell, 8 a complete second shell, and the remaining 1 a highly incomplete third shell (see Fig. 3.2). If this atom were to *lose* the single electron in the third shell, its second shell would then become the outermost shell. Since this second shell is already complete, the atom would have satisfied its tendency for completeness and would be stable. Thus, chlorine is unstable because it has one electron too few, and sodium, because it has one electron too many. Both atoms could then become stable simultaneously if an electron were transferred from sodium to chlorine. Such *electron transfers* can actually occur, and they represent one major class of chemical reactions (Fig. 3.3).

Since electrons carry negative charges, their transfer has important electric consequences. In the sodium-chlorine reaction, for example, neither atom is electrically neutral after the transfer. Sodium has lost a negative charge and has therefore become electropositive; and chlorine has gained a negative charge, hence it has become electronegative. Atoms or groups of atoms that have lost or gained electrons are called *ions;* electron transfer produces an *ionization* of the participating atoms. One of the ions formed is always electropositive, the other electronegative. And since positively and negatively charged particles attract each other, a positive and a negative ion will similarly exert mutual attraction. It is this attraction that forms a chemical bond between the ions, and it is this bond that unites the ions as a compound. Atoms that tend to lose electrons and thereby become positively charged ions are otherwise known as *metals;* and atoms that gain electrons and become negatively charged ions are *nonmetals.* Sodium is a metal, chlorine, a nonmetal.

Compounds formed by electron transfers and mutual attraction of the resulting ions are *ionic compounds.* They represent a major category of chemical substances, and they are abundant in living matter. The chemical bonds in an ionic compound are *ionic,* or *electrovalent, bonds.* The number of such bonds in a compound generally equals the number of electrons transferred. For example, the ionic compound sodium chloride contains a single bond; the attracting force between the sodium and chloride ion results from transfer of a single electron:

$$\left.\begin{array}{l} \mathrm{Na} \longrightarrow \mathrm{Na}^+ \\ \quad\quad e^- \\ \mathrm{Cl} \longrightarrow \mathrm{Cl}^- \end{array}\right\} \longrightarrow \mathrm{Na}^+\mathrm{Cl}^-$$

Because sodium and chlorine can form one ionic bond, they are each said to have an electrovalence of 1. The numbers and signs of the electric charges on ions are indicated by so-called *oxidation states.* For example, since the sodium ion carries one unit of positive charge, it is said to have an oxidation state of +1. Similarly, the chloride ion with one unit of negative charge has an oxidation state of −1. Atoms that transfer two, three, or more electrons between them form compounds containing a correspondingly larger number of electrovalent bonds. For example, magnesium can lose two electrons by transfer to other atoms: $Mg \rightarrow Mg^{++} + 2\,e^-$. Magnesium thus has an electrovalence of 2, and the magnesium ion has an oxidation state of +2. The two electrons could be transferred to two fluorine atoms, each of which could gain one: $2\,e^- + 2\,F \rightarrow 2\,F^-$. Fluorine has an electrovalence of 1, and the fluoride ion, an oxidation state of −1. Two ionic bonds would then maintain the compound magnesium fluoride, $Mg^{++}F_2^-$.

In general, metal ions have positive oxidation states and nonmetal ions, negative ones (see Table 4). Since oxidation states indicate the numbers and signs of charges, whole neutral atoms have oxidation states of zero. Also, the arithmetic sum of oxidation states of all the ions in an ionic compound adds up to zero, since the compound as a whole is electrically neutral.

molecules

Atoms can become stable not only by transferring but also by *sharing* electrons. For example, suppose that chlorine atoms are prevented from gaining electrons from other kinds of atoms because such other atoms are not present. A chlorine atom can then complete its outer shell of seven electrons by interacting with another chlorine atom. We already know that a chlorine atom can attract one additional electron quite strongly. If two such atoms come into contact, each will therefore attract an electron of the other with equal force. But each atom holds on to its own electrons, and an electronic "tug of war" will take place that neither atom can "win"; and without a decision, the mutual tugging will continue indefinitely. As a result the atoms will remain linked together, just as equally matched opponents of a real tug of war remain linked by the mutual pull they exert on each other. In this case electrons are not transferred and ions are not formed. Instead, as each atom pulls on an electron of the other, a pair of electrons is shared: each atom has its own seven outer electrons plus

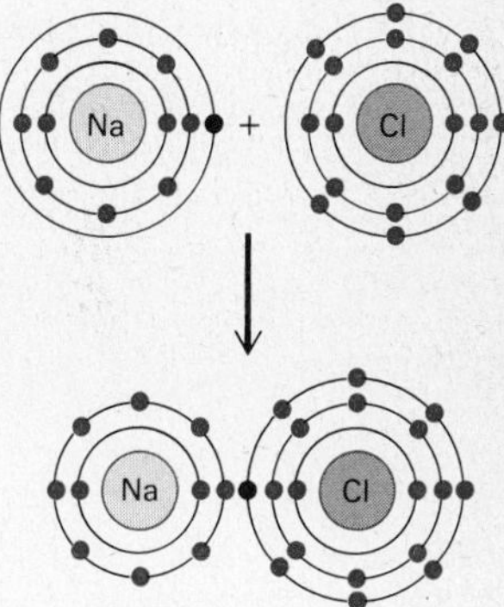

3.3 Electron transfer and ionic compounds. *In a reaction between one atom of sodium and one of chlorine, the single electron in the third shell of sodium is transferred to the third shell of chlorine. Sodium thereby acquires a complete outer (second) shell of eight electrons, and chlorine, a complete outer (third) shell of eight electrons. In this form sodium and chlorine are ions, and both together represent the ionic compound sodium chloride.*

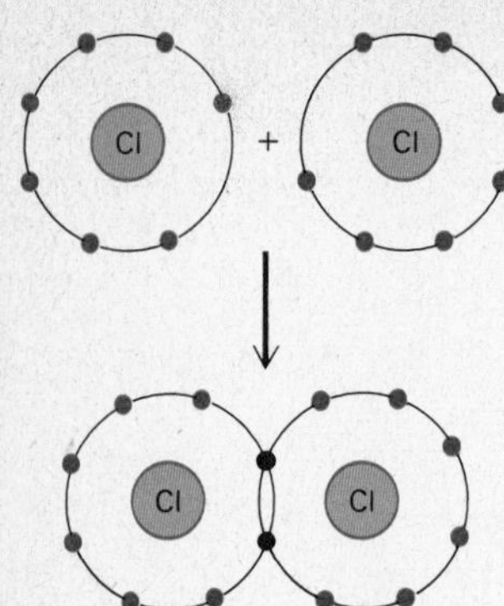

3.4 Electron sharing and molecular compounds. *Two chlorine atoms with their seven outer electrons are shown at top. If the two atoms share one pair of electrons as at bottom, each atom acquires a complete outer shell of eight electrons. The result is a molecule of chlorine,* Cl_2.

one that it attracts from the other. Both atoms then behave as if they actually contained eight outer electrons each, and this suffices to establish their stability (Fig. 3.4).

Hydrogen atoms too can share electrons:

$$H\cdot + H\cdot \longrightarrow H{:}H$$

The two electrons then "belong" to both atoms equally, and each atom has a sphere of attracting influence over the two electrons it requires for a complete orbital shell. In many cases more than one pair of electrons can be shared. For example, an oxygen atom with six outer electrons can share two pairs with another oxygen atom:

$$\underset{\cdot\cdot}{\ddot{O}}{:} + {:}\underset{\cdot\cdot}{\ddot{O}} \longrightarrow \underset{\cdot\cdot}{\ddot{O}}{::}\underset{\cdot\cdot}{\ddot{O}}$$

Each oxygen atom now has a sphere of attracting influence over eight electrons, the required number for a complete outer shell. Oxygen can also share two pairs of electrons with, for example, hydrogen:

$$H\cdot + \cdot H + \cdot\underset{\cdot\cdot}{\ddot{O}}\cdot \longrightarrow H{:}\underset{\cdot\cdot}{\ddot{O}}{:}H$$

Here each of the three participating atoms attracts just enough electrons for a complete outer shell—oxygen a shell of eight electrons and each hydrogen a shell of two.

Atoms such as chlorine or hydrogen either transfer or share electrons, depending on what other kinds of atoms are available for reaction. Another group of atoms (including sodium, magnesium, and many other metals) reacts almost exclusively by electron transfer. And in a third group (represented by oxygen, nitrogen, carbon, and others), electrons are almost always shared. Carbon, for example, can share its four outer electrons with four hydrogen atoms:

$$\cdot\underset{\cdot}{\dot{C}}\cdot + 4\,H\cdot \longrightarrow \begin{array}{c} H \\ H{:}\underset{\cdot\cdot}{\ddot{C}}{:}H \\ H \end{array}$$

Or, carbon can also react with two oxygen atoms:

$${:}C{:} + 2\,\underset{\cdot\cdot}{\ddot{O}}{:} \longrightarrow \underset{\cdot\cdot}{\ddot{O}}{::}C{::}\underset{\cdot\cdot}{\ddot{O}}$$

As the electron distributions here indicate, each of the participating atoms again attracts just the number of electrons required for a complete outer shell.

Electron-sharing represents a second major way in which compounds are formed. Compounds of this type are *molecular compounds,* or simply *molecules.* The chemical bonds in molecules are *covalent bonds,* each represented by a shared electron pair. The number of such bonds an atom can form indicates its *covalence.* Thus, hydrogen has a covalence of 1, oxygen of 2, nitrogen usually of 3, and carbon usually of 4. The atoms of a molecule also have oxidation states, according to how strongly they attract shared electron pairs. In

$$\begin{array}{c} H \\ H{:}\underset{\cdot\cdot}{\ddot{C}}{:}H \\ H \end{array}$$

for example, the four shared pairs are attracted more strongly to the carbon atom than to the hydrogen atoms; carbon here is said to have an oxidation state of −4, and each H atom, an oxidation state of +1. Conversely, in

$$\underset{\cdot\cdot}{\ddot{O}}{::}C{::}\underset{\cdot\cdot}{\ddot{O}}$$

it is the oxygen atoms that attract electron pairs more strongly, hence each oxygen atom is assigned an oxidation state of −2, whereas the carbon atom has an oxidation state of +4. Since a molecule is electrically neutral, the arithmetic sum of all the oxidation states of the participating atoms is zero.

In present contexts it will usually not be necessary to distinguish between electrovalent and covalent bonds, but the position of bonds will need to be shown fairly often. A compound can then be symbolized by means of a *structural* formula, in which the location of bonds (either electrovalent or covalent) is indicated by short dashes between appropriate atoms. For example,

NaCl	or	**Na—Cl**	*sodium chloride*
Cl_2	or	**Cl—Cl**	*chlorine molecule*
H_2O	or	**H—O—H**	*water molecule*
O_2	or	**O═O**	*oxygen molecule*
N_2	or	**N≡N**	*nitrogen molecule*
CH_4	or	$\begin{array}{c} H \\ \vert \\ H—C—H \\ \vert \\ H \end{array}$	*methane molecule*
CO_2	or	**O═C═O**	*carbon dioxide molecule*

The chemical properties of a compound are determined by the *arrangement,* the *numbers,* and the *types* of atoms present. Two molecules might contain the same set of atoms, but if these are arranged differently the molecules will have different properties. For example, the molecules

$$\begin{array}{ccccccccc} & H & & H & & H & & H & \\ & | & & | & & | & & | & \\ H- & C & - & C & - & C & - & C & -H \\ & | & & | & & | & & | & \\ & H & & H & & H & & H & \end{array} \quad \text{and} \quad \begin{array}{ccccc} & H & H & H & \\ & | & | & | & \\ H- & C & -\!\!-\!\!-\;C\;-\!\!-\!\!- & C & -H \\ & | & | & | & \\ & H & H-C-H & H & \\ & & | & & \\ & & H & & \end{array}$$

contain identical atoms, and both molecules can be symbolized as C_4H_{10}. But since their atoms are bonded in different patterns, they are actually different molecules with different properties. Variations in the bonding patterns of otherwise similar molecules are particularly significant in the chemistry of living matter.

dissociation

Practically all chemicals of biological interest occur in a water medium. When ionic compounds are put into water, they generally exist as free ions, physically separate from one another; water molecules become interposed between the ions of the compound. When molecular compounds dissolve in water, one of two events can occur. Some types of molecular compounds simply continue to exist as whole, intact molecules, with water interposed between individual ones. Ordinary sugar is a good example. By contrast, other types of molecules do not remain intact in water; instead they break up, or *dissociate,* into free ions. For example,

$$\underset{\textit{acetic acid}}{CH_3COOH} \xrightarrow{H_2O} \underset{\textit{acetate ion}}{CH_3COO^-} + \underset{\textit{hydrogen ion}}{H^+}$$

$$\underset{\textit{ammonium hydroxide}}{NH_4OH} \xrightarrow{H_2O} \underset{\textit{ammonium ion}}{NH_4^+} + \underset{\textit{hydroxyl ion}}{OH^-}$$

Inasmuch as dissociation produces equal amounts of positive and negative electric charges, solutions containing dissociated compounds remain electrically neutral. However, the presence of free ions permits passage of electric currents through such solutions. Dissociable compounds are therefore also called *electrolytes,* and undissociable ones are *nonelectrolytes.*

Note that, in the first equation above, acetic acid dissociates in such a way that hydrogen ions are formed. This is what actually makes acetic acid an acid; any compound that dissociates and yields hydrogen ions (H^+) is called an *acid.* Similarly, any compound that dissociates and yields hydroxyl ions (OH^-), as in the second equation above, is a *base,* or *alkali.*

Acids and bases are molecular compounds in pure form; they dissociate in water and give rise to ions as a result. If ions derived from a dissociated acid interact chemically with ions from a dissociated base, a *salt* is produced. Thus, because they are composed of ions, salts are ionic compounds. For example, sodium chloride (NaCl) is a salt formed by interaction of hydrochloric acid (HCl) and the base sodium hydroxide (NaOH):

$$\begin{array}{lcl} HCl & \xrightarrow[\textit{dissociation}]{} & H^+ + Cl^- \\ NaOH & \longrightarrow & Na^+ + OH^- \\ \hline HCl + NaOH & \longrightarrow & NaCl + H_2O \end{array}$$

Every electrolyte is an acid or a base or a salt (Fig. 3.5).

An electrolyte is said to be "strong" or "weak" according to the *extent* to which it is dissociated. With some exceptions unimportant in biological contexts, salts dissociate completely and *all* their chemical units exist in the form of ions. Salts are therefore very strong electrolytes. By contrast, acids and bases are not always dissociated fully, different ones dissociating to different degrees. For example, the molecular compound hydrochloric acid (HCl) is a strong acid, for in water practically all the molecules of the compound dissociate into ions. But the molecular compound acetic acid (CH_3COOH) is a weak acid, for in water only a few ion pairs are formed; most of the

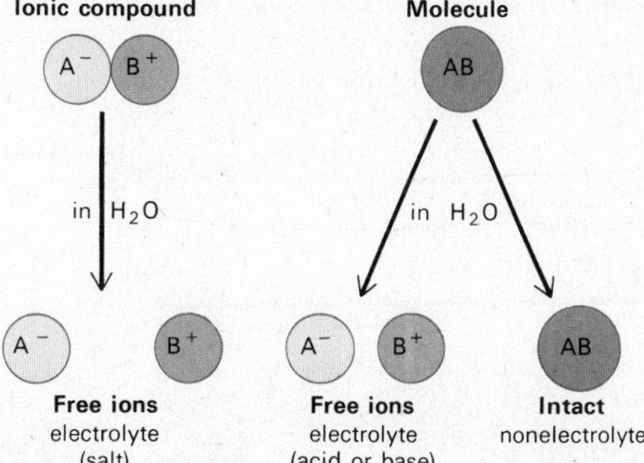

3.5 Dissociation. *Salts in water exist in the form of the ions of which they are composed. Molecules in water either dissociate as free ions if they are electrolytes or remain as intact molecules if they are nonelectrolytes.*

molecules remain whole and intact, and only relatively few break up into free acetate and hydrogen ions. Strong and weak bases can be distinguished similarly. The weakest of all electrolytes in effect are the nonelectrolytes, which do not dissociate at all.

It is often important to determine the acid or alkaline strength of a solution, or the degree to which the compounds in the solution are dissociated. This can be done with an electrical apparatus that measures the relative number of H^+ ions (actually H^+ bound to water in the form of $H_3{}^+O$) and OH^- ions in the solution; for the more of these ions are found, the more the acids and bases present are dissociated. The result is expressed as a number, called the *pH* of the solution. In living material, the numbers that indicate the pH usually range from 0 to 14. A pH of 7 indicates chemical *neutrality;* the solution is neither acid nor basic because the number of H^+ ions equals the number of OH^- ions. Below 7, a solution is the more acid the lower its pH; it contains more H^+ ions than OH^- ions. Conversely, a solution is the more alkaline the more its pH exceeds 7 (Fig. 3.6).

Living matter, which contains a mixture of variously dissociated acids, bases, and salts, has a pH usually very near neutrality. For example, the pH of human blood is generally 7.3. Distinctly higher or lower pH levels do occur, however, but usually in restricted regions only. For example, lemons or stomach cavities are characteristically quite acid. Living material does not tolerate significant variations in its normal acid-base balance, and its pH must remain within fairly narrow limits. If these limits are greatly exceeded, major chemical and physical disturbances result that can be highly damaging or even lethal.

Many normal processes in organisms yield small amounts of excess acids or bases, but these hardly affect the pH because living matter is *buffered;* it is protected to some extent against pH change. For example, one of the usual constituents of living material is the bicarbonate ion, $HCO_3{}^-$. If an acid is now added, this acid will yield an excess of hydrogen ions (H^+) that ordinarily might be damaging. However, when H^+ and $HCO_3{}^-$ are present together they cannot remain free ions to any great extent, for they react together and form carbonic acid, H_2CO_3. This compound happens to be a weak acid that cannot dissociate very much. Dissociation of H_2CO_3 into free ions will therefore take place only to a minor extent, but the reverse process that joins H^+ and $HCO_3{}^-$ into whole H_2CO_3 molecules will occur abundantly. As a result, the H^+ ions derived from the added acid are "taken out of circulation" by combination with $HCO_3{}^-$, and the pH therefore will not change appreciably despite the addition of the acid.

The bicarbonate ions in effect function as buffers against pH change. Phosphate ions have a similar buffering effect against added acids, and several positively charged ions in living matter protect against added bases. To be sure, if living material or any buffered system is flooded with large quantities of additional acids or bases, then pH protection will be inadequate.

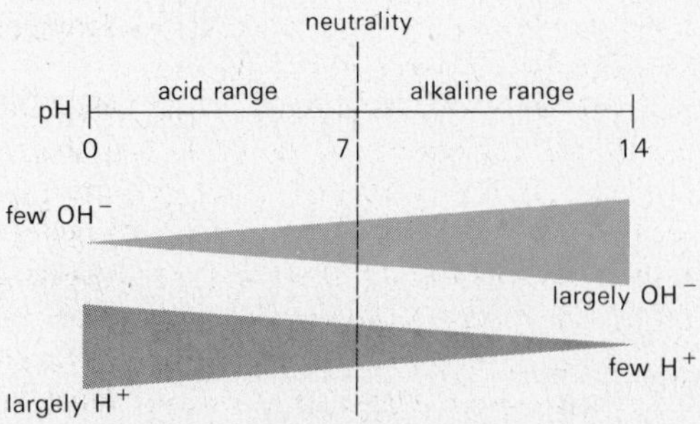

3.6 *The pH scale.*

chemical changes

reactions

Any process in which at least one bond between two atoms is formed or broken can be regarded as a chemical reaction. Such processes generally occur as a result of *collisions* among molecules or ions; direct contact is necessary if compounds are to be close enough together for bond breaking or bond formation.

Inasmuch as reactions always imply changes in chemical bonding, the invariable outcome of any reaction is a *rearrangement* of atoms and bonding patterns. For example:

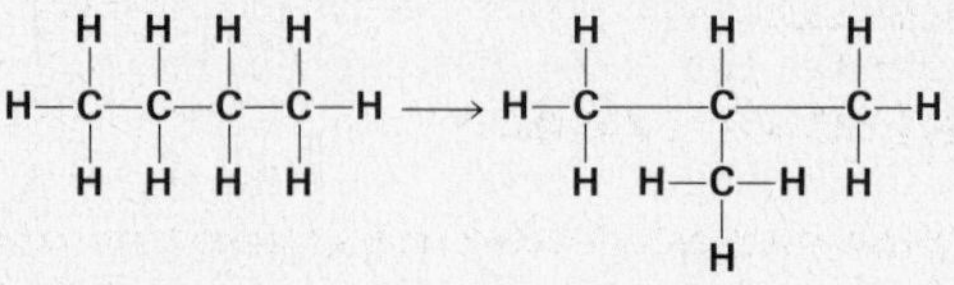

```
  H H H H          H     H     H
  | | | |          |     |     |
H-C-C-C-C-H  -->  H-C-----C-----C-H
  | | | |          |     |     |
  H H H H          H   H-C-H   H
                         |
                         H
```

Or generally,

$A \longrightarrow B$

If reactions take place between two or more types of compounds, then the atomic rearrangements are usually accompanied by three kinds of broader results. First, two or more molecules or ions can come together and form a single larger unit; a *synthesis* can occur. For example:

$$\underset{\text{bicarbonate ion}}{HCO_3^-} + \underset{\text{hydrogen ion}}{H^+} \longrightarrow \underset{\text{carbonic acid}}{H_2CO_3}$$

Or generally,

$$A + B \longrightarrow AB$$

Reactions of this general type include the processes of synthesis which, as noted in the preceding chapter, represent a major metabolic activity of living matter.

Second, a single molecule or ion can become fragmented into two or more smaller units; a chemical *decomposition* can take place, the reverse of synthesis. For example:

$$H_2CO_3 \longrightarrow H^+ + HCO_3^-$$

Or generally,

$$AB \longrightarrow A + B$$

Reactions of this general type include the decomposition reactions of respiration, another metabolic activity referred to in Chap. 2.

Third, synthesis and decomposition can occur simultaneously; the decomposition products of one set of compounds can become the building blocks for the synthesis of another set. In such a process, one or more of the atoms or ions of one compound trade places with one or more of the atoms or ions of another compound. This is an *exchange* reaction. For example:

$$\underset{\text{hydrochloric acid}}{H{-}Cl} + \underset{\text{sodium hydroxide}}{Na{-}OH} \longrightarrow \underset{\text{water}}{H{-}OH} + \underset{\text{sodium chloride}}{Na{-}Cl}$$

Or generally,

$$AB + CD \longrightarrow AD + BC$$

Note that each of these reaction types actually does include a rearrangement of atoms and bonding patterns. In every case one or more bonds are broken and one or more new ones are formed. However, the total numbers and types of atoms are exactly the same before and after the reaction; atoms are neither gained nor lost. In symbolic representations of reactions, therefore, it is important to make sure that equations balance; the total numbers and types of atoms to the left of the reaction arrow must equal exactly those on the right.

Apart from belonging to one of the reaction types just described, any chemical process has two fundamental characteristics. The first is *direction.* In the examples above the directions of the reactions have been indicated by arrows, but this has been possible only because of knowledge gained from earlier experience. If such experience were lacking, it would not necessarily be clear whether a given reaction would proceed to the right or to the left. What determines the actual direction? The second characteristic is reaction *rate,* a measure of how fast and for how long a reaction proceeds. Reactions result from collisions of chemical units, as noted, and the generalization can be made that reaction rate is directly proportional to collision rate. Any factor or condition promoting collisions will also promote rates. What are these rate determinants?

The direction of a reaction is governed by the *energetics* of the reacting chemicals; and the rate is determined by *temperatures,* by *pressures* and *concentrations,* and by *catalysts.*

energetics

Like all other kinds of changes in the universe, chemical changes obey and are governed by certain laws of *thermodynamics.* These most fundamental rules of nature deal with the *energy* relations of a system and its surroundings. The general concept of energy is roughly equivalent in meaning to work potential, or the capacity to do work. A ''system'' can be regarded as any set of materials on which attention is focused at the moment, such as a group of chemicals undergoing reactions. The surroundings then are all other parts of the universe, the total environment in which the system exists.

A *first law* of thermodynamics, also called the law of *conservation of energy,* states that, in any process, the sum of all energy changes must be zero. Expressed differently, energy can be neither created nor destroyed. Thus if a chemical system gains energy, that amount of energy must be lost by the environment of the system. Or if a chemical system loses energy, that amount must be

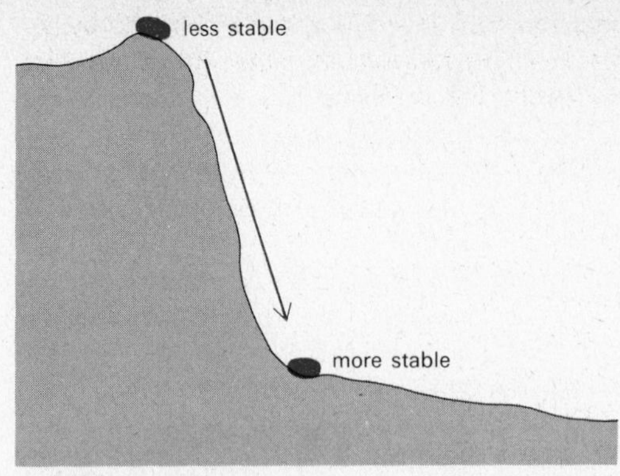

*3.7 **Thermodynamics and stability.** A stone on a hillside can be regarded as a closed thermodynamic system. If the stone is left to itself a unidirectional process can occur: the stone can fall to the valley and thereby assume a more stable state.*

gained by the environment. The first law therefore implies that energy can only be redistributed, changed in form, or both.

A *second law* of thermodynamics, already referred to in Chap. 2, states that if left to itself any system tends toward a state of greatest stability. A stone near the top of a hillside represents a less stable (and also a more ordered and less probable) system than a stone at the bottom of the slope. The second law indicates that, whereas such a stone might roll downhill to a more stable state, by itself it can never roll uphill. To be sure, a stone can be *brought* uphill if an environmental agent expends energy and pushes the stone up; but in that case the system is no longer "left to itself." Evidently, natural processes tend to be *unidirectional,* even though they are inherently reversible. Correspondingly, all chemical processes are theoretically reversible, but in actuality they proceed either in one direction or the other, according to which one of these leads to a more stable state (Fig. 3.7).

The actual stability of chemical systems depends mainly on two factors, both involving the energy of compounds. One factor is *enthalpy,* symbolized by the letter *H;* it denotes the *total energy content* of a chemical system. As already pointed out, a compound is held together by chemical bonds resulting from mutual electric attraction between atoms or ions. These bonding forces represent *chemical energy,* or *bond energy.* The greater the attraction between two atoms or ions, the greater is the bond energy. Two bonded atoms or ions will become disunited only if some external force pushes them apart and thereby breaks the bond. Such forcible separation requires work, or energy, and the amount of energy needed clearly must be at least great enough to overcome the attraction between the two atoms or ions. In other words, the energy required to break a bond equals, and defines, the bond energy. Accordingly, the enthalpy, or total chemical energy, of a compound can be defined as the energy needed to break all the bonds in the compound.

If now two or more compounds are close together, such a chemical system will be most stable if and when its total chemical energy is at a *minimum.* The second law of thermodynamics shows that, for any system, a state of minimum available energy is the most likely; and it is because of this greatest likelihood that minimum energy states are the most stable. Chemical reactions will therefore tend to proceed in such a way that, at the end, the total energy content of all participants will be least. For example, assume that in the generalized reaction

$$\boldsymbol{A + B \longrightarrow C + D}$$

the total energy of all the bonds in *A* and *B* together is greater than the total energy of all the bonds in *C* and *D* together. In other words, more potential energy is available in the bonds of the starting materials than is needed to form the bonds of the endproducts. If all other conditions are suitable, such a reaction can occur readily because $C + D$, containing less total energy, is more stable than $A + B$. The energy difference will be lost from the reaction system to the environment. The energy differential, or *total energy change,* is customarily symbolized as ΔH. And since ΔH passes from the reaction system to the environment, it is given a negative sign:

$$\boldsymbol{A + B \longrightarrow C + D - \Delta H}$$

Such a liberation of energy can become evident, for example, through a spontaneous rise of temperature in the reaction mixture. Reactions that yield energy as above are said to be *exergonic* (or *exothermic,* if the energy is liberated in the form of heat). Decomposition reactions, including respiratory decompositions in living matter, tend to be of this type (Fig. 3.8).

Conversely, assume that the total energy of $A + B$ is less than that of $C + D$. In this case $A + B$ is more stable, and the second law stipulates that no process can proceed by itself from a more stable to a less stable state. However, the reaction could be made to occur if energy were supplied *from* the environment *to* the reaction system, in an amount at least equal to ΔH. For example, the starting materials could be heated over a flame. Then, so long as external energy continues to be supplied, the reaction can proceed:

$$A + B \longrightarrow C + D + \Delta H$$

Reactions that *require* external energy, as above, are said to be *endergonic* (or *endothermic,* if the energy is required in the form of heat). Synthesis reactions generally, including those in living matter, are of this type. Evidently, chemical (or any other) synthesis tends to be expensive in terms of energy.

The second factor that determines the relative stability of a chemical system is its *entropy,* or *energy distribution,* symbolized as S. A system is most stable if S is at a maximum, with energy distributed as uniformly or randomly as possible. It can be shown that, of all possible energy distributions in a system, the most random or unordered is the most likely; and it is because of this greatest likelihood that maximum entropy states are the most stable.

For example, consider again the reaction $A + B \rightarrow C + D$, and assume that the total energy content is the same before and after the reaction ($\Delta H = 0$). Assume however that A is energy-rich and B energy-poor, and that C and D each contain intermediate amounts of energy. The energy distribution in $A + B$ is therefore more uneven or less random than in $C + D$, and $C + D$ will be more stable. The reaction to the left thus can occur, and it will increase the entropy of the system. If the entropy differential between $A + B$ and $C + D$ is symbolized as ΔS, the reaction can be written as

$$A + B \longrightarrow C + D + \Delta S$$

Consider now the reaction

$$A + B + C \longrightarrow D$$

and again assume that ΔH is zero. On the left side the total energy is distributed among three particles, but on the right all the energy is concentrated in one. With everything else being equal, the $A + B + C$ state thus has a more scattered, more random energy distribution, and this state will be more stable and have a greater entropy than the D state. The reaction will therefore not be possible if the system is left to itself. However, energy supplied from the environment could conceivably lower the entropy of $A + B + C$ sufficiently to make the reaction to D possible. Symbolically,

$$A + B + C \longrightarrow D - \Delta S$$

Entropy is temperature-dependent. For example, if equal amounts of water under otherwise equivalent conditions exist in the form of ice, liquid water, and steam, then ice will have the lowest and steam the highest entropy; water molecules are most scattered and disordered in the form of steam. In general, entropy tends to increase with rising temperature. For this reason entropy changes are usually symbolized as a mathematical product of ΔS and T, where T is the absolute temperature at which a reaction occurs.

The overall stability change during a reaction is therefore a function of two variables, ΔH and $T\,\Delta S$. By conceptual definition these two are of opposite algebraic sign, since stability changes as enthalpy increases and entropy decreases (or as enthalpy decreases and entropy increases). This circumstance finds expression in the formulation

$$\Delta F = \Delta H - T\,\Delta S$$

an important equation representing a symbolic statement of the second law. The term ΔF denotes overall change in system stability and is generally referred to as the *free-energy change.*

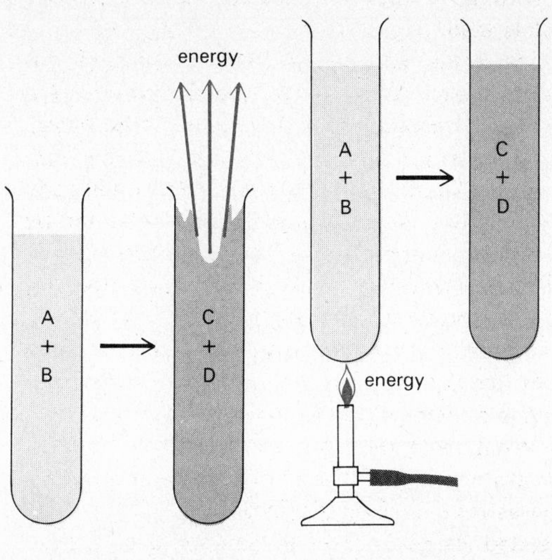

3.8 Energy and reactions. *Left, exergonic reaction. The mixture A + B contains more total energy than C + D, and the energy difference escapes the reacting system. Right, endergonic reaction. The mixture A + B contains less energy than C + D. Hence if a reaction is to take place the energy difference must be supplied to the reacting system from an external source.*

This change is a measure of the theoretical amount of *usable* work that can be obtained from a reacting system. For example, if a piece of wood is burned in a fireplace, the original energy of the wood less the energy of all the ashes and other combustion products represents ΔH, the total energy change. This total is not usable as such to perform work—to heat a room, for example; for in the process of burning, the compact piece of wood has scattered into ashes and escaping gases. This dispersal represents an increase in entropy, or loss of some of the potential energy of the original wood. The amount of this lost energy is equivalent to the energy that would have to be spent to reassemble the dispersed combustion products back in one place. This quantity, equal to $T\,\Delta S$, is therefore not available to heat the room, and the net amount that does remain available is $\Delta H - T\,\Delta S$, or ΔF.

Changes in free energy, enthalpy, and entropy are expressed as *heat equivalents*. The unit of heat is a *calorie* (cal), the amount of heat (or equivalent quantities of other energy forms) required to raise the temperature of 1 gram (g) of water by 1°C. A commonly used biological unit is a kilocalorie (kcal), or "dietary" calorie, equal to 1000 cal. (For example, when an average slice of bread is burned completely, either in a furnace or in the body, the energy liberated is roughly 100 kcal.)

A negative ΔF is largely characteristic of *decomposition* reactions, a positive ΔF, of *synthesis* reactions. Under suitable conditions some of the energy liberated in a decomposition reaction can be made to perform useful work. For example, it could drive an engine, as in the decomposition of fuels by burning, or it could simply provide useful heat as such. Or, indeed, it can make possible energy-requiring synthesis reactions. In living systems, actually, decompositions are intimately *coupled* with syntheses; as already pointed out in Chap. 2, energy obtained from respiratory decomposition supports metabolic synthesis.

The energetics of a chemical system thus determine one basic attribute of reactions, their direction. The second attribute, rate, is specified by factors that influence the collision frequency among chemical units.

pressure, temperature, concentration

The effect of pressure on reacting systems varies greatly, depending on the gaseous, liquid, or solid nature of the participating chemicals. Reaction rates among gases are the higher the greater the environmental pressure; increasing pressure forces gases into progressively smaller volumes, and the possibility of direct contact among gas ions or molecules is thereby enhanced. Pressure has far less effect on liquids, which are virtually incompressible, and on solids, which may or may not be compressible,

More significant than pressure is the environmental temperature. Reactions depend on contact among chemical units, and the usual agency that brings chemical units into contact is *heat* motion. All atoms, ions, and molecules, regardless of whether they are in a gas, a liquid, or a solid, vibrate uninterruptedly in random back-and-forth movements, and in gases and liquids they also move from place to place over relatively greater distances. We feel these movements as heat and we measure them as temperature. At a high temperature chemical units are in violent motion. Conversely, at $-273°$C, the theoretical absolute zero of temperature, heat is by definition entirely absent and all chemical units are stationary. But every known natural or experimentally produced material always contains at least some heat, and the chemical units undergo more or less intense motions. Such thermal movements produce collisions among the chemical units. At a given temperature, chemical units therefore have a characteristic collision rate, and the collision rate in turn is a major determinant of the reaction rate among the units.

Ordinary room temperature often provides enough heat to agitate chemical units adequately for chemical reaction. But for many reactions room heat is insufficient. For example, a mixture of fat and water reacts so slowly at room temperature that the result is quite unnoticeable. However, molecular collisions, hence the speed of reaction, can be increased by heating the mixture, for example.

The external energy needed to produce significant reaction rates is called *activation energy*. Most materials in the physical world, as also in the living world, actually require activation energies far greater than those provided by ordinary temperatures. That is why, for example, the oxygen molecules in air and the molecules of wood or coal do not interact spontaneously, despite the numerous collisions between these substances. As is well known, combustible fuels must be heated substantially, or activated effectively, before they will react with aerial oxygen and thus burn. To start any reaction, therefore, enough activation energy must first be supplied from the outside. Interaction of the chemical units can then begin.

Activation energies interrelate with free-energy changes, as can be illustrated by considering a stone lying near the edge of a cliff. If the stone fell over the edge, its descent to the valley would yield energy that could be used to perform work. But some external force must first move the stone over the cliff edge, and this force is equivalent to the activation energy. Assume that, in Fig. 3.9, point *A* represents the degree of stability of a chemical system before a reaction has started, and position *C*, the degree of stability at the end of the reaction. The net stability change, or free-energy change ΔF, therefore can be represented as the difference in the levels of *A* and *C*. The lower position of *C* signifies that, as with a falling stone, stability is greater at the end of the reaction. But note that the stability curve from *A* to *C* passes through point *B*, located at a higher level than either *A* or *C*. This means that the stability of the system first decreases from *A* to *B* before it increases from *B* to *C*. The amount of this decrease from *A* to *B* represents the activation energy, E_{act}, which must be supplied from the outside to bring the reaction system "over the cliff." Thereafter, just as a stone falls on its own, the reaction proceeds by itself; and in the process it not only "pays back" the energy expended for activation but also yields net free energy usable for work, in the amount of ΔF.

In the reverse reaction from *C* to *A*, adequate activation requires external energy in an amount equal to ΔF plus E_{act}. Here only E_{act} is paid back when the reaction later "falls" from *B* to *A*. The net energy expenditure therefore is ΔF, far greater than in the reaction from *A* to *C*; more work must be done to move a stone up from a valley onto a cliff than in the opposite direction.

After having been activated, a reaction will proceed the faster the more heat is supplied to it. It has been found that every temperature rise of 10°C increases the speed of reactions approximately two to three times (or, stated in technical language, the *temperature coefficient* Q_{10} is 2 to 3 for chemical reactions in general). The implications for reactions in living systems are important. Plants and most animals lack internal temperature controls, and the temperatures in their bodies largely match those of the external environment. As a result the life-maintaining chemical processes in a housefly, for example, will occur two to three times as fast on a day that is 10°C warmer than another. By contrast, temperature controls are present in birds and mammals, and these animals maintain constant internal temperatures. In these "warm-blooded" types, therefore, the rates of chemical reactions do not fluctuate directly with changes in environmental temperature.

Apart from pressure and temperature, reaction rates also depend on the amount per volume, or *concentration*, of the reacting compounds present; for the greater the concentration of the starting materials, the more frequently collisions can occur and the faster the reaction will proceed. Other factors being equal, therefore, the rate of a reaction is proportional to the concentrations of the participating compounds. This generalization is sometimes referred to as the *law of mass action*.

Assume that the reversible reaction

$$1 \text{ glycerin} + 3 \text{ fatty acids} \rightleftharpoons 1 \text{ fat} + 3 \text{ water}$$

is in *equilibrium;* concentrations are constant and all other conditions are such that the reaction to the right occurs at the same rate as the reaction to the left. A *net* change will not occur so long as the equilibrium conditions are maintained. However, the equilibrium will be disturbed when some fat or water is removed from the system. The glycerin and fatty acids then in effect will have a relatively higher concentration, and according to the principle of mass action the reaction to the right will now take place at a greater

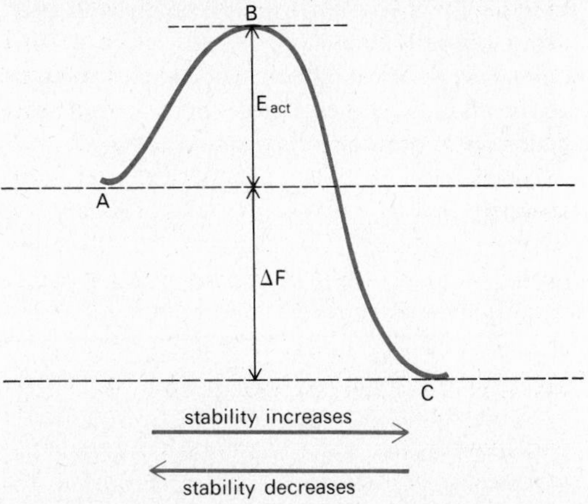

3.9 Activation energy. *If A represents a less stable chemical system than C, an exergonic reaction from A to C can occur when activation energy (E_{act}) is first applied to A. E_{act} brings the reacting system over an energy barrier (symbolized by B), and as A then becomes C, energy is released. This energy release "pays back" the E_{act} expended earlier, and it also yields additional energy, ΔF, the "free-energy change." The net energy gain of the reaction thus is ΔF, an amount of energy that varies in proportion with the stability difference between A and C. Conversely, in an endergonic reaction from C to A, C must not only be activated (E_{act}) but must also be supplied with external energy in the amount of ΔF. The only energy gain then is E_{act}; hence the net energy expenditure is ΔF.*

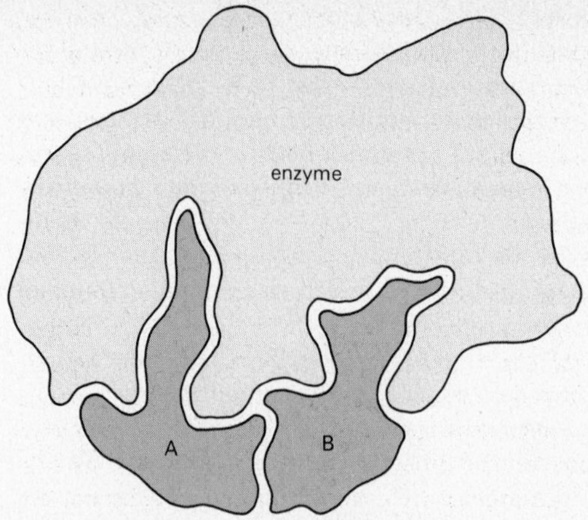

enzyme

A

B

3.10 ***Enzyme action.*** *The surfaces of molecules A and B fit into the surface of the enzyme. Reaction between A and B can thereby be speeded up, for contact between A and B does not depend now on chance collision.*

rate than the reaction to the left. If we keep on removing the endproducts as fast as they form, the reaction to the right will proceed to completion and the yield of fat and water will become maximal. Reactions often proceed to completion and maximum yield if one of the endproducts is an escaping gas (↑) or a relatively insoluble precipitate (↓); either circumstance is equivalent to removing one of the participating substances. For example,

$$H_2CO_3 \longrightarrow H_2O + CO_2\uparrow$$
$$Ca^{++} + CO_3^{=} \longrightarrow CaCO_3\downarrow$$

Another way of upsetting the equilibrium in the glycerin-fat reaction above would be to *add* glycerin, fatty acids, or both to the reaction system. The concentrations of these substances then would always remain high, and according to the principle of mass action the reaction would always be "driven" to the right. More and more fat and water would form as more and more glycerin and fatty acids were added.

This rule of mass action also applies to the energy changes of exergonic and endergonic reactions. Consider the reversible reaction

$$A \rightleftharpoons B - \Delta H$$

Proceeding to the right, the reaction is exergonic. Energy here is as much an endproduct as *B,* and if energy escapes as fast as it is produced the reaction to the right will not reach equilibrium but will proceed to completion. The reverse reaction is endergonic. Here energy must be added continuously if all of *B* is to be converted to *A.* If the supply of energy is stopped prematurely, the reaction to the left will cease and the reverse reaction to the right will take place and proceed to completion.

catalysis

Most chemical reactions of biological interest require fairly high activation energies—so high, indeed, that environments far hotter than room temperature would be needed. As noted, for example, a fat-water mixture at room temperature (or even at body temperature) remains virtually unchanged for days. In the body, however, fat and water react appreciably within an hour or so, yet body temperature remains comparatively low. In living matter generally, sufficiently high rates of molecular collisions are produced without additional heat through *catalysis,* or acceleration of reactions by means of *catalysts* instead of heat.

Catalysts of various kinds are well known and widely used by chemists dealing with nonliving processes. The special catalysts that occur in living matter are called *enzymes.* These substances are *proteins,* compounds about which more will be said in the next chapter. Virtually every one of the thousands of chemical reactions in living matter is speeded up enormously by a particular enzyme protein. Without enzymes the reactions could not occur fast enough at ordinary temperatures to sustain life. Enzymes therefore represent a supplement to thermal motion, a means by which reactions requiring high temperatures in test tubes can occur at low temperatures in living organisms. The effect of enzymes is to lower the activation-energy requirements. These catalysts thereby promote appreciable reaction rates at lower temperatures than would be possible otherwise.

An enzyme produces such an effect by combining temporarily with the reacting compounds. Mutual contact of these compounds is then no longer a matter of chance collision but a matter of certainty; hence reactions are faster. The protein nature of enzymes is essential to this accelerating action. Protein molecules are huge, and an almost unlimited number of different kinds of proteins exists. The surface shapes of such molecules appear to be the key to the effects of enzymes. Consider the reaction

$$\text{fat} + \text{water} \longrightarrow \text{fatty acids} + \text{glycerin}$$

A fat molecule has a particular surface geometry, and so does a water molecule. Enzymatic acceleration of this reaction now occurs if the surfaces of both fat and water happen to fit closely against the surface of a particular protein molecule. When the reacting molecules then become attached to this suitably shaped enzyme surface, they will be so close to each other that they interact chemically (Fig. 3.10).

The enzyme itself remains almost passive here. It merely provides a uniquely structured "platform," or *template,* on which certain molecules can become trapped. Such trapping brings reacting molecules into contact far faster than chance collisions at that temperature. Reactions are therefore accelerated. When they are held by the enzyme, fat and water interact and become fatty acid and glycerin, and these endproducts then disengage from the enzyme surface. The enzyme itself remains unaffected. It reappears unchanged at the end of the reaction, free to combine with a new set of starting compounds. Being passive platforms, enzymes speed up reaction in *either* direction; the reaction to the right, above, is accelerated by the same enzyme that speeds up the reverse reaction. Thus, like heat, enzymes influence only the rates of reactions, not the directions.

In describing enzyme-accelerated reactions, it is customary to speak of reacting molecules such as fat and water as the *substrates.* When substrate molecules are attached to an enzyme, the whole is referred to as an *enzyme-substrate complex.* Formation of such complexes can be thought of as a "lock-and-key" process. Only particularly shaped keys fit into particularly shaped locks. Just so, only molecules of certain shapes will establish a close fit with a given type of enzyme protein (Fig. 3.11).

Because enzyme proteins are huge molecules compared to most substrates, the whole surface of an enzyme is often not required to promote a reaction; in many cases it has been shown that only one or at most a few limited surface regions, called *active sites,* are involved. Hence even if other parts of enzyme molecules become altered chemically or physically, the enzymes can still be effective if their active sites remain intact.

Until recently enzymes were generally believed to be rigid molecular structures, templates of fixed shapes, and enzyme activity was thought to depend on this permanence of the geometry. Newer research indicates, however, that enzyme molecules are actually flexible in a physical sense and that the structure of a particular substrate can *induce* the enzyme to bend or mold itself over the substrate. Such an "induced fit" effect is consistent with the observation that only active sites, not necessarily whole enzyme molecules, need to retain permanent configurations. Moreover, induced fits also account in part for the long-established observation that many enzymes operate adequately only in the presence of certain *cofactors.* These are of various kinds and include, for example, metal ions such as Mg^{++}. Cofactors appear to be agents that, by virtue of their own properties, aid in molding an enzyme (or its substrates) into the shape required for a proper enzyme-substrate fit (Fig. 3.12).

Differences in the surface configuration of different protein types result in *enzyme specificity:* a particular type of enzyme normally accelerates only one particular type of reaction. For example, the enzyme in the fatty acid–glycerin reaction above, called *lipase,* is specific and catalyzes only that particular reaction. Living matter actually contains almost as many different kinds of enzymes as different varieties of reactions. This specificity of enzymes is an important corollary of the more general phenomenon of *protein specificity,* about which more will be said in the next chapter. Because of protein specificity, some proteins are enzymes to begin with and some are not. If a protein happens to have surface regions that can fit with the surfaces of some other compounds, then the protein could function as an enzyme for such compounds.

The effectiveness of enzymes varies greatly with changes of temperature, pH, and environmental conditions in general, just as all proteins are affected by such changes. More specifically, as either temperature or pH rises, the effectiveness of enzymes increases up to a certain optimum but decreases thereafter. Most enzymes operate optimally in a temperature range of about 25 to 40°C (human body temperature is 37°C) and in a pH range of about 6.0 to 7.5. At lower temper-

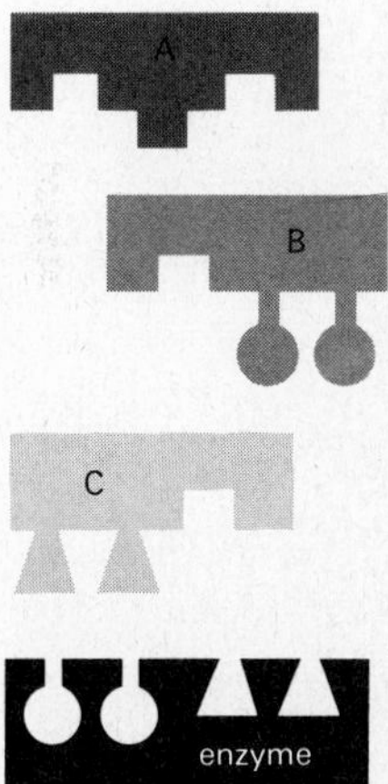

3.11 Enzyme specificity. *Reactants A and B fit partially into the surface of the enzyme, but reactant C does not. Hence the enzyme can speed up the reactions involving A and B but not those involving C.*

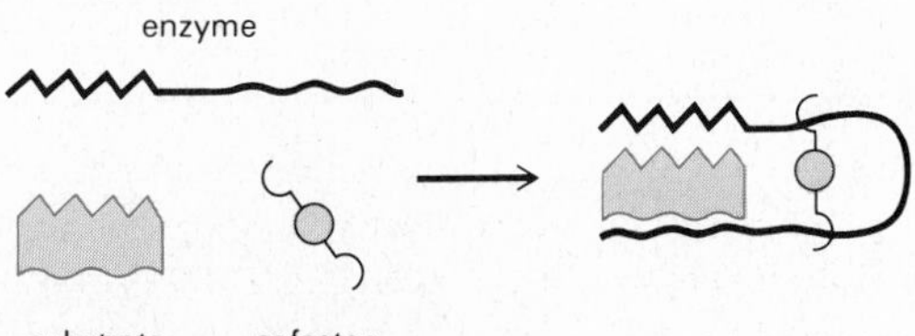

3.12 Cofactors. *The enzyme diagrammed here is assumed to have an active site at each end. A cofactor can aid in producing a fit between the substrate and the active sites of the enzyme. Cofactors include various mineral ions and a variety of coenzymes. These organic substances are specific, each operating in conjunction with a particular enzyme (often called "apoenzyme" in this context).*

atures reactions of all kinds decrease in rate, as noted earlier, and at higher temperatures the thermal motion of the atoms in an enzyme becomes intense enough to disrupt the physical structure of the enzyme protein. Similarly, pH changes to either side of the optimum range produce structural changes that result in enzyme inactivation. These are basic reasons why excessive temperature or pH changes can be lethal to living matter.

Enzymes are usually named according to the kinds of compounds they affect. Thus enzymes that accelerate reactions of so-called "carbohydrate" compounds are *carbohydrases.* Similarly, *proteinases* and *lipases* are enzymes catalyzing certain reactions of, respectively, proteins and fatty substances (lipids). The suffix *-ase* always identifies a name as one of an enzyme (although all enzyme names need not have this suffix). In writing an enzymatic reaction symbolically, the enzyme is conventionally indicated just above the reaction arrow. For example,

$$\text{fatty acids} + \text{glycerin} \xrightarrow{lipase} \text{fat} + \text{water}$$

The above discussion of chemicals of all kinds prepares the way for a consideration of the particular kinds of chemicals that form the building blocks of living matter.

review questions

1 Define element, atom, compound, ion, molecule, chemical energy, chemical bond.

2 What is an electrovalent bond? How is such a bond formed? Explain in terms of atomic structure. What is a covalent bond? Describe a way in which such a bond can be formed. Again explain in terms of atomic structure.

3 Consider the following equation:

$$\mathbf{Ca(OH)_2} + 2\ \mathbf{HCl} \longrightarrow \mathbf{CaCl_2} + 2\ \mathbf{H_2O}$$

a. Identify the different atoms by name.
b. Rewrite the equation to show bonds in each compound.
c. Is the equation balanced?
d. Is this an exchange, synthesis, or decomposition reaction?

4 Define dissociation, electrolyte, acid, base, salt. Is H_2SO_4 an acid, a base, or a salt? How does sodium sulfate (Na_2SO_4) dissociate? The magnesium ion is Mg^{++} and the nitrate ion is NO_3^-; write the formulas for magnesium hydroxide, nitric acid, and magnesium nitrate.

5 What does the pH of a solution indicate? What would you expect the pH of a solution of NaCl to be? Of HCl? Of NaOH?

6 What is a chemical reaction and what kind of event produces it? What general types of reactions are known? What factors determine the directions and rates of reactions?

7 State the first and second laws of thermodynamics and describe their general implications. Describe also their specific implications for chemical processes. Why are most natural processes unidirectional in practice?

8 Define enthalpy, entropy, free-energy change. How does each of these concepts apply to a reacting system? What does the ΔF of a reaction indicate? How do energy changes differ for exergonic and endergonic reactions? Define calorie.

9 How do pressure and concentration affect a reaction? Review the effect of environmental heat on reactions. What is activation energy? How is this energy related to free-energy changes?

10 What is a catalyst? What is an enzyme and how does it work? What is an active site of an enzyme? A cofactor? How does enzyme activity affect the activation energy of a reaction?

11 Show how enzyme activity varies with temperature and pH. What are the usual optimal conditions for enzyme activity? Review the general characteristics of enzymes.

12 Why is a carbohydrase ineffective in accelerating the reaction glycerin + fatty acids $\rightarrow$ fat + water? What kind of enzyme does such a reaction actually require?

collateral readings

Baker, J. J. W., and **G. E. Allen:** "Matter, Energy, and Life," Addison-Wesley, Reading, Mass., 1965. This paperback contains accounts of reaction energetics, catalysis, reaction rates and equilibria, and thermodynamics. Recommended.

Frieden, E.: The Enzyme-substrate Complex, *Sci. American,* Aug., 1959. A popularly written article on enzymatic reactions.

Grunwald, E., and **R. H. Johnsen:** "Atoms, Molecules, and Chemical Change," Prentice-Hall, Englewood Cliffs, N.J., 1964. Introductory, directly pertinent to the topics of this chapter.

King, E. L.: "How Chemical Reactions Occur," Benjamin, New York, 1963. A paperback especially relevant to the contents of this chapter. Highly recommended.

Lessing, L.: The Life-saving Promise of Enzymes, *Fortune,* March, 1969. An excellent popular review of recent advances in our knowledge and applications of enzyme action.

Phillips, D. C.: The Three-dimensional Structure of an Enzyme Molecule, *Sci. American,* Nov., 1966. The makeup and manner of action of an antibacterial enzyme are examined.

Sienko, M. J., and **R. A. Plane:** "Chemistry," 3d ed., McGraw-Hill, New York, 1966. A recommended basic text, containing good accounts of the energetics and nature of reactions.

Speakman, J. C.: "Molecules," McGraw-Hill, New York, 1966. This paperback contains detailed but not too difficult accounts of atomic and molecular structure, written from both a chemical and a biochemical point of view. Some parts are clearly relevant to the topics of this chapter.

White, E. H.: "Chemical Background for the Biological Sciences," Prentice-Hall, Englewood Cliffs, N.J., 1964. A chapter on chemical reactions is included in this paperback.

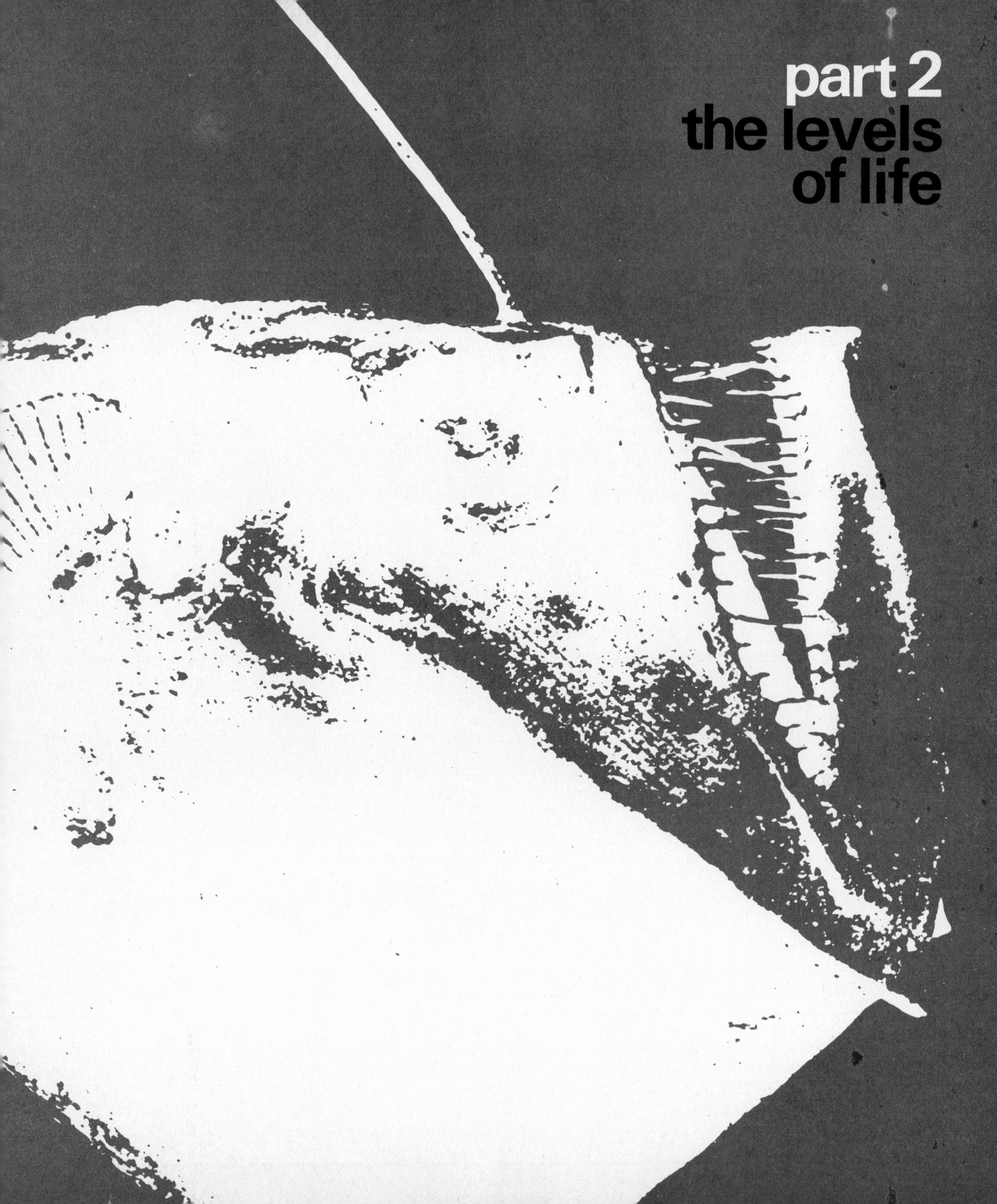

part 2
the levels of life

part 2
the levels of life

chapter 4
molecule and cell

chapter 5
cell and organism

chapter 6
species and ecosystem

chapter 7
habitat and biosphere

In this part we examine the structure of the living hierarchy in some detail. Our first concerns are the chemical makeup of living matter and the ways in which living matter forms organisms composed of cells, tissues, organs, and organ systems. Whole organisms in turn are components of higher living levels, notably populations, species, communities, and supercommunities. The organization of these larger units is our second subject of discussion. Groups of this kind live in, and indeed are greatly influenced by, the geographic localities that serve as their homes. Such environmental considerations lead to the most inclusive levels that encompass all living matter on earth as well as the physical parts of the globe. The organization of these levels and the extraordinary impact of man on this organization is the concluding topic in this series of chapters.

chapter 4 molecule and cell

No living unit is ever exactly like any other or exactly the same from moment to moment; living matter is not a static, passive material. In a cell, for example, new substances enter continuously, wastes and manufactured products leave continuously, and substances in the interior are continuously transformed chemically and redistributed physically. As a result, living matter is always in an agitated state. To the casual human observer a tree might appear to be a rather placid, inactive structure; but if the cell contents of the tree could be seen, they would all be noted to be in unceasing motion, interacting and changing. Consequently, a tree as a whole changes continuously, and so indeed does every kind of living material.

However, despite such changes between and within cells, certain very basic features nevertheless remain the same. Representing the universal heritage passed on by the very first cells on earth, these basic characteristics are in part *chemical,* part *physical,* and in part *biological.* The first two of these aspects of cell organization are discussed in this chapter, and the third is examined in the next.

chemical organization

elements and compounds

Four of the most widely distributed chemical elements on earth—oxygen, carbon, hydrogen, and nitrogen—make up approximately 95 percent of the weight of cells (Table 5). Some 30 other elements contribute the remaining 5 percent of the weight. All these elements are present in the ocean; organisms have originated in water, and their cells still reflect the composition of the sea.

Most of the elements are joined together as compounds. One major class of such compounds comprises water, minerals, metallic and nonmetallic materials, and in general those substances that make up the bulk of the physical, nonliving universe. A good many of such substances occur also in living matter. This class represents the so-called *inorganic compounds.* Directly or indirectly, all inorganic compounds in cells are of mineral origin and are ultimately derived as finished nutrients from the external physical environment. The most abundant cellular mineral is *water,* present in amounts ranging from 5 to 90 or more percent. For example, the cellular water content of certain plant seeds and of tooth enamel is about 5 to 10 percent; of muscle, 75 percent; of brain, milk, or mushrooms, 80 to 90 percent; and of algae and jellyfish, 90 to 95 or more percent. As a general average, cellular matter is about 65 to 75 percent water.

The other inorganic components of cells are *mineral solids.* Such substances are present in amounts averaging about 1 to 5 percent. A considerable fraction of the minerals often forms hard deposits such as crystals inside cells or secreted precipitates on the outside of cells. Silicon- or calcium-containing deposits are common. For example, diatoms, certain protozoa, and the surface cells of certain grasses are protected externally with layers of glasslike silica; the hard part of bone is largely calcium phosphate, secreted in layers around bone-forming cells; clamshells consist of secreted calcium carbonate.

Other cellular minerals are in solution, either as free ions or combined with other compounds. The most abundant positively charged inorganic ions are H^+, hydrogen ions; Ca^{++}, calcium ions; Na^+, sodium ions; K^+, potassium ions; and Mg^{++}, magnesium ions. Abundant negatively charged mineral constituents include OH^-, hydroxyl ions; $CO_3^=$, carbonate ions; HCO_3^-, bicarbonate ions; $PO_4^{\equiv}$, phosphate ions; Cl^-, chloride ions; and $SO_4^=$, sulfate ions. In general, the kinds of minerals found in cells occur also in the ocean and in rocks. This is not a coincidence, for rocks are dissolved by water, water finds its way to the ocean and into soil, and living organisms ultimately draw their mineral supplies from these sources.

The second large group of cellular chemicals comprises the *organic compounds.* These are so named because they occur almost exclusively in living or once-living matter. Organic compounds are often exceedingly complex, and they in particular are responsible for the ''living'' properties of cells. Moreover, organic compounds represent the *foods* required by all organisms; inorganic compounds too serve as nutrients, but they are not foods. Chemically, organic substances are compounds of *carbon,* or more specifically, compounds in which the main chemical bonds join two or more carbon atoms or carbon and hydrogen atoms. Thus, carbon dioxide (CO_2), carbonate ions ($CO_3^=$), and materials derived from them are not organic, since the carbon here is bonded to oxygen. But methane, CH_4, with its carbon-hydrogen bonds, is an organic compound. Most

Table 5. The relative abundance of chemical elements in living matter

element	*symbol*	*weight percent*
oxygen	O	62
carbon	C	20
hydrogen	H	10
nitrogen	N	3
calcium	Ca	2.50
phosphorus	P	1.14
chlorine	Cl	0.16
sulfur	S	0.14
potassium	K	0.11
sodium	Na	0.10
magnesium	Mg	0.07
iodine	I	0.014
iron	Fe	0.010
subtotal		99.244
trace elements		0.756
total		100.00

of the organic compounds of biological interest contain not only carbon-hydrogen but also numerous carbon-carbon bonds.

In this respect carbon is a rather unusual element. The atoms of most other elements link to atoms of like kind too, but the number of atoms so bondable is usually quite limited. For example, a hydrogen atom can join with one other hydrogen atom at most (H—H, H_2); sulfur can form molecules of eight atoms, S_8. But a carbon atom is far more versatile. It can form as many as four (covalent) bonds with other atoms, including other carbon atoms. Long *chains* of carbon atoms can form in this way:

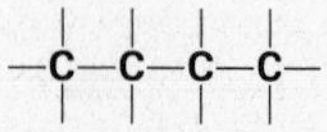

```
  |  |  |  |
 —C—C—C—C—
  |  |  |  |
```

Such chains represent parts of organic molecules in which various other atoms are attached to the carbons. Further, carbon atoms can be joined in ringlike fashion, as in *benzene,* for example:

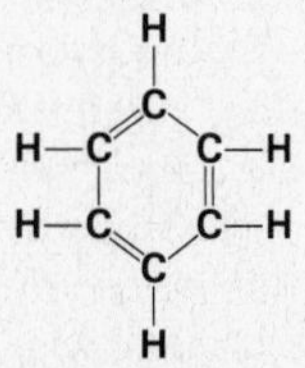

```
      H
      |
      C
    //  \
H—C      C—H
   |     ||
H—C      C—H
    \\  /
      C
      |
      H
```

Many other types of configuration exist. Thus, carbon chains can be branched, rings and chains can become joined to one another, and any of these carbon structures can also be three-dimensional. Carbon combinations can therefore be exceedingly complex and varied. Organic substances actually display more complexity and more variety than all other chemicals put together.

Cells contain hundreds of different classes of organic compounds. Of these, four classes in particular are found in all cells and form the organic basis of living matter. The four are

1 carbohydrates

2 lipids

3 proteins

4 nucleotides

Like mineral compounds, some of these organic substances contribute to the formation of hard body parts. For example, the wood of plants and horny animal materials such as claws and hoofs are predominantly organic. More generally, however, organic compounds are dissolved or suspended in cellular water. In a plant such as corn, carbohydrates make up about 18 percent of the total weight, proteins about 2 percent, and all other organic constituents together not more than about 1 percent. An animal such as man contains about 15 percent protein, about 15 percent fat, and other organic components to the extent of about 1 percent. In both cases, evidently, the inorganic matter (mainly water) far outweighs the organic. It is also generally true that, per unit weight, plant cells contain less organic matter and more water than animal cells.

carbohydrates

Carbohydrates are so named because they consist of carbon, hydrogen, and oxygen, the last two in a 2 : 1 ratio, as in water. The general atomic composition usually corresponds to the formula $C_x(H_2O)_y$, where *x* and *y* are whole numbers.

If *x* and *y* are low numbers, from 3 to about 7, then the formula describes the composition of the most common carbohydrates, the simple sugars, or *monosaccharides.* In these the carbon atoms form a chain to which H and O atoms are attached. Several classes of monosaccharides are distinguished on the basis of the numbers of carbons present: C_3 sugars are *trioses;* C_4 sugars, *tetroses;* C_5 sugars, *pentoses;* C_6 sugars, *hex-*

oses; and C_7 sugars, *heptoses.* The suffix *-ose* always identifies a sugar.

According to the pattern in which H and O atoms are attached to the carbon chains, two series of sugars can be distinguished, the *aldose* and the *ketose* sugars. As shown in Fig. 4.1, their main difference is that a $\overset{|}{\underset{|}{C}}=O$ group is terminal in aldoses and subterminal in ketoses. Among individual sugars referred to in several later contexts are certain pentoses, particularly the aldose *ribose* and the ketose *ribulose;* and certain hexoses, notably the aldose *glucose* (possibly the most common of all sugars) and the ketose *fructose* (Fig. 4.2).

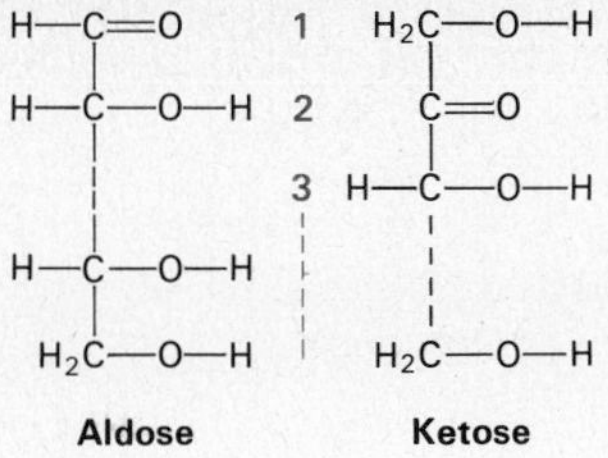

Two or more similar or identical monosaccharides can become joined together end to end as chainlike larger molecules. If two monosaccharides are joined in this way, a double sugar, or *disaccharide,* is formed. For example, combination of two glucose units yields the disaccharide *maltose,* malt sugar; combination of glucose and fructose yields *sucrose,* the cane or beet sugar used familiarly as a sweetening agent; and combination of glucose and the hexose sugar galactose yields *lactose,* milk sugar. All three of these disaccharides have the formula $C_{12}H_{22}O_{11}$, and their formation is described by the same equation:

$$2\ C_6H_{12}O_6 \longrightarrow H_2O + C_{12}H_{22}O_{11}$$

If many more than two monosaccharide units are joined together, multiple sugars, or *polysaccharides,* are the result. The general chemical process through which large molecules are built up from smaller units of like type is known as *polymerization.* Polysaccharides are said to be *polymers* of simple sugars. A polymer consisting of some hundreds or thousands of glucose units forms *glycogen,* an animal polysaccharide of considerable importance. Another polysaccharide is *cellulose,* a polymer of up to 2,000 glucose units, rare among animals but very common in plants. Also common in plants is *amylose,* a polysaccharide of 300 to 1,000 joined glucose units and a main component of starch.

In a good many polysaccharides the joined sugar units form straight, unbranched chains. The union between adjacent sugar units in such cases is said to be a 1,4 link: the first carbon of one unit links to the fourth carbon of the adjacent unit. Cellulose and amylose are good examples of polysaccharides containing 1,4 links exclusively.

Aldose **Ketose**

4.1 Aldose and ketose sugars. *In an aldose, an aldehyde group (—CHO) is terminal at position 1; in a ketose, a ketone group (—CO—) is subterminal at position 2. All other terminal positions carry —CH_2OH groups, and at all other nonterminal positions are —CHOH groups. Aldoses differ according to the number of —CHOH groups they contain and the alignment of these groups relative to each other (—CHOH— or —HOHC—); similarly for ketoses.*

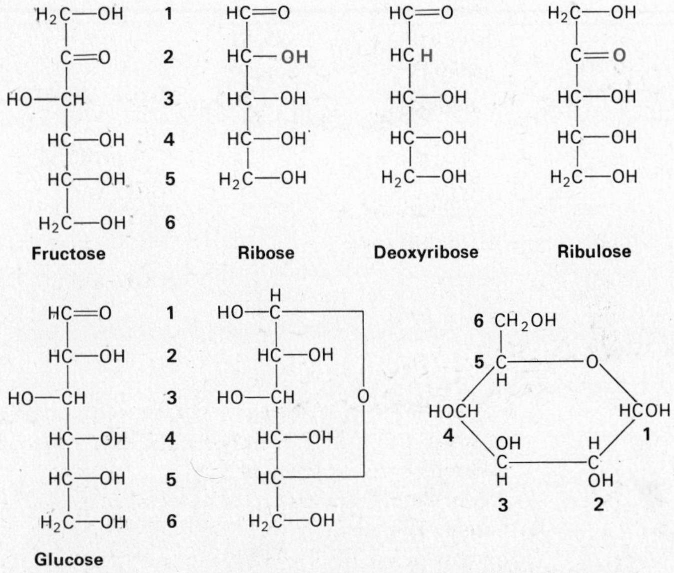

Fructose **Ribose** **Deoxyribose** **Ribulose**

Glucose

4.2 Pentoses and hexoses. *Among the pentoses shown, ribose is an aldose and ribulose is the corresponding ketose. Deoxyribose is an aldose derivate of ribose that carries an —H instead of an —OH at position 2. Among the hexoses, fructose is the ketose corresponding to the aldose glucose. The structure of glucose (as of other sugars) can be depicted in several ways, either as a chain or as a ring, as illustrated in the bottom row.*

In glycogen and other polysaccharides, however, so-called 1,6 linkages occur as well: not only carbon 4 but also carbon 6 of a given sugar unit links to carbon 1 of adjacent units. Such polysaccharide molecules are variously forked and branched as a result (Fig. 4.3).

As a group, carbohydrates function in cells in two general capacities: they are structural building blocks of the cellular substance, and they are energy-rich molecules suitable as fuels in respiration. Carbohydrates are therefore important foods. Glycogen specifically represents the chief form in which carbohydrates are stored in animals, and starch is a major storage form of car-

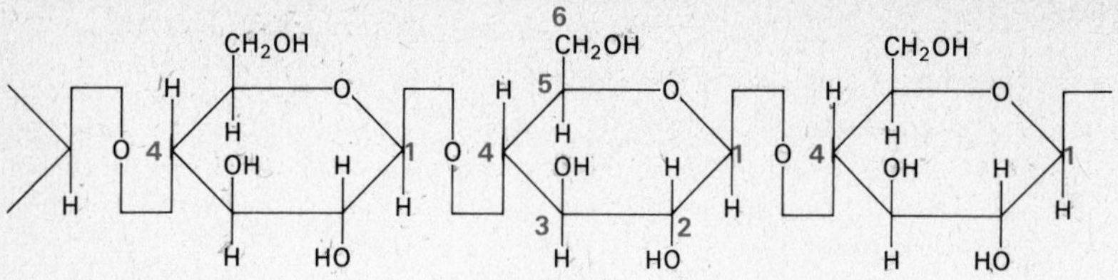

Cellulose

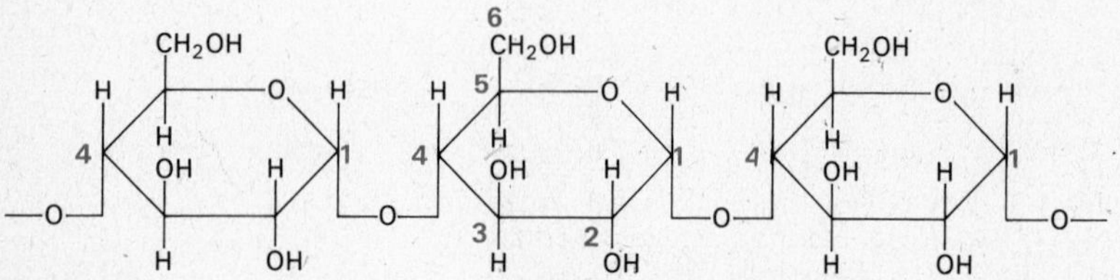

Amylose

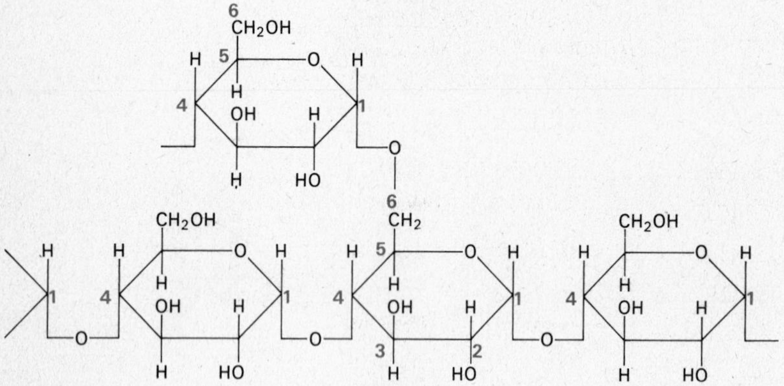

Glycogen

4.3 ***Polysaccharides.*** *All three shown here are composed entirely of glucose units. In cellulose and amylose two adjacent glucose units are joined by a 1,4 link (the difference being the alignment of the atoms in such links). Both these polysaccharides are straight-chain compounds. In glycogen the straight-chain portions have 1,4 links (as in amylose) and branch-chain portions are joined by 1,6 links (carbon 6 of one glucose unit joins carbon 1 of another glucose unit).*

bohydrates in plants. Glucose is the chief form in which carbohydrates are transported from cell to cell in all organisms and over greater distances by sap in plants and by blood in animals.

lipids

Fats and their derivatives are known collectively as lipids. The principal lipids are the *fatty acids.* Like the sugars, these acids are composed of C, H, and O, the carbon atoms being arranged as chains of various lengths. At one end each such chain carries a *carboxyl* group, —COOH, which confers acid properties on a fatty acid; the H of the carboxyl group can dissociate:

$$\text{—COOH} \longrightarrow \text{—COO}^- + \text{H}^+$$

The simplest fatty acid is *formic acid* (HCOOH). A series of increasingly more complex fatty acids is formed by successive addition of $—CH_2—$ groups to HCOOH. For example, addition of one such group produces *acetic acid* (CH_3COOH), the active ingredient of vinegar. Beyond acetic acid, fatty acids have the general formula

$$CH_3(CH_2)_nCOOH$$

where n is an integer other than zero (Fig. 4.4).

In most naturally occurring fatty acids, n is an even number; cells synthesize fatty acids from acetic acid (2-carbon, or even-numbered) building units. Common fatty acids in most plant and animal matter include, for example, *palmitic acid,*

$$CH_3(CH_2)_{14}COOH \quad (\text{or } C_{16}H_{32}O_2)$$

and *stearic acid,*

$$CH_3(CH_2)_{16}COOH \quad (\text{or } C_{18}H_{36}O_2)$$

Fatty acids like these are said to be *saturated;* all available bonds of the carbon chains are filled with hydrogen atoms. By contrast, *unsaturated* fatty acids have one or more double bonds in the carbon chains. For example, the widely occurring *oleic acid,* $CH_3(CH_2)_7CH{=}CH(CH_2)_7COOH$ (or $C_{18}H_{34}O_2$), contains one double bond. Fatty acids having more than one double bond are said to be *polyunsaturated.*

In a fat molecule, three fatty acid units are joined to one glycerin unit (Fig. 4.5). The properties of a fat are determined by the chain lengths and the degrees of saturation of the fatty acids present. Fats containing fatty acids that are short-chained, unsaturated, or both tend to be volatile or oily liquids. For example, oleic acid is oily, and fats containing oleic acid tend to be oily too. By contrast, fats with long-chained and saturated fatty acids tend to be hard tallow. This is the case in tristearin, for example, a common animal fat that contains three stearic acids per molecule.

Fats and fatty acids are important food-storage compounds in most organisms. Like carbohydrates, fats also play significant roles as structural components of cells. For example, they are present in cellular membranes, where they probably contribute to controlling the traffic of materials into and out of cells. Moreover, fats and fatty acids are even richer sources of respiratory energy than carbohydrates.

Related to fats are various compounds in which not three but only two fatty acid units are attached to glycerin. The third carbon of glycerin holds some other atomic grouping. Substances of this type include *lecithin* and *cephalin,* found in small amounts in most accumulations of animal fat. Also related are compounds in which fatty acids are joined not to glycerin but to some other carrier molecule. Most *waxes* are of this type.

More distantly related are *carotenoids,* fatty acid–like carbon chains carrying carbon rings at each end (Fig. 4.6). These compounds are pigments, and they produce red, orange, yellow, cream, and brown colors in both plant and animal matter. Carotenoids include the *carotenes* and the *xanthophylls.* Carotenes occur widely in all leaves and are also responsible for the colors of, for example, tomatoes, pumpkins, egg yolk, butter, milk, and other plant and animal products. Vitamin A is a derivative of carotene. Xanthophylls are as widely distributed as the carotenes. For example, *lutein* is a common xanthophyll of leaves, responsible for the yellow colors in autumn foliage, and *fucoxanthin* is an important pigment in brown and other algae.

Also related to lipids are *steroids,* complex ring structures that form the molecular framework of vitamin D and of several animal hormones, including the sex hormones and adrenal hormones of vertebrates (see Fig. 4.6). Still more distantly related to lipids are the *tetrapyrrols,* a group of pigmented compounds serving a wide variety of functions in plants and animals. Among these compounds are red, blue, yellow, and other pigments found, for example, in several algal groups, in the shells of robin and other bird eggs, and in mammalian feces and urine. Some of the tetrapyrrols are complex ringlike molecules that contain a single atom of a metal in the center of such rings (see Fig. 4.6). Two important tetrapyrrols of this type are *cytochrome* and *heme,* red pigments in which the metal atom is iron. Cytochrome is a hydrogen-transporting compound required in the respiration of all cells and in the photosynthesis of green cells; and heme is the oxygen-transporting component of hemoglobin present in the blood of many animals. The green pigment of photosynthetic organisms, *chlorophyll,* similarly is a ringlike tetrapyrrol, the central metal atom here being magnesium (see Chap. 16, Fig. 16.3).

proteins

These compounds are polymers of molecular units called *amino acids.* The general structure of an amino acid is represented by the formula

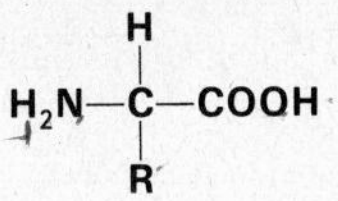

$$H_2N-\underset{\substack{|\\R}}{\overset{\substack{H\\|}}{C}}-COOH$$

where $-NH_2$ is an amino group, $-COOH$ a carboxyl group, and R— an atomic grouping that can vary in composition considerably. For example, the simplest amino acid is *glycine,* where R = H; if R = CH_3, the amino acid is called alanine. Many other amino acids are characterized by comparatively more complex R— groups. Cells typically contain 23 different types of amino acid.

Hundreds and even thousands of amino acid units can be joined together in a single protein

Structure	Composition	Name
$H-COOH$	CH_2O_2	formic
$\overset{\alpha}{CH_3}-COOH$	$C_2H_4O_2$	acetic
$\overset{\beta}{CH_3}-\overset{\alpha}{CH_2}-COOH$	$C_3H_6O_2$	propionic
$\overset{\gamma}{CH_3}-\overset{\beta}{CH_2}-\overset{\alpha}{CH_2}-COOH$	$C_4H_8O_2$	butyric
$CH_3(CH_2)_4COOH$	$C_6H_{12}O_2$	caproic
$CH_3(CH_2)_5COOH$	$C_8H_{14}O_2$	caprylic
$CH_3(CH_2)_{14}COOH$	$C_{16}H_{32}O_2$	palmitic
$CH_3(CH_2)_{16}COOH$	$C_{18}H_{36}O_2$	stearic

4.4 Fatty acids. *The (incomplete) series is arranged according to increasing molecular complexity. Carbon positions are identified by Greek letters, starting at the carbon next to the carboxyl group.*

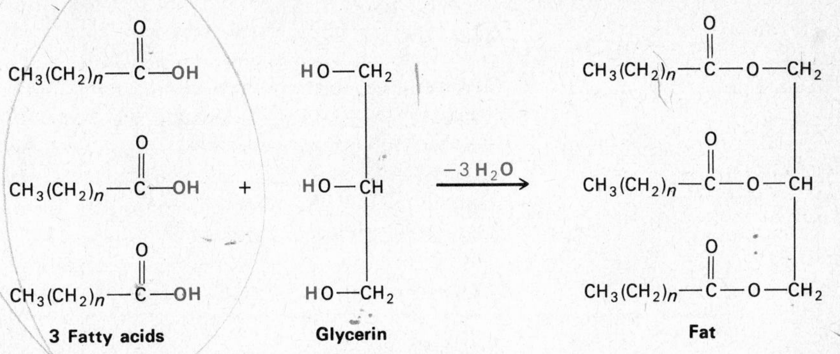

$$3\ CH_3(CH_2)_n-\overset{O}{\overset{\|}{C}}-OH + \begin{matrix} HO-CH_2 \\ | \\ HO-CH \\ | \\ HO-CH_2 \end{matrix} \xrightarrow{-3\,H_2O} \begin{matrix} CH_3(CH_2)_n-\overset{O}{\overset{\|}{C}}-O-CH_2 \\ | \\ CH_3(CH_2)_n-\overset{O}{\overset{\|}{C}}-O-CH \\ | \\ CH_3(CH_2)_n-\overset{O}{\overset{\|}{C}}-O-CH_2 \end{matrix}$$

3 Fatty acids **Glycerin** **Fat**

4.5 Fat formation. *Three molecules of fatty acid combine with one molecule of glycerin, resulting in three water molecules and one fat molecule.*

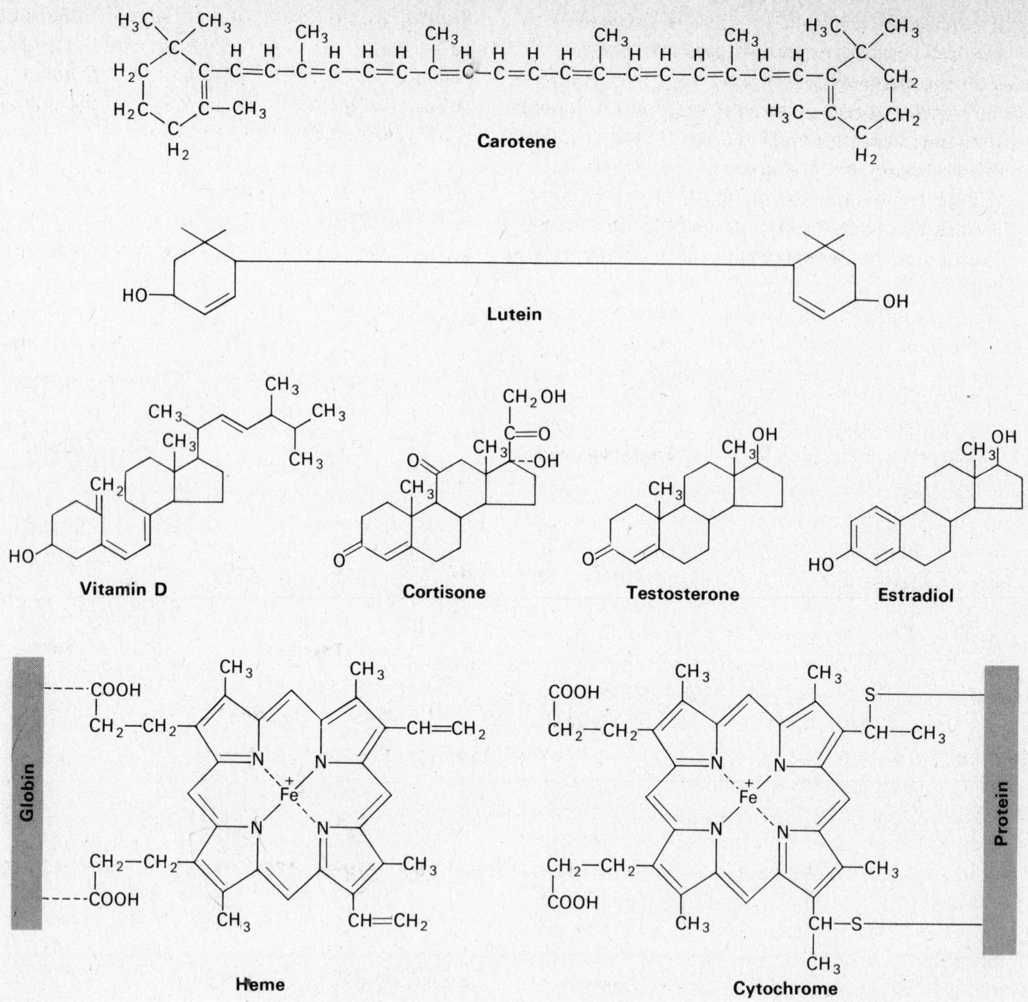

4.6 Lipid derivatives. *Top: the carbon chain of the xanthophyll pigment lutein is quite similar to that of the carotenoid pigment carotene. Middle: four steroid compounds. Cortisone is a hormone of the adrenal cortex. Note the structural similarity of testosterone and estradiol, the most potent of the male and female sex hormones, respectively. Bottom: the ringlike tetrapyrrols heme and cytochrome are each bonded to a protein in cells. Hemoglobin transports oxygen in vertebrate blood, and cytochrome is an electron-carrying participant in photosynthesis and in the respiration of all cells. See also Fig. 16.3 for the structure of chlorophyll, another ringlike tetrapyrrol.*

molecule (Fig. 4.7). Whenever molecules attain exceedingly large sizes, they are referred to as *macromolecules.* Proteins are very often macromolecules, and some of them are among the largest chemical structures known. As such, proteins are associated most intimately with the phenomenon we call "life."

Adjacent amino acids in a protein are united in such a way that the amino group of one acid links to the carboxyl group of its neighbor; the bond is formed by removal of one molecule of water (Fig. 4.8). The resulting grouping —NH—CO— represents a *peptide bond,* and two amino acids so joined form a *dipeptide.* If many amino acids are polymerized by means of peptide bonds, the whole chainlike complex is a *polypeptide.*

Chemically, polypeptides can vary in practically unlimited fashion:

1 They can contain any or all of the 23 different naturally occurring *types* of amino acids.

2 They can contain almost any *number* of each of these amino acid types.

3 The specific *sequence* in which given numbers and types of amino acids are joined as a chain can vary almost without restriction.

In other words, amino acid units can be envisaged to represent an "alphabet" of 23 "letters," and an astronomically large number of different polypeptide "sentences" can be constructed from this alphabet. Correspondingly, the possible number of chemically different proteins is likewise astronomical. Indeed no two organisms possess exactly the same types of proteins. A polypeptide chain with its particular sequence of amino acid units and peptide bonds represents the so-called *primary* structure of a protein.

Such a chain has the physical form of a twisted ribbon. If a line were drawn through all the R— portions of the consecutive amino acids present, the line would mark out a spiral (Fig. 4.9). Such spirals are in some cases "right-handed" (*α-helix*), in others "left-handed" (*β-helix*). In either configuration the backbone of the spiral is a bonded sequence of

—N—C—C—N—C—C—N—

atoms, each —N—C—C— portion representing

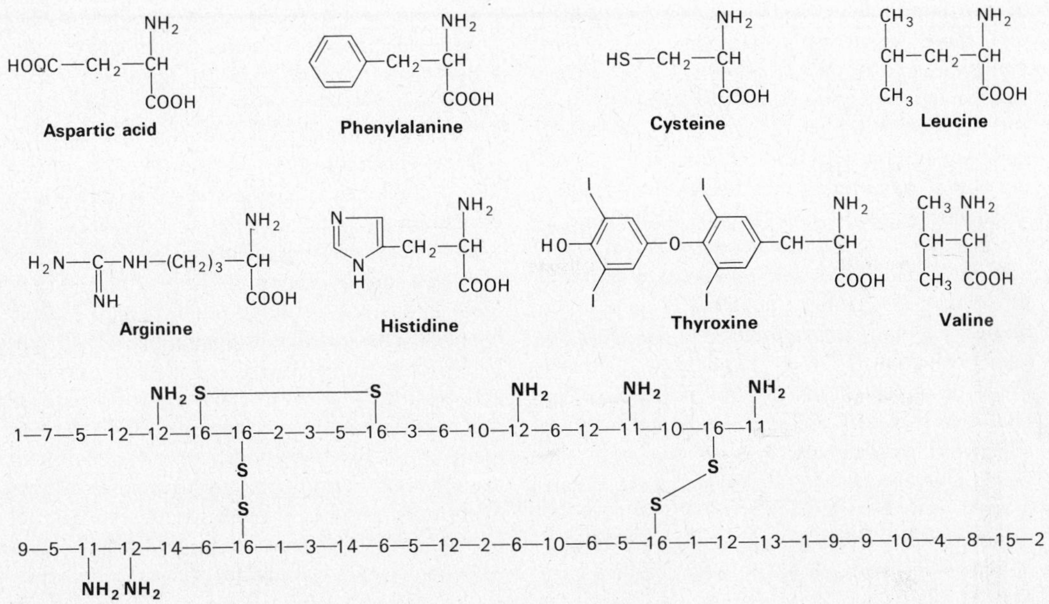

Aspartic acid

Phenylalanine

Cysteine

Leucine

Arginine

Histidine

Thyroxine

Valine

1, glycine	5, valine	9, phenylalanine	13, arginine
2, alanine	6, leucine	10, tyrosine	14, histidine
3, serine	7, isoleucine	11, aspartic acid	15, lysine
4, threonine	8, proline	12, glutamic acid	16, cysteine

4.7 Amino acids and proteins. *Top, the structure of eight representative amino acids. Bottom, the structure of the insulin molecule, a protein consisting of 51 amino acid units. One chain consists of 21 units, another of 30 units, and the two are held together by sulfur-containing cysteine units. Insulin is one of the smallest proteins known.*

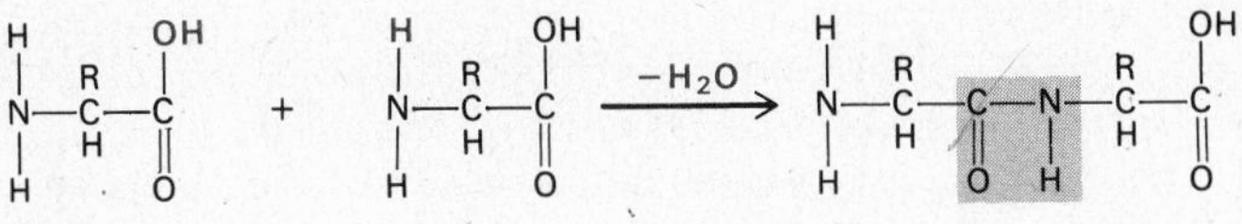

4.8 Amino acid bonding. *Two amino acids combine with loss of water. The result is a peptide bond, as indicated in the tinted area at right.*

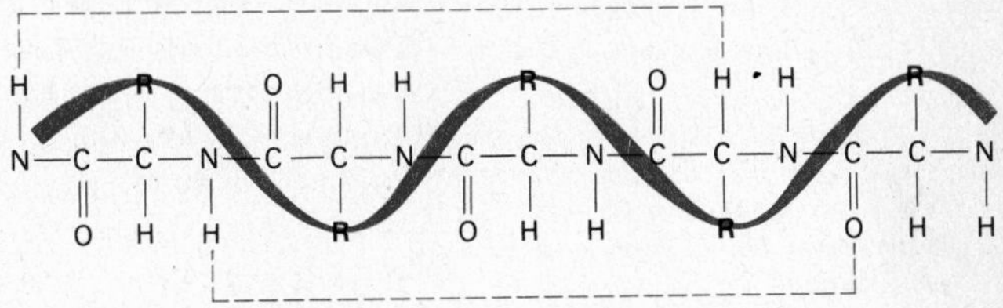

4.9 The spiral structure of protein. *A line connecting the R— fractions of consecutive amino acid units in a polypeptide chain marks out a spiral called an α-helix. Such a helix is held together by hydrogen bonds between the H of the —NH of one amino acid unit and the O of a —CO— in another amino acid three units distant (colored broken lines).*

the skeleton of one amino acid unit. Projecting out from this ribbon are the H—, O═, and R— groups of the amino acid unit. In most proteins the polypeptide spirals have fairly similar geometric properties. Thus there are on the average 3.7 amino acid units per turn of a spiral. Accordingly, a chain of some 18 units forms a helix with five complete turns.

This spiral configuration is held together by *hydrogen bonds.* Such a bond is formed here when a H atom is shared between the nitrogen of one amino acid unit and an oxygen of a nearby unit. More precisely, the H of the —NH of one unit is bonded to the O of —C═O three amino acid units away (see Fig. 4.9). All —NH and —C═O groups of a polypeptide chain are hydrogen-bonded in this fashion, each such bond linking amino acids three units apart. The resulting spiral configuration is relatively stable, and it represents the *secondary structure* of a protein.

If long coils of this sort remain extended and threadlike, the protein molecule is said to be *fibrous.* In many cases, however, the coils are looped and twisted and folded back on themselves, in an almost infinite variety of ways. Protein molecules then are *globular,* balled together somewhat like entangled twine. Such loops and bends give a protein a *tertiary structure.* Where present, a tertiary configuration is held together chiefly by three kinds of bonds (Fig. 4.10). One is again the hydrogen bond, which in this case links together more or less distant portions of a polypeptide chain. Another is an *ionic bond,* formed when a carboxyl group and an amino group of two distant terminal amino acid units come to lie near each other. A third type of link is the *disulfide bond,* which arises between sulfur-containing amino acids. Sulfur occurs most often in the form of —SH groups, and the most common —SH-containing amino acid is *cysteine.* If then two distant cysteine units in a folded polypeptide come to lie close to each other, their —SH groups can link together and form a "disulfide bridge," —S—S—.

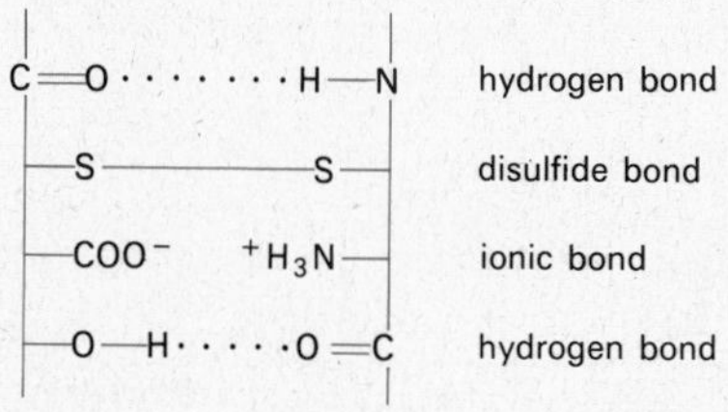

C═O · · · · · · · H—N hydrogen bond

—S————————S— disulfide bond

—COO⁻ $^{+}H_3N$— ionic bond

—O—H · · · · ·O═C hydrogen bond

4.10 Bonds in protein. *Separate polypeptide chains on different segments of a single chain (vertical lines) can be held together by bonds such as shown. In a hydrogen bond, a H atom is held in common by two side groups on the polypeptides (top and bottom). Disulfide bridges are formed by S-containing amino acid units, mainly cysteine. Ionic links between charged side groups on polypeptide chains hold together by electric attraction.*

Some proteins consist of not one but several separate polypeptide chains bonded to one another, often in the form of a bundle. Proteins of this type are said to possess a *quaternary structure.* The polypeptides here are held together largely by the bond types already referred to above. For example, one of the hormones of the pancreas, *insulin,* is a protein made up of two parallel polypeptide chains, and these are held together by two disulfide bonds (see Fig. 4.7). Similarly, in a hemoglobin molecule of vertebrate blood the protein component consists of four linked polypeptide chains. Differences in the properties of proteins thus can arise from differences in as many as four aspects of structure. For example, even if two proteins have identical primary structure, they will have different properties if their secondary, tertiary, or quaternary structures are not the same.

Of all the bonds that maintain a globular protein configuration, hydrogen bonds are the weakest. Such bonds are disrupted readily by physical or chemical changes in the environment of a protein—for example, by excessive heat, pressure, pH, electricity, heavy metals, and other agents that create suboptimal conditions. When some or many of its hydrogen bonds are broken, a protein cannot retain its globular configuration, and its quaternary, tertiary, or even secondary structure will be lost. An originally highly folded molecule will then become a straight, fibrous one. Also, in the original globular state the protein might have been soluble in water, for ball-like particles disperse readily; but long fibrous molecules pile together like a log jam and generally become insoluble in water.

Such changes in protein configuration are called *denaturation.* If the disruptive effect is mild and of brief duration, denaturation is often temporary and the protein can later revert to its original *native* state. But if the environmental change is drastic and lasting, then denaturation becomes permanent and irreversible and the protein will be *coagulated.* For example, the protein of egg white, albumen, is globular (and water-soluble) in the raw native state, but becomes fibrous (and water-insoluble) in the cooked, coagulated state (like boiled egg white). Denaturation usually destroys the biological properties a protein has in the native state—a major reason why excessive heat or other excessive environmental changes kill cells.

Proteins differ considerably from carbohydrates

or fats in their nearly unlimited structural variations. Even a highly complex carbohydrate, for example, is structurally the same whether we obtain it from mushrooms or mangoes, from mice or from men. A given lipid, similarly, is the same lipid regardless of where we find it. Not so for proteins, however; these compounds vary so much that, as noted, no two organisms contain precisely the same types. Even twin organisms have slightly different proteins, and the differences are the greater the less closely two organisms are related. Proteins evidently have a high degree of *specificity:* the proteins of an organism are unique for that organism.

Protein specificity has well-known consequences. For example, transfer of protein from one organism into the cells of another amounts to an introduction of foreign bodies, and disease can follow. Thus the proteins of plant pollen or of parts of other organisms can produce allergic reactions in man. Or when blood of one animal is mixed with incompatible blood of another, the recipient can suffer protein shock that can be lethal. Partly because bacterial proteins differ from those of other organisms, infectious bacteria produce many diseases. And when body parts of one animal are grafted to another animal, the transplants normally do not heal into place and are rejected sooner or later because the two sets of proteins differ. Special medication can sometimes retard or forestall graft rejection in man.

To some extent, normally far less than carbohydrates or fats, proteins are used in cells as foodstuffs. But proteins serve mainly in two far more important cellular roles. First, they represent vital construction materials out of which much of the basic framework of cells is built. Carbohydrates, fats, minerals, and other cellular components are organized around such *structural proteins* that form the molecular "scaffolding" of living material. Second, many proteins serve as reaction-catalyzing enzymes. Life depends on enzymatic acceleration of reactions, and "living" therefore means dependence on enzymatic *functional proteins.* Enzymes share the chemical and physical properties of proteins generally. As proteins are specific, so enzymes are specific; and if denaturation of enzyme proteins alters or destroys the native configuration, then specific enzymatic capacities will be lost (unless the active sites remain intact and accessible).

For both structural and functional reasons, therefore, cellular life would probably not be possible without molecular agents such as proteins. But even with proteins and all the other cellular compounds already described, a cell could not yet be alive; the chemicals discussed thus far only endow a cell with the *potential* of having a structure (proteins and other constituents), the *potential* of performing functions (enzymes), and the *potential* of accumulating usable foods (carbohydrates and fats). The cell has not yet been equipped chemically to make these potentials actual: *how* to use the foods, *what* actual structure to develop, and *which* functions to carry out. These all-important capacities emerge from the organic compounds considered next.

nucleotides

A nucleotide is a molecular complex of three units: a *phosphate group,* a *pentose sugar,* and a *nitrogen base.* Phosphate groups are derivatives of phosphoric acid (H_3PO_4), an inorganic mineral substance. If this formula is rewritten as $H—O—H_2PO_3$, then the $—O—H_2PO_3$ part represents the phosphate group of present concern. And if the $—H_2PO_3$ portion of the group is represented simply as P, the whole phosphate group can be symbolized as —O—P.

The pentose sugar in a nucleotide is one of two kinds, *ribose* or *deoxyribose* (see Fig. 4.2). Therefore, according to the kind of sugar present, two types of nucleotides can be distinguished: *ribose nucleotides* (or *ribotides*) and *deoxyribose nucleotides* (or *deoxyribotides*).

The nitrogen base of a nucleotide is one of a series of ring compounds that contain nitrogen as well as carbon. A single ring occurs in *pyrimidines,* and a double ring characterizes *purines* (Fig. 4.11). Pyrimidines include three variants of significance, *thymine, cytosine,* and *uracil.* Among purines are two important types, *adenine* and *guanine.*

The nitrogen base in a ribose nucleotide usually is either uracil or cytosine or adenine or guanine. Similarly, a deoxyribose nucleotide typically contains either thymine or cytosine or adenine or guanine. Thus, nucleotides occur in the following two series:

ribotides	*deoxytibotides*
adenine—ribose—**O—P**	adenine—deoxyribose—**O—P**
guanine—ribose—**O—P**	guanine—deoxyribose—**O—P**
cytosine—ribose—**O—P**	cytosine—deoxyribose—**O—P**
uracil—ribose—**O—P**	thymine—deoxyribose—**O—P**

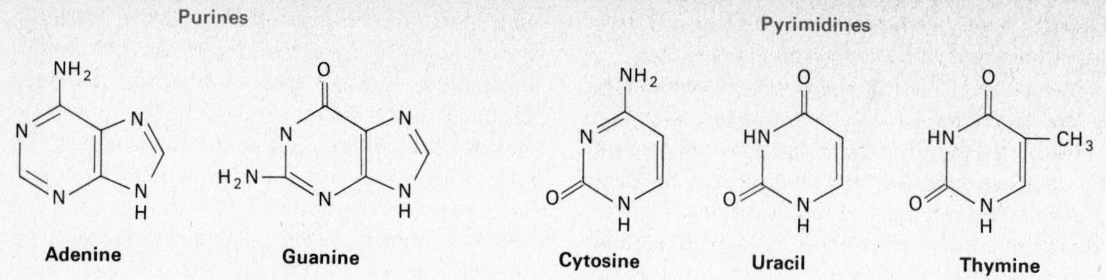

4.11 *Nitrogen bases.*

Uracil occurs only in the ribose series, thymine only in the deoxyribose series; adenine, guanine, and cytosine occur in both. Each of these nucleotides has at least three different but equivalent names. For example, adenine—ribose—O—P can be called *adenine ribotide* or *adenylic acid* or *adenosine monophosphate* (AMP for short). The other nucleotides have similarly constructed designations (for example, guanylic acid or guanosine monophosphate or GMP; cytidylic acid or cytidine monophosphate or CMP; uridylic acid or uridine monophosphate or UMP; thymidylic acid or thymidine monophosphate or TMP).

Nucleotides are building blocks of larger molecules that serve three crucial functions in cells: some are *energy carriers;* others are *coenzymes;* and still others form *genetic systems.*

energy carriers

A nucleotide can link up in serial fashion with one or two additional phosphate groups. For example, if to adenosine monophosphate (AMP) is added one more phosphate, then *adenosine diphosphate,* or ADP, is formed; and if a third phosphate is added to ADP, the result is *adenosine triphosphate,* or ATP:

adenine—ribose—**O—P**	AMP
adenine—ribose—**O—P—O∼P**	ADP
adenine—ribose—**O—P—O∼P—O∼P**	ATP

the wavy symbol in the added —O ∼ P groups indicates the presence of a so-called *high-energy bond.* The significance of such bonds will become clearer in Chap. 15. Here it need be noted only that the formation of bonds between certain atoms, notably the —O ∼ P— bonds, requires particularly large amounts of energy. They also release correspondingly large amounts of energy when they are broken. Thus, to convert AMP to ADP and ADP to ATP requires not only additional phosphate groups but also considerable energy inputs. This energy is derived in cells from respiratory fuels, and we shall find that the primary function of respiration actually is to create the high-energy bonds of ATP. The compound is the significant energy-rich endproduct of respiration. In effect ATP is an *energy carrier,* the most widespread of such carriers in cells. Derivatives of some of the other nucleotides play a more limited energy-carrying role. For example, by addition of phosphate groups and energy, UMP can become UDP and UTP.

coenzymes

A coenzyme is a carrier molecule that functions in conjunction with a particular enzyme. It happens often in a metabolic process that a group of atoms is removed from one compound and is transferred to another. In such cases a specific enzyme accelerates the decomposition reaction that brings about the removal, but a specific coenzyme must also be present to carry out the transfer. The coenzyme temporarily joins with, or accepts, the removed group of atoms and later transfers it to another compound. The majority of coenzymes happen to be chemical derivatives of nucleotides.

More specifically, in many coenzymes the nitrogen base of a nucleotide is replaced by another chemical unit, usually a derivative of a particular vitamin. For example, one of the B vitamins is *riboflavin* (B_2). This compound consists of a ribose portion and, attached to it, a complex *flavin* portion. In cells a phosphate group becomes linked to riboflavin, and the result is nucleotidelike complex flavin—ribose—O—P. Called *flavin mononucleotide,* or FMN for short, this complex can then become joined to the nucleotide AMP, resulting in a double nucleotide known as *flavin adenine dinucleotide,* FAD (Fig. 4.12). Both FMN and FAD are cellular coenzymes that serve as carriers in many processes in which hydrogen is transferred from one compound to another.

Two other hydrogen-carrying coenzymes, called NAD and NADP, are constructed from adenine-containing nucleotides and from nicotinamide, a derivative of the B vitamin nicotinic acid (niacin). Nucleotides and still another B vitamin, pantothenic acid, contribute to the structure of *coenzyme A,* or CoA, a compound that carries not hydrogen but another specific group of atoms. In later contexts we shall encounter not only the coenzymes mentioned here but also some others that are not nucleotide derivatives.

genetic systems

If any single group of chemicals could qualify as the ''secret'' of life, that group would unquestionably have to be the *nucleic acids.* (But since we can actually make such an identification today, it is really no longer possible to speak of any ''secret.'') Nucleic acids are *polynucleotides,* extended chains of up to thousands of joined nucleotide units.

Such chains are of two types, according to whether the nucleotides composing them belong to the ribose series or the deoxyribose series. A chain consisting of ribotides is a *ribose nucleic acid,* or RNA for short; and a chain of deoxyribotides is *deoxyribose nucleic acid,* DNA for short.

In either type, the sugar component of one nucleotide unit bonds to the phosphate component of the next. Thus, the sugar (*S*) and phosphate (*P*) components form an extended molecular thread from which nitrogen bases (*N*) project as side chains:

```
—P—S—P—S—P—S—P—S—
   |   |   |   |
   N   N   N   N
```

In the case of RNA, the particular types, numbers, and sequences of the four possible kinds of nitrogen bases can vary almost infinitely. A short segment of a long RNA molecule might, for example, contain nitrogen bases in a sequence such as

```
—P—R—P—R—P—R—P—R—P—R—
   |   |   |   |   |
   A   U   G   G   C
```

where *R* stands for ribose and *A, U, G, C,* for adenine, uracil, guanine, and cytosine, respectively. In effect, RNA molecules differ as the sequences of their nitrogen bases differ; and that is actually the key to their importance. For the four possible nitrogen bases can be regarded as a four-letter ''alphabet'' out of which, just as with amino acids in proteins, any number of ''words'' and ''sentences'' can be constructed. As will become apparent later, the protein ''sentences''

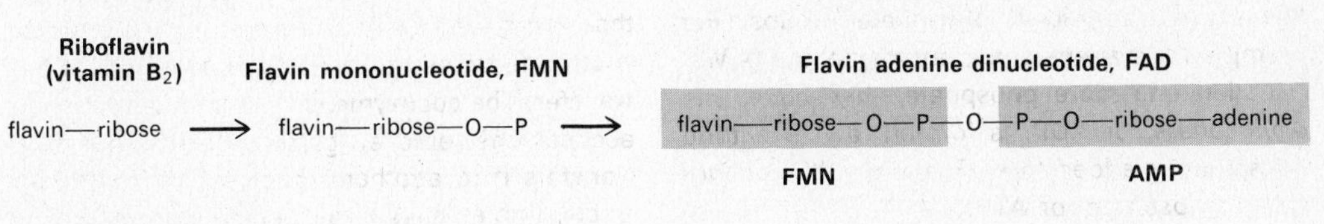

Niacin (vitamin B)

nicotinic acid

↓

nicotinamide

↓

Nicotinamide adenine dinucleotide, NAD

nicotinamide—ribose—O—P—O—P—O—ribose—adenine (AMP)

→ **Nicotinamide adenine dinucleotide phosphate, NADP**

nicotinamide—ribose—O—P—O—P—O—ribose—adenine, with O—P attached to the second ribose

Pantothenic acid (vitamin B) → **Coenzyme A, CoA**

[carbon-sulfur chain]—pantothenic acid—O—P—O—P—O—ribose—adenine, with P—O attached to the ribose

4.12 ***Coenzymes.*** *In the examples shown here, coenzymes are derived in part from vitamins, in part from nucleotides. Top, from the B vitamin riboflavin cells manufacture the coenzyme FMN by addition of a phosphate group, and the coenzyme FAD by the further addition of adenosine monophosphate (AMP). Center, the B vitamin niacin is the cellular source for the formation of nicotinamide, a compound used in the syntheses of the coenzymes NAD and NADP. Bottom, the B vitamin pantothenic acid is a component in the construction of coenzyme A in cells.*

precisely correspond to, and indeed are determined by, the RNA "sentences."

The original source of the sentences is not RNA itself, but DNA. This type of nucleic acid is a long *double* chain of nucleotides; two parallel single chains are held together by hydrogen bonds between pairs of nitrogen bases (Fig. 4.13). By virtue of their particular structure these bases can be paired only in four different ways: adenine with thymine or the reverse, and guanine with cytosine or the reverse. But there is apparently no limit to the number of times each of these combinations can occur in a long double chain. Nor do there appear to be restrictions as to their sequence. Thus *A · T, T · A, G · C,* and *C · G* can be regarded as an original four-symbol alphabet, and sequences of any length can be constructed by using these symbols as often as desired and in any order. The possible number of different DNA's is therefore practically unlimited. A final structural characteristic of DNA is that the double chain of the molecule is spiraled, not straight (Fig. 4.14). The molecular structure outlined here is referred to as the *Watson-Crick model,* after the investigators who proposed it on the basis of X-ray diffraction studies of DNA.

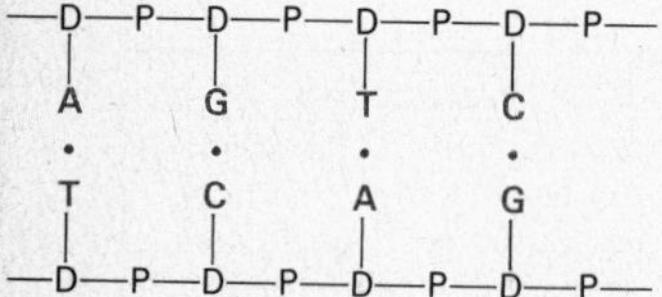

***4.13 The Watson-Crick model** of DNA structure (P, phosphate; D, deoxyribose; A, T, G, C, purines and pyrimidines. A P—D—A unit represents one of the nucleotides.) In the —P—D—P—D— double chain, four kinds of purine-pyrimidine pairs are possible: A·T, T·A, G·C, and C·G. Each of the four can occur many times, and the sequence of the pairs can vary in unlimited fashion.*

Functionally, DNA exhibits three properties that make it the universal key to life. First, as will be shown in Chap. 17, DNA provides the cell with instructions on how to manufacture specific proteins. And through this control of protein manufacture, DNA ultimately controls the entire structural and functional makeup of every cell. Second, cellular DNA has the property of being self-duplicating; DNA is a *reproducing* molecule. That a chemical should be able to multiply itself under certain conditions may perhaps be astounding, but this capacity is nevertheless a known, unique property of DNA. Reproduction of DNA is at the root of all reproduction, and in a fundamental sense even the reproduction of a whole plant or animal is, after all, a reproduction of "chemicals." Third, under certain conditions DNA can undergo *mutations,* or become slightly but permanently altered in its nitrogen-base content. When such changes occur the structural and functional traits of a cell can become changed correspondingly. Through changes in its cells a whole organism and its progeny can then become changed in the course of successive generations—a process equivalent to *evolution.*

In short, DNA is the material that forms *genes.* These cellular components have long been recognized as the carriers of heredity, but now they are known to be the ultimate controllers of all metabolism and all self-perpetuation. DNA molecules, or genes, thus are the basis of life. Chapter 17 will show how the structure of the genetic nucleic acids actually permits these molecules to function as they do.

Carbohydrates, lipids, proteins, and various nucleotide derivatives form the organic bulk of living matter. However, hundreds of other kinds of organic substances exist in cells. Although such substances are often present in only very small quantities, they are nevertheless of extreme importance in the maintenance of life. Some of these compounds are not related chemically to the four main categories above. Others are derivatives of one of the four groups, and still others are combinations of two or more of the basic four.

Thus, even without a lengthy listing of the enormous number of different cellular compounds, a general conclusion can be discerned: almost the whole vast array of organic substances in cells is related to or derived from only a half dozen or so fundamental types of compounds; and among these the main types are sugars, fatty acids, amino acids, and nucleotides. Nature apparently builds with but a limited number of fundamental construction units, yet the possible combinations and variations among them are practically unlimited.

It should be kept in mind also that the diverse chemical components of a cell are not "just there," randomly and passively dissolved or suspended in water like the ingredients of a soup. Instead the components interact and form a highly organized *living* system. This system consists of a mixture of particular macromolecular and micromolecular substances, some organic and some inorganic; and as certain of them do and others do not dissolve in the water medium of a cell, the whole cell acquires a well-defined physical organization. Its nature is examined in the following section.

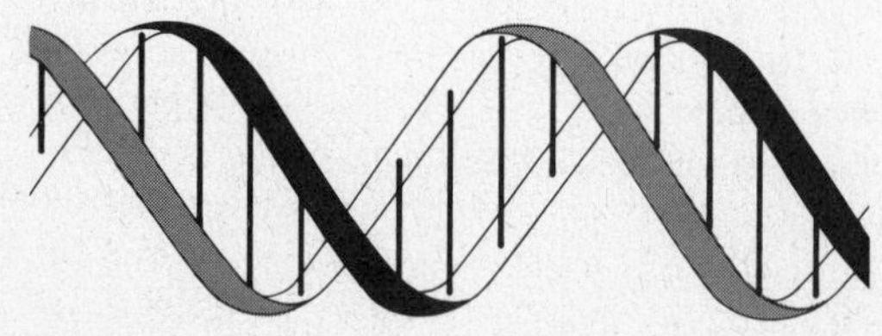

***4.14 The DNA spiral.** The two spirals symbolize the —P—D—P—D— chains, and the connections between the spirals represent the purine-pyrimidine pairs.*

colloids

Any system composed of particles that are dispersed in another medium may be classified as belonging to one of three categories, depending on the size of the particles. If the particles are small enough to dissolve in the medium, the system is a true *solution.* If the particles are large—the size of soil grains, for example—they soon settle by gravity to the bottom of a container. Such a system is a coarse *suspension.* But if the particles are of intermediate size, from about 1/1,000,000 to 1/10,000 mm in diameter, they neither form a solution nor settle out. Such a system is a *colloid,*

Any system composed of two kinds of components is a colloid if one of the components consists of particles of appropriate size. Eight general types of colloidal systems exist: a gas dispersed in either a solid or a liquid; a liquid in either a liquid, a solid, or a gas; and a solid in either a liquid, a solid, or a gas. The most common types are *sols,* in which solid colloidal particles are dispersed in liquids (for example, colloidal $Mg(OH)_2$ in water, as in milk of magnesia); *gels,* in which liquid colloidal particles are dispersed in solids (for example, colloidal water in protein, as in stiff gelatin or Jell-O); *emulsions,* in which colloidal liquids are dispersed in liquids (for example, colloidal fat in water, as in milk); and *aerosols,* in which either solids or liquids are dispersed in a gas (for example, colloidal ash in air, as in cigarette smoke, or colloidal water in air, as in fog).

The cell substance is partly a true solution, partly a colloidal system, Water is the medium in which many materials are dissolved, and it is also the *liquid phase* in which many insoluble materials of colloidal size are dispersed. This colloidal *dispersed phase* includes, for example, macromolecular solids such as proteins and nucleic acids, and liquids such as oily fats. What prevents these dispersed colloidal particles from setting out? As noted in Chap. 3, the molecules of a liquid are in continuous thermal motion, the more so the higher the temperature. If dispersed particles are present, they are buffeted and bombarded constantly by the moving molecules of the liquid. Very large particles are unaffected by these weak forces, and they settle to the bottom of a container. But smaller bodies of colloidal size will be pushed in all directions. Such movements override the effect of gravity and the particles will remain suspended. This random movement of small particles, called *Brownian motion,* is readily demonstrable under the microscope.

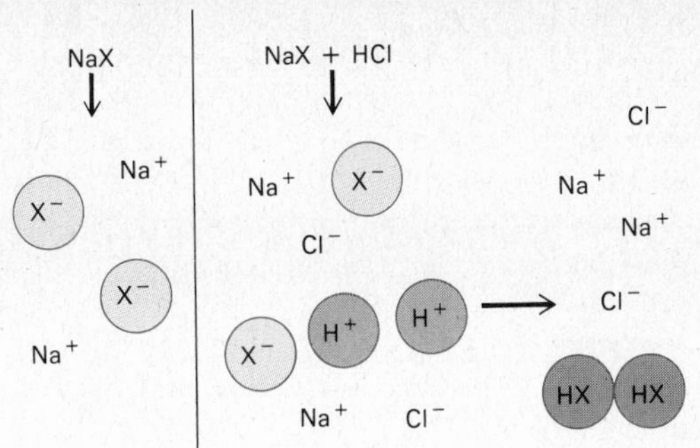

4.15 Dispersion in colloids. *Left, if a material dissociates in water and if one of the ion types formed is of colloidal size (X^-), then the repulsion of like charges can maintain dispersion of the colloid. Right, if particles of opposite charge (H^+) are added to dispersed and charge-carrying colloidal particles (X^-), then the colloid can become neutralized electrically by formation of HX and settle out.*

Brownian movement aids in keeping colloidal particles from settling out, but they cannot remain suspended by this force alone. They stay dispersed mainly because most types of colloids are ionized and therefore carry *electric charges.* One member of an ion pair is usually noncolloidal and fully dissolved, and the other member is colloidal. Thus all colloidal particles of a particular type carry like charges, and the particles are kept apart by their electric repulsion. If the charges are neutralized by addition of oppositely charged substances that reduce the degree of ionization, then the colloid particles often do settle out (Fig. 4.15).

The relative quantities of the two components of a colloid often determine whether the system will form a *sol* or a *gel.* For example, if a little gelatin is added to a large amount of water, a sol will be formed. If more gelatin is added or, alternatively, if water is withdrawn, the gelatin particles will be brought closer together until, ultimately, they come into contact. They will then interlock as a spongelike meshwork of solid material, and in the spaces of the mesh discontinuous droplets of water will be dispersed. The original sol thus becomes transformed to a quasi-solid, pliable jelly, or a gel. Conversely, addition of water or removal of solid particles can transform a gel to a sol (Fig. 4.16). In living materials *sol-gel transformations* of this sort occur normally and repeatedly as the concentrations of particles in a given region increase or decrease with time. In some cases a region remains more or less permanently in a gel state, like skin, or in a sol state, like blood plasma (which becomes a gel

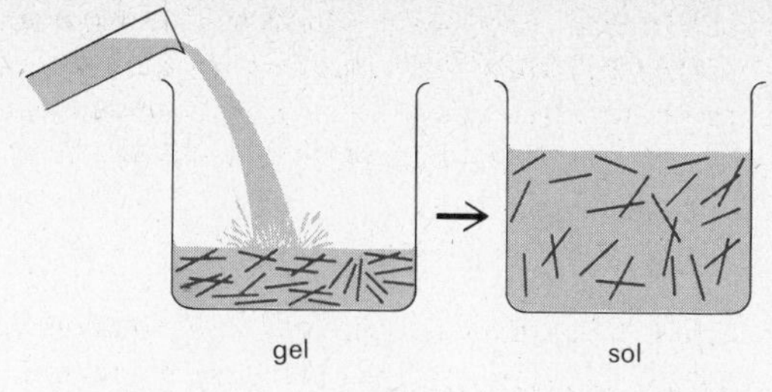

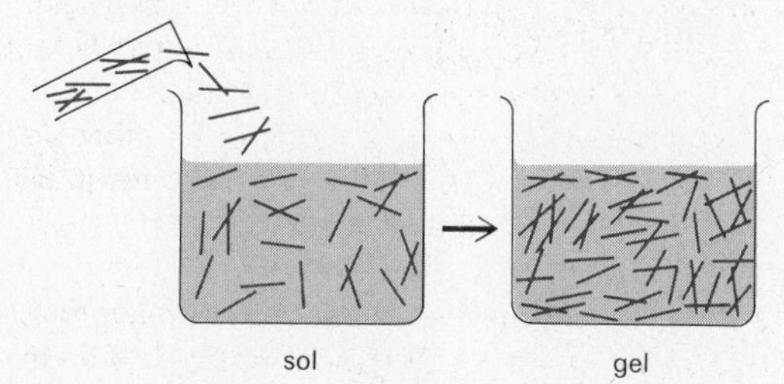

4.16 ***Phase reversals.*** *A gel can be transformed to a sol either by addition of more liquid (top) or by withdrawal of solid particles. A sol can be transformed to a gel either by addition of more solid particles (bottom) or by withdrawal of liquid.*

on clotting). Gels maintain definite forms and shapes despite high water contents. For example, a jellyfish is predominantly a gel, with a water content of 95 or more percent. Similarly, brain tissue is largely a gel, with a water content of about 80 percent.

Sol-gel reversals can be brought about also by temperature changes. At higher temperatures the thermal motion of the colloidal particles in a gel is more intense, and the gelled meshwork is disrupted (as in the liquefaction of Jello-O by heating). Conversely, lower temperatures promote conversion of sols to gels. Many other physical and chemical influences—low or high pH or pressure, for example—likewise affect sol-gel conditions.

All colloids *age.* The particles in a young, freshly formed colloidal system are enveloped by layers of water that are adsorbed to the particle surface by electric attraction. It is largely because of these forces that water in a gel does not "run out" through the gel meshes. With time, however, the binding capacity of the particles decreases, and some of the water does run out. The colloid "sets," contracting and gelating progressively; examples are exudation of water from long-standing milk curd, custard, or mustard.

In colloids, and also in true solutions, *migratory movements* occur as a direct result of the thermal motion of the particles. If ions, molecules, or colloidal particles are distributed unevenly, more collisions take place in more concentrated regions. For example, if a particle in the circle in Fig. 4.17 is displaced by thermal motion or by Brownian bombardment *toward* a region of higher concentration, it will soon be stopped by collision with other particles. But if it is displaced *away* from a high concentration, its movement will not be interrupted so soon, since neighboring particles are farther apart. On an average, therefore, a greater number of particles is displaced to more dilute regions than to more concentrated ones. In time, particles throughout the system will become distributed evenly. This equalization resulting from migration of particles is called *diffusion.*

Diffusion plays an important role in living cells, for it often happens that particles inside a cell are distributed unevenly. Diffusion will then tend to equalize the distribution. This is one means by which materials in cells can be transported from place to place.

membranes

At the boundary between a colloidal system and a different medium (air, water, solid, surfaces, or another colloid of different type), the molecules are usually subjected to complex physical forces that act on the boundary from both sides. The result is that the molecules there pack together tightly and become oriented in parallel or in layers and form a *membrane.* Good examples are the "skins" on puddings, custards, and boiled milk. Complex molecular skins arise also in living colloids. This property well may be the fundamental reason why living material does not occur in large undivided masses, but is organized in discrete units such as cells and smaller bodies inside cells, all separated from one another by membranes. The structure of these living membranes is more complex than that of simple nonliving ones, yet a simple colloidal structure appears to be the basis on which greater complexity is superimposed. If a living membrane is punctured, a new *surface precipitation membrane* develops over the opening within seconds, before appreciable amounts of material can flow through—a property displayed also by the boundary membranes of nonliving colloids.

Representing the gateways through which the chemical traffic to either side must pass, living membranes have different *permeability* to different substances. Most membranes are completely permeable to water molecules, which can pass through freely in either direction. As for other materials, organic or inorganic, there is no rule by which their passage potential can be determined beforehand. In general, three classes of materials can be distinguished: those that can pass through a membrane in either direction; those that can pass in one direction but not in the other; and those that cannot penetrate at all. These categories vary considerably for different kinds of membranes.

In the past, traffic through living membranes has been compared with traffic through nonliving ones like cellophane. Such nonliving membranes let water or small ions through, but not proteins, for example. Particle penetration here can be explained by diffusion. Particles would strike the barrier, most of them would bounce off, but some would pass through *pores* in the membrane. If the concentration were greater on one side of the membrane than on the other, more particles on an average would migrate to the dilute side, thus equalizing concentrations.

However, a hypothesis of diffusion through pores is generally inadequate for living membranes. If such membranes were indeed inert films with holes like cellophane, then it should not be possible to poison them—passive inert structures could not be affected by poisons. But the functioning of cellular membranes actually is impaired or stopped by poisons, indicating that such membranes are not simply passive films. Moreover, if living membranes really contained small holes, then only the size of a particle should determine whether or not it could pass through. Yet particle size is often of little importance. For example, under certain conditions large protein molecules can pass through a given membrane readily, whereas very small molecules sometimes cannot. Also, sugars such as glucose, fructose and galactose all have the same molecular size ($C_6H_{12}O_6$), yet they pass through living membranes at substantially different rates (fructose passes most readily and galactose least readily).

In short, membranes are highly *selective.* Although ordinary diffusion appears to play some role in most cases, membranes often act as if they "knew" which substances to transmit and which to reject. Also, energy-consuming work is often done by a living membrane in transmitting materials, and in a few cases complex chemical reactions are known to take place in the process (see Chap. 14). Cellular membranes must therefore be regarded as dynamic structures in which entering or leaving particles are actively "handed" across from one side to the other. The precise means by which cells accomplish such *active transport* across their boundaries is understood as yet for only a few types of materials.

osmosis

When a membrane separates one solution or colloid from another kind of medium, it often happens that some of the particles on either side cannot go through the membrane. Suppose that one side has a very low concentration of such particles (side *A* in Fig. 4.18), and the other side (*B*) a very high concentration. What events will occur in such a system?

1 In the beginning, relatively more water molecules are in contact with the membrane *X* on the *A* side than on the *B* side, since fewer of the solid particles occupy membrane space on the *A* surface than on the *B* surface.

2 Therefore, more water molecules on an average are transmitted through the membrane from *A* to *B* than from *B* to *A*.

3 As a result, the water content decreases in *A* and increases in *B*. Particles in *A* become crowded into a smaller and smaller volume, and more and more of them therefore take up mem-

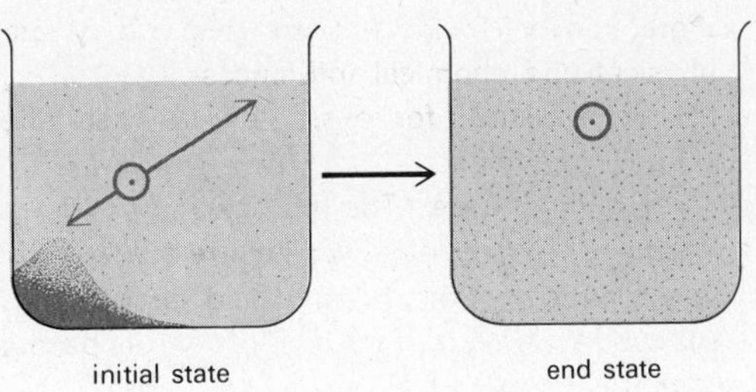

***4.17* Diffusion.** *In the initial state at left, particles are distributed unevenly. A given particle (for example, the circled one) will therefore have more freedom to move in the direction of lower concentrations. This eventually leads to an even distribution of particles, as in the end state at right.*

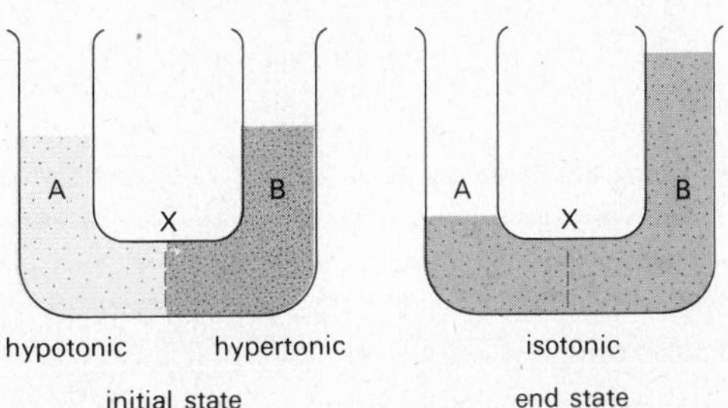

***4.18* Osmosis.** *In the initial state A is less concentrated than B, and water will therefore move from A to B. This eventually leads to an isotonic end state, where concentrations in A and B are equal. From this point on further net migration of water does not occur (just as much water moves from A to B as from B to A). The broken line (X) represents a semipermeable membrane.*

brane space on the *A* surface. On the *B* side, the increasing water content permits the particles to spread into progressively larger volumes; hence the particle concentration along the *B* surface of the membrane will fall.

4 A stage will be reached at which the number of particles along the *A* surface equals that along the *B* surface. From then on the number of water molecules transmitted from *A* to *B* will equal the the number transmitted from *B* to *A*. Thereafter no further *net* shift of water will occur.

This movement of water is called *osmosis.* The amount of osmosis depends on the *concentration differential,* the relative *numbers* of particles in *A* and *B.* If the difference in particle number is great enough—for example, if *A* contains only pure water but *B* contains a large number of particles—then *A* might dehydrate completely and collapse, while *B* might burst and thus also collapse. The side that loses water in osmosis is said to be *hypotonic,* and the side that gains water, *hypertonic.* When neither side gains or loses the two sides are said to be *isotonic* to each other.

The net effect of osmosis is to pull water *into* the region of higher concentration, from the hypotonic to the hypertonic side. The process will continue until the two sides are isotonic. And note that osmosis will occur whenever certain particles cannot pass through a membrane. Then nothing moves across except *water,* as well as those particles that *can* diffuse through the membrane. In living cells osmosis serves as one of the means by which water is distributed and redistributed across membranes.

In its physical organization, therefore, the substance of cells is a mixed colloidal system that has variously permeable boundary membranes, that undergoes localized sol-gel transformations, and that is kept agitated continuously by thermal and Brownian motion, by diffusion displacements, and by osmotic forces. As a result, the living material is subjected unceasingly to physical changes as profound as the chemical ones. Indeed, physical changes initiate chemical ones and vice versa. From any small-scale point of view, cellular matter clearly is never the same from moment to moment.

Superimposed on and ultimately resulting from its chemical and physical organization, the cell substance also displays a highly distinctive biological organization. The next chapter focuses on this biological makeup of cells.

review questions

1 What are inorganic compounds? Organic compounds? What main classes of each occur in living matter, and in what relative amounts? Which of these substances are electrolytes and which are nonelectrolytes?

2 Review the chemical composition and molecular structure of carbohydrates. What are pentoses, hexoses, aldoses, and ketoses? Give examples of each.

3 What are monosaccharides, disaccharides, and polysaccharides? Give examples of each. Distinguish between 1,4 and 1,6 linkages in polysaccharides, and give specific examples of compounds having such links.

4 Review the composition and structure of fatty acids. Distinguish between saturated and unsaturated kinds, and give examples. How is a fat formed? What general functions do carbohydrates and fats have in living matter?

5 Describe the general molecular structure of waxes, carotenes, xanthophylls, steroids, and tetrapyrrols. What roles do some of these substances play in living matter?

6 Review the structure of amino acids, and show how these compounds differ among themselves. Write out the formation of a peptide bond. What is a polypeptide, and in what ways can polypeptides differ in composition?

7 What is the primary, secondary, tertiary, and quaternary structure of a protein, and what kinds of bonds produce such structures? What is an α-helix? What are globular and fibrous proteins?

8 What is protein specificity? How is a coagulated protein different from a native or a denatured protein? Review the general role of proteins in cells.

9 Distinguish between nitrogen bases, nucleotides, ribotides, and deoxyribotides. Give examples

of each. What are adenosine phosphates? Review the structure and function of coenzymes, and give the names of some of them.

10 What is the chemical composition and molecular structure of nucleic acids? In chemical terms, what are DNA and RNA? What different kinds of nucleotides occur in nucleic acids?

11 What makes nucleic acids specific, and what are the general functions of such acids? How are they related to genes?

12 What is a colloidal system? How does such a system differ from a solution? Review the properties of colloidal systems.

13 Define diffusion and show how and under what conditions this process will occur. What is the significance of diffusion in cells?

14 How and where do colloidal membranes form? What are the characteristics of such membranes? What roles do they play in cellular processes?

15 Define osmosis. Show how and under what conditions this process will occur. Distinguish carefully between osmosis and diffusion. What are isotonicity, hypertonicity, and hypotonicity?

---

collateral readings

Baker, J. J. W., and **G. E. Allen**: "Matter, Energy, and Life," Addison-Wesley, Reading, Mass., 1965. This paperback contains a good general discussion of all classes of cellular chemicals. Recommended for further reading.

Loewy, A. G., and **P. Siekevitz**: "Cell Structure and Function," Holt, New York, 1963. Part 2 of this paperback is highly recommended for further background on the topics dealt with in this chapter.

All the following articles in *Scientific American* are popularly written; they deal with particular cell constituents identified in the titles:

Buswell, A. M., and **W. H. Rodebush**: Water, Apr., 1956.

Crick, F. H. C.: Nucleic Acids, Sept., 1957.

Fieser, L. F.: Steroids, Jan., 1955.

Frank, S.: Carotenoids, Jan., 1956.

Hokin, L. E., and **M. R. Hokin**: The Chemistry of Cell Membranes, Oct., 1965.

Kendrew, J. C.: The 3-Dimensional Structure of a Protein Molecule, Dec., 1961.

Perutz, M. F.: The Hemoglobin Molecule, Nov., 1964.

Preston, R. D.: Cellulose, Sept., 1957

Schmitt, F. O.: Giant Molecules in Cells and Tissues, Sept., 1957.

Stein, W. H., and **S. Moore**: The Chemical Structure of Proteins, Feb., 1961.

Thompson, E. O. P.: The Insulin Molecule, May, 1955.

chapter 5 cell and organism

The generalization that all organisms consist entirely of cells and cell products is known as the *cell theory.* Formulated in 1838 by the German biologists Schleiden and Schwann, this theory rapidly became one of the fundamental cornerstones of modern biology, and, with minor qualifications, it still has that status today. In 1831 the English biologist Robert Brown discovered nuclei in cells, and in 1839 the Bohemian biologist Purkinje coined the general term *protoplasm* for the living substance out of which cells are made. Virchow in 1855 concluded that "*omnis cellula e cellula*"—new cells can arise only by reproduction of preexisting ones. This was an important recognition of the continuity of life, well in line with what was then already known about the growth and development of organisms and about evolution.

cells

Examination of living or killed cells under various kinds of microscopes shows that cell diameters vary considerably, from about 0.2 μ to as much as several millimeters and more [1 micron (μ) = 1/1,000 mm]. However, the order of size of the vast majority of cells is remarkably uniform, a diameter of 0.5 to 15 μ being fairly characteristic generally. Too small a size presumably would not provide enough space for the necessary parts, and too large a size would increase the maintenance problem and at the same time reduce operating efficiency. For as a cell increases in size its surface enlarges as the *square* of its radius, and the available surface area determines how much nutrient uptake and waste elimination are possible. However, cell volume increases with the *cube* of the radius, and the volume determines how much mass a cell must keep alive. Hence if a cell kept on enlarging, its mass would eventually outrun the food-procuring capacity of its surface and cell growth then would cease. The actual sizes of cells appear to be governed in part by these surface-volume relations.

nucleus and cytoplasm

The two fundamental subdivisions of most cells are the *nucleus* and the substance surrounding the nucleus, called the *cytoplasm.* The nucleus is bounded by a *nuclear membrane,* the cytoplasm by a *cell membrane* (also called *plasma membrane*). Surrounding the cell membrane in many cases is a *cell wall* (Fig. 5.1).

Most cells contain a single nucleus each, but there are many exceptions. For example, bacteria and blue-green algae lack membrane-bounded nuclei. Similarly, when mammalian red blood corpuscles and several types of plant cells become mature, they lose their nuclei. Conversely, many kinds of unicellular organisms are *binucleate* or *multinucleate,* with two or more nuclei each. In some cases the individuality of cells becomes obscured altogether. In certain tissues, for example, the membranes of adjacent cells dissolve at particular stages of development, and the results are fused, continuous living masses with numerous nuclei dispersed through them. Such a structure is a *coenocyte* in plants and a *syncytium* in animals.

A nucleus typically consists of three kinds of components: the more or less gel-like nuclear sap, or *nucleoplasm,* in which are suspended *chromosomes* and one or more *nucleoli* (Fig. 5.2).

The chromosomes are the main nuclear organelles. Indeed, a nucleus as a whole may be regarded primarily as a protective housing for these threadlike bodies. Chromosomes consist largely of nucleic acids and proteins, joined here as complexes called *nucleoproteins.* DNA is the main nucleic acid, but RNA is also present. Functionally, chromosomes are the carriers of the genes which, as noted previously, are the ultimate controllers of cellular processes.

Chromosomes are conspicuous only during cell reproduction, when they become thickly coated with additional nucleoprotein. At other times such coats are absent, and chromosomes then are very fine filaments. The exact number of chromosomes in each cell nucleus is an important species-specific trait. For example, cells of human beings contain 46 chromosomes each. The cells of every other type of organism have their own characteristic chromosome number.

A nucleolus ("little nucleus") is a spherical body composed largely of protein and RNA. Produced by chromosomes, nucleoli participate in the process of protein synthesis. Each cell is characterized by a fixed number of nucleoli. The whole nucleus is separated from the surrounding cytoplasm by the nuclear membrane, composed like most other living membranes mainly of proteins and lipids. It governs the vital traffic of materials between cytoplasm and nucleus. Examination with the electron microscope shows that the

5.1 General cell structure, *A, cells of a plant root (approx. ×700). B, blood cells of a frog (approx. ×2,000). Note the darkly stained cell nuclei, the cell membranes, and the cytoplasms between nuclei and cell membranes.*

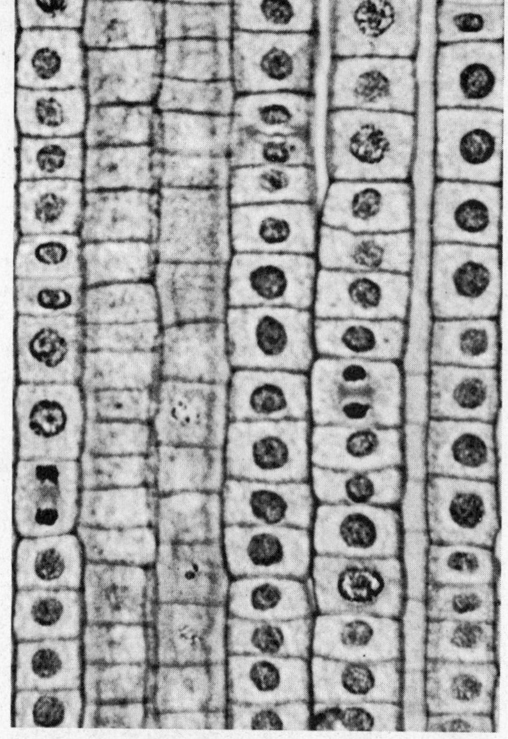

A

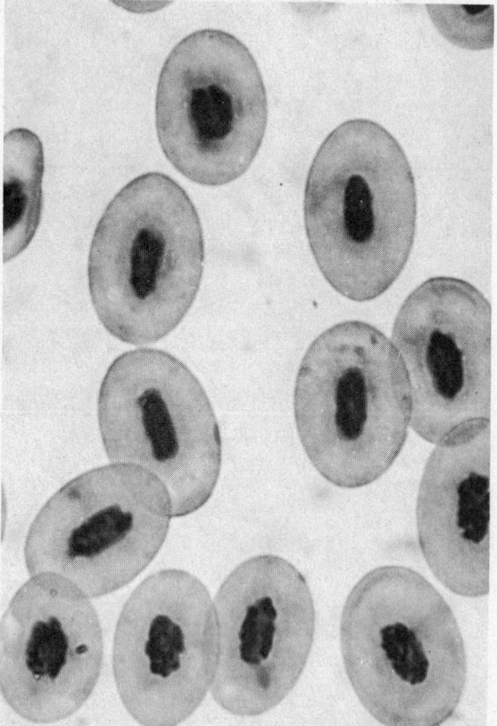

B

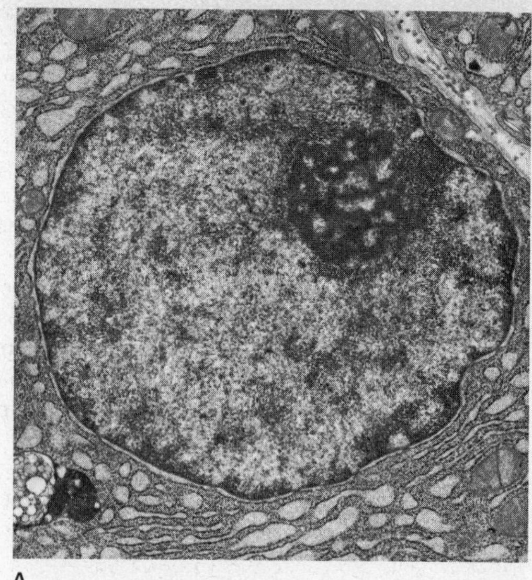

A

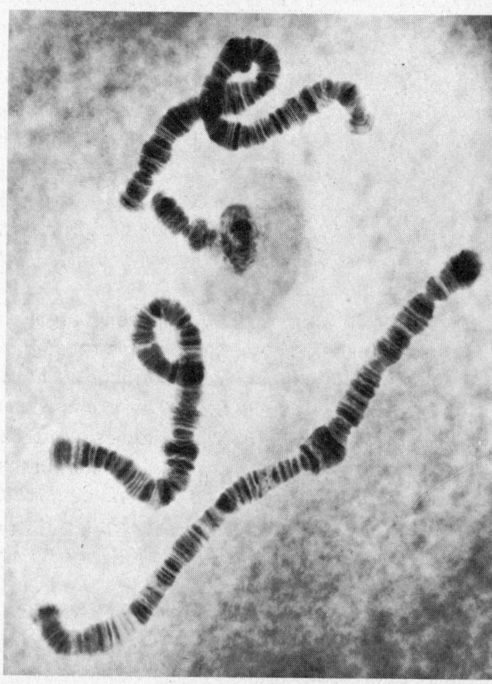

B

5.2 The cell nucleus. *A, electron micrograph of a whole nucleus, covering most of the photo. Inside the nucleus the large dark patch is a nucleolus and the dark speckle elsewhere is the gene-containing chromosomal material (which in stained preparation has a filamentous appearance only during cell division) (×40,000). B, a stained preparation of insect chromosomes (×3,000). Note the characteristic cross bands, found in all chromosomes studied. See also Fig. 17.4. (B, courtesy of Drs. D. F. Poulson and C. W. Metz, from Fig. 1, J. Morph., vol. 63, p. 366, 1938.)*

nuclear membrane actually is a double layer pierced by tiny pores (Fig. 5.3).

By virtue of its genes the nucleus is the control center of cellular activities. The cytoplasm is the executive center in which the directives of the nucleus are carried out. But although the nucleus primarily controls, it also executes many directives of the cytoplasm; and although the cytoplasm primarily executes, it also influences many nuclear processes. A reciprocal interdependence thus links nucleus and cytoplasm, and experiment has repeatedly shown that the one cannot long survive without the other. For example, amoebas can be cut into halves so that one half includes the nucleus. Such a nucleated half then carries on in every respect like a normal amoeba, but the nonnucleated half invariably dies eventually. Yet just as survival of the cytoplasm depends on the nucleus, so survival of the nucleus depends on the cytoplasm; a naked isolated nucleus soon dies. Cellular life must therefore be viewed against a background of cyclical interactions between nucleus and cytoplasm.

Cytoplasm consists of a semifluid *ground substance,* which is in a sol or a gel state at different times and in different cellular regions, and in which are suspended large numbers of several kinds of organelles. The following are widespread among many or all cell types (Fig. 5.4.).

Endoplasmic reticulum. Composed largely of lipids and proteins, the endoplasmic reticulum is a network of exceedingly fine double membranes (Fig. 5.5 and see Fig. 5.4). These membranes traverse all regions of the cytoplasm and are continuous with the cell and nuclear membranes. In some cases the endoplasmic reticulum also passes from one cell to adjacent ones. Attached to this membrane system are many of the other cytoplasmic organelles.

The endoplasmic reticulum appears to function broadly in two ways. First, it can serve as a network of traffic pathways and conducting channels. Materials in transit from one cell region to another, or from the cell to the outside and vice versa, can migrate along the narrow spaces between the membranes. Second, by interconnecting other organelles, the endoplasmic reticulum forms an ultrastructural framework that keeps the nonfluid components of cytoplasm in certain relative positions. The membranes can form, dissolve, and re-form rapidly, often in conjunction with the frequent shifts of position and streaming movements of the other cell contents. Thus although the cell as a whole is readily deformable and the interior contents flow and intermix unceasingly, the endoplasmic reticulum nevertheless keeps other organelles properly stationed and distributed in relation to one another. As a result little is really "loose" in a cell, and an orderly organization is maintained.

Mitochondria. These organelles are again constructed predominantly out of lipids and proteins. Small amounts of DNA and RNA are known to be present as well. The main functional compo-

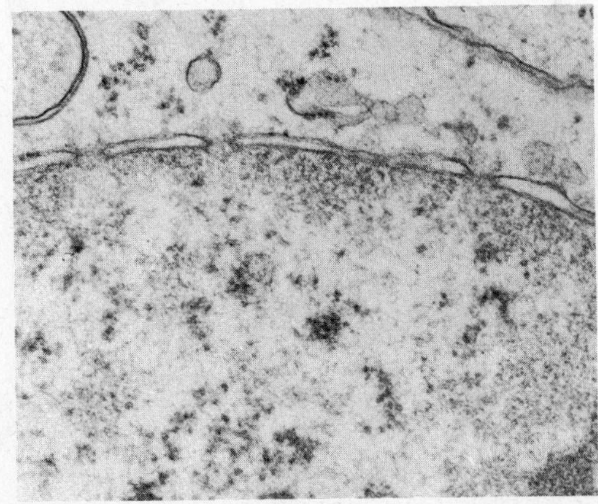

5.3 The nuclear membrane. *In this electron-micrographic close-up of a cell in the spinal cord of a bat, the nuclear substance is at bottom of photo, cytoplasmic substance at top. Note that the nuclear membrane is a double layer with pores (×40,000).*

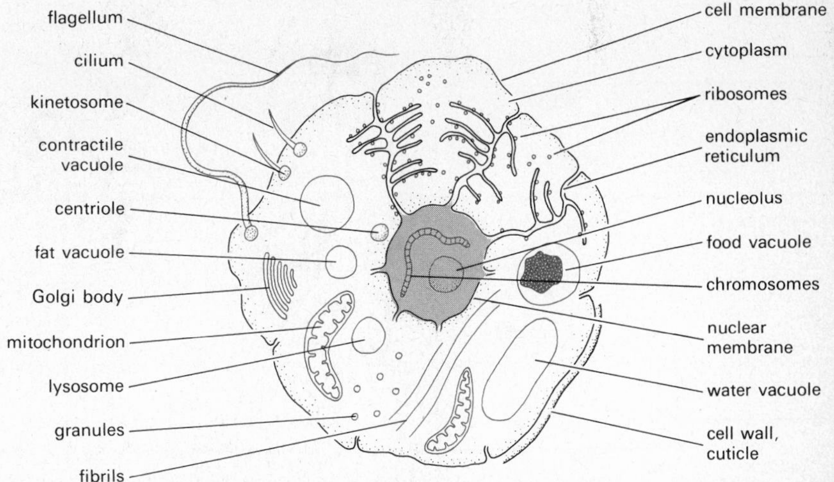

5.4 Cell structure. *No single cell contains all the organelles shown in this composite drawing. For clarity and simplicity most components are shown in only part of the cell. For example, the endoplasmic reticulum traverses all parts of the cytoplasm.*

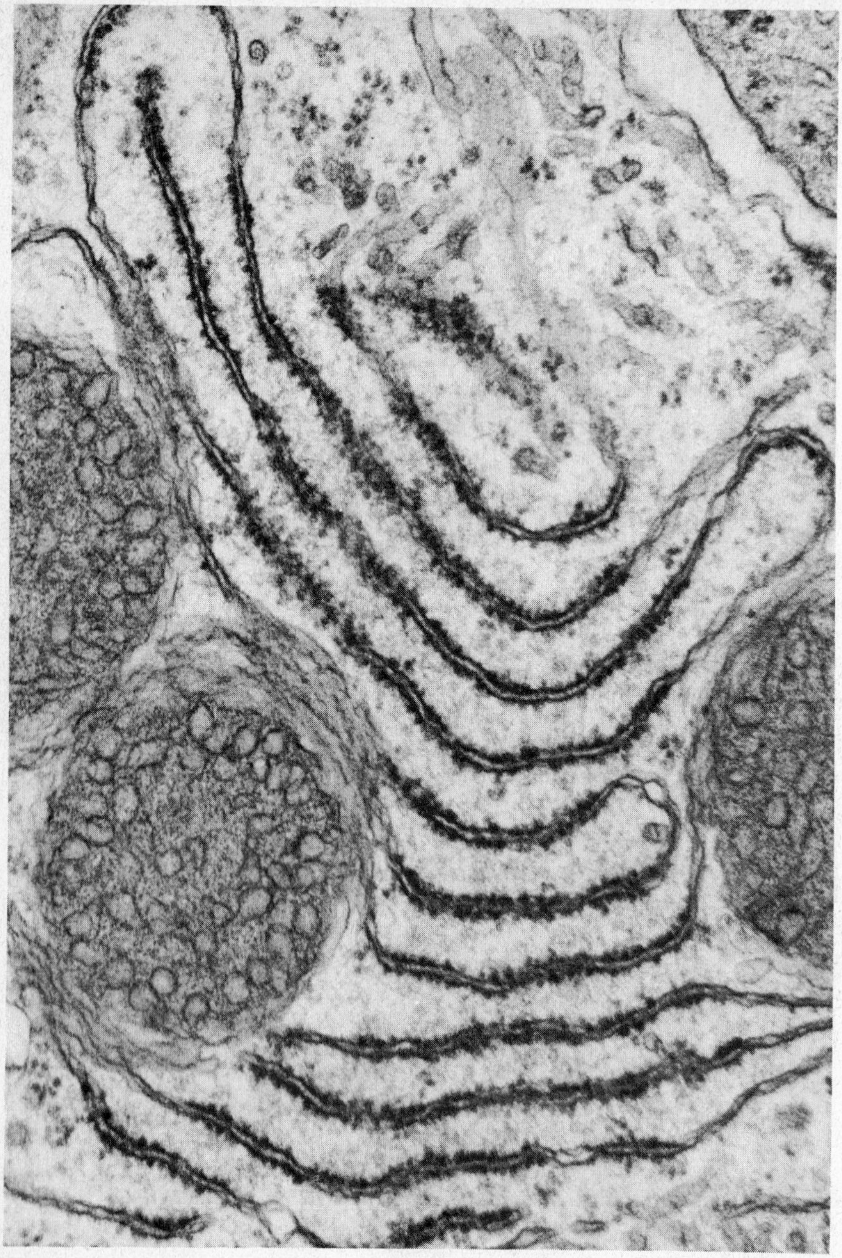

5.5 Endoplasmic reticulum. *Electron micrograph of a portion of a monkey adrenal gland. Note the endoplasmic reticulum, a continuous double membrane passing throughout the cytoplasm. Note also the (dark) granular ribosomes that adhere to the membranes. The large round structures are mitochondria (× 100,000).*

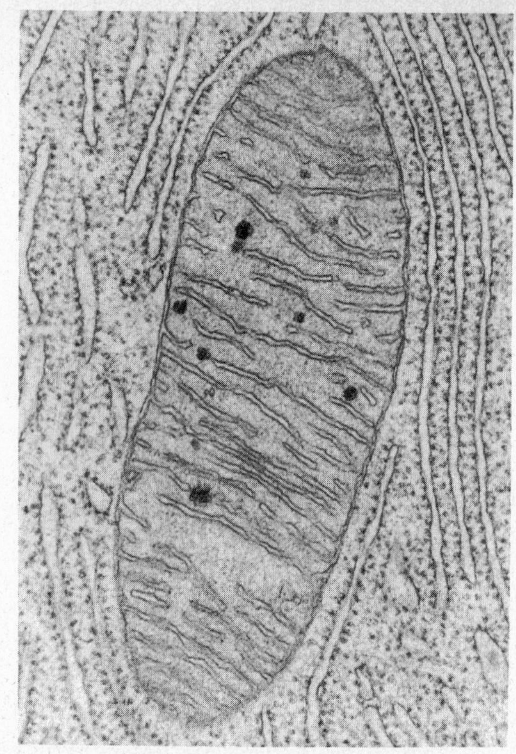

A

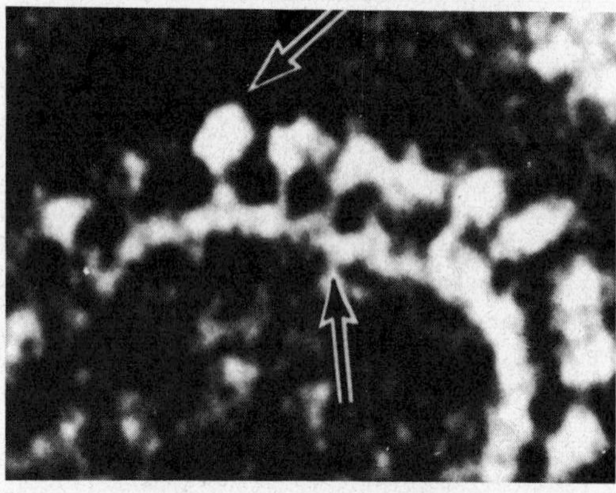

B

5.6 Mitochondria. *A, electron-micrographic section through a mitochondrion of a mammalian pancreatic cell (× 45,000). Note the double-layered exterior boundary and the many infoldings of the inner membrane (mitochondrial cristae). The dark spots in the interior of the mitochondrion are calcium-rich granules. Outside the mitochondrion are parts of the endoplasmic reticulum (double membranes with clear channels inside) and numerous ribosomes (small dark granules). B, highly enlarged portion of a mitochondrial crista (in beef heart muscle), showing array of stalked particles attached to the cristal membrane. Arrows point to head piece and base piece of such a particle. Particles of this kind appear to contain the enzymatic apparatus for respiratory reactions (× 700,000).*

nents are respiratory enzymes and coenzymes; mitochondria are the chief chemical "factories" in which cellular respiration is carried out. Under the light microscope mitochondria appear as short rods or thin filaments averaging 0.5 to 2 μ in length. The electron microscope shows that the surface of a mitochondrion consists of two fine membranes (Fig. 5.6). The inner one has folds that project into the interior of the mitochondrion. These folds (*mitochondrial cristae*) bear numerous tiny stalked microgranules, probably the specific locations where respiratory reactions take place.

Ribosomes. These are tiny granules visible under the electron microscope (see Fig. 5.6). Many of them are usually attached to the endoplasmic reticulum, others lie free in the cytoplasm. Ribosomes contain RNA (hence the "ribo-" portion of their name) and the enzymes for protein manufacture. The granules thus are the "factories" where protein synthesis is carried out, a function probably performed by groups of them (*polyribosomes*) acting in concert.

Golgi bodies. Under the electron microscope these bodies are seen as stacks of thin, platelike layers (Fig. 5.7). The organelles function in the synthesis of cellular secretion products, and Golgi bodies are particularly conspicuous in actively secreting cells. For example, whenever gland cells manufacture their characteristic secretions, the Golgi bodies of such cells become very prominent.

Lysosomes. Known to occur in various types of animal cells, these organelles are tiny membrane-bounded sacs or vesicles. They contain digestive enzymes that are released into the cytoplasm when the vesicles burst open. The enzymes probably participate in various normal decomposition processes in a cell—chemical breakdown of nutrients prior to their utilization, breakdown of cellular organelles prior to their reconstruction or remodeling, breakdown of foreign particles, and the like. It is known also that simultaneous disruption of many or all lysosomes leads to rapid dissolution and death of a cell. Lysosomes therefore might play a role in processes of tissue maintenance, in which old cells are replaced by new ones formed through cell reproduction.

Plastids. These round, oval, or disk-shaped bodies occur in the cells of most algae and all green plants. Three kinds of plastids can be distinguished on the basis of their pigment content. One kind lacks pigments, and such *leucoplasts* often serve as starch-storing organelles, as in the cells of potatoes, for example. A second kind, called *chromoplasts,* contains a variety of carotenoid pigments. For example, carrots and tomatoes owe their colors to carotenoids localized in chromoplasts. The third type of plastid usually contains carotenoid pigments too, but their colors

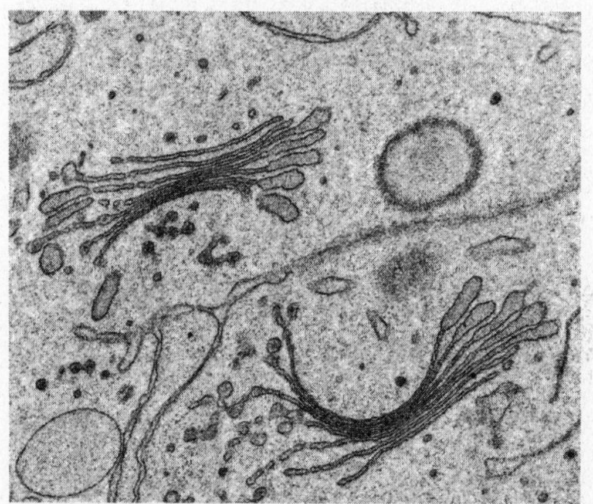
A

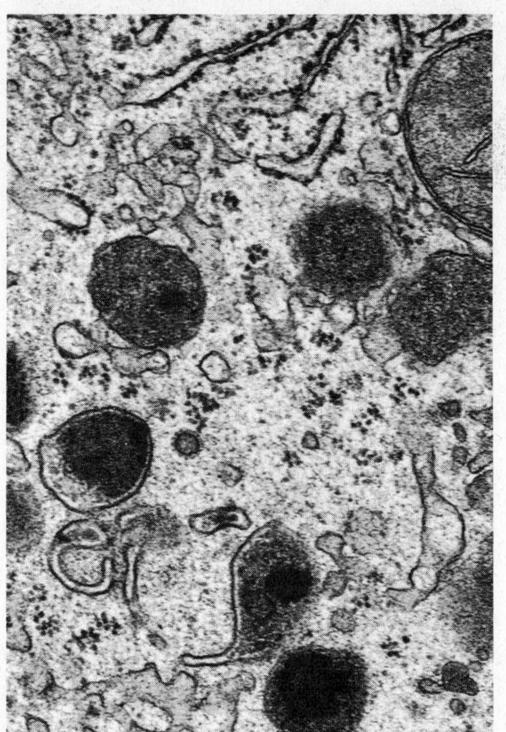
B

5.7 Golgi bodies and lysosomes. *A, an electron micrograph of cytoplasm with two Golgi bodies, each composed of a stack of parallel double membranes (×50,000). B, a portion of a rat liver cell, with dark membrane-covered lysosomes in lower half of photo. In the upper half are portions of a mitochondrion and the endoplasmic reticulum (×48,500).*

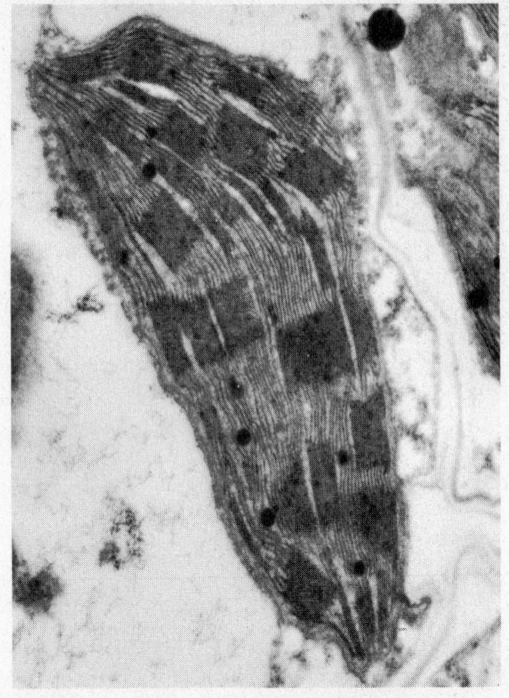

A

B

5.8 ***Chloroplasts and grana.*** *A, electron micrograph of section through whole chloroplast (×35,000). Note layered structure and denser layers of the grana. B, higher magnification of a single granum (×200,000). (Courtesy of Dr. A. J. Hodge, California Institute of Technology, and J. Biophys. Biochem. Cytol., vol. 1, p. 605.)*

are masked by large quantities of the green pigment *chlorophyll.* Plastids with chlorophyll are *chloroplasts,* and they endow leaves and other plant parts with their characteristic green color.

Averaging 4 to 6 μ in diameter, chloroplasts have a protein framework arranged as a stack of parallel layers (Fig. 5.8). In the spaces between the layers are smaller organelles, so-called *grana.* Each of these contains a dense framework of protein layers of its own, and the spaces between these layers contain DNA, enzymes, chlorophyll and the other pigments, and indeed the whole chemical machinery for food manufacture. Grana in effect are the structural and functional units for photosynthesis.

Centrioles and kinetosomes. A centriole is a small granule located near (and in some cases inside) the nucleus (see Fig. 5.4). Centrioles occur in some algae, some fungi, and all animals (but not in most of the cells of plants). As will be shown later, these granules play a specific role in cell reproduction. Another type of granule, called *basal granule* or *kinetosome,* is found in cells that have surface flagella or cilia (see below). Kinetosomes anchor and control the motion of such surface structures. Centrioles and kinetosomes appear to have arisen from a common evolutionary source, a single type of granule that served simultaneously as a centriole and a kinetosome. Many primitive cell types today still contain such granules with joint dual functions. In later cell types the originally single granule evidently evolved into two separate ones, one retaining the centriole function only, the other, the kinetosome function only. Moreover, ancestral cells that evolved into plants largely lost both centrioles and kinetosomes.

The electron microscope reveals centrioles and kinetosomes to have a common, complex structure (Fig. 5.9). Each such granule is made up of a ringlike array of nine sets of parallel tubules, with a fine layer of boundary material around the ring. On one side of the granule the tubules continue into the cytoplasm as a spreading bundle of *microtubules;* and on the other side in a kinetosome the tubules form the basal parts of a flagellum or cilium (see also page 75).

Additional structures. Apart from structures just described, cytoplasm generally contains additional *granules* and fluid-filled droplets called *vacuoles.* Such organelles perform a large variety

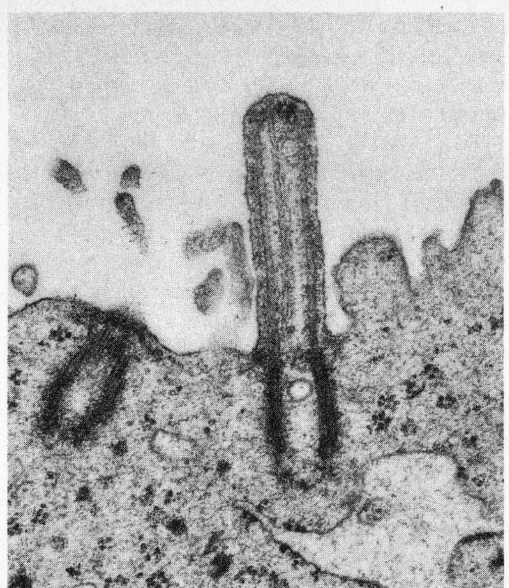

A

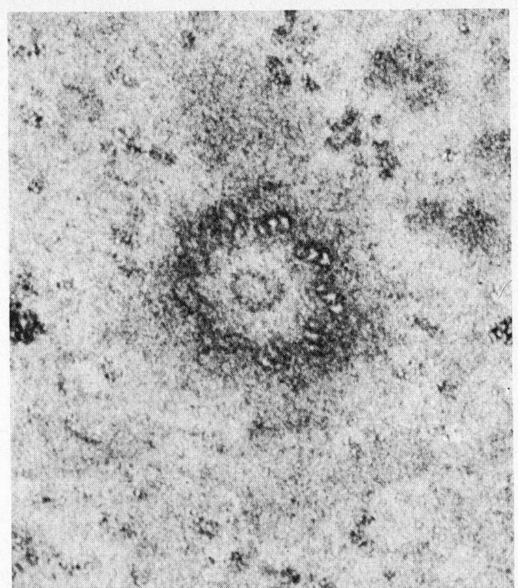

B

5.9 Kinetosomes and centrioles. *A, electron-micrographic section through a kinetosome (of a cell in a monkey oviduct), with a cilium growing out from this basal granule. Note that the ciliary fibrils (tubules) are continuous with those of the basal granule. Also note the small vesicle inside the kinetosome (×40,000). B, electron-micrographic cross section through a centriole (of a cell in a monkey oviduct). Note the central core material and the surrounding circular array of nine (triplet) tubules (which correspond to a ring of nine tubules in a kinetosome) (×50,000).*

of functions. For example, they transport nutrients from the cell surface to the interior (*food vacuoles*) or finished products in the opposite direction (*secretion granules*); they are places of storage (*starch, granules, glycogen granules, fat vacuoles, water vacuoles, pigment granules*); or they carry waste materials to points of elimination (*excretory vacuoles*).

In addition to all these, cytoplasm may or may not contain a variety of long, thin protein *fibrils,* such as contractile *myofibrils* or conducting *neurofibrils.* Various other inclusions, unique to given cell types and serving unique functions, may also be present. In general, every function a cell performs involves a particular structure in which the machinery for that function is housed.

Cytoplasm as a whole is normally in motion. Irregular eddying or streaming occurs often, and at other times the substance of a cell is subjected to cyclical currents known as *cyclosis.* The organelles, nucleus included, are swept along passively in these streams. The specific cause of such motions is unknown, but there is little doubt that they are a consequence of the unceasing chemical and physical changes taking place in a cell. Whatever the specific causes might be, the apparently random movements might give the impression that nothing is fixed in a cell and that cytoplasm is simply a collection of loose bodies suspended in "soup." As already pointed out, however, such an impression is erroneous, for a cell does have an orderly, though deformable, interior organization.

cell surfaces

Composed predominantly of protein and lipid substances, the cell membrane plays a critical role in *all* cell functions, since directly or indirectly every such function depends on *absorption* of materials from the exterior, *excretion* of materials from the interior, or both.

Nearly all plant cells have a *cell wall* around the cell membrane. Such walls are usually composed of cellulose and other polysaccharide derivatives, among them *hemicellulose* and *pectin.* A *primary cell wall* forms while a cell grows and develops. Mature, nongrowing cells often have a *secondary cell wall* on the inner surfaces of their primary walls (Fig. 5.10). Adjacent plant cells in a tissue are held together by a thin layer of pectinlike cementing material, called a *middle lamella.* In many cases adjacent cells are interconnected further by *plasmodesmata,* fine strands of cytoplasm that pass through the cell walls and the middle lamella. Parts of the endoplasmic reticulum are included in such plasmodesmata.

Thin cell walls are more or less elastic; thicker ones, more or less rigid. These envelopes maintain cell shape and aid in mechanical support against gravity. Plant cells exposed directly to the

5.10 Cell surfaces in plants. *A, primary and secondary cell walls and plasmodesmata between adjacent cells. B, portion of a leaf showing epidermal cells with thick walls (dark) and a waxy cuticle along the exposed side at top.*

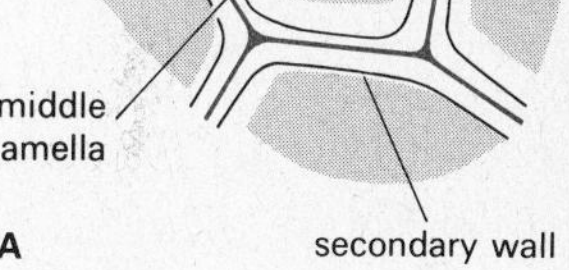

A

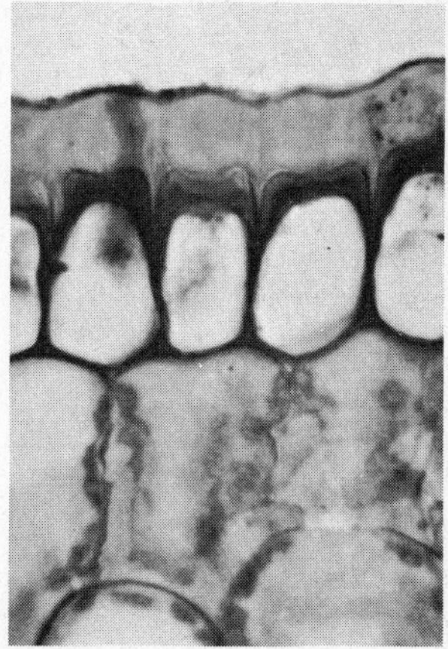

B

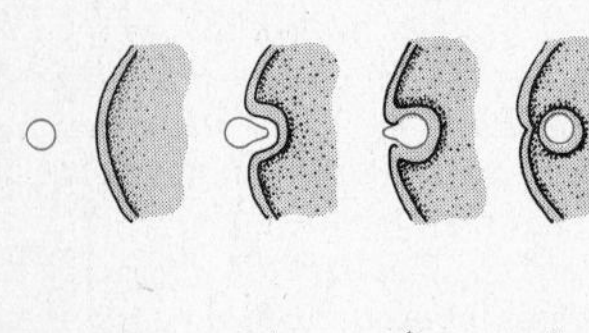

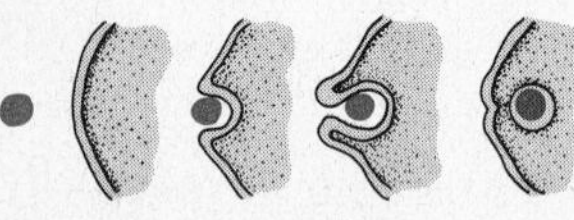

5.11 Cellular engulfment. *Top, pinocytosis, or cellular engulfment of fluid droplets. Bottom, phagocytosis, or cellular engulfment of solid particles.*

5.12 Cell surfaces in animals. *A, many cells without surface secretions develop fingerlike projection like those shown here. If two such cells are in contact, their projections usually interlock. B, many cells have cilia along exposed surfaces, like the separated tissue cells shown here. See also Fig. 5.13.*

external air also secrete *cuticles* on their exposed surfaces, in addition to cell walls. Composed of waxy and fatty materials, cuticles make the exposed cells relatively impermeable to water. Unlike plant cells, most animal cells and also many algal and protozoan cells lack exterior walls. In many cases the surfaces of such naked cells are fairly smooth, but in certain compact animal tissues numerous fingerlike extensions project from one cell and interlock with similar extensions from neighboring cells. Occasionally one such cell nips off a protrusion of an adjacent cell—one of the means by which material can be transferred from cell to cell. Also, a cell sometimes develops a deepening surface depression that eventually nips off on the inside as a fluid vacuole. Through this type of fluid engulfment, or *pinocytosis,* a cell can transfer liquid droplets to its interior (Figs. 5.11 and 5.12).

All such transfers are specialized forms of the more general phenomenon of *amoeboid motion,* in which temporary fingerlike extensions, or *pseudopodia,* are again formed at any point on the cell surface (see Fig. 2.6). Some algae and protozoa move and feed by means of pseudopods. In feeding, pseudopods engulf a bit of food by flowing around it and forming a food vacuole that comes to lie in the cell interior. Many kinds of animal cells are similarly capable of amoeboid movement. For example, many types of eggs engulf sperm cells in fertilization, and several categories of blood cells engulf foreign bodies, bacteria, and other potentially harmful materials. When one cell "swallows" particles in amoeboid fashion, the process is often called *phagocytosis.*

Animal cells exposed directly to the external environment are usually not naked but are enveloped partially or wholly by wall-like *cuticles* or *pellicles.* For example, a protective horny coat of secreted *chitin* is found on the skin cells of insects and related groups. Numerous other animals secrete horny protein coats on their outer cells; and the skin cells of most vertebrates secrete coats of the protein *keratin,* a substance that also covers surface structures such as feathers and hair. In many other cases surface cells secrete slimy protective films of mucus or *shells* of lime, glass (*silica*), or various organic materials.

Many cell types have the capacity of locomotion. Those that do not move in amoeboid fashion are usually equipped with specialized locomotor organelles on the cell surface. Among these are *flagella,* long, slender, threadlike projections from cells (Fig. 5.13). The base of a flagellum is anchored in the cell cytoplasm on a motion-controlling kinetosome granule. In some cases a threadlike fibril, or *rhizoplast,* connects

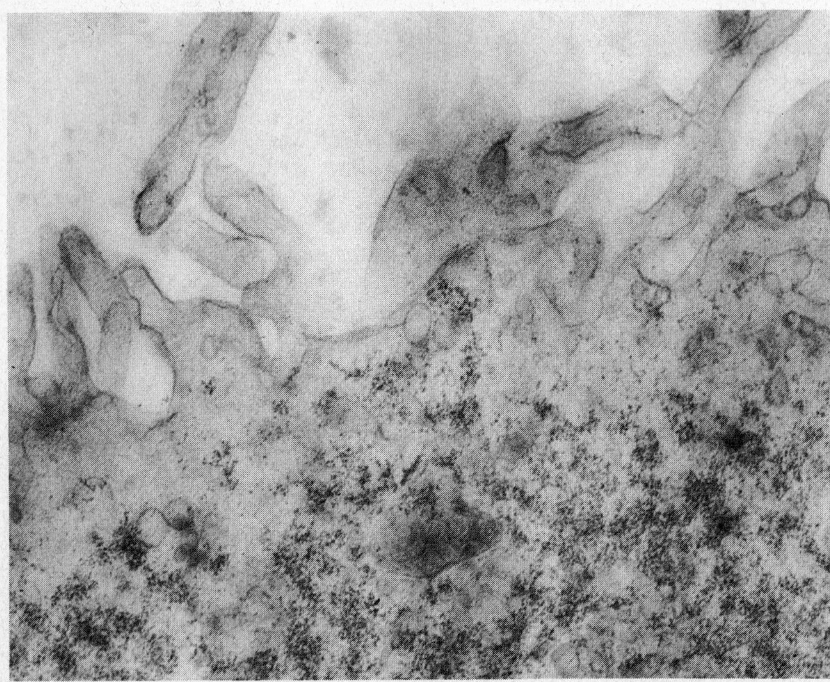

A

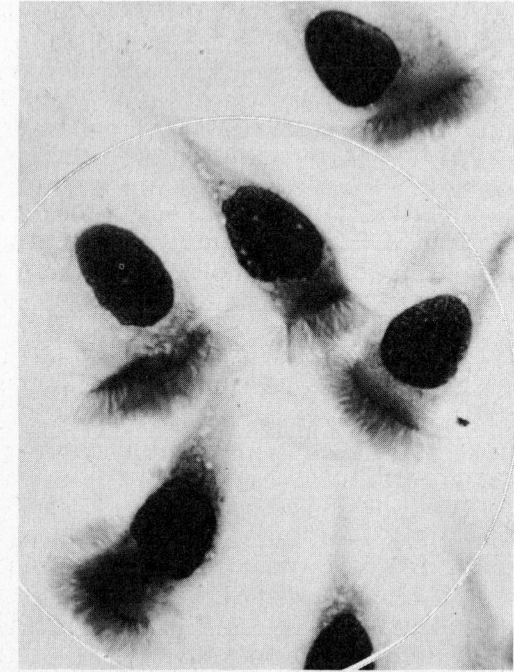

B

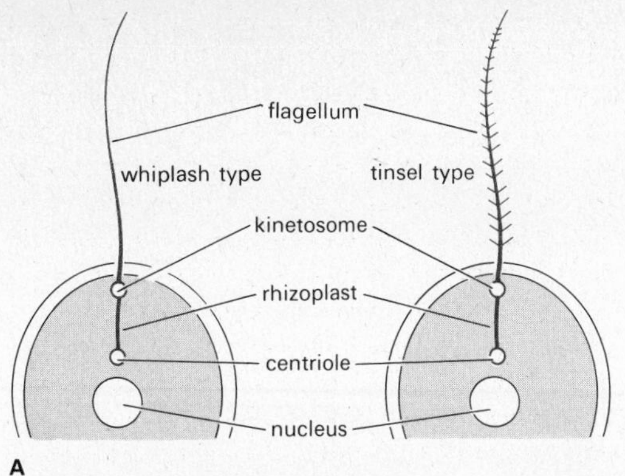

A

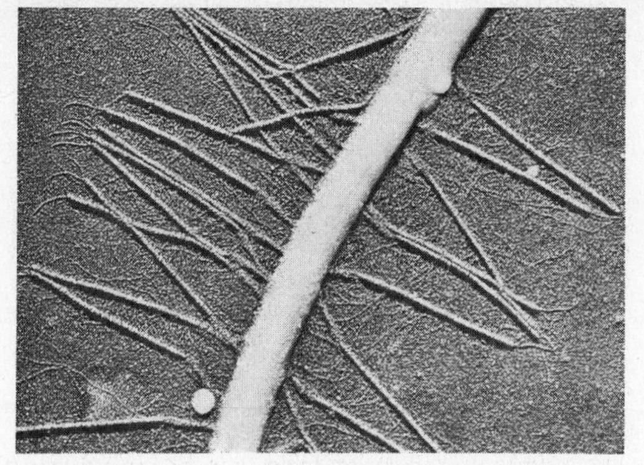

C

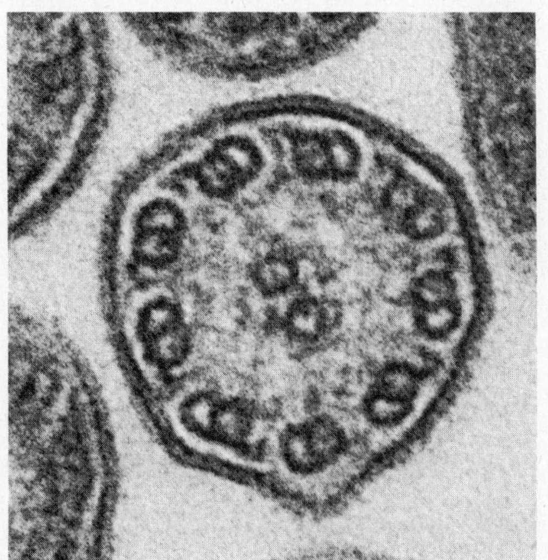

B

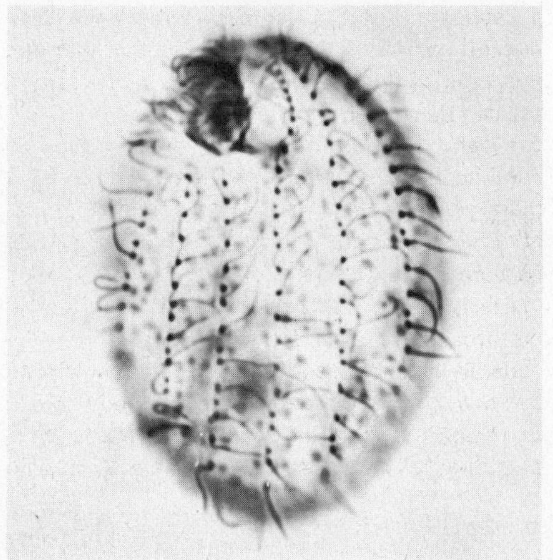

D

5.13 Flagella and cilia. *A, types of flagella (color) and their insertion in cells. B, electron-micrographic cross section through a cilium (from a cell in a monkey oviduct), showing the central two and the nine peripheral fibrils inside. The peripheral fibrils are continuous with the tubules of the kinetosome (and/or the centriole) (× 100,000). C, electron micrograph of a portion of a tinsel-type flagellum, showing the fine lateral filaments (× 35,000). D, the ciliate protozoan Tetrahymena stained to show the rows of cilia on the body surface (× 500).*

the kinetosome with the centriole in the cell interior. A cell usually bears one flagellum, but often many more are present, all anchored in the same kinetosome region. Flagella with smooth external surfaces are said to be of the *whiplash* type. Some have very fine side branches and are said to be of the *tinsel* type.

Numerous types of cells have shorter variants of flagella called *cilia.* These are usually present in large numbers and cover all or major portions of a cell like tiny bristles (see Fig. 5.12). Each cilium has its own separate kinetosome at its base. Internally all flagella and cilia have the same structure. The electron microscope reveals a flagellum or cilium to be a bundle of eleven exceedingly fine fibrils, two of them central and nine arranged in a ring around the central two (see Fig. 5.13). The nine in the ring are continuations of the microtubules of the kinetosome. How motion is actually produced is as yet understood only poorly.

Flagella are the locomotor structures in numerous algae and protozoa and in most sperm cells of plants and animals. In most of these cases the flagellum is at the anterior end of a cell and its whiplike beat pulls the cell behind it. By contrast, in many sperms and in some fungal cells the flagellum is at the posterior end and its beat pushes the cell forward. Flagella or cilia also occur in many embryos, larvae, and small adult animals, which have flagellate or ciliated skins that serve in locomotion, in creating food-bearing water currents, or both. Moreover, most animals have flagellate or ciliated cells in the interior of the body. For example, such cells occur in certain sense organs; in the lining tissues of breathing, alimentary, and reproductive channels; and generally in any location where air, water, or solid

Table 6. Some structural components of cells and their main functions

	structure	function
nucleus	chromosomes	gene carriers, ultimate control of cell activities
	nucleolus	auxiliary to protein synthesis
	nuclear membrane	traffic control to and from cytoplasm
cytoplasm	endoplasmic reticulum	secretion channels, connection between cell parts, attachment surfaces
	mitochondria	site of respiration
	ribosomes	site of protein synthesis
	Golgi bodies	site of specific secretion synthesis
	lysosomes	stores of hydrolytic enzymes
	chloroplasts	site of photosynthesis
	centrioles	auxiliary to cell division
	kinetosomes	anchor and control flagella, cilia
	myofibrils	contraction
	neurofibrils	conduction
	granules, vacuoles	transport, storage, processing centers
surface	plasma membrane	traffic control to and from cell
	cell wall	support, protection, cell shape
	cuticles, pellicles	support, protection, waterproofing
	cilia, flagella	locomotion, current creation, feeding
	pseudopodia	locomotion, feeding, phagocytosis

materials must be moved over a surface or through a duct.

In any cell, evidently, certain of the structural components of the nucleus, the cytoplasm, or the surface serve directly as the machinery for particular cell functions. For example, photosynthesis, respiration, and protein synthesis are distinct functions performed in distinct cytoplasmic structures; see Table 6 for a summary of such relations. But many cell functions cannot be localized so neatly. For example, cell reproduction or amoeboid movement requires the cooperative activity of many or all of the structural components of a cell. Functions of this kind cannot be referred to any particular part of a cell but are performed by the cell as a whole.

Also, whereas many organelles are bulky enough to be visible under the microscope, many more are not visible; individual molecules in a cell "function" no less than larger bodies. Be it a single dissolved molecule or a whole group of large suspended organelles, each cellular structure performs a function, and as the structures differ among cells so do the functions.

tissues, organs, systems

As an organism matures most of its cells specialize; they become more or less diversified in external appearance and internal structure, and they develop the capacity to perform some function or functions especially well. Such characteristics tend to become fixed and irreversible. In general, the more a cell has become specialized in one way, the less readily can it change and respecialize in another way.

A *tissue* can be defined as a set of cells that *cooperate* in the performance of a particular group function. Similarly, an *organ* is a cooperating set of tissues, and an *organ system* is a cooperating set of organs. Not all multicellular organisms necessarily contain organs and organ systems. In some of the most primitive multicellular types the whole body consists of but a single tissue. More advanced organisms usually have several tissues, and some of these often form organs. Numerous organs and sets of organ systems occur only in the most advanced plants and animals.

the plant pattern

The ways in which plant cells of various types are joined as tissues are illustrated clearly by young flowering plants. In the stems and roots of such plants the tissues are arranged in a concentric, radially symmetrical pattern (Fig. 5.14).

On the outside is the *epidermis,* a covering tissue one cell layer thick. Where the epidermal cells of leaves and green stems face the atmosphere the cell walls are usually thicker than elsewhere, and thick waxy cuticles are usually present as well (see Fig. 5.10). The epidermis of leaves and green stems also contains numerous *guard cells,* sausage- or crescent-shaped cells placed pairwise in such a way that the concave side of one faces the concave side of another (Fig. 5.15). The open space between two paired guard cells is a *stoma* (pl. *stomata*). Through changes of osmotic conditions in guard cells stomata can open and close, an important process controlling the entry and exit of atmospheric gases through the body surface of a plant (see Chap. 19). Guard cells are usually the only epidermal cells that are green and photosynthetic.

Epidermal cells of roots usually lack waxy cuticles and guard cells. But near the root tips the epidermis contains a zone of *root-hair cells.* These carry elongated fingerlike extensions of the cytoplasm on the side exposed to soil. Such "hairs" greatly increase the surface area of the cells, an important factor in nutrient absorption (see Fig. 5.15).

Underlying the epidermis in both stem and root is a tissue called the *cortex.* Its most abundant components are food- and water-storing *parenchyma cells* (Fig. 5.16). In stems such cells are often also green and food-producing. Under appropriate conditions parenchyma cells can specialize further and develop into a large variety of other cell types. Groups of such cells can even develop into whole roots or stems or into complete new plants.

Parenchyma cells usually have large intercellular spaces and only relatively thin primary walls. If such cells develop into other cell types, thicker secondary walls are often laid down inside the primary ones. Certain areas along these walls then usually remain thin *pits,* and adjoining pits of two neighboring cells may come to form *pit pairs.* The

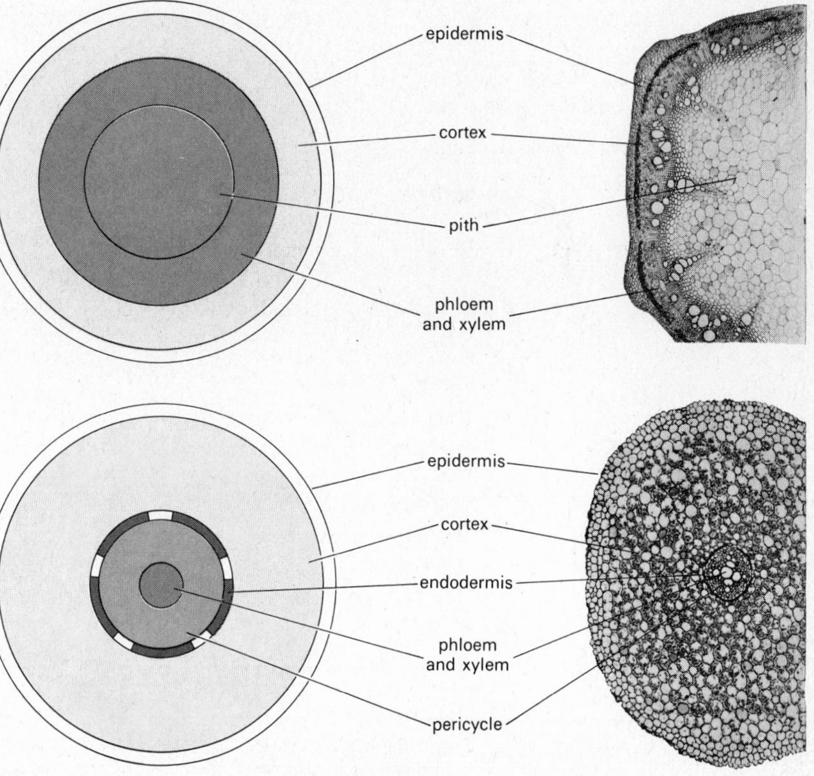

5.14 Tissue arrangements in plants. *Top, stem tissues at left and bean-stem section at right. Bottom, root tissues at left and buttercup-root section at right (Photos courtesy Carolina Biological Supply Company).*

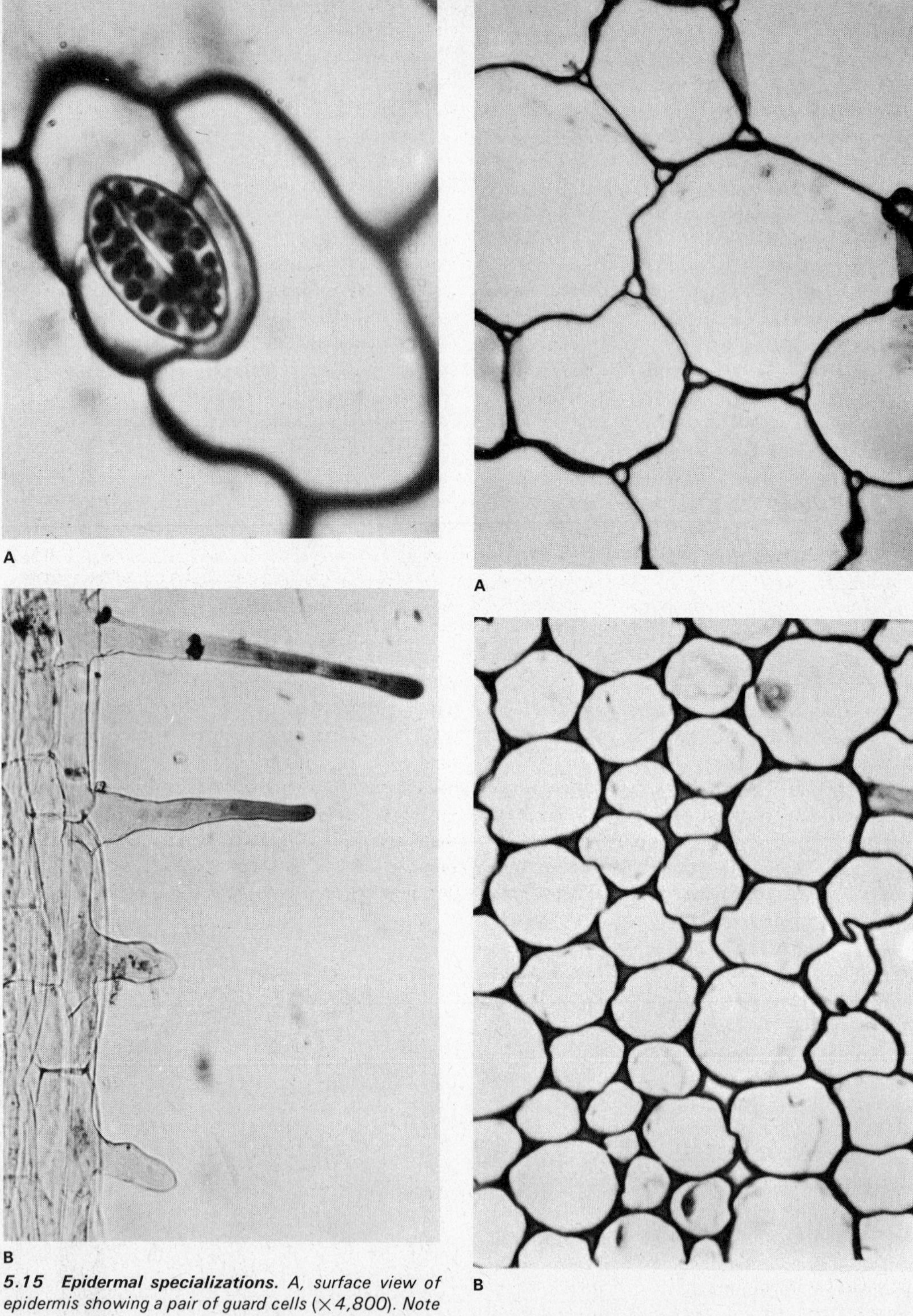

5.15 Epidermal specializations. *A, surface view of epidermis showing a pair of guard cells (×4,800). Note the chloroplasts in them and the stoma between them. B, root epidermis with root hairs at various stages of growth (×400).*

5.16 Cortex cell types. *A, parenchyma. B, collenchyma. (×5,000).*

two pits of a pair are separated by a *pit membrane,* composed of the middle lamella and the primary wall along each side (Fig. 5.17).

Somewhat more specialized variants of parenchyma are *collenchyma cells,* usually elongated cells with thick but fairly elastic primary walls. Collenchyma cells are abundant in developing leaves and stems, where the thick cell walls aid greatly in support against gravity (see Fig. 5.16).

The cortex often also contains highly specialized *sclerenchyma cells,* which function mainly in providing mechanical support. Such cells have thick primary walls, very thick secondary walls, and they are strong and quite inelastic. After sclerenchyma cells have developed fully, their nuclei and cytoplasms usually disintegrate. Only the thick walls are left, and mature sclerenchyma therefore is wholly nonliving and no longer "cellular" (Fig. 5.18). Of two cell types classified as sclerenchyma, *fibers* are greatly elongated and they usually have tapered ends. Such cells lend support to stems and other elongated plant parts. For example, the stems of flax plants are rich in fibers. These are used commercially in the manufacture of linen. The second type of sclerenchyma comprises variously shaped *sclereids,* which serve primarily in providing rigidity or hardness. For example, sclereids called *stone cells* occur in the flesh of pears, where they give this fruit a characteristic gritty texture.

Adjoining the innermost layer of the cortex is the *endodermis,* prominent usually only in roots. This tissue is composed of a single layer of fairly large cells, most of them impregnated along their outer surfaces with a waterproofing substance called *suberin.* Some groups of endodermis cells do not manufacture suberin; these are *passage cells,* which play an important role in lateral water transport through the root (Fig. 5.19).

The endodermis surrounds a group of tissues known collectively as the *stele.* The outermost of these, directly adjacent to the endodermis, is the *pericycle.* It is conspicuous usually only in roots and consists of one or more layers of parenchyma cells (see Fig. 5.19). Along the inner boundary of the pericycle is a second component of the stele, the *primary phloem.* This is a complex tissue composed of parenchyma cells, sclerenchyma fibers and sclereids, and cellular complexes called *sieve tubes.* A sieve tube usually develops from a vertical column of adjacent embryonic cells (Fig. 5.20). Each of these cells divides, and one of the two resulting cells is a *sieve-tube cell.* Remaining joined to it, the other cell forms one or more smaller *companion cells.* The nuclei of sieve-tube cells disintegrate during the maturation of the tissue, and thereafter the activities of such cells appear to be controlled by the companion cells, in which nuclei are retained.

Maturation of a sieve-tube cell also includes formation of pits in several regions. Pits that develop along the upper and lower ends of the cell actually become perforations right through the cell wall. These specialized perforated end walls are *sieve plates.* Passing through the perforations are cytoplasmic strands that connect with the cytoplasm of adjoining sieve-tube cells. These cytoplasmic bridges play an important role in food conduction through a long sieve tube (see Chap. 14). The long-distance transportation of organic materials is actually the chief function of sieve tubes and of phloem tissue as a whole. Because primary phloem thus serves as a system of conduction vessels, it is also referred to as a *vascular* tissue.

A third tissue of the stele is the complex *primary xylem,* located typically along the inner boundary of the primary phloem (see Fig. 5.19). It contains parenchyma cells and sclerenchyma fibers, as well as *tracheids* and *vessels.* Tracheids are elongated, spindle-shaped cells, up to 5 mm long and 0.03 mm wide, that form vertical columns extending from root to leaf. Like a sclerenchyma cell, a tracheid loses its nucleus and cytoplasm during development, and the remaining walls then enclose only water. These walls contain primary as well as secondary layers, both rigid and impregnated with *lignin,* a chemically com-

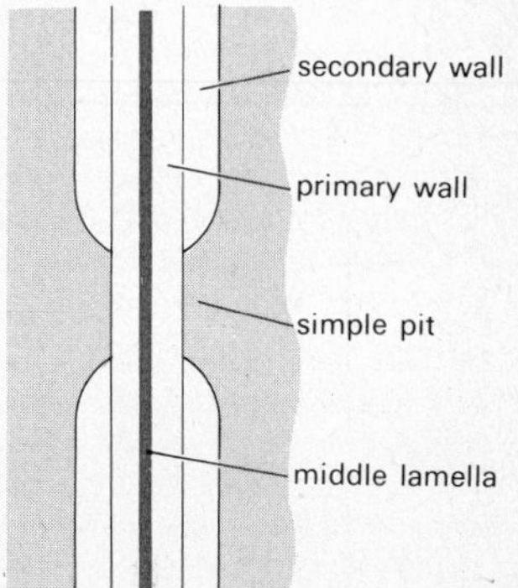

5.17 Parenchyma pits. *A simple pit pair in two adjacent parenchyma cells is shown. The pit membrane is formed by the middle lamella and the primary wall on each side of it.*

5.18 Sclerenchyma. *A, fibers in longitudinal view. B, fibers in cross-sectional view. C, stone cells in cross-sectional view. Note the exceedingly thick walls.*

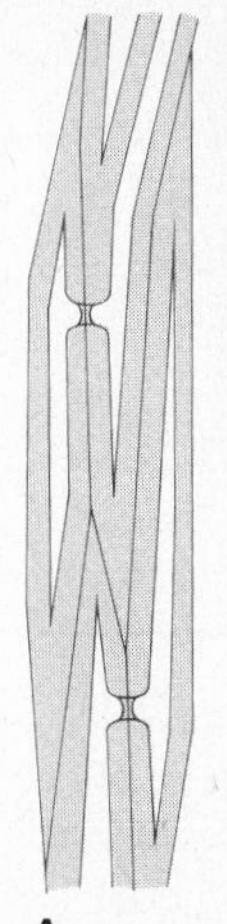

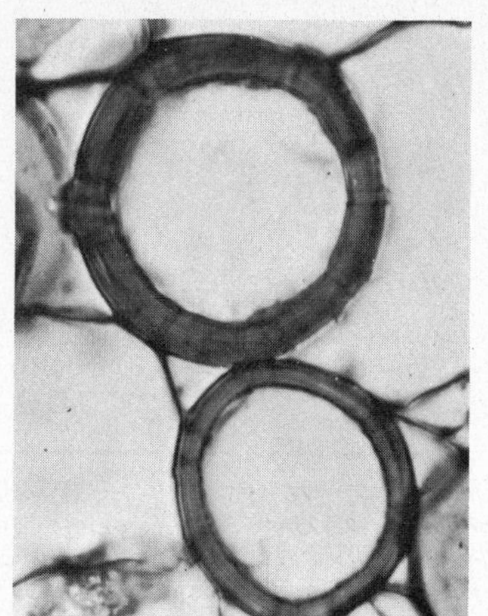

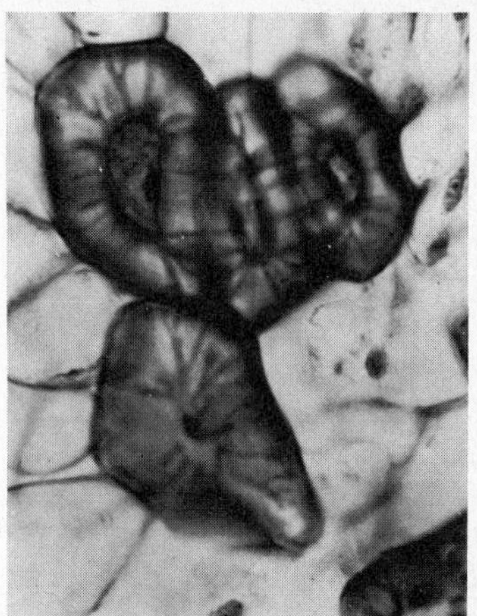

plex strengthening material. In many cases the secondary wall lines the primary layer completely, as an uninterrupted inner coat. In other cases the secondary wall is incomplete and is deposited in the form of rings or spiral bands or transverse bars or networks. Such incomplete inner walls add strength, yet still permit a long tracheid to bend without breaking (Fig. 5.21).

Also present in the walls of tracheids are elaborate *bordered pits,* specialized regions similar in some respects to the pits of parenchyma cells. In a bordered pit primary cell wall material forms a *torus,* a small round or oval plug attached to the pit membrane. The secondary wall overhangs the pit around its rim and is absent in the region of the torus. Thus, if water pressure in an adjoining cell pushes the pit membrane and the torus into the tracheid, the torus is prevented from moving too far by the rim of the secondary wall. The torus in effect functions like a valve.

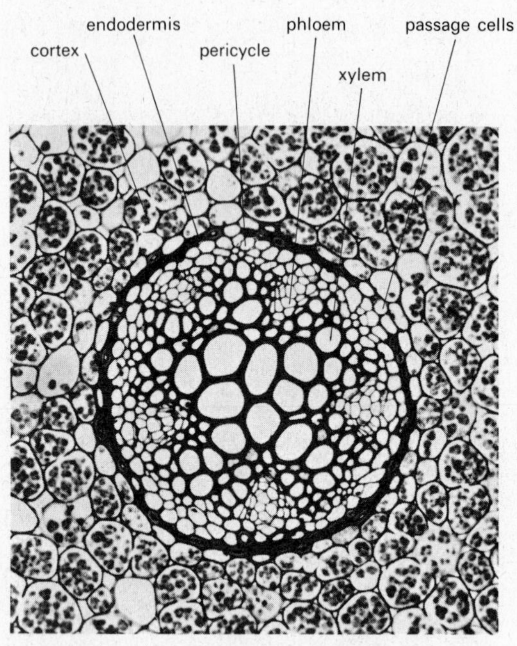

5.19 (At right) ***Root tissues.*** *Surrounded by the cortex and the endodermis, the stele tissues of a buttercup root are shown here in magnified view (approx. ×85). See Fig. 5.14 for section through whole buttercup root.*

5.20 (Below) ***Sieve tubes and their development.*** *A, left, column of cells from which a sieve tube will form. Middle, division gives rise to a smaller companion cell (at left). Right, the companion cell remains as before, but in the other cell, sieve plates develop at the top and bottom and the nucleus disintegrates. A column of such specialized cells forms a sieve tube. B, sieve plate in top view. C, sieve tube, with sieve plates along the side walls.*

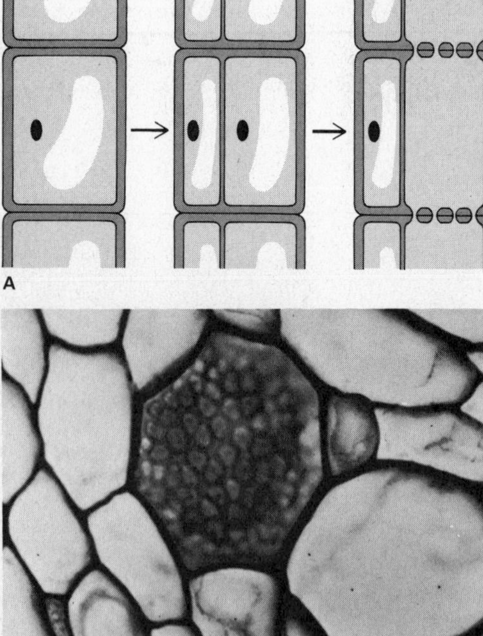

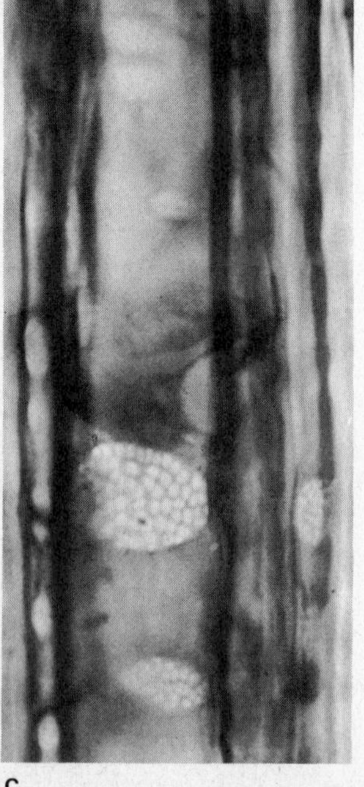

The vessels of primary xylem develop from vertical columns of adjacent embryonic cells (Fig. 5.22). As each such cell matures it produces primary walls and lignin-impregnated secondary walls with bordered pits, just like tracheids. Eventually the nucleus and the cytoplasm disintegrate, and the transverse end walls, where one cell of the column abuts against the next, develop one or more openings or often dissolve altogether. In effect, the column becomes a hollow water-filled tube, with remnants of transverse cross walls still present in places. Such a nonliving structure is a vessel.

By virtue of its tracheids and vessels, primary xylem is both a vascular and a supporting tissue; it functions in long-distance conduction of water and it supports a plant against gravity. The plants that possess these two vascular tissues, primary phloem and xylem, are appropriately called "vascular plants." Note that another name of xylem is *wood.* However, if only a little xylem is present, as is usually the case in primary xylem, the tissue is not bulky enough to make a plant distinctly "woody" in external appearance. For example, although a green bean stem technically contains wood, or primary xylem, the stem of such a plant is not "woody."

The innermost of the basic tissues of the stele is the *pith.* It is not present in roots, and in stems it is located right at the center, surrounded by primary xylem. Pith is composed of parenchyma cells which, as in the cortex, store foods and conduct water from cell to cell (see Fig. 5.14).

Clearly, these various tissues are not "just there," but are organized in a definite structural pattern. Because of this structural organization, functional cooperation among the tissues becomes possible. The main cooperative functions

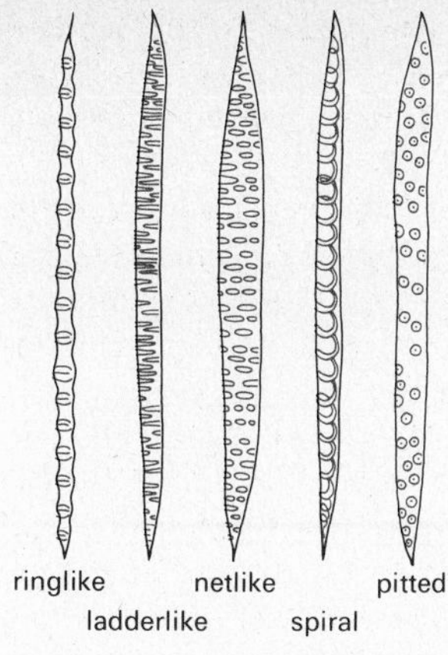

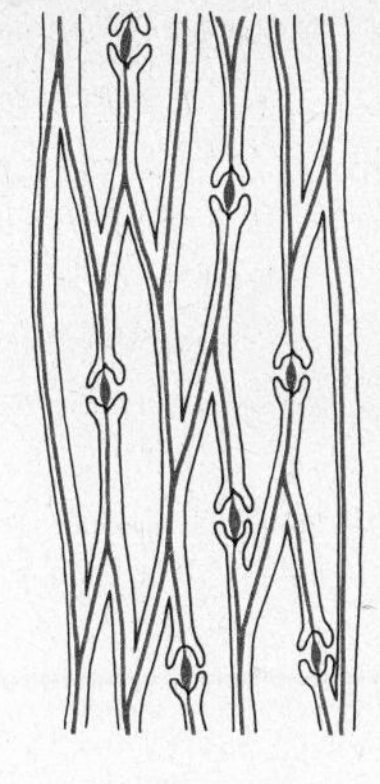

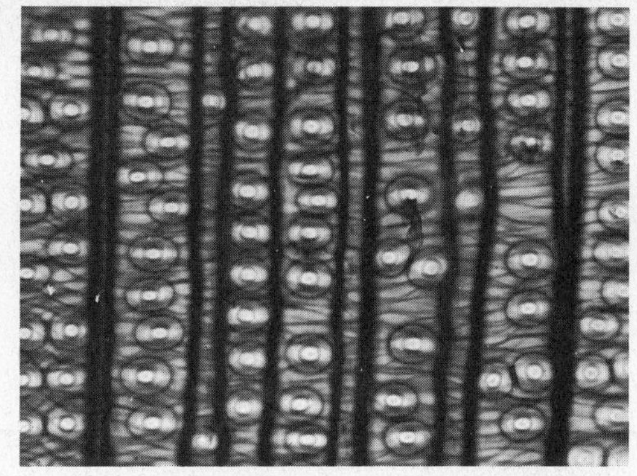

5.21 Tracheids. *A, tracheids with various kinds of secondary thickenings. B, tracheids with pits in longitudinal section. The thin pit membranes provide lateral pathways from one cell to an adjacent one. The thickening in the middle of the pit membranes (torus) serves as a stopper that prevents the membrane from ballooning out too far to either side. C, section through tracheids of a fir showing pits in surface view (approx. × 1,000).*

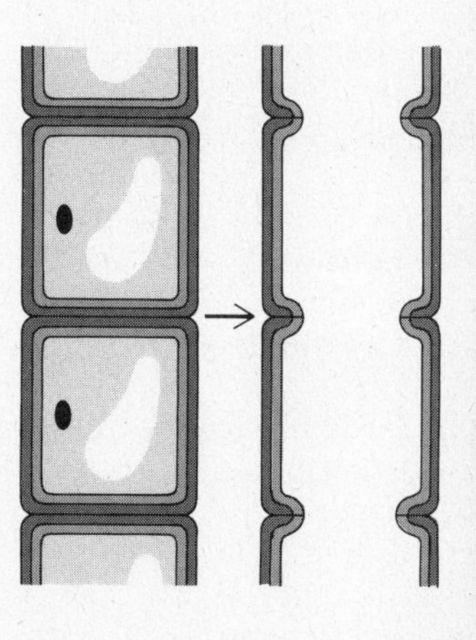

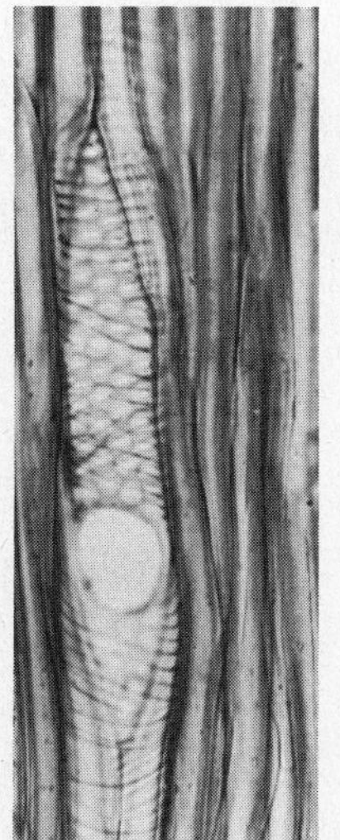

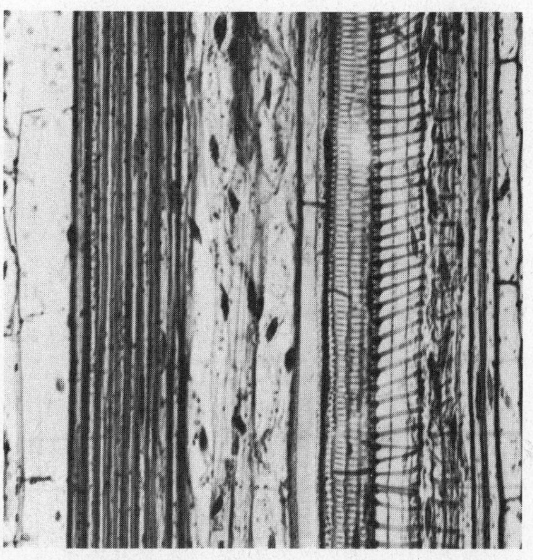

5.22 Xylem vessels and their development. *A, left, column of cells from which a vessel will form. Right, primary and secondary walls at top and bottom have degenerated, leaving a continuous vertical vessel. B, longitudinal section of xylem vessels. One of the vessels has a conspicuous simple pit (the white opening) and spiral thickenings along the wall. C, primary xylem in sunflower stem, longitudinal section. Note the ringlike, spiral, and netlike wall thickenings in various groups of vessels.*

are, in the stem, support against gravity, conduction, and manufacture of foods; and in the root, support in soil, conduction, and absorption of nutrients from soil. Group functions performed by several tissues are characteristic of organs, and stems and roots actually are two of the kinds of organs found in a plant.

Two other sets of organs occur in plants, *leaves* and *reproductive organs.* These are formed largely from the same cell types and tissue types that occur in stems and roots (see Chap. 10). In at least one instance, several whole organs cooperate functionally and form an *organ system.* This is the case in cones and flowers. As will become apparent later, such structures consist of several reproductive and other associated organs, all contributing to the one overall function of propagation.

the animal pattern

tissues

Most tissues of most animals can be classified either as *connective tissues* or as *epithelia.* Not normally included in this classification are three specific tissues, *nerve, muscle,* and *blood.*

Connective tissues are identified by comparatively widely separated cells and by various fluid or solid materials in the spaces between the cells.

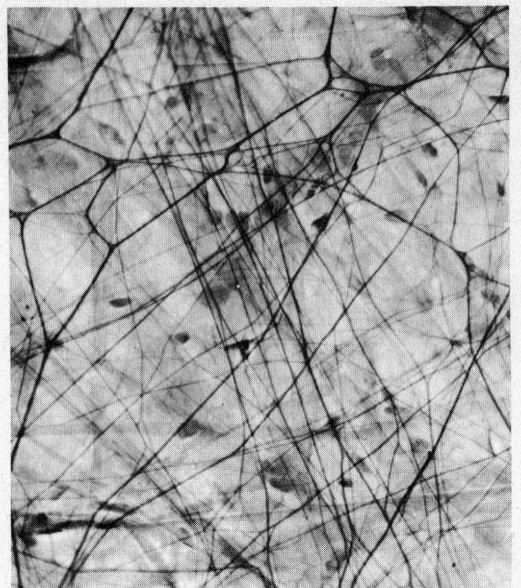

5.23 Fibroelastic connective tissue. *Fibers form a network, and the cells (small dark dots) secrete the fibers and are embedded in the network (×500).*

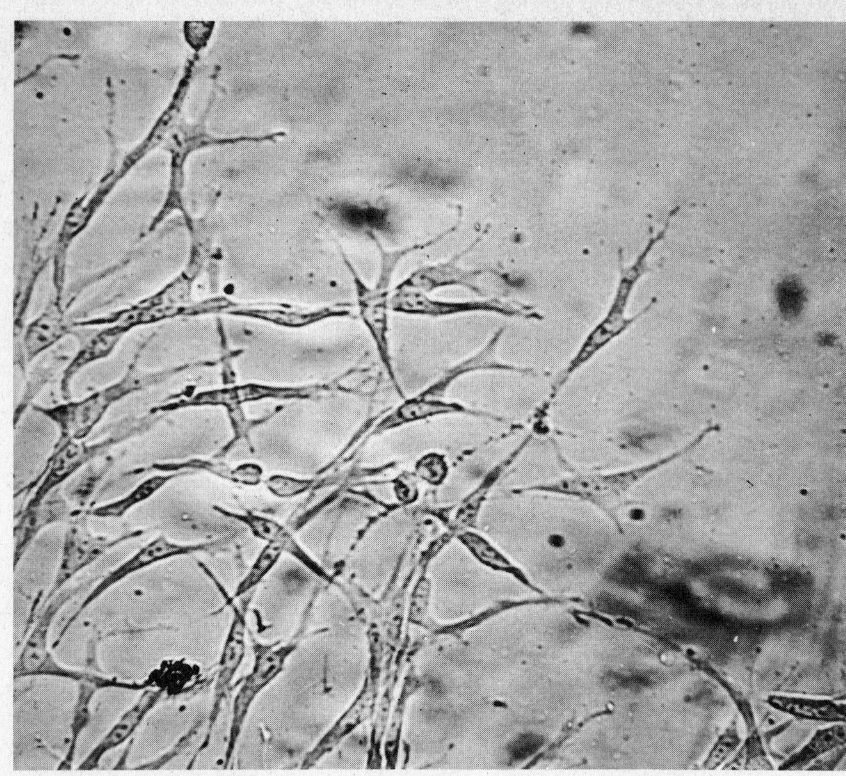

A

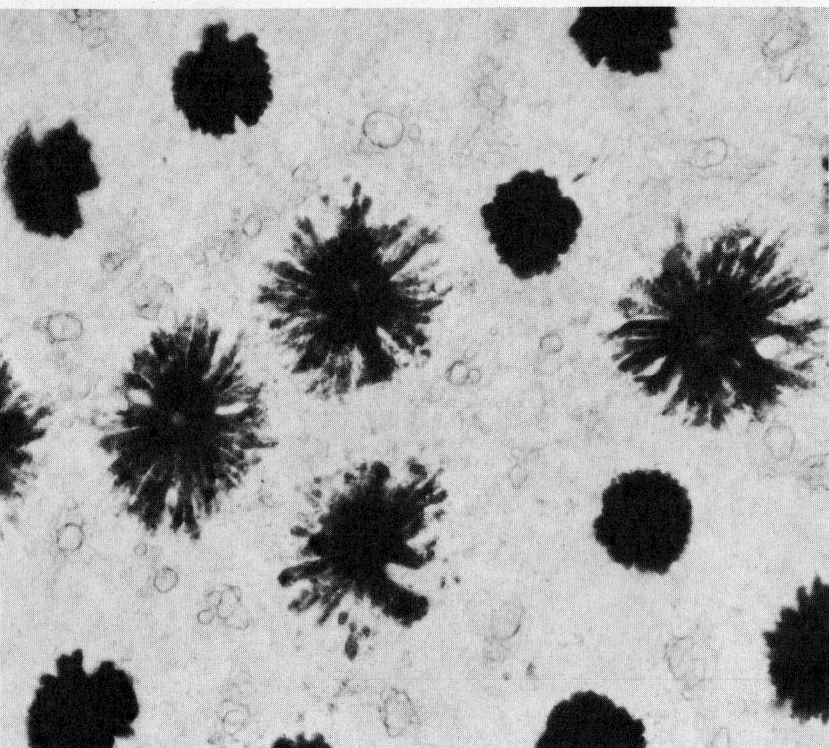

B

5.24 Connective tissue cell types. *A, mesenchyme cells in tissue culture (×5,000). B, pigment cells (from skin connective tissue of flounder) in various states of expansion (×5,000).*

color figure 1

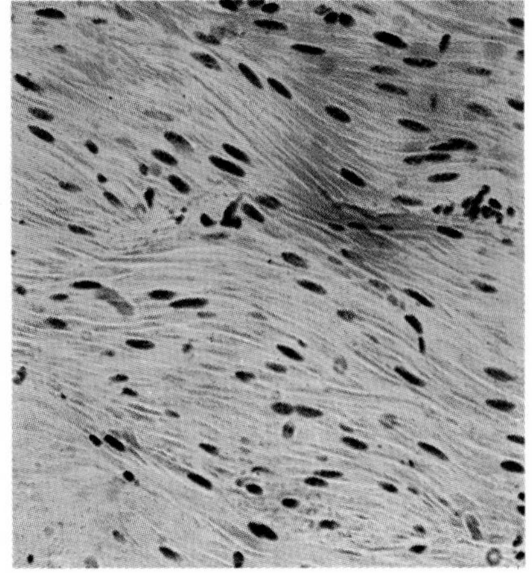

A

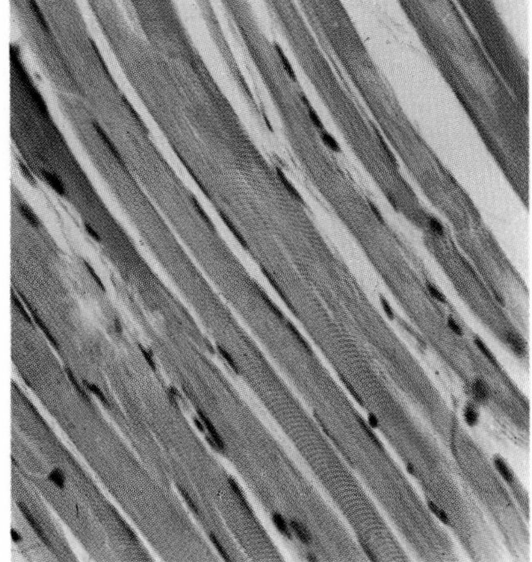

B

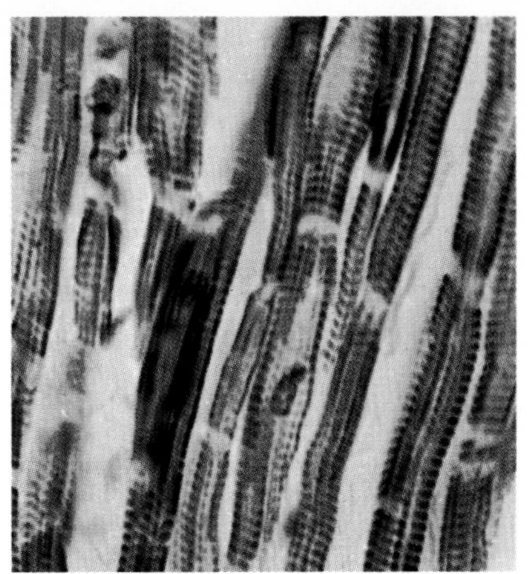

C

1. Muscle types. *A, smooth muscle. Note the spindle-shaped cells. B, a few fibers of skeletal muscle. Note the cross striations and the nuclei in each fiber. C, cardiac muscle. Note the branching fibers, the nuclei, the faint longitudinal fibrils in each fiber, and the cross striations. (A, C, courtesy Carolina Biological Supply Company.)*

2. ***Caterpillar*** *of a moth, carrying the pupal cocoons of a parasitic wasp. (Courtesy Carolina Biological Supply Company.)*

3. ***Mutualism.*** *Lichens, which are mutualistic associations of algae and fungi, are shown here encrusting a tree branch. (Courtesy Carolina Biological Supply Company.)*

A

B

*4. **Camouflage.** A, a stick insect and B, a caterpillar, both resembling the branches of plants. C, D, a flatfish (plaice) against two different backgrounds. The animal can adapt the pattern of its skin pigmentation to the environment. In such cases information about the environment is communicated to the skin via eyes, nerves, and hormones. Pigment cells in the skin respond to the information by contracting or expanding, thereby altering body coloration.*

C

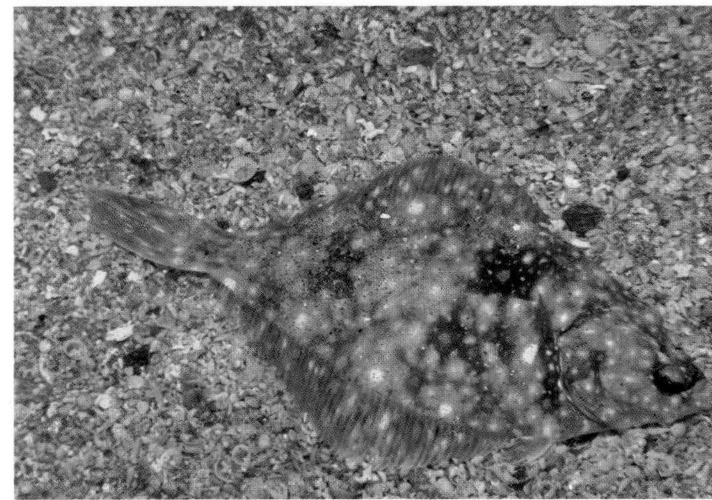

D

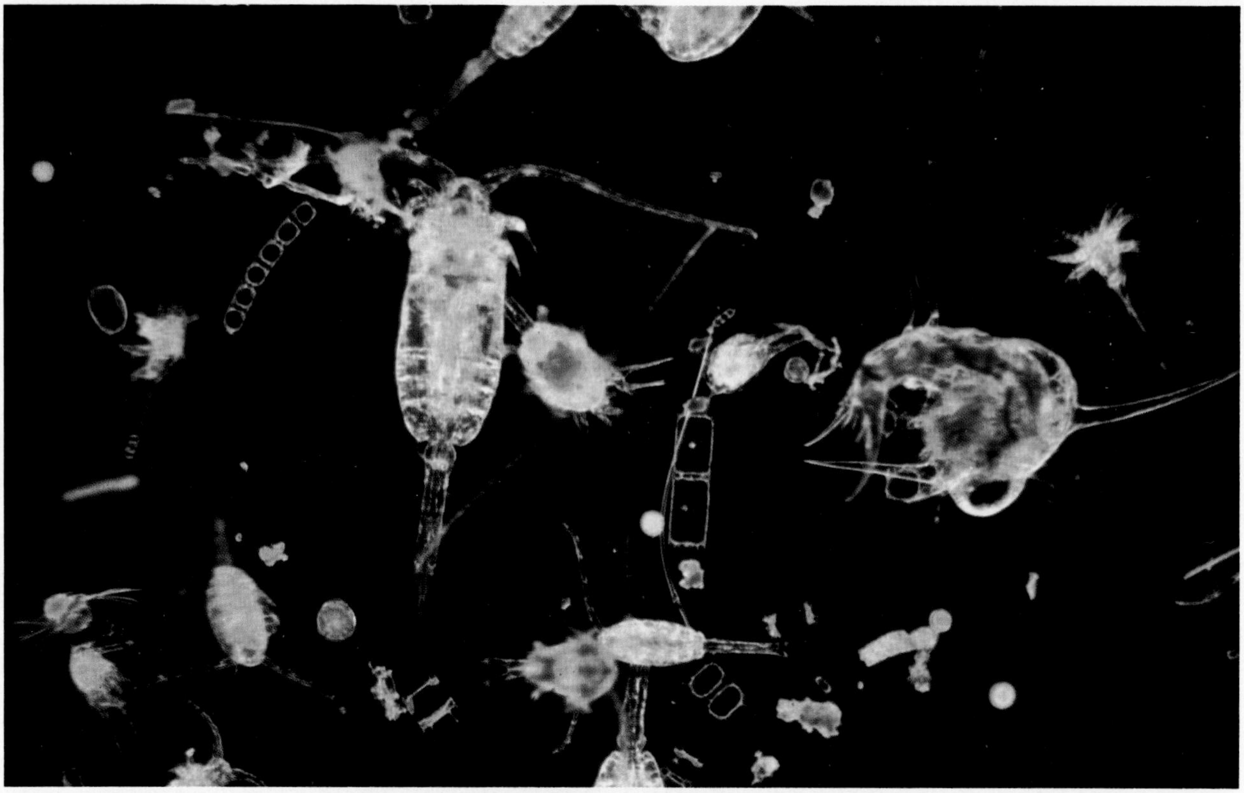

A

5. Marine plankton. *A, diatoms, copepods, crustacean larvae, protozoa, animal eggs, and other organisms. B, diatoms.*

B

color figure 5

Another identifying characteristic is the relatively unspecialized nature of the cells. With appropriate stimulation they can transform from one connective tissue cell type to another. In this respect they are roughly equivalent to the parenchyma cells of plants.

The most fundamental of the connective tissues is *fibroelastic tissue* (Fig. 5.23). Conspicuous in it are large numbers of threadlike fibers, some tough and strong, others elastic. These are suspended in fluid and form an irregular, loosely arranged meshwork. The cells of the tissue are dispersed throughout the mesh, and they secrete materials that give rise to the fibers outside them.

The cells are of various types. Many are *fibrocytes,* generally spindle-shaped and believed to be the chief fiber-forming cells. Others, the *histiocytes,* are capable of amoeboid motion and of engulfing foreign bodies (such as bacteria in infected regions). Also present are *pigment cells, fat cells,* and above all, *mesenchyme cells.* These are undeveloped and relatively quite unspecialized. They form all the connective tissues of an embryo and later give rise to the various cell types of adult connective tissues. Thus it is possible to define connective tissues as all those that have a mesenchymal origin in the embryo (Fig. 5.24).

In many animals, mesenchyme cells "left over" from embryonic stages play an important role in healing and regeneration. The cells can migrate to injured body regions and contribute to the redevelopment of lost body parts and to formation of scar tissue. Most of the adult cell types of fibroelastic tissue likewise can transform into one another. For example, a fibrocyte might become a fat cell, then perhaps a histiocyte, then a fibrocyte again, and then a pigment cell. The specializations of any of these cells evidently are not fixed.

By virtue of its cellular components, fibroelastic tissue thus functions in food storage and in body defense against infection and injury; and by virtue of its fibers, the tissue is a major binding agent that holds one body part to another. For example, fibroelastic tissue connects skin to underlying muscle. The tough fibers provide connecting strength, yet the elastic fibers still permit the skin to slide over the muscle to some extent.

The relative quantities of cellular and fibrous components vary greatly, and on the basis of such variations other types of connective tissue may be distinguished (Fig. 5.25). For example, *tendons* are dense tissues containing only fibrocytes and tough fibers, the latter arranged as closely packed parallel bundles. Tendons typically connect muscles to parts of the skeleton. A *ligament* is similar to a tendon, except that both tough and elastic fibers are present and that these are arranged more or less irregularly. Another variant of fibroelastic tissue is *adipose tissue,* in which fat cells are the most abundant components. Each fat cell contains one or more large fat vacuoles that fill almost the entire cellular space. A collection of such cells has the external appearance of a continuous mass of fat. Still other variants of fibroelastic tissue are known.

Many animals contain *jelly-secreting* connective tissues. The cells in such cases are mesenchymal, and as they secrete gelatinous substances the cells become separated from one another more and more. Mesenchymal jelly tissue can become quite bulky, as in jellyfishes, for

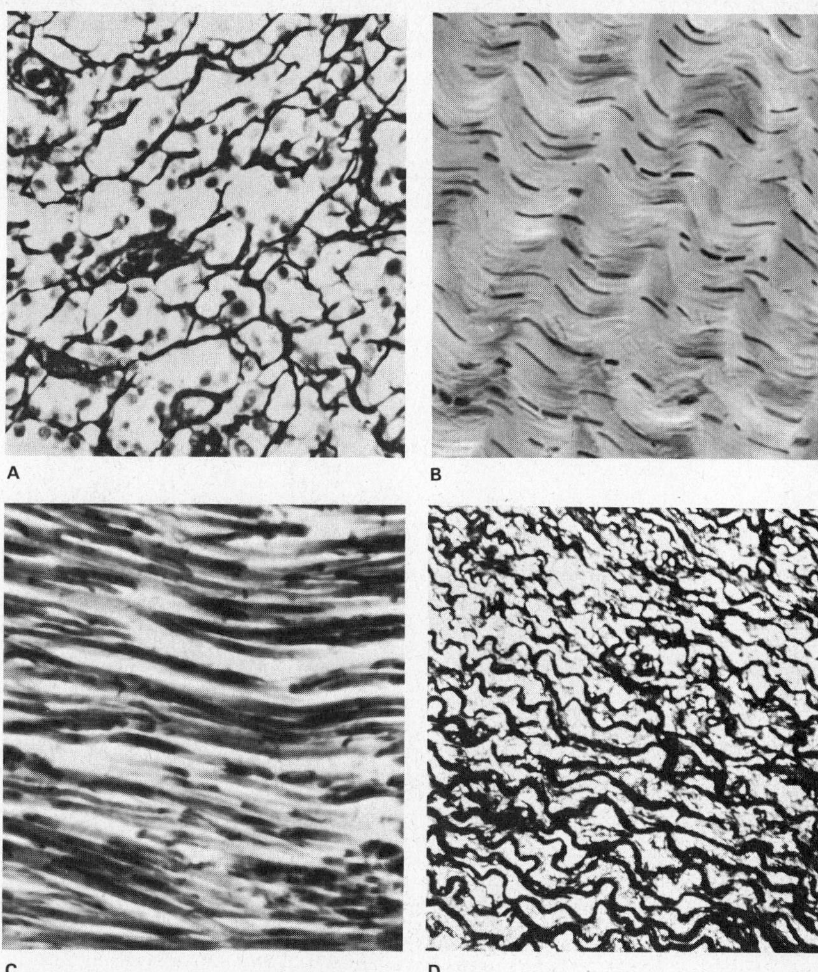

5.25 Variants of fibroelastic connective tissue. *A, reticular tissue, composed of fibrous and cellular components. This type of tissue is found in lymph nodes and lungs and in preadult stages is also a forerunner of mature fibroelastic tissue. B, tendon. C, ligament. D, elastic tissue, as in the walls of the large arteries. Elastic fibers predominate here. (D, courtesy Carolina Biological Supply Company.)*

example. Such tissues also occur abundantly in numerous other animals (for example, around and in the eyes of man and most other vertebrates).

In some connective tissues the cells secrete organic and especially inorganic materials that form a solid precipitate around the cells. Such cells therefore appear as islands embedded in hard intercellular deposits. The chief variants of this tissue type are *cartilage,* encountered in several invertebrate groups and in all vertebrates, and *bone,* characteristic of vertebrates (Fig. 5.26). Both cartilage and bone arise from mesenchymal cells, and both function in support and protection. For example, the long bony rods of the appendages support other tissues around them, and the flat bony plates of the skull cover and protect the underlying brain.

A

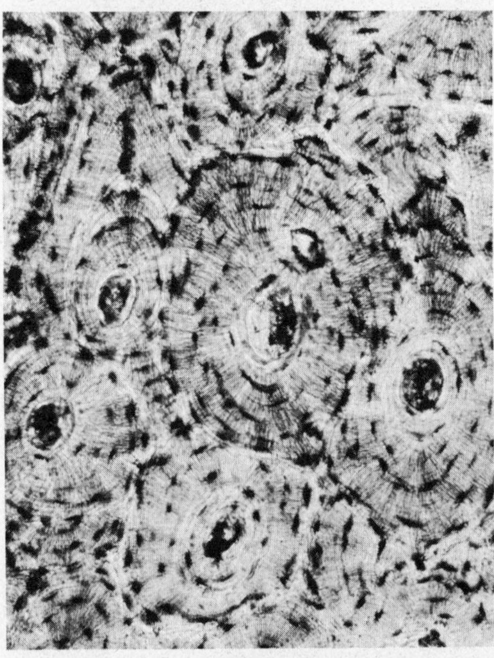

B

5.26 Cartilage and bone. *A, the many cartilage-forming cells are surrounded by their own secretions. B, bone-forming cells are in the dark patches, arranged in concentric patterns. Hard bone substance appears light. A unit of concentric bone layers represents a so-called Haversian system; a cell-filled Haversian canal is in the center of such a system.*

Among vertebrates, cartilage is the only skeletal tissue in types such as lampreys and sharks. In other vertebrates, man included, the skeleton is largely bony. Bone develops in two ways. Skeletal parts that consist of flat plates and lie close to the body surface—skull bones and shoulder blades, for example—arise as *dermal bones,* directly from the connective tissue in the inner layers of the skin. All other skeletal parts—those that form deep-lying and predominantly elongated supports—develop as *replacement bones;* they are first laid down in cartilage, which is replaced later by bone substance (Fig. 5.27). In man such replacement of cartilage by bone is usually not completed until approximately the twentieth year of life. A few regions do not become bony at all, as illustrated by the cartilages of the nose and the outer ears.

By and large, the connective tissues serve to provide a structural framework for the animal body. Epithelial tissues by contrast form primarily those body parts that carry out most of the vital functions. An epithelium is a tissue in which the cells adhere directly to one another. Such cell groups can occur as single-layered sheets, as many-layered sheets, or as compact, irregularly shaped masses.

Epithelia that form sheets generally rest on *basement membranes,* flat networks of tough fibers secreted as supporting fabrics. Sheets consisting of single layers of cells are called *simple* epithelia (Fig. 5.28). Distinctions among them are made mainly on the basis of cell shape. If the cells are flat and joined along their edges, the tissue is a "pavement" or *squamous* epithelium. Many tissue membranes and the surface layer of the skins of many animals are of this type. If the cells have the shape of cubes, the tissue is a *cuboidal* epithelium. The walls of ducts and glands frequently consist of such tissues. If the cells are prismatic and are joined along their long sides, a *columnar* epithelium is formed. In many animals this type occurs in, for example, the

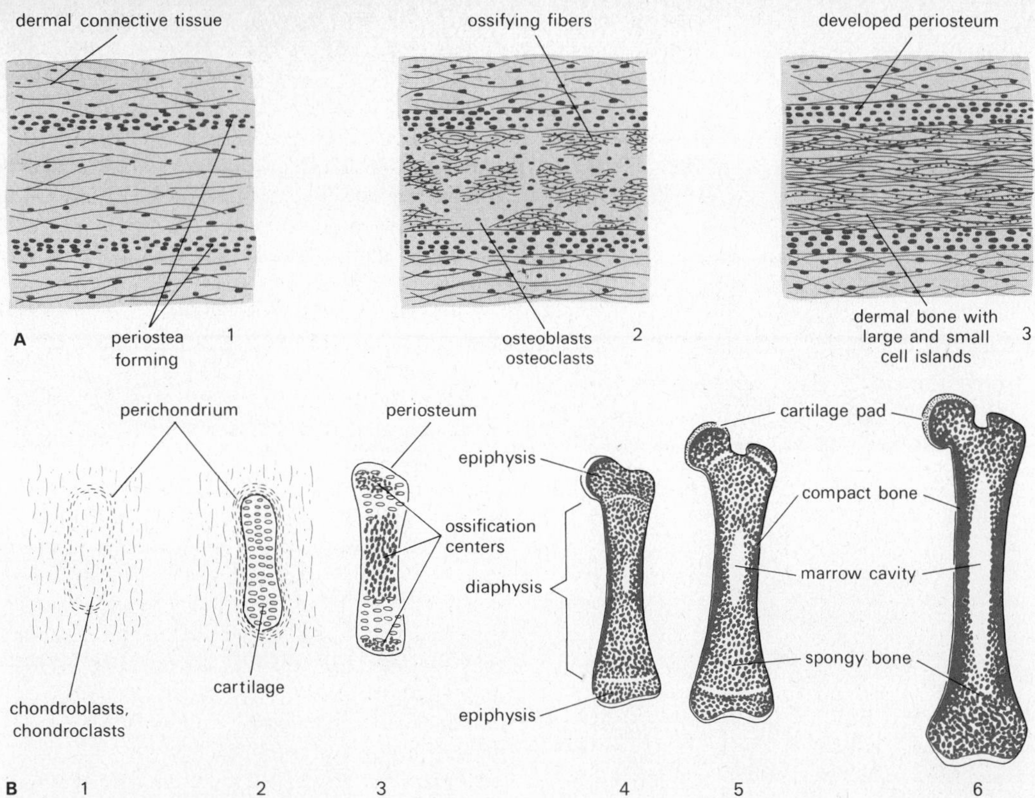

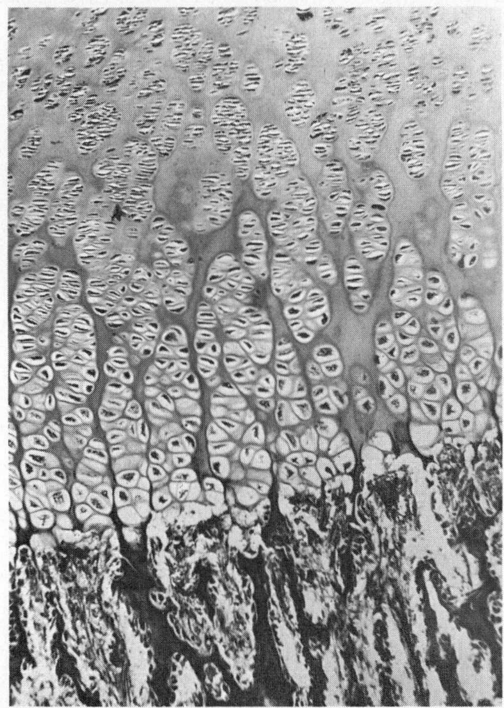

***5.27 Bone development.** A, formation of dermal bone. A periosteum (1) is layer of connective tissue that produces bone-forming and bone-destroying cells (osteoblasts and osteoclasts, respectively, 2), and that also covers a bone after it is formed (3). B, formation of replacement bone. A cartilage rod is first shaped by cartilage-forming and cartilage-destroying cells (chondroblasts, chondroclasts) that have been produced from a perichondrium (1, 2). The latter then becomes a periosteum, and osteoblasts produced by it begin secretion of bone substance at three ossification centers (3). Spongy bone replaces all cartilage except in regions near joints (white bands); compact bone begins to form at surface of shaft, and marrow cavity, in center of shaft (4, 5). In a mature bone (6), cartilage layers near joints have been replaced by bone, the marrow cavity is large, and spongy bone is largely replaced by compact bone (solid color). C, section through ossification center; cartilage (top) in process of resorption, bone (bottom) in process of formation. Bone deposits are dark.*

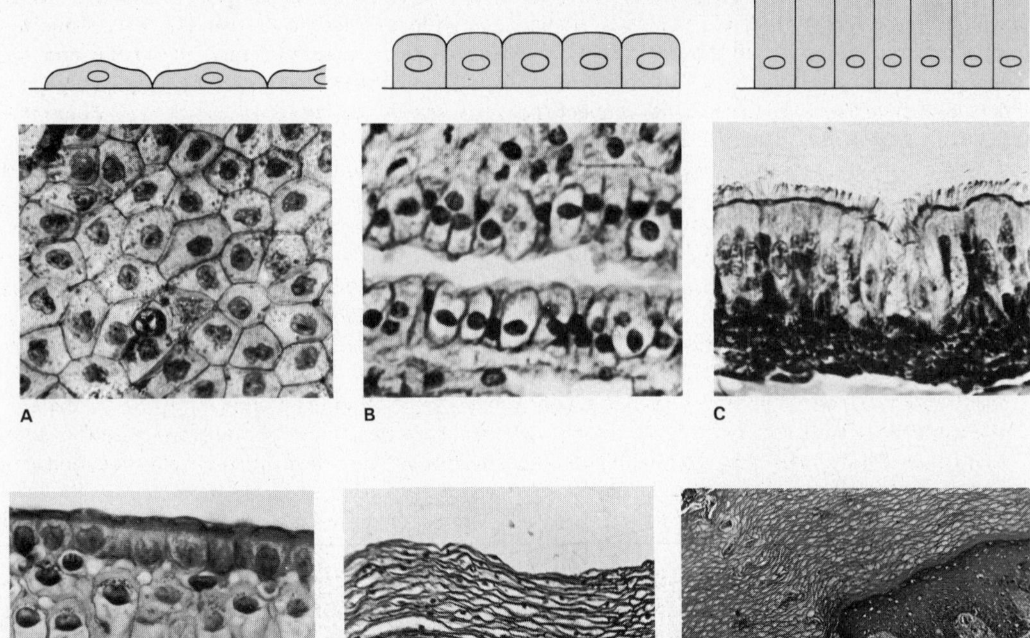

5.28 Epithelia. *A, squamous epithelium, diagram of cross section and photo of surface view of frog epidermis. Note close packing of cells, flat shapes, and angular outlines produced by mutual pressure of cells (×1,000). B, cuboidal epithelium, diagram and photo of cross section of lining of tubule in kidney (×1,400). C, columnar epithelium, diagram and photo of inner lining of frog gut. Note surface cilia (×1,500). (B, C, courtesy Carolina Biological Supply Company.)*

5.29. Stratified epithelia and skin. *A, section of skin of frog tadpole, showing stratified epidermis (dark tissue) and connective tissue dermis under it. Note progressive flattening of epidermal cells toward skin surface (see also Fig. 5.28) (×1,500). B, section through lining of human uterus. This lining tissue resembles the epidermis of skin. Again note flattening of cells toward surface (×50). C, section through mammalian skin. Note stratified epidermis near top of photo and dermis near bottom. Parts of the duct of a sweat gland can be seen meandering from the dermis through the epidermis to the skin surface (×50).*

innermost (digestive-juice-secreting) layer of the intestine.

If several epithelial layers are stacked as a multilayered sheet, they are said to form a *stratified* epithelium. The outermost tissue of the mammalian skin, the epidermis, is a good example of a mixed, stratified epithelium; the cells are squamous along the outer surface and become increasingly cuboidal with greater distance from the surface (Fig. 5.29). In contrast to the connective tissues, the epithelia are all fairly highly specialized. Once their cells are mature, they do not thereafter change in their basic structural and functional characteristics.

Blood, nerve, and muscle cannot be classified strictly as either connective or epithelial tissues because they share certain characteristics of both. Blood is generally like a connective tissue in that it contains cells and extensive intercellular deposits, fluid in this case (see Fig. 20.2). But although some of the blood cells have a mesenchymal origin, some do not. Nerve tissue on the contrary has an epithelial origin, and it resembles an epithelium in some respects. But in others—for example, its frequent netlike arrangement—it does not (see Chap. 21). Muscle tissue has a mesenchymal origin, yet adult muscle resembles an epithelium more than a connective tissue. Muscle is usually the most abundant tissue in animals. In man, for example, as much as two-thirds of the total body weight is muscle weight.

Muscle tissues occur as *smooth, striated,* and *cardiac* types (Color Fig. 1). In the smooth variety, the cells are elongated and spindle-shaped, and groups of such cells are often oriented in parallel and form a layer. In vertebrates smooth muscle is generally not connected to the skeleton and is not under voluntary nervous control. Striated, ''skeletal,'' or ''voluntary'' muscle is made up of syncytial units. Each such unit, a *muscle fiber,* develops through repeated division of a single cell, a process during which the boundaries between daughter cells disappear. Groups of such fibers are enveloped by fibroelastic connective tissue and form a *muscle bundle.* Several of these bundles in turn form a *muscle,* enclosed by a connective tissue sheath of its own. At either end a muscle merges gradually with a tendon and connects to a part of the skeleton. Cardiac muscle composes the bulk of the heart. Like smooth muscle it is not under voluntary control; like striated muscle its fibers are syncytial. Indeed, cardiac fibers are themselves fused together in intricate patterns, and the whole heart is a continuous, multinucleate mass.

All muscle fibers innervated by a single nerve fiber form a *motor unit* (Fig. 5.30). Hundreds of such units can be present in a whole muscle. Each motor unit operates in an all-or-none manner; either it contracts fully or it does not contract at all. The motor units in a whole muscle work in relays, different ones contracting at any given moment.

Muscles actually are never relaxed completely. Even at rest they are in a partially contracted state in which very little energy is expended. Such mild contractions maintain a muscle ''tone,'' and it is through this that muscles preserve body shape and posture and provide mechanical support in general. (Numerous animals—worms, for example—do not contain a skeleton, and muscles are their main supporting structures.) Only stronger contractions, above and beyond tonic ones, result in outright movement of parts and in pronounced energy expenditure.

Striated muscles operate far more rapidly than smooth muscles, and they usually also contain many more motor units than smooth muscles of equivalent size. The striated musculature can therefore produce faster, more abruptly alterable, and more finely adjustable motions. On the other hand, the smooth musculature requires comparatively less energy, and its slower, more sustained motions are well suited in steady, continuing activities—maintenance of digestion through gut-wall contractions, for example.

organs and systems

An animal organ typically consists of one or more epithelia and one or more connective tissues. The epithelia carry out the characteristic specialized functions of the organ, and the connective tissues serve in the necessary auxiliary roles. Thus the connective tissues maintain the shape and the position of the organ as a whole, and they carry the nerves, blood vessels, and other ducts that pass to and from the epithelia.

For example, in a compact organ like the liver, connective tissues form an external enveloping layer and they also extend into the interior as partitions. The connective tissues thus make up a *stroma,* a supporting framework that subdivides the liver into islands of epithelial cells (Fig. 5.31). Such islands usually represent complete functional units of the organ, and the traffic of materials to and from the units is carried by the surrounding stroma. Smaller or larger groups of such islands often form anatomically recognizable *lobules* or *lobes.*

In sheetlike organs such as skin, epithelia and connective tissues are usually arranged in adjacent layers. For example, vertebrate skin consists of two main layers, an outer *epidermis,* which is

__5.30 Motor endplates,__ the knobbed terminals of nerve branches on individual muscle fibers. The group of muscle fibers so innervated by a single nerve fiber and its terminal branches is a motor unit, a set of muscle fibers that functions together (×2,000).

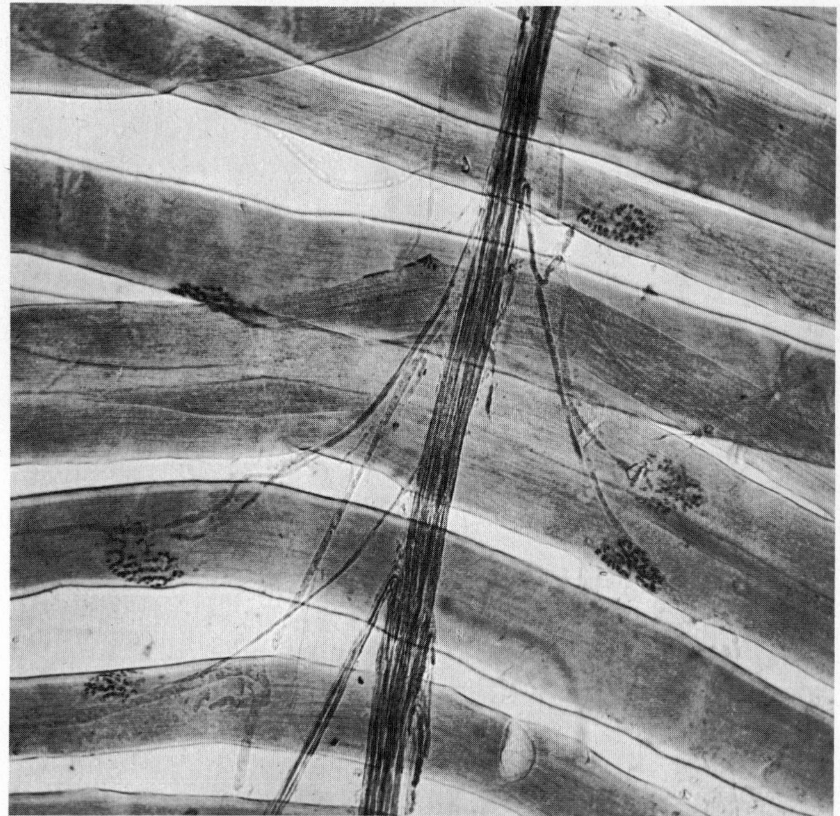

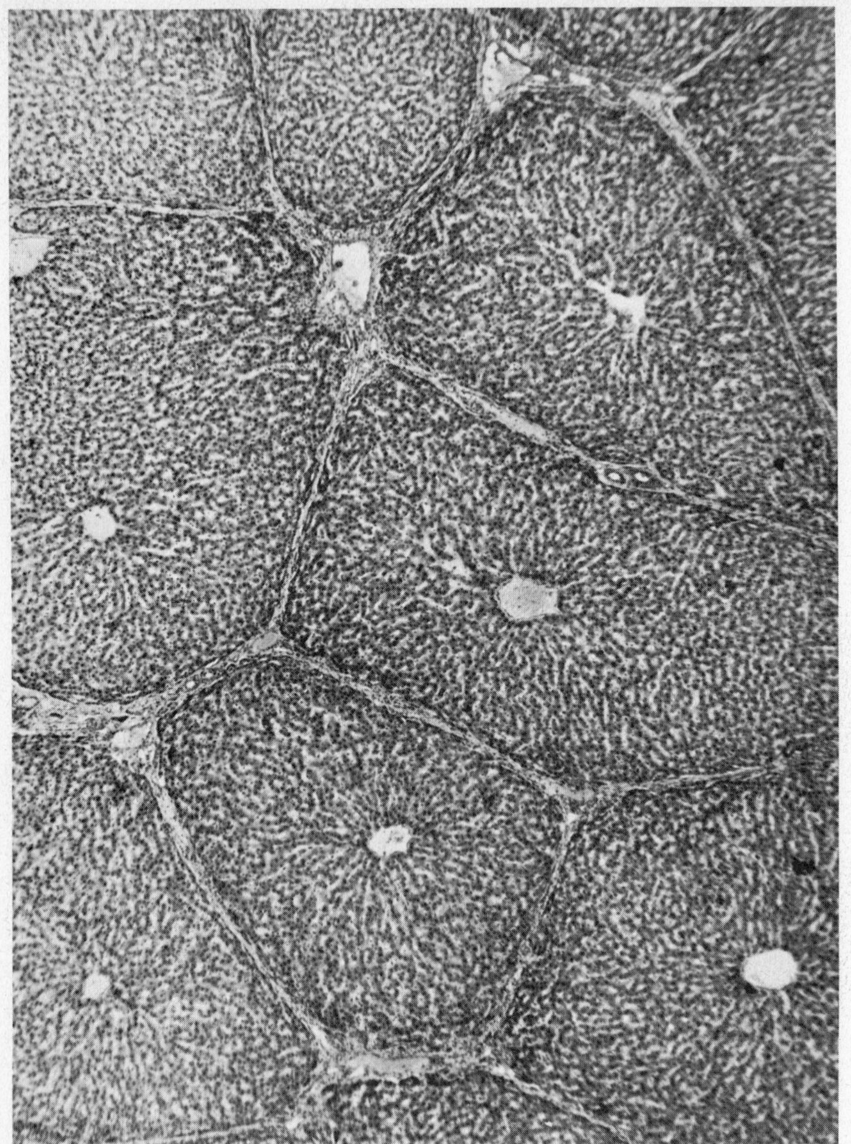

5.31 Mammalian liver. *In this section of a pig liver are seen a few of the epithelial lobules, separated from one another by layers of the connective tissue stroma. Branches of the hepatic portal vein in the stroma carry blood to a lobule. Blood then passes freely through the canal-like spaces between the strands of lobule cells, and it is eventually carried off by a branch of the hepatic vein, seen as a large clear space in the center of a lobule (×200). See also Fig. 14.12 for additional details on liver structure.*

a multilayered stratified epithelium, and an inner *dermis,* a multilayered fibroelastic connective tissue (see Fig. 5.29). Each of these layers also gives rise to other tissues and organs in various body regions. Thus the epidermis produces series of glandular ingrowths into the dermis (for example, excretory *sweat glands,* oil-secreting *sebaceous glands*), as well as numerous outgrowths such as beaks, claws, hoofs, nails, scales, feathers, and hair. The dermis produces dermal bones, as noted earlier (the scales of fishes are included here), as well as teeth, combs, and wattles in birds, and pigment cells that give various vertebrates their characteristic skin colorations. In effect, the skin as a whole, or *integument,* is not merely a single organ but an integrated group of numerous organs; it is an organ system.

In tubular organs such as the gut, epithelia and connective tissues are again arranged in alternating layers. For example, the wall of the mammalian small intestine consists of four main layers formed by at least six or seven different tissues (Fig. 5.32). The innermost layer is the *mucosa,* which contains a surface layer of simple columnar epithelium and a sublayer of fibroelastic connective tissue. Its chief function is to complete the digestion of foods and to absorb the digested nutrients from the cavity of the gut. Adjoining the mucosa is the *submucosa,* a substantial layer of fibroelastic connective tissue that contains numerous blood vessels, lymph vessels, and nerve fibers. The function of the submucosa is to transfer nutrients from the mucosa to the blood and lymph circulations for further distribution to other body parts. Surrounding the submucosa is the *muscularis,* the chief muscle tissue of the gut wall. This tissue is composed of smooth muscle, and it contains an inner circular and an outer longitudinal sublayer. More nerve tissue is present between these two muscle layers. The muscularis maintains the tubular shape of the gut, and it also produces a series of gut movements that play an important role in digestion. The outermost layer of the intestinal wall is the *serosa,* composed of an inner sublayer of fibroelastic tissue and an outer sublayer of squamous epithelium. The serosa as a whole is the limiting membrane of the gut, and it is continuous with the membranes that keep the entire intestine in place in the body.

All these tissues of the small intestine cooperate in performing the single group function of food processing. A series of other organs, each similarly composed of two or more tissues, carries out other functions of food processing. Included here are, for example, mouth, stomach, liver, pancreas, salivary glands, large intestine, and others. Together these organs form a specialized organ system, the *alimentary system.*

The most complex animals, man included, contain a total of 10 organ systems. Directly or indirectly all of them are necessary and just sufficient to maintain the life-sustaining functions of metabolism and self-perpetuation. Conversely, all functions also contribute importantly to the maintenance of all systems. For example, although the alimentary system serves primarily in nutrition, it also contributes indirectly toward all other functions of metabolism and self-perpetuation, including even evolution: without a properly nourished reproductive system there can be no reproduction, hence also no heredity and no evolution. It is easy to verify similarly that every body part must provide functional support for every other part, and that only through such interdependent activities can all of metabolism and self-perpetuation take place.

Some systems nevertheless function more directly in certain metabolic or self-perpetuative processes than in others. Thus, five systems serve mainly in various supporting, protecting, and coordinating activities; as a group they primarily coordinate the internal processes of an animal with particular conditions imposed by the external environment. These five are:

the *integumentary* system, which includes the skin and all skin-derived structures, and which serves as boundary and protective cover for the whole animal

the *skeletal* and *muscular* systems, which provide support, protection, and the means of motion, and which also maintain body shape and the position of body parts

the *nervous* and *endocrine* systems, which coordinate the activities of all body parts in a harmonious pattern and which adapt the behavior of the whole animal to particular environmental situations

Four other systems are internal "service" systems; their primary functions are supply, removal, and transport of all the materials associated with the proper operation of individual cells. These four are:

the *alimentary* system, which processes foods available in the environment into actually usable ones

the *breathing* system, which brings respiratory oxygen into the animal and respiratory waste gases out of it

the *excretory* system, which ensures the retention of usable substances and the elimination of unusable wastes

the *circulatory* system, which is the general internal transport apparatus; as the circulation passes by all cells of the body, it supplies the cells with nutrients and oxygen and carries off their wastes; and as the system passes through the alimentary, breathing, and excretory systems, it delivers the wastes to all three of these and picks up fresh nutrient supplies from the first and oxygen supplies from the second

The remaining, tenth system is the *reproductive* system, which accomplishes the propagation of the animal.

In various animal groups some or others of these systems are not present. As already noted, for example, worms lack skeletal systems. Similarly, many primitive animals lack circulatory or breathing or excretory systems. In such animals, as indeed also in plants, the functions performed elsewhere by systems are performed by individual cells, tissues, or organs. An organism consisting of but a single cell is alive just as fully and completely as one composed of 10 elaborate organ systems. The differing degrees of structural complexity or simplicity are reflections of the comparative *specializations* of organisms and their parts.

Because the parts of an organism are interconnected physically, an individual organism generally is the most readily identifiable unit of the living world, a distinct whole usually separated clearly from other such wholes. However, very real and powerful interconnections unite even organisms that are structurally separate. Such bonds are predominantly functional, and they create larger living units at higher organizational levels. This consideration leads to our next topic.

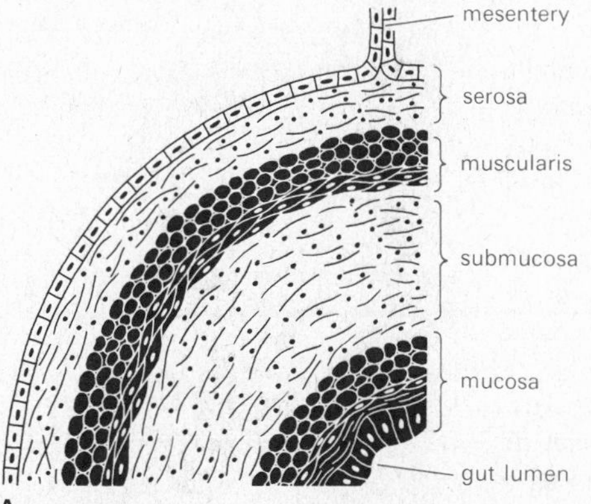

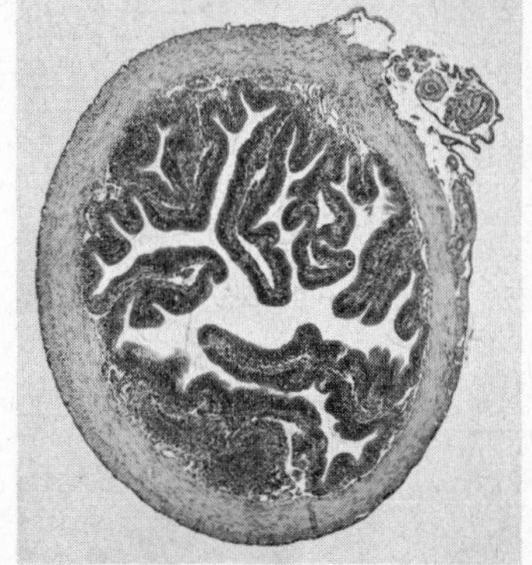

5.32 Mammalian intestine. *A, cross section through a portion of the intestinal wall. The mucosa, adjacent to the lumen (gut cavity), consists of columnar epithelium, connective tissue, and thin layers of muscle; the submucosa, of connective tissue, nerves, and blood vessels; the muscularis, of thick layers of inner circular and outer longitudinal muscles; and the serosa, of connective tissue and squamous epithelium, the latter continuous with a membrane (mesentery) that holds the whole intestine in place. B, section through the intestine (at the level of the duodenum), showing the highly folded condition of the mucosa.*

review questions

1 What are the structural subdivisions of cells? What are the main components of each of these subdivisions, where are they found, and what functions do they carry out?

2 List cytoplasmic organelles encountered in all cell types and organelles found only in certain cell types. What is cyclosis? How do plant and animal cells differ structurally?

3 What kinds of structures occur on the surfaces of various cell types? Which of these structures are primarily protective? What do they protect against? What are the functions of other surface structures? How do the surfaces of plant and animal cells differ?

4 Define "cell" (*a*) structurally and (*b*) functionally. Define tissue, organ, organ system, organism.

5 Review the characteristics of various cell types among plants. Which cell types function primarily in conduction? In mechanical support? What cell types are unique to roots? To stems?

6 Describe the development and structure of xylem vessels and of sieve tubes. What is a stele, and what tissues does it contain? What justifies the designation of a stem or a root as an organ?

7 What is a connective tissue? Describe the makeup of several types of connective tissue, and state their general functions.

8 What is an epithelium? List several variants of this type of tissue. Give specific examples of each. In what patterns are tissues arranged as organs? What is a stroma and what is its role?

9 Describe the development and structure of dermal and of replacement bone. What types of muscle tissue are there, and how are they distinguished? What makes a muscle or a bone an organ?

10 Name and state the function of the various organ systems of man and the familiar organs belonging to each of these systems. Show how each system contributes specifically to metabolism and self-perpetuation. How many organ systems does a flowering plant contain?

collateral readings

Allen, R. D.: Amoeboid Movement, *Sci. American,* Feb., 1962. A hypothesis as to how this form of cellular motion might be brought about.

Allison, A.: Lysosomes and Disease, *Sci. American,* Nov., 1967. On the role of these organelles in normal and abnormal cellular processes.

Brachet, J.: The Living Cell, *Sci. American,* Sept., 1961. A very good general account on our modern knowledge of cell structure.

deDuve, C.: The Lysosome, *Sci. American,* May, 1963. The structure and function of this cytoplasmic organelle are discussed in a nontechnical style.

Dippell, R. V.: Ultrastructure of Cells in Relation to Function, in "This Is Life," Holt, New York, 1962. An exceedingly good and well-illustrated article on the electron-microscopic fine structure of various cellular organelles. Highly recommended.

Galston, A. W.: "The Life of the Green Plant," 2d ed., Prentice-Hall, Englewood Cliffs, N.J., 1964. This paperback contains a section on the structure of plant cells.

Green, D. E.: The Mitochondrion, *Sci. American,* Jan., 1964. An instructive description of the structure and function of this organelle.

Hokin, L. E., and **M. R. Hokin**: The Chemistry of Cell Membranes, *Sci. American,* Oct., 1965. The article describes the role of the chemical components of membranes and the transport of materials through the membranes.

Jensen, W. A.: "The Plant Cell," Wadsworth, Belmont, Calif., 1964. In this paperback the structure of plant cells is discussed in relation to their functions. Recommended.

Montagna, W.: The Skin, *Sci. American,* Feb., 1965. A good review of the structure and function of this organ system in man.

Racker, E.: The Membrane of the Mitochondrion, *Sci. American,* Feb., 1968. On the structure and respiratory function of the mitochondrial cristae.

Robertson, J. D.: The Membrane of the Living

Cell, *Sci. American,* Apr., 1962. A good account of the exterior cell membrane and its continuations in the cellular interior.

Satir, P.: Cilia, *Sci. American,* Feb., 1961. A thorough description of the electron-microscopic fine structure of these surface organelles.

Solomon, A. K.: Pores in the Cell Membrane, *Sci. American,* Dec., 1960. The structure of cellular membranes is discussed in relation to the traffic of materials through them.

Swanson, C. P.: "The Cell," 2d ed., Prentice-Hall, Englewood Cliffs, N.J., 1964. This paperback is recommended particularly for further background reading on the structure and function of cells.

chapter 6 species and ecosystem

Because every organism is specialized, it invariably depends on the environment, and particularly on other organisms, for some essential product or process; survival requires group association. Such associations, and the interrelations of organisms and their environments in general, are the special concern of the biological subscience of *ecology.*

This chapter deals with two major ecological associations above the level of the organism, the *species* and the *ecosystem.* A species consists of like individuals that live together in *populations.* Groups of populations belonging to several different species form the next higher level, that of the *community.* And a community together with the physical space in which it exists represents an ecosystem. Two special forms of community life are *symbiosis,* discussed in this chapter, and *societies,* examined in another context in Chap. 23.

the species

structures and functions

As pointed out in Chap. 2, a species is a taxonomic unit that encompasses organisms capable of interbreeding with one another. Thus, all the corn plants on earth, all the bullfrogs, all the human beings, each group represents a species. Several types of bonds unify the members of a species as a *natural* grouping of organisms.

First, a species is a *reproductive* unit; by definition the member organisms are capable of interbreeding, but members of two different species normally are not cross-fertile. Actually not all species can be defined uniquely in this way. Certain closely related ones, and occasionally even more distantly related ones, are known to be interfertile in some cases, although in nature they are often isolated from one another by various geographic or biological breeding barriers. Among plants, for example (where this phenomenon is more common than among animals), cross-breeding of cabbages and radishes is known to produce new, fertile organisms. Among animals, similarly, horses and asses have long been used to produce *mules.*

In some cases, on the contrary, interbreeding is not possible between two members of the same species. For example, the protozoan taxonomic species *Paramecium aurelia* contains 16 distinct, hereditary mating groups called *syngens,* or "biological species." Mating within a syngen can occur, but mating between syngens cannot. Such infertility among the members of a species reaches its extreme form in asexual organisms, in which fertilization does not occur at all and in which interbreeding is therefore completely absent (Fig. 6.1). Common reproductive bonds evidently characterize what appears to be more than a single species in some cases and less than a whole species in others. But for the vast majority of organisms the definition of a species as an interbreeding unit does hold, and reproduction does represent an important unifying link for species members.

Because it is a reproductive unit, each species is also an *evolutionary* unit; since interbreeding has taken place in a species throughout its history, the member organisms are more closely related to one another than to members of any other species. As a result, the members of a species have in common a basic set of structural and functional traits. However, no two organisms are exactly alike, and the members of a species actually differ from one another quite considerably; superimposed on the common traits, *variations* of structure, function, or both, occur in each species. The range of such variations in one species can be directly continuous with the range in a closely related species. Therefore, two organisms of two different species sometimes might not differ too much more than two organisms of the same species (Fig. 6.2).

Variations can be *inheritable* or *noninheritable.* The first are controlled genetically and can be transmitted to offspring. Noninheritable variations

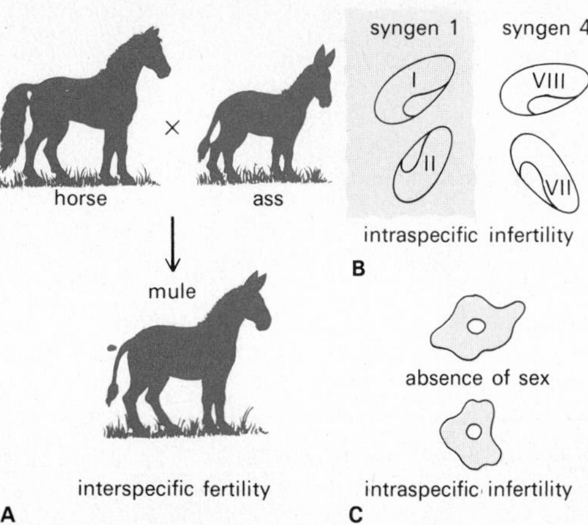

6.1 Species definition: exceptions. *A, horses and asses are distinct species, yet matings between them can occur. B, mating of types I and II of Paramecium aurelia forms a syngen within which mating can occur. Similarly, types VII and VIII form a mating syngen. But cross-mating between syngens cannot occur, even though all such syngens belong to the same species. C, organisms such as Amoeba proteus are sexless and thus by definition infertile; yet all individuals belong to the same taxonomic species nevertheless.*

A

B

6.2 ***Individual variation.*** *A and B are umbrella birds that belong to the same species, Cephalopterus ornatus. But they are members of different populations, and the structural differences between the birds are quite pronounced. Technically these birds are said to belong to different subspecies of the same species.*

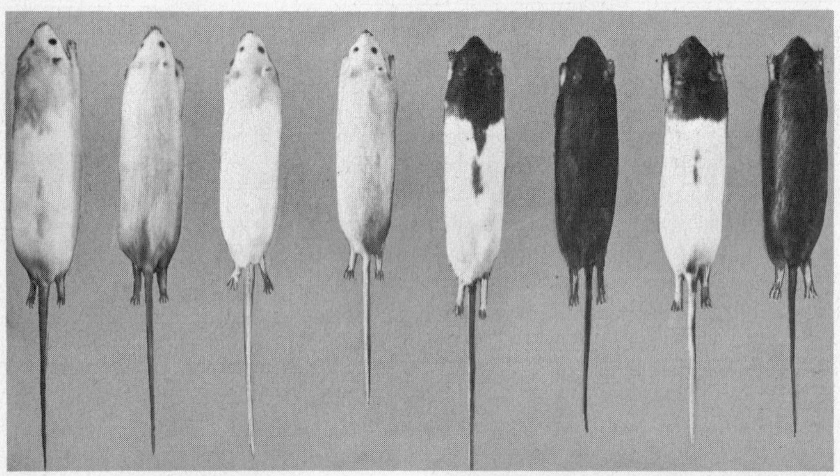

6.3 ***Inheritable variations.*** *These are litter-mate rats produced by the same two parents. Considerable variation in coat color is evident. Such differences are controlled genetically and are superimposed on common basic traits. For example, despite the color differences, all the litter mates are distinctly rats and share not only the traits common to the species but also those that are specifically characteristic of their breeding line.*

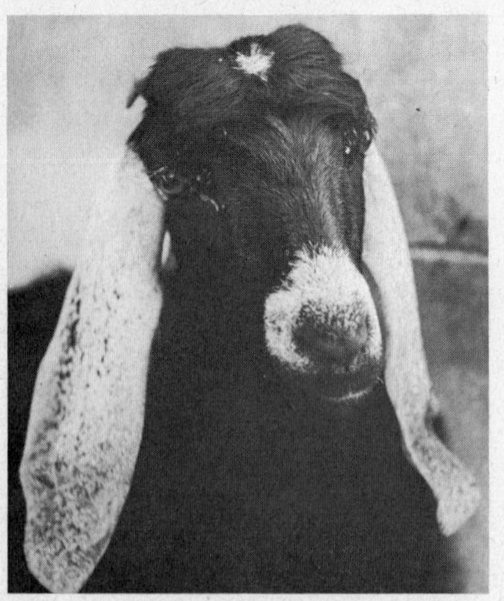

A

B

6.4 ***Variations and climate.*** *Evaporation surfaces tend to be larger in warm-climate animals than in corresponding cool-climate ones. For example, the Arabian desert goat shown here (A) has external ears very much larger than those of related types in temperate regions (B).*

A

B

C

6.5 ***Polymorphism.*** *A, the Portuguese man-of-war Physalia. This coelenterate is a floating colony of numerous individuals of various structural types—feeding, reproductive, protective, and float-forming polymorphs. See also Chap. 11. B, ants (as well as bees and other social insects) exhibit polymorphism in that queens (shown here) are winged whereas all other individuals of a species are wingless. See also Chap. 23. C, sexual dimorphism, a special form of polymorphism, is illustrated by the fur seals shown here. The male at right is far larger and more colorful than the female at left.*

are the result of developmental or environmental influences, and they therefore disappear with the death of the individuals that exhibit them. Thus only inheritable variations are significant in determining the lasting traits of a species. If a man is an athlete, his muscular system is likely to be developed much more than in the average person. This is a noninheritable variation; the degree of muscular development depends primarily on exercise, not on heredity. By contrast, blood type or skin color are examples of hereditary variations. They are part of the genetic inheritance from parents and earlier forebears and will in turn influence the traits of future generations (Fig. 6.3).

Some variations appear to be associated with climates and geography. In warm areas, for example, individuals of many animal species tend to have smaller body sizes, darker colors, and longer ears, tails, and other protrusions than fellow members of the same species living in cold climates (Fig. 6.4). Such structural variations are usually adaptive, or advantageous in the different environments. Thus, smaller bodies and longer ears give animals larger skin surface relative to the body volumes. Surface evaporation is then comparatively rapid, and the resulting cooling effect is of considerable benefit. The converse holds in a cool climate. However, in many instances it is difficult to recognize the adaptive value of a variation. Indeed some variations well might be nonadaptive, without inherent advantage to the possessors. The possible adaptive significance of variations in the human species is examined in Chap. 30, in the context of racial differences.

Because of the variations of their members, all species exhibit a greater or lesser degree of *polymorphism;* the members have "many shapes." For example, a species always includes variant individuals in the form of immature and mature organisms. Often also males and females differ in appearance, a form of polymorphism called *sexual dimorphism.* Moreover, a species usually encompasses subordinate groups such as subspecies and subsubspecies, and these too are distinguished by particular variations (Fig. 6.5). Polymorphism can actually be so pronounced that the close relation of two individuals of the same species becomes evident only through careful study. Among social insects, for example, a species can include queens, drones, soldiers, workers, and others, all quite dissimilar in structure. Such instances of polymorphism are expressions of structural *specialization.* And where organisms exhibit great polymorphic diversity, a high degree of functional interdependence usually follows as well. In a colony of social insects, for example, only the whole colony, with representatives of all types of polymorphic variants, is functionally self-sufficient.

By virtue of being evolutionary units all species are also *ecological* units. Each is defined by its *ecological niche,* its place in nature: it inhabits a certain geographic region, it uses up particular raw materials in that region, and it produces particular byproducts and endproducts. For example, the environment offers numerous opportunities for carnivorous modes of animal existence, all differing from one another in hundreds of fine details. Thus, a carnivorous species can subsist by being terrestrial, aquatic, or aerial; sessile or motile; a cold-, temperate-, or warm-climate type; a type that hunts in daytime or nighttime; a form that specializes in small prey or large prey. And each such coarse category contains innumerable finer categories of possible carnivorous ways of life. All such different opportunities represent ecological niches, and given species occupy them. Therefore, just as each species is identified by a particular set of structural, functional, and evolutionary characteristics, so it is also identified uniquely by its ecological niche. No two species have precisely identical niches, and a given niche cannot be occupied indefinitely by more than one species (Fig. 6.6).

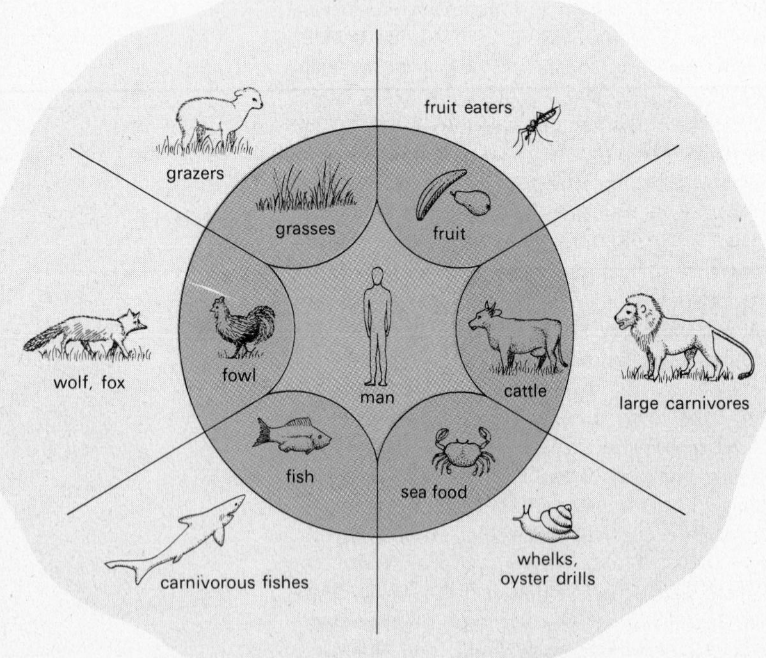

6.6 The ecological niche of man. *It is characterized in part by man's requirement of foods shown inside the circle around man. These food organisms also happen to form parts of the ecological niches of other animals, as indicated outside the circle, but such animals also use foods not used by man. Thus although these niches partly overlap man's, each is nevertheless distinct and characteristic of a particular species. Ecological niches are defined not only by food organisms but also by geographic territory, waste products, structures, and other attributes of species.*

Such niches are associated intimately with geography; in similar kinds of environments, even if widely separated, species with similar ways of life will be found. For example, widely different localities offering similar conditions of soil and climate will support prairies composed of grass species having similar requirements. Prairies in turn offer opportunities for grazing animals, and each prairie region of the world actually has its own animal species filling available grazing niches—antelopes in Africa, bisons in North America, kangaroos in Australia. In like manner, plant and animal species on high mountains occupy similar ecological niches. Several similar niches may also be available in a single territory. For example, the Central African plains support not only one but several species of grasses, and not only numerous types of antelopes but also zebras, giraffes, and other grazing species. The ways of life of such species overlap in many respects, but they are not precisely identical in all details; each species normally fills a unique niche.

By being adapted to the same niche, the members of a species are linked together through powerful bonds that have cooperative and competitive aspects. For example, *intraspecific cooperation* is often necessary to execute the way of life of an animal species; hunting may have to be done in cooperative packs, migrations may have to be undertaken in the comparative safety of herds or flocks, and groups may be required for the construction of complex nests or hives. But inasmuch as the members of a species must share the living space and food sources in their common niche, *intraspecific competition* occurs as well. With the exception of occasional animal competition by direct combat, most animal and all plant competition occurs only indirectly through the environment, and physical or visual contact is not or need not be involved.

development and geography

A species occupies its ecological niche for the duration of its evolutionary life—on the order of a million years on the average. In the course of this time a species typically has a characteristic history. It originates in a small home territory, spreads from there over as wide a geographic

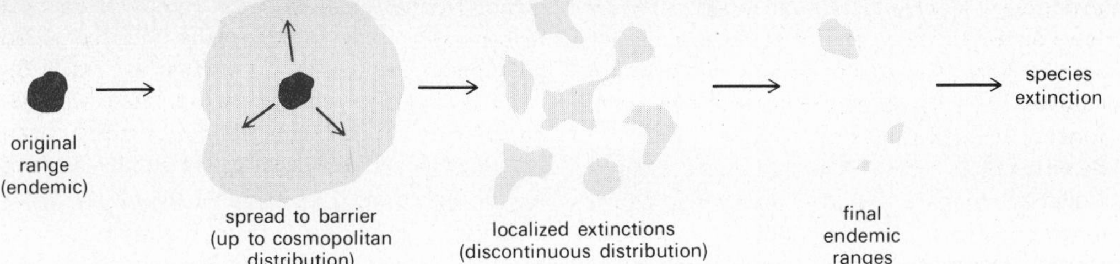

6.7 ***Species:*** *general life history.*

range as conditions permit, then dies out in various localities of that range and eventually becomes extinct (Fig. 6.7). Species extinction is not a theoretically inherent necessity, but no past species is known to have survived longer than a few million years at most. What factors govern this pattern of species development?

As will be shown in Chap. 28 in greater detail, species formation, or *speciation,* occurs when, in a parent species, a population becomes isolated reproductively from neighboring sister populations. Such isolation can develop in various ways, but the common consequence of all is that the isolated population can no longer interbreed with the rest of the parent species and in time comes to form a new descendant species. In this process of being ''born,'' a new species also acquires its own ecological niche. It can do so, for example, by occupying a niche that had been free in the territory. Or if a change in the physical environment has created a new niche, the new species may come to occupy it. Or the new species can create its own niche by evolving a way of life that overlaps partially with the ways of life of similar species in the area. Or the new species may simply encroach on a niche that another species in the area already occupies.

During its early development a new species is said to be *endemic;* its members form just one or a few populations, all localized in a single small territory. Further development depends on the geographic extent of the ecological niche of the species. In general, a species tends to expand in widening circles around the home territory until the boundaries of its niche are reached—until ecological barriers impose conditions to which the species is not adapted. Such barriers are biological as well as physical. For example, further spreading in a particular direction may be blocked by the presence of competing species or by the absence of appropriate food sources. Physical barriers include water, deserts, or mountains that can stop the expansion of a terrestrial species; land usually prevents an aquatic species from spreading. Among more subtle physical barriers on land are seasonal and daily temperatures, precipitation and soil characteristics, water supply, and numerous other variables. In the ocean, species may be confined to given temperature zones, salinity zones, pressure zones, oxygen zones, illumination zones, current zones, and many more. Similarly, dispersal opportunities in fresh water may depend on strengths of currents, amount of silting and pollution, oxygen content, bottom conformation, and a wide variety of other conditions.

Thus if the boundaries of its ecological niche are close to the original home territory, a species cannot expand significantly and it must then remain endemic. Such species usually become extinct comparatively rapidly, as soon as physical or biological changes in the geographically limited environment make survival impossible. But most species can find the living conditions they require in more extensive areas and they usually succeed in spreading quite widely. Many cover all or major parts of a continent or an ocean, and many others expand even farther and become *cosmopolitan,* distributed around the world.

But after a species becomes cosmopolitan or at least manages to become distributed widely, its populations in numerous localities cease to exist sooner or later. On a time scale of thousands of years, such local disappearances are brought about in three ways: a population dies out; or it emigrates; or it evolves into a new species. The underlying causes can be physical, biological, or both. For example, if a locality undergoes slow physical changes, a population living there must respond to such changes in one of the three ways mentioned. Biological change is promoted by other species living in the same locality. For example, if two populations of different species have a predator-prey relationship, then disappearance of the prey for any reason will be a biological change to which the predator in many cases must

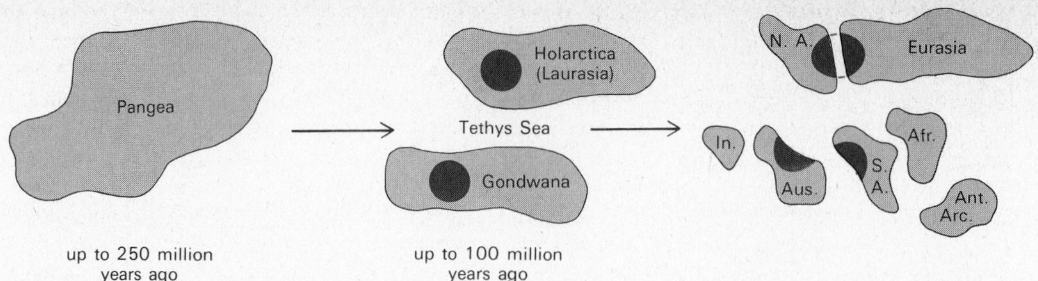

6.8 Continental drift. *Continental areas at right, identified by abbreviations, are assumed to have drifted to their present positions during the last 100 million years. Color areas in Holarctica and at right indicate how the distribution of eels might be accounted for. Color areas in Gondwana and at right similarly suggest an explanation for the distribution of marsupials.*

respond in one of the three ways above. Another frequent cause of biological change is the invasion of a region by populations of other species that occupy very similar ecological niches. The result then is *interspecific competition* for the same living space or the same food sources or both. Coexistence might be possible at first, but in time one population usually becomes dominant and those of other species then must emigrate, evolve into new species, or die out.

In widely distributed and cosmopolitan species, therefore, population gaps are likely to appear in various parts of the territorial range. In time such gaps tend to become progressively more numerous, and what may have been a fairly continuously distributed species earlier eventually becomes a discontinuous array of more or less isolated populations. Literally hundreds of species actually consist of widely separated populations in various parts of the globe. They represent remnants of previously contiguous populations. Ultimately a species again becomes endemic and consists of but few localized populations or even just a single one. Total extinction then is usually not far off.

If species are considered singly, the pattern of their life histories in most cases accounts adequately for their present global distribution. But the distribution of groups of species is not always explainable so readily. For example, we know that pouched marsupial mammals (a group that includes kangaroos) exist today not only in Australia but also in North America, where the opossum is the only surviving representative. It is also known from fossils that, about 100 million years ago, groups of marsupials lived in South Asia as well as South America, and that from these regions they later spread to Australia and North America, respectively. To explain this distribution we could postulate that the first ancestral marsupials evolved either in some Asian or in some American territory, and that they then expanded from this single original location to both South Asia and South America. Such a hypothesis cannot be ruled out entirely, but the available evidence makes it rather unlikely. Or we could postulate that marsupials originated independently in two different regions of the world. Such a hypothesis is again possible, but not particularly promising. A third and most likely explanation is based on the idea of *continental drift.*

First proposed in the early part of this century, this hypothesis postulates that all the land mass of the globe formed a single continent, *Pangaea,* until roughly 250 million years ago (Fig. 6.8). Pangaea then is assumed to have split into a northern *Laurasia* (or *Holarctica*) and a southern *Gondwana,* with a *Tethys* sea between them. Later each of these land masses is considered to have split further, Laurasis into what eventually was to become North America and Eurasia, Gondwana into land now represented by Antarctica, Africa, India, Australia, most Pacific islands, and South America. All these fragments are thought to have drifted to their present locations and to have become joined here and there, forming the familiar land masses of today.

The hypothesis was suggested originally by the contours of the present continents, some of which seem to fit together like pieces of a jigsaw puzzle (for example, South American and Africa). Moreover, continental drift could account for numerous other geographic and geologic features of the earth. Above all, the drift hypothesis was neatly consistent with the known biogeographic attributes of the world. For example, marsupials could have originated on Gondwana, and when this continent later foundered the animals would have become split into South Asian and South American groups. A drift hypothesis could also explain curious migration patterns such as those of eels. These animals travel to common North Atlantic spawning grounds from both American and European rivers (see Chap. 22). Thus if North America and Europe actually were part of a Holarctic land mass as postulated, ancestral eels could originally have spawned in a common central Holarctic river system. Their present descendants therefore still might travel from both west and east to the same ancestral spawning area, which now however happens to lie in the middle of an ocean (see Fig. 6.8).

Geologic evidence for continental drift has recently become quite strong and convincing, and many former puzzles of biogeography soon may be on the way of being solved.

population

Every species consists of one or more populations, or *species-populations.* Examples of such relatively stable, geographically localized groups are the dandelions in a field, the minnows in a pond, the earthworms in a plot of ground, or the people in a village. Individual organisms multiply and die, emigrate or immigrate, but collectively a population persists. It may split into subpopulations or fuse with adjacent sister populations, yet the basic characteristics of the group as a whole do not thereby change. All members of a population share the same food sources and the same local territory, and the members also interbreed more or less preferentially with one another. In addition, interbreeding with members of sister populations occurs fairly frequently. A population thus is a reproductively cohesive unit, integrated more loosely with other such units.

The significant structural characteristics of populations are their *dispersion* and *growth* patterns. Dispersion is a measure of the population density. The growth pattern is influenced by the extent and the resources of the territory, by the balance between reproduction and mortality, by rates of emigration and immigration, and by the effects of population density on growth. Such effects can be of three kinds. In some species population growth occurs the more rapidly the lower the population density. In other species growth rates tend to increase geometrically until the limits of the available living space and food supply are reached. And in still other species population growth is most intense at intermediate densities; both undercrowding and overcrowding here depress growth.

The usual net result of all variables affecting population growth is that, over appreciable periods of time, *natural populations tend to remain constant in size.* The conditions that promote and those that limit growth tend to balance each other, and the numbers of individuals in a population then normally do not change significantly on a long-term basis (see also below). Many human populations are notably exceptions to this rule, a subject discussed in the next chapter.

A significant functional attribute of populations is that they *interact* with all components of their surroundings. The members of a population interact with one another, with sister populations, with populations of other species in the same territory, with the territory itself, and with the physical environment in general. Indirect interactions are extensive and continuous; each member of a population affects every other one through its impact on the environment. Thus even two rooted plants some distance apart affect each other by, for example, drawing on the same supply of raw materials in the soil. Direct interactions may not occur or, as among solitary animals, may be limited to reproductive contact. By contrast, the members of certain animal populations interact far more extensively, directly as well as indirectly. The animals in such cases live together as more or less closely knit *social* populations, a topic examined in Chap. 23 in the context of behavior.

Direct and indirect interactions among the several populations that usually inhabit a particular territory produce *community* life, and the interactions of all these living components of an area with the physical environment maintain an *ecosystem.* It is to these higher levels of organization we now turn.

the ecosystem

A community is a localized association of several populations of *different* species. Almost always, a community contains representatives of plants, animals, and microorganisms, all being required for group survival. Moreover, a community also contains populations of parasites and other organisms that live together in so-called *symbiotic* associations.

Communities together with the physical environments in which they live represent ecosystems. All ecosystems on earth collectively form the *biosphere,* which thus encompasses the entire inhabited part of the globe, including all nonliving and living components. Ecosystems represent the largest subunits of the biosphere; examples are a pond, a forest, a meadow, a section of ocean shore, a portion of the open sea, a coral reef, or a village with its soil, grasses, trees, people, bacteria, cats, dogs, and other living and nonliving contents.

structure and growth

The living portion of an ecosystem exhibits a characteristic species structure: a few species are represented by large populations and many species are represented by small populations. For example, the animals in a jungle community often comprise a few large populations of just two or three kinds of monkeys but many small populations of numerous kinds of birds, bats, snakes, and other animals. Plants are likely to be represented by several dozen species of trees, but populations of just two or three species can make up to 70 to 80 percent of the total number of trees. In general also, species diversity in an ecosystem is inversely proportional to the sizes of organisms. Thus a forest is likely to contain more species of insects than of birds and more species of birds than of large mammals. The reasons for such correlations will soon become apparent.

Like other living units communities grow, develop, pass through mature phases, reproduce, and ultimately die. The time scale may be in hundreds and thousands of years. Such life cycles result from an interplay between the living and the nonliving components of an ecosystem. Being specialized to occupy particular ecological niches, different species must live in different types of environment. The physical characteristics of a given region therefore determine what types of organism can settle there originally. By its very presence, however, a particular set of organisms gradually alters local conditions. Raw materials are withdrawn from the environment in large quantities, and metabolic wastes are returned. The remains of dead organisms also return to the environment, but not necessarily in the same place or the same form in which they were obtained. In time, therefore, communities bring about profound redistributions and alterations of vast quantities of the earth's substance.

Later generations of the original community then may find the changed local environment no longer suitable, and the populations must resettle elsewhere or readapt or die out. The result, as noted earlier, is gradual development of population gaps in species. A new community of different plant and animal populations may therefore come to occupy the original territory, and as this community now alters the area according to its own specializations, type replacement, or *ecological succession,* will eventually follow once more.

Continued ecological succession ultimately produces a *climax community:* a set of populations that changes the local environment but repeatedly re-creates the original conditions more or less exactly. Good examples are the North American prairie and forest belts, and the communities in large lakes and in the ocean. Climax communities represent ecological steady states that last as long as local physical conditions are not altered drastically by climatic or geologic upheavals. If that happens, communal death usually follows. New communities might then develop by immigration, or the remnants of the old community might undergo major evolutionary readjustment.

In an ecological succession leading to a climax community, each developmental stage is a *sere* (Fig. 6.9). A sequence of seres is usually characterized by repeated changes in the types of population present and by an increase in species diversity and the total quantity of living matter. The particular seres that can be expected in a given region are often fully predictable. For example, if the original physical environment is sand or equivalent virgin territory, then the succession of seres generally includes a sequence in which the following types of organism dominate the community: soil-forming organisms (bacteria, lichens, mosses) → annual grasses and herbs → perennial grasses and herbs → shrubs → trees. Characteristic animal populations are associated with each seral plant population. Development from sand to forest climax can require on the order of 1,000 years. If soil is already present at

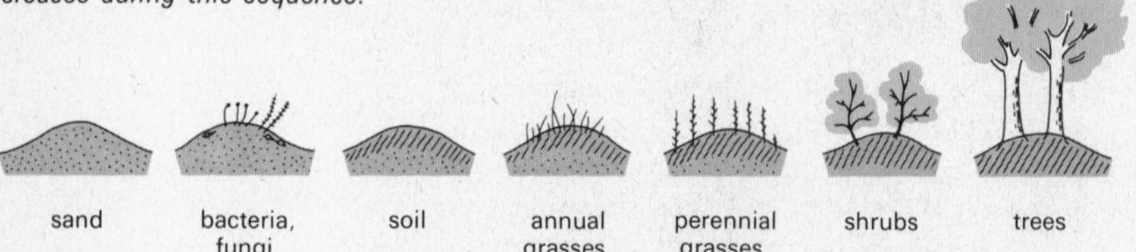

6.9 Ecological succession. *Left to right, a sequence of seres from virgin land (sand) to climax (trees). The total living mass increases during this sequence.*

the start, then a grass climax can be attained in about 50 to 100 years, a forest climax in about 200 years or more.

Clearly, *turnover* occurs on the level of the ecosystem, just as it does on all other levels of living organization. After a climax has been attained, a community exhibits a numerical steady state in all populations present: the numbers of individuals remain relatively constant on a long-term basis. In a large, permanent pond, for example, the numbers of algae, frogs, minnows, and other organisms stay more or less the same from decade to decade. Annual fluctuations or cycles of several years are common, but over longer periods of time constancy of number is characteristic in most natural communities.

Three key factors create and control these striking numerical balances: *nutrients, reproduction,* and *protection.* They are the main links that make the populations of a community interdependent.

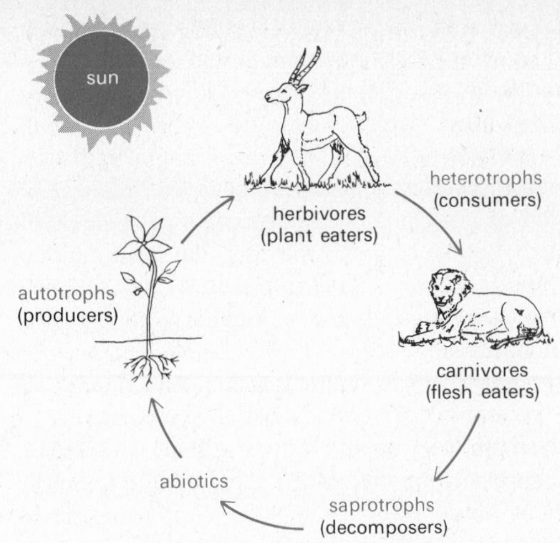

6.10 Nutritional structure of an ecosystem. *Abiotics represent the physical, nonbiological components of the system. Arrows indicate flow of energy and materials.*

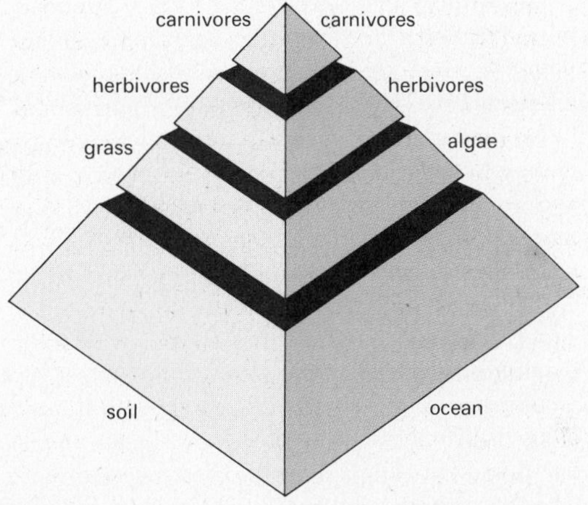

6.11 Food pyramids. *Soil and ocean support plant life; plant-eating animals (herbivores) subsist on the plants; and flesh-eating animals (carnivores) subsist on the herbivores.*

links and balances

A stable ecosystem generally has a four-part nutritional structure (Fig. 6.10). The *abiotics* are the nonliving physical components of the environment on which the living community, or *biomass,* ultimately depends. The *producers* are the green photosynthetic food-creating autotrophs that live entirely on the abiotic portion of the ecosystem. The *consumers* are the heterotrophs, largely animals. Plant-eating consumers feed on the producers, and flesh-eating types consume one another as well as the plant-eaters. Lastly, the *decomposers* (or saprotrophs) are bacteria and fungi that live on the excretion products and the dead bodies of all producers and consumers. Decomposers bring about decay and a return of raw materials to the abiotic part of the ecosystem. The physical substance of an ecosystem thus *circulates,* from the abiotic part through the biomass back to the abiotic part. This circulation is maintained by the continuous influx of energy from the sun.

However, energy dissipates in the course of such cycles, and as raw materials pass from the environment to plants and from plants to animals, these transfers are not 100 percent efficient. More than a pound of inorganic materials is needed to make a pound of plant matter, and more than a pound of plant food is needed to make a pound of animal matter. Similarly, more than 300 lb of antelope meat or even lion meat is required to produce a 300-lb lion. This inescapable circumstance results in *food pyramids* in the ecosystem (Fig. 6.11). So many tons of soil can support only so many *fewer* tons of grass. Grass in turn supports plant-eating animals that together weigh less than the grass. And only a relatively small weight of flesh-eaters can find sustenance in such a community. Several acres of ground therefore might just suffice to support a 150-lb man. Such a pyramid of productivity and weights also describes a pyramid of numbers and sizes. Prey is generally smaller than predator, and the balanced community might contain millions of individual grass plants but only one man.

Food pyramids are among the most potent

contributors to communal steady states; significant variations of numbers at any level of a pyramid soon bring about automatic adjustments at every other level. For example, extensive growth of land plants soon results in nutritional depletion of soil. This depletion eventually leads to a starvation of the plants and decimation of their numbers. But the bodies of the dead plants now enrich the soil again, and the fewer plants that still live make less total demand on the raw materials once more present in soil. These living plants therefore can become well nourished; they can reproduce relatively rapidly, and this circumstance increases their numbers again. The cycle then is repeated (Fig. 6.12). Similar cycles occur among animals. As a result, although the numbers of all kinds of organisms can undergo short-term fluctuations, the total quantities generally remain relatively constant over the long term.

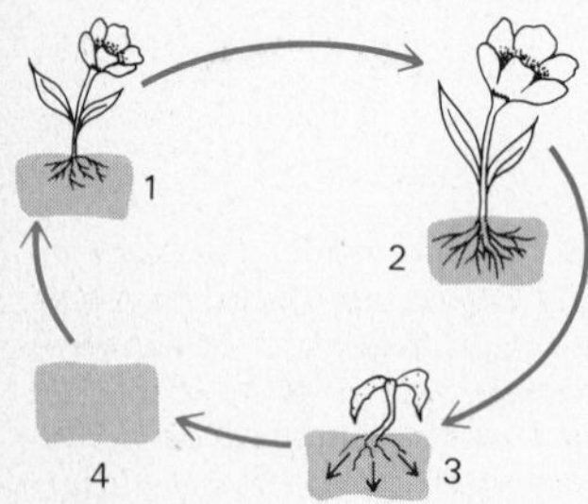

6.12 Population balance. *A large plant population reduces the soil nutrients available (1, 2). This eventually leads to starvation of plants and reduction of their numbers (3). But the dead plants now enrich the soil (4), and an increase in the number of living plants therefore can occur again. Through continued repetition of such a cycle the size of the plant population is maintained relatively constant over the long term. Quite similar cycles occur in animal populations.*

The territory of an ecosystem usually supports more than one food pyramid. Each represents a different *food chain* that usually ends with a different flesh-eater. For example, a lion would find it extremely expensive in terms of locomotor energy to live on insects, worms, or even lizards and mice. Bigger prey like antelope or zebra is more appropriate. On the other hand, insects and worms are suitable food for small birds, and small birds, lizards, and mice provide adequate diet for larger predatory birds. In this example two food pyramids are based on the same plot of land. The pattern is generally much more complex. Different types of plants in one territory can sustain many different plant-eating animals. These can form the basis of different, intricately interlocking animal food chains. As in the case of elephants, a plant-eater may itself represent the peak of a food pyramid.

In a balanced ecosystem the total biomass yields just enough dead matter and other raw materials to replenish the soil or the ocean. This circumstance permits the continued existence of the various food pyramids above ground or in water. In such delicate nutritional interdependencies, minor fluctuations are rebalanced fairly rapidly. But serious interference, by disease, by man, or by physical factors, is likely to topple the whole pyramid. If that happens the entire community often ceases to exist. Man's impact has been particularly detrimental in this respect, a subject examined further in Chap. 7.

A second link between the populations of a community is reproductive interdependence. Familiar examples are the pollinating activities of insects and the seed-dispersing activities of a large variety of animals, man included. It is fairly obvious how such activities contribute to population balance: any reduction of the animal populations restricts the reproduction of the plant populations, and vice versa. Many other examples illustrate the same type of population control. Thus, birds like cuckoos lay eggs in nests of other birds. Insects such as gall wasps embed their eggs deep in the tissues of particular plants, where the hatching larvae find food and protection. And many insects deposit eggs on or under the skin of various animals (Color Fig. 2).

Reproduction and nutrition play important roles in the growth and geographic expansion of a community. In new territory, a pioneer community will first form a small food pyramid that might still be too "low" to support any large animals. Abundance of food and absence of competition will promote high reproduction rates and a rapid increase of numbers at all levels of the pyramid. The base of the pyramid will therefore widen and a larger area of the territory will be occupied. Sizable plant-eaters and even a few larger flesh-eaters might gradually be assimilated into the community. As a result the rate of predation will increase, which in turn will slowly decrease the net reproductive gain. A turning point will be reached eventually. Prior to it the community grows at an increasing rate; after it the community still grows, but at a decreasing rate. Net expansion finally comes to a standstill, and from then on the pyramid retains relatively stable proportions (Fig. 6.13)

6.13 Population growth. *As the number of individuals increases, more territory will be occupied and the food pyramid will become wider and higher (left part of diagram). Rates of population increase are indicated in the curve at right; rates increase to a turning point (arrow), then decrease.*

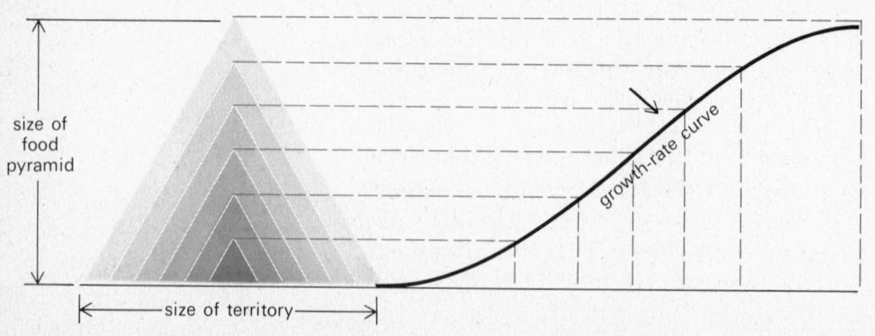

Such a growth pattern depends on the absence of external restrictions on the expansion of a community. If geographic or biological barriers do limit expansion, then communal growth is stopped prematurely. The food pyramid in such a limited community might never become high enough to support large animals. One searches

A

B

C

6.14 Camouflage. *A, dead leaf butterfly (top of photo), resembling foliage in form and color. B, leaf insect, resembling a dried and fallen leaf. C, South African mantis, resembling stem and branches of a bush. See also Color Fig. 4.*

in vain for stag in a tiny forest, for large fish in a small pond. But the one is likely to abound in worms, mice, and small birds, the other in algae, protozoa, and frogs.

In a community incapable of further expansion, steady reproduction can produce a centrifugal *population pressure.* If emigration is not possible or if it is not sufficiently effective, numbers will be decimated by starvation or even sooner by epidemic diseases. The latter spread rapidly through an overpopulated, undernourished, spatially restricted community. Even if disease affects only one of the component populations, the whole communal web is likely to be disrupted.

The third main link in a community is protective interdependence. Plants usually protect animals by providing shelter against enemies and adverse weather. If the opportunities for protection are reduced, both the animal and plant populations can suffer. For example, if an overpopulation of insects makes plant shelter inadequate, the insects will become easier prey for birds and bats. But this circumstance can also decimate the plant populations, for their major pollinating agents may no longer be sufficiently effective.

In many cases, organisms are protected from others by *camouflage* involving body color or body shape or both. Probably the most remarkable instance of color camouflage is *mimicry,* widespread particularly among butterflies and moths. In certain of these animals the pigmentation patterns are virtually indistinguishable from those of other, unrelated species. Such mimicked species are usually strong or fast and have few natural enemies. An animal resembling even superficially another more powerful one will then be protected too, by scaring off potential predators. Insects also display a variety of structural camouflages. For example, the individuals of certain species are shaped like leaves, branches, or thorns, an adaptive device serving not only defensively but also as a disguise that misleads potential victims (Fig. 6.14 and Color Fig. 4).

Many other protective devices are common. Various birds and some mammals mimic the song and voice of other species, either defensively or as an aggressive lure. The hermit crab protects its soft abdomen in an empty snail shell of appropriate size. Schools of small pilot fish scout ahead of large sharks and lead their protectors to likely prey. Significant protection is also afforded by man, through domestication, game laws, parks, and sanctuaries.

These various examples illustrate how the member populations of a community are specialized nutritionally, reproductively, and protectively. Flesh-eating populations cannot sustain themselves on plant food and not even on every kind of animal food. Plant-eating populations are incapable of hunting for animals. The photosynthesizing populations depend on soil or ocean, and the decomposers cannot do without dead organisms. These are profound specializations in structure and function, and they imply a lack of self-sufficiency of individual populations. Communal associations of populations evidently are a necessity. Indeed they are but extensions, on a higher biological level, of the associations of cells in the form of tissues, organs, and organ systems.

In a large number of cases such specializations of the populations in a community are even more profound; for a community contains not only free-living populations but also organisms of different species that live together in more or less permanent physical contact. These associations are instances of *symbiosis,* an expression of the most intimate form of communal life.

symbiosis

There is no major group of organisms that does not include symbiotic species, and there is probably no individual organism that does not play *host* to at least one *symbiont.*

6.15 ***Root nodules.*** *These growths are mutualistic combinations of nitrogen-fixing bacteria and roots of legumes, including the pea plants shown here.*

Symbiosis occurs in two basic patterns. In *facultative* associations, two different organisms "have the faculty" of entering a more or less intimate symbiotic relationship. But they need not necessarily do so, being able to survive as free-living forms. In *obligatory* associations, one organism *must* unite symbiotically with another, usually a specific one, if it is to survive. The ancestors of obligatory symbionts have invariably been free-living organisms that in the course of history have lost the power of living on their own. Before becoming obligatory symbionts, they formed facultative associations with organisms on which they came to depend more and more.

A symbiont affects its host in different ways. In *mutualism,* both associated partners derive some benefit from living together. *Commensalism* benefits one of the partners and the other is neither helped nor harmed by the association. *Parasitism* is of advantage to the parasite but is detrimental to the host to greater or lesser extent.

mutualism and commensalism

An example of mutualism is the tickbird-rhinoceros relationship. Tickbirds feed on skin parasites of rhinoceroses; the latter are relieved of irritation and are warned of danger when the sharp-eyed birds fly off temporarily to the security of the nearest trees. This is an example of facultative mutualism; both tickbirds and rhinoceroses can get along without each other if necessary.

A more intimate form of mutualism is illustrated by *lichens,* variously colored incrustations commonly found on rock surfaces and on tree bark (Color Fig. 3). These crusts are associations of threadlike fungi and photosynthesizing algae (see Chap. 9). The algae produce food for themselves and for the fungus. The fungus in turn contributes water, nitrogen-containing waste compounds, and respiratory carbon dioxide, substances that permit continued algal photosynthesis and food production. Lichens consequently can survive in relatively dry terrestrial environments. Separately the fungi and the algae are merely two types of organisms not particularly different from many others like them. But together they become a combination of considerable evolutionary and ecological importance: by contributing to the crumbling of rock and the formation of soil, they also pave the way for a colonization of land by mosses and other plants.

The most intimate forms of mutualism involve

A

B

6.16 **Commensalism.** *A, ferns grow on tree trunk as epiphytes. B, shark with three suckerfish (remoras) attached to it.*

symbionts that live directly inside their hosts. For example, the roots of legumes like soybeans, clover, and peas form important multualistic associations with so-called *nitrogen-fixing bacteria.* Roots infected by such bacteria develop *root nodules.* In them, the host plant provides nutrients for the bacteria, and the bacteria in turn "fix" atmospheric nitrogen; they make this essential element chemically usable for both themselves and the host (Fig. 6.15 and see Chap. 7).

In the gut of termites live flagellate protozoa capable of digesting the cellulose of wood. Termites chew and swallow wood, the intestinal flagellates then digest it, and both kinds of organisms share the resulting carbohydrates. Thus, to the detriment of man, termites can exploit unlimited food opportunities open to very few other animals. And the protozoa receive protection and are assured of a steady food supply.

Virtually every animal with an alimentary canal houses billions of mutualistic bacteria in the lower gut. The bacteria draw freely on substances not digested by the host, and the result of this bacterial activity is the decay of materials that the host later eliminates. The host generally benefits from this auxiliary bacterial digestion and in many instances is also dependent on certain of the bacterial byproducts. For example, man and other mammals obtain many vitamins in the form of "waste" materials released by the bacteria of the gut.

Many mutualistic associations have probably evolved from parasitic ones. For example, mutualistic intestinal bacteria might be descendants of originally parasitic ancestors. It is advantageous to a parasite not to jeopardize its own survival, and in the course of evolution this circumstance well might have tended to change a parasitic relation into one that might be beneficial or at least harmless for the host. Commensalism is illustrated among plants by numerous *epiphytes.* An epiphyte is a plant that grows on another plant host, but the latter is neither harmed nor helped. For example, trees frequently support epiphytic ferns (Fig. 6.16). Among animals, commensalism is exemplified by the so-called *shark sucker,* or *remora.* In this fish a dorsal fin is modified as a holdfast device. By means of it the fish attaches to the underside of sharks and thereby secures scraps of food, wide geographic dispersal, and protection. The shark neither benefits nor suffers significantly. In another example, barnacles can attach to the skin of whales and can thereby secure geographic distribution and wider feeding opportunities. In this instance a trend toward parasitism is in evidence; in some cases the barnacles send rootlike outgrowths into the whale that eat away bits of host tissue.

parasitism

parasitic ways of life

Symbiosis in general and parasitism in particular tend to be most prevalent among organisms that must obtain nutrients from other organisms, and among which competition for food is therefore most intense—viruses, bacteria, fungi, and animals. Many animal groups are wholly parasitic, and practically all others include at least some parasitic subgroups. Parasites also form the majority of the bacteria and fungi, and viruses are exclusively parasitic.

A virus is neither an organism nor a cell; it consists of only a core of nucleic acids and an external mantle of protein (Fig. 6.17). In the free state viruses are quite inert, and they become activated if, and only if, they infect a living host cell. In this process the nucleic acid core becomes squeezed into the cell but the protein mantle remains outside. Inside the host the nucleic acids parasitize the resources of the cell for the formation of more viruses; the nucleic acids reproduce and direct the metabolism of the host cell to construct new protein mantles around them. The offspring viruses then escape, often disintegrating the host cell in the process.

As a way of life parasitism is almost as ancient as life itself. So advantageous and economical is the parasitic mode of existence that many parasites are infested with smaller parasites of their own. For example, a mammal might harbor parasitic worms; these can be invaded by parasitic bacteria; and the bacteria are often infected by *bacteriophages,* or viruses that parasitize bacteria (see Fig. 6.17). The presence of one parasite inside another is called *hyperparasitism.* This common conditon represents a natural consequence of the very principle of parasitism. Hyperparasitic relationships form inverted food pyramids in the pyramids of the larger community.

In most cases a host cannot readily prevent a parasite from becoming attached to its body surface. Numerous *ectoparasites* exploit this possibility. Equipped with suckers, clamps, or adhesive surfaces, they hold on to the skin of a host and feed on the internal body fluids with the aid of cutting, biting, or sucking mouth parts. Examples are leeches, lice, ticks, mites, lampreys, and many fungi. Inside the body of a host live *endoparasites,* which must breach more formidable defenses. Cellular enzymes of a host, digestive juices and strong acids in the alimentary tract, antibodies in the blood, and cells that engulf foreign bodies in amoeboid fashion are among the defensive agents guarding against the invader. Overcoming such defenses means *specialization:* formation of resistant outer cuticles or cyst walls, development of hooks or clamps that hold on to the gut wall, or secretion of enzymes that erode a path through host tissues (Fig. 6.18).

Specialization also involves selection of *specific* hosts. Parasites can survive only in hosts that, for example, contain particular types of nutrients and that offer appropriate invasion routes by which such nutrients can actually be reached. Once an infection is achieved, it is to the obvious advantage of a parasite to keep its host alive; for when a parasite kills a host, the killer generally is killed as well. Indeed, the virulence of a parasite often decreases with time. When a parasite-host relationship is first established, the invader is likely to be disease-causing, or *pathogenic.* Two parallel evolutionary trends then tend to reduce

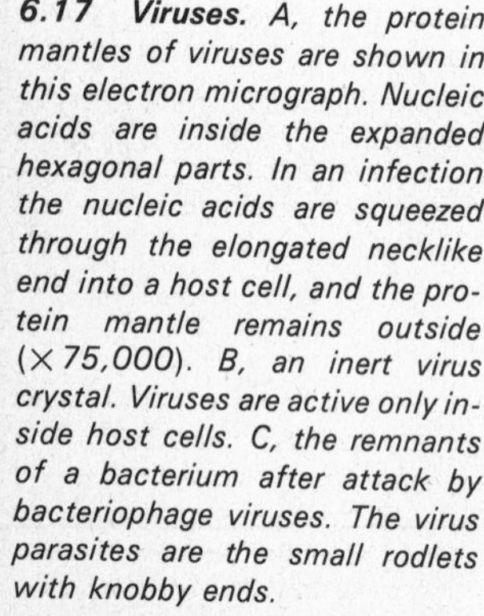

6.17 Viruses. *A, the protein mantles of viruses are shown in this electron micrograph. Nucleic acids are inside the expanded hexagonal parts. In an infection the nucleic acids are squeezed through the elongated necklike end into a host cell, and the protein mantle remains outside (×75,000). B, an inert virus crystal. Viruses are active only inside host cells. C, the remnants of a bacterium after attack by bacteriophage viruses. The virus parasites are the small rodlets with knobby ends.*

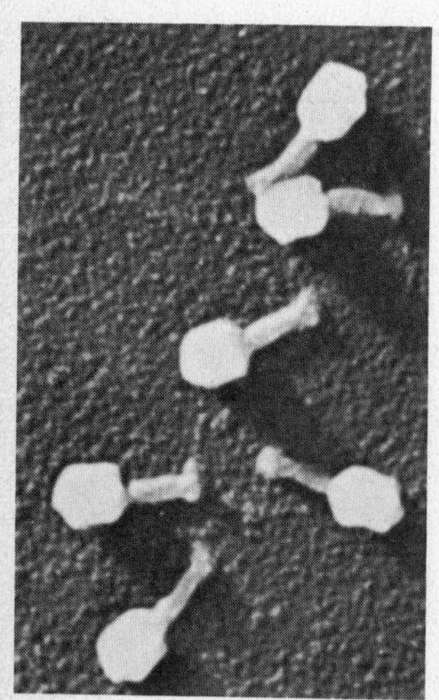

A

B

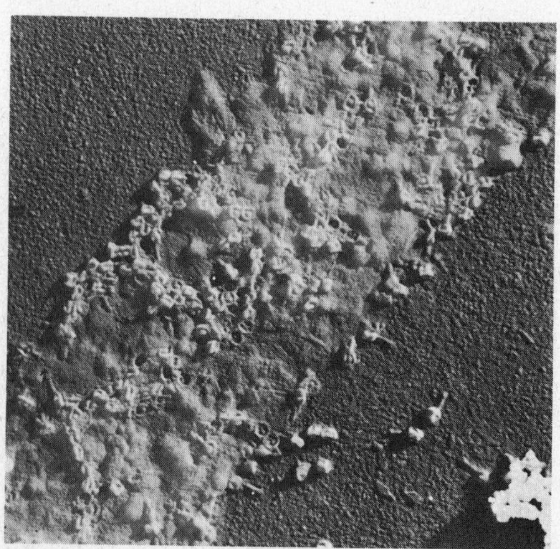

C

A

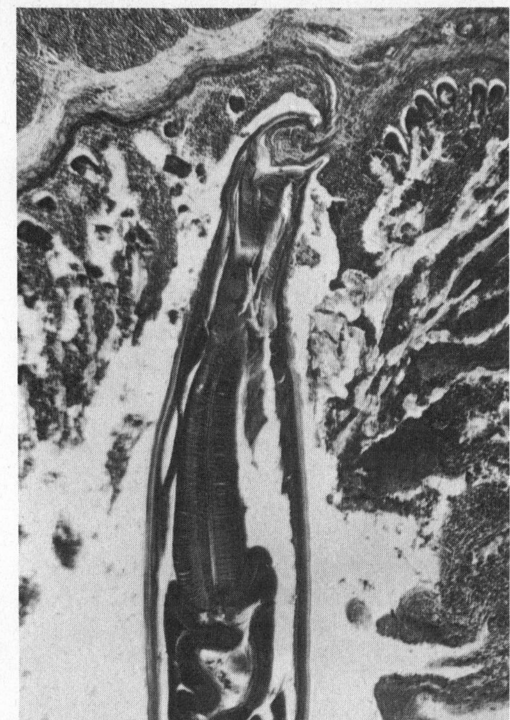

B

6.18 ***Parasite attachment.*** *A, an ectoparasitic wood tick attached to the fur of a deer. B, section through the anterior part of an endoparasitic hookworm (a nematode) clamped to the mucosal lining in the gut of a host.*

this pathogenicity. One is natural discrimination against infected hosts—the least resistant will have less chance of surviving. At the same time, the less harmful a parasite the better will be its own chance of surviving. Many parasites are only mildly pathogenic, or not at all, often indicating long association with a particular host. In time the parasitic relation can actually become commensalistic or mutualistic.

Once established in a host, a parasite is more or less embedded in nutrients and does not require much locomotor equipment, many sense organs, or fast nervous reflexes. Indeed, structural and functional *simplification* is a nearly universal characteristic of parasites. Here is the ultimate expression of the principle that loss of self-sufficiency tends to be proportional to the degree of interdependence of organisms.

Structural simplification is exhibited, for example, by mistletoes. The dwarf mistletoe, common on western cone-bearing trees, has only the slightest vestiges of leaves. Moreover, absorption of water and inorganic materials from the host occurs not through true roots but through rows of parenchyma cells that grow like fungus filaments through the host tissue (Fig. 6.19). Among animal parasites, structural simplification is pronounced in tapeworms, for example. They have only a reduced nervous system, a greatly reduced muscular system, and not even a vestige of a digestive system (see Fig. 11.24). Almost like blotting paper, the worms soak up through their body walls the food juices in the host gut.

6.19 ***Parasitic plants.*** *Mistletoe on branch of pine tree.*

Simplification also affects metabolic activities. For example, the synthetic capacities of a parasite

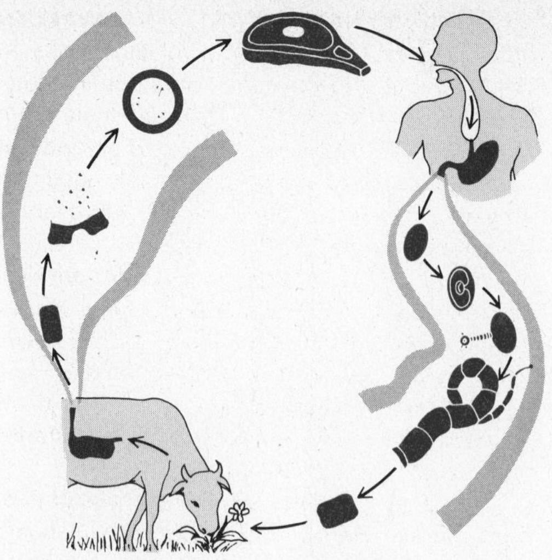

6.20 Beef tapeworm life cycle. *Ripe sections of the worm pass with the feces from the human gut. Eggs are released from these sections in the gut of cattle. Walled, hook-bearing tapeworm embryos then encapsulate in beef muscle, and the embryos become adults in the intestine of man. The head (scolex) of the worm is invaginated at first, but it soons everts, and with the hooks and newly developed suckers it attaches to intestinal tissues. See Fig. 11.24 for illustration of adult worm.*

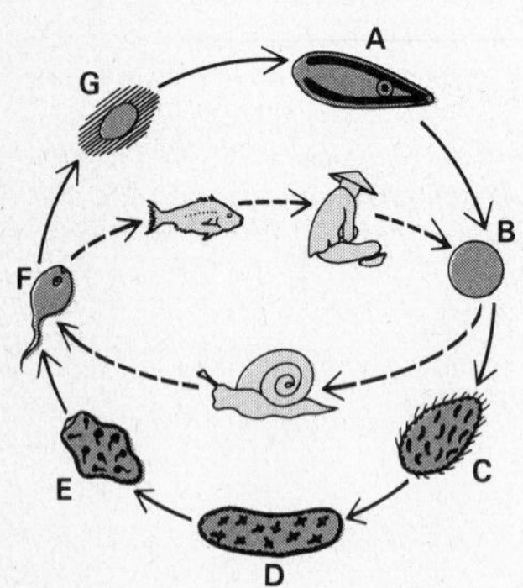

6.21 Chinese liver fluke life cycle. *The structure of the adult is shown in greater detail in Fig. 11.23. A, adult in liver of man. B, egg released with feces and eaten by snail. C, miracidium larva in snail. D, sporocyst. E, one of many redias formed from a sporocyst. F, cercaria. G, cercarias escape from snail and encapsulate in fish muscle. Man then eats undercooked fish, and an adult fluke develops in the host alimentary system.*

are almost invariably restricted. Thus in the presence of nitrogen sources and simple carbohydrates, a *free-living* soil bacterium or fungus can synthesize all the complex compounds that make up its living substance. But a parasitic bacterium or fungus promptly dies when given nitrogenous and simple organic substances alone. It has reduced synthesizing capacities and depends on its host for most of the components of its living substance.

In this respect viruses are the most simplified; they are active only inside living host cells, and outside of such hosts they become inert chemicals. Other parasites are free-living at least at some stage of their life cycle, but viruses are never free-living. Their parasitism is total, complete, obligatory. (However, since viruses are chemical complexes, not cellular organisms, they should not actually be put into the same category as other parasites.)

Simplification is probably an adaptive advantage, for the reduced condition tends to be more economical than the fully developed condition of the free-living ancestor. A tapeworm, for example, need not divert energy and materials toward maintenance of elaborate nervous, muscular, or digestive systems, which are unnecessary anyway in this parasitic way of life.

parasitic reproduction

Parasites typically are exceedingly prolific. The enormous reproductive potential represents a solution of a major problem confronting the parasite, particularly the endoparasite: how to get from one host to another of the same species.

Parasites succeed by *active transfer* and *passive transfer,* both of which involve reproduction. In active transfer, one stage of the life cycle is free-living and motile, and this stage transfers from one host to another through its own powers of locomotion. For example, the adult may be parasitic but the embryo or larva is free-living and capable of locomotion. Or the immature phase may be the parasite, the adult then being free-living and motile.

Passive transfer is encountered where a parasite is not motile at any life-cycle stage. Propagation here is accomplished by wind, by water, or by *intermediate hosts.* The last offer a means of transfer not quite as chancy as distribution by wind or water. For example, tapeworms use one of the easiest routes into and out of their human hosts, the alimentary tract. Entering through the host's mouth by way of eaten food, tapeworms spend their life directly in the gut cavity of man, and they release their eggs through the anus of the host, along with feces. The problem now is to transfer by passive means to another human host.

Since man does not eat feces, the eggs cannot reach new human hosts directly. However, tapeworms take advantage of the food pyramids of which man is a member; man eats beef, and cattle eat grass. A ready-made pathway from grass to man thus exists, and transfer can be achieved if, as happens on occasion, human feces are deposited on grass. Tapeworm eggs clinging to such vegetation then are often eaten by cattle (Fig. 6.20).

In the intestine of a cow, a tapeworm egg develops into an embryo that bores a path through the gut wall into the cow's blood stream. From there the embryo is carried to beef muscle, where it encapsulates and matures. If man later eats raw or partially cooked beef, the capsule surrounding the young tapeworm is digested in the human gut and the free worm hooks on to the intestinal wall of its new host.

This history is by no means unusual, for many kinds of parasites use well-established food chains in transferring to new hosts. Often there is more than one intermediate host, as in the life cycle of the Chinese liver fluke (Fig. 6.21). The adults of this parasitic flatworm infest the liver of man. Fertilized eggs are released through the bile duct into the gut of the host and pass to the outside with the feces. If the feces get into ponds or rivers, as happens frequently, the eggs develop into so-called *miracidium* larvae.

Such a larva must then enter a snail and there the miracidium develops into another larval type, called a *sporocyst.* Inside it develop many *redia* larvae, which escape and feed on snail tissue. Then each of the redias produces yet another set of many larvae, called *cercarias.* These fourth-generation larvae escape from the snail; if within a short time they happen to encounter a fish, they bore into it and encapsulate in muscular tissue. If man later eats raw or incompletely cooked fish, the young adult flukes find their way from the human gut to the liver.

This cycle involves two intermediate hosts, the snail and the fish. Transfer is partly passive (man to snail, fish to man), partly active (snail to fish). Note particularly the multistage, larva-within-a-larva type of development. Characteristic of flukes generally, larval polymorphism of this sort represents a highly efficient method of enormously increasing the number of reproductive units. A single fluke egg is estimated to yield a final total of some 10,000 cercarias—and a single adult fluke can produce many tens of thousands of eggs. Hence the chances become fairly good that at least some of the millions or billions of larvae will reach final hosts.

Through active locomotion, through physical agents such as air and water, and through routes involving food pyramids and intermediate hosts, parasites have solved their transfer problems most successfully. So successfully, indeed, that there are many more individual parasites in existence than free-living organisms.

A community consists of various kinds of free-living and various kinds of symbiotic populations. Which particular ones of each type actually compose a given community is determined largely by the nature of the physical, abiotic portions of ecosystems, as the following chapter will show.

---

review questions

1 Define ecosystem, biosphere, species, polymorphism, dimorphism, community, and give examples. What characteristics does a species exhibit as an evolutionary unit, a reproductive unit, and an ecological unit? What is an ecological niche?

2 Describe the typical life cycle of a species. What are endemic and cosmopolitan species? Describe the continental drift hypothesis, and show how it helps to explain the geographic distributions of certain organisms.

3 What are individual variations? Distinguish between inheritable and noninheritable variations, and give examples of each. Is the usual definition of "species" applicable to all organisms? What is a syngen?

4 What is a species-population, and what is its relation to a species? What are the structural characteristics of a population with reference to dispersion and growth? What are some of the physical and biological limiting factors of population growth? In what ways does a population interact with its physical environment? Its biological environment?

5 Describe the species structure of a community. What factors produce and maintain such a structure? Describe the life cycle of a community.

6 What are ecological succession, climax communities, seres? Describe the nutritional structure of a community. What factors maintain such a structure?

7 What are food pyramids, and what conditions produce and maintain them? Show how nutritional factors contribute to the long-range numerical constancies in communities.

8 Describe reproductive and protective links that make the population of communities interdependent. Show how such links contribute to numerical population balances. Give examples of mimicry and other forms of camouflage in organisms.

9 What are the various forms of symbiosis, and how are they defined? Give specific examples of each. What are lichens, root nodules? Distinguish between obligatory and facultative symbiosis.

10 What general structural and functional characteristics distinguish parasites from free-living organisms? What is hyperparasitism? What is the adaptive advantage of parasitic simplification?

11 Distinguish between active and passive transfers in parasite life cycles. What is the role of food pyramids in parasite transfers? What are intermediate hosts?

12 Review the life cycle of tapeworms and liver flukes and show what general modes of parasite transfer are illustrated by this cycle.

collateral readings

Billings, W. D.: "Plants and the Ecosystem," Wadsworth, Belmont, Calif., 1964. In this paperback the sections on dynamics and types of ecosystems are particularly pertinent to the topics of this chapter.

Cole, L. C.: The Ecosphere, *Sci. American,* Apr., 1958. The amount of life sustainable on earth is assessed from the point of view of ecological interrelations or organisms and their environment.

Dodson, E. O.: "Evolution: Process and Product," Reinhold, New York, 1960. This book contains comprehensive sections on biogeography and species distribution, both plant and animal.

Fraenkel-Conrat, H.: Rebuilding a Virus, *Sci. American,* June, 1956. An article on virus structure and on making artificial viruses by combining parts of different original ones.

Harzen, W. E.: "Readings in Population and Community Ecology," Saunders, Philadelphia, 1964. A compilation containing discussions of many topics covered in this chapter.

Horne, R. W.: The Structure of Viruses, *Sci. American,* Jan., 1963. Electron-microscopic studies on the organization of these bodies.

Hurley, P. M.: The Confirmation of Continental Drift, *Sci. American,* Apr., 1968. An account on some of the most recent evidence in support of the hypothesis.

Jacob, F., and **E. L. Wollman**: Viruses and Genes, *Sci. American,* June, 1961. An account on how bacteriophage infections have thrown light on the mechanism of heredity.

Lamb, I. M.: Lichens, *Sci. American,* Oct.,1959. A case study of symbiosis.

Limbaugh, C.: Cleaning Symbiosis, *Sci. American,* Aug., 1961. This article describes mutualistic and commensalistic relationships among marine fishes.

Odum, E. P.: "Ecology," Holt, New York, 1963. This is a useful paperback for general background on topics covered in this and the following chapter.

Rogers, W. P.: "The Nature of Parasitism," Academic, New York, 1962. Well worth consulting for a more thorough study of this aspect of symbiosis.

Smith, R. L.: "Ecology and Field Biology," Harper & Row, New York, 1966. The first sections of this book provide a good discussion of basic ecological principles.

Wilson, J. T.: Continental Drift, *Sci. American,* Apr., 1963. A historical outline of the hypothesis and a description of some of the recent supporting evidence. See also the more recent article by Hurley, above.

chapter 7 habitat and biosphere

The sum of all ecosystems on earth represents the *biosphere,* and the physical portion of this largest ecological unit is the global environment. Everything living ultimately depends on this environment; it sustains life, orients evolution, and provides the specific homes, or *habitats,* in which communities actually exist.

habitats

With the possible exception of the most arid deserts, the high, frozen mountain peaks, and the perpetually icebound polar regions, probably no place on earth is devoid of life. The two main types of habitat are the *aquatic* and the *terrestrial.* Both range from equator to pole and from a few thousand feet below to a few thousand feet above sea level. *Ocean* and *fresh* water are the main subdivisions of the aquatic habitat, and *air* and *soil* of the terrestrial.

the sea

The most familiar attribute of sea water is its high mineral content. The proportions of the different types of salt are almost the same all over the globe, as a result of thorough mixing of all waters by currents. Fifty-five percent of all ions present are chlorine, 30 percent are sodium. Thus, more than four-fifths of the total mineral content consists of table salt.

However, the total salt concentration, or *salinity,* varies considerably from region to region. The highest salinities occur in tropic waters, where high temperatures and extensive evaporation concentrate the oceanic salts. In the Red Sea the salt concentration is 4 percent, one of the highest known. At higher latitudes, by contrast, sea water evaporates less and is therefore less salty. Moreover, salinities are lower for often several hundred miles around the mouths of great rivers. The lowest known salinity is that of the Baltic Sea, where it is 0.7 percent (that of human blood is 0.9 percent). Salinity determines the density, or buoyancy, of ocean water, density being the greater the higher the salinity. Both salinity and buoyancy are of considerable significance to all marine life; salinity affects, for example, the mineral and osmotic balances of living matter, and buoyancy aids organisms in counteracting the pull of gravity.

An ocean basin has the general form of an inverted hat (Fig. 7.1). A gently sloping *continental shelf* stretches away from the coastline for about 100 miles (discounting often extreme deviations from this average). The angle of descent then changes fairly abruptly, and the shelf grades over to a steep *continental slope.* This slope eventually levels off and becomes the ocean floor, a more or less horizontal expanse called the *abyssal plain.* Mountains rise from it in places, with peaks sometimes so high that they rear up above sea level as islands. Elsewhere the plain is scarred by rifts, the deepest being the approximately 7-mile-deep Japan and Philippine Trenches along the western edge of the Pacific.

Three major habitats can be distinguished in such a basin. The sea floor from the shore out to the edge of the continental shelf forms a *littoral zone.* Beyond it, the sea floor along the continental slope and the abyssal plain represents the *benthonic zone.* And the water that fills the ocean basin is the *pelagic zone.* Sunlight penetrates water only to an average depth of about 250 ft, and to at most 600 ft in certain seas. Within this sunlit *photic zone* light dims progressively to zero. As a consequence, photosynthesizing organisms can exist only in the uppermost layers of the sea. Animal life directly dependent on these organisms must therefore remain near the surface as well. In sharp contrast, the dark region below the sunlit water, called the *aphotic zone,* is completely free of photosynthetic organisms and contains only animals, bacteria, and possibly fungi.

On the basis of its relationship to these habitats, marine life can be classified generally as *plankton, nekton,* and *benthos.* Plankton includes all drifting or floating types. Most of them are microscopic and are found largely in the photic zone. Although many of these forms have locomotor systems, they are nevertheless too weak or too small to counteract water currents (Color Fig. 5). Nekton comprises the strong swimmers, capable of changing stations at will. All nektonic types thus are animals, and they are found along the surface as well as in the sea depths. The benthos consists of crawling, creeping, and attached organisms along the sides and the bottom of the ocean basin.

The planktonic organisms in the surface waters include teeming trillions of algae that as a group probably photosynthesize more than twice as much food as all land plants combined. Collectively called *phytoplankton,* this oceanic vegetation represents the richest pasture on earth; di-

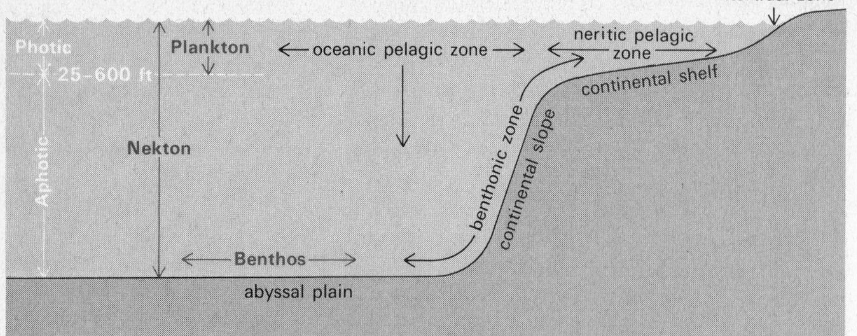

7.1 (Above) ***The structure of an ocean basin.*** *The littoral zone (not labeled) is the part of the benthonic zone that forms the floor of the continental shelf.*

7.2 ***Macroplankton.*** *Not all phytoplankton is microscopic. The photo shows Sargassum weed, a brown alga. A related species forms the main seaweed that floats in the Sargasso Sea. The bulbous structures on the algae are air bladders.*

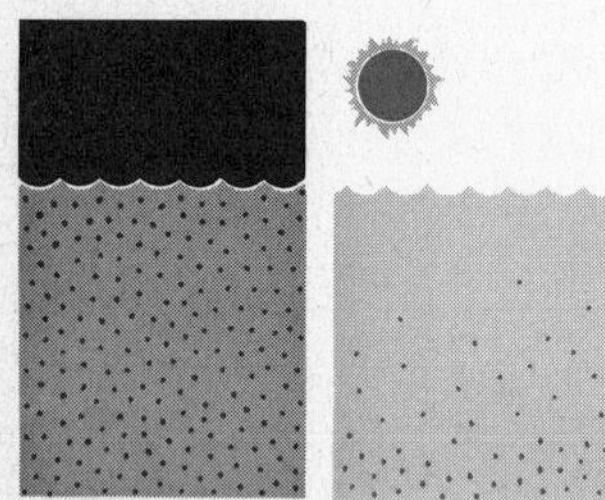

7.3 ***Diurnal migrations of plankton.*** *At night (left) plankton is distributed throughout the dark surface water. In daytime (right) plankton migrates away from the surface to darker, deeper waters.*

rectly or indirectly it forms the nutritional basis of all marine life. Most of the algal types in this ''grass of the sea'' are microscopic, and among them the single-celled, yellowish- or brownish-green *diatoms* are probably the most abundant (Fig. 7.2 and see Color Fig. 5).

Living side by side with the phytoplankton in open surface water are the small nonphotosynthetic forms. These include bacteria, protozoa, and members of the *zooplankton;* eggs, larvae, tiny shrimp, and other small animals carried along by surface drift. They feed directly on the microscopic vegetation. Most of the nekton, largely fishes and marine mammals, comes to these waters and feeds either on zooplankton or on photoplankton directly.

Through its influence on water temperature the sun has important effects on the distribution and abundance of plankton, hence on marine life in general. When the temperature of surface water is high, as in tropical seas throughout the year and in northern and southern seas in summer, the surface water cannot mix readily with the colder water below; a warm-water layer is less dense and therefore lighter than a colder layer, and it ''swims'' on top of the colder layer without mixing. The boundary between the two layers is a *thermocline.* Organisms above such a thermocline deplete the water of mineral raw materials, and after the organisms die these materials sink down without being returned to the surface by vertical mixing. As a result the amount of surface life is limited, and warm seas actually are relatively barren. In cold seas, by contrast, surface and deeper waters have roughly the same low temperature, thermoclines tend to be less pronounced or even absent, and vertical mixing of water can occur more readily. Minerals are then recirculated more rapidly and surface life can be correspondingly more abundant. The perennially cold arctic, antarctic, and subpolar waters actually support huge permanent plankton populations. And as is well known, the best commercial fishing grounds are in the high north and south, not in the tropics, and the best fishing seasons are spring and fall, not summer.

Warm and cold seas differ not only in the total amount but also in the diversity of life: warm oceans typically sustain small populations of many species, and cold oceans harbor large populations of comparatively few species. The reason is that higher temperatures promote all reactions, including those leading to evolution. Warm-climate life will therefore tend to become more diverse than cold-climate life. However, the limited mineral content of warm seas will keep the numbers of individuals low.

The sun also produces *diurnal migrations* of most planktonic organisms. During the night the organisms are distributed vertically throughout the surface waters, but during the day most of the plankton shuns the bright light and moves down to the dim layers of the photic zone. Larger animals feeding on plankton migrate up and down correspondingly. As a result even richly populated seas are quite barren on the surface during the daytime, and it is well known that surface fishing is most successful at night (Fig 7.3).

Nearer to shore, in the water above the littoral zone, even a bottom dweller is likely to be within the range of sunlight. The main problem here is to remain attached to solid ground, for the force of waves and ground swells is considerable. In the tide zone, moreover, a still greater problem is the rhythmic alternation between aquatic and essentially terrestrial conditions twice every 24 hours. As the meeting ground of water, land, and air, the tidal region actually is among the most violently changing habitats on earth.

Vegetation in this coastal region is again largely algal. In addition to the single-celled and small planktonic types, multicellular algae abound. Most of these seaweeds are equipped with specialized holdfasts that anchor the organisms to underlying ground. Green, brown, and red algae are particularly common. For example, the soft, slippery mats of vegetation that encrust rocks along the shore are familiar to many, as is *Fucus*, a common leathery brown alga found in dense populations on coastal rock. Animals in these waters include representatives of almost all major groups. In addition to planktonic types the region contains numerous nektonic animals, largely fish, as well as attached, burrowing, and creeping forms adapted to rocky, muddy, or sandy bottoms (Fig. 7.4).

The contrast between the surface habitat within reach of the sun and the aphotic zone below it is dramatic. As the one is forever fluctuating, so the other is perennially steady and relatively unchanging. Several unique physical conditions characterize this world of the sea depths.

First, in the total absence of sunlight, the region is pervaded with an eternal blackness of a kind found nowhere else on earth. Second, seasons and changing weather are practically absent. Localized climatic changes do occur, either as a result of occasional submarine volcanic activity, or, more regularly, through deep-sea currents. These produce large-scale shifts of water masses and, incidentally, bring oxygen to even the deepest parts of the ocean. The deep waters are also perpetually cold. Temperatures range from about 10°C at the top of the dark zone to about 1°C along the abyssal plain.

Third, water pressure increases steadily from the surface down, 1 atmosphere (atm) for every 33 ft of descent. In the deepest trenches of the ocean the pressure is therefore about a thousand times as great as at sea level. And last, a continuous slow rain of the remains of dead surface organisms drifts down toward the sea bottom. A good deal of this material dissolves completely during the descent. But much microscopic mineral matter reaches the abyssal plain, where it forms ever-thickening layers of ooze. Accumu-

A

B

C

D

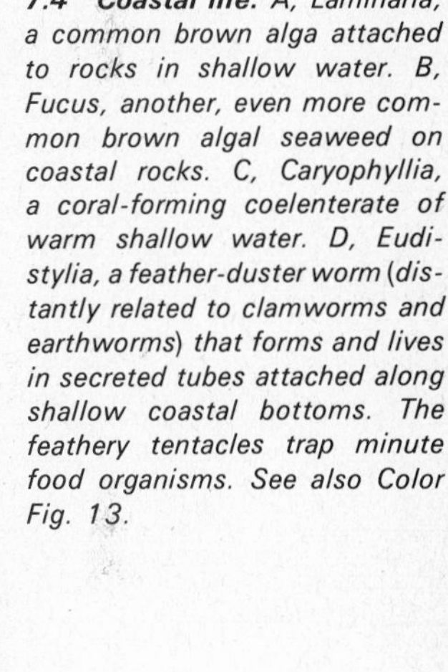

7.4 ***Coastal life.*** *A, Laminaria, a common brown alga attached to rocks in shallow water. B, Fucus, another, even more common brown algal seaweed on coastal rocks. C, Caryophyllia, a coral-forming coelenterate of warm shallow water. D, Eudistylia, a feather-duster worm (distantly related to clamworms and earthworms) that forms and lives in secreted tubes attached along shallow coastal bottoms. The feathery tentacles trap minute food organisms. See also Color Fig. 13.*

A

B

C

D

7.5 ***Deep-sea life.*** *A, an angler fish with a stalked, luminescent "lantern" over the mouth. Note the vertical position of the mouth, which facilitates catching prey lured to the light of the lantern. B, the angler fish shown here is a female. The structure above the eye is a parasitic male, which is carried about permanently attached. This neatly solves the problem of finding a mating partner in the dark. Many of these large-mouthed, dagger-toothed fishes are surprisingly small; for example, the fish shown here fits comfortably into a person's palm. C, another "lantern" fish, in which not only the organ above the mouth but also the "beard" is probably bioluminescent. D, a school of luminescent deep-sea squids.*

lating over the millennia, the older layers are eventually compressed to rock. Vertical bore samples of such rock have revealed a great deal about the past history of the oceans and their former surface inhabitants.

Contrary to early beliefs that life should be impossible in such an environment, a surprisingly rich diversity of organisms has been found to exist in it virtually everywhere. Apart from bacteria and perhaps fungi, the community is characteristically animal; photosynthetic organisms cannot live in perpetual darkness. Nearly all animal groups are represented, many by strange and bizarre types uniquely adapted to the locale (Fig. 7.5). With the exception of animals such as toothed whales, which can traverse the whole ocean from bottom to surface, most of the nektonic deep-sea forms are adapted to particular water pressures. Such animals are therefore rigidly confined to limited pressure zones at fixed depths. Food must be obtained either from the dead matter drifting down from the surface—a meager source, particularly in deeper water—or from other nektonic types.

This last condition makes the deep sea the most fiercely competitive habitat on earth. The very structure of the animals underscores their violently carnivorous, "eat-or-be-eaten" mode of existence. For example, most of the fishes have enormous mouths equipped with long, razor-sharp teeth, and many can swallow fish larger than themselves. Since the environment is pitch-black, one of the critical problems for these animals is, to begin with, *finding* food. A highly developed pressure sense provides one solution. Turbulence in the water created by nearby animals can be recognized and, depending on the nature of the disturbance, can be responded to by flight or approach.

Another important adaptation to the dark is

bioluminescence. Many of the deep-sea animals have light-producing organs of different shapes, sizes, and distributions. The light patterns emitted probably serve partly in species recognition. Identification of a suitable mate, for example, must be a serious problem in an environment where everything appears equally black. Another function of the light undoubtedly is to warn or to lure. Certain fish, for example, carry a "lantern" on a stalk protruding from the snout. An inquisitive animal attracted to the light of the lantern will discover too late that it has headed straight into powerful jaws (see Fig. 7.5).

the fresh water

Physically and biologically the link between ocean and land is the fresh water. Among descendants of ancestral marine organisms that invaded the rivers, some adapted to the brackish water in river mouths or to a life spent partly in the ocean, partly in fresh water (for example, salmon, eels). Most could leave the ocean entirely. Certain of such freshwater types then managed to gain a foothold on land. Of these, some continued to spend part of their lives in or near fresh water (for example, mosses, frogs), but more became wholly terrestrial. And among the terrestrial forms, some later returned to water and adapted secondarily to an aquatic existence (for example, reed grasses, some snails, many insects). Thus, organisms that inhabit the fresh water today represent a rich and major subdivision of the living world.

In addition to rivers, freshwater habitats also include lakes, ponds, and marshes. Three main conditions distinguish all such environments from the ocean. First, the salinity is substantially lower—indeed, lower than the salt concentrations inside organisms. As a result water will move osmotically from the environment into organisms and the contents of their tissues will tend to become diluted.

But freshwater organisms can counteract this tendency of absorbing too much water. Where rigid cell walls are present, as in plants, the walls protect against internal dilution; once such cells contain given amounts of water, no more can be drawn in osmotically because the walls will not permit any further cell enlargement. If rigid cell walls are lacking, as in animals, water balance is maintained by excretion of excess internal water. Excretory systems and also digestive systems and gills serve in this function.

A second condition characterizing much of the freshwater environment is the presence of strong, swift currents. Where these occur, passively floating life so typical of the ocean surface is not likely to be encountered. On the contrary, the premium will be either on maintaining firm anchorage along the shores and bottoms of rivers or on ability to resist and overcome the force of currents by muscle power.

Indeed, the vegetation found in rivers consists almost entirely of plants with rootlike holdfasts or actual roots. Pertinent examples are reed grasses, water foxtails, wild rice, and watercress. But where fresh water is not flowing strongly, not only rooted but also floating planktonic vegetation can be exceedingly abundant. In stagnant or near-stagnant water, algal communities forming continuous layers of green surface scum are particularly conspicuous. Among animals, similarly, those in quiet fresh waters include both planktonic and nektonic types, but those in swiftly flowing water are either attached or nektonic. The eggs of nektonic animals are enveloped by sticky jelly coats that adhere firmly to plants or other objects in the water, and the young are strongly muscled from the moment they hatch (for example, fishes and freshwater vertebrates in general; Fig. 7.6).

A third major distinction of the fresh water is that, with the exception of the very large lakes, it is affected much more by climate and weather than the ocean. Bodies of fresh water often freeze over in winter and can dry up completely in summer. Water temperatures change not only seasonally but also daily. Gales or floods bring bottom mud and silt to the surface. A large number of factors can alter flow conditions and produce, for example, stagnant water, or significantly altered chemical content, or situations facilitating infectious epidemics. In effect, the fresh water shares the environmental inconstancies of the land in very large measure.

the land

All land life is sustained by air and, directly or indirectly, also by soil. Air and soil are to the terrestrial habitats what the surface waters of the ocean are to the marine.

Like air, soil is itself a terrestrial home, providing a habitat for a vast array of subsurface organisms. And by creating the conditions necessary for the survival of all other terrestrial organisms, soil transforms the land surface into ac-

A

B

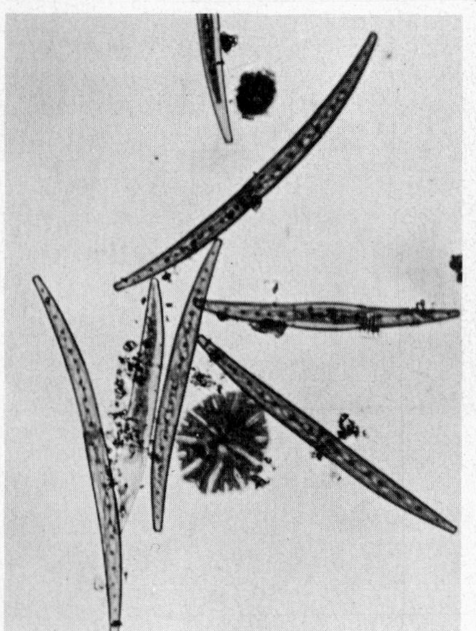

C

D

***7.6 Freshwater life.** A, a swamp region, characterized by many plants adapted secondarily to aquatic existence. These plants can resist displacement by flowing water. B, cattails are among the many rooted aquatic plants found along stream banks in swampy areas. C, desmids, unicellular green algae that form pond scum on stagnant fresh water. D, amphibian eggs enveloped by sticky jelly coats. Attachment of such eggs to aquatic vegetation is an animal adaptation to flowing fresh water.*

tually usable living spaces. Two other factors play a vital role, annual *temperature* and *precipitation.* As these vary with geographic latitude and altitude, they divide soil-covered land into a number of distinct habitat zones, or *biomes.* The six main biomes are *desert, grassland, rain forest, deciduous forest, taiga,* and *tundra.*

The first three are common in but not confined to the tropics. These biomes are characterized by comparatively high annual mean temperatures and by daily temperature variations that are greater than the seasonal variations; day and night temperatures tend to differ more than the average summer and winter temperatures. Variations in the amount of precipitation account for many of the different characteristics of these habitats.

A *desert* usually has less than 10 in. of rain per year, concentrated mainly in a few heavy cloudbursts. Desert life is well adapted to such conditions. Most plants grow, bloom, and produce seeds, all in a matter of days after a rain. Since the growing season is therefore restricted greatly, such plants stay relatively small. Leaf surfaces are often reduced to spines and thorns (as in cacti), which minimize water loss by evaporation. Desert animals too are generally small, and they include many burrowing forms that can escape the direct rays of the sun under the ground surface. In most deserts, mammals and birds are comparatively rare or absent altogether; maintenance of constant body temperature is difficult or impossible under conditions of great heat and practically no water. Cold-blooded animals can get by much more easily (Fig. 7.7).

The *grassland* extends from the tropics to much of the temperate zone. The more or less synonymous terms "prairie," "pampas," "steppe," "puszta," and many other regional designations underscore the wide distribution of this biome. A common feature of all grasslands is intermittent, erratic precipitation, usually amounting to about 10 to 40 in. annually. Grasses of various kinds, from short buffalo grass to tall elephant grass and thickets of bamboo, are particularly adapted to irregularly alternating periods of precipitation and dryness. Grassland probably supports more animal species than any other terrestrial habitat. Different kinds of mammals are particularly conspicuous (Fig. 7.8).

In those tropical and subtropical regions where torrential rains fall practically every day and where a well-defined rainy season occurs in winter, plant growth continues the year round. Such areas support *rain forests,* composed of populations of up to several hundred different species of trees. Rain forests cover much of central Africa, south and southeast Asia, Central America, and the Amazon basin of South America. Trees in such forests are normally so crowded together that they form a continuous overhead canopy of branches and foliage. This cover cuts off practically all the sunlight, much of the rain water, and a good deal of the wind. As a result the forest floor is exceedingly humid and quite dark, and it is populated by plants that require only a minimum of light. Animal communities too are stratified vertically, according to the several very different habitats offered between canopy and ground (Fig. 7.9).

Apart from extensive grasslands and occasional deserts, the most characteristic biome of the temperate zone is the *deciduous forest.* The basic climatic conditions here are cold winters, warm summers, and well-spaced rains that bring some 30 to 40 in. of precipitation per year. Moreover, day and night temperatures tend to differ less than

7.7 The habitat of the desert. *A, a desert landscape with tall saguaro cacti, barrel cacti (center foreground), cholla cacti (foreground), and palo verde trees. B, bobcat, a mammal characteristic of many deserts.*

A

B

7.8 (*Below*) **The habitat of the grassland.** *A, a typical grassy plain. B, oryx, a mammal characteristic of African grasslands.*

A

B

A B

7.9 The habitat of the rain forest. *A, Caribbean rain forest, with palms the predominant (but not only) trees. Note dense population of plants. B, an African rain forest. Note moss plants hanging from tree branches. The high moisture content of the atmosphere (resulting from release of much vapor by flora) permits growth of the epiphytic mosses in such forests.*

A B

7.10 The habitat of the deciduous forest. *A, a typical deciduous forest, with maples the predominant trees. B, mountain lion, a mammal characteristic of many deciduous forests.*

the average summer and winter temperatures. Winters make the growing season discontinuous, and the flora is adapted to this condition. Trees are largely deciduous—they shed their leaves and hibernate; and although annual plants die in winter, they produce seeds that withstand the cold weather. A deciduous forest differs from a rain forest in that trees are spaced farther apart and in that far fewer species are present, perhaps no more than ten to twenty. Maple, beech, oak, elm, ash, and sycamore are among the common trees of a deciduous forest. The many familiar animal types in this biome include deer, bears, raccoons, foxes, squirrels, and, characteristically, woodpeckers (Fig. 7.10).

North of the deciduous forests and the grasslands, across Canada, northern Europe, and Siberia, stretches the *taiga*. This is a biome of long, severe winters and of growing seasons limited to the few months of summer. Moose, wolves, and bears are most representative of the fauna, and hardy conifers of the forest flora. These forests differ from others in that they usually consist of a single species of tree. For example, spruce may be the only kind of tree present over a very large area. Another conifer species might be found in an adjacent, equally large area. The taiga occurs mainly in the northern hemisphere—little land exists in corresponding southern latitudes (Fig. 7.11).

The same circumstance makes the *tundra* a predominantly northern biome. Much of the tundra lies inside the Arctic Circle; hence there can be continuous night during the winter season and continuous daylight of comparatively low intensity during the summer. Some distance below the surface ground is frozen permanently (*permafrost*). Above ground frost can form even during the summer—plants often freeze solid and remain dormant until they thaw out again. The effective growing season is very brief, as in the desert, and indirectly the limiting factor is again water supply: frozen water is functionally equivalent to absence of water. Trees are completely absent, and the vegetation consists largely of lichens, mosses, and low shrubby plants. Also present are herbs with brilliantly colored flowers, many blooming simultaneously during the growing season. Conspicuous among the animals are hordes of insects, particularly flies, and a considerable variety of mammals: caribou, artic hares, lemmings, musk oxen, and polar bears. Birds are largely migratory, leaving for more southern latitudes with the coming of winter (Fig. 7.12).

Life does not end at the northern margin of the tundra but extends farther into the ice and bleak rock of the soilless polar region. Polar life is almost exclusively animal and includes types such as walrus, seals, and penguins. This fauna is not really terrestrial, however, but is based on the sea (see Fig. 23.9).

The horizontal sequence of biomes between equator and pole is repeated more or less exactly in a vertical direction, along the slopes of mountains (Fig. 7.13). Here too temperature and precipitation are the decisive variables. On a high mountain in the tropics, for example, the succession of biomes from mountain base to snow line is tropical rain forest, deciduous forest, coniferous forest, and lastly low shrubby growths and lichens. The farther north a mountain is situated, the more northern a biome covers its base and the fewer biomes cover its slopes. In the taiga, for example, the foot of a mountain is coniferous forest and the only other biome higher up is the zone of low shrubby plants. Thus, habitats spread over thousands of miles of latitude are telescoped into a few thousand feet of altitude.

A

B

7.11 The habitat of the taiga. *A, a typical taiga landscape, with single (coniferous) tree species covering a large area. B, moose, a mammal characteristic of the taiga.*

A

B

7.12 ***The habitat of the tundra.*** *A, Alaskan tundra landscape. Note complete absence of trees. B, muskox, a mammal characteristic of the tundra.*

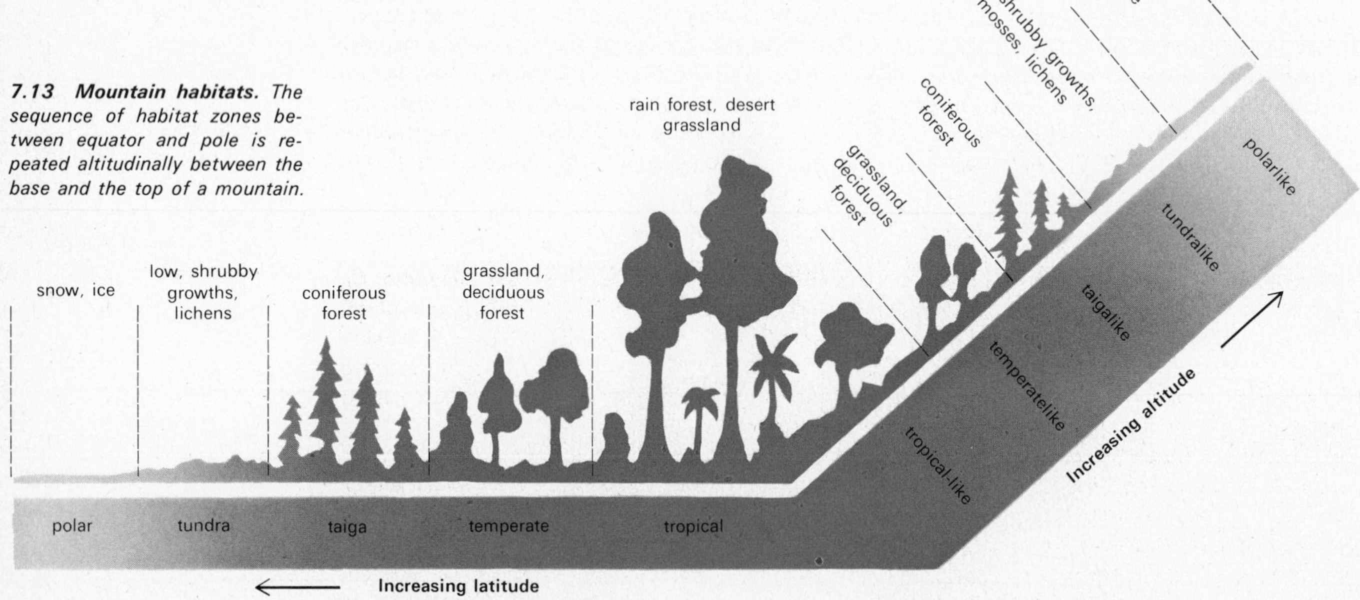

7.13 ***Mountain habitats.*** *The sequence of habitat zones between equator and pole is repeated altitudinally between the base and the top of a mountain.*

The nature of any kind of communal home, terrestrial, freshwater, or marine, evidently is determined by a few recurring physical variables. Among them are solar light, solar heat, geographic latitude, vertical depth and altitude, precipitation, wind and water currents, and the chemical composition of the locale. Variables like these are global in scope, and together they add up to large-scale ''environment.'' Thus we reach the most comprehensive ecological unit on earth, the biosphere as a whole, in which a thin surface layer of the planet maintains a carpet of life.

the biosphere

The most important general property of the environment is that it is forever changing, at every level from the submicroscopic to the global. Astrophysical, meterologic, geologic, geochemical, and biological forces alter every component of the earth sooner or later, very rapidly in some cases, slowly in others. A basic reason for this unceasing change is that the earth as a whole, living matter included, is an *open system.* Such systems exchange materials, energy, or both with their surroundings. By contrast, a *closed system* exchanges nothing with its surroundings (see also Chap. 3). To be sure, the amounts of material exchanged between earth and space are negligible. But *energy* enters and leaves all the time: heat, light, X rays, ultraviolet rays, electric waves, and other forms of solar energy beam to earth uninterruptedly, and emormous amounts of energy radiate away, mainly in the form of heat. So long as the sun shines and the earth spins, therefore, the energy flow creates balance-upsetting disturbances. Every imbalance then creates new imbalances of its own, and as a general consequence the earth's environment is forever changing.

Being produced primarily by the sun and the motion of the earth, such changes tend to occur in rhythmic *cycles.* Daily and seasonal climatic cycles are familiar examples. Other cycles are less readily discernible, for their scale is often too vast or too minute or they occur too fast or too slowly for direct observation. Living matter is interposed in these cycles; and as the earth's components circulate, some become raw materials in living processes.

Living organisms can therefore be envisaged as temporary constructions built out of materials "borrowed" from the environment for a short time. Billions of tons of materials are withdrawn from the environment by billions of organisms all over the world, are made components of living matter, are redistributed among and between organisms, and are finally returned to the environment. Through such *nutrient cycling* organisms contribute actively to the large-scale movement of earth substances. And because of such cyclic movements the physical earth *conserves* all its raw materials on a long-term basis. An indefinitely continued, repeated re-creation of living matter thereby becomes possible, and the continuity of life clearly depends on the parallel continuity of death.

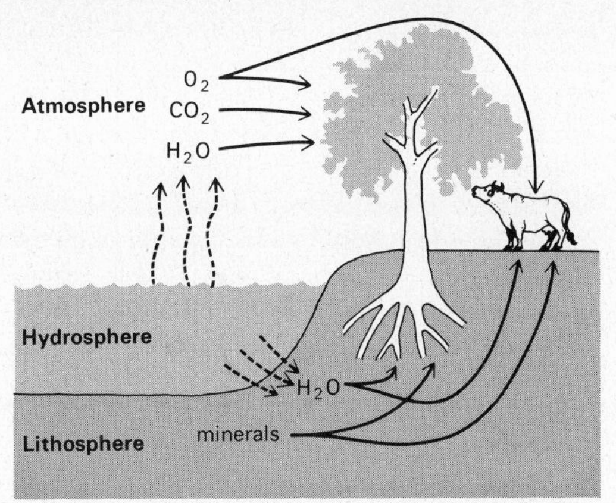

7.14 Environment and living matter. *An illustration of the material contributions of each of the three subdivisions of the environment to the maintenance of living matter.*

The physical portion of the biosphere consists of three global subdivisions. The *hydrosphere* includes all liquid components—the water in oceans, lakes, rivers, and on land. The *lithosphere* comprises the solid components, the rocky substance of the continents. And the *atmosphere* is the gaseous mantle around the hydrosphere and the lithosphere. Living organisms depend on raw materials from each of these subdivisions. The hydrosphere supplies *water;* the lithosphere contributes all other *minerals;* and the atmosphere is the source of *oxygen, nitrogen,* and *carbon dioxide.* Together, these inorganic materials provide all chemical elements for construction and maintenance of living matter (Fig. 7.14).

the hydrosphere

Representing the most abundant mineral of the planet, water covers some 73 percent of the earth's surface entirely and it is a major constituent of the lithosphere and the atmosphere. Water is also the most abundant component of living matter (see Chap. 4).

The basic cycle that moves and conserves water in the environment is quite familiar. Solar energy evaporates water from the hydrosphere to the atmosphere. Later cooling and condensation of the vapor at higher altitudes produces clouds, and precipitation as rain or snow then returns the water to the hydrosphere. This is the most massive process of any kind on earth, consuming more energy and moving more material than any other.

Aquatic organisms obtain water directly from their liquid environment, and they excrete some of it back while they live. After death the remainder is returned through decay. Terrestrial plants and animals draw liquid water from the reservoir in soil and in bodies of fresh water. The organisms retain some of the water in their bodies and the rest is excreted, partly as liquid water back to the hydrosphere but more particularly as water vapor to the atmosphere. Indeed, water moves from hydrosphere to atmosphere far faster through the "pump" of living organisms than if it were simply allowed to evaporate directly from the hydrosphere. Terrestrial organisms therefore actively accelerate the global water cycle. Sometimes this can have an effect on climate. For example, the trees in jungles release so much water vapor that the air over vast areas remains permanently saturated with moisture, cloudbursts then occurring almost every evening. After terrestrial organisms die, any liquid water in their bodies returns again to the hydrosphere through decay.

Apart from being a prime nutrient water also influences organisms through its effect on almost all aspects of climate and weather. In the ocean, water warmed in the tropics becomes light and rises to the surface, whereas cool polar water sinks. These up-down displacements bring about massive horizontal shifts of water between equator and pole. The rotation of the earth introduces east-west displacements. These effects, together with the driving force of similarly patterned winds, result in *ocean currents.* Such currents influence climatic conditions not only in the sea but also in air and on land.

Another climatic effect is a consequence of the thermal properties of water. Of all liquids water is one of the slowest to heat or cool, and it stores a very large amount of thermal energy. The oceans thus become huge reservoirs of solar heat. The result is that sea air chilled at night becomes less cold because of *heat radiation* from water warmed by day. Conversely, sea air warmed during the day becomes less hot because of *heat absorption* by water cooled at night. Warm or cool onshore winds then moderate the inland climate in daily patterns. Similar but more profound effects produce seasonal summer and winter patterns.

Third, global climates are influenced by the relative amount of water locked in *polar ice.* Temperature variations averaging only a few degrees over the years, produced by still poorly understood geophysical changes, suffice for major advance or retreat of polar ice. Ice ages have developed and waned during the last million years, and warm *interglacial* periods, characterized by ice-free poles, have intervened between successive advances of ice. At present the earth is slowly emerging from the last ice age, which reached its peak some 50,000 to 20,000 years ago. As polar ice is melting water levels are now rising and coast lines are gradually being submerged. Moreover, deserts are presently expanding; snow lines on mountains are receding to higher altitudes; in given localities more days of the year are snow-free; and the flora and fauna native to given latitudes are slowly spreading poleward.

Evidently, by influencing temperature, humidity, amount of precipitation, winds, waves, and ocean and river currents, the hydrosphere plays a major role in determining what kinds and amounts of organisms can live in particular regions.

the lithosphere

This subdivision of the environment supplies most *mineral* nutrients to living organisms. Also, it forms the inorganic base of *soil,* required specifically by terrestrial plants and by numerous subterranean animals.

minerals

Like the world's water, the rocky substance of the earth surface moves in a gigantic cycle. But here the rate of circulation is measured in thousands and millions of years. One segment of this global mineral cycle is *diastrophism,* the vertical uplifting of large tracts of the earth's crust through a variety of geologic forces. Major parts of continents or indeed whole continents can undergo such slow diastrophic movements. The most striking example is *mountain building.* Presently the youngest and highest mountains are the Himalayas, the Rockies, the Andes, and the Alps. All of them were thrown up some 70 million years ago, and the earth surface in these regions is not completely settled even now.

Quite apart from the tremendous upheaval caused by mountain formation itself, such an event has long-lasting effects on climate, hence on organisms. The appearance of a high mountain barrier is likely to interfere drastically with continental air circulation, and moisture-laden ocean winds may no longer be able to pass across the barrier. Rain will then continue to fall in the region between ocean and mountain and this region can become lush and fertile. But the region on the other side of the mountain will be arid, and desert conditions are likely to develop (Fig. 7.15). Along the Himalayas, for example, India on the oceanside is fertile but a belt of deserts lies north of the mountains. Similarly, California on the oceanside of the Sierras is fertile, but deserts lie east of the Rockies, in Arizona and New Mexico. Organisms living on either side of a newly formed mountain range must adapt to the new environmental conditions by evolution. Indeed, periods of extensive mountain building have always been followed by major evolutionary turnover among organisms (Chap. 29).

The second segment of the global lithospheric cycle involves *gradation,* the lowering of high land and the leveling of mountains. These changes occur by actual geologic sinking of land and by *erosion.* Physical erosion through water, wind, and changes in temperature results in a breaking of rock. For example, the shearing and pulverizing effects of water and ice on rock are well known (Fig. 7.16). Chemical erosion, brought about by the often acid products of decay, leads to a dissolution of rock. All such erosive forces contribute to converting large stones to smaller ones and small pebbles to tiny sand grains and microscopic rock fragments. Erosion thereby plays a major role in forming the mineral components of soil.

Through chemical erosion, moreover, water dissolves small quantities of rock and acquires a mineral content as a result. Accordingly, as rain water runs off high land it becomes progressively laden with minerals. Dissolved in streams, rivers, and soil water, such minerals serve as raw materials for terrestrial and freshwater organisms. After these die and decay the minerals return to the hydrosphere and are eventually carried to the sea. Therefore, as the lithosphere is slowly being denuded of mineral compounds the marine portion of the hydrosphere accumulates them. It was partly by this means that the early seas on earth acquired their original saltiness, and as the global water cycle now continues it makes the oceans even saltier. Organisms in the sea freely use the mineral ions as nutrients.

The death of marine organisms then helps to complete the global mineral cycle. Many marine forms use mineral nutrients in the construction of protective shells and supporting bones. After these organisms die their mineral components rain down to the sea floor where, as already pointed out, the accumulating layers of ooze ultimately compress to rock. The global lithospheric cycle becomes complete when such a section of sea bottom or low-lying land generally is subjected to new diastrophic forces. High ground or mountains are thereby regenerated, and parts that were sea floor originally are thrust up as new land in the process (Fig. 7.17).

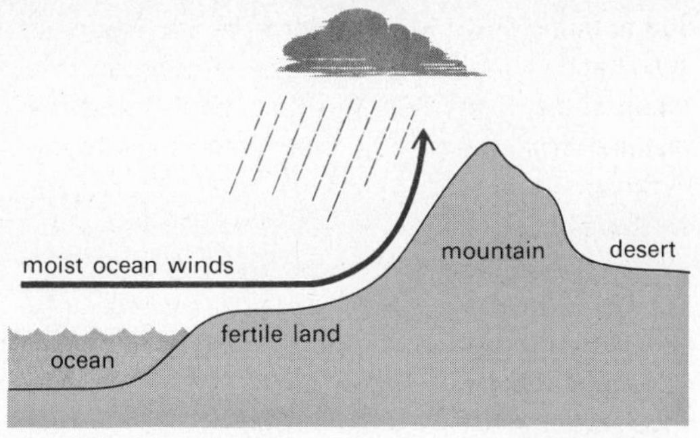

7.15 Mountains and climate. *A mountain deflects moisture-rich ocean winds upward and causes rain to remain confined to the slope facing the ocean. That slope will therefore be fertile, but the far slope will become a desert.*

7.16 Erosion. *This canyon was cut by the erosive action of the stream seen in the photo.*

soil

As noted, the lithosphere plays a special role in the life of land plants in that it contributes importantly to the formation of soil. This complex material provides mechanical anchorage for plants without hindering growth and aeration of roots. Also, soil holds water and mineral ions, the source from which land plants obtain supplies of these inorganic nutrients.

Before ancestral plants invaded the terrestrial environment the land was bare of soil. But the

7.17 ***The global mineral cycle.*** *Minerals absorbed by terrestrial plants and animals return to soil by excretion and death. Rivers carry soil minerals to the ocean, where some of them are deposited at the bottom. Portions of sea bottom then are occasionally uplifted by geologic forces, which reintroduce minerals to a global cycle.*

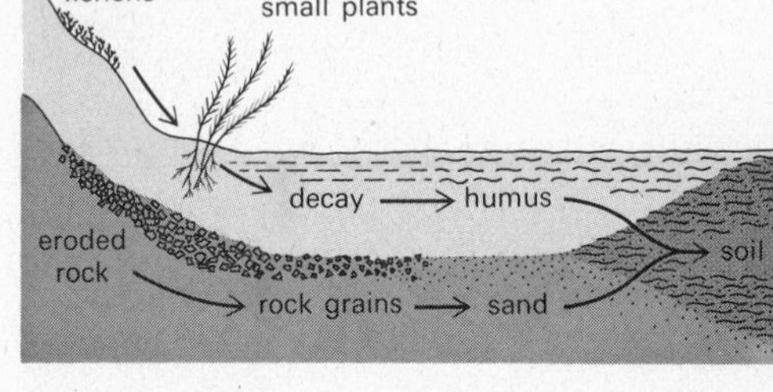

7.18 ***Soil formation.*** *Chemical and physical decomposition of rock yields humus and sand, respectively, and these two components together form soil.*

7.19 (*Below*) ***Soil profile.*** *In this grass-covered area, topsoil extends to a depth of about 1 ft, clay lies underneath to about the 2-ft level, and below that is rock consisting of sandstone and shale.*

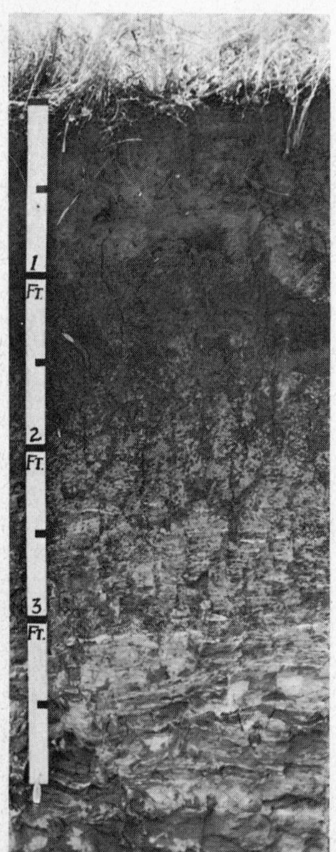

forces of gradation produced tiny particles of rock, or *sand,* which became one component of soil. Sand particles generally have a rough, jagged texture, and when they pack together they still leave small air spaces between them. Extremely small rock particles pack together very tightly, leaving hardly any air spaces. This kind of sand is *clay.* Sand and clay form the hard mineral portion of soil. The second main portion consists of complex organic materials collectively called *humus.* Sand can become inhabited by bacteria, fungi, and other organisms that do not require soil themselves, and such organisms add excretion products and their dead bodies to the sand. Such organic materials then decay and the decay products represent humus. To some extent humus binds the sand particles together and gives soil its crumbly, water-retaining characteristics (Fig. 7.18).

Actually soil is not an essential medium for plant maintenance. For example, floating aquatic plants do very well without it. Moreover, land plants too can be maintained adequately without soil if they are immersed in mineral-rich water. Such *hydroponic* cultures are used today in many experimental and commercial situations. Evidently, so long as the environment provides water and minerals at all, it does not matter too much through what medium the plant obtains these materials. Soil happens to be the most common and therefore most treasured large-scale supplier.

General references to "soil" are usually references to the *topsoil,* the upper, most valuable layer. Topsoils differ widely in color, according to the types of minerals and humus components present. The roots of small plants are embedded entirely in topsoil. Larger plants send their roots to the extensive *subsoil* underneath. Here the proportion of clay is generally higher than in topsoil, and subsoil therefore can be relatively dense. Also, the proportion of humus may be reduced. Subsoil is usually underlain by *loose rock,* and this layer extends down to the continuous *bedrock* of the continent (Fig. 7.19).

A good topsoil is neither too dense to prevent the growth of roots nor too loose to be blown or washed away. Plant cover itself tends to protect the soil, and as the soil holds the plant so the plant also holds the soil (Fig. 7.20). Also, a good soil contains a high proportion of water-retaining humus and is underlain by a substantial layer of subsoil, which prevents water from draining away too fast.

The chemical value of a soil depends on its usable water and mineral content. Three major ways by which these nutrients are replenished have already been mentioned: inflow of new mineral-laden water, direct chemical dissolution of soil particles by soil water, and decay of dead plants and animals. Decay not only returns minerals to soil but also adds new organic substances and thereby raises the humus content. In cultivated areas these relatively slow natural processes of replenishment are usually augmented by man, through conservation procedures designed to prevent nutritional exhaustion of soil. For example, man can add mineral-rich *fertilizers* to soil. He can let soils rest for one or more seasons. He can enrich soil by not harvesting a crop but plowing it under. Or he can adopt a program of *crop rotation,* whereby different crops are planted in successive seasons, each crop requiring a different set of minerals from the soil (Fig. 7.21).

Some natural replenishment of soil minerals is accomplished also by certain bacteria, as will become apparent in the next section.

the atmosphere

Like the hydrosphere, the atmosphere is subjected to physical cycles by the sun and the spin of the

A

B

7.20 ***Erosion.*** *A, eroded land with sandy gullies. These would normally erode further and enlarge. B, same landscape after planting and about 3 years of growth. Erosion has been halted. Plants evidently protect land against wind and water erosion.*

earth. Warmed equatorial air rises and cooled polar air sinks, and the axial rotation of the earth shifts air masses laterally. The resulting global air currents have basically the same general pattern as the ocean currents, and indeed these winds are the main forces that produce the ocean currents. Like the water circulation, moreover, the global air circulation influences climatic conditions substantially.

Equally significant to organisms are the chemical cycles of the atmosphere. Air consists mainly of oxygen (O_2, about 20 percent); carbon dioxide (CO_2, about 0.03 percent); nitrogen (N_2, about 79 percent); water (in varying amounts, depending on conditions); and minute traces of inert gases. Except for the inert gases, all these components of air serve as raw materials, and each circulates in a global cycle in which organisms play a conspicuous role. Also, all the gases are dissolved in natural waters; hence aquatic as well as terrestrial organisms have access to the aerial raw materials.

Atmospheric oxygen enters the living world as a respiratory gas, and in the course of respiration it combines with hydrogen and forms water (see Chap. 15). This water becomes part of the general water content of living matter, and as such it undergoes three possible fates. First, it can be excreted immediately to the hydrosphere or atmosphere. Second, it can be used in the construction of more living matter as a source of the elements hydrogen and oxygen. Structural oxy-

7.21 ***Contour plowing.*** *Plow lines are run at right angles to the slope of the land to reduce wind and water erosion.*

7.22 ***The oxygen cycle.*** *The parts of the cycle that occur inside organisms are shown in the colored rectangle.*

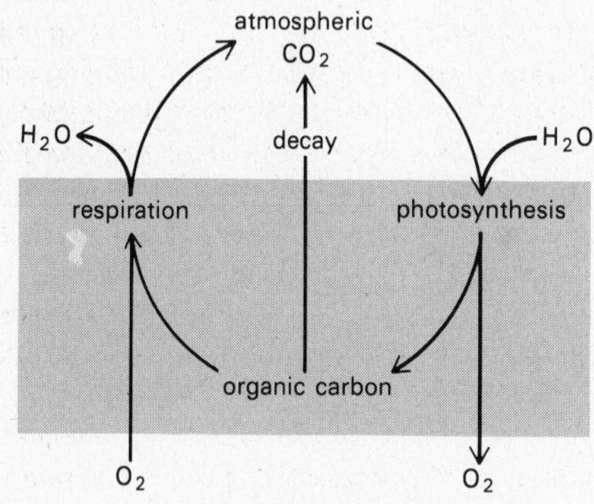

7.23 ***The carbon cycle.*** *The parts of the cycle that occur inside organisms are shown in the colored rectangle.*

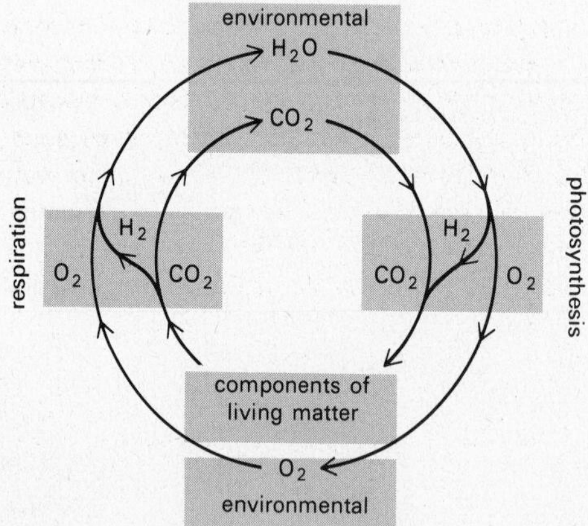

7.24 Interrelations of O_2, CO_2, and H_2O cycles.

gen of this sort remains in an organism until decay after death converts most of it to H_2O or CO_2, which return to the environment. Third, water is a raw material in photosynthesis, where the hydrogen participates in food manufacture and the oxygen returns to the environment as a byproduct (Fig. 7.22).

In effect, oxygen enters organisms only through respiration and leaves only through photosynthesis. In intervening steps the oxygen is incorporated in water, and in this form it can interlink with the water cycle or indirectly with the carbon cycle. Atmospheric oxygen is the source of an ozone (O_3) layer that envelops the earth at an altitude of some 10 miles. This layer shields organisms by preventing most of the solar ultraviolet and X rays from reaching the earth's surface.

Atmospheric carbon dioxide is the exclusive carbon source of living matter. The gas enters the living world through photosynthesis, in which it is a fundamental raw material (Fig. 7.23). In this manner CO_2 contributes to the formation of food substances, and these are partly respired, partly used in construction of more living matter. In the first case CO_2 reappears as a byproduct that is returned to the environment immediately, and in the second it is a decay product returned only after death. The interrelations of the CO_2, O_2, and H_2O cycles are outlined in Fig. 7.24.

The carbon dioxide content of the atmosphere is replenished also through forest and other fires and through burning of industrial fuels. Such processes actually represent a long-delayed completion of the carbon cycle. The combustible substances in wood, coal, oil, and natural gas all are organic compounds that were manufactured through photosynthesis, in many cases millions of years ago. Aerial CO_2 was then used up, and the gas is returned to the atmosphere only now. Atmospheric CO_2 acts as a heat screen. Solar energy that reaches the earth's surface is largely converted to heat, but CO_2 retards radiation of earth heat into space. The gas therefore has a "greenhouse" effect that probably contributes to the present warming up of global climates (see also next section).

The nitrogen of the atmosphere is the ultimate source of this element in living organisms. However, aerial nitrogen is chemically relatively inert, and the majority of organisms cannot use it directly. For example, although terrestrial animals obtain an abundance of nitrogen with every breath, all of it is again exhaled unused. Aerial N_2 can be used directly only be so-called *nitrogen-fixing* organisms, mainly certain bacteria and blue-green algae living in soil and water. These absorb N_2 as a nutrient and are able to make it part of organic substances. Some nitrogen-fixing bacteria are mutualistic symbionts on the roots of leguminous plants. The bacteria here induce growth of root nodules (see Fig. 6.15), and the nitrogen "fixed" by the bacteria becomes available to the legumes as usable nitrogen.

Usable fixed nitrogen in plants passes through plant foods to animals (Fig. 7.25). Another important source of usable nitrogen is the nitrate ion, NO_3^-, present in water and soil. Plants (but not animals) can convert nitrates to usable organic substances, and these again become available to animals via plant foods. Through decay after excretion and death, nitrogenous compounds in plants and animals then return to water and soil in the form of ammonia, NH_3. This substance is a nutrient for so-called *nitrifying bacteria.* One type of these converts ammonia to *nitrite* ions, NO_2^-; a second type absorbs the nitrite and converts it to *nitrate* ions, NO_3^-. This combined action of the nitrifying bacteria thus replenishes the supply of environmental nitrates.

Replenishment is achieved also in at least three other ways, through dissolution of rock by water, through addition of fertilizers to soil by man, and to a small extent through formation of nitrates in air, when lightning combines aerial nitrogen and oxygen. The nitrate supply in the environment is then drawn on not only by plants but also by so-called *denitrifying bacteria.* They use nitrates as nutrients and ultimately convert them to molecular nitrogen, N_2. This gas escapes to the atmosphere, and the global nitrogen cycle is thereby completed.

The cycle evidently depends on four different sets of bacteria: nitrogen fixers, decay causers, nitrifiers, and denitrifiers. These bacteria act as they do, not because they are aware of the grand plan of the global nitrogen cycle, but because they derive immediate metabolic benefits from their action; the nitrogenous compounds they absorb are nutrients, and the altered compounds they eliminate are their waste products. The nitrogen cycle also illustrates, perhaps as sharply as any one process can, how thoroughly the living and nonliving components of the biosphere are interdependent and interconnected. Indeed such a total ecological integration is absolutely essential for the continued existence of the biosphere and all its subordinate parts.

the ecological crisis

The interrelation of all parts of the biosphere is probably the single most important factor that man today must be concerned with if he is to survive as a species. Of all biospheric components man is by far the most influential, and his net ecological impact to date has been to bring about a rapidly accelerating disruption of the links and balances on which the existence of the biosphere depends. As a result, human survival itself is now seriously threatened by this "environmental decay." Broadly speaking the man-made ecological crisis manifests itself in three parts of the biosphere: the physical environment, in which we face a crisis of resources; the biological environment, in which we must cope with the twin crises of overpopulation and undernourishment; and the cultural environment, which has generated a crisis of technology and science.

Our physical resources include all environmental components on which our lives depend—land, water, and air, the providers of living space and basic raw materials. A crisis arises because our withdrawals from these finite resources and our additions to them have been excessive and have seriously impoverished both our space and our raw materials. On land, for example, we increasingly withdraw growing space for plants by building houses, roads, and other installations incompatible with vegetation. The result is a curtailment of photosynthesis, with a corresponding reduction in the amount of oxygen liberated by plants to the air. At the same time we withdraw and burn enormous quantities of oil, coal, and gas, which further depletes the oxygen of the atmosphere. Moreover, we add so much nitrogen- and phosphorus-containing waste to our water resources that many of them become overfertilized. The consequence is overgrowth of aquatic microorganisms and depletion of oxygen in water, often followed by death of the microorganisms and all other aquatic life as well. Lake Erie is a good example of a body of water that is virtually

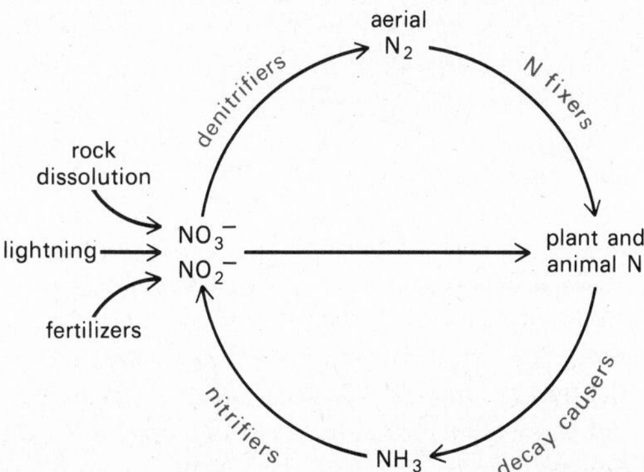

7.25 The nitrogen cycle. *In this simplified representation the participating bacterial types are indicated in color over the curved arrows.*

A

B

C

7.26 ***Pollution*** *of land, water, and air. A, country road in Florida. B, detergent foam on the Mississippi River near Alton. C, smog over New York City.*

dead biologically—and such results tend to be irreversible for many decades. A continuing oxygen depletion ultimately can be lethal for man, too, for once the rate of depletion through fuel combustion and pollution exceeds the rate of global photosynthesis, the atmosphere will begin to lose oxygen. Some 70 percent of all photosynthesis on earth occurs in the ocean, to be sure, but even there, especially in coastal regions, man now adds pollutants to such an extent that algal life and hence oxygen liberation are affected adversely (Fig. 7.26).

Furthermore, our burning of fossil fuels (particularly in automobiles and planes) adds so much CO_2 to the atmosphere that the "greenhouse" effect referred to earlier becomes immediately worrisome. It has been estimated that at present combustion rates the amount of excess CO_2 accumulated by the end of this century will be enough to cause polar ice to melt in from 400 to 4,000 years. Assuming a melting time of 1,000 years for the Antarctic cap alone, the sea level would rise 4 ft every 10 years, enough to inundate most major cities and all coastal areas around the globe. Moreover, the effect of excess CO_2 and other pollutants on air quality and local climates is appreciable even now, especially in urban areas. In a city like Los Angeles, for example, the *daily* outpouring of aerial pollutants includes some 150 tons of volatile acids, 400 tons of sulfurous compounds, 500 tons of nitrogenous substances, and 1,500 tons of organic materials (among which the hydrocarbons become irritants in smog after exposure to sunlight and oxygen). To that should be added some 2 tons of dust settling on every square mile every year. There can be little question that the combined deleterious effects on plant crops and the clinical and subclinical effects on people are substantial; and they are usually so pervasive and diverse that they defy precise measurement.

Aerial pollutants absorbed by water and wastes added to water directly affect us quite as decisively. Many of them decay too slowly or not at all, and they then pass through aquatic food chains to fish and other water animals eaten by man, or from water animals to land forms that in turn are eaten by man. An important *amplification* phenomenon is usually observed in such cases: both in water and on land the concentration of a pollutant increases at each step during its transfer through a food chain. For example, it has been shown that for any given concentration of insecticide in soil, earthworms in that soil acquire concentrations up to 40 times higher; and in birds feeding on such earthworms the concentration rises up to 200 times. Similar amplifications have been demonstrated for many other pesticides, for synthetic detergents, and for the components of radioactive fallout. Since 1965 the use of undegradable detergents has been banned by law; but slowly decaying pesticides such as DDT still persist practically everywhere, some 20 years after their first use—and long after many kinds of insects have become resistant to the compound. Similarly, fallout products such as strontium-90 will persist for decades or centuries. An additional problem is that the despoilation of resources required by man is often irreversible or nearly so and that such effects are cumulative. The overall result is a continuing impoverishment of our physical environment and a steadily deepening resource crisis.

The sheer massiveness of the human presence aggravates this crisis enormously. Human protoplasm well might outweigh the amount of living matter of any other land animal, and our increasing numbers actually create or seriously contribute to all other ecological crises. Indeed, overpopulation is generally considered the single most critical of all the critical problems we face. Mankind now doubles in numbers every 30 to 35 years, or once every generation, so that by the year 2000 there will be $7\frac{1}{2}$ billion people, roughly twice as many as at present. The annual growth rate currently is about 2 percent, but this rate itself is increasing. Our net global population gain amounts to 2 persons every second, which means 200,000 more people, or a new Peoria, every day; 6 million more, or a new Moscow, every month; and 70 million more, or a new Brazil, every year. The basic problem—though by no means the only one—is food supply, which is inadequate now and is bound to become more so. According to expert consensus global food production is not likely to keep pace with the inexorable population increase, and widespread famines are believed to be virtually unavoidable in the years ahead (Fig. 7.27).

New food technologies conceivably might help to forestall catastrophe. Indeed, laboratory methods are rapidly becoming available for a "made-to-order" creation of so far nonexistent food plants. For example, two cells of different plants can be fused together, and the resulting single cell can be reared into a new plant that has the joint characteristics of the "parental" types. Protein quantity and quality can be improved in this way. Similarly, new genetic variants of corn and wheat are now being developed in which the protein content is substantially increased. It should be recognized, however, that accelerated and ever more ingenious research by itself cannot solve the global food problem. To be effective, technical advances must become part of routine agricultural practices; yet for various reasons this is often difficult or impossible.

For example, many new strains and varieties of food plants developed in the United States do not grow well in tropical regions, the main centers of the food crisis. And when an attempt is made to develop new strains in tropical and subtropical areas directly, success is hardly ever rapid. A project to create the right kinds of high-yield corn in Mexico took 25 years to complete (quite apart from concentrated research aid by the United States and an expenditure of millions of dollars). That much time is simply no longer available today in most food-poor regions. Besides, successful introduction of modern agricultural practices and new food technologies depends on full support of local farming populations, yet in many places such support is lacking or takes too long to foster. Until recently, food-rich nations have

7.27 Overpopulation and undernourishment.

A

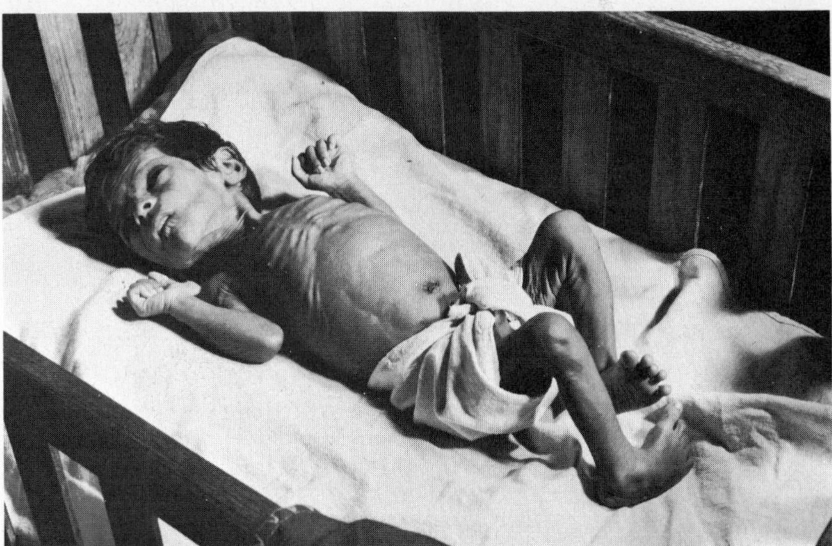

B

shipped their surpluses to needy countries, but by now the extensive reserves are long gone. In many cases, moreover, receiver nations that have come to rely on donated food have delayed improving their own food production, and unchecked population increases in such nations have more than nullified the very temporary effects of food shipments. Thus, the two-thirds of mankind that was undernourished 20 years ago is still undernourished today, except that now this two-thirds comprises not 1 but 2 billion people. And the degree of malnutrition is still increasing.

A more direct way of solving the population problem would be birth control. Widely regarded as a more hopeful and more effective procedure than attempts to increase the food supply, birth control has indeed been successful in technically advanced nations. But success has been far less impressive in countries where the population and food crises are at their worst. In many places large populations are still considered evidence of national strength, and in others various religious and economic beliefs continue to foster excessively large families. For example, many people in Asia, Africa, and South America regard having numerous children as the best or only security for their old age; and if many of these children die from starvation or disease before maturity, as they do, the usual response is having even more children. In view of the general poverty in such areas, there actually is no better substitute at present for the economic rationale that perpetuates large families. Here and there local governments have introduced modern birth-control techniques, but so far the results have been largely disappointing. Taking birth-control pills requires attention to schedules and motivation, yet as just noted the motivation is usually in the opposite direction. And intrauterine devices (IUDs) must be fitted by trained personnel, which is often in short supply. Besides, in countries like India close to 1 million women reach reproductive age every year, and it takes at least 3 to 5 min to install one IUD; hence IUDs almost cannot be installed fast enough.

Some ecologists now believe that a solution of the population crisis, and of the ecological crisis as a whole, will require a new worldwide morality, a kind of eleventh commandment: at your death leave the ecosystem in a state no worse than it was at your birth; or, in specific relation to the population problem, make it part of your personal philosophy that two people should leave no more than two children. Such an ethic would lead to a voluntary but nevertheless absolute restriction of human numbers, and like other moral precepts it could have social and even legal reinforcement. Thus, exceeding the birth limitation could come to be regarded morally just as reprehensible, and just as punishable, as theft or murder; in a real sense excessive reproduction does rob and murder the life of future generations. Similarly, while any population would retain the freedom to breed itself into starvation, it would be immoral for outsiders to donate food since such a course would aggravate the global problem and indeed the local problem itself. To be effective, a morality of this sort clearly would have to be truly worldwide; and in view of a lack of global agreement on far lesser issues one has reason to doubt its rapid adoption. Yet without it only two other solutions appear to remain: reduction of numbers through nuclear holocaust, conventional wars no longer being sufficiently destructive to affect global population growth; and the "natural" solution through which the ecosystem always balances itself on its own accord—large-scale periodic waves of famine and death whenever the food supply falls below minimum sustenance levels.

While the food crisis is the most serious consequence of overpopulation in developing nations, the main consequence in advanced nations has been a cultural and technological crisis. Excessive numbers are a primary cause of crowded communities, sprawling slums, noise and congestion, foul air and environmental ugliness, and all the other physical manifestations of the "urban crisis." Biologically, moreover, life is often stunted, too tense, or simply dissatisfying, and in many cases life spans are shortened unduly by the excessive stresses generated by crowded conditions. Above all, overpopulation produces an increasingly automated, computerized, dehumanized culture, in which impersonal institutions frequently overwhelm many of the aspirations of the individual. Machines already control us as much as we control them, and some of the cultural possibilities based on future technology are even more disquieting: a drug-dependent, illusion-seeking populace readily manipulated by central authority; semimechanical people with plastic substitute organs; cells and tissues taken from donors and later cultured back into whole donor-duplicates; direct biochemical interference with genes and minds to control human characteristics and human thought; test-tube babies grown to order according to authorized specifications; electronic spy systems and computerized regulation of lives; machine-prepared liquid food rations dispensed through pipes to each habitation; and more, all against a background of barely manageable numbers subsisting in a machine-regulated environment.

Many people have therefore been prompted to wonder if science and technology have not gone "out of control," and if it thus might not be better to abolish these enterprises. It should be quite apparent, however, that suggestions of this kind are merely superficial responses to the symptoms, not the causes, of our cultural crisis. Our basic problem is not science and technology as such, but knowing—or rather not knowing—what to use them for. Too often have science and technology been employed simply to abet human greed or nationalistic ends, and too often has there been little concern about the consequences of their employment. Thus detergents and gasoline engines have proved to be exceedingly useful products, but it was not foreseen that they also polluted; and after their pollutant effects had become known it has taken too long and too much opposition to institute remedies. Similarly, nuclear explosions have served primarily as experiments in engineering and as instruments of national policy, and even now they are not treated as they should be, as major ecological interventions that affect *all* parts of our biosphere. Each technological advance always introduces risks as well as benefits, and deciding on a particular balance between risk and benefit is fundamentally *not* a scientific matter; as pointed out in Chap. 1 it is a social and cultural one, involving value judgments by all.

The answer in effect is not less science but more, for only through science are we at all likely to have some hope of coming out of the ecological crisis as a still viable species. Realization of this hope actually would not even require major scientific advances or new technologies; we already have enough information and know-how to make a significant start at improving our ecosystem now. The essential requirement, rather, is a collective willingness to put our knowledge to work. However, development of such a willingness demands certain basic changes in our attitudes. First, human action would have to be guided by the recognition that man and his environment form a single, closed, global system of integrated components. In this system every man is bound to every other not simply through common biological ancestry or through philosophic dreams of oneness, but, far more directly, through the same atmosphere, the same water, the same food-producing soil. The ancient query, "Am I my brother's keeper?" demands a very *practical* answer today.

Second, mankind would have to moderate its arrogant habit of trying to dominate the environment and would have to begin living with it in true *partnership.* We would have to cultivate the idea of being stewards only, not self-appointed masters, of what one observer has called our common "spaceship Earth." And as watchful stewards we would have to recognize that our technology by its very nature tends to be parasitic on the environment, and that destructive forces nearly always work more rapidly than those of rebirth; the tree we saw down in 30 sec may have taken 30 years to develop. If we started the environmental restoration right now, it would take us from one to three generations, or on the order of 100 years at the very least, to resolve the present ecological crisis. We would need to be patient, therefore, and we would need to launch an immediate, permanent program of *planned ecological management.* Our basic aim would have to be an improvement in the quality of life—*all* life—, with considerations of quantity being distinctly secondary.

And third, in our role of environmental stewards, we could no longer afford to have our technological innovations produce unexpected ecological side effects; we would have to foresee and prepare for such effects. The necessary foresightedness can be generated today through "systems analysis," a computer-based management technique. Mathematical models of our ecosystem and its subordinate parts could be constructed, and any change contemplated by us could be fed into these models. Computer analysis could then show how all elements of the system will be affected. We would then be able to decide ahead of time if these effects were consistent with our goals or, if not, how contemplated changes would have to be modified to make their total effects acceptable. Ecological analyses of this sort have not yet begun; they are exceedingly laborious and would require all our ingenuity and dedication, with contributions from all fields of knowledge. Yet we know *how* to begin them. And we also know that, unless we do begin them, man who uncaringly tried to overwhelm the earth is about to be overwhelmed by his own hand.

review questions

1 What is the structure of an ocean basin? What are the major habitats of such a basin? What role does the sun play in creating subdivisions in these habitats? What physical conditions characterize the various subdivisions?

2 Define plankton, nekton, and benthos. Give specific examples of each. Where in the ocean are each of these types of organisms found?

3 How do different oceans vary in water density and salinity? What are the proportions of oceanic salts? What factors make life in tropic waters generally less abundant but more diverse than in temperate and subpolar waters?

4 What are thermoclines, diurnal migrations? What physical and biological conditions characterize the sea depths?

5 Review the physical characteristics of freshwater habitats. What major groups of organisms occur in fresh water, and in what general ways are they adapted to this habitat?

6 What are the main terrestrial habitats, and what physical and biological conditions characterize each of them? In what way are the terrestrial habitats at different latitudes related to those at different altitudes?

7 What factors maintain the global environment in a state of continuing change? What are open and closed physical systems? How do organisms contribute to cyclic environmental change?

8 Describe the global water cycle. What forces maintain it? How do organisms participate in this cycle? In what different ways does the world's water influence climates?

9 What are diastrophism and gradation? How does the formation of mountains influence climates? Cite examples. In what ways is the global lithospheric cycle of nutritional importance?

10 What are the main components of soil? In what ways does soil serve in the maintenance of plant life? What factors determine the quality of a soil? What are hydroponics?

11 Review the ways in which soil minerals are replenished. Describe the general pattern of mineral cycles. On the basis of this, construct diagrams showing the pattern of global phosphate and calcium cycles.

12 Describe the oxygen and carbon cycles and show how they are interlinked.

13 Outline the global nitrogen cycle. How many different groups of bacteria aid in the maintenance of this cycle? What is the role of decay in the atmospheric, lithospheric, and hydrospheric cycles?

14 Identify the main contributing factors to our present ecological crisis. Describe the amplification effect of pollutants. What specific conditions jeopardize the supply of atmospheric oxygen? The maintenance of aquatic life?

15 What are the ecological consequences of human overpopulation? Outline your own solutions to our various environmental crises, and systematically examine the ecological consequences of these suggestions.

collateral readings

Billings, W. D.: "Plants and the Ecosystem," Wadsworth, Belmont, Calif., 1964. A section on terrestrial biomes is included in this paperback.

Calhoun, J. B.: Population Density and Social Pathology, *Sci. American,* Feb., 1962. Experiments on rats reveal some of the drastic effects of overcrowding.

Carson, R.: "The Sea Around Us," Oxford, Fair Lawn, N.J., 1951. A classic nontechnical book on the physics, chemistry, and biology of the sea, written for popular consumption. Strongly recommended.

———: "The Silent Spring," Houghton Mifflin, Boston, 1962. This book (which caused considerable controversy when it first appeared) examines the disruptive effect of man's use of chemicals and other agents on the ecological balance of nature.

Cole, L. C.: The Ecosphere, *Sci. American,* Apr., 1958. The amount of life sustainable on earth is assessed by examining the relation of organisms and their environment.

Commoner, B.: "Science and Survival," Viking Press, New York, 1966. A penetrating examination of our resource crisis and the cultural crisis generated by our advanced technology. Strongly recommended.

Deevey, E. S.: The Human Population, *Sci. American,* Sept., 1960. An examination of the total amount of human life the earth may be able to support.

Dubos, R.: "So Human an Animal," Scribner, New York, 1968. An exceedingly well-written, nontechnical analysis of all the undesirable ecological and cultural aspects of the contemporary human scene.

Ellison, W. D.: Erosion by Raindrop, *Sci. American,* Nov., 1948. A discussion of the physical and chemical effects of environmental water on the lithosphere generally and on soil conservation specifically.

Fairbridge, R. W.: The Changing Level of the Sea, *Sci. American,* May, 1960. This article discusses the effects of ice ages and of diastrophic movements of the ocean floor.

Fremlin, J. H.: How Many People Can the World Support? *New Scientist,* vol. 24, p. 285, 1964. A physicist estimates the possible upper limit of human numbers on the basis of the total body heat produced, and he indicates the changes in way of life that would be necessary to maintain such a population. Extremely thought-provoking.

McDermott, W.: Air Pollution and Public Health, *Sci. American,* Oct., 1961. An examination of the subtle effects of aerial pollutants on human health.

Opik, E. J.: Climate and the Changing Sun, *Sci. American,* June, 1958. Changes in the radiation rate of the sun may have contributed to the development of ice ages.

Pirie, N. W.: Orthodox and Unorthodox Methods of Meeting World Food Needs, *Sci. American,* Feb., 1967. An examination of required changes in cultural attitudes in attempts to solve the food crisis.

Plass, G. C.: Carbon Dioxide and Climate, *Sci. American,* July, 1959. CO_2 contributes to the regulation of global temperature, and the gas therefore plays an important ecological role.

Woodwell, G. M.: The Ecological Effects of Radiation, *Sci. American,* June, 1963.

———: Toxic Substances and Ecological Cycles, *Sci. American,* March, 1967. The ecological amplifications and other effects of pollutants are discussed in both articles.

The following readings from *Scientific American* have self-explanatory titles; they deal with the relation of the living to the nonliving components of the biosphere and with the nature of various habitats:

Deevey, E. D.: Life in the Depths of a Pond, Apr., 1951.

Ingle, R. M.: The Life of an Estuary, May, 1954.

MacInnis, J. B.: Living Under the Sea, March, 1966.

Munk, W.: The Circulation of the Oceans, Sept., 1955.

Nicholas, G.: Life in Caves, May, 1955.

Pequegnat, W. E.: Whales, Plankton, and Man, Jan., 1958.

Powers, C. F., and **A. Robertson**: The Aging Great Lakes, Nov., 1966.

Ryther, F. H.: The Sargasso Sea, Jan., 1956.

Stetson, H. C.: The Continental Shelf, March, 1955.

Vevers, H. G.: Animals of the Bottom, July, 1952.

Walford, L. A.: The Deep-sea Layers of Life, Aug., 1951.

Went, F. W.: The Ecology of Desert Plants, Apr., 1955.

part 3
the world of life: nonanimal organisms

part 3

the world of life: nonanimal organisms

chapter 8

the earliest organisms

chapter 9

protists

chapter 10

plants

Following an introductory discussion of the probable beginning of life on earth, this part consists of an examination of three of the four major groups of organisms living today—Monera, Protista, and Metaphyta.

One main objective of this (and the succeeding) part is to provide insight into the vast diversity of existing living creatures. An appreciation of this diversity should show clearly that workable, successful solutions to the universal requirements of life have been found countless times and under exceedingly varied environmental circumstances. A second main objective is to supply a background for the analysis of living functions following later. We know that these functions are metabolism and self-perpetuation and that they are performed in specific individual organisms. If therefore the functions are to be understood, it is necessary that the performers themselves be understood.

chapter 8 the earliest organisms

category	phylum
monera	schizophyta
	cyanophyta

As noted in Chap. 2, the Monera and Protista living today appear to be descendants of some of the first organisms that ever existed on earth. Monera in particular well might have had the longest history, and their structural primitiveness presumably provides clues to the possible nature of the earliest living types. The ways in which life could have originated, the likely characteristics of the first creatures, and the known characteristics of modern Monera are the subjects of this chapter.

origins of life

It is thought today that life began through a progressive series of chemical synthesis reactions that raised the organization of inanimate matter to successively higher levels. Atoms first formed simple compounds, these later formed more complex ones, and the most complex of them eventually became organized as living cells.

The details of these processes are at present known only partly. Some information can be obtained by deducing from viruses, bacteria, and other primitive existing forms what the earliest living systems might have been like. Other clues come from astronomy, physics, and geology, sciences that supply data about the probable physical characteristics of the ancient earth. Important insights are also gained from chemical experiments designed to duplicate in the laboratory some of the steps that may have led to the beginning of life.

What has been learned in this way indicates that living creatures on earth are a direct product of the earth. There is also every reason to believe that living things owe their origin entirely to certain physical and chemical properties of the ancient earth. Nothing supernatural appears to be involved—only time and natural physical and chemical laws operating within the peculiarly suitable earthly environment. Given such an environment life probably *had* to happen; once the earth had formed, with particular chemical and physical properties, it was then virtually inevitable that life would later originate on it also. Similarly, if other solar systems have planets where chemical and physical conditions resemble those of the ancient earth, then life is likely to originate on such planets as well. It is now believed strongly that life occurs not only on earth but probably widely throughout the universe.

chemical evolution: cells

According to the most widely accepted hypothesis, the solar system started out some 10 billion years ago as a hot, rotating ball of atomic gas. In it, hydrogen atoms probably were the most abundant, and other, heavier kinds of atoms were present in lesser quantities. The sun was formed when most of this gas gravitated toward the center of the ball. Even today the sun is composed largely of hydrogen atoms. A swirling belt of gas remained outside the new sun. In time this belt broke up into a few smaller gas clouds; these spinning masses of fiery gases were the early planets.

The earth thus probably began, about 4.5 to 5 billion years ago, as a glowing mass of free hydrogen and other elements. These eventually became sorted out according to weight. Heavy ones such as iron and nickel sank toward the center of the earth, where they are still present today. Lighter atoms such as silicon and aluminum formed a middle shell. The very lightest, such as hydrogen, nitrogen, oxygen, and carbon, collected in the outermost layers. In time the temperature of these surface gases became low enough to permit the formation of compounds, and free atoms then largely disappeared.

On the basis of the known chemical properties and the presumed relative abundance of hydrogen, carbon, oxygen, and nitrogen, the surface gases should have given rise to some half-dozen different combinations: water (H_2O); methane (CH_4); ammonia (NH_3); carbon dioxide (CO_2); hydrogen cyanide (HCN); and hydrogen molecules (H_2). We have evidence that at least the first three of these compounds actually came into being not only on the early earth but on other planets as well. On Jupiter, for example, water, methane, and ammonia appear to be present today in the form of thick surface layers of permanently frozen solids. These compounds apparently formed there as on earth, but at that great distance from the sun the surface of the planet probably froze before much additional chemical change could occur. On the hot earth, by contrast, the early compounds remained gaseous and could give rise to new compounds later.

Temperatures in the outer layers of the earth eventually became low enough to allow some of the gases to liquefy and some of the liquids in turn to solidify. Thus although to this day the earth contains a hot, thickly flowing center, the middle shell of lighter substances became a solid, gradually thickening crust. And as this crust thickened and cooled, it wrinkled and folded and gave rise to the first mountain ranges. Overlying the crust was the outer atmospheric mantle, which remained gaseous.

When the crust had cooled below the boiling point of water, most of the water in the atmosphere must have fallen as rain and formed oceans. Dissolved in these must have been some of the atmospheric methane and ammonia, as well as salts and minerals that leached out slowly from the solid crust of the earth and that spewed forth from numerous volcanoes. The oceans apparently acquired their saltiness relatively early, and to a small extent they became saltier still during succeeding ages (Fig. 8.1).

The stage was then set for synthesis reactions. Such reactions among water, methane, and ammonia resulted in *organic* compounds that contained *linked* carbon atoms. That simple organic materials can indeed be created by reactions among these gases was demonstrated in the early 1950s through dramatic and now classic laboratory experiments. In them the presumed environment of the early earth was duplicated in miniature. Mixtures containing water, methane, and ammonia were put into a flask, and electricity was discharged through these mixtures for several days to simulate the lightning discharges of the early earth. When the contents of the flask were examined, many amino acids, fatty acids, sugars, and other simple organic compounds were found to be present.

Thus there is excellent reason to think that, with energy from lightning and also from solar radiation, simple inorganic materials could give rise to a variety of organic compounds that accumulated in the ancient seas. Such compounds would have represented the chemical "staples" out of which more complex organic materials could be synthesized later (Fig. 8.2). At some point in the course of this *chemical* evolution, *biological* evolution must have begun: formation of the very complex chemicals so characteristic of life, and development of cells, the first actual living units.

It is physically and chemically most plausible to assume that the critical events in the creation of cells took place not in the open sea, where the necessary ingredients would not have remained together, but along the shores of the early ocean. The sand and clay particles there would

8.1 Sources of ocean salt. *Some came from volcanoes, both submarine and terrestrial; some was dissolved out at the sea bottom; some resulted from tidal action, which crumbled and dissolved the shorelines; and some originated on the land surface, leached out by rain and rivers.*

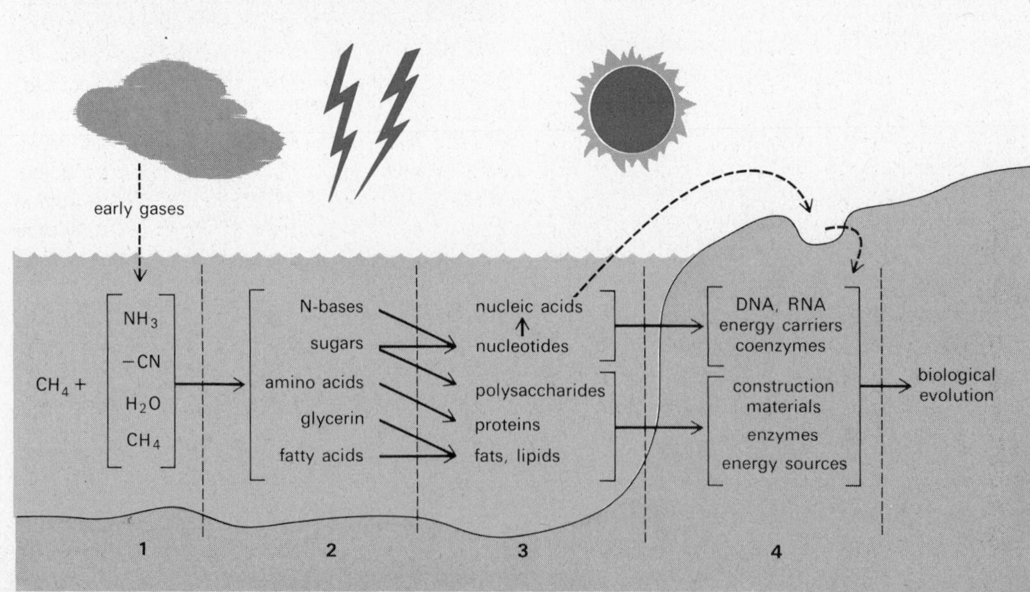

8.2 Chemical evolution: *summary of probable early synthesis reactions. At least three or four successive phases appear to have been involved. The original gaseous raw materials came from the early atmosphere (1), and, with the aid of energy from lightning and the sun, key biological compounds were synthesized progressively in the ocean (2, 3). The later, more complex synthesis reactions perhaps took place in sand pockets along the shore, where required ingredients could become highly concentrated by evaporation of water (4). The outcome was the origin of the first living units, and further biological evolution then followed.*

have provided surfaces to which oceanic molecules could have adhered, and evaporation of water would have increased the concentrations of such molecules. Indeed, microscopic sand pockets containing highly concentrated, nearly dry accumulations of simple organic materials well could have been the birthplaces of cells. This surmise again is reinforced by experimental data. For example, if concentrated mixtures of amino acids are heated under nearly dry conditions, proteinlike complexes are formed. Moreover, these develop surface films resembling cell membranes quite closely. Furthermore, if mixtures of simple starting compounds such as ammonia and certain amino acids are heated under almost dry conditions, products appear that have the characteristics of nitrogen bases.

It is therefore possible that, inside minute membrane-bounded droplets along the shore, some of the proteinlike materials formed at the time could have been active enzymatically. These could then have promoted a combination of nitrogen bases, simple sugars, and phosphates into nucleotides. And nucleotides are only a simple chemical step away from energy carriers such as ATP. Further, once enzymes and ATP are available, a few additional chemical steps can lead to nucleotide derivatives such as coenzymes and to nucleic acids such as genetically active DNA and RNA. In their turn, the DNA molecules in the droplets would have controlled the formation of particular, *specific* proteins, just as they are known to do today.

In the laboratory it is now possible to create DNA, RNA, and specific proteins artificially from simpler organic precursors, and by steps that virtually duplicate those taking place in a living cell (see also Chap. 17). Thus there exists important experimental support for the hypothesis that progressive synthesis reactions, roughly as outlined above, must have been the critical steps in the original development of living matter. In effect, the droplets on the ocean shore would have been distinctly individual units marked off from the surrounding ocean water, and they would have remained individualized even if they absorbed more water and were later washed back to the open ocean. Such units would have been primitive cells (Fig. 8.3).

Undoubtedly numerous trials and errors must have occurred before the first actual cells left their places of birth. Many and perhaps most of the accumulations on the shore probably were "unsuccessful." In given cases, for example, the right kinds of starting ingredients might not have come together; or the right amounts of ingredients might not have accumulated; or the mixture might have dried up completely; or it might have been washed out to sea prematurely and dispersed. Clearly, numerous hazards must have led to many false starts and to many incomplete endings. Yet when an appropriate constellation of materials did accumulate, the formation of a living cell would have been a likely result.

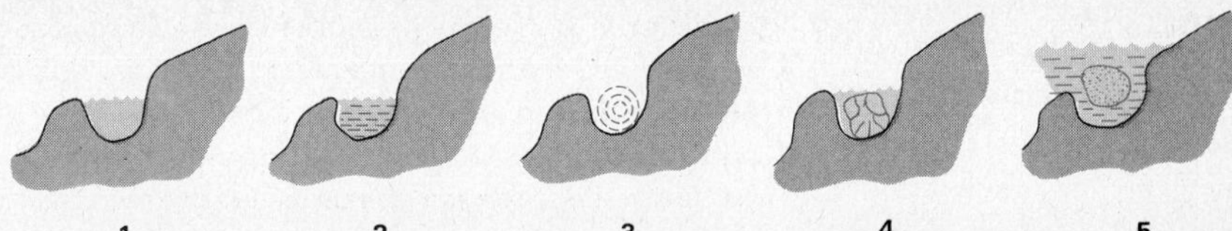

8.3 The possible origin of the first cells. *Appropriate chemical ingredients might have accumulated by adsorption in microscopic pockets along the seashore* (*1*), *and these ingredients could have become concentrated progressively* (*2*). *Under relatively dry conditions and perhaps with the aid of ATP, which might have been present, nucleic acids and proteins could have formed* (*3*). *Some of the proteins then could have made possible enzymatically accelerated reactions and formation of structural membranes and internal fibrils* (*4*). *Finally, primitive cellular compartments might have been washed out to sea* (*5*).

A basic problem in tracing the possible origin of cells (and of later groups of organisms in general) is to decide whether they evolved *monophyletically,* from a single common ancestral stock, or *polyphyletically,* from several separate ancestral stocks. Did early cells arise from a single first cell, an "archancestor" of all life, or did numerous "first" cells originate independently? The answer to such questions simply is not known.

Monophyletists invoke a *probability* argument: cells are so complex that multiple origins of such complexities are statistically quite unlikely. The argument leads logically to the view that all life started in a single place at a single time, from a single cell formed by "lucky accident." Proponents of polyphyletism counter with a probability argument of their own. They point out that, compared to their later complexities, the original cells could not really have been so complex. At first they probably were little more than accumulations of mixed chemicals surrounded by membranes, and structural complexity must have evolved later, in gradual steps. Moreover, if the conditions for cell formation could develop in one place at one time, it is statistically most likely that such conditions would develop also in other places and at other times.

In one sense, therefore, chance undoubtedly did play a role in cell formation: many droplets never became cells, and those that did owed their existence to the chance accumulation of the right ingredients. But in another sense cell formation was not simply an enormously "lucky accident," a one-time occurrence of very remote probability. On the contrary, given an early earth so constituted that certain compounds could form, and given these compounds and their special properties, then cell formation *had* to take place sooner or later. The only element of chance here was time; the uncertainty was not a matter of "if" but of "when" and "how often." The origin of cells was therefore as little an accident as is the eventual appearance of sevens and elevens in a series of dice throws.

Monophyletists also invoke a *similarity* argument: all cells are fundamentally so remarkably alike in chemical composition, microscopic structure, and function, that a common origin from a single ancestry seems clearly indicated. Polyphyletists here counter with the observation that all living cells must *necessarily* share certain basic structural and functional characteristics; for those early droplets that did not exhibit such characteristics simply would never have been "alive," by definition of this term. The similarities among cells therefore are not necessarily an indication of common ancestry, but might merely reflect the universal attributes anything living must have regardless of origin.

Best estimates at present suggest that the first cell or cells probably arose perhaps 3 or 4 billion years ago, or about 1 or 2 billion years after the formation of the earth. Yet no one point in the earth's early history really qualifies as a "beginning" of life. The cell is the major product of the first few billion years, and we regard this product as being alive. But the earlier organic compounds dissolved in the ocean already had the properties that eventually made life possible. Such compounds in turn did not originate their characteristic properties, but acquired them when they were formed from various simpler compounds. The potential of life clearly traces back to the original atoms, and the creation of life out of atoms was but a step-by-step exploitation of their properties.

In short, life did not burst forth from the ocean finished and ready. Instead it *developed,* and here is perhaps the most dramatic illustration that small beginnings can have surprisingly large endings. Development has been the hallmark of life ever since, and life today is still unceasingly forming and molding. Indeed it will never be finally "finished" until its last spark is extinguished.

biological evolution: premonera

For present purposes the earliest cells can collectively be called *Premonera,* or organisms that preceded the evolution of the Monera.

In later ages, premoneran cells must have become diversified as numerous new cell types in response to a powerful environmental stimulus: the gradual disappearance of free organic molecules from the ocean. For as more and more such molecules were used as food by an ever-increasing multitude of reproducing cells, the global rate of food consumption must eventually have become greater than the rate of food formation from methane, ammonia, and water. In time, therefore, the ocean became a largely inorganic medium, as it still is today. Unless the early cells then could have evolved new ways of obtaining food they would soon have nourished themselves into extinction. Evidently they did not.

One of the first evolutionary responses to dwindling food supplies probably was the development of *parasitism.* If foods could not be obtained from the open ocean, they still could be obtained inside the bodies of living cells. Methods of infecting cellular hosts could well have evolved almost as soon as cells themselves had originated, and parasitism must have been an effective new way of life for many of the early cells (Fig. 8.4).

Another new way that required relatively little evolutionary adjustment was *saprotrophism.* Here a cell drew food molecules from the bodies of dead cells or disintegrated cellular material. Organic *decay* of such material was a result and has occurred ever since. Saprotrophic types are so abundant today in all environments that practically every organic substance begins to decay almost immediately after exposure. A third new process that permitted survival despite dwindling food supplies was *holotrophism,* "eating" other living cells whole. This method of feeding presumably originated through phagocytosis, the general capacity of a cell to engulf microscopic particles (see Chap. 5). Amoeboid pseudopodia and permanent cellular mouths (*gullets*) must have been later elaborations.

But all three of these new food-gathering procedures were ultimately self-limiting. Collectively they represent the *heterotrophic* forms of nutrition, exhibited even today by organisms that require preexisting foods and that therefore depend on other organisms. Early heterotrophic nutrition among Premonera thus merely redistributed organic materials that already existed. If totally new food sources had not been obtained, life would have had to cease sooner or later.

The raw materials for new foods were still present in abundance. Water was in inexhaustible supply and, in addition to methane, an even better source of carbon now existed directly inside cells in the form of respiratory carbon dioxide. With CO_2 and water available, organic molecules could be manufactured by cells, provided that new external sources of energy could be found. Internal energy was still obtainable from ATP, to be sure, but ATP was itself among the very organic molecules that were in danger of disappearing.

We know by hindsight that some Premonera actually did evolve means of using new external sources of energy. One group included cell types that could absorb sulfur, iron, nitrogen, or one of a number of other mineral materials obtainable in the environment. Such inorganic substances could be made to undergo various exergonic, energy-yielding reactions in the cells, and chemical energy so obtained could then serve in transforming internal CO_2 and water to organic food molecules. Nutrition by such a process of *chemosynthesis* is still encountered today in some of the bacteria (Fig. 8.5).

However, chemosynthesis was probably far less widespread right from the start than another new nutritional process, *photosynthesis,* evolved by other groups of Premonera. In photosynthesis the external energy source is light, and with the aid of the green photosensitive compound *chlorophyll* the energy of light is used to transform CO_2 and water to foods. Collectively, chemosynthesis and photosynthesis represent the *autotrophic* forms of nutrition, exhibited by organisms that can survive in an exclusively inorganic environment and that therefore do not depend on other organisms.

Thus once the autotrophic production of new organic compounds was assured, it did not matter that the supply of free molecular foods in the ocean finally became inadequate. Photosynthetic cells could make foods for themselves; holotrophic forms could swallow such cells as well as one another; parasites could invade photosynthesizers or holotrophs; and saprotrophs could find foods in the dead bodies of any of these. Today photosynthesis still supports all living creatures except the chemosynthesizers.

As photosynthesis occurred on an ever-increasing scale, it brought about far-reaching changes in the physical environment. A byproduct of photosynthesis is free molecular oxygen (O_2), a gas that combines readily with other substances. The gas escaped from photosynthetic cells into the ocean and from there to the atmosphere, and it must have reacted promptly with everything it could. A slow, profound "oxygen revolution" then occurred. In the course of it the ancient atmosphere was transformed to the modern one, which no longer contains methane, ammonia, and cyanide. Instead it consists mainly of water vapor, carbon dioxide, and molecular nitrogen, plus large quantities of free molecular oxygen itself (Fig. 8.6).

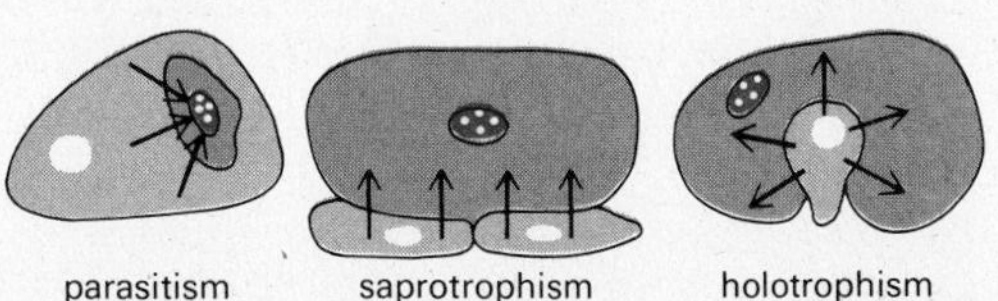

8.4 ***Heterotrophic nutrition.*** *In parasitism one organism obtains food from another living one (a small parasitic cell is shown inside a larger host cell). In saprotrophism food is obtained from dead organisms. And in holotrophism one organism eats another in whole or in part. These three methods are noncreative; they merely redistribute already existing foods and do not generate new supplies.*

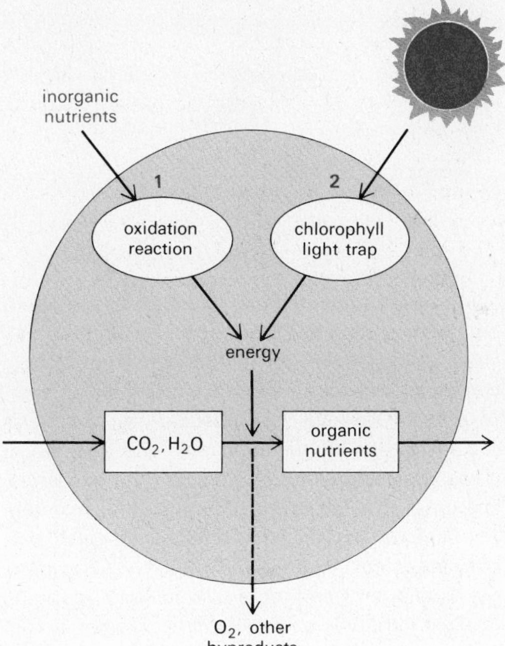

8.5 ***Autotrophic nutrition.*** *In chemosynthesis (1) energy is obtained from inorganic raw materials, and with the aid of this energy the organism creates organic materials out of carbon dioxide and water. Various inorganic byproducts result as well. In photosynthesis (2) energy is obtained from the sun by means of energy-trapping molecules such as chlorophyll. The organism then again creates organic nutrients out of carbon dioxide and water. Oxygen is a byproduct here (derived from water, which is split into separate hydrogen and oxygen fractions).*

$CH_4 + 2\,O_2 \longrightarrow CO_2 + 2\,H_2O$

$4\,NH_3 + 3\,O_2 \longrightarrow 2\,N_2 + 6\,H_2O$

$O_2 + 2\,O_2 \longrightarrow 2\,O_3$, ozone

metals, minerals + $O_2 \longrightarrow$ ores, rocks

organisms + $O_2 \longrightarrow$ aerobic respiration

8.6 ***The oxygen revolution.*** *Oxygen from photosynthesis reacted with other materials. A major result was the establishment of a new, modern atmosphere that contained* N_2*,* CO_2*, and* H_2O*, in addition to* O_2 *itself.*

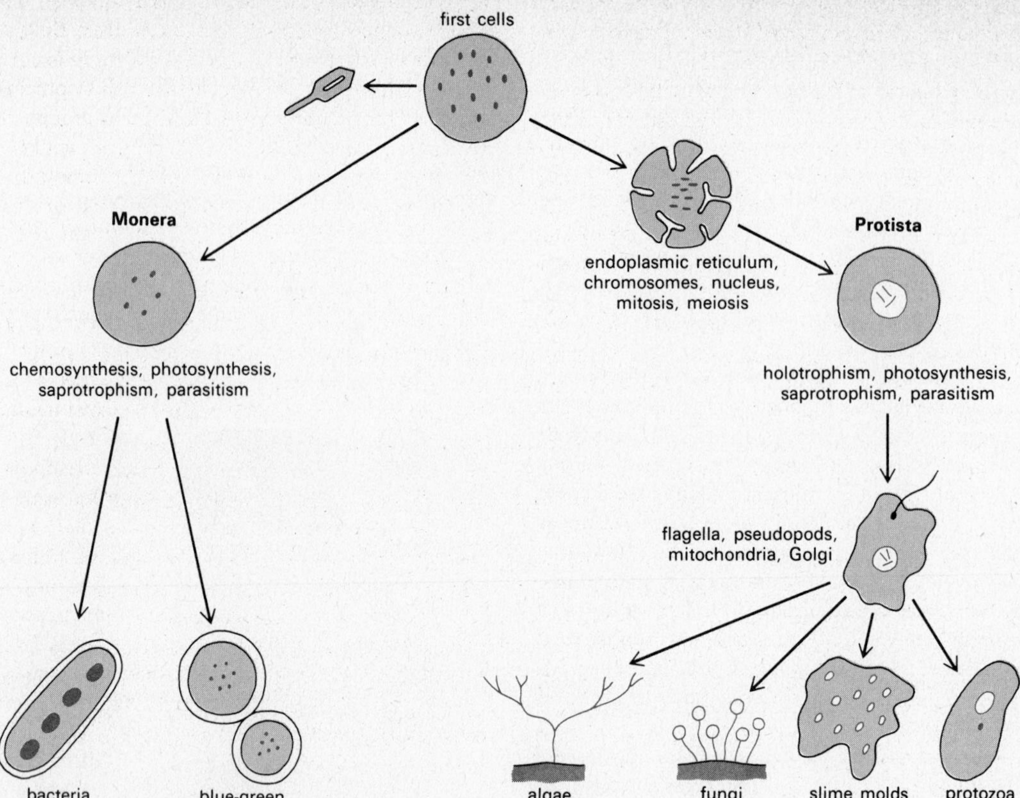

8.7 Early cell evolution. *The earliest cells (with dispersed genetic material, as indicated) probably gave rise to two structural types, one without nuclear membranes and referred to as moneran cells, the other with nuclear membranes and referred to as protistan cells. The presumed later evolutionary history of these two cellular stocks is sketched at right.*

Moreover, under the impact of X rays and other high-energy radiation from space, oxygen molecules several miles up in the new atmosphere combined with one another and formed a layer of *ozone* (O_3). This layer became an excellent screen against high-energy rays, and ever since it has protected living organisms from excessive amounts of such space radiation. Free oxygen also reacted with the solid crust of the earth and converted most metals and minerals to *oxides,* the familiar ores and rocks now making up much of the land surface. Finally, free oxygen made possible a new form of respiration. The earliest cells respired *anaerobically,* without oxygen, and to a small extent all living organisms still do so (see Chap. 15). But when environmental oxygen became available in quantity, organisms newly evolving at the time developed means of using this gas. Since then the far more efficient oxygen-requiring, or *aerobic,* form of respiration has been perpetuated.

Evidently, the activities of the early organisms greatly altered the physical character of the earth and also the biological character of the organisms themselves. So has it been ever since: the physical earth creates and influences the development of the biological earth, and the biological earth then reciprocates by influencing the development of the physical earth.

In parallel with the nutritional evolution of the Premonera an internal structural evolution must have taken place as well. At first the gene-forming DNA molecules were probably suspended free in the cell substance. Occasionally such nucleic acid molecules could have escaped from a cell to the open ocean and by accident could have encountered other cells and entered them. Such transferable nucleic acids conceivably might have been ancestral to the viruses. As noted in Chap. 6, modern viruses have similarly transferable nucleic acids, and it is possible that ancestral viruses were perhaps little more than naked nucleic acid molecules. If so, introduction of such molecules from one early cell to another must have had important consequences. For the transferred acids were cellular genes, and as these became shuffled among cells, so did the activities that such genes controlled. Exchanges of nucleic acids thus would have altered the genetic constitution of cells, and this process could have contributed to the evolution of a great variety of new cell types. Certain kinds of modern viruses still transfer genes from one cell to another, a phenomenon known as *transduction* (see Chap. 27).

Judging from the results today, we know that two of the new structural cell types came to have particular significance in later evolution (Fig. 8.7). In one line of descent, the originally freely suspended nucleic acids later must have become joined together as threadlike filaments that formed loose clumps. Such clumps remained embedded in and in direct contact with the rest of the cell substance. The organisms exhibiting this type of internal cellular arrangement collectively form the *Monera* (or *Prokaryota,* organisms preceding the evolution of cell nuclei). They are represented today by the *bacteria* and the *blue-green algae.* As a group they exhibit four of the five methods of nutrition. Bacteria are variously photosynthetic, chemosynthetic, parasitic, or saprotrophic; blue-green algae are largely photosynthetic. Evidently, all methods except holotrophic eating occur.

In a second major line of descent, the gene-forming nucleic acids in each cell again condensed as threadlike filaments. However, proteins became an integral structural part of such filaments, and these nucleoprotein organelles represented *chromosomes.* Furthermore, a membrane formed around the chromosomes in a cell, setting off a distinct *nuclear* region from a surrounding *cytoplasmic* region. In the cytoplasm then evolved all the organelles we now find in a "modern" cell. Organisms exhibiting such an internal cellular structure collectively constitute the *Protista* (or *Eukaryota,* organisms with distinct nuclei). Four groups descended from early Protista represent a major part of the living world today: the *algae* (other than the blue-greens), the *fungi,* the *slime molds,* and the *protozoa.* Collectively they exhibit all nutritional methods except chemosynthesis—photosynthesis, holotrophism, saprotrophism, and parasitism. Certain groups of protists, notably some primitive algae, actually can carry out two or more of these methods simultaneously. Thus a given individual of this type might either photosynthesize or eat holotrophically or do both together.

Monera and Protista probably were the only organisms in existence for long ages. Eventually, perhaps a billion years ago, certain of the protists gave rise to a basically new group of organisms. Neither the date of this event nor the exact evolutionary source of the new group can be pinpointed well. But it is clear that these organisms must have lost all nutritional methods except holotrophism, that they were multicellular, and that they attained new levels of structural complexity: they had *organs* and later also *organ systems,* and their individual development passed through distinct *embryonic* and *larval* phases. This new group, the *Metazoa,* comprised the *animals.*

Much later, about 350 million years ago, ancient protists also gave rise to another basically new group. In this case the date is somewhat more certain, and the specific ancestors appear to have been some of the multicellular green algae then in existence. The new group descended from these lost all nutritional methods except photosynthesis, and the structural complexity again reached the organ and organ-system levels. Moreover, the organisms characteristically also passed through embryonic phases of development. This group, the *Metaphyta,* comprised the *plants.*

Today the living world is a collection of Monera, Protista, Metazoa, and Metaphyta (see Fig. 2.8). The characteristics of these organisms will occupy our attention in the following sections and chapters.

Monera

As might be expected in view of their presumed evolutionary antiquity, Monera are distinguished largely by negative characteristics (Fig. 8.8). A moneran cell does *not* contain an organized nucleus with a distinct surrounding membrane. Experiments indicate that the genetic material is arranged in the form of filaments (and that these filaments may be closed rings); but the internal structure of these filaments does *not* correspond to that of chromosomes of the type found in other organisms.

Under the light microscope the genetic material appears as one or more clumps exposed directly to the surrounding cytoplasm.

The cytoplasm itself does *not* appear to contain vacuoles, and it can *not* be observed to undergo the cyclosis and streaming movements typical of other cell types. Many Monera are photosynthetic, and these do *not* have complexly organized chloroplasts like those found in all other photosynthetic cells. Instead the structural unit of photosynthesis is a *chromatophore,* a protein disk that greatly resembles a single layer of a granum of a true chloroplast (see Chap. 5). Many such chromatophores are normally present. Monera also are without endoplasmic reticula, mitochondria, or Golgi bodies, but they do contain an abundance of ribosomes, the only organelles present that appear to be equivalent to those of other cell types. These many features of nonpossession clearly suggest that, at the time the Monera arose, the internal elaboration and specialization of cellular structure had not yet progressed very far.

Within the moneran category, the bacteria form the phylum *Schizophyta,* and the blue-green algae, the phylum *Cyanophyta.* The exact evolutionary relation of one phylum to the other is still relatively obscure.

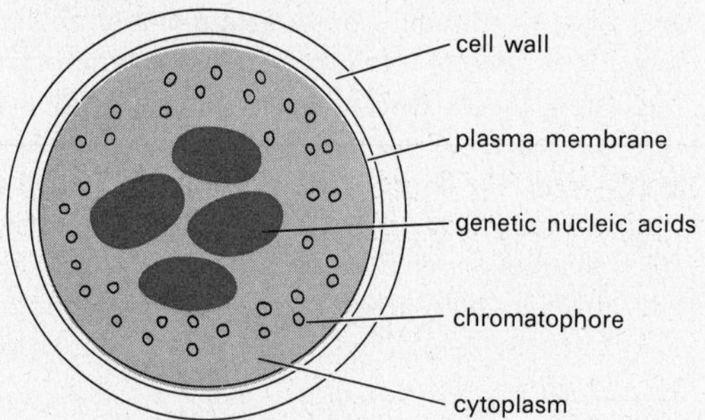

8.8 The moneran cell, *diagrammatic.*

Bacteria

Phylum Schizophyta 2,000 species

Bacteria probably outnumber all other organisms. They occur whenever life on earth is possible at all, and they are present in numerous places where other organisms cannot exist. Bacteria actually play a major role in the economy of nature and of man. They are also suitable test organisms in genetic and biochemical research, and much of our present understanding of the molecular basis of life has come from studies on bacteria.

Schizophytes are the smallest cells known (Fig. 8.9). They average 1 to 3 μ in length, as compared with about 10 μ for most other kinds of cells. Bacteria usually have a cell wall, made of polysaccharides, proteins, and frequently also lipids. Often this wall in turn is surrounded by a gelatinous capsule, variously composed of mixtures of carbohydrates and amino acids. In many instances it is the presence or absence of a capsule that determines whether a bacterium will be disease-producing or not.

Certain bacteria are flagellate, and the flagella are structurally unique. Each consists of just a single fibril, chemically different from the flagellar fibrils of other cell types (see Chap. 5). A bacterium can have flagella at either or both ends of the cell, or many flagella can be distributed over the entire cell surface.

Among the many shapes of bacterial cells, the three most common are the spherical, or *coccus* type, the straight-rod, or *bacillus* type, and the curved-rod, or *spirillum* type (Fig. 8.10). Bacteria are basically unicellular, but in many species two or more cells form filamentous, disk-shaped, or three-dimensional *colonies.* For example, common kinds of colonies among cocci include pairs of cells (*diplococcus*), disks of four cells (*tetracoccus*), straight chains of cells (*streptococcus*), cuboidal arrays of eight or several more cells (*sarcina*), and irregular clumps of cells (*staphylococcus*). The planes of cell division determine what form a colony will have.

In their usual active state bacterial cells are said to be in a *vegetative* condition. Some bacteria can also exist in an alternative state as *endospores.* An endospore forms by development of a membrane or wall that encloses an oval or spherical portion of the cell substance, including genetic DNA and some of the cytoplasm. The part of the cell outside the wall eventually degenerates, but the enclosed part persists as the endospore. Endospores are *dormant* and do not feed or multiply. Their walls are highly resistant to injurious agents, and bacteria so protected can survive in environments that would kill vegetative cells. Under favorable conditions endospores germinate; the walls break open and normal vegetative cells emerge (Fig. 8.11).

With the exception of animal-like eating, all possible forms of food procurement occur among the bacteria. Some species are chemosynthesizers or photosynthesizers that produce their own food. The photosynthetic types contain unique varieties of chlorophyll (including one called *bacteriochlorophyll*) located on the chromatophores. Bacterial photosynthesis also is chemically unique in that it never produces oxygen as a byproduct.

Most bacteria are heterotrophs that depend on other organisms for food. Of these, some are free-living saprotrophs in terrestrial and aquatic environments, and the rest are parasitic, commensalistic, or mutualistic symbionts. Also, some bacteria must have oxygen for respiration, others can do without it, and still others can survive both with and without oxygen. In most of these types reserve foods are stored in the form of the polysaccharide glycogen. Bioluminescence is fairly common in the phylum (see Fig. 17.14).

Bacteria as a whole have come to be of major significance to all other life on earth. Three general groups are of particular ecological importance: the saprotrophic *decay-causing* types in soil and water; the chemosynthetic *nitrogen-using* types (nitrifiers, denitrifiers, and nitrogen fixers), which contribute to the maintenance of the global nitrogen cycle; and the parasitic *pathogenic* bacteria, which produce disease. In Table 7 are listed the names of the main groups of bacteria (each equivalent in taxonomic rank to an order) and some of the characteristics of each group.

The so-called *rickettsias* appear to be vaguely related to the bacteria and perhaps also to the

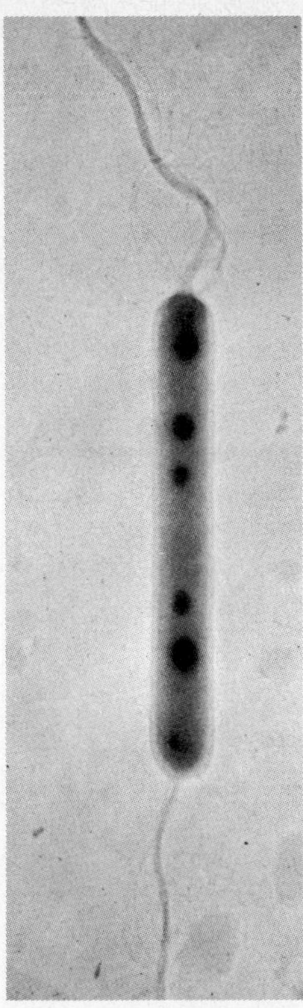

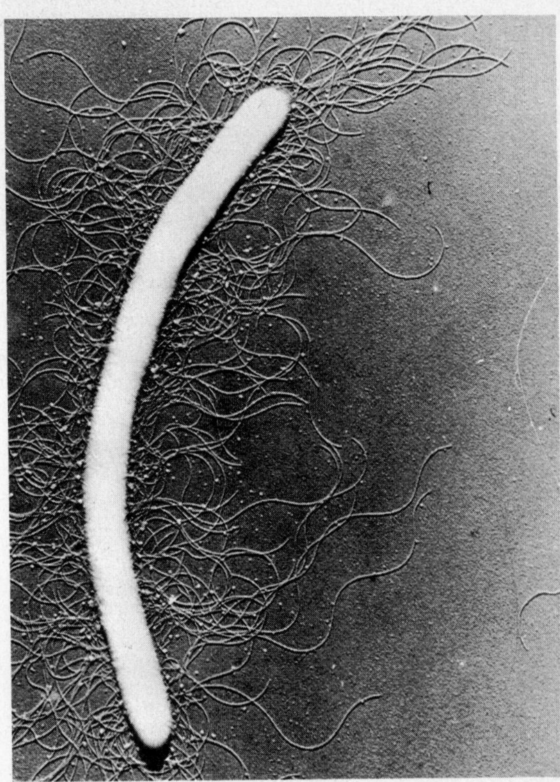

8.9 The bacterial cell. *Left, general structure. Note cell wall, internal clumps of genetic nucleic acids, and locomotor flagellum at each end. Only comparatively few bacterial types have such locomotor organelles. Right, electron micrograph of Proteus vulgaris, a flagellate bacterium. See also the following figures.*

8.10 Bacterial cells and colonies. *A, cocci in chains. B, bacilli. C, spirilla. D, some of the types of colonies formed by cocci; the nature and designation of a colony varies according to whether cell divisions occur in 1, 2, 3, or numerous planes.*

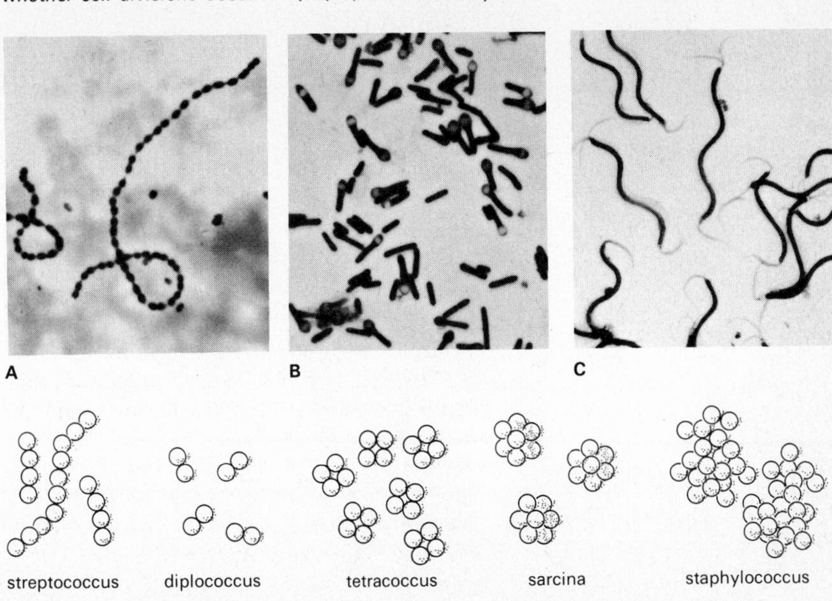

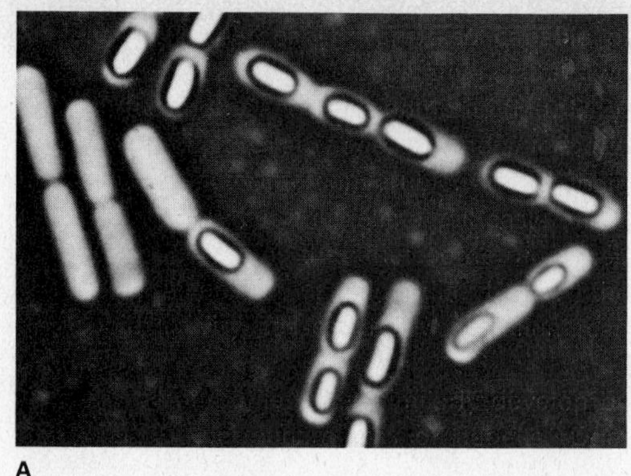

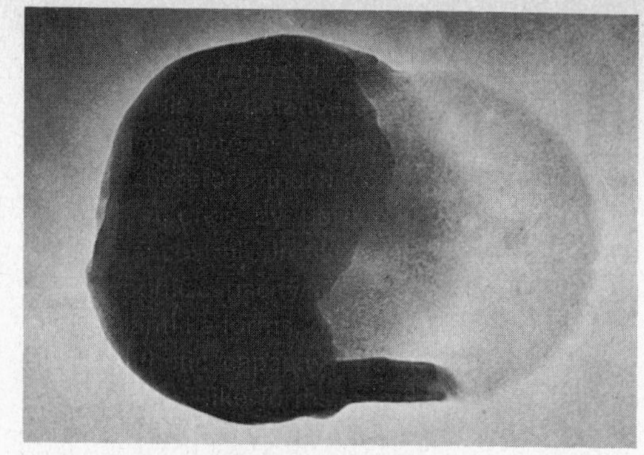

A B

8.11 ***Endospores.*** *A, thick-walled endospores have formed in bacilli. B, electron micrograph of a germinating endospore of Bacillus mycoides.*

Table 7. The main groups of bacteria and some of their characteristics

name of group	*chief characteristics*
Pseudomonadales: pseudomonads	most primitive group; generally flagellate; chemosynthetic, photosynthetic, and heterotrophic
Eubacteriales: true bacteria	largest group; some flagellate; all kinds of heterotrophism and symbiosis; many pathogenic; example: *Escherichia coli,* commensal in human gut
Actinomycetales: branching bacteria	in branching, filamentous colonies; antibiotic producers (streptomycin, aureomycin, etc.)
Spirochaetales: spiral bacteria	large spiral cells; whirling and spinning aids propulsion; example: *Treponema pallidum,* syphilis-causing parasite
Myxobacteriales: gliding slime bacteria	secrete slime track on which cells creep and glide; collect in masses and form ''fruiting bodies'' superficially like those of slime molds
Beggiatoales: gliding bacteria	in filamentous colonies; propulsion by jerky, oscillating movements; great resemblance to certain blue-green algae, except nonphotosynthetic

viruses. Uncertainty still exists as to whether or not rickettsias are cellular ''organisms'' at all. Their spherical or rodlike body is far smaller than that of even small bacteria, and like viruses they are obligate intracellular parasites, unable to carry out living functions outside the cells of specific hosts. Such hosts are ticks and lice. One rickettsial species is the causative agent of Rocky Mountain spotted fever and another of epidemic typhus fever, both diseases of man. Ticks in the first case and body lice in the second transfer the rickettsias to man.

Another group with possible affinities to bacteria includes the viruses themselves (see also Chap. 6 and preceding section). At least some of the viruses now in existence could be descendants of nucleic acid fragments that broke away from the genetic material of early bacterial cells. If so, the cells of other organisms very possibly could have given rise to viruses in similar fashion. Virus creation of this sort actually might still be taking place today.

Blue-green Algae

Phylum Cyanophyta 2,500 species

This phylum name is somewhat misleading, since many cyanophytes are not blue-green but red, yellow, green, blue, black, and of various intermediate shades. These colors are produced by different proportions of several pigments: a variety of chlorophyll called *chlorophyll a; carotene;* various *xanthophylls;* a blue *c-phycocyanin;* and a red *c-phycoerythrin.* The last two are tetrapyrrol derivatives occurring uniquely in the cyanophytes.

The blue-greens live in virtually all environments that contain water. The organisms range from the tropics to the poles, and they occur in soil, fresh water, and the ocean. In lakes and in the ocean they often form part of the plankton. Extensive growths of the algae frequently occur in areas that are wetted only intermittently, such as tidal flats, stream banks, tree bark, and rocks sprayed with sea water. Some cyanophytes live in the icy waters of glaciers; others, in hot springs where temperatures reach 85°C or more. Some blue-green algae live as symbionts with other organisms. For example, they often are the algal members of lichens.

A cyanophyte cell is enclosed in a wall that contains *cellulose* and frequently also *pectin.* In some species the pectin dissolves immediately after being secreted, but in others it persists and forms a thick gelatinous sheath around the cell wall. Flagella are entirely absent, and if locomotion occurs at all it is of gliding or jerky type similar to that of some of the bacteria.

The cell interior of a cyanophyte consists of a colorless central part and a surrounding pigmented region (Fig. 8.12). The central portion contains the genetic material as well as granules believed to be phosphate-containing crystals. This region is not separated from the surrounding parts by any membrane or other structure. In the outer cytoplasm are found chromatophores with chlorophyll, various other pigments, and *cyanophycean starch,* a food-storage compound unique to the blue-greens.

Like certain bacteria, many cyanophytes can fix atmospheric nitrogen, and many are bioluminescent. Nearly all are photosynthetic, oxygen being released as a byproduct. Numerous species grow as single cells, but many are multicellular and form filaments or colonies of more complex shapes. Such types are often embedded in a gelatinous mass secreted by the cells (Fig. 8.13 and Color Fig. 6).

The phylum contains three subgroups (orders): *Chroococcales, Chamaeosiphonales,* and *Hormogonales.* The first two include solitary and colonial species (see Fig. 8.13), and the Hormogonales are distinctly filamentous (see Color Fig. 6). In such filaments groups of adjacent cells

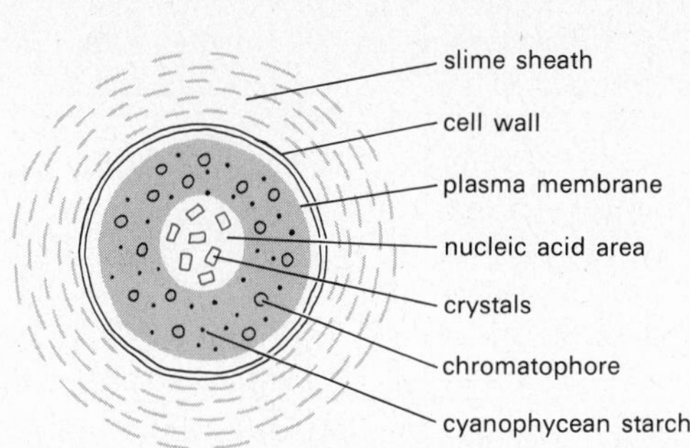

8.12 ***Cell structure in blue-green algae,*** *diagrammatic.*

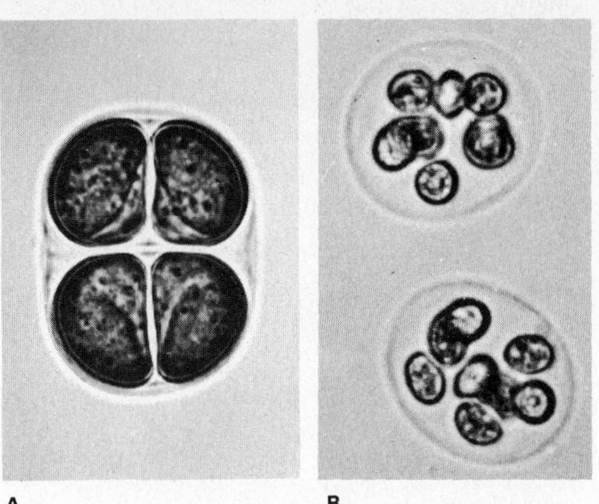

8.13 ***Blue-green algae.*** *A, a four-celled growth stage of Chroococcus. B, two colonies of Gloeocapsa. Note the gelatinous capsules in both figures (approx. ×150). See also Color Fig. 6.*

(*hormogones*) are often enclosed by a common wall, and two neighboring hormogones are joined by a unit called a *heterocyst.* This structure appears to be a transparent cell with a double wall. A filament can break readily at these heterocysts, and their main function may be to make such breaks possible. The separated hormogones then can settle elsewhere and grow into new filaments. In contrast with the other two groups, the Hormogonales are motile and display the jerky, rolling type of motion already mentioned.

Two common representatives of the Hormogonales are *Oscillatoria,* so named after its characteristic motion, and *Nostoc* (see Color Fig. 6). The latter is found in clear fresh water, where it forms gelatinous balls of up to 2 ft in diameter. Such balls contain numerous filaments and their surrounding sheaths. *Nostoc* colonies can enter a dormant state and survive the winter in this condition. The organisms also occur as mutualistic symbionts in many lichens.

review questions

1 Which gases in the early atmosphere of the earth appear to have contributed to the formation of biologically important compounds? What were some of these compounds, and what evidence do we have that they could actually have formed?

2 Review the role of (*a*) temperature, (*b*) water, (*c*) organic compounds, and (*d*) enzymes in the origin of life.

3 Review the synthesis reactions through which compounds required for the origin of living systems might have occurred. Describe experiments duplicating some of these reactions.

4 How are the first cells believed to have evolved? Distinguish between chemical and biological evolution. What was the physical character of the earth (*a*) at the time it formed, (*b*) before living systems originated, and (*c*) after living systems originated?

5 Review the events of the oxygen revolution and describe the consequences of this revolution. How many years ago did (*a*) the earth form, (*b*) life originate? Distinguish between monophyletism and polyphyletism as related to the origin of cells.

6 How are moneran and protistan cell types distinguished, and how could both have arisen from the first cells? What living groups belong to the Monera and the Protista? What are viruses, and how are they believed to have originated?

7 Through what processes of evolution could moneran and protistan nutritional patterns have arisen? What processes probably necessitated and promoted such nutritional evolution?

8 Describe the basic events of, and the differences between, chemosynthesis and photosynthesis. What are the basic forms of heterotrophic nutrition, and which of these forms occur among Monera and Protista? Review the identifying traits of Monera, of bacteria, and of blue-green algae. What traits distinguish the two moneran phyla?

9 Describe the general structure of a bacterial cell. How do these organisms feed and move? How are bacteria distinguished in shape and growth pattern? What is an endospore? What are rickettsias?

10 Describe the general structure of a cyanophyte cell. How do these organisms feed and move? Where do blue-greens occur in nature? Define hormogone, heterocyst. Name representative groups within the phylum.

collateral readings

Brown, H.: The Age of the Solar System, *Sci. American,* Apr., 1957. Estimations are based on the radioactivity of meteorites and rocks.

Cairns, J.: The Bacterial Chromosome, *Sci. American,* Jan., 1966. An article discussing the structure and duplication of this DNA-containing organelle.

Echlin, P.: The Blue-green Algae, *Sci. American,* June, 1966. On the biology of these organisms and their importance to man.

Eglinton, G., and **M. Calvin**: Chemical Fossils, *Sci. American,* Jan., 1967. On organic compounds found in 3-billion-year-old rocks.

Ehrlich, P. R., and **R. W. Holm**: "Process of Evolution," McGraw-Hill, New York, 1963. The first chapter of this book is a discussion of the origin of life.

Kerkut, G. A.: "The Implications of Evolution," Pergamon, New York, 1960. This stimulating little book examines some of the assumptions underlying evolutionary thinking, including the problem of monophyletism versus polyphyletism.

Landsberg, H. E.: The Origin of the Atmosphere, *Sci. American,* Aug., 1953. The history of the atmosphere is traced on the basis of data from various sciences.

Miller, S. L.: The Origin of Life, in "This Is Life," Holt, New York, 1962. This article gives details on the atmosphere experiments referred to in this chapter and also discusses the general problem of the origin of life. References at the end of the article cite all pertinent original sources.

Morowitz, H. J., and **M. E. Tourtellotte**: The Smallest Living Cells, *Sci. American,* March 1962. Certain microbes smaller than some viruses are described, leading to the question of the smallest unit compatible with life.

Oparin, A. I.: "Life: Its Nature, Origin, and Development," Academic, New York, 1962. This author fathered modern thinking on the subject in a book published in 1936; the present volume is the latest revision of it.

Ross, H. H.: "A Synthesis of Evolutionary Theory," Prentice-Hall, Englewood Cliffs, N.J., 1962. This highly recommended book contains two early chapters on the origin of the universe and of life; the heating experiments referred to in this chapter are reviewed as well.

Wald, G.: The Origin of Life, *Sci. American,* Aug., 1954. A reexamination of the meaning of spontaneous generation in the light of modern thinking about the creation of life.

chapter 9 protists

category	phylum	subphylum	class
protista	chlorophyta		
	charophyta		
	euglenophyta		
	chrysophyta		chrysophyceae
			xanthophyceae
			bacillariophyceae
	pyrrophyta		cryptophyceae
			dinophyceae
	phaeophyta		
	rhodophyta		
	mycophyta		phycomycetes
			ascomycetes
			basidiomycetes
			fungi imperfecti
	myxophyta		myxomyceteae
			acrasieae
			labyrinthuleae
	protozoa	mastigophora	
		sarcodina	
		sporozoa	
		ciliophora	

Of the four protistan groups now in existence—algae, fungi, slime molds, and protozoa—the algae probably include the descendants of the most ancient protists. Primitive living algae actually are thought to resemble the original protistan ancestors to a considerable degree, and from such primitive types we can infer what the first protists might have been like.

general characteristics

In the course of probably millions of years, the cell type we now recognize as protistan gradually must have evolved all the specialized organelles we have examined in Chap. 5. Thus, a definite membrane-bounded nucleus must have come to include nucleoli and filamentous nucleoprotein chromosomes. The cytoplasm must have become equipped with endoplasmic reticulum, mitochondria, Golgi bodies, chloroplasts, centrioles, and kinetosomes, as well as flagella, cilia, and the capacity to form pseudopods. Ribosomes must have been inherited from earlier premoneran ancestors, but protistan cells in addition must have evolved different kinds of vacuoles, granules, and fibrils (Fig. 9.1).

Cell division must have become associated with new processes of chromosome duplication (*mitosis* and *meiosis;* see Chap. 24) not encountered as such in the Monera. Also, early protists must have been capable of existing alternately as vegetative and dormant cells in response to particular environmental conditions. Like many of its algal descendants today, for example, the ancient protist undoubtedly could secrete a thick, resistant wall and become *encapsulated* or *encysted.* Or it could secrete a sheath of water-retaining jelly and survive periods of drought in this fashion.

Above all, judging from primitive algal types today, early protists must have had the capacity to obtain food by two or more methods simulta-

9.1 Protistan cell structure. *Diagram of basic components.*

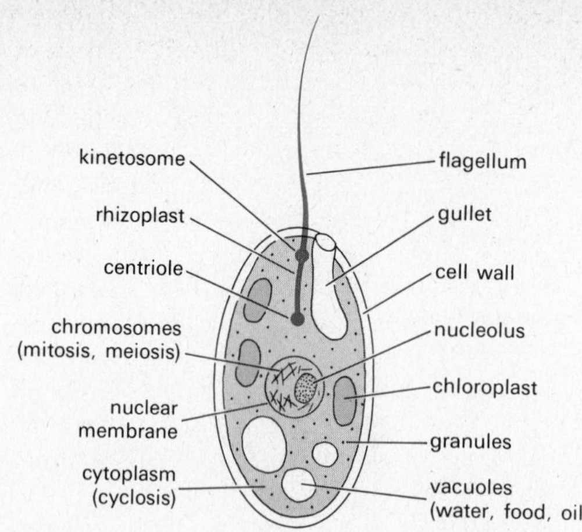

9.2 Vegetative states in protists. *A flagellate cell can become amoeboid, and later that same cell or any of its offspring can revert to a flagellate state. Loss of flagella and development of multinuclearity leads to the nonmotile coccine state, in which, after cell-boundary formation during reproduction, the offspring cells can either remain coccine or resume flagellate or amoeboid existence. Loss of flagella and successive vegetative divisions produce the sporine state. The resulting cells can separate or stay together as colonies, and any of the cells can also assume the flagellate or the amoeboid condition.*

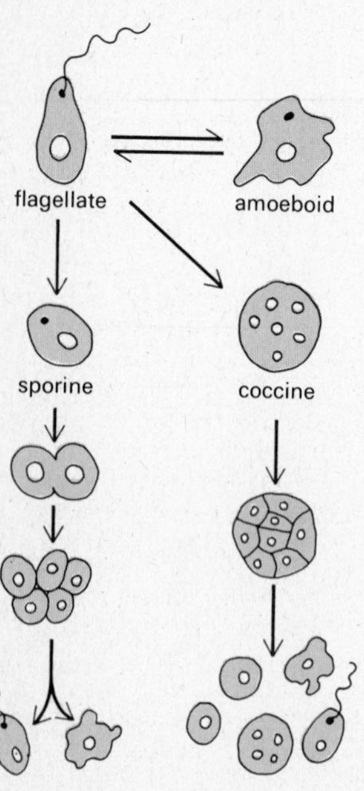

neously. For example, it must have been quite common for a protist to engulf or absorb preexisting food from the external environment *as well as* photosynthesize new food internally. In this respect the ancient protists probably were both plantlike and animal-like at once.

In conjunction with these alternative forms of nutrition, and again judging from living types, ancient protists probably were also capable of existing in four alternative vegetative states, two of them locomotor and two nonmotile (Fig. 9.2). The locomotor states are *flagellate* and *amoeboid,* and they are readily interconvertible. An amoeboid state can arise when a flagellate cell casts off its flagellum (but retains the kinetosome) and then moves by means of pseudopodia. If later the amoeboid activity ceases, a new flagellum can grow out.

The two nonmotile states similarly develop by temporary or permanent loss of flagella. One, which we may call the *coccine* condition, is a special type of multinucleate state. The nucleus of a nonmotile cell here continues to divide, but the cytoplasm does not. The result is a progressively more multinucleate but still unicellular organism. Cytoplasmic division occurs only at the time of reproduction, when *multiple fission* takes place: the cell becomes partitioned into numerous offspring cells simultaneously, each containing a nucleus. Such new cells (*spores*) then either become temporarily flagellate or amoeboid or grow into new nonmotile multinucleates directly. In the second nonmotile condition, conveniently called the *sporine* state, a cell does divide regularly during its vegetative life. The resulting nonmotile daughter cells then often remain attached to one another and form a multicellular aggregate. At any time, however, any of the cells can develop flagella or become amoeboid and disengage from the aggregate.

Of these four different states of vegetative existence, the flagellate condition occurs in the most primitive protists known and is therefore believed to be basic; all other states might be derived from it. The adaptive advantage of such multiple alternative states must have been great, particularly in conjunction with the multiple means of nutrition. Thus, by permitting cellular locomotion, the two motile states must have made possible heterotrophic nutrition generally and holotrophic feeding specifically. At night or on the dimly lit bottoms of natural waters, an ancestral protist could actively hunt for food. But in the presence of ample light in the daytime, photosynthesis could occur and locomotor energy could be reduced to zero by assumption of one of the nonmotile states.

Among some modern Protista given individuals still can exist in two or more of these four alternative states, and certain species of unicellular algae can both photosynthesize and feed heterotrophically. However, most living protists exhibit just one particular vegetative state and one method of nutrition more or less permanently. It can be inferred, therefore, that ancestral groups gave rise to modern ones by partial losses of function. Certain ancestral protists could have lost the heterotrophic capacity and thus evolved into more nearly plantlike forms, or they could have lost the photosynthetic capacity and evolved into more nearly animal-like forms. Similarly, different ancestral groups could have become specialized to exist in but one of the four vegetative states and lost the capacity to exist in the others. That such differential losses of function can actually occur is demonstrable in the laboratory. For example, primitive living algae with multiple means of nutrition can be converted by various experimental procedures to either purely photosynthetic or purely heterotrophic organisms. Similarly, experimental removal of, for example, kinetosomes can convert flagellate cells to permanently nonmotile ones.

If we therefore regard specialization in photosynthetic and heterotrophic nutrition as two possible directions of evolution, and if each of these two could at the same time evolve four different vegetative states of existence, then there must have been at least eight possible evolutionary pathways that ancient protists could have followed. Moreover, modern protists include not only unicellular but also multicellular members. Accordingly, we can assume that the available evolutionary paths could be further multiplied by a factor of 2, depending on whether the organisms remained unicellular or became multicellular. Thus there must have existed at least 16 different ways in which early protists could have evolved further.

These 16 lines of descent are represented today by the modern Protista (Fig. 9.3). Some unicellular algae now living still display the ancestral traits of being both plantlike and animal-like simultaneously. All other algae are exclusively photosynthetic. They are variously flagellate, amoeboid, coccine, and sporine, and each of these lines includes both unicellular and often quite complex multicellular members. The remaining Protista represent the exclusively heterotrophic lines of descent. Fungi exemplify a culmination of the coccine state; all fungi are or become multinucleate organisms that form distinct uninucleate cells only at the time of reproduction. Slime molds exemplify a culmination of the amoeboid state. These largely saprotrophic organisms are creeping multicellular or multinucleate amoeboid masses without permanent shape. Protozoa are holotrophic, parasitic, and in some cases saprotrophic, and the cells are mostly flagellate or amoeboid, though a few groups are coccine. The multicellular condition has developed to only a limited degree, but protozoa appear to have exploited the unicellular way of life perhaps more fully than any other group of protists.

It may be noted that most of the modern protists, unicellular or multicellular, that remain in one vegetative state permanently still reveal at the time of reproduction the ancestral potential of developing other states. Thus even where the organisms are nonmotile, the reproductive cells generally are flagellate or amoeboid. Indeed, cells of both kinds are often formed at the same time; flagellate cells become sperms, amoeboid cells become eggs.

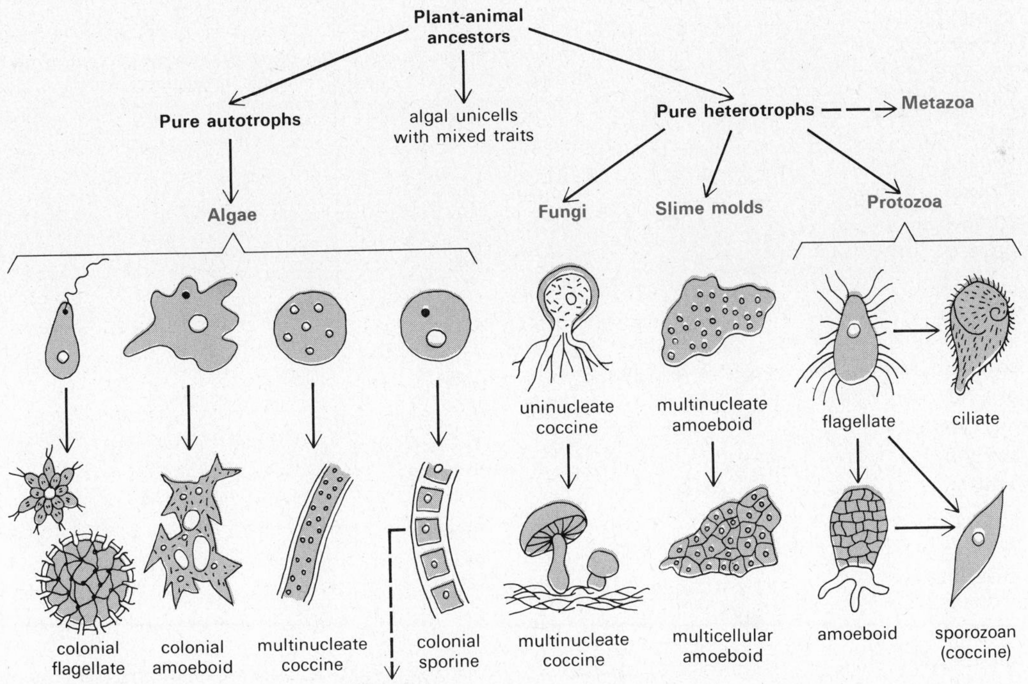

9.3 ***Protistan evolution.*** *Ancestral protists (top) probably were both autotrophic and heterotrophic simultaneously. From such stocks with joint plantlike and animal-like traits appear to have evolved purely autotrophic and purely heterotrophic types, represented today by the groups indicated. Also in existence are a few types that still retain mixed traits. In the algal groups, the colonial flagellates shown are Synura (top) and Volvox (bottom). Colonial sporine types also include branched filaments, sheets, and three-dimensional aggregates. Note that the heterotrophic groups do not include any sporine types—they might never have evolved or, if they did, have all become extinct.*

Algae

In this superphylum three main groups may be distinguished on the basis of the types of chlorophyll present. All three contain chlorophyll *a*. In addition, one also contains chlorophyll *b*, the second chlorophyll *c* (or in some cases *e*), and the third chlorophyll *d*. In conjunction with other pigments, these chlorophylls produce characteristic visible colors: some shade of green in the *a* plus *b* types, brown in the *a* plus *c* types, and red in the *a* plus *d* types. It is therefore possible to distinguish a *green line*, a *brown line*, and a *red line* of algae (Table 8). The possible evolutionary interrelations of these lines are outlined in Fig. 9.4.

Table 8. Some comparative biochemical characteristics of algae

group	*phylum*	*chlorophyll*	*food-storage compounds*	*cell walls*
green line	Chlorophyta	*a, b*	starch	cellulose
	Charophyta	*a, b*	starch	cellulose
	Euglenophyta	*a, b*	paramylum, fats	usually none
brown line	Chrysophyta	*a, c* (*e*)	leucosin, fats	cellulose, silica, or none
	Pyrrophyta	*a, c*	starch, polysaccharides, fats	cellulose or none
	Phaeophyta	*a, c*	laminarin, mannitol	cellulose, algin
red line	Rhodophyta	*a, d*	floridean starch	cellulose

9.4 ***Algae:*** *probable evolutionary affinities of the major phyla. Read from bottom up. The top row indicates the basic flagellation pattern of each group, either in the adult or in sex cells. Four basic patterns are encountered: two equally long whiplash flagella; one (or more) tinsel flagellum; one tinsel and one whiplash flagellum; one tinsel and one short whiplash flagellum. The flagellation aids in assessing evolutionary affinities.*

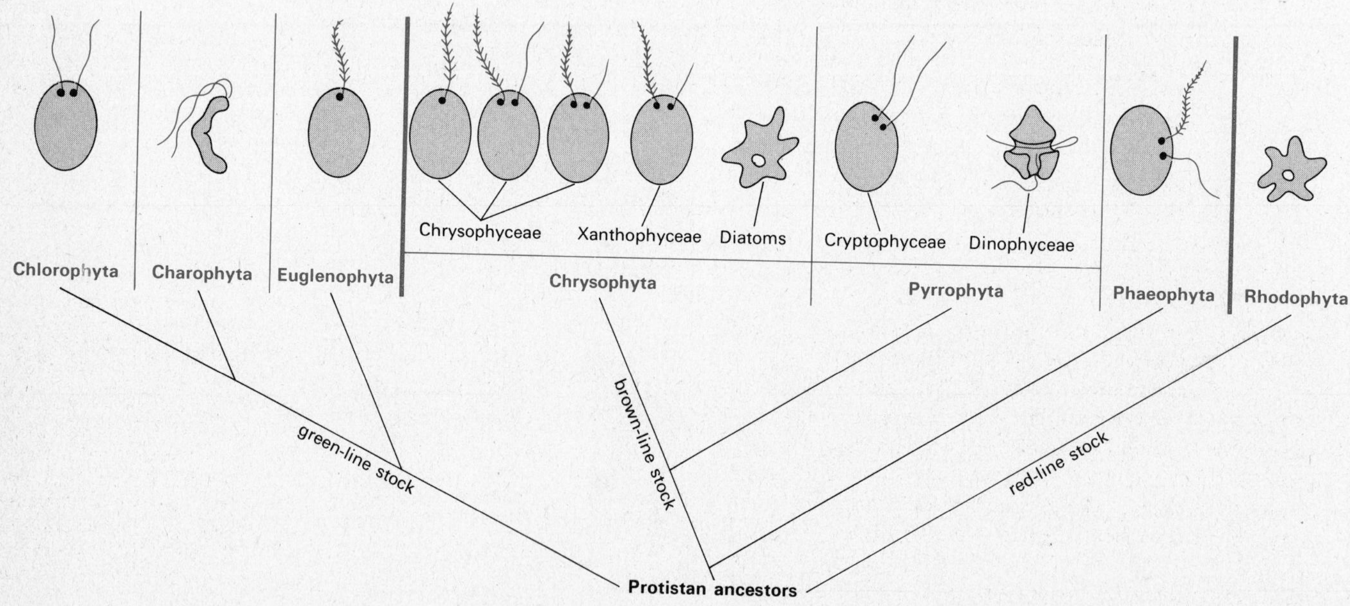

Green Algae

Phylum Chlorophyta 6,000 species

Apart from chlorophylls *a* and *b,* the phylum is identified also by red *carotene* and yellow *xanthophyll* pigments, by comparatively rigid cell walls containing cellulose, by reserve foods stored in most cases as starch, and by flagellate cells or stages that bear two (or rarely four or more) equally long anterior flagella with smooth surfaces (whiplash type). These characteristics occur in precisely this combination only in the green algae and the Metaphyta. Early chlorophyte stocks are therefore believed to have been in the specific ancestors of plants.

On the pigment-containing chloroplasts of the green algae are located small, often highly refractile bodies called *pyrenoids* (Fig. 9.5). Starch deposits accumulate around them, and for this reason pyrenoids are believed to be specialized centers for starch manufacture. Many flagellate algal cells also have an *eyespot* (*stigma*) near the anterior end. This organelle consists of a cup containing the photosensitive pigment *hematochrome,* chemically related to carotene and vitamin A; and of a ''lens,'' a transparent, light-concentrating body covering the pigment cup. A functional connection, if not also a structural one, is believed to exist between the eyespot and the nearby kinetosomes of the flagella. By virtue of this complex of photosensory and locomotor structures, the cell can distinguish regions of light and dark and move accordingly.

Chlorophytes include a *flagellate* group, a *coccine* group, and a *sporine* group. Each is represented by both unicellular and colonial forms. Flagellate algae are exemplified by single-celled types such as *Chlamydomonas* (see Fig. 9.5). Very closely related is *Polytoma,* a genus nearly identical to *Chlamydomonas* except that it is colorless and nonphotosynthetic; it lives as a saprotroph. Type-pairs of this sort are also encountered in some of the other algal phyla. Undoubtedly such paired photosynthetic and colorless forms represent branch lines descended from a relatively recent common ancestor, one line having retained and the other having lost the photosynthetic method of nutrition. In certain cases such evolutionary processes have been duplicated experimentally.

Cells rather like *Chlamydomonas* form flagellate colonies, usually composed of fixed numbers of cells—4, 8, 16, 32, 64, or larger multiples. If there are relatively few cells they form disks or cup-shaped colonies; and if the cell number is comparatively large, the colony is usually a hollow sphere, as in *Volvox.* In this organism a network of presumably impulse-conducting fibrils joins the kinetosomes of all cells, and the flagella beat in a highly coordinated, locomotion-producing pattern (Color Fig. 7).

Chlorophytes in the coccine line of evolution include *Chlorella,* used extensively in research on photosynthesis (Fig. 9.6). At the time of reproduction the nucleus of *Chlorella* divides several times, and each offspring nucleus together with some of the surrounding cytoplasm becomes partitioned off as a spore cell. In *Chlorella* such spores are nonmotile, but in other coccine algae the spores are flagellate. Remarkable for its size and structural elaboration is the green coccine *Acetabularia.* This marine alga, up to 2 or 3 in. long, consists of a stalk, an umbrellalike cap at the top, and fine outgrowths at the bottom of the stalk that anchor the organism on the sea floor. A single nucleus is in the base of the stalk. At the time of reproduction the nucleus migrates to the cap, where it divides several times. Spores then form as in *Chlorella.* Other coccine algae become highly multinucleate in the mature state,

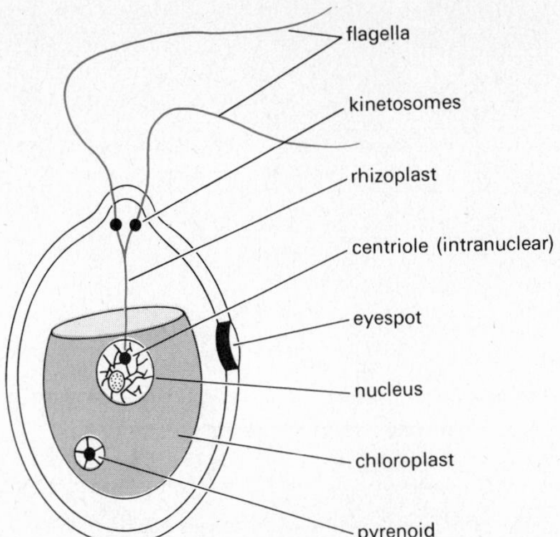

9.5 Chlamydomonas, *a unicellular flagellate green alga. The chloroplast is cup-shaped. On it, the pyrenoid is a refractile, presumably light-concentrating organelle, around which starch deposits accumulate. This organism is very similar to Polytoma, a nonphotosynthetic type in which chloroplast and pyrenoid are lacking. See also Color Fig. 7.*

yet they too remain undivided single cells. Such algae usually have branched, tubular bodies capable of indefinite extension in length. A good example of these so-called *siphonaceous* types is *Bryopsis.*

The sporine line is the most diversified of the chlorophytes (Fig. 9.7). Unicellular types include the common *Protococcus,* which usually grows on moist tree bark in the form of loose colonies. More complexly organized are the filamentous green algae, among them *Spirogyra, Ulothrix,* and *Oedogonium,* freshwater forms commonly used in laboratories. Cell division extends the filaments of such organisms in length. The most complex green algae are types in which cell division produces extensive sheets of cells, as in the sea lettuce *Ulva,* or compact three-dimensional bodies composed of several layers of cells, as in *Schizomeris.* Such algae may be considered to have attained the tissue level of organization.

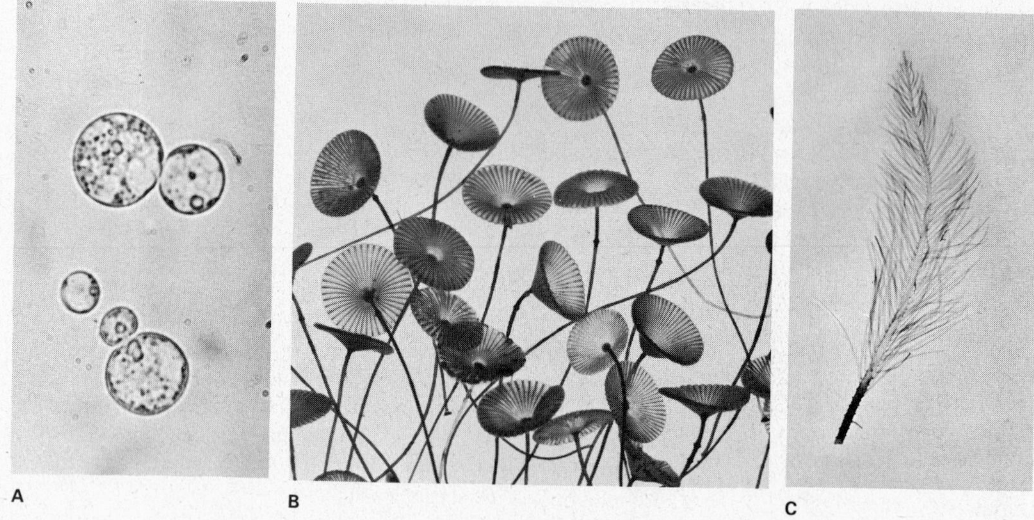

9.6 Coccine green algae. *A, Chlorella. B, Acetabularia. C, Bryopsis.*

9.7 Sporine green algae. *A, Spirogyra. Terminal cells of a filament. B, Ulothrix. In each cell of the filament at right the cell substance has become subdivided into many smaller sex cells. C, Oedogonium. The enlarged cell is an egg. D, Cladophora, a branching chlorophyte.*

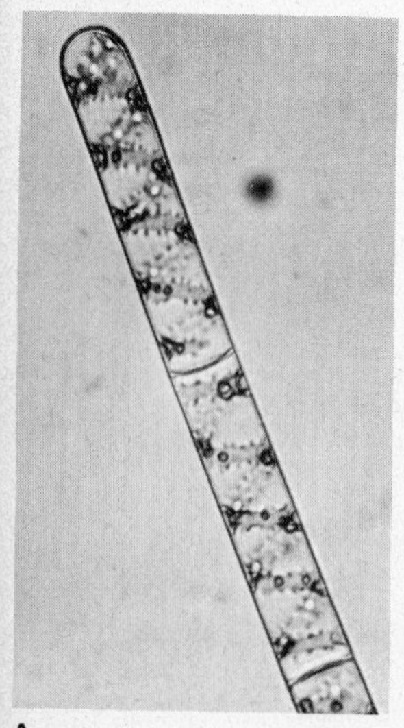

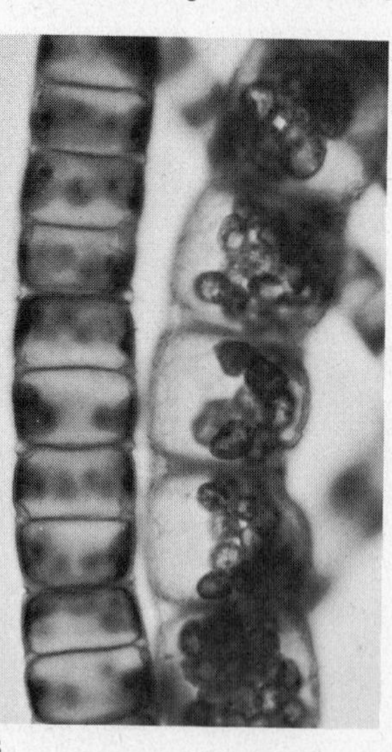

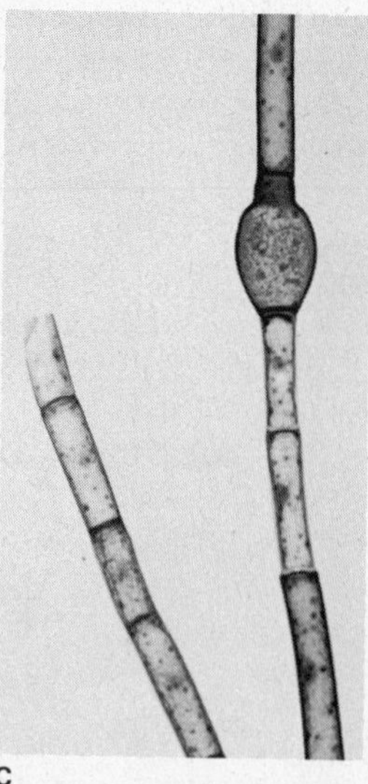

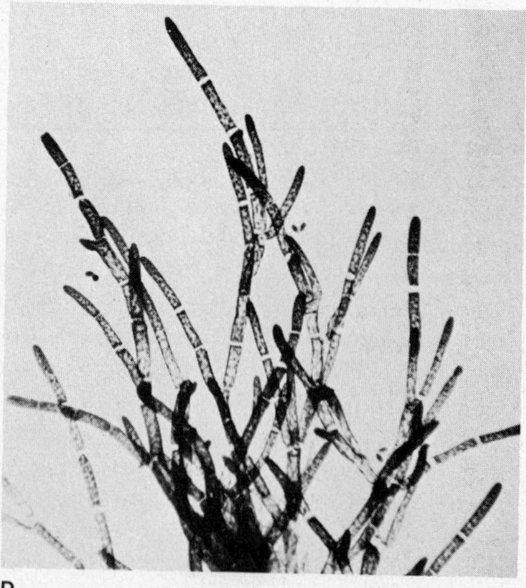

Stoneworts
Phylum Charophyta 250 species

In many ways these organisms are similar to the most advanced green algae, but they differ enough to be classified as a separate phylum. Stoneworts live in freshwater ponds. They resemble miniature trees, with whorls of leaflike branches attached at more or less regular intervals to a stemlike stalk. This stalk is anchored to the ground by rootlike processes (Fig. 9.8). Growth occurs only at the branch tips (*apical* growth), not diffusely as in chlorophytes. And stoneworts have multicellular reproductive structures that are true organs. This exceptional feature suggests an advanced evolutionary status; the phylum may represent an evolutionary line descended from complex sporine green algae in parallel with the line that gave rise to the Metaphyta.

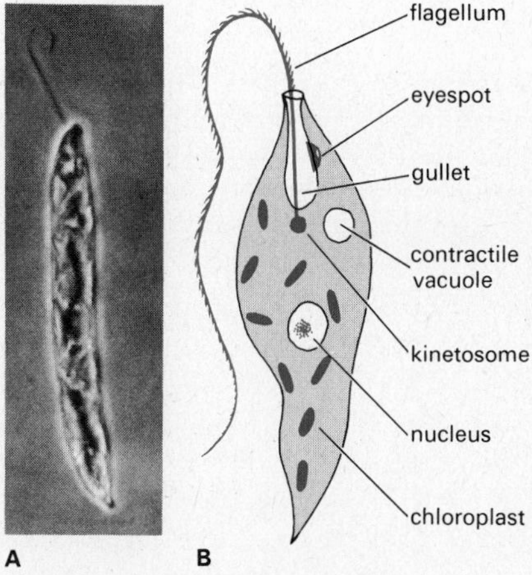

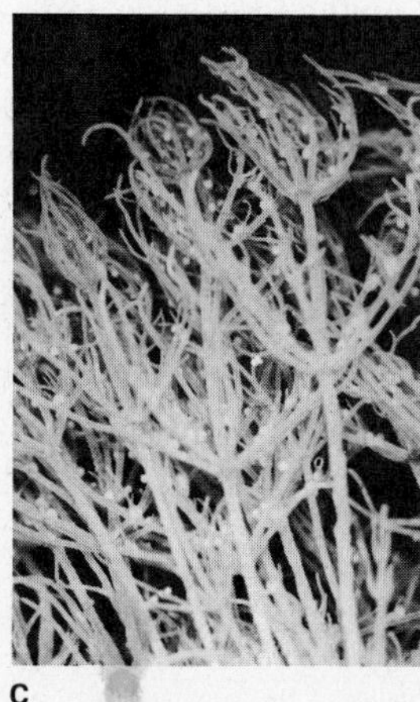

9.8 Green-line algae. *A, B, the euglenoid Euglena (photo approx. ×25,000). The genus Astasia is entirely similar to Euglena except that chloroplasts are lacking. C, upper portions of the charophyte stonewort Chara.*

Euglenoids
Phylum Euglenophyta 350 species

By virtue of its pigments this phylum belongs to the green-line algae, but the organisms are distinct in several respects. First, euglenoids are almost exclusively unicellular flagellates. Second, there may be a single anterior flagellum, or two flagella of equal length, or one long and one short, or even three. All these flagella have fine side branches (tinsel-type), and they pass through a *gullet,* another characteristic feature of euglenoids. Third, the cells are naked, without rigid cell walls, and very pliable and deformable. Fourth, food is stored not as starch but partly as fatty material and partly as *paramylum,* a polysaccharide chemically related to starch.

Paired green and colorless euglenoids are common. For example, *Euglena* is a green photosynthesizer, interesting also in that it can and probably must occasionally feed as a saprotroph, whether light is present or not. And *Astasia* is a colorless saprotroph otherwise entirely similar to *Euglena* (see Fig. 9.8).

Golden-brown Algae
Phylum Chrysophyta 6,000 species

Class Chrysophyceae yellow-brown algae

Class Xanthophyceae yellow-green algae

Class Bacillariophyceae diatoms

This phylum encompasses more different structural types than any other algal group. Early chrysophytes, particularly the early yellow-browns, may have been ancestral not only to all other chrysophytes but also to all other brown-line algae, as well as to some of the slime molds, fungi, protozoa, and possibly even sponges.

Chrysophytes are identified by chlorophylls *a* and *c* (*e* in some cases) and by various carotene and xanthophyll pigments. The xanthophylls include the conspicuous yellow-brown *fucoxanthin*. Foods are stored not as starch but partly as *oils*, partly as the polysaccharide *leucosin*. Cell walls can be absent or present. Where present the wall is in two halves, the rim of one half tightly overlapping the rim of the other. Such walls are usually made of glassy silica.

The first two classes listed above are exceedingly diversified. Each includes flagellate, amoeboid, coccine, and sporine lines, and each of these contains unicellular and multicellular members (Fig. 9.9). Paired photosynthetic and colorless forms are common in each of the two classes, and some of these colorless types well could have been ancestors of other Protista. For example, a colorless chrysophycean amoeba is virtually indistinguishable from a protozoan amoeba.

In contrast to the first two classes, the diatoms (see Color Fig. 5) are mainly sporine, unicellular, and occasionally colonial. As noted in Chap. 7, diatoms are the most abundant single group of plankton organisms, and as such they support much of the life in the sea and in fresh water.

__9.9 Golden-brown algae.__ A, chrysophyceans. The coccolithophorid is flagellate, Chrysamoeba is amoeboid, Epichrysis is coccine, and Phaeothamnion is sporine. B, C, xanthophyceans. B, Botrydiopsis. C, Ophiocytium. Both are coccine types. D, bacillariophyceans, or diatoms. See also Color Fig. 5.

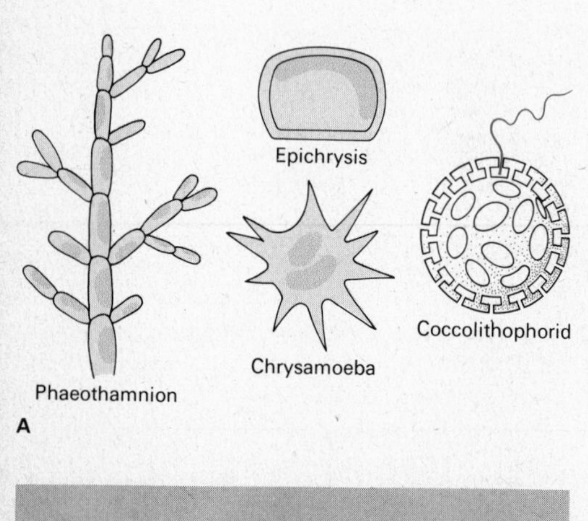

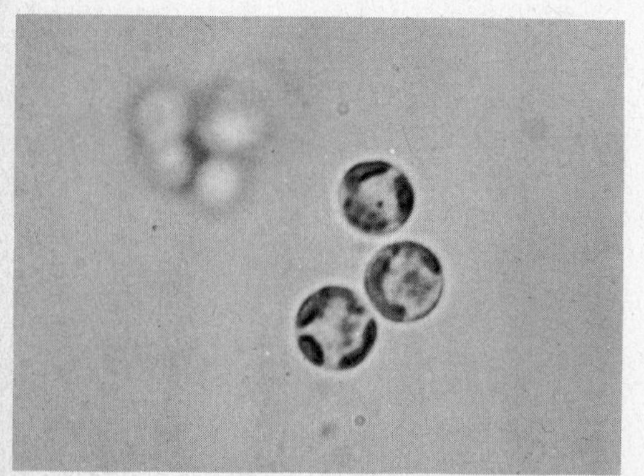
B

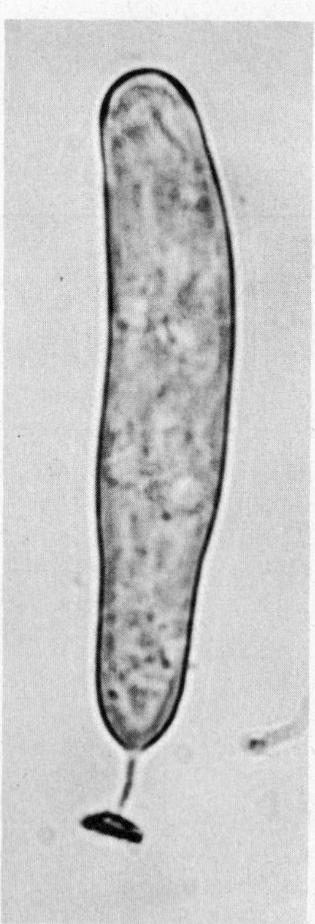
C

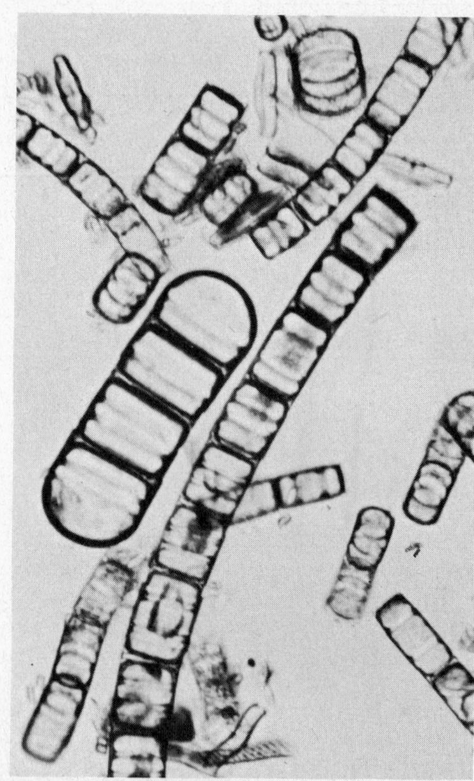
D

The silica shells of dead diatoms make up large tracts of the ocean floor. Geologically uplifted parts of this floor are the source of *diatomaceous earth,* mined for its abrasive and various other properties. For example, it is a common component of toothpaste. Moreover, much of the petroleum used in industry today is probably derived from the oils synthesized and stored by diatoms of past ages.

Fire Algae

Phylum Pyrrophyta 1,000 species

Class Cryptophyceae cryptoflagellates

Class Dinophyceae dinoflagellates

The pigments in this phylum include chlorophylls *a* and *c* and *fucoxanthin.* Foods are variously stored in the form of starch, starchlike carbohydrates, and fats and oils. Cell walls are absent in some of the dinoflagellates. In others, as well as in the cryptoflagellates, walls composed of cellulose are present.

Cryptophyceae are mostly biflagellate unicells with gullets. Paired photosynthetic and colorless types are represented by, for example, *Cryptomonas* and *Chilomonas* (Fig. 9.10). The Dinophyceae are a major component of plankton. Most are dinoflagellates, unicellular flagellate forms. The remaining Dinophyceae include amoeboid, coccine, and sporine types, but not nearly so elaborately developed as in other algal groups (Fig. 9.11).

Many of the dinoflagellates have cellulose walls

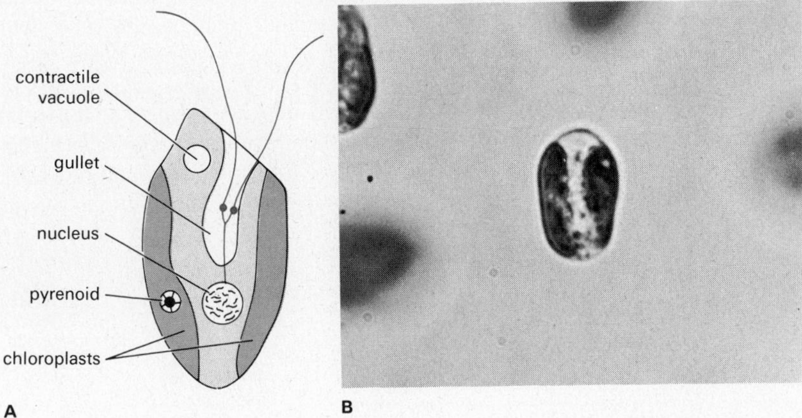

9.10 Cryptophyceans. *Diagram and photo of Cryptomonas. The genus Chilomonas is entirely similar except that it lacks chloroplasts.*

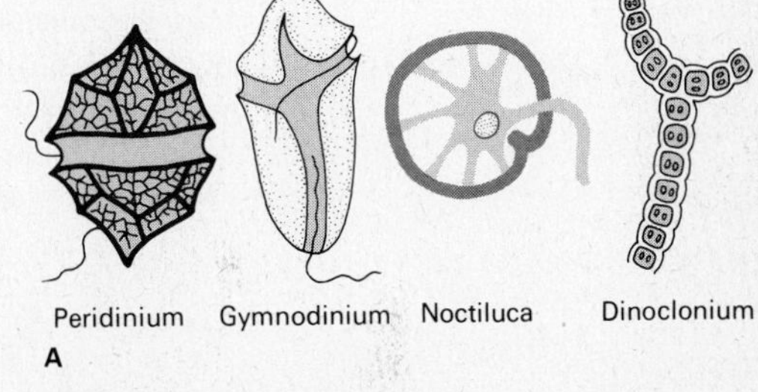

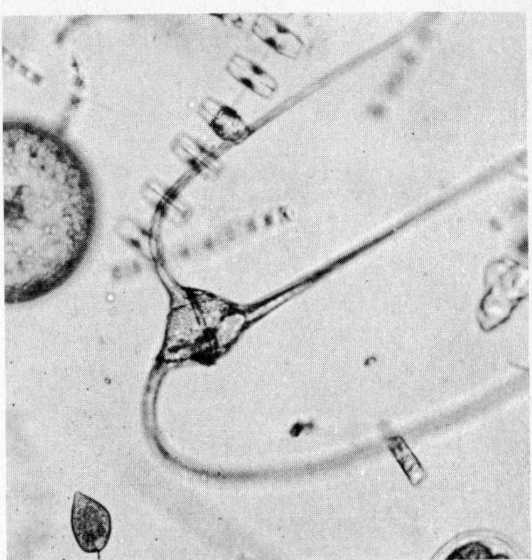

9.11 Dinophyceans. *A, Peridinium and Gymodinium are armor-plated dinoflagellates. Noctiluca is a bioluminescent dinoflagellate. Dinoclonium is a multicellular sporine type with flagellate sex cells. B, Ceratium, a dinoflagellate common in plankton.*

in the form of distinct interlocking "armor" plates, as in *Peridinium* or *Ceratium.* Two flagella are present, one directed backward in swimming, the other undulating in a transverse groove formed by the armor. Different nutritional variants are common. For example, *Ceratium* is photosynthetic, *Blastodinium* is a colorless parasite in animals, and *Noctiluca* either photosynthesizes or feeds holotrophically. Paired photosynthetic and colorless types are known as well. Many marine dinoflagellates are bioluminescent (*Noctiluca,* for example). On occasion some dinoflagellates proliferate locally in fantastic numbers. For example, the reddish *Gymnodinium* is one of several forms that often produces so-called *red tides* (hence the name of the phylum).

Brown Algae
Phylum Phaeophyta 1,000 species

Among the identifying pigments of these algae are chlorophylls *a* and *c* and the brown fucoxanthin. The last occurs in amounts sufficient to mask all other pigments. Foods are stored partly as *laminarin,* a unique polysaccharide, partly as *mannitol,* a complex alcohol. The cell walls are composed of cellulose and *algin,* an organic material unique to the phylum.

Phaeophytes are exclusively multicellular and attached, and nearly all are marine. Colorless types are unknown, and photosynthesis is the only food-supplying process. The organisms have the form of filaments and of more complex, tissue-level organizations (Fig. 9.12).

Most of the seaweeds are brown algae. They live in shallow water and in the tide zone, attached to rocky bottoms by holdfasts. Ebb tides often expose the organisms to air for several hours, but their algin coating retains considerable amounts of water and protects the organisms from drying out. The most familiar of the brown algae is probably the rockweed *Fucus,* found along many shores, and the most spectacular are the giant kelps. For example, the kelp *Macrocystis* along the Pacific coast of North America sometimes attains lengths of more than 100 yd. *Laminaria,* the commonest of the kelps, is of worldwide distribution. Torn pieces of it can often be found washed up on beaches along with other algae.

Brown algae are the source of several substances useful to man. For example, the algae contain high concentrations of iodine, and algin finds wide use in many manufacturing processes (ice cream production, for example).

Red Algae
Phylum Rhodophyta 3,000 species

The members of this phylum contain chlorophylls *a* and *d* and the pigments *r-phycocyanin* and *r-phycoerythrin.* The last two are chemically not the same as the pigments of like name in the blue-green algae. Rhodophytes store food in the form of *floridean starch,* chemically very much like glycogen. The cell walls are of cellulose. The *stony coralline algae* deposit calcium compounds on their surfaces and thereby contribute importantly to the formation of coral reefs (Color Fig. 8).

A few genera of red algae are unicellular. Most are multicellular, however, and their cells often become multinucleate. Red algae are exclusively marine, and they live in somewhat deeper water than the brown algae. The red pigment *r*-phycoerythrin appears to be an adaptation to this dimmer environment; *r*-phycoerythrin absorbs blue light particularly well, and the blue wavelengths of sunlight actually penetrate deeper into water than red wavelengths. Indeed, *r*-phycoerythrin has been found to play an important

A

B

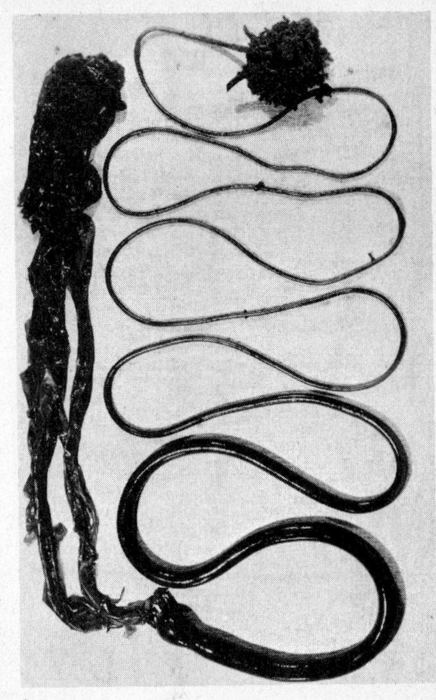

C

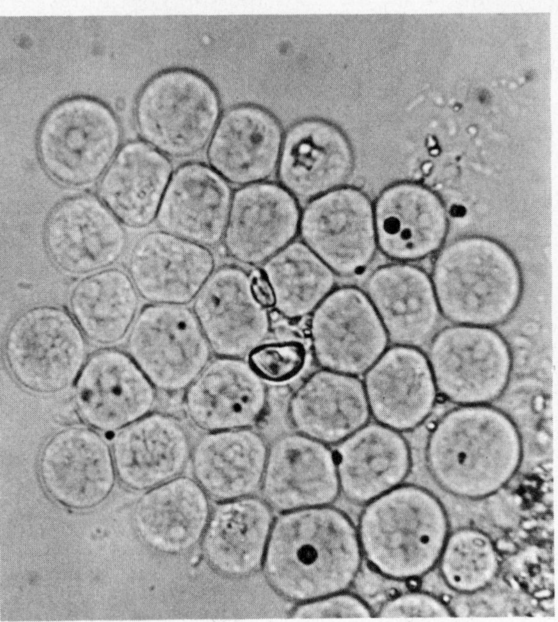

D

E

9.12 Brown and red algae. *A, B, C, brown algae (see also Fig. 7.4). A, Fucus. Note reproductive receptacles at tips and air bladders lower down. B, Ascophyllum, a common seaweed. Note air bladders. C, Macrocystis, a type that often becomes extremely long. Note conspicuous holdfast (top), the long stalk, and the leaflike blades (bunched up in this photo). D, E, red algae (see also Color Fig. 8). D, Porphyridium, a unicellular form (shown here as a group of many). E, Polysiphonia, a branched, delicately structured type.*

auxiliary role in the photosynthesis of these algae. Rhodophytes are lacier and more delicate than the sturdy brown algae. The latter are adapted to withstand pounding surf, but in deeper water the red algae are not so much subject to wave action.

Some of the red algae are used commercially. The genus *Gelidium* is the source of agar jelly, used as a medium for culturing microorganisms; and *Porphyra, Rhodymenia,* and *Chondrus crispus,* the Irish moss, are among several types eaten as vegetables in various parts of the world.

Fungi

Phylum Mycophyta 90,000 species

Class Phycomycetes filamentous fungi; water molds, downy mildews, blights, bread molds

Class Ascomycetes sac fungi; yeasts, molds, powdery mildews, truffles, cup fungi

Class Basidiomycetes club fungi; rusts, smuts, bracket fungi, mushrooms, toadstools, puffballs, stinkhorns

Class Fungi Imperfecti provisional collection of types with incompletely known reproductive processes, not yet assignable to any of the above groups

This huge phylum (now sometimes divided into more classes than those listed) has representatives in almost every available habitat on earth, and many fungi are of major economic or medical significance to man. The organisms are partly free-living saprotrophs, partly symbionts of all possible types. They store foods as glycogen and lipids. Primitive members of the phylum are aquatic and produce flagellate reproductive cells. More advanced fungi are terrestrial, with nonmotile reproductive cells dispersed passively by wind, water, and animals.

As a group fungi can be regarded as a culmination of the coccine state in protistan evolution. The body of a fungus is multinucleate and without internal cell boundaries, though incomplete partitions do occur in the sac and club fungi (Fig. 9.13). Thus, a fungus is a continuous living mass that can grow in size and in the number of nuclei. True cells, with complete individual boundaries and one nucleus each, are formed only during reproduction.

A fungus is covered by a rigid wall composed of cellulose in primitive types but of chitin in most cases. The basic unit of the fungus body usually is a *hypha,* a tubular, often branched filament. As it grows it extends in length and can branch increasingly. Numerous hyphae are usually intermeshed as an irregular network, a so-called *mycelium* (see Fig. 9.13). Hyphae can also pack together in more orderly patterns and produce, for example, bodies structured like mushrooms.

The class Phycomycetes is probably the most primitive. Some members are entirely aquatic and often microscopic in size (Fig. 9.14). Other, larger forms are amphibious, able to live under both aquatic and terrestrial conditions. For example, *Saprolegnia* is a common saprotrophic water mold that can live both in calm fresh water and in irrigated soil. The most advanced members are strictly terrestrial; to this group belongs the familiar mold *Rhizopus,* which grows on stale bread. The mycelium of this fungus on and in bread is visible externally as a fuzzy whitish growth.

The Ascomycetes, nearly all terrestrial, appear to have evolved from advanced ancestral stocks of terrestrial Phycomycetes. Sac fungi are so

A

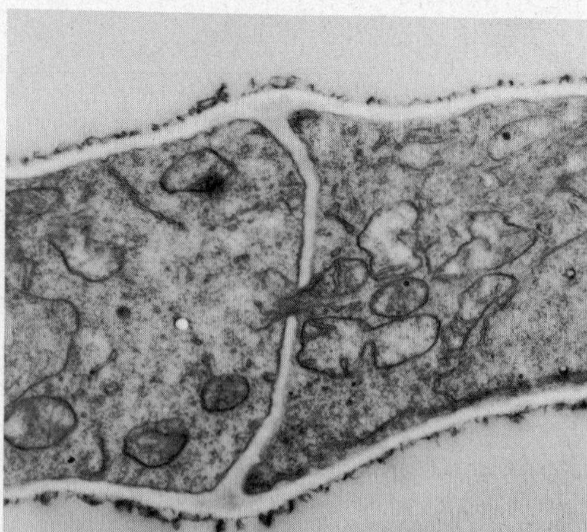

B

9.13 Fungus hyphae. *A, numerous hyphae as in this photo make up a mycelium. B, section through a hypha of the ascomycete Neurospora, showing one of the incomplete internal partitions. Note the continuity of the cytoplasm through the pore in the cross partition (approx. ×4,000).*

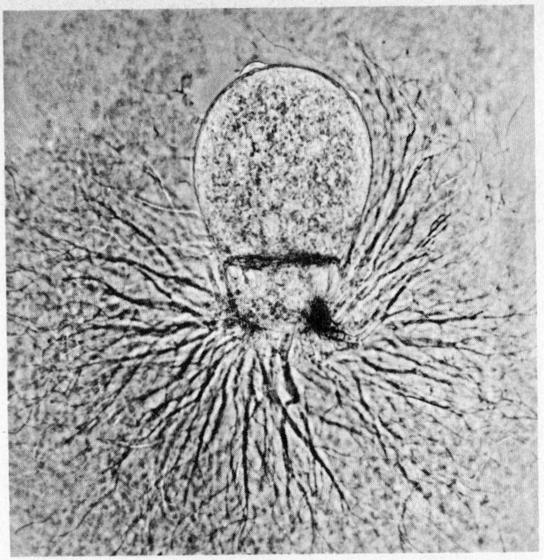

A

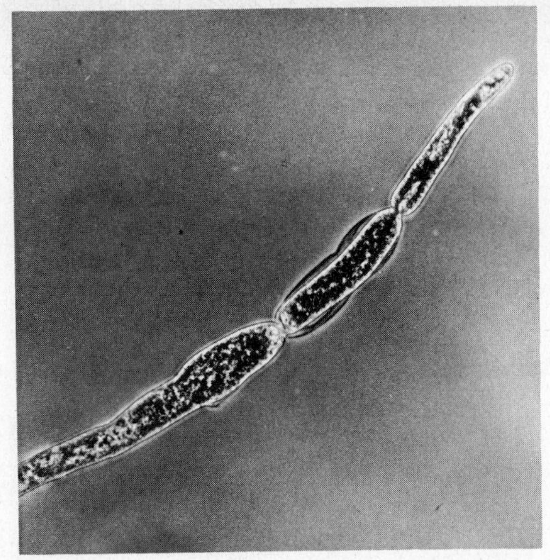

B

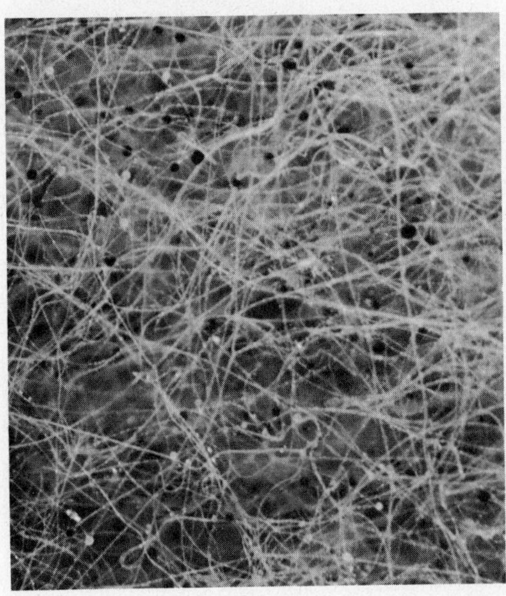

C

9.14 Phycomycete fungi. *A, Karlingia, a simply constructed aquatic type. Note the two cellular compartments. From the lower one absorptive extensions (rhizoids) radiate away. The upper one is spore-producing. B, Saprolegnia, a water mold. The terminal portion of a hypha is shown. C, Rhizopus, a bread mold. Small (black) spore-containing sporangia (on stalks, not visible) have matured among the mat of tangled hyphae of the mycelium (×10).*

called because their principal spores are manufactured in elongated sacs, or *asci* (see Chap. 25). Among these fungi are the *yeasts,* which are secondarily reduced, largely unicellular forms, and the fleshy, edible *morels* and *truffles* (Fig. 9.15 and Color Fig. 9). Various ascomycete molds also produce the characteristic flavors of Roquefort, Camembert, and other cheeses. Parasitic forms include types responsible for Dutch elm disease, ergot disease in rye, and scabs, rot, and mildewing of numerous fruits. But the class also includes *Penicillium,* one species of which is the source of the disease-curing antibiotic penicillin.

Ascomycetes are the most common fungal members of lichens. The algal members of these symbiotic associations are usually blue-green and coccine green algae. The fungus forms a mycelial framework in which the algae are held and supported. Lichens can be crustlike (*crustose*), leaflike (*foliose*), or branching (*fruticose*, Fig. 9.16). They are often epiphytic on trees, but more commonly they live independently on rock, where they aid in fragmenting the stone surfaces and thus contribute to the formation of soil (see Chap.

9.15 Ascomycetes. *A, yeasts. Note budding cells. B, Penicillium. Note chains of spores (conidia) at ends of hyphae. C, Monolinia producing brown rot on peach. D, Venturia inequalis causing mildewing of apple.*

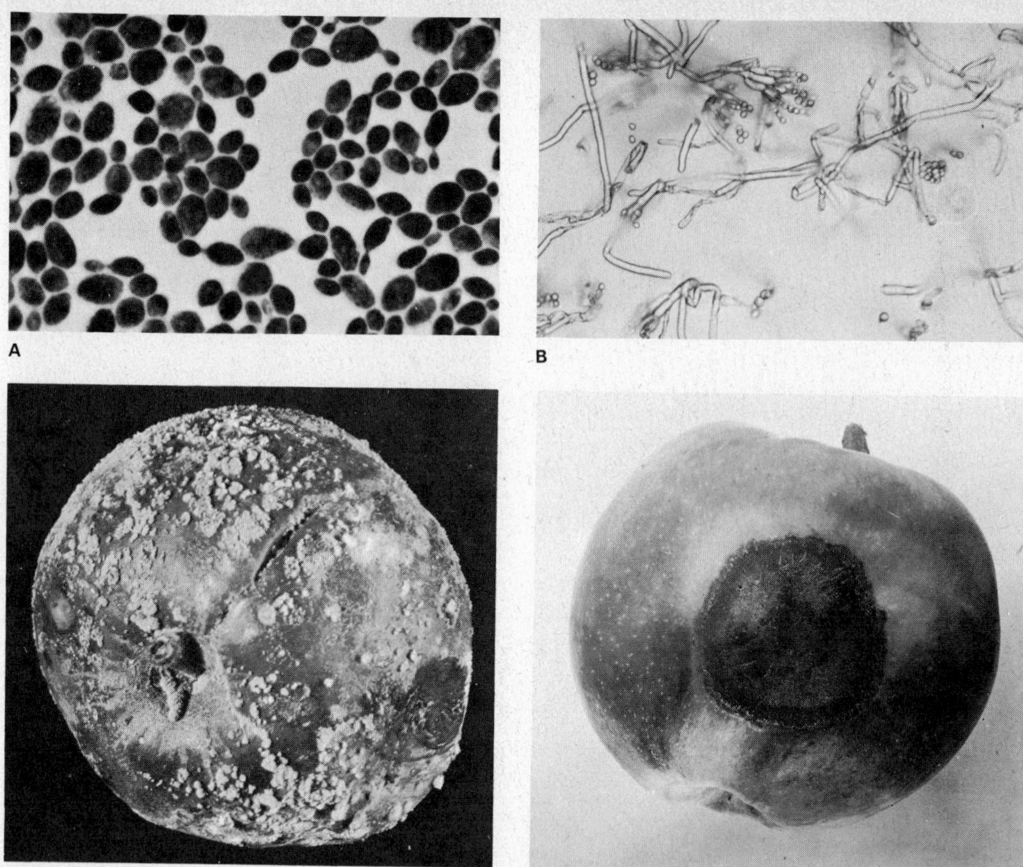

A B C D

9.16 *(Below)* **Lichens.** *A, a leafy (foliose) type; B, a branching (fruticose) type. See also Color Fig. 3.*

A

B

A

B

C

9.17 Basidiomycetes. *A, a mushroom. Note gills on underside of cap. B, jelly fungus. C, a bracket fungus on a tree branch. See also Color Fig. 10.*

6). Ascomycetes also appear to make up most of the Fungi imperfecti. The reproductive stages known in this artificial class are at present only the nonsexual ones. Species for which sexual stages are discovered are assigned to one of the other fungal classes. In this way the class Ascomycetes has enlarged most, and the membership of the Fungi imperfecti is decreasing.

Early ascomycete ancestors probably have given rise to the class Basidiomycetes, identified by hyphae with spore-producing terminal units called *basidia* (see Chap. 25). In some cases basidium-bearing hyphae are combined as large, stalked structures familiarly called *mushrooms* (Fig. 9.17).

Not all Basidiomycetes form mushrooms, however. Among those that do not are the *jelly fungi,* saprotrophic on dead tree branches and decaying logs, and the *bracket fungi,* parasitic on living trees. Of great economic importance are the *rusts* and *smuts,* destructive parasites of plants such as wheat and corn. Saprotrophic types also include *bird's-nest fungi, stinkhorns,* and *puffballs,* some of the latter attaining diameters of about 5 yd (Color Fig. 10). Such giant puffballs probably have the distinction of being the most prolific of all living organisms. A single one can manufacture as many as 100 *trillion* spores; if each of these were to grow into a mature fungus, a mass of living matter nearly 1,000 times the size of the earth would be produced.

Slime Molds
Phylum Myxophyta

Class Myxomyceteae multinucleate types

Class Acrasieae multicellular types

Class Labyrinthuleae multicellular types without fruiting bodies

These interesting organisms represent the evolutionary culmination of the colonial *amoeboid* state; the body of a slime mold is a naked, creeping, amoeboid mass, in some cases as much as 1 ft in diameter (Fig. 9.18).

In the Myxomyceteae the adult form is a *plasmodium,* an amoeboid sheet containing hundreds or thousands of nuclei. Internal cell boundaries are absent, however, and the whole organism is a continuous living mass. Some of these slime molds are parasitic on flowering plants, but most of them are free-living in moist wooded areas, where they creep over fallen leaves and rotting logs like supergiant amoebas (*Physarum,* for example). The Acrasieae are superficially similar, but the adult form is a *pseudoplasmodium,* a true cellular colony composed of hundreds or thousands of uninucleate amoeboid cells that do not lose their cell boundaries.

These two classes of slime molds form *fruiting bodies,* thickened regions or stalked outgrowths in which spore cells are produced (see Color Fig. 24). Ripe spores then escape and divide repeatedly. The resulting cells are or become amoeboid, and eventually they migrate together and form a common amoeboid mass in which the cell boundaries may or may not disappear, depending on the class. New generations of plasmodia or pseudoplasmodia are formed in this manner (see also Chap. 25).

In the class Labyrinthuleae, multicellular pseudoplasmodia are typical but fruiting bodies are not. Migrating cells again are a phase of the life cycle, but the locomotion of these cells is neither flagellate nor amoeboid. Indeed, clearly identifiable locomotor structures are not visible at all, and the cells appear to be sliding along surfaces without noticeable change of shape. Just how their propulsion is accomplished is unknown.

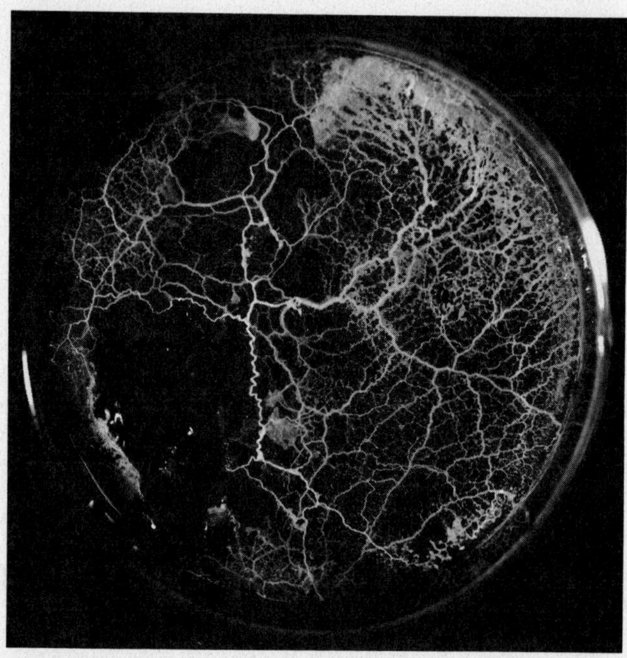

***9.18* Slime molds.** *A plasmodium of Physarella is shown.*

Protozoans

Phylum Protozoa 15,000+ species

Subphylum Mastigophora flagellate protozoa

Subphylum Sarcodina amoeboid protozoa

Subphylum Sporozoa spore-forming protozoa

Subphylum Ciliophora ciliate protozoa

As algae are the most nearly plantlike protists, so protozoa are the most nearly animal-like. It is difficult to pinpoint the exact ancestry of these organisms, but there is little doubt that they are highly polyphyletic; they appear to be descended from several different ancestral groups among other Protista. By loss of chlorophyll, primitive algae in particular could have given rise to protozoa early and directly, or later and indirectly via other protistan types. There is fairly general agreement that flagellate and amoeboid protozoa are closely interrelated (they are often classified as a single group); that flagellate ancestors probably have also given rise to the ciliate group; and that the origin of the spore-forming group is obscure. Sporine states of existence are not represented in the phylum, and colonial types are comparatively rare; most protozoa are unicellular.

Protozoa are components of all ecosystems in all aquatic environments, in soils, and generally in any environments containing some moisture. Most types are free-living and holotrophic. So-called ''herbivorous'' protozoa subsist largely on bacteria and microscopic algae, and ''carnivorous'' forms feed on minute animals such as rotifers or on other protozoa (including fellow members of their own species in cannibalistic types; Color Fig. 11). Some protozoa are saprotrophic; all of the Sporozoa and certain subgroups of the other subphyla are parasitic. Very many animals harbor at least one parasitic protozoan type, which means that protozoan species could well number in the hundreds of thousands. Thus although only some 15,000 species have been described to date, at least 100,000 species may actually be presumed to exist on a conservative estimate.

Moreover, each protozoan subphylum well might be regarded as a separate phylum. On the cellular level the differences between, for example, an amoeba and a paramecium are just as profound as those between a green and a golden-brown algal unicell—or indeed between an earthworm and a caterpillar. If such pairs represent two different phyla, as they do, so should amoebas and paramecia. Protozoa could thus represent a superphylum, like algae.

The protozoan cell is either naked or surrounded by a nonrigid *pellicle,* a cuticle composed of a variety of horny substances. Cellulose is not present. In many cases shells of various inorganic compounds are secreted as external covers. Foods are stored as glycogen and fats. In free-living flagellate and ciliate types, gullets are usually well developed. Amoeboid protozoa use pseudopodia for feeding (see Color Fig. 11). Underneath the cell surface in a number of protozoan groups are neurofibrils (presumably conductile), contractile myofibrils, and contractile vacuoles. The last occur in nearly all freshwater forms as well as in a few marine and parasitic types. Where present, such vacuoles excrete excess water drawn into the cell osmotically. Protozoa are largely uninucleate, but all ciliates and many amoeboid types are multinucleate, often highly so. Sporozoa become multinucleate at particular life-cycle stages.

Various protozoa ''taste'' food and refuse to ingest unsuitable materials; they give distinct avoidance responses to unsuitable temperatures, light, electric charges, pH, mechanical stimuli, and chemicals in the water; they seek out optimum environments by trial-and-error behavior; and some of them have been trained through conditioning to give ''learned'' responses to particular stimuli.

The most primitive members of the Mastigophora, or *zooflagellates,* are generally free-living and holotrophic, and they greatly resemble colorless flagellate algae (Fig. 9.19). For example, the *collar flagellates* resemble certain flagellate chrysophytes. The flagellum of collar flagellates creates a current that sweeps food toward the cell, where it is trapped in the collar and then en-

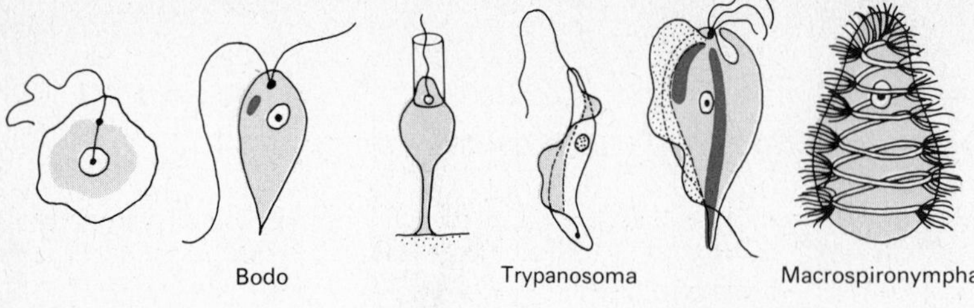

9.19 (*Above*) **Zooflagellates.** *The first three are free-living types. Note the trichocyst (color oval) in Bodo, the rhizoplast in Mastigamoeba, and the collar in the attached collar flagellate Codosiga. The remaining three types are symbiotic. In Trypanosoma note the posterior kinetosome and the undulating membrane edged by the flagellum. Trichomonas has a gullet, an undulating membrane, a nucleus with intranuclear centriole, and a kinetosome with additional flagella. Macronspironympha contains a spiral, ribbonlike kinetosome and hundreds of flagella emanating from it. Trichonympha (not shown) is similarly hyperflagellate.*

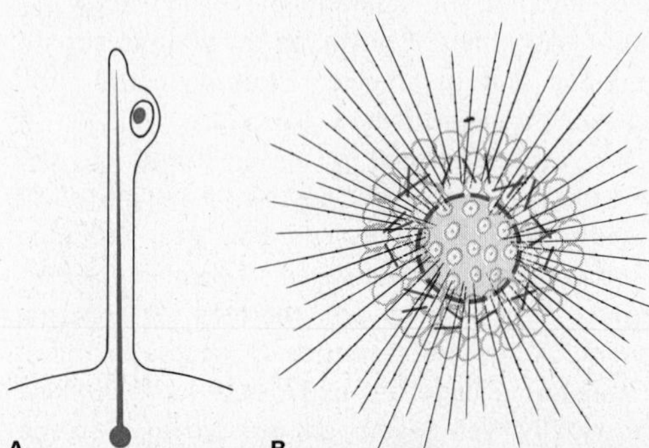

9.20 (*Right*) **Sarcodina:** *actinopod types. A, an axopodium, with a stiff supporting flagellum (axoneme) emanating from a kinetosome and a layer of cytoplasm covering it. Near the tip is a food vacuole. B, general structure of a radiolarian. Note outer foamy layer (with free silica needles) around a perforated skeletal silica shell, and interior nucleated region. Axonemes emanate from this inner region. C, skeletal shells of radiolarians. Note latticelike construction (approx. ×50).*

gulfed. Some of these organisms are stalked and solitary, others form colonies. In many of the free-living zooflagellates the flagella can be lost temporarily and the organisms then become amoeboid. Indeed the cells of some species are both flagellate and amoeboid at the same time, a strong indication that flagellate and amoeboid protozoa are closely related.

Early free-living zooflagellates undoubtedly gave rise to the many symbiotic forms living today. For example, different species of *Trypanosoma* live parasitically in lymph and blood cells of various vertebrates. One such species produces sleeping sickness in man. Other symbiotic zooflagellates include *Trichomonas,* a commensal in the gut of man and other vertebrates, and *Trichonympha,* a wood-digesting symbiont in the gut of termites. This zooflagellate is one of many in which hundreds of flagella grow from an enlarged, ribbon-shaped kinetosome (see Fig. 9.19).

The Sarcodina are almost certainly derived from several evolutionary sources. As already noted, an algal amoeba that loses its chlorophyll can hardly be distinguished from a protozoan amoeba. Sarcodina move and feed by means of pseudopods. In the class *Actinopodea,* each pseudopod is supported internally by a straight, rigid spike (*axoneme*) that resembles a flagellum structurally (Fig. 9.20). To this group belong the largely freshwater *Heliozoa,* in which numerous permanent pseudopods radiate out from the cell like sun rays. The marine, planktonic *Radiolaria* have a similar appearance. Some Heliozoa and all Radiolaria have beautifully sculptured, latticelike silica shells, with pseudopodia protruding though the spaces in such lattices. Some 5 percent of the area of the world's ocean floor consists of "radiolarian ooze," composed of the skeletons of these organisms. Compressed to rock, these bottom deposits form *flint* and *chert.*

In a second class, *Rhizopodea,* the pseudopods are unsupported internally and they therefore flow and change their contours freely. The most familiar member of this group is the common amoeba, *Amoeba proteus* (see Fig. 2.6 and Color Fig. 11). Closely related is the parasitic *Entamoeba histolytica,* which causes amoebic dysentery in man, and *Pelomyxa,* a large, free-living, highly multinucleate amoeba (Fig. 9.21). Other such types encase their bodies in various kinds of shells. For example, *Arcella* secretes a chitinous housing and extrudes pseudopodia through an opening in this shell. *Difflugia* cements tiny sand grains to a chitinous envelope. Most widespread are the *Foraminifera,* planktonic marine organisms that have spiraled and coiled calcareous shells of many different forms. Pseudopods are extruded through holes in these shells, hence the name of the group (signifying "hole bearers"). Shells of dead organ-

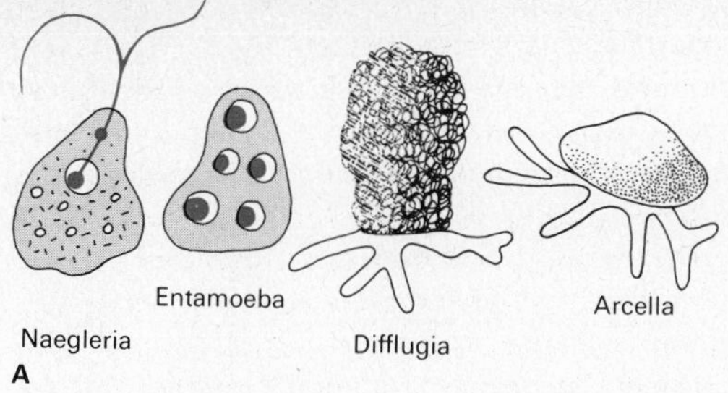

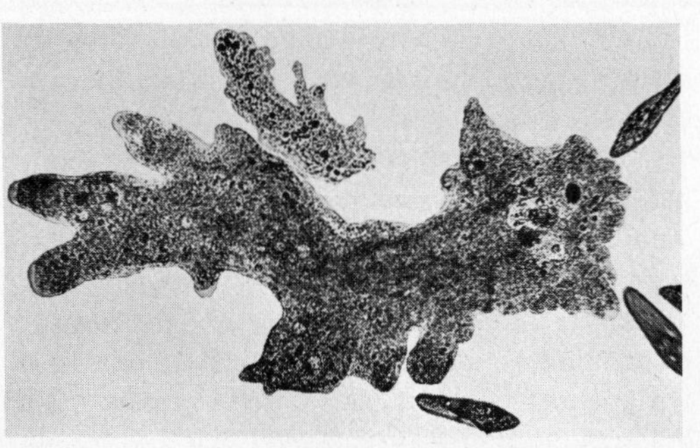

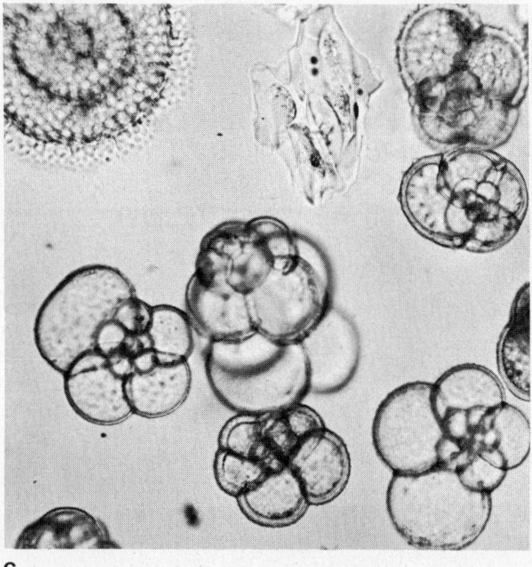

9.21 Sarcodina: *rhizopod types. A, Naegleria is an amoeboid type that also has flagella. Entamoeba histolytica is shown with ingested blood corpuscles in food vacuoles. The shell of Difflugia is made of sand grains, that of Arcella, of chitinous substances. B, Pelomyxa, one of the naked, multinucleate amoeboid types (with paramecia around it and Amoeba proteus near top, for comparison; approx. ×70). An amoeba is also shown in Fig. 2.6. C, Globigerina, a common foraminiferan. The coiled shells have minute openings through which the pseudopodia project (approx. ×100). See also Color Fig. 11. (B, courtesy Carolina Biological Supply Company.)*

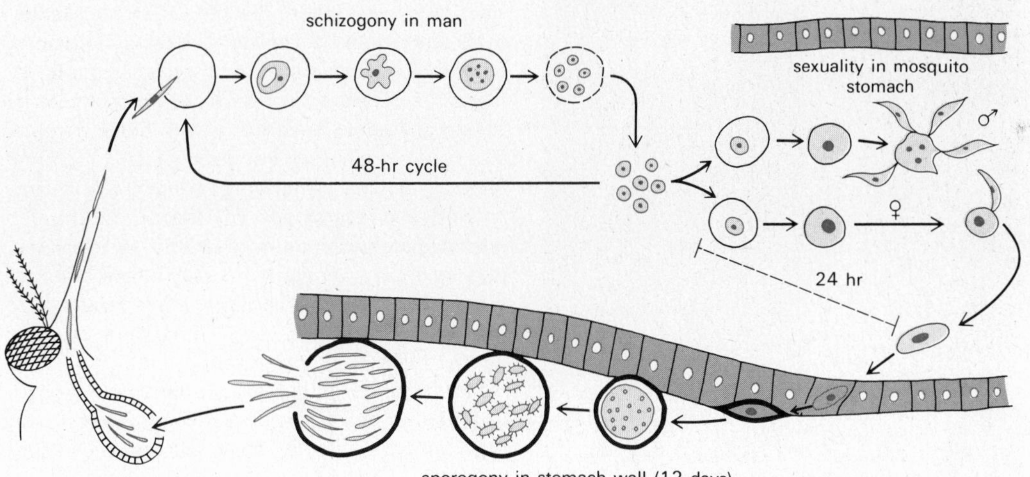

9.22 Malaria: *life cycle of the sporozoan parasite Plasmodium vivax. Mature parasitic cells invading human red blood corpuscles (top left) undergo multiple fission (schizogony) either inside the corpuscles, as shown, or outside them. Offspring cells (merozoites) destroy corpuscles and cause an attack of fever. They also reinfect new corpuscles and then lead to repetition of a 48-hr fever cycle. Merozoites entering red corpuscles also function as gamete producers, and if human blood is sucked by an Anopheles mosquito, the gamete producers break free in the mosquito stomach, transform to male and female sex cells, and bring about fertilization. The fertilization product then encysts in the stomach wall and undergoes multiple fission (sporogony). The resulting free spore cells later migrate through the body cavities and organs of the insect, including the salivary glands. From there the spores are injected into the human circulation when the mosquito bites a man. Spores mature in human liver cells, and fully formed parasites then begin a new life cycle.*

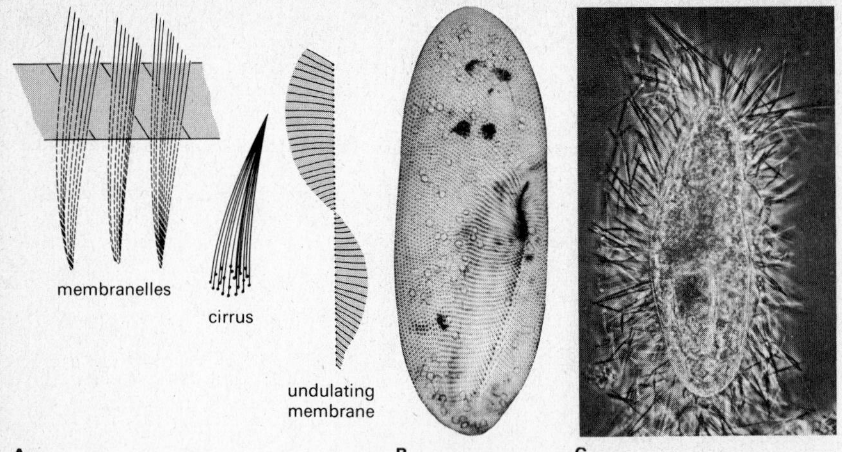

9.23 ***Surface organelles in ciliates.*** *A, locomotor structures formed from variously fused cilia. Each membranelle has a triangular basal portion that forms an anchor in the cytoplasm; in the diagrams of a cirrus and an undulating membrane only the parts that project beyond the cell surface are shown. B, the chitin-like pellicle of Paramecium. The dark dots are pores through which the cilia project. C, Paramecium discharging its trichocysts.*

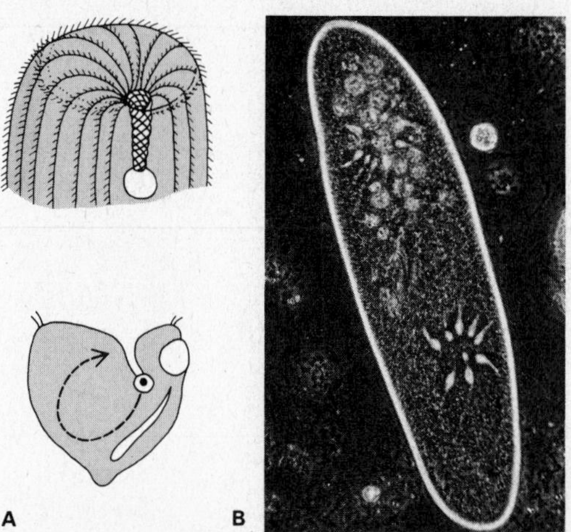

9.24 ***Ciliate feeding and excretion.*** *A, top, the oral region as in Stentor. The diagram shows anterior end of the organisms, with shallow vestibular depression ringed by membranelles. The depression leads to a deep funnel-shaped gullet (cytopharynx), with mouth and food vacuoles at the bottom. Bottom, sectional view. Dashed line indicates path of food vacuoles. Arrow points to area of egestion (cytopyge), here located along the wall of the gullet. Contractile vacuole and water drainage channel are indicated in right part of diagram. See also Fig. 9.25 and Color Fig. 11. B, the rosette-shaped system of contractile vacuoles in Paramecium. One rosette is near each end of the organism.*

isms cover some 30 to 40 percent of the world's ocean floor as "foraminiferan ooze." The rocky products here are *limestone* and *chalk.* Uplifted geologically, they form limestone mountain ranges and chalk cliffs such as those along the English Channel coast.

The parasitic Sporozoa pass through complex life cycles that, as indicated by the name of the group, include spore-forming stages; a single-celled sporozoan undergoes *multiple fission* and divides into numerous smaller cells simultaneously. Each of the resulting cells is a spore with a single nucleus. After such a cell has become established in a given host as a mature parasite it eventually becomes multinucleate, in preparation for another fission. In certain sporozoans as many as three successive spore-forming generations occur in a single sexual life cycle. Also, each cycle may require one or more intermediate hosts in addition to a main host. Sporozoa evidently are largely coccine forms; cell division takes place primarily during reproduction. The spore cells produced by multiple fission are amoeboid in many cases, flagellate in others, and often they also become encapsulated in a cyst wall for passive dispersal.

Many sporozoan parasites are relatively harmless, but many others are not. The best known of all sporozoans is *Plasmodium,* various species of which produce malaria in mammals and birds (Fig. 9.22). Here repeated cycles of multiple fission and spore release from red blood corpuscles result in successive attacks of fever. The time interval between attacks is a main distinction between the several types of malaria. The specific intermediate host in human malaria is the *Anopheles* mosquito, in which the parasites mature in the intestine and the salivary glands. From these glands the parasites reach the blood of new human hosts through mosquito bites.

The Ciliophora, the most complexly elaborated protozoa, represent the most diversely specialized of all known cell types. The organisms move and feed by means of their cilia, which in most cases are arranged in orderly rows. Corresponding rows of kinetosomes lie under the cell surface. Also present there is a system of neurofibrils and, in many species, contractile myofibrils. Furthermore, rows of dischargeable *trichocysts* occur in given species (Fig. 9.23).

Cilia often occur as modified compound organelles. For example, cilia in a row can be fused as a sheetlike *undulating membrane,* which functions in locomotion or in producing food-bearing currents. Tapered tufts of fused cilia are *cirri,* strong bristlelike organelles functioning as locomotor legs. Fused cilia from several rows form *membranelles,* tiny paddles that create an extra strong beat (see Fig. 9.23).

Most ciliates have permanent gullets. Food vacuoles migrate over a more or less definite path in the ciliate body, and digestive remains are cast out at a fixed point often located in or near the gullet. Contractile vacuoles occur at fixed positions near the body surface, and in many cases definite cytoplasmic channels form an internal drainage system leading to the contractile vacuoles (Fig. 9.24).

Ciliates are always multinucleate. They contain at least one and often many (up to several hundred) *micronuclei,* and at least one or many (up to several dozen) *macronuclei* (Fig. 9.25). The micronuclei contain typical chromosomes, but in the macronuclei the genetic material is clumped together and not organized as identifiable chromosomes. Micronuclei produce the macronuclei and exert long-range control over them, and the micronuclei are also the chief controllers of sexual processes. Macronuclei govern all metabolic and developmental functions, and they are directly responsible for the maintenance of the visible traits of the organism. Micronuclei can be lost or removed, and a ciliate can survive and even divide without difficulty. But if the macronuclei are removed or lost, even if the micronuclei are still present, all formed structures degenerate and the organism dies.

In comparatively primitive ciliates (such as *Prorodon*) simple cilia are distributed uniformly over the whole body, and the gullet is little more than a shallow depression at one end (Fig. 9.26). In somewhat more advanced forms the gullet is a deep funnel, with specialized ciliary structures around the rim and along the walls. The large, trumpet-shaped *Stentor* and the well-known *Paramecium* are good examples. In the most advanced types a general body ciliation is reduced or even absent, but specialized membranelles, cirri, and other ciliary derivatives occur in particular regions. For example, *Euplotes* uses cirri on the underside of its flattened body as miniature legs, and *Halteria* uses long surface bristles as tiny stilts in a jumping form of locomotion.

A good many ciliates are symbiotic, and most free-living types are motile. The comparatively few sessile forms include, for example, *Vorticella,*

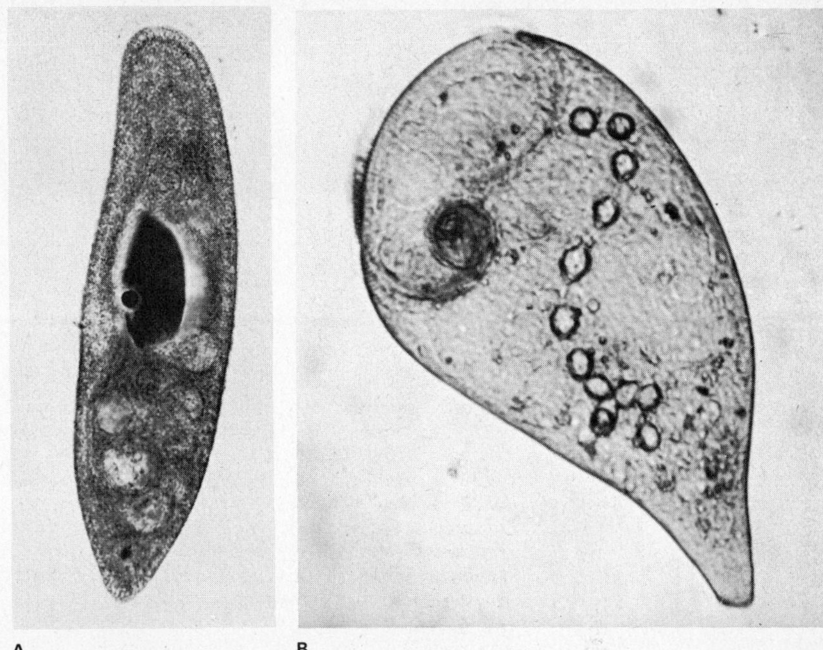

9.25 Ciliate nuclei. *A, Paramecium caudatum stained to reveal the macronucleus (large dark central body) and the smaller micronucleus, which partly overlaps it on one side (approx. ×600). B, Stentor coeruleus, from life. Note region of vestibule, ring of membranelles, gullet, macronuclear chain, and holdfast (partly contracted at end opposite gullet). Faint rows of body cilia are also visible (approx. ×200). (A, courtesy Carolina Biological Supply Company.)*

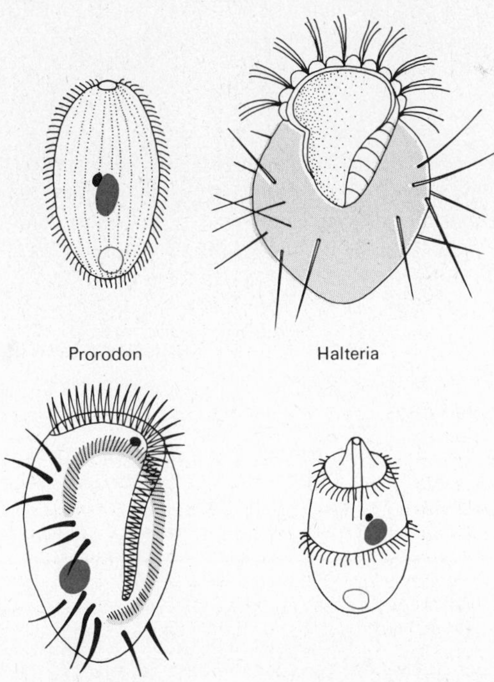

9.26 Ciliate types. *Prorodon is a relatively primitive form with uniform body cilia and a simple mouth. In Didinium the mouth is at the tip of a proboscis; in addition to the rings of cilia shown here, an otherwise uniform body ciliation is also present (but not indicated). Halteria and Euplotes are advanced types; simple cilia are absent, but various kinds of membranelles and cirri are situated in specific regions.*

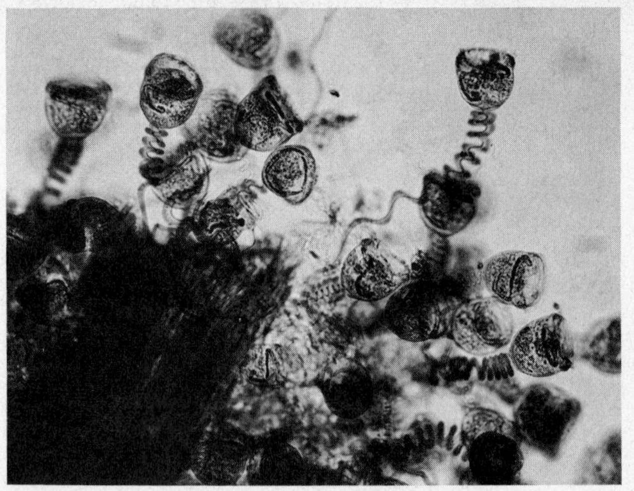

A

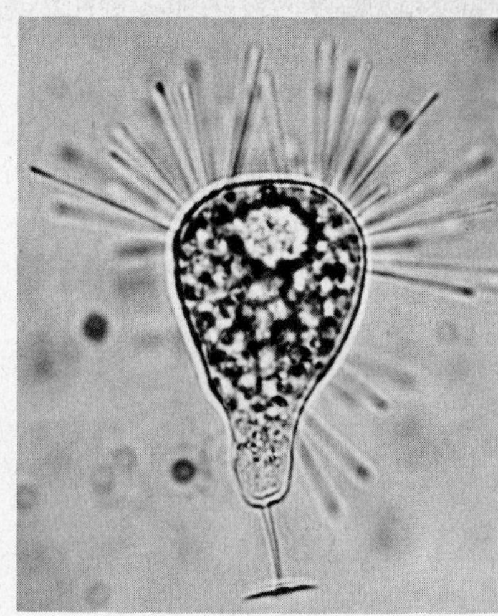

B

9.27 ***Sessile ciliates.*** *A, a group of Vorticella. Each individual is attached by a stalk that contains a conspicuous contractile myoneme. In the contracted state the stalk is coiled, as in most individuals in the photo (×800). B, a suctorian. The tentacles radiating out from the attached cell body suck up the juices of trapped prey (×400). (A, courtesy Carolina Biological Supply Company.)*

a type attached by a contractile stalk (Fig. 9.27). Similarly sessile are the interesting *suctorians,* which trap microscopic food organisms by means of tentacles and suck the contents of such prey into their bodies. Immature suctorians swim about with the aid of cilia, but when the organisms become attached adults the cilia are lost.

Evidently, protozoa specifically and Protista generally are far from "simple." Many of these organisms have remained unicellular and microscopic in size, yet in this very smallness lies perhaps their most remarkable characteristic: despite being limited to the dimensions of single cells they are as diverse, varied, and complex in the microsphere of life as only very few groups of far larger organisms can be in the macrosphere.

review questions

1 What are the unifying traits of the Protista? Why should the various protistan groups no longer be classified simply as "plants" and "animals"? Describe the probable ancestral type from which Protista are believed to have evolved.

2 What states of existence could early protists probably exhibit? Define each of these states and give specific examples.

3 What were the probable methods of nutrition of early protists? In view of the nutritional possibilities and the various states of existence, how many different evolutionary directions could ancestral protists probably follow? Show how the diversity of existing protists supports such assumptions.

4 What are the group characteristics of the algae? What are the special characteristics of the green-line, brown-line, and red-line algal groups? Review here the (*a*) pigments, (*b*) food-storage compounds, and (*c*) cell-wall compounds of these organisms.

5 What is the probable evolutionary significance of pairs of algae of which one is photosynthetic and the other not? Give specific examples of such pairs for three or four algal phyla.

6 In what ways are (*a*) charophytes and (*b*) euglenophytes similar to chlorophytes, and in what ways are they different?

7 Describe the characteristics of chrysophytes generally and of each chrysophyte class specifically. What groups are included among the Pyrrophyta, and what features identify each of these groups?

8 Review the identifying features of brown and red algae.

9 Review the structural characteristics of fungi generally. What are the possible evolutionary relations of this phylum to other protistan groups? Name the main groups of fungi.

10 Describe the general characteristics of the various fungal classes. What are Fungi imperfecti? Lichens?

11 What traits identify the slime molds? What justifies inclusion of these organisms among Protista? Which features of slime molds are reminiscent of other protists?

12 Distinguish between protozoa and (*a*) other protists, (*b*) animals. What states of existence are exhibited by (*a*) fungi, (*b*) slime molds, (*c*) protozoa?

13 Describe the general structural characteristics of protozoan cells. What cytoplasmic and nuclear organelles are typical of such cells?

14 Describe the characteristics of various representatives of the Mastigophora and the Sarcodina. Describe the life cycle of the malarial parasite *Plasmodium.*

15 What is the general structure of a ciliate? What are cirri, membranelles, and undulating membranes? What are the functions of micronuclei and macronuclei?

---

collateral readings

Bonner, J. T.: How Slime Molds Communicate, *Sci. American,* Aug., 1963. An examination of the mechanism by which solitary amoebas of slime molds aggregate as pseudoplasmodia.

Brook, A. J.: Water Blooms, *New Biol.,* vol. 13, 1957. An article on the waxing and waning of algal life in water.

Doyle, W. T.: "Nonvascular Plants: Form and Function," Wadsworth, Belmont, Calif., 1964. This paperback reviews the biology of all protistan groups except the protozoa. Recommended.

Emerson, R.: Molds and Man, *Sci. American,* Jan., 1952. The importance of harmful and beneficial fungi for man is discussed by a noted mycologist.

Gibor, A.: Acetabularia: A Useful Giant Cell, *Sci. American,* Nov., 1966. An account of the interesting research on nucleocytoplasmic relations in this large unicellular alga.

Ingold, C. T.: Famous Plants—The Mushroom, *New Biol.,* vol. 18, 1955. An interesting article dealing with the economically most important of all fungi.

Jahn, T. L., and **F. F. Jahn**: "How to Know the Protozoa," Wm. C. Brown, Dubuque, Iowa, 1949. This book greatly facilitates the identification and characterization of these protists.

Jane, F. W.: Famous Plant-Animal—Euglena, *New Biol.,* vol. 19, 1955. A short biology of a commonly used laboratory alga.

Lamb, I. M.: Lichens, *Sci. American,* Oct., 1959. The biology and ecology of these symbiotic alga-fungus combinations are examined.

Milner, H. W.: Algae as food, *Sci. American,* Oct., 1953. The title adequately describes the subject matter.

Newton, L.: Famous Plants—Fucus, *New Biol.,* vol. 17, 1954. A study of the most common of the coastal brown algae.

Niederhauser, J. S., and **W. C. Coob**: The Late Blight of Potatoes, *Sci. American,* May, 1959. The nature and control of a serious fungus pest is discussed.

Preston, R. D.: Plants without Cellulose, *Sci. American,* June, 1968. On the composition of algal cell walls.

Russell, P. F.: The Eradication of Malaria, *Sci. American,* June, 1952. Problems in the control of this widespread sporozoan parasite are examined.

Wichterman, R.: "The Biology of Paramecium," McGraw-Hill, New York, 1953. Highly recommended not only for further data on this ciliate but also for additional background on protozoa generally.

chapter 10 plants

category	phylum	subphylum	class	subclass	order
metaphyta	bryophyta		bryopsida		
			hepaticopsida		
			anthoceropsida		
	tracheophyta	psilopsida			
		lycopsida			
		sphenopsida			
		pteropsida	filicineae		
			gymnospermae	cycadophytae	cycadales
				coniferophytae	ginkgoales
					coniferales
					gnetales
			angiospermae	dicotyledoneae	
				monocotyledoneae	

At some points during their evolutionary history, the Protista gave rise to the two largest groups of organisms now in existence, the *Metaphyta* and the *Metazoa,* or plants and animals proper. In both groups the cell structure is typically protistan, and flagellate, amoeboid, and sporine states of cellular existence are common. Sperms and many other cell types are flagellate (or ciliate); eggs, connective tissue cells, and others are actually or potentially amoeboid; and the vast bulk of the plant or animal body is sporine, composed of nonmotile cells that divide during their vegetative life.

Plants evolved only some 350 million years ago, much later than animals, and thus they represent the newest major branch of life.

general characteristics

Plants are distinguished from Protista in their organ and organ-system levels of organization, in having reproductive structures that are at least tissues and in most cases organs, and in passing through distinct embryonic stages during development. Also, plants are exclusively photosynthetic and nonmotile. The evolutionary derivation of plants from sporine green algae is suggested strongly by the presence of chlorophylls *a* and *b,* by carotenoid and xanthophyll pigments nearly identical with those of chlorophytes, by cell walls made of cellulose, by the deposition of food stores in the form of starch, by the presence of usually two whiplash flagella in most motile cells, and by a body composed very largely of sporine cells.

Most distinguishing characteristics of plants are adaptations to terrestrial ways of life developed during the evolution from aquatic protistan ancestors. For example, in the absence of the buoyant action of water, plants contain antigravity *skeletal tissues.* These reach their most advanced form in the sclerenchymas and woods of the tracheophytes. The requirement of mechanical support is met also by the generally *upright, radial* structure, though this is not an invariable feature. Such a construction distributes the weight equally around the vertical axis and permits lower body portions to support upper ones directly. In the absence of open water around all surfaces, plants have specialized *absorbing tissues* that project into soil. These are either *rhizoids* or more elaborate *roots.* Since such structures occur only in specific body regions, plants also contain nutrient-distributing or *conducting* tissues, the most highly developed being those of *vascular* plants.

Exposed to air, plants minimize the danger of

drying out through *waxy cuticles* on free surfaces, which let light pass but not water or atmospheric gases. But gases must be exchanged with the environment, and plants actually contain gas-transmitting surface pores, or *stomata* (see Chap. 5). The structures and processes of reproduction likewise represent adaptations to life in an aerial environment. Reproductive structures are organs containing at least two tissues: an exterior sterile tissue that protects against drying out and an interior tissue that produces the actual spores or sex cells. Spores themselves are always encapsulated, and sex cells either are released only during wet or rainy periods or remain surrounded by protective tissues. Moreover, the life cycle of plants always includes an embryonic phase, which provides the developmental time necessary for the elaboration of the many specialized tissues of the mature plant. Since this internal elaboration is an adaptation to terrestrial conditions, the plant embryo too can be regarded as an evolutionary response to the requirements of land life.

Finally, the life cycle of plants always consists of two successive adult generations. One, the *gametophyte,* produces sex cells only, from which new adults develop. Such an adult, the *sporophyte,* then produces spores only, which grow into new gametophytes. The mature plants of these two generations are structured quite differently; they are excellent examples of polymorphism. Life cycles characterized in this way by an *alternation of generations* originated among the Protista, in adaptation to their own problems of aquatic life (see Chaps. 24 and 25). Plants then inherited such life cycles and adapted them to the requirements of terrestrial life.

The ancestors of plants probably *had* to adapt to terrestrial conditions if they were to survive at all. For the algal ancestors occasionally must have experienced prolonged droughts, not an unusual hazard in freshwater habitats. Various evolutionary responses to these hazards then permitted them to withstand drought and thus allowed them to survive as basically aquatic organisms. Almost incidentally, however, gradual perfection of the adaptations to temporary terrestrial living must eventually have produced plants able to survive without open water. Such organisms could then be permanently terrestrial.

Two phylum groups of plants have evolved, the moss plants, or *bryophytes,* and the vascular plants, or *tracheophytes.* The latter are far more abundant and important and will occupy most of our attention.

A

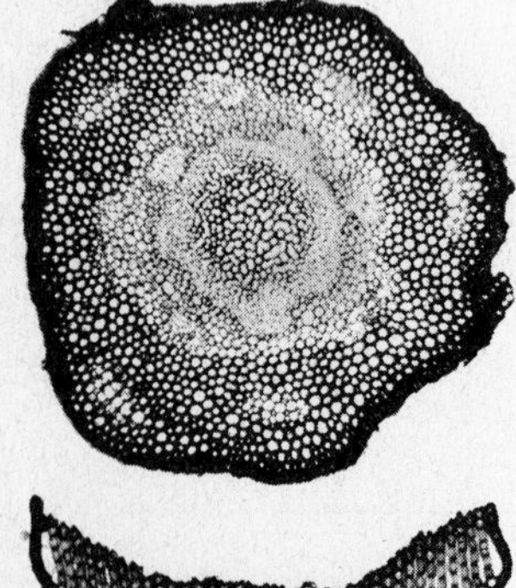

B

***10.1* Moss structure.** *A, a horizontal protonema, with rhizoids growing into the ground and buds and young shoots growing upward. B, cross section through the stem and a leaf of a shoot. In stem (top) note thick-walled cortex cells and thin-walled core cells. In leaf (bottom) note columns of cells along the upper surface and air spaces between the columns.*

Bryophytes

Moss Plants
Phylum Bryophyta 25,000 species

Class Bryopsida mosses

Class Hepaticopsida liverworts

Class Anthoceropsida hornworts

The members of this cosmopolitan phylum generally live in more or less shady, perpetually moist places, where the danger of drying out is minimized. Some bryophytes inhabit bogs and swamps, others grow in the cold regions of the world, in the tundra and high on mountains. Still others grow in deserts, near hot springs, and in the tropics. In tropical rain forests bryophytes occur abundantly as epiphytes on the leaves, branches, and trunks of trees. Several species of bryophytes live in fresh water; none is marine.

Bryophytes frequently are important soil formers and soil protectors. They can settle where lichens have begun to convert bare rock surfaces to small patches of soil, and by their metabolism and decay bryophytes then contribute to a further transformation of rock to soil. Moreover, many bryophytes form dense, soil-covering carpets that minimize soil erosion and retain water between the closely spaced plants. Many bryophytes also absorb water directly through their leaves, which spares the water supplies of soil.

Bryophytes are distinguished from tracheophytes by a life cycle in which the gametophyte generation is always *dominant.* This generation lasts longer, is physically larger and more conspicuous, is nutritionally independent, and in general represents the "main" plant. Casual reference to a "moss," for example, is a reference to the gametophyte. By contrast, the sporophyte is small, short-lived, and nutritionally dependent on the gametophyte (see Chap. 25).

Mosses are believed to be the most primitive members of the phylum. The gametophyte body

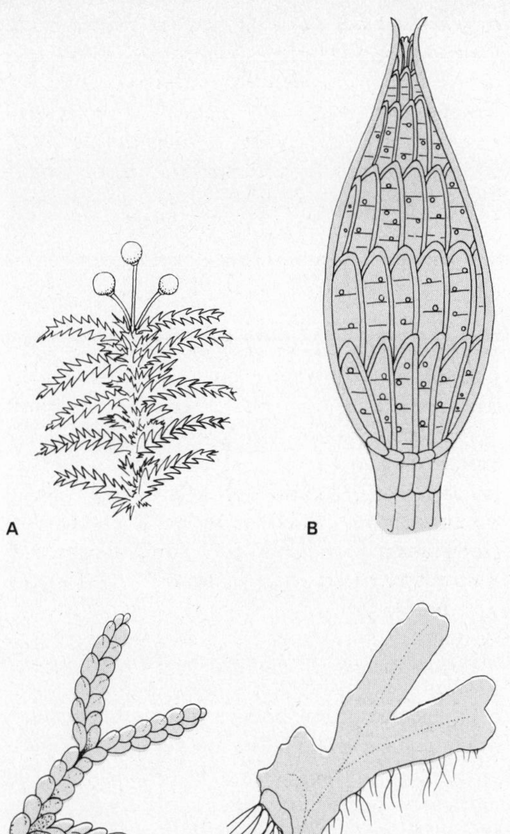

10.2 Peat moss. *A, branching shoot of Sphagnum (protonema not shown). Sporophytes are attached at the top of the shoot. B, a Sphagnum leaf. Note boxlike nonliving hulls of cells. These are filled with water and air.*

10.3 Liverwort body shapes. *Left, a leafy (foliose) type. Right, a sheetlike (thallose) type.*

of a moss typically consists of a branched network of green filaments spread flat over the ground (Fig. 10.1). From such a *protonema* grow small nongreen extensions into soil, and these *rhizoids* absorb water and minerals. The protonema also gives rise to one or more green *shoots* that project in the air. Each shoot consists of an upright *stem* to which are attached radially arranged *leaves.* At maturity a shoot also bears terminal *sex organs.* The stem is composed of an outer *epidermis* without stomata, a parenchymatous *cortex* underneath, and a core of water- and nutrient-transporting cells (in which the cytoplasm degenerates during development, leaving only the walls). The leaves of some mosses are formed from a single layer of green cells, but in other cases several differently specialized layers are present. They usually leave air spaces near the upper leaf surface that permit even deep-lying green cells to exchange gases directly with the external atmosphere (see Fig. 10.1).

Among mosses of more than small-scale ecological significance are the peat mosses (*Sphagnum*). These plants live in swamps and bogs all over the world, but particularly in the tundra and in colder regions generally. Metabolic activities make the plants and the water in which they grow too acid for most decay bacteria. As a result, old plants pile up in beds of considerable thickness, filling in swamp areas and forming the main organic component of peat. The body of these plants is specialized for water storage. The protonema is a flat, broad sheet bearing a highly branched system of long shoots (Fig. 10.2). In the cortex of the mature shoots are thick-walled water-storing hulls of disintegrated cells. Leaves too contain large water-filled cells, of which only the walls remain in the mature plant. This spongy, water-holding property has made peat mosses useful as, for example, packing material for moisture-requiring goods.

Whereas mosses typically have vertical, radially symmetrical parts, liverworts are horizontal plants (Fig. 10.3). Some are leafy like moss shoots, and in others the body is a flat sheet, or *thallus,* along the ground. An example of the leafy (*foliose*) types is *Porella,* a liverwort with a horizontal stem bearing usually three rows of leaves. The plant is often epiphytic on trees. Sheetlike (*thallose*) types are exemplified by *Marchantia.* The thallus of this plant is ribbon-shaped and lobed, with a median furrow along the upper surface. From the underside project numerous rhizoids. At the forward margin of a thallus is a *growing point* consisting of a cluster of cells. As these produce new cells on either side two new lobes are formed, and the growing point thus comes to be located in a notch between the lobes. Later the growing point usually becomes divided into two cell groups, each of which can then produce a thallus branch. A growth pattern of this sort therefore leads successively to the formation of two equal branches from one main branch.

Internally a thallus contains three distinct zones, each composed of one or more tissues (Fig. 10.4). The bottom zone is largely absorptive and consists mainly of the nongreen rhizoids. The middle zone is formed from nongreen parenchyma and functions in storage and conduction of nutrients. The upper zone is photosynthetic and includes elaborate air chambers and air pores. In types like *Marchantia* the location of the internal air chambers is marked externally by fine diamond-shaped lines on the surface of the thallus. Some thallose liverworts are secondarily simplified. In *Sphaerocarpos,*

10.4 Liverwort structure. *A, thalli of Marchantia. In each thallus note the pair of lobes at the forward margin (well seen at upper left, for example). The growing point is located in the notch between the two lobes. B, the internal structure of the Marchantia thallus.*

for example, the thallus is only one cell layer thick.

In hornworts the body is likewise a thallus, irregularly scalloped along the margins but without notches, surface furrows, or midribs. Rhizoids are present on the underside. Internally the tissue of the thallus is parenchymatous, and each cell contains a single large chloroplast with a conspicuous pyrenoid (as in green algae). In this respect hornworts differ from the other bryophyte classes, in which each cell contains numerous chloroplasts without pyrenoids. The central portions of a hornwort thallus are usually several cell layers thick, and air chambers or air pores are often absent. The best known hornwort is probably *Anthoceros,* fairly common on damp soils (see also Chap. 25 and Fig. 25.22).

Tracheophytes

Vascular Plants

Phylum Tracheophyta 260,000+ species

Subphylum Psilopsida psilopsids

Subphylum Lycopsida club mosses

Subphylum Sphenopsida horsetails

Subphylum Pteropsida

Class Filicineae ferns

Class Gymnospermae cone-bearing seed plants

Class Angiospermae flowering seed plants

The earliest tracheophytes gave rise to four separate lines of descent, represented today by the four subphyla listed above. The first three are little more than evolutionary relics, and today the pteropsids unquestionably are the dominant group of plants. Flowering plants in particular include more species than all other Metaphyta and plantlike Protista combined. These plants in fact form the largest group of photosynthetic organisms and, after the insects, the second largest group of all types of organisms.

patterns of life

The phylum as a whole is identified by independent and *dominant sporophytes,* and by

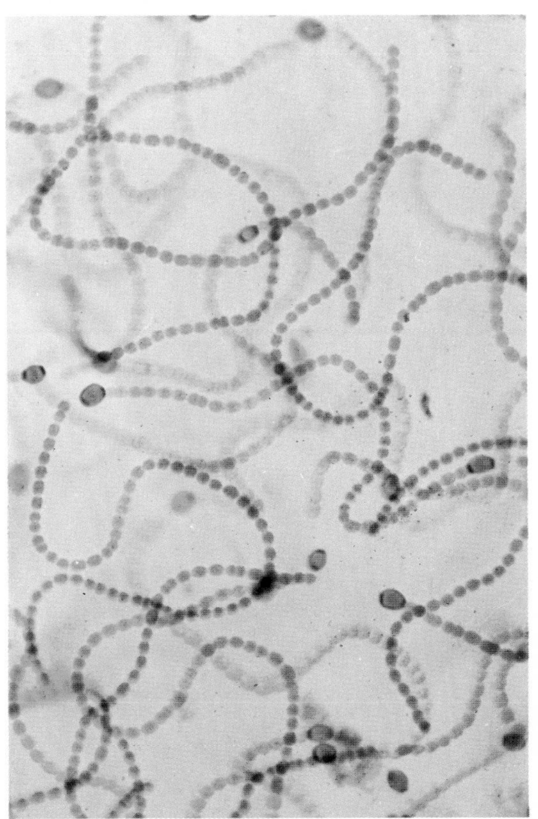

6. ***Nostoc,*** *a colonial blue-green alga. The cellular filaments are embedded in gelatinous sheaths. The enlarged cells are heterocysts, regions where a filament can fragment and give rise to separate filaments capable of growing independently as new colonies. (Courtesy Carolina Biological Supply Company.)*

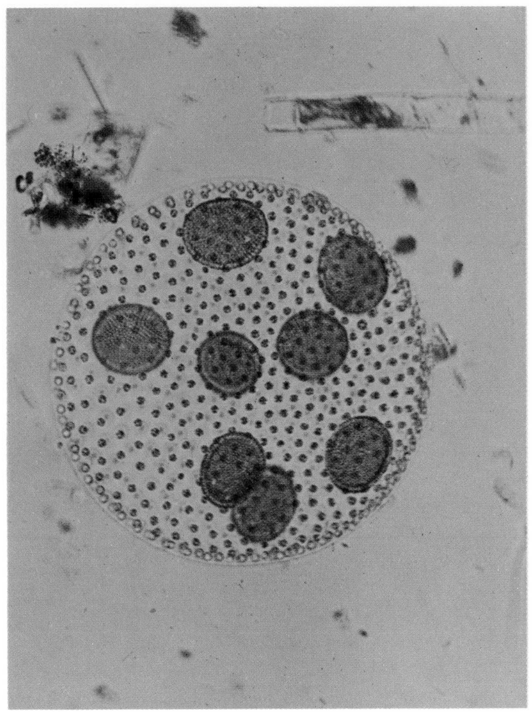

7. ***Volvox,*** *a colonial green alga composed of many flagellate cells. The cells are arranged as a single-layered sphere, each cell of it in direct contact with the water environment. In the interior are several offspring colonies, which develop there and eventually burst through the parent.*

color figure 8

A

B

8. Red algae. *A,* Antithamnium, *a branched type. B,* Corallina, *a stony coralline type. (Courtesy Carolina Biological Supply Company.)*

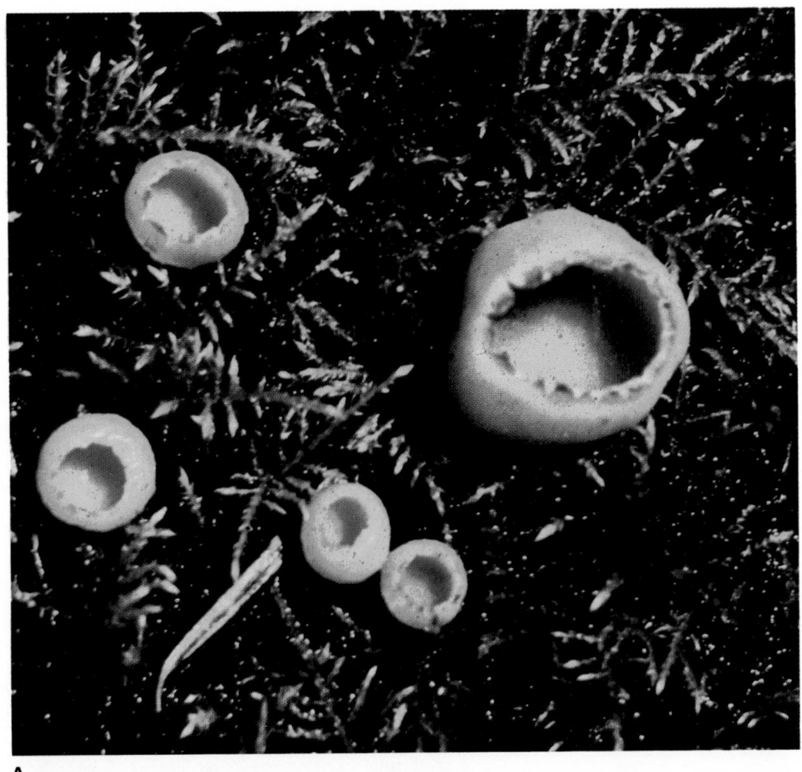

A

B

9. Ascomycete fungi. *A, fruiting bodies of* Peziza, *a cup fungus. B, fruiting bodies of* Morchella, *the edible morel. (Courtesy Carolina Biological Supply Company.)*

color figure 10

10. Basidiomycete fungi. *A, puffball. B, stinkhorn. C, bird's-nest fungi. The globular bodies in the cups are reproductive dispersal units. (B, courtesy Carolina Biological Supply Company.)*

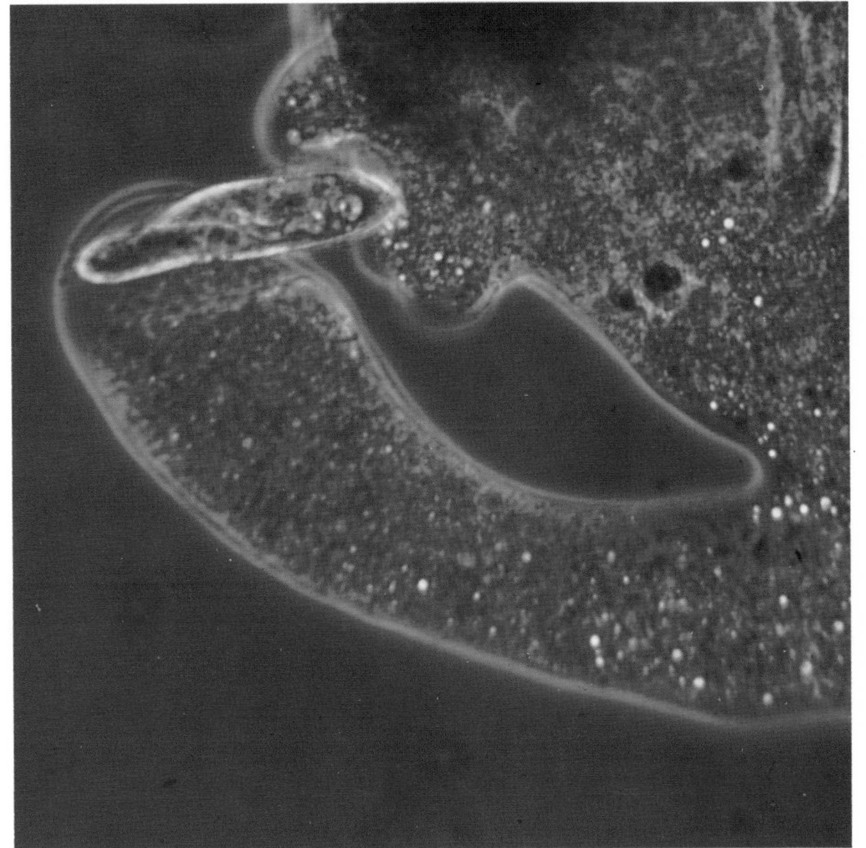

A

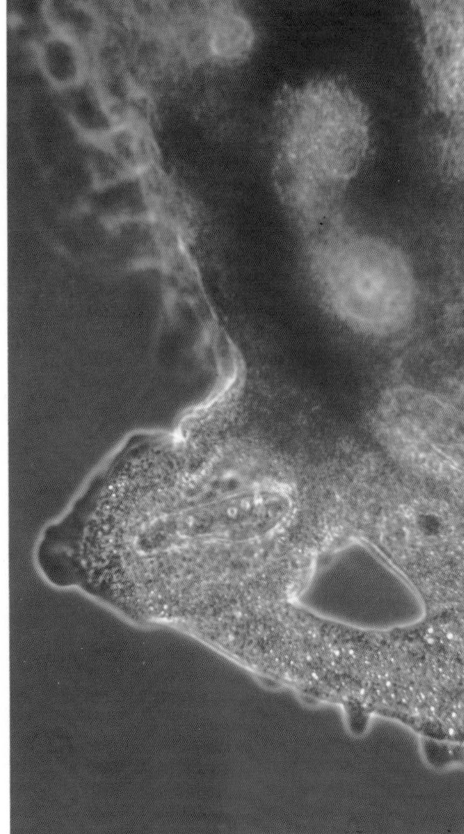

B

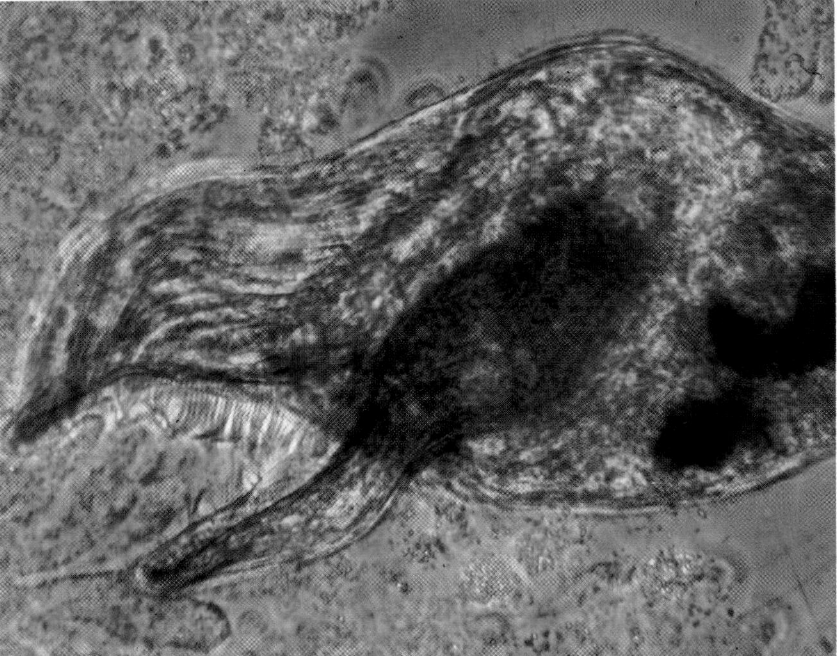

C

11. Feeding in protozoa. *A, B, two stages of ameba engulfing a paramecium. C, a large cannibalistic ciliate* Blepharisma *engulfing a smaller fellow member of the species.*

color figure 12

A

12. Early tracheophyte groups. *A, one of the groundpines,* Lycopodium. *B, one of the club mosses,* Selaginella. *C, one of the horsetails,* Equisetum.

B

C

13. Motion and feeding. *Animals obtain food either by active locomotion or by trapping small moving food organisms, as among the sessile featherduster worms* (Sabella) *shown here. Related distantly to earthworms,* Sabella *lives in an attached tubular housing and projects its feathery food-trapping crown from the open end of the tube.*

color figure 14

14. Life cycle stages *of amphibians symbolize the main stages in the sexual development of animals generally. A, eggs. B, embryo. C, larva. D, adult. The transition from embryo to larva is achieved by hatching, that from larva to adult, by metamorphosis. The photos are not reproduced to the same scale.*

gametophytes that are either independent or dependent but never dominant (see Chap. 25). Casual reference to a tracheophyte is a reference to the sporophyte generation. The phylum is further distinguished by the presence of two specialized vascular tissues in the sporophytes, the water-conducting *xylem* and the food-conducting *phloem*. Also, the typical tracheophyte body is subdivided into *roots, stems,* and *leaves,* each such body part representing a true organ.

Tracheophytes have a vertical main axis and a conspicuous radial symmetry around this axis. Such a construction permits efficient nutrient absorption from all sides around the plant, and it also provides a mechanically balanced body. Many tracheophytes taper upward, which allows the greatest weight to rest on the broadest foundation. Support is also provided by collenchyma, sclerenchyma, and the cellulose and lignin of wood. By virtue of such construction patterns and materials, plants can attain considerable sizes.

Large size necessitates long-distance nutrient conduction. Moreover, because the plant is exposed to both air and soil, the aerial and subterranean portions can be expected to differ in function if not also in structure. The characteristic root-stem-leaf organization of the tracheophyte is a specific adaptation to these requirements. Roots absorb from the ground, leaves photosynthesize, and stems interconnect, conduct, and support.

In a stationary organism in which water is vital and in which food cannot be produced during the night and often also not during the winter, *storage* of water and food is of major importance. Indeed, water storage is a function of nearly every living tracheophyte cell. Such cells are *succulent,* with large amounts of water, much of it in vacuoles. This condition also makes the cells highly *turgid.* Water is confined by rigid cell walls and this constraint puts the water under considerable pressure. Such cellular turgor gives tissues additional mechanical support and permits even ''soft'' plant parts like leaves to maintain their shape well. But if water is in insufficient supply, succulence, turgor, and mechanical support all become reduced and the plant wilts.

Food storage too is a function of many plant cells, parenchymatous cells most particularly. Moreover, many tracheophytes have enlarged body parts often adapted especially for food storage. Stems and roots are modified more frequently for this function than leaves. Some of the main types of modified stems are (Fig. 10.5): *rhizomes,* horizontal underground stems common particularly in primitive tracheophytes; *tubers,* expanded portions of underground stems usually adapted for food storage, as in potatoes; *bulbs,* shortened underground stems to which thickened storage leaves are attached, as in onions; *corms,* shortened bulky underground storage stems that resemble bulbs superficially but have scalelike leaves on the outer surfaces, as in gladioli; *runners,* horizontal stems flat on the ground, as in strawberries; and *twining stems,* which wind around upright on other objects and obtain support from them, as in beans.

Variant types of roots include (Fig. 10.6): *fibrous roots,* in which numerous branch roots lead off from the stem base into soil in all directions, as in grasses; *taproots,* single thick vertical storage roots from which small branch roots lead off, as in carrots; *adventitious roots,* which sprout from any region of the plant (except a root), even from regions near the tip of the stem; *prop roots,* which are adventitious roots specially adapted to provide mechanical support, as in banyan trees

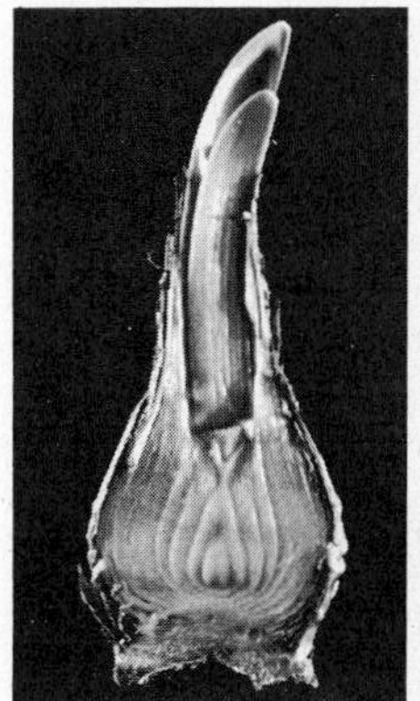
A

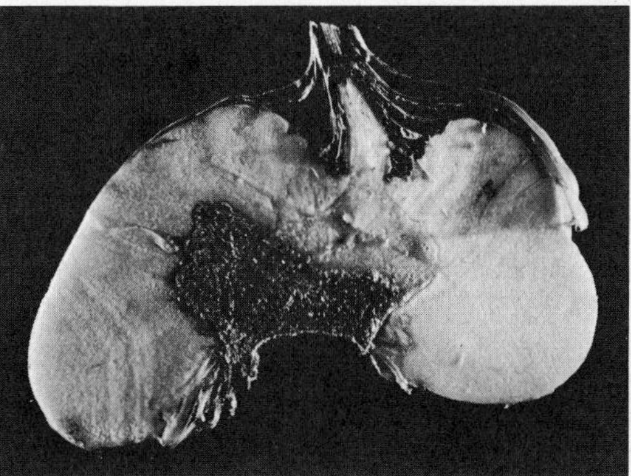
B

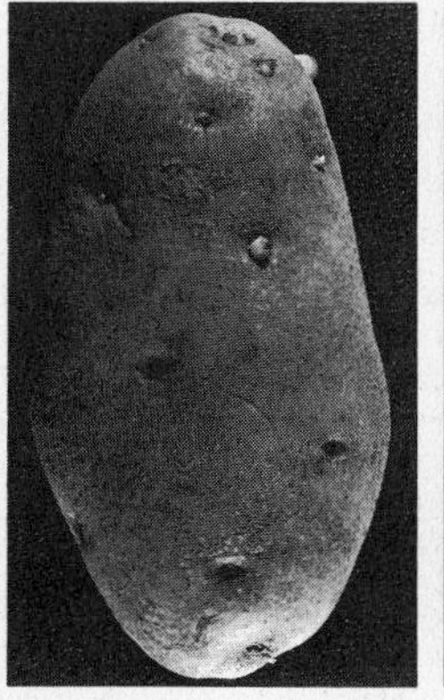
C

D

***10.5* Stem types.** *A, a bulb. The central vertical stem is surrounded by leaves, which form the bulk of the bulb. B, a corm. Leaves are borne at the top. C, a tuber (potato). D, a runner.*

A

B

C

10.6 *(Above)* ***Root types.*** *A, fibrous roots. B, taproots. C, prop roots.*

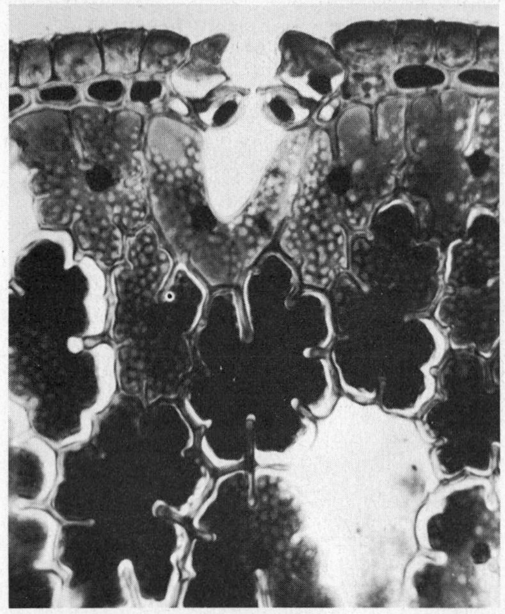

10.7 Adaptations to dry conditions. *Section of pine leaf showing sunken stoma (top center) and lobed parenchyma cells in interior. See also Fig. 5.10 for thick waxy cuticle over epidermis.*

and older corn plants; and *aerial roots,* which are not in contact with the ground but absorb water from sources available above ground, as in orchids. Such roots have a many-layered epidermis in which the cells die and the remaining walls then serve in water storage.

A suitable body construction is only one requirement for a successful nonmotile way of terrestrial life. Another is adaptability to potentially lethal changes in local weather, for a plant rooted to the ground cannot escape extremes of temperature. It can only attempt to protect against them. Water poses the key problem here. In summer heat and in deserts the plant is in danger of having too little internal water; and in winter or at high latitudes and altitudes there is often too much, for if internal water freezes, it can damage and kill cells.

The heat problem is one of internal *water conservation,* and it affects the exposed stems and leaves far more than the underground roots. Tracheophytes living in dry, warm, or hot climates, so-called *xerophytes,* are protected in various ways against excessive evaporation of interal water. For example, waxy cuticles over exposed surfaces are greatly thickened, sometimes becoming even thicker than the epidermal cells that secrete them (see Fig. 5.10). Stomata in stem and leaves are often reduced in number, and in leaves they can be located mostly or entirely on the underside, away from direct sunlight and settling dust. Or they are sunk deep in microscopic epidermal pits, which provide shade except when the sun shines straight into them (Fig. 10.7).

Under near-desert conditions the rate of evaporation may nevertheless be too high. However, water vaporization will be lessened if the area of exposed parts is reduced in proportion to their volume. Thus, xerophytic plants often have but a few leaves or small scalelike or needle-shaped leaves. In the extreme case, well exemplified by cacti, leaves do not develop at all and the function of food manufacture is taken over largely by massive green stems. Exposure can also be reduced if much of the plant is underground, and underground organs actually are particularly common in xerophytes. Water-storing capacity can be increased through bulky, succulent leaves, as in many ornamental house plants. Through adaptations such as these, some tracheophytes are able to survive even in the hottest, driest regions provided that at least *some* water is available at *some* time. Quite a number of tracheophytes have overcome the water-conservation problem altogether by adapting secondarily to an aquatic habitat and living as *hydrophytes* (see Fig. 7.6).

Where water supplies are neither overly abundant nor overly sparse, as in much of the temperate zone, the plants are *mesophytes.* Such plants must still cope with considerable fluctuations in climatic conditions. For example, a summer day might be excessively hot and dry, and the mesophytic tracheophyte then will droop and begin to wilt. But if water becomes available within a few days, conditions in the plant are soon restored to normal. In winter, by contrast, frost for even an hour is likely to kill; below the freezing point water that is not part of colloidal gels is transformed to ice crystals. These can tear the structural framework of cells and this is why very low temperatures are potentially lethal.

Probably in response to yearly cold seasons or outright winters, tracheophytes have evolved major adaptations profoundly affecting their whole way of life. On the basis of these adaptations three groups of vascular plants can be distinguished, *perennials, biennials,* and *annuals* (Fig. 10.8).

In perennials, major or all portions of the plant body last through many successive winters. Although such plants do not live indefinitely, their individual life spans in many cases are far longer than those of any other organisms. At the approach of winter perennials usually manufacture large quantities of colloidal materials that convert the interior of cells to a gel state. Little water then remains free inside cells, and ice formation is forestalled. In *evergreen* plant groups, such *winter hardening* is particularly effective. Even leaves can be retained, as in most conifers, and vital processes can continue as in summer though at a slower pace.

Other perennials, the *deciduous* plants, cannot protect their foliage against the cold and they shed leaves in the fall. But the rest of the plant lives on. Buds and embryonic leaves have developed during the preceding summer, and they sprout the next spring as new foliage. In the absence of mature leaves during the cold season little or no food can be produced. However, such plants accumulate food reserves at other seasons and store them in roots and stems. Flowering trees living in the temperate zone are familiar examples of deciduous perennials.

Still other perennials are soft-bodied and *herbaceous.* In such plants, exemplified by asparagus or dandelions, the leaves as well as the aerial parts of the stem die off in the fall. But the roots

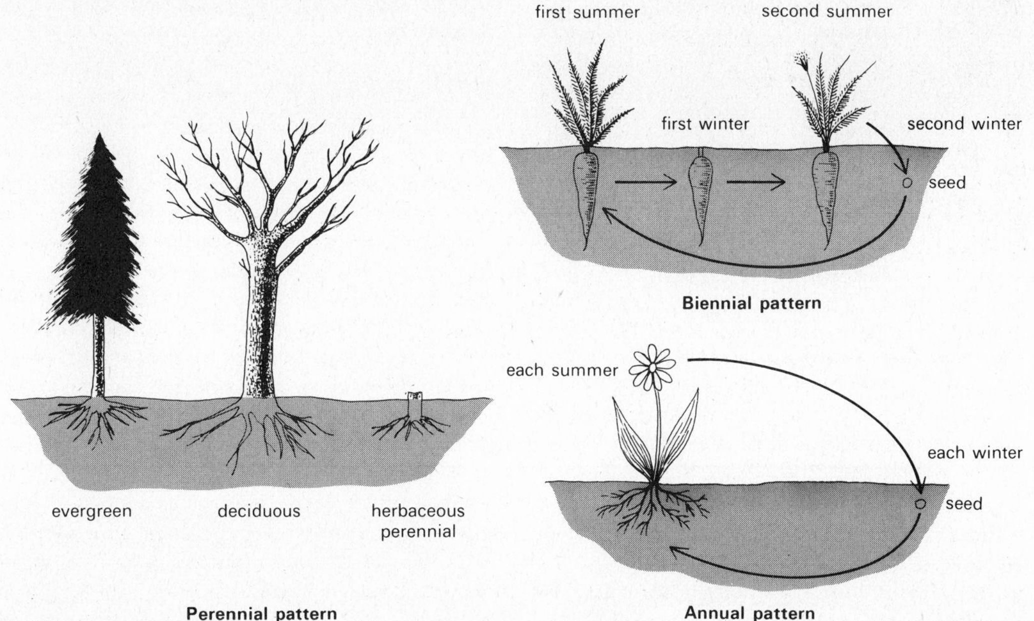

10.8 Survival patterns of plants. *In perennials such as conifers, the whole plant survives the winter. In deciduous perennials foliage is shed in the cold season but the rest of the plant survives. In herbaceous perennials only the roots and a small piece of stem survive the winter. Biennial plants retain only the roots and a small piece of stem during a first winter, and only seeds survive the second winter. In an annual the whole plant dies every year and is perpetuated only by seeds.*

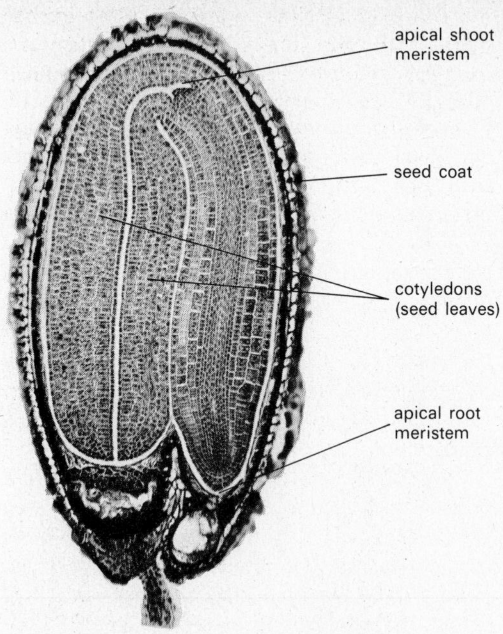

10.9 The tracheophyte embryo, *in seed.*

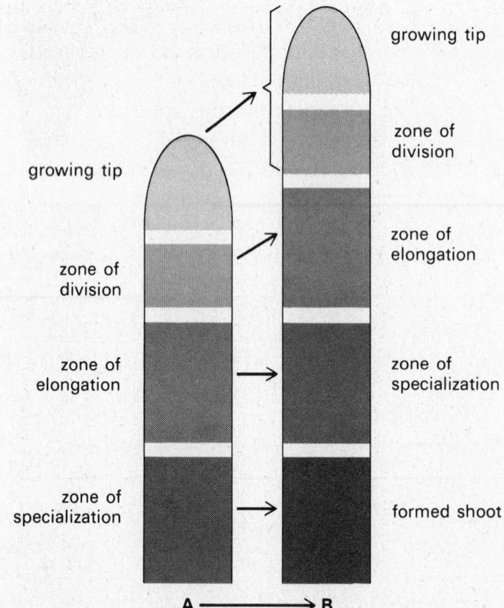

10.10 Shoot development. *The condition depicted in A changes to that of B after a period of growth. Note how any given zone transforms to the more mature condition of the zone originally below it. The growing tip not only perpetuates itself but also generates new zones of division.*

and a short underground piece of stem survive. Reserve foods in these underground body parts last through the winter and suffice in spring for the development of a new aerial shoot. Leaves and a mature stem then grow from this shoot. Since the aerial portions of such plants live only during a relatively brief growing season, they never become very extensive; bulky wood is neither required nor formed, and the plants remain nonwoody herbs. For many perennials it is evidently more advantageous to retrench when life becomes difficult than to maintain elaborate aerial structures against heavy odds.

Winter retrenchment goes even further in biennial and annual herbaceous plants. In biennials, well exemplified by carrots, food reserves are stored in the bulky taproots and the leaves then die off at the approach of winter. The roots and portions of the shoot survive that winter, and from them develops a new plant the following spring. This second-year plant flowers and forms seeds. At the approach of the second winter the entire plant dies, roots included. Only the seeds survive, and they later begin a new two-year cycle. An annual plant such as wheat flowers and produces seeds every year. The whole plant dies in the fall, and its seeds give rise to a new generation the following spring (see Fig. 10.8).

Evidently, vascular plants have found several workable solutions to the problem of cold. They can winterproof the whole body or some part of the body, or they can rely entirely and most economically on the handful of hardy cells that make up seeds. These often contain as little as 5 percent water and are therefore excellently adapted to withstand the rigors of winter. Thus, tracheophytes make the most of their difficult terrestrial habitat. Actually there are only two types of land environment in which a tracheophyte cannot live: the glacial regions at very high altitudes and latitudes, and the permanently arid deserts. But most other organisms cannot live there either.

growth and structure

primary growth: stem and root

The sporophyte of a vascular plant begins its life history as a fertilized egg that divides and becomes a multicellular, elongated *embryo.* Such an embryo has a *shoot apex* at one tip and a *root apex* at the other (Fig. 10.9). At these tips certain cells called *apical meristems* remain permanently embryonic. They continue to divide, and new cells formed by them are added behind each tip to the embryonic tissues already present. The whole embryo continues to elongate in this manner.

The embryonic tissues behind the apical meristems soon begin to specialize as adult stem and root tissues, and as their distance from the tips increases the tissues become progressively more mature. Thus, a lengthwise view of a shoot or a root exhibits an orderly sequence of zones corresponding to the stages each adult stem or root tissue has passed through during its development (Fig. 10.10). As already described in Chap. 5, the concentrically arranged adult tissues are, from the outside inward, epidermis, cortex, endodermis (in roots), and stele. The stele consists of pericycle (in roots), phloem, xylem, and pith (in stems; see Fig. 5.14).

In the root, the root-hair cells of the epidermis are usually in a distinct zone some distance behind the root tip (Fig. 10.11). Root hairs are temporary structures; ahead of the root-hair zone they have not yet developed and behind it they have already disappeared. The root-hair zone therefore advances as the root tip advances. Also present is a *root cap,* several layers of cells that envelop the root tip externally. Formed by the apical root meristem, a root cap is an important adaptive device. As the root tip advances, hard soil grains would soon macerate unprotected meristem tissue. But in the presence of a root cap the cap cells wear off instead and the growing tip is shielded effectively. New cap cells continue to be formed by the root meristem.

The roots of most tracheophytes are without pith, and the steles in such cases are called *protosteles.* The simplest type of protostele is a *haplostele,* in which xylem, phloem, and pericycle have a cylindrical arrangement. Most tracheophyte roots have *actinosteles,* or variants of protosteles in which the xylem has a starlike appearance in cross section (Fig. 10.12).

In the stem, the epidermis is cutinized and contains paired guard cells with stomata. The endodermis and pericycle are reduced or absent, but a pith is present in most cases. Steles with

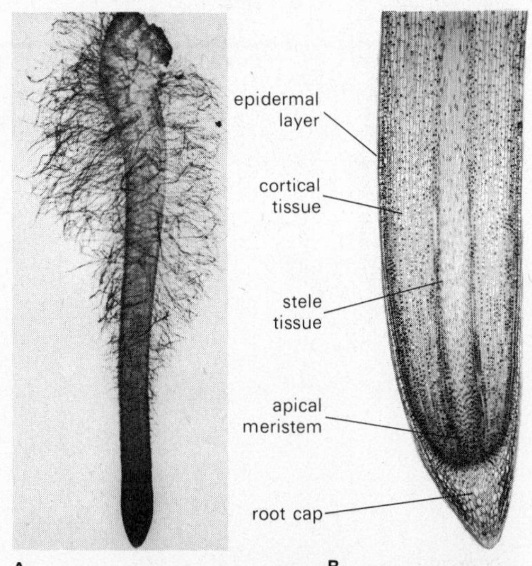

***10.11* Root structure.** *A, terminal part of a root, showing the root-hair zone and the thickened root-cap region at the tip. See Fig. 5.15 for a close-up view of root hairs. B, longitudinal section through a root tip, showing the cells of the root cap and, immediately behind them, the dense small cells of the apical root meristem. The tissues that will later become the stele form a central column, and around it is the developing cortex. The epidermis covers the exterior.*

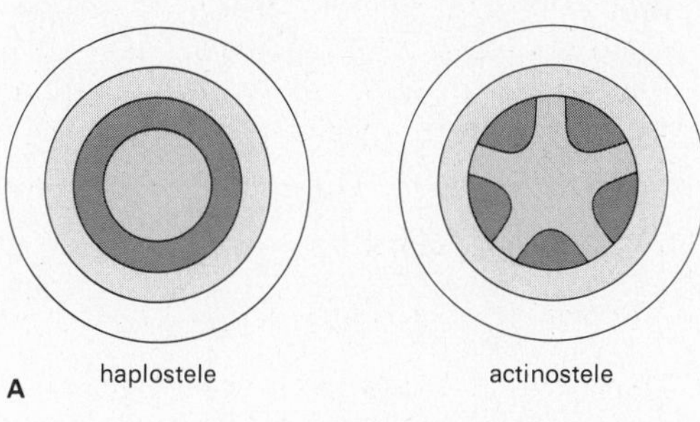

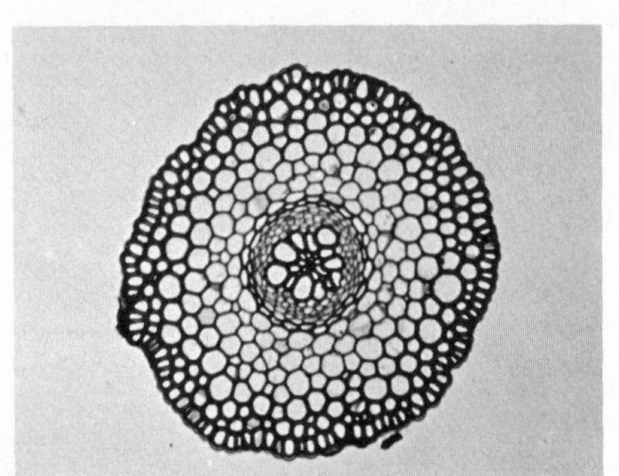

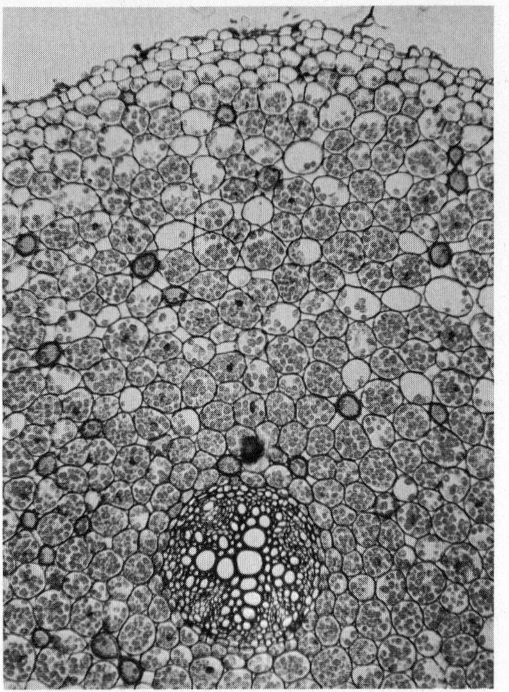

***10.12* Root structure: steles.** *A, protosteles, or steles without pith. The two most common protostele types are shown. Xylem, gray; phloem, dark, pericycle, light color; cortex, white. B, section through a rootlike organ of Selaginella; the tissues of the central haplostele can be identified from left diagram in A. C, part of a section through a buttercup root, showing a four-pointed protostelic actinostele, the surrounding cortex (with starch-storing amyloplast granules in the cells), and the epidermis (×80). A higher-power view of a five-pointed buttercup actinostele is illustrated in Fig. 5.19, and see also Fig. 5.14.*

10.13 Stem structure: steles. *A, steles with pith. Phloem, dark; xylem, light gray; pith, stippled. Phloem and xylem form vascular bundles in which phloem is toward the outside. The bundles have a circular arrangement in a dictyostele, characteristic of the stems of gymnosperms and dicot angiosperms. The bundles are scattered in atactosteles, characteristic of the stems of monocot angiosperms. B, cross section through a buttercup stem, showing the dictyostelic pattern of the vascular bundles. The stem core of these particular plants happens to be hollow. C, cross section through a corn stem, showing the atactostelic pattern of the vascular bundles.*

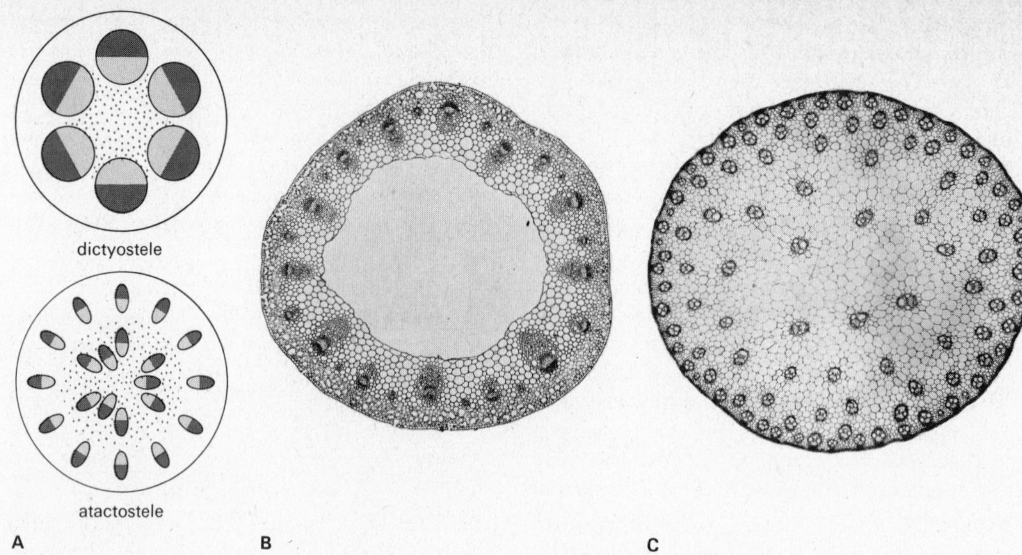

10.14 Leaf and branch growth. *A, longitudinal section through a shoot tip, showing apical meristem and various stages in leaf and branch development. B, the buds and tissues in a shoot tip. Note the leaf gap, branch gap, and leaf trace.*

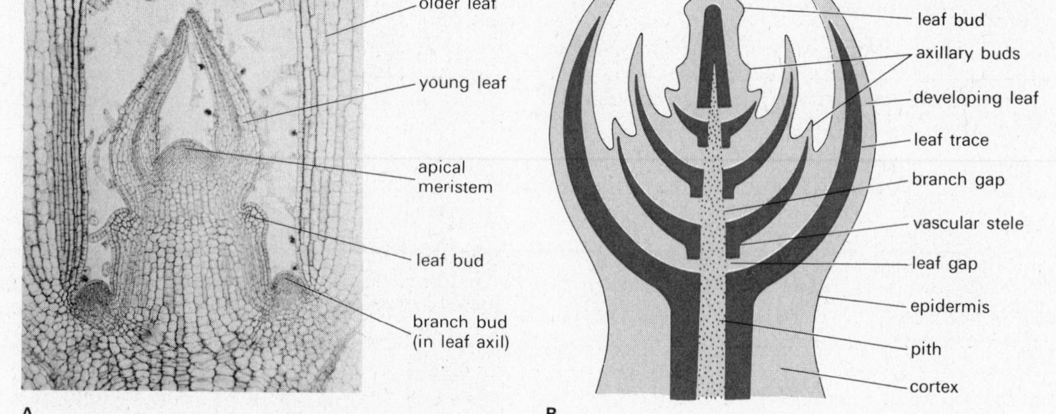

10.15 Microphylls and megaphylls. *A: left, the leaf-stalk base of a microphyll, identified by single vascular bundle (bottom) and absence of leaf gap (top); right, leaf-stalk base of a megaphyll, with numerous vascular bundles (bottom) and distinct leaf gap (top). B, the basal parts of a mature leaf (megaphyll).*

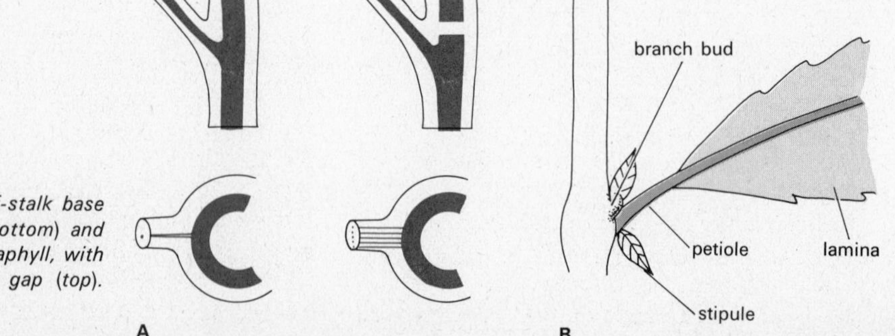

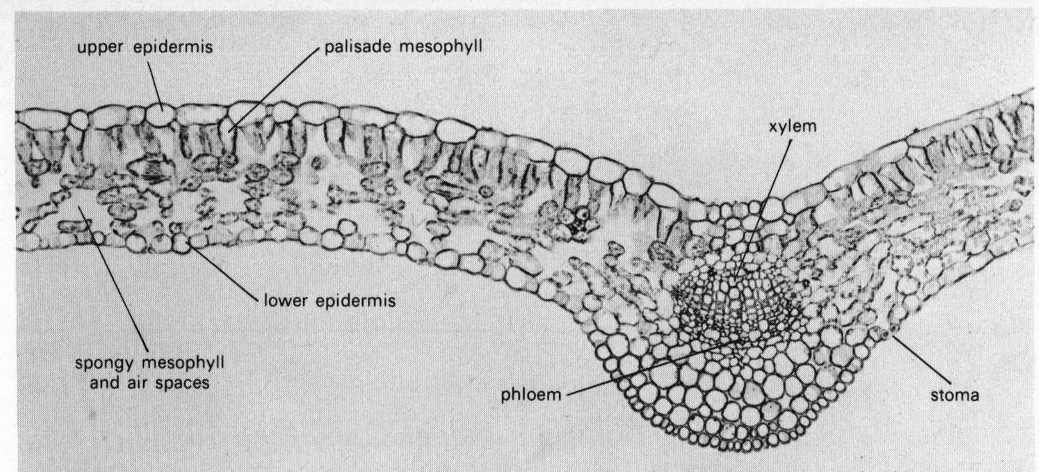

10.16 Leaf structure. *In this cross section the xylem and phloem (and usually also surrounding fiber tissue) form a vein. Note stomata in the lower epidermis.*

pith occur in a large number of variant forms. In the class of gymnosperms and one subclass of angiosperms (the dicots, see below), so-called *dictyosteles* are encountered (Fig. 10.13). Here the xylem and phloem tissues are arranged as distinct and separate *vascular bundles,* and these are grouped in more or less circular patterns in the stem. Such a circle of bundles surrounds the pith, which is continuous with the cortex outside the ring of bundles. In a second subclass of angiosperms (the monocots), the steles are *atactosteles.* Here xylem and phloem again form vascular bundles, but they are scattered randomly throughout the stem. It is therefore often difficult to distinguish precisely between pith and cortex.

primary growth: leaves and branches

Stem and root growth proceed indefinitely as a result of the continuous production of new cells at the shoot and root tips. By contrast, leaf growth is usually limited in time, for a leaf generally does not possess an apical meristem of its own.

A *leaf bud* forms embryonic tissue just below the shoot apex (Fig. 10.14). Sometimes a single cell but more often several cells give rise to the leaf bud. These embryonic cells divide repeatedly, most divisions occurring along the margins of the expanding and flattening blade. Concurrently a column of future xylem and phloem tissue, a so-called *leaf trace,* branches away from the stele of the stem and grows into the leaf.

Two leaf types can be distinguished according to the amount of vascular tissue formed by a leaf trace. In a *microphyll,* the amount of xylem and phloem is equivalent to at most a single vascular bundle. Such leaves occur only in the primitive subphyla of tracheophytes. By contrast, the subphylum of pteropsids is characterized by *megaphylls,* in which the xylem and phloem are equivalent to numerous vascular bundles. Where a leaf trace of a megaphyll branches away from the stele of the stem, a small region of the stele just above this branch point does not specialize as vascular tissue. Such regions are *leaf gaps,* which do not form during the development of microphylls (Fig. 10.15 and see Fig. 10.14).

When their tissues are mature, the leaves of the vast majority of tracheophytes have attained their final sizes and do not grow thereafter. A microphyll consists of a leaf blade only. A mature megaphyll usually includes a *petiole,* a thin basal stalk that attaches the leaf to the stem; two *stipules,* small appendages that grow out near the base of the petiole in many species; and a *lamina,* the leaf blade itself.

The epidermis of a leaf is continuous with that of the stem. As in the stem the leaf epidermis is cutinized and contains green guard cells with stomata (Fig. 10.16). The interior of the leaf consists of parenchymatous *mesophyll,* normally the chief food-producing tissue of the plant; all mesophyll cells contain chlorophyll. In most tracheophytes the mesophyll is organized as two distinct zones. Just underneath the upper epidermis in horizontally placed leaves and underneath the whole epidermis in most upright and needle-shaped leaves, mesophyll cells form compact layers, or *palisade* parenchyma. Elsewhere mesophyll consists of *spongy* parenchyma, loose layers honeycombed extensively with *air spaces.* These connect with one another and lead to the exterior through open passages in the palisade

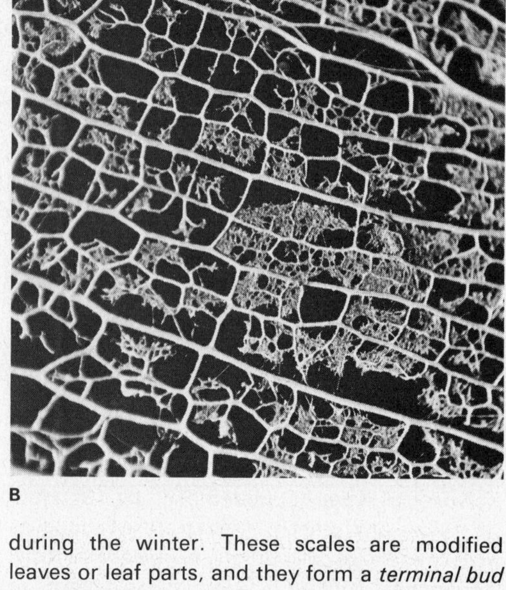

10.17. ***Leaf types.*** *A, simple (single-bladed) types are at top, compound (many-bladed) types at bottom. B, the vein pattern in a net-veined leaf.*

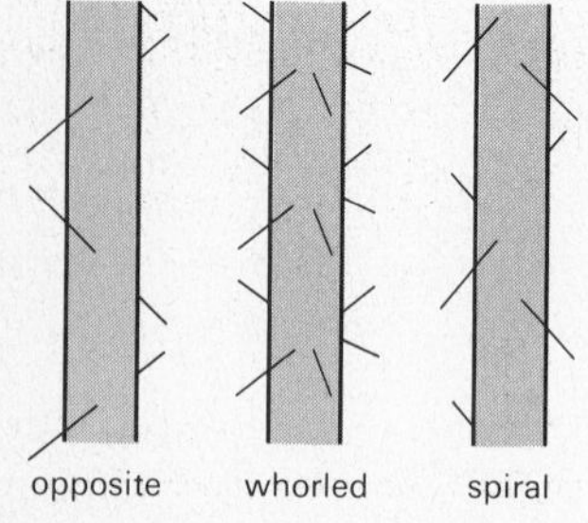

10.18 ***Phyllotaxis.*** *Leaf stalks are arranged on a stem in various geometric patterns, as shown.*

tissue and the stomata. Such a structural arrangement permits the greater part of every mesophyll cell to come into direct contact with fresh external air.

Embedded in mesophyll are leaf *veins,* composed of supporting fiber tissue and of xylem and phloem bundles that are continuous with the vascular tissues of the stem. Veins give mechanical support and carry nutrients to and from all parts of the leaf. The veins usually form networks (as in dicot angiosperms) or parallel strands (as in monocot angiosperms). In external form, leaves are most often *blade*-like, *needle*-like, or *scale*-like. Leaves with single blades are said to be *simple,* those with more than one blade, *compound* (Fig. 10.17).

Leaves are arranged along a stem in different patterns (*phyllotaxis*). In an *alternate* pattern, single leaves are attached at successive stem levels and the leaf bases mark out a spiral winding up along a stem (Fig. 10.18). The geometric characteristics of such spirals are usually quite distinct for given species. Leaves are *opposite* if two of them grow out at the same stem level, and they are *whorled* if more than two arise at the same level. The regions of the stem where leaves are attached are called *nodes;* the leaf-free regions between nodes are *internodes.*

In deciduous plants leaves that have dropped off in the fall leave permanent *leaf scars* on the stem (Fig. 10.19). Such plants also develop *bud scales,* which cover the apical shoot meristem during the winter. These scales are modified leaves or leaf parts, and they form a *terminal bud* on a dormant stem in winter condition. When growth resumes the following spring, bud scales fall off and leave densely placed *bud-scale scars* on the elongating stem. By counting the number of stem regions where such scars occur it is often possible to determine the age of a plant.

Stems usually produce many *lateral branches.* These arise from *branch buds,* developed in the apical shoot meristem in the *leaf axil.* This is the upper angle where a leaf joins the stem. Wherever a leaf is formed, a branch bud forms in the leaf axil as well. Branch buds leave their own *branch gaps* in the stele of the parent stem (see Figs. 10.14 and 10.15).

Branch buds often do not mature immediately. Some remain dormant for many years, and others may not develop at all. In wintering stems dormant branch buds are usually clearly visible just above leaf scars. When a branch bud does mature, it develops an apical shoot tip of its own and grows in every respect like the parent stem. Evidently, an important difference between a branch and a leaf is that one does and the other does not acquire a growing tip in the bud stage.

Roots are without nodes, but branches form nevertheless. However, the process of branch development differs from that in the stem (Fig. 10.20). At varying distances behind the apex of the main root, cells in localized regions of the pericycle divide and form a pad of tissue, a so-called *root primordium.* During its later development such a primordium pushes through the peripheral tissues of the primary root. By the time it emerges through the epidermis, a root meristem and a root cap have been formed. A stele with vascular tissues then matures, and these tissues become continuous with corresponding ones of the main root. At this stage the *lateral root* is fully established and continues to grow like a main root.

secondary growth

The whole organization of the tracheophyte body described up to this point represents the product of *primary growth:* all body parts are direct derivatives of the apical meristems and the original immature tissues of the embryo. Primary growth essentially permits extension in *length,* and any increase in the thickness of stems and roots results mainly from an enlargement of cells in a lateral direction. In many tracheophytes primary growth is the only means of increasing body size. However, numerous tracheophytes are capable of growing not only in length but also in thickness, through lateral increase of cell *number.* These plants undergo processes of *secondary growth,* superimposed on a continuing primary growth. Apart from comparatively enormous increases in stem and root girth, the large-scale result of secondary growth is the development of *bark* and of *wood.*

Wood tends to be formed in relatively large quantities, and new layers are added each year to those already accumulated. Plants of this type develop as trees and become recognizably *woody* in appearance. Primary growth actually gives rise to "wood," or primary xylem, too, but in the vast majority of cases this xylem is formed in such small amounts that the plant is left in a *herbaceous* condition; and if a distinctly woody plant is to develop, abundant wood must be formed by secondary growth. Thus the phrase "woody plants" refers largely to plants in which secondary growth occurs (specifically angiosperms; see below).

In these woody plants young shoots and roots begin to develop, as in all other cases, through primary growth. The plant also continues to elongate through primary growth at each tip, and the regions immediately behind the tips maintain the characteristic primary structure of nonwoody roots and stems. More specifically, the primary

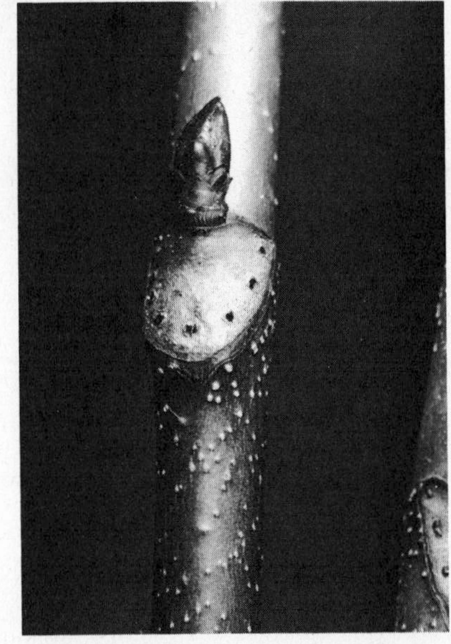
A

B

10.19 Stem buds. *A, a dormant lateral bud just above a leaf scar, a stem region representing a node. An internode is the stem region between two successive nodes. B, a terminal and two lateral buds in dormant condition.*

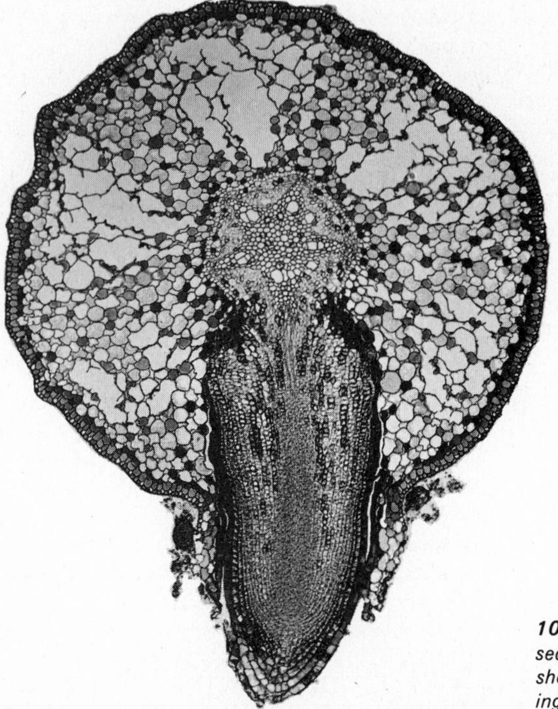

10.20 Lateral roots. *This cross section through a primary root shows a lateral branch root growing out from the pericycle region.*

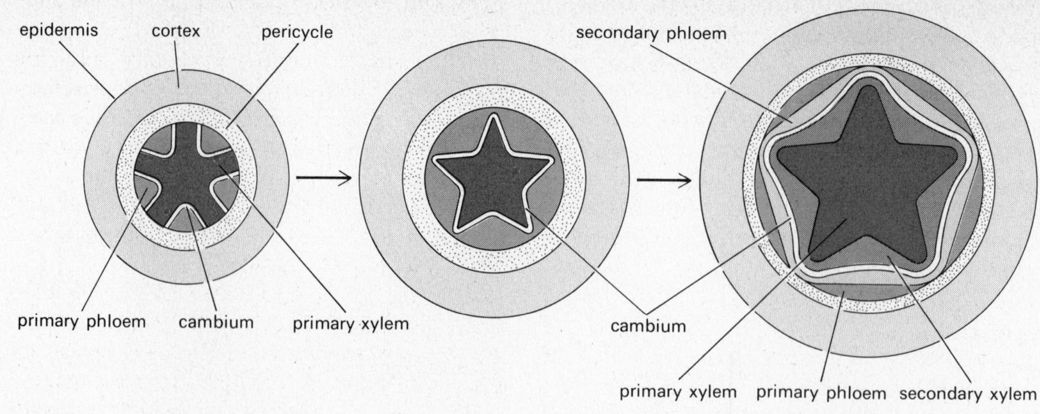

10.21 Root cambium. *Stages in development of cambium and of cambium-derived secondary tissues are shown.*

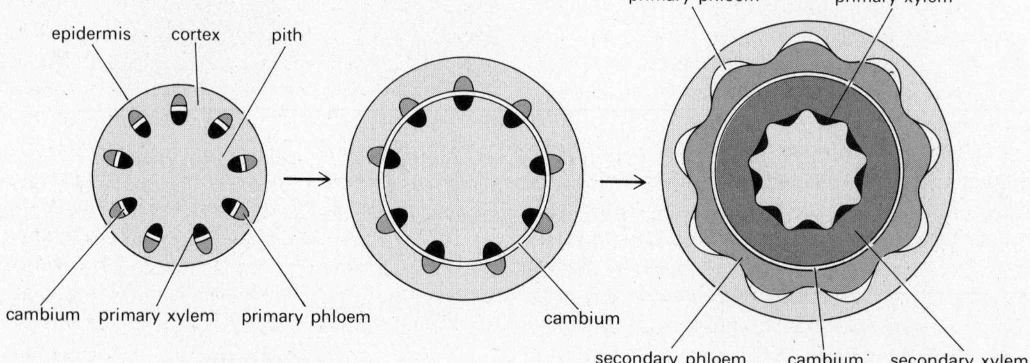

10.22 Stem cambium. *Stages in development of cambium and of cambium-derived secondary tissues are shown. Note that such stems are dictyostelic originally.*

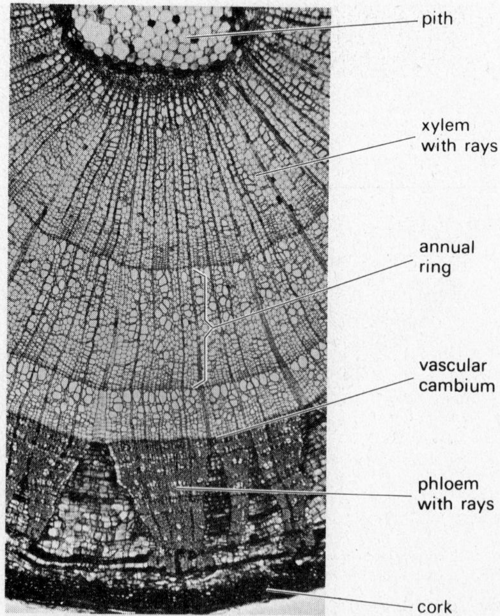

10.23 The woody stem. *This is a cross section through a portion of a 3-year-old (basswood) stem. Note that the tissues outside the vascular cambium collectively represent bark.*

root pattern is actinostelic and the primary stem pattern is largely dictyostelic. But in older regions, well behind each tip, these primary patterns later become transformed to secondary ones. The early shoots and later growing tips thus remain "green" even in woody plants. Since leaves bud off near the shoot apex and do not have growing tips of their own, they do not participate in secondary development at all.

The transformation of roots and stems from primary to secondary states is brought about by *secondary meristems,* or *cambia.* Two kinds of cambium develop, a *vascular cambium* and a *cork cambium.* Each arises from different primary tissues, and the process of formation differs somewhat in root and stem.

In a root, the vascular cambium forms between the primary xylem and phloem in the stele (Fig. 10.21). A layer of cells here remains permanently embryonic and relatively unspecialized. This layer becomes the vascular root cambium, which ultimately surrounds the primary root xylem completely.

In a stem, part of the vascular cambium again forms from a cell layer between primary xylem and phloem (Fig. 10.22). Since these tissues in the dictyostelic stem form a ring of vascular bundles, the cambium layer between the xylem and phloem is interrupted between neighboring bundles. Such interruptions soon disappear, however, for a layer of parenchyma cells between the bundles acquires the properties of a cambium. The vascular stem cambium thereby becomes a complete tube, continuous with the corresponding tube in the root. In the course of the further elongation of the stem-root axis through primary growth at the apical tips, the open-ended cambial tube lengthens as progressively more cambium develops behind the shoot and root tips.

In both the root and the stem, the cells of the vascular cambium continue to divide and bud off new cells toward both the inside and the outside. In this manner whole *layers* of cells continue to be deposited at both sides of the cambium. Most of the cells that are budded off toward the inside of the cambial layer soon mature as the various components of xylem tissue; and cells that are budded off toward the outside become components of phloem tissue. Vascular tissues so generated by cambium represent *secondary xylem* (or *wood* proper) and *secondary phloem* (Fig. 10.23).

These secondary tissues are traversed in places by radial *xylem rays* and *phloem rays*. Such rays are strands of parenchymatous tissue that are generated by small patches of cells (*ray initials*) in the cambium. New cells budded off by these patches both toward the inside and the outside do not become vascular xylem and phloem, but instead they grow out as columns of cells that form the xylem and phloem rays, respectively. The rays function in lateral transport of nutrients in stems and roots (see Fig. 10.23).

As secondary xylem continues to be formed in successive concentric layers inside the cambial tube, it cannot grow too far inward for this space is already occupied by the primary xylem and the pith. An outward expansion will therefore take place, and the thickness of the stem or the root will increase. Similarly, as secondary phloem develops outward it increases the thickness of stem or root still more. Indeed, as secondary phloem presses increasingly against primary phloem, cortex, and epidermis, these primary tissues must ultimately rupture; for being adult and thus no longer able to grow, they cannot keep pace with the ever-expanding girth of the stem or the root.

The smallest amounts of secondary tissue are always near the apical tips, where cambial activity is just beginning; the largest amounts have accumulated at the stem-root juncture, the region that has grown for the longest period and is the oldest. This is therefore the region of greatest girth, and from here the stem tapers up and the root tapers down (Fig. 10.24).

The second of the cambial tissues is the cork cambium. This single layer of cells develops from the pericycle in roots and from the cortex or the phloem in stems. Like the vascular cambium, the cork cambium produces new cell layers toward the inside and outside (Fig. 10.25). Layers budded off toward the inside develop as *cork parenchyma* (or *phelloderm*). Layers generated toward the outside form *cork* (or *phellem*). During their maturation cork cells deposit heavy suberin coats on their walls, and the cell interiors then disintegrate; mature cork is wholly nonliving. (The cork cambium and its products, phelloderm and phellem, are collectively also known as *periderm*.)

Cork cells are usually packed close together, an arrangement that makes the outer covering of woody plant quite impervious to water and air. At various places, however, the cork cambium produces loosely arranged cork cells separated by intercellular spaces. Such spongy regions are *lenticels*. They permit gas exchange between the atmosphere and the interior living tissues of root or stem (Fig. 10.26).

Cork first develops where the epidermis and

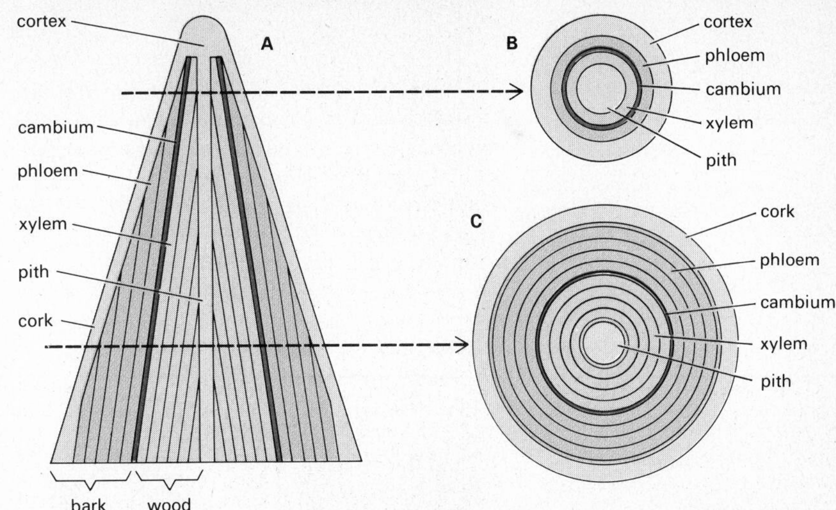

10.24 Tissue arrangements in a shoot. *A, diagrammatic longitudinal view, showing the formation of successive tissue layers to the outside and inside of the cambium. A cross section at the level of the upper broken line would appear as in B; at the level of the lower broken line, as in C. The arrangement in a root corresponds to a mirror image of A.*

10.25 ***Cork cambium*** *and its products in a woody stem. Phelloderm is the layer of parenchyma budded off by the cork cambium (or phellogen) toward the inside of the stem. This layer becomes part of the cortex. Cork (or phellem) is budded off by the cork cambium toward the outside. Cork, cork cambium, and phelloderm collectively represent the periderm, which is shown in the photo.*

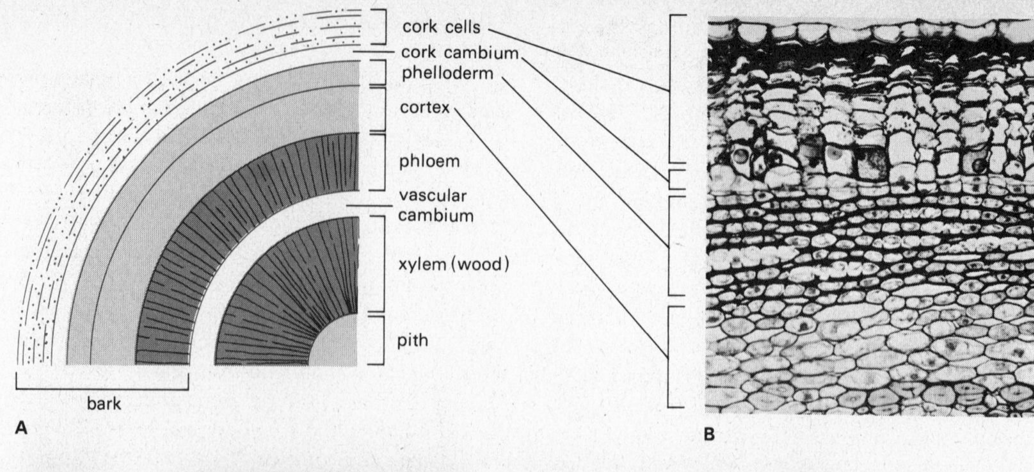

10.26 ***Lenticels.*** *A, external and B, cross-sectional views.*

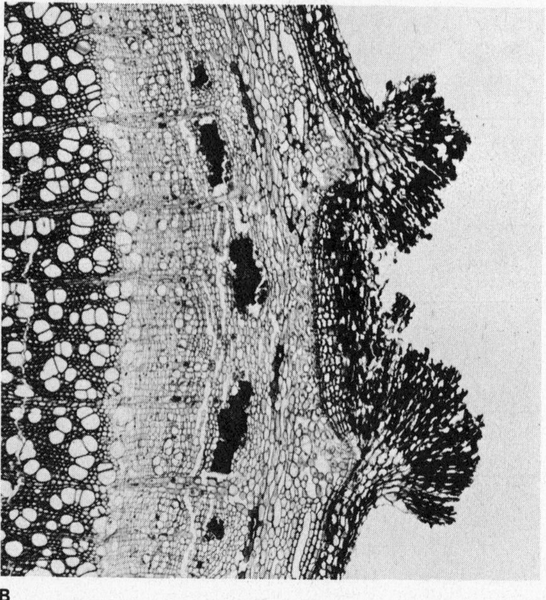

the cortex have ruptured as a result of the outward expansion of xylem and phloem. Later, after epidermis and cortex have torn away completely, a continuous layer of cork comes to surround the entire outside surface of stem and root. Further increases in stem and root diameter then cause a rupturing and flaking off of the original cork, but new cork is produced in its place. This new tissue in turn ruptures and flakes off, and the cycle of new formation and flaking off repeats indefinitely. In roots the pericycle itself soon ruptures and flakes off, and secondary phloem then becomes the chief source for the regeneration of cork cambium, as in the stem.

All tissues outside the vascular cambium are collectively called *bark*. In a cut section of a tree the main tissues then are, concentrically from the outside inward: cork; the microscopically thin layer of cork cambium; cork parenchyma; secondary phloem; the microscopic layer of vascular cambium; and wood, which fills the space within the ring of vascular cambium. In a stem section a microscopic accumulation of pith is in the very center (see Fig. 10.23).

Older phloem, right below the surface of a tree trunk, continually flakes off as the trunk thickens. At any given time, therefore, only a thin rind of young phloem is present in bark. Similarly, only young xylem is functional. Older xylem near the center of a trunk in time gradually blocks up with resins and gums, and water conduction through these channels is then no longer possible. Such

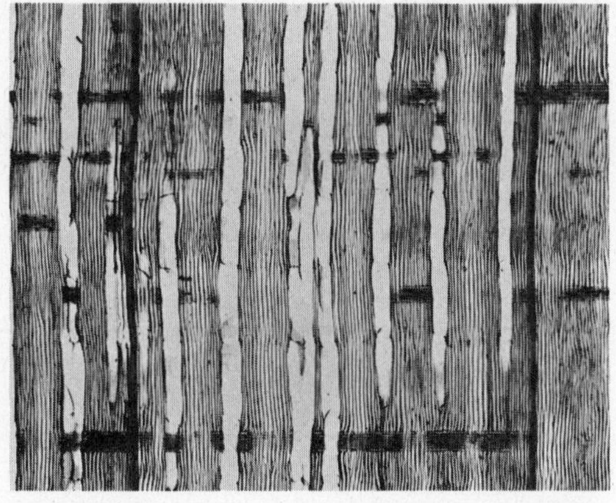

10.27 Wood and annual rings. *A, portion of a tree trunk showing 12 rings. B, longitudinal section through wood showing xylem channels. The two dark vertical lines mark the extent of one annual ring.*

central regions are called *heartwood.* The core of a tree can therefore be hollowed out without interfering with xylem conduction. But the outer, young wood of a tree, called the sapwood, must remain intact if a tree is to remain alive.

In an older tree growing in the temperate zone, the xylem vessels laid down during spring generally have a larger diameter than those formed in summer. In spring, melting snow provides the tree with much water, and wider conducting channels formed at that season accommodate the greater flow. This alternation of narrow summer xylem and wider spring xylem is recognizable with the naked eye as a concentric series of dark and light bands, or *annual rings* (Fig. 10.27 and see Fig. 10.23). The number of rings indicates the age of a tree. Moreover, from the comparative widths of spring and summer rings it is often possible to estimate the amount of rainfall, hence general climatic conditions, during the past seasons as far back in time as the tree has lived.

Through the secondary growth processes described, a young, green shoot is slowly transformed to a tall, thick, tapering woody tree. As noted, the bulk of a tree trunk is nonliving, and a woody plant expends large amounts of energy and materials every year in producing new tissues that soon become nonliving too. In this respect a herbaceous plant is far more economical; for the tissues formed by primary growth just suffice to maintain life and they serve the plant as long as it lives.

To be sure, even a tiny herb is built on a lavish structural scale when compared with a microscopic unicellular alga floating in the ocean. But such lavishness is the price of survival on land; of all photosynthetic organisms really only the tracheophytes have become completely successful as terrestrial types. In this success the evolution of vascular tissue has been one basic factor. Another has been the evolution of seeds, a topic examined later in another context.

Psilopsids

Subphylum Psilopsida leaves are microphylls; roots absent, absorption through rhizoids; *Psilotum, Tmesipteris;* 3 species

These most primitive of all living vascular plants are xerophytes. Two species of *Psilotum* grow in tropical and subtropical regions of the Americas, and *Tmesipteris* is found in Australia and on some Pacific islands. Some of the plants live as epiphytes on trees, others in soil.

A

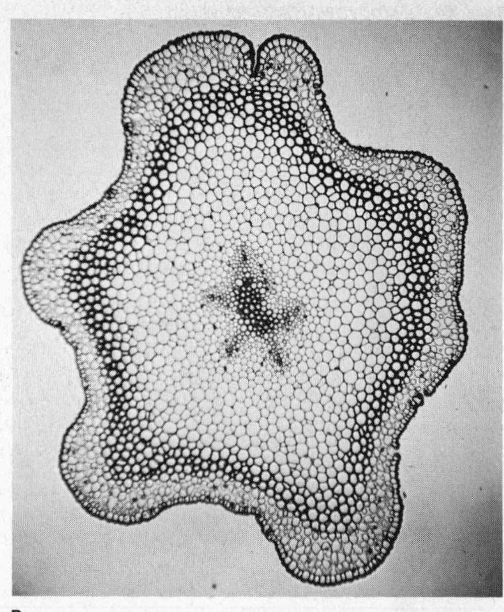

B

10.28 ***Psilopsids.*** *A, aerial parts of a mature Psilotum sporophyte. Note spore sacs along branch stems. B, stem cross section. Note epidermis with cuticle and stomata, the thick underlying cortex with a layer of scleren-chymatous cells, and the central actinostele with xylem in the core and surrounding phloem.*

The traits of psilopsids are remarkably similar to those of their fossil ancestors (Fig. 10.28). Stems are partly horizontal rhizomes, underground in the nonepiphytes, partly upright and aerial. Unicellular rhizoids grow from the horizontal portions of a stem. The aerial portions have a heavily cutinized epidermis with sunken stomata, and they bear tiny microphylls. These are without stomata or vascular tissue in *Psilotum* but do contain a single strand of vascular tissue as well as stomata in *Tmesipteris.*

Lycopsids

Subphylum Lycopsida leaves are microphylls; roots present; *Lycopodium,* club mosses, ground pines; *Selaginella,* spike mosses, resurrection plants; *Isoetes,* quillworts; 900 species

Many ancestral lycopsids were large woody trees, but their present-day relatives are invariably small and nonwoody. These plants still range in respectable numbers from the tropics to north temperate regions, and the ground pine *Lycopodium* in particular is relatively common. Many lycopsids are creepers with horizontal rhizomes, others are erect, and some are epiphytes (Color Fig. 12).

The roots of *Lycopodium* are frequently adventitious, the pericycle of the stem being the tissue from which such roots arise. In erect forms, adventitious roots sometimes originate near the shoot apex and grow down right *through* the stem cortex. The microphylls contain air spaces in the mesophyll and stomata on both surfaces.

Selaginella lives largely in damp, shady places in the tropics. Stems are often partly horizontal, partly upright, and the epidermis is cutinized and without stomata. Young plants develop typical roots, but nearly all later roots form from so-called *rhizophores.* These are stemlike downgrowths from forks in aerial stems. The portions of a rhizophore that enter the ground reorganize structurally and functionally as a root. The microphylls have stomata, and each leaf also bears a *ligule,* a small tuft of tissue attached to the upper leaf surface near the juncture with the stem. Neither the function nor the evolutionary history of ligules is known.

Quillworts are the only surviving lycopsids that, by virtue of a special cortical cambium, are still capable of secondary growth. They do not become

A

B

C

10.29 **Lycopsids.** *A, upper portion of the ground pine Lycopodium (with spore-forming cone at top). B, aerial portion of Selaginella. C, aerial parts of the quillwort Isoetes. See also Color Fig. 12.*

woody, however. The plants live as deciduous perennials in marshy areas, and their underground stems are *corms*. From these project dense clusters of erect microphylls, which give quillworts part of their English name as well as a superficial resemblance to patches of lawn grass (Fig. 10.29).

Sphenopsids

Subphylum Sphenopsida leaves are microphylls; stems with nodes bearing whorls of leaves; roots present; *Equisetum* (horsetails, scouring rushes); 25 species

A

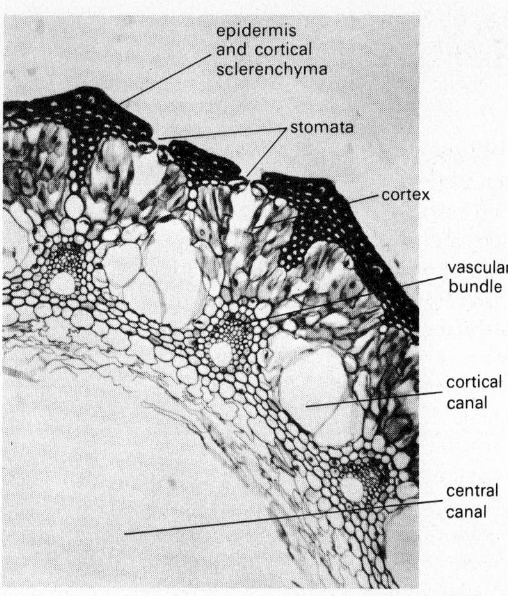

B

10.30 **Sphenopsids.** *A, portion of aerial stem of a horsetail, Equisetum. Note whorled arrangement of leaves (microphylls). B, cross section through portion of aerial stem.*

All surviving sphenopsids are members of the single genus *Equisetum*, found from the tropics to the temperate zone. The plants have underground rhizomes and aerial stem parts that have nodes. Narrow microphylls grow out in whorls at such nodes (Fig. 10.30 and see Color Fig. 12). The stems are usually ribbed lengthwise, strengthened with silica deposits, and hollow internally. Stomata occur between the ridges of the stem and in the leaves. Roots are largely adventitious and grow out along the rhizome. The underground portions are perennial; the aerial structures of temperate-zone plants are regrown each year.

Pteropsids

Subphylum Pteropsida leaves are megaphylls with veins; leaf gaps present; stems largely with pith; *ferns, coniferous plants, flowering plants*

Class Filicineae ferns; growth primary only; xylem with tracheids but without vessels; seeds not formed; 10,000 species

Class Gymnospermae cone-bearing seed plants; growth primary and secondary; xylem with tracheids but without vessels in most cases; reproductive organs in cones; seeds formed, not enclosed; 800 species

Class Angiospermae flowering seed plants; growth primary and secondary or primary only; xylem with tracheids as well as vessels; seeds formed in flowers, enclosed in fruits; 250,000 species

---

Ferns

Class Filicineae

These plants are most conspicuous in tropical rain forests, where many attain heights of 50 to 60 ft, with leaves 10 to 15 ft long (Fig. 10.31). Even so, such tree ferns are not woody. In temperate regions, deciduous forests and other well-watered areas harbor many fern species as

A

B

10.31 Ferns. *A, tree ferns. B, the rolled-up condition ("circinate vernation") of developing fern leaves. See also epiphytic ferns in Fig. 6.16.*

abundant ground cover. Some few ferns are secondarily aquatic.

The stems of the plants are largely underground perennial rhizomes, often covered with fibrous remnants of leaf bases that give stems a somewhat "hairy" appearance. Internally a stem has a thick sclerenchymatous cortex that gives strength like wood and permits some ferns to attain the size of trees. Leaves growing from rhizomes are large, upright, and complexly shaped. They are regrown every year in most species of the temperate zone, but in other cases the leaves last several seasons. Fern leaves are interesting also in that they have functional apical meristems unlike leaves of other plants, and thus they can grow continuously. These leaves also commonly exhibit *circinate vernation;* young leaves form tight coils, and as they grow they unroll and straighten up.

Cone-bearing Seed Plants

Class Gymnospermae

Subclass Cycadophytae wood not extensive

Order Cycadales cycads, "sago palms;" 100 species

Subclass Coniferophytae wood extensive

Order Ginkgoales maidenhair trees; 1 species

Order Coniferales conifers; 600 species

Order Gnetales 70 species

Practically all gymnosperms are perennial evergreens. Primary growth first produces actinostelic roots and dictyostelic stems. Active secondary growth occurs thereafter, and the woody habit is nearly universal in the class.

One subclass is represented by the *cycads.* These usually small trees have an extensive pith, which is surrounded by a relatively narrow, slowly developing band of xylem. Cycads thus form comparatively little wood. The plants are most common today in tropical and subtropical regions (Fig. 10.32).

More distinctly woody and generally much more massive are the *coniferous* gymnosperms. In this subclass *Ginkgo biloba* is the only surviving member of a once flourishing group. These maidenhair trees are large, up to 100 ft high, and in temperate regions they are fairly common

A

B

***10.32* Gymnosperms.** *A, cycads. B, a ginkgo, the maidenhair tree.*

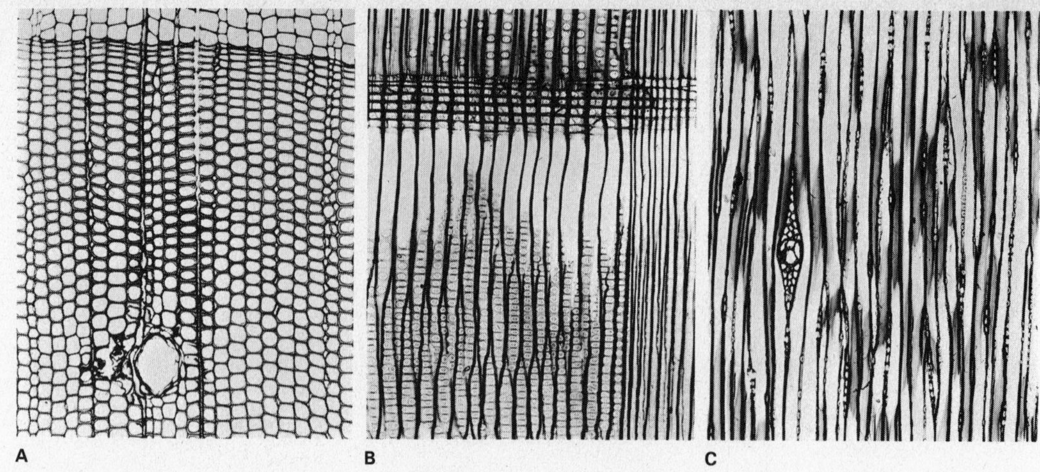

10.33 ***Pine wood.*** *A, transverse section; note resin canal near bottom. B, radial section; note pits in tracheids and xylem ray traversing upper part of photo. C, tangential section; note pits in mid-region of photo.*

shade trees. Of the conifers proper, many are familiar members of the flora in the temperate zone and in the taiga: pines, spruces, firs, cedars, yews, and redwoods. All these are evergreens; larches and bald cypresses are deciduous. The largest are the giant redwoods of California, which reach heights of nearly 400 ft and are the largest living things now in existence.

Because conifers develop much wood in proportion to other tissues, they are used widely as lumber and in paper manufacture. In the vascular tissues of conifers are *resin canals,* ducts formed from the vascular cambium. These channels secrete the aromatic gums and resins so characteristic of conifer wood and which probably participate in the process of winter hardening (Fig. 10.33).

Among the three surviving genera of the Gnetales, a distinguishing feature is the presence of true xylem vessels, a trait not otherwise encountered in gymnosperms. Gnetales possibly might represent remnants of one or more quite independent lines of pteropsid evolution.

Flowering Seed Plants

Class Angiospermae

Subclass Dicotyledoneae dicots; leaves net-veined; stems dictyostelic; flower parts in fours, fives, or multiples; two cotyledons in seed; 200,000 species

Subclass Monocotyledoneae monocots; leaves parallel-veined; stems atactostelic; flower parts in threes or multiples; one cotyledon in seed; 50,000 species

This most varied, most abundant, and most familiar group of plants is distinguished by a xylem that characteristically contains not only tracheids, as in most other vascular plants, but also true *vessels.* The components of sclerenchyma are not only sclereids, as in other tracheophytes, but also *fibers.* Angiosperms are distinguished further by their flowers and fruits, and by a number of other reproductive features to be discussed in Chap. 25. Flowering plants inhabit nearly all environments except the open ocean. They include aquatic types, symbiotic and parasitic types, saprotrophic types, and partly carnivorous types. They enrich the world with color and scent, but they also exude poison and stench. Some survive only a single growing season; others live for

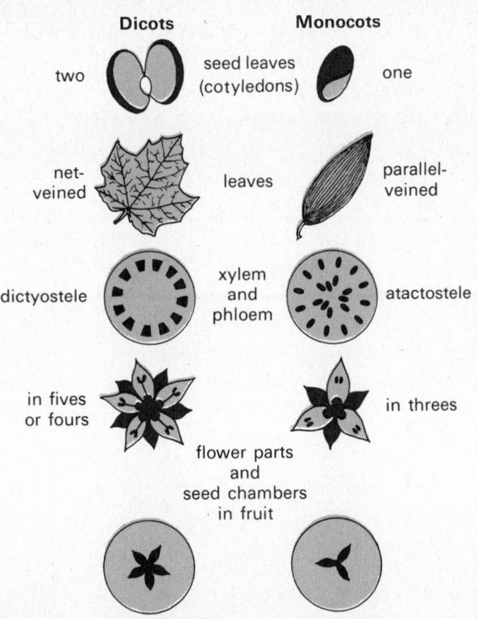

10.34 Dicots and monocots. *Some of the structural differences between these two angiosperm subclasses are illustrated in the center panel (the arrangement of xylem and phloem is illustrated also in Fig. 10.13). Photos at left and right illustrate the subclass differences in flower structure.*

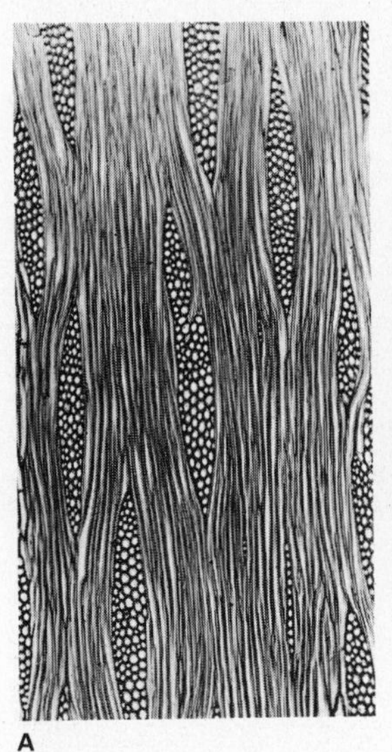

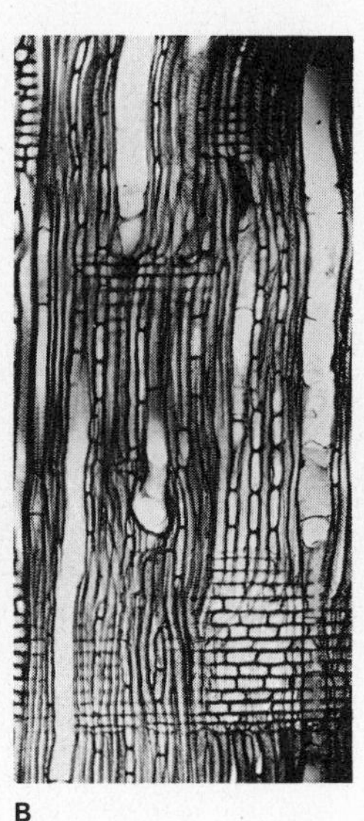

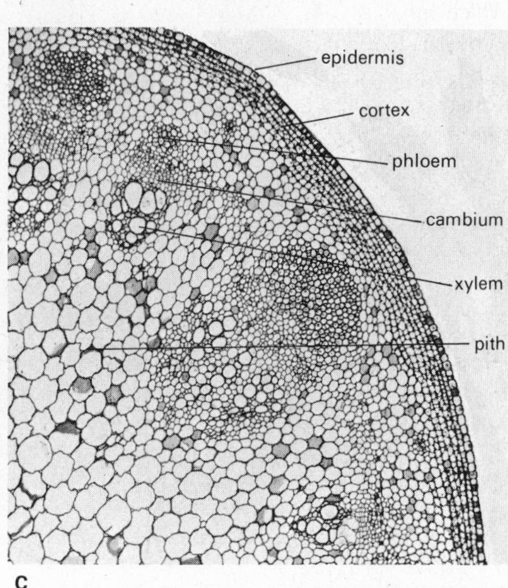

10.35 Woody and semiherbaceous stems. *A, B, the woody stem of oaks. A, tangential section. Note xylem vessels and spindle-shaped cell bundles of xylem rays, here seen in cross section. B, radial section. Xylem vessels here are again vertical, and the xylem-ray bundles lie horizontal (and are seen in lengthwise cut). C, the semiherbaceous stem of a sunflower. Vascular bundles have a circular arrangement, and in older (lower) stem regions some of the parenchyma cells between neighboring bundles acquire the properties of a vascular cambium. Herbaceous stems are illustrated in Fig. 10.13.*

centuries. Some complete an entire generation from seed to seed within a few days; others require decades. Terrestrial animals owe their continued existence largely to the angiosperms, for these plants are the essential food producers for all life on land. Far more so than in other cases, an unqualified reference to ''plants'' implies reference to flowering plants.

The two subclasses of angiosperms are named and distinguished on the basis of the number of their *cotyledons,* food-storing leaflike structures in the seeds. Monocots generally have one such seed leaf, dicots usually two. A corn kernel and a bean seed illustrate this difference (see Fig. 25.39). Several other distinctions are outlined in Fig. 10.34.

The dicots are the more abundant and presumably more primitive group. They include, in addition to fully *woody* types, plants that exhibit secondary growth only to a reduced degree; such *semiherbaceous* dicots become woody only in old, basal portions of the stem and root (Fig. 10.35). A third group is incapable of any secondary growth, and these dicots are fully *herbaceous* (see buttercup stem, Fig. 10.13). Among familiar members of the subclass are all the flowering trees and shrubs, including apple, peach, cherry, oak, chestnut, walnut, elm, rubber trees, and many others; as well as strawberry, bean, cabbage, turnip, cotton, cocoa, coffee, avocado, celery, carrot, parsely, spinach, citrus, lilac, blueberry, cranberry, potato, tomato, tobacco, pepper, melon, cucumber, lettuce, goldenrod, rhubarb, artichoke plants, and thousands more.

Among monocots the primary stem is not dictyostelic as it is in the dicots but atactostelic (see corn stem, Fig. 10.13). Moreover, nearly all monocots are herbaceous and without secondary growth. The main exceptions are palms and bamboos, in which complex and rather atypical forms of secondary growth occur. Although the number of species is smaller than in dicots, monocots have at least equal or even greater economic importance; for in this subclass are wheat, corn, rye, rice, oat, barley, sugar cane, and all other grasses; as well as lilies, irises, pineapples, bananas, and orchids.

review questions

1 How are Metaphyta distinguished from Protista? Review the identifying characteristics of Metaphyta.

2 Describe the group characteristics and the basic structure of bryophytes. Name the classes of bryophytes and their identifying features. Define thallus, rhizoid, protonema.

3 State the identifying characteristics of tracheophytes. How is this phylum classified into subphyla and classes? What is the probable evolutionary relation of (*a*) tracheophytes as a whole to bryophytes and protists, and (*b*) the subgroups in the tracheophyte phylum?

4 Review the architectural adaptations of tracheophytes to life on land. Name different modifications of (*a*) stems and (*b*) roots, and state the adaptive roles of such modifications.

5 How do tracheophytes conserve water? How do they protect against (*a*) heat and (*b*) cold? What are perennial, biennial, and annual tracheophytes, and what are the life cycles of such plants?

6 Show how the embryo of a tracheophyte develops into a mature plant by primary growth. Name specific tissues and their anatomic relations. Describe the organization of different types of stele.

7 Define leaf trace, leaf gap, mesophyll. What is the difference between a microphyll and a megaphyll? Describe the structure of a leaf. What types of leaves and leaf arrangements can be distinguished? How does a leaf develop?

8 How does a stem or a root grow in length? What is secondary growth? Show how a vascular cambium forms secondary xylem and phloem. Describe the activities of a cork cambium.

9 Define lenticel, ray initial, phellogen, periderm, phloem ray, phellem, annual ring, heartwood, bark, wood.

10 Describe the complete structural organization of a mature woody plant in (*a*) the woody part of the stem, (*b*) the woody part of the root, (*c*) the nonwoody apical part of the stem, and (*d*) the nonwoody apical part of the root.

11 Review some of the identifying traits of psilopsids, lycopsids, sphenopsids. Name representatives of each group, and indicate where they live.

12 Define branch gap, ligule, rhizophore, circinate vernation, atactostele, cotyledon, internode, phyllotaxis.

13 Review the identifying features of pteropsids. Describe the structural organization of a fern (sporophyte). How are gymnosperms subclassified? Describe the structural characteristics of gymnosperms. What are the identifying features of angiosperms?

14 Name the subclasses of angiosperms and their identifying features. Name representative plants of each subclass. What distinguishes ferns from gymnosperms and both these groups from angiosperms?

15 Describe the internal structure of (*a*) a woody angiosperm, (*b*) a semiherbaceous angiosperm, and (*c*) a herbaceous angiosperm.

collateral readings

Bold, H. C.: "The Plant Kingdom," 2d ed., Prentice-Hall, Englewood Cliffs, N.J., 1964. A good source for further information on Metaphyta. The book also deals with bacteria, fungi, and algae.

Clevenger, S.: Flower Pigments, *Sci. American,* June, 1964. An article on the chemical nature and genetic control of plant pigments.

Doyle, W. T.: "Nonvascular Plants: Form and Function," Wadsworth, Belmont, Calif., 1964. The last chapter contains a concise account of the biology of bryophytes.

Galston, A. W.: "The Life of the Green Plant," 3d ed., Prentice-Hall, Englewood Cliffs, N.J., 1964. This paperback contains chapters on the structure, nutrition, growth, and development of plants.

Gates, D. M.: Heat Transfer in Plants, *Sci. American,* Dec., 1965. The roles of radiation, transpiration, and convection in the temperature regulation of plants are discussed.

James, W. O.: Succulent Plants, *Endeavor,* vol. 17, 1958. This article shows how xerophytic plants can conserve water and protect themselves against heat.

Mangelsdorf, P. C.: The Mystery of Corn, *Sci. American,* July, 1950. An interesting account on the search for the evolutionary ancestor of domesticated corn.

———: Wheat, *Sci. American,* July, 1953. The article describes the origin of domesticated wheat and the basis of the usefulness of this plant to man.

Richards, P. W.: Famous Plants—The Liverwort Marchantia, *New Biol.,* vol. 27, 1958. One of the best-known bryophytes is examined in this article.

Salisbury, F. B., and **R. V. Parke**: "Vascular Plants: Form and Function," Wadsworth, Belmont, Calif., 1964. This paperback deals in introductory fashion with the anatomy and the functional processes of tracheophytes.

Wardlaw, C. W.: Famous Plants—The Banana, *New Biol.,* vol. 11, 1951. An economically important monocot is examined in some detail.

Watson, E. V.: Famous Plants—Funaria, *New Biol.,* vol. 22, 1957. The biology of one of the mosses is given special attention.

White, D. J. B.: The Stem Apex of a Dicotyledon, *New Biol.,* vol. 16, 1954. Recommended for further data on apical organization and growth.

Williams, S.: Wood Structure, *Sci. American,* Jan., 1953. A better appreciation of the anatomy of woody plants can be obtained through this article.

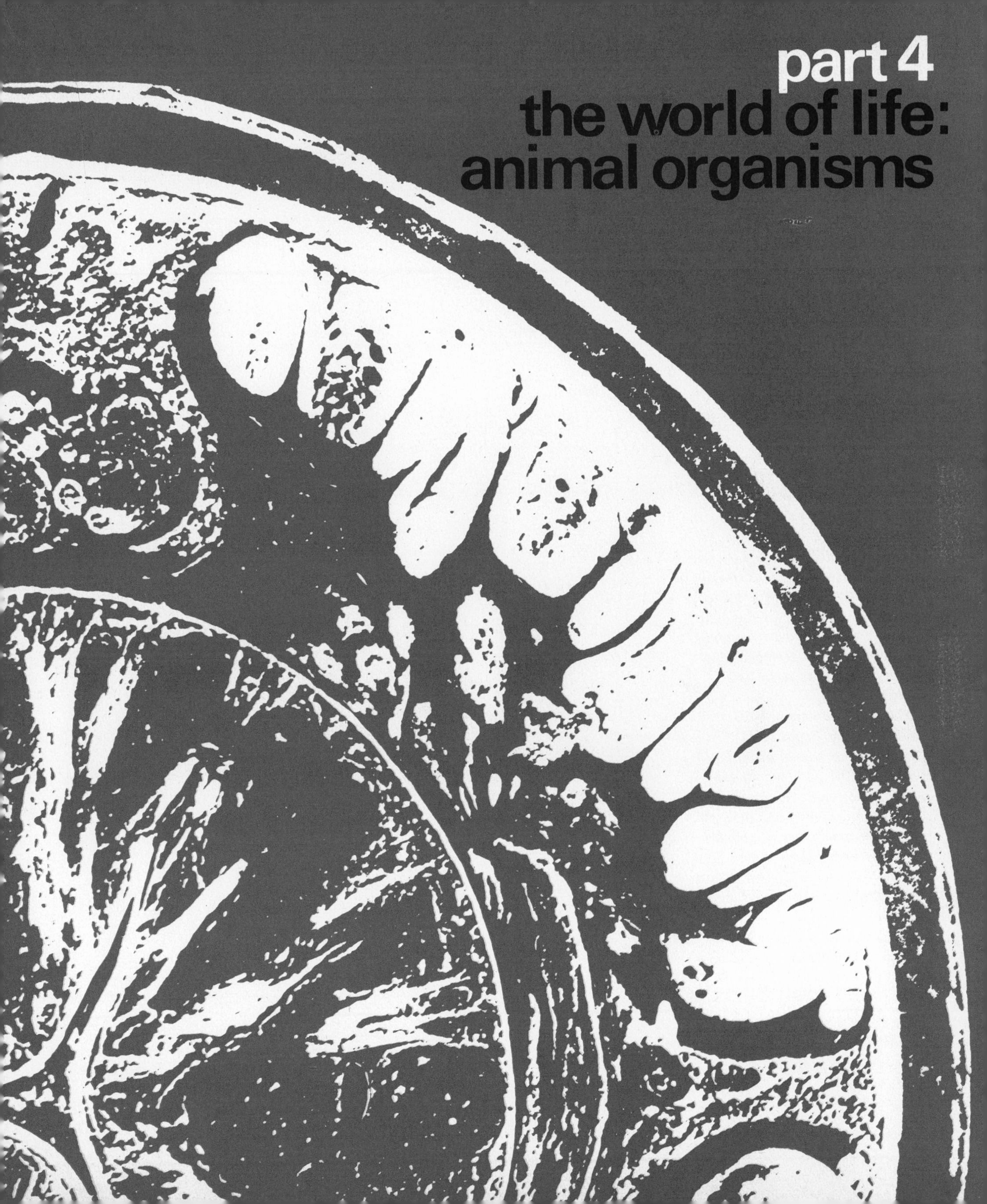

part 4
the world of life: animal organisms

part 4
the world of life: animal organisms

chapter 11
animal nature and noncoelomates

chapter 12
coelomate groups: protostomes

chapter 13
coelomate groups: deuterostomes

The evolutionary origin of animals is obscure. That they arose from ancestral Protista is hardly in doubt, but it is impossible at present to be sure exactly which protistan group was directly ancestral. According to early hypotheses, Metazoa are assumed to have evolved from protozoa; but there is actually very little evidence for such a view. Any of the early protistan stocks could have given rise to animals, and indeed long before protozoa as such had originated.

Moreover, numerous early protistan types could have contributed to animal evolution independently, and at different times. Thus, apart from uncertainty regarding the identity of the immediate precursors of animals, it is equally uncertain whether animals form a monophyletic or a polyphyletic assemblage of organisms. Such clues as are available appear to point to a limited polyphyletism as the most likely possibility. The nature of these clues is examined in part in later contexts, in part in this series of chapters.

chapter 11 animal nature and noncoelomates

category	branch	grade	subgrade	phylum	class
metazoa	parazoa			porifera	calcarea
					hexactinellida
					demospongiae
	eumetazoa	radiata		cnidaria	hydrozoa
					scyphozoa
					anthozoa
				ctenophora	
		bilateria	acoelomata	platyhelminthes	turbellaria
					trematoda
					cestoda
				nemertina	
			pseudocoelomata	aschelminthes	rotifera
					gastrotricha
					kinorhyncha
					priapulida
					nematoda
					nematomorpha
				acanthocephala	
				entoprocta	
			coelomata		

Like the Metaphyta, Metazoa exhibit a complex multicellular construction encompassing the organ and organ-system levels of organization. Animals differ from plants in that their cells typically contain centrioles, and that cells not in direct contact with the external environment are naked, without walls or cuticles. Further, metazoan development passes not only through embryonic but typically also through *larval* stages. Most obviously, animals are exclusively heterotrophic and nearly all are holotrophic: they ingest bulk foods, digest them thereafter, and then egest unusable remains. This collective function of *alimentation* is an almost universal animal characteristic, the counterpart of photosynthesis in plants.

patterns of life

Directly or indirectly the function of alimentation influences the whole nature of an animal. One immediate consequence is the necessity of active motion, for movement by passive means—such as random dispersion by water or wind—would in most cases not carry animals to appropriate kinds or amounts of food.

Flagella, cilia, and particularly a *muscular system* are the means of animal motion, and this motor capacity is used in two major ways to obtain food. In the more common case an animal carries out some form of *locomotion;* it propels its whole body toward the location of a likely food source. In the second case the animal remains stationary and *sessile* and lets the food source move toward it. All sessile animals are aquatic. They employ their motion-producing equipment to create water currents that carry food organisms to them or to trap food organisms that happen to pass close by.

Once the capacity of motion is given, it can serve not only in feeding but also secondarily in other vital activities. As is well known, for example, locomotion is a significant means of protection inasmuch as it permits animals to avoid or to escape from potential environmental dangers. Locomotion also plays an important role in mate selection and in reproduction generally. Yet the most frequent locomotor effort is usually made in the search for food.

Before an animal can effectively move toward food or vice versa, it is clearly essential for the animal to recognize that, at a given place in the environment, an object is located that is or appears to be a usable food. Moreover, after food has been localized it is equally essential to *control* the ensuing motion—to set and adjust course and speed, and to determine when movement is to begin and to terminate. What is evidently needed is a complete guidance apparatus, and most animals have it in the form of a *nervous system.* In it, sense organs of various kinds permit recognition of environmental detail, impulses in nerves produce control over motion, and a brain or brainlike organ correlates, coordinates, and fits a given set of recognitions to an appropriate set of motions.

Motion depends not only on muscles but on practically all other components of an animal as well, for all body parts contribute directly or indirectly to the fitness of muscles. Neural control over muscles therefore necessitates neural control over almost all other functions, too. Most animals actually have *chemical* control systems in addition to the neural ones. In many instances internal chemical coordination is exercised by parts of other organ systems (for example, blood, kidneys, gills), and in some groups, notably arthropods and vertebrates, chemical regulation is also achieved by hormone-producing *endocrine systems.*

Because the supply of appropriate food is limited, animals must compete for it more or less openly. Under the pressure of such competition numerous animals have adopted symbiotic and particularly parasitic ways of life, and among free-living types some have become predators whereas others are prey. Associated with such patterns of living are many familiar specializations in offensive or defensive modes of *behavior* and also in eating habits. Thus, *herbivores* can eat only plant foods; *carnivores* subsist only on other animals; and *omnivores* can eat both animal and plant foods, living or dead. Plant material contains much water and also cellulose that is indigestible and that makes tissues tough and difficult to tear. The nutritive value of a unit amount of plant food therefore is usually less than that of animal food. Accordingly, herbivores generally eat more, and more often, than other animals, and they also tend to have longer alimentary tracts that allow more time for digestion. Carnivores are specialized to overcome not only herbivores but also smaller carnivores and omnivores. And omnivores live on whatever nourishment they can find or catch.

The requirement of motion influences the architecture of animals in major ways. Movement is most efficient when the external medium offers the least possible resistance. Unlike a plant, therefore, which is constructed in a branching shape for maximum exposure to light, air, and soil, an animal is built as compactly as possible, for minimum surface exposure. Most motile animals also tend to be *bilaterally symmetrical* and *elongated* in the direction of motion, a shape that aids in further reducing resistance to movement. Moreover, since one end of an elongated animal necessarily enters new environments first, that end will serve best as the place for the chief sense

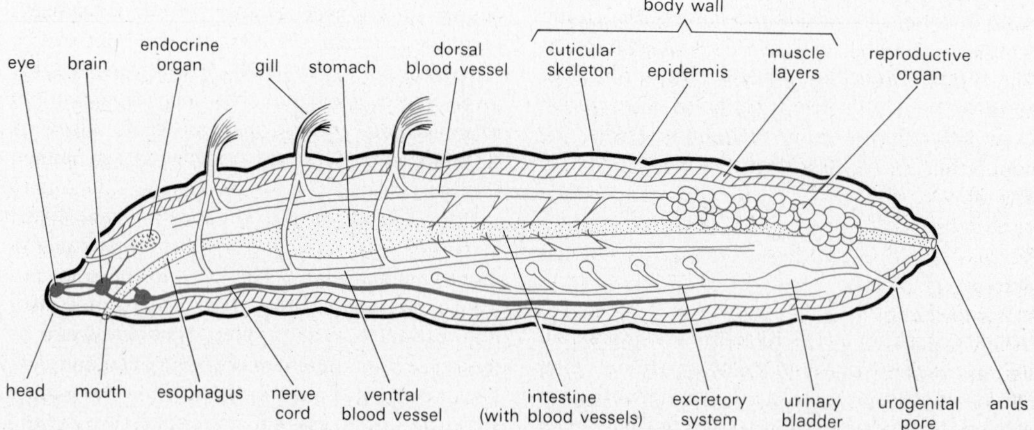

11.1 Structure in motile animals. *This diagram depicts a hypothetical animal and shows the general position of organ systems. The integumentary and nervous systems are at or near the surface; the alimentary, breathing, excretory, and reproductive systems communicate with the surface; and the circulatory and muscular systems extend throughout the body. Endocrine and skeletal systems if present often range throughout the body as well, and a skeletal system can be on the outside or the inside (see Fig. 11.2).*

organs and nerve centers and for the food-catching apparatus. The leading part of the body so becomes a *head.* At the same time elimination products of all kinds are best released at the hind end, where they do not impede forward progression. A general build of this sort is actually standard and nearly universal among moving animals (Fig. 11.1).

By contrast, sessile animals and also many of the slow and sluggish types face their environment more or less equally from all sides, as plants do, and this circumstance is reflected in their architecture. They are or tend to be *radially symmetrical,* and a distinct head is usually not present. Also, with locomotion absent or limited, nervous systems and sense organs tend to be greatly reduced (Color Fig. 13).

Numerous important characteristics of animals result from the bulkiness and compactness of the body. Since animal cells have comparatively little inherent rigidity, a large collection of such cells is likely to sag to a formless mass under the influence of gravity. Animals therefore require antigravity supports, and they have them in the form of muscular and particularly *skeletal systems.* That muscles function not only in motion but also in support is well illustrated in animals such as earthworms, which lack a skeleton. The same muscles that move such animals also hold them together and maintain their shapes. Moreover, even an animal with a skeleton would sag out of shape if muscles did not maintain a firm organization. Conversely, that skeletons function in support as well as locomotion is also clear. A large, heavy animal without rigid supports could neither hold its shape nor propel itself forward by muscles alone.

Animal skeletons are calcium-containing *calcareous* supports or silicon-containing *silicaceous* supports or variously composed *horny* supports. The skeletons are organized as *exoskeletons* or as *endoskeletons* (Fig. 11.2). In an exoskeleton, exemplified by the shells of clams or snails, the supporting material is on the outside of the animal and envelops the body partly or wholly. In an endoskeleton, as in the cartilage- and bone-possessing vertebrates, the supports are internal and soft tissues are draped over them. With increasing body size an exterior skeleton rapidly becomes inadequate for the support of deep-lying tissues. Interior supports, however, can buttress all parts of even a large animal. It is not an accident, therefore, that the largest animals are the vertebrates, and that animals with exoskeletons or without skeletons of any kind are comparatively small.

The bulky construction of animals also creates problems of internal logistics. For example, after food is eaten and digested, the usable nutrients must be distributed to all parts of the animal body. If the distance between the alimentary system and the farthest body parts is appreciable, as in the majority of animals, then some sort of internal transport system becomes essential. The *circulatory systems* of animals serve to meet this requirement (Fig. 11.3). In such networks of vessels the transport vehicle of food is blood, and one or more muscular pumping organs, or hearts, usually maintain a circulation of blood throughout

A

B

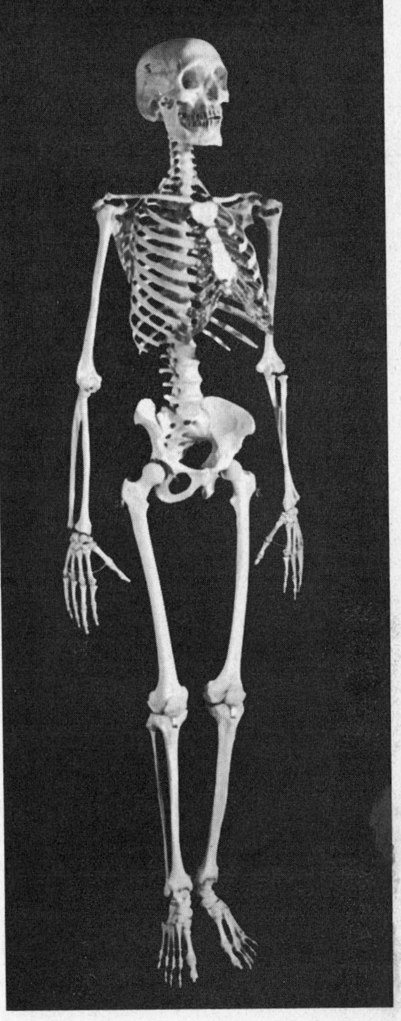

C

11.2 Skeletal types. *A, the calcareous exoskeleton of a snail. B, the horny exoskeleton of a stag beetle. C, X-ray photograph of a girl, showing the human endoskeleton.*

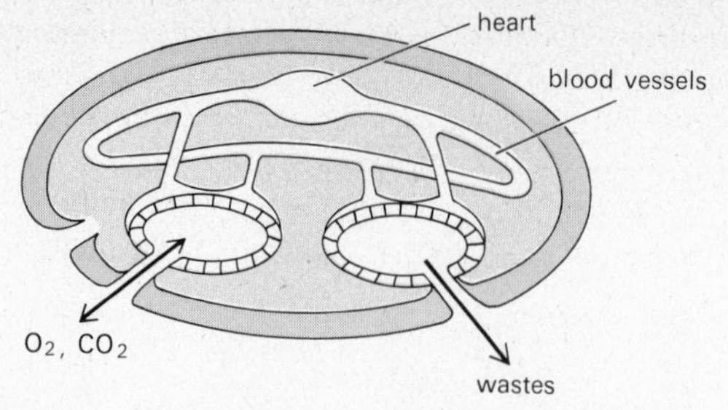

11.3 Surface structure and animal complexity. *In complexly structured animals, as symbolized here, the surface layers are generally thick and impermeable and the breathing and excretory surfaces usually are parts of specialized, interiorized organ systems. Internal transport of materials is accomplished by distinct circulatory systems.*

the body. Blood is not pigmented in all animals. Where it is, the pigments function specially in transport of oxygen, not food, a circumstance pointing up another problem of internal logistics.

Because of the compact construction of an animal, most of the cells are not in immediate contact with the external environment. Yet all cells require environmental oxygen for respiration, and every cell also must release waste substances to the environment. In the majority of animals blood in the circulatory system again serves as the main traffic vehicle between the environment and the interior of the body. In animals such as earthworms and frogs, exchange of materials between blood and the external environment can occur through the whole skin, which is thin and permeable. In most animals, however, the integumentary system is elaborated more complexly and is relatively impermeable. Animals so covered can exchange materials with the environment only at restricted areas, where surface thinness and permeability are preserved and where the blood supply is particularly abundant. For protection, such thin and sensitive areas are frequently tucked well into the body. These areas represent parts of *breathing systems* and *excretory systems.* Gills and lungs are the main types of oxygen collectors, but these organs also contribute importantly to waste excretion. Serving primarily in excretion are kidneys and other, functionally equivalent types of organs (see Fig. 11.3).

Bulk and complex organization affect yet another aspect of animal nature, the process of reproduction and the pattern of the life cycle. Like plants, animals too have *reproductive systems* that manufacture sperms and eggs and thereby contribute to the formation of fertilized eggs. Yet the growth of such eggs must be considerably more complex than in plants, for animal development must produce elaborate body parts that plants do not possess: nervous systems, muscular systems, skeletal supports with jointed components, alimentary structures—all those, in short, that are required in a way of life based on heterotrophism and locomotion.

The maturation of animals actually does occur in a unique manner; early development typically includes two distinctive stages, the *embryo* and the *larva.* The embryonic phase starts with the fertilized egg and usually terminates in a process of *hatching.* The following larval phase then continues up to *metamorphosis,* or transformation to the adult. Both embryo and larva can be regarded as developmental devices that provide the necessary time, and the means, for the production of a complexly structured adult animal out of a single cell (see Color Fig. 14).

All major aspects of animal nature thus can be considered consequences of the basic conditions of heterotrophism and great structural complexity. As noted, these two conditions at once necessitate the presence of nervous, muscular, skeletal, alimentary, circulatory, excretory, breathing, and integumentary systems. And if to these we add a reproductive system and in some cases also an endocrine system, we have a complete list of all the architectural ingredients that compose an animal. Implied also is a good deal about how an animal moves, behaves, feeds, develops, copes with its environment—in short, pursues life. Moreover, we know in broad outline how the structural ingredients must be put together to form a sensibly functioning whole. As suggested in Fig. 11.1, some of the organ systems must be in surface positions in whole or in part (integumentary, nervous); others can lie deep but must at least communicate with the surface (alimentary, breathing, excretory, and also reproductive); and still others must extend through all portions of the body (skeletal, circulatory, nervous, endocrine).

On the basis of such a preliminary sketch, the fundamental anatomy of a motile, elongated animal can be visualized as a complex tube that has a triple-layered construction. The outermost layer of the tube is the body wall, which includes mainly the integumentary system and parts of the nervous system. The innermost layer, which encloses the open channel through the tube, is represented chiefly by the alimentary system. And the bulky middle layer contains all other organs and systems. Such a triple-layered picture of animal architecture actually is more than a rough analogy; for at an early stage of development most animal embryos do consist of just three layers, one inside the other and each originally not more than one cell thick. From the outside inward these *primary germ layers* are the *ectoderm,* the *mesoderm,* and the *endoderm* (Fig. 11.4). Later they each proliferate greatly and give rise to the triple-layered adult. Ectoderm forms, for example, the integumentary and nervous systems. Mesoderm develops in part into the muscular, circulatory, and reproductive systems. And endoderm produces the alimentary system. Other systems arise from different germ layers in different animal groups.

Inasmuch as such developmental processes produce a large variety of distinct animal anatomies, the differences among the processes are important aids in distinguishing animal types taxonomically.

growth and structure

The most general trait of animals, and the first to appear during development, is their *level of organization.* All animals typically begin life as single cells, and some then develop to a tissue level of complexity. But others pass beyond this level and become more complex. Accordingly, Metazoa are considered to include two taxonomic *branches.* In the branch *Parazoa,* the highest level of organization is the tissue. This branch happens to encompass just one phylum, the *sponges.* All other animals belong to the branch *Eumetazoa,* characterized by the presence of organs and organ systems (Fig. 11.5).

After level of organization, the next most general trait to appear in animal development is that of *symmetry.* At first all animal embryos are radially symmetrical; they are solid or hollow balls composed of a few cells. Some animal groups then retain this radiality right to the adult stage, but in others the embryos soon become bilateral and the later larval and adult stages usually remain bilateral as well. On this basis the branch Eumetazoa can be subclassified into two *grades,* the *Radiata* and the *Bilateria.* Radiates are identified by a basic radial symmetry throughout life and also by a structural organization in which the organ is the highest level. The grade contains two phyla, the coelenterates and the comb jellies. All other animals belong to the Bilateria, characterized by the presence of organ systems and by bilateral symmetry after early embryonic stages. (Most Bilateria retain this symmetry, but a few groups—starfishes, for example,—acquire a secondary radiality when they metamorphose into adults; such adults tend to be sluggish or sessile and headless like the Radiata; see Fig. 11.5).

After symmetry is established in the embryo, the next most general trait to appear is the pattern

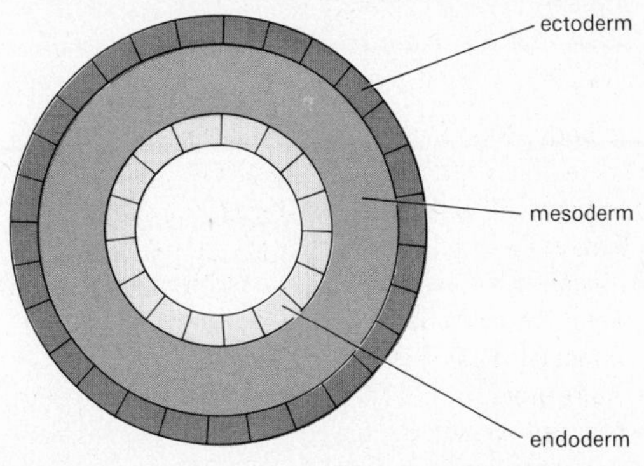

11.4 Primary germ layers. *These embryonic layers will give rise to the triple-layered "tube" of the adult body (as in Fig. 11.1). Ectoderm generally forms epidermis and nervous system, endoderm forms the alimentary system, and mesoderm develops into muscular, circulatory, and reproductive systems. The other systems arise from different germ layers in different animal groups.*

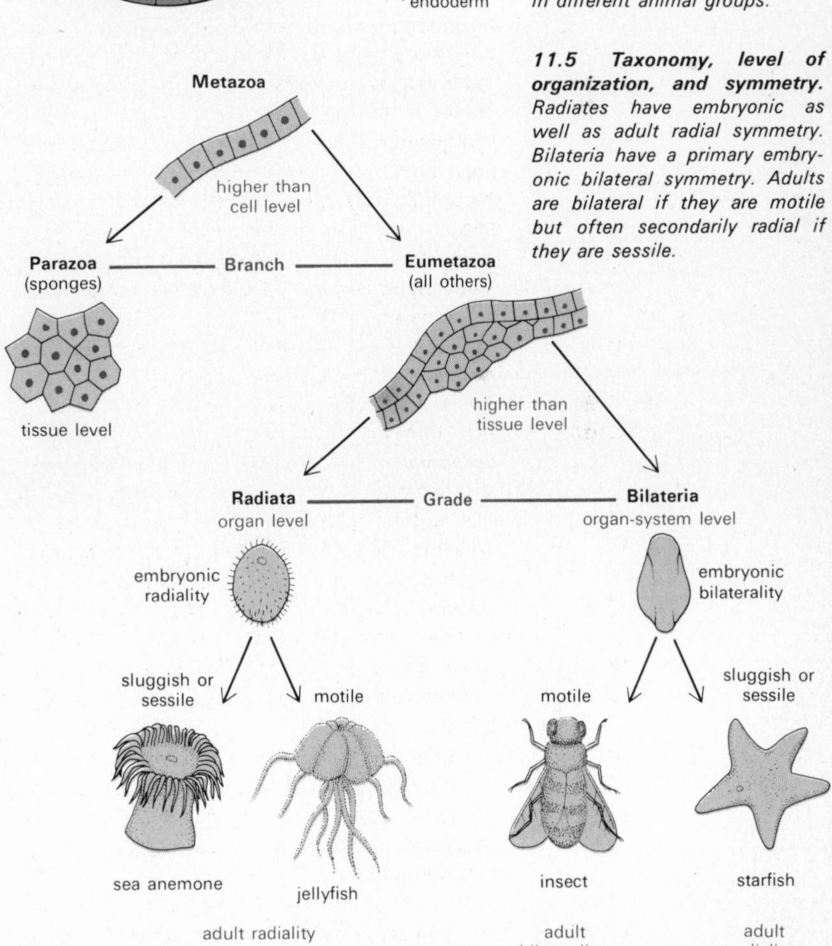

11.5 Taxonomy, level of organization, and symmetry. *Radiates have embryonic as well as adult radial symmetry. Bilateria have a primary embryonic bilateral symmetry. Adults are bilateral if they are motile but often secondarily radial if they are sessile.*

of the alimentary structures. Three major patterns are known, and they add to the distinctions between Parazoa, Radiata, and Bilateria (Fig. 11.6). In sponges, the alimentary structures are unique *channel networks:* food-bearing water flows through systems of channels that branch throughout the body. In Radiata and one phylum of Bilateria (flatworms), the alimentary pattern is a *one-hole sac.* A single opening in the sac serves as both mouth and anus, and the layer of cells that forms the sac represents the endoderm, one of the primary germ layers. In all other Bilateria the alimentary structures form a *two-hole tube.* Such a tube develops in the embryo from a sac that later acquires a second opening, typically opposite the first one. One opening then specializes as a mouth, the other as an anus, and the tube interconnecting them becomes the alimentary tract in which food passes only one way, from mouth to anus. In one group of Bilateria (*Protostomia*) the first opening becomes the mouth, the second the anus; in another group (*Deuterostomia*), the first opening forms the anus and the second the mouth.

Taken together, the level of organization, the symmetry, and the alimentary pattern provide a broad outline of the fundamental body form of any animal. Alimentary pattern and symmetry specify the basic interior and exterior architecture, respectively, and the organizational level specifies

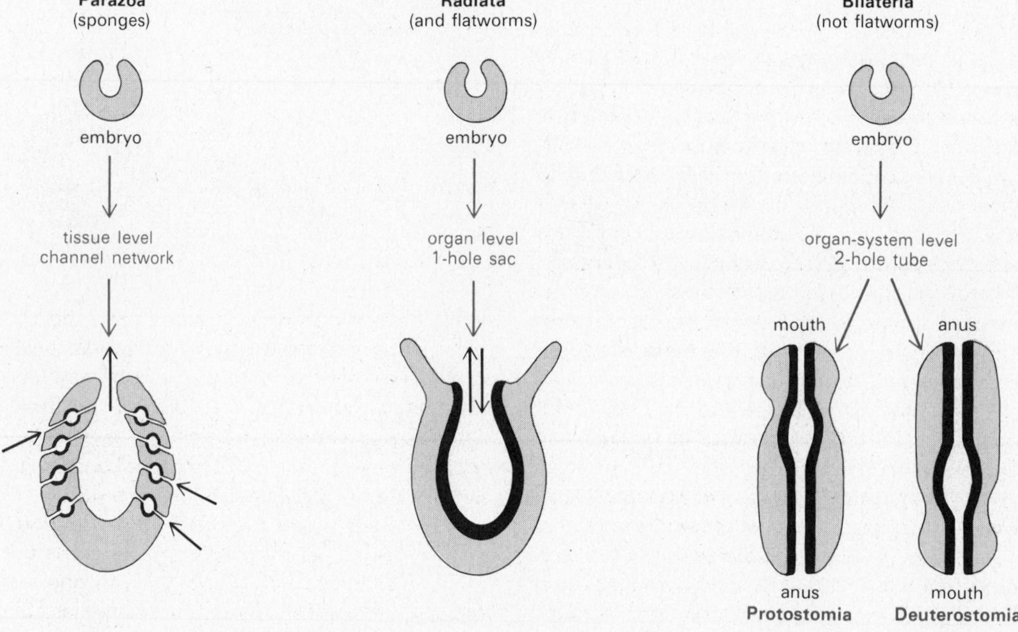

11.6 ***Alimentary patterns.*** *The position of the alimentary cells is shown as dark layers (endoderm in Radiata and Bilateria). In radiates the single alimentary opening of the embryo becomes a joint mouth-anus in the adult. In bilaterial types the embryonic alimentary opening becomes the mouth in Protostomia, the anus in Deuterostomia. In each case a second alimentary opening develops later at the opposite end.*

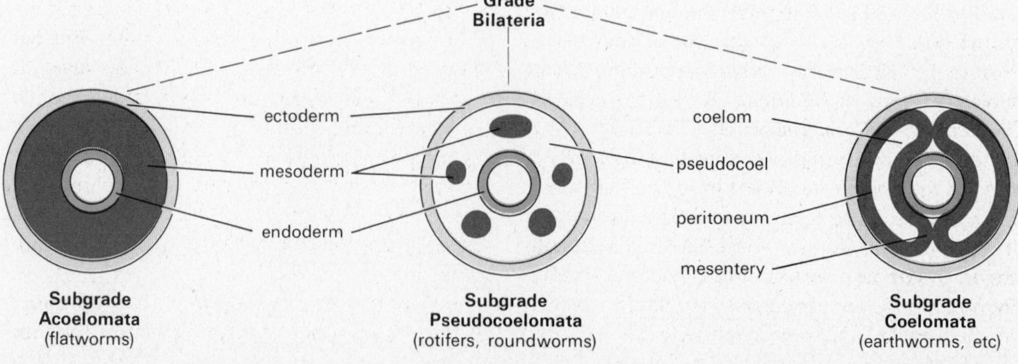

11.7 Mesoderm and coelom *in Bilateria. The main body cavity is a pseudocoel in the Pseudocoelomata and a peritoneum-lined coelom in the Coelomata. In coelomates a dorsal and ventral mesentery (formed by two mesodermal layers) supports the alimentary tract.*

the complexity of the architectural building blocks. At such a stage of development an embryo is already clearly recognizable as, for example, a bilaterial type, and in it at least two of the three primary germ layers are already present: integumentary ectoderm outside and alimentary endoderm inside. Between these two the mesoderm now develops, from cells produced by ectoderm, endoderm, or both layers as in most cases. The pattern of mesoderm formation is an important criterion that can be used to divide the grade Bilateria into *subgrades* (Fig. 11.7).

In one bilaterial group, mesoderm comes to fill completely the available space between ectoderm and endoderm. Animals so constructed lack an internal body cavity; they form the subgrade *Acoelomata,* and they are exemplified by, for example, flatworms. In all other Bilateria mesoderm comes to occupy only part of the space between ectoderm and endoderm, and the remainder later becomes a fluid-filled *principal body cavity.* The presence of such a cavity makes the motions of the alimentary tract independent of those of the body wall and the animal as a whole. Moreover the cavity permits an animal to attain considerable size, for the fluid in the cavity can provide internal support as a hydraulic ''skeleton.'' It can also aid in transporting food and wastes, a necessary function that in a large animal could not be accomplished by direct diffusion between surface and deep-lying parts alone.

One group of Bilateria has a body cavity bounded on the outside directly by the body wall and on the inside directly by the alimentary system. The mesoderm here consists of cells and tissues that accumulate in certain restricted regions only. Animals with body cavities of this type make up the subgrade *Pseudocoelomata.* It is exemplified by, for example, rotifers and roundworms. In all remaining Bilateria, one portion of the developing mesoderm is situated along the inner surface of the ectoderm and another portion forms around the alimentary tract. Most of the free space left between these mesodermal layers typically comes to be enclosed by a mesodermal membrane, the *peritoneum.* The vertical portions of this membrane represent *mesenteries,* which suspend the alimentary tract from the body wall.

Any space or body cavity enclosed completely by mesodermal tissues, and especially by a peritoneal membrane, is known as a *coelom.* Accordingly, animals with a coelom are said to belong to the subgrade *Coelomata.* The terms ''acoelomate'' and ''pseudocoelomate'' now become clear. Acoelomates are animals without a coelom and indeed without a body cavity of any kind. Pseudocoelomates have a *pseudocoel,* or ''false'' coelom, a body cavity lined directly by ectoderm and endoderm, not by a peritoneum. Such a cavity resembles a true coelom superficially.

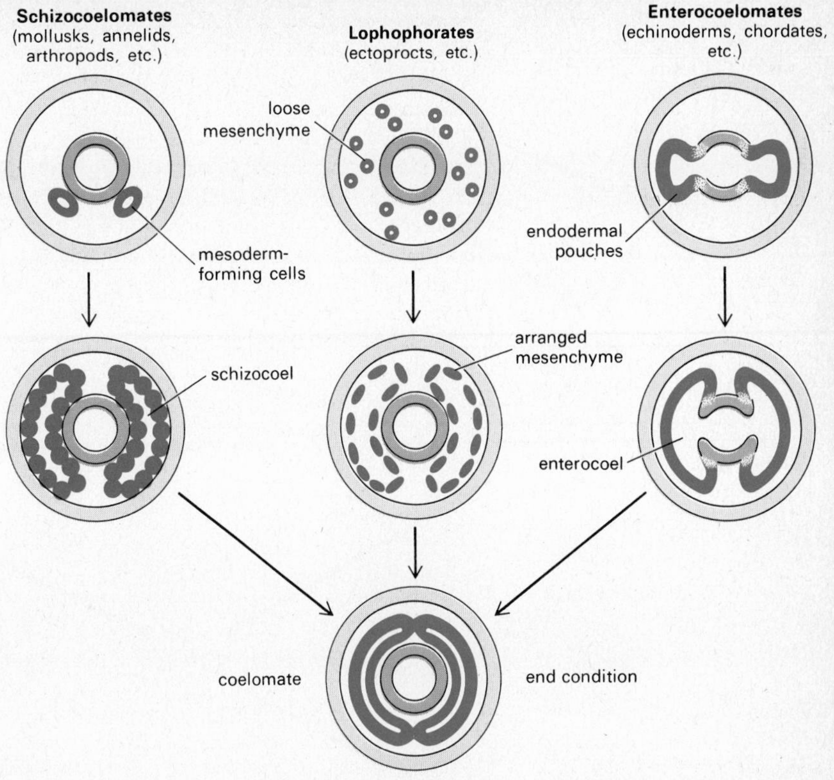

Among coelomate Bilateria in turn, subgroups can be distinguished according to how the coelomic cavities develop (Fig. 11.8). In one subgroup, exemplified by mollusks, annelids, and arthropods, all adult mesoderm arises from two endoderm-derived cells, one on each side of the future gut. Each of these so-called *teloblast cells* then forms a *teloblastic band* of tissue. This band later splits into an outer mesodermal layer that lies along the ectoderm and an inner layer that surrounds the endoderm. Because the coelom here forms by a splitting process, it is called a *schizocoel;* and animals with coelomic body cavities of this type make up the *schizocoelomates,* an assemblage roughly equivalent to a superphylum.

In another such superphylum, represented mainly by echinoderms and chordates, the meso-

***11.8* Coelom formation** *in the subgrade Coelomata. The pattern shown for lophophorates is but one of several known to occur in that group.*

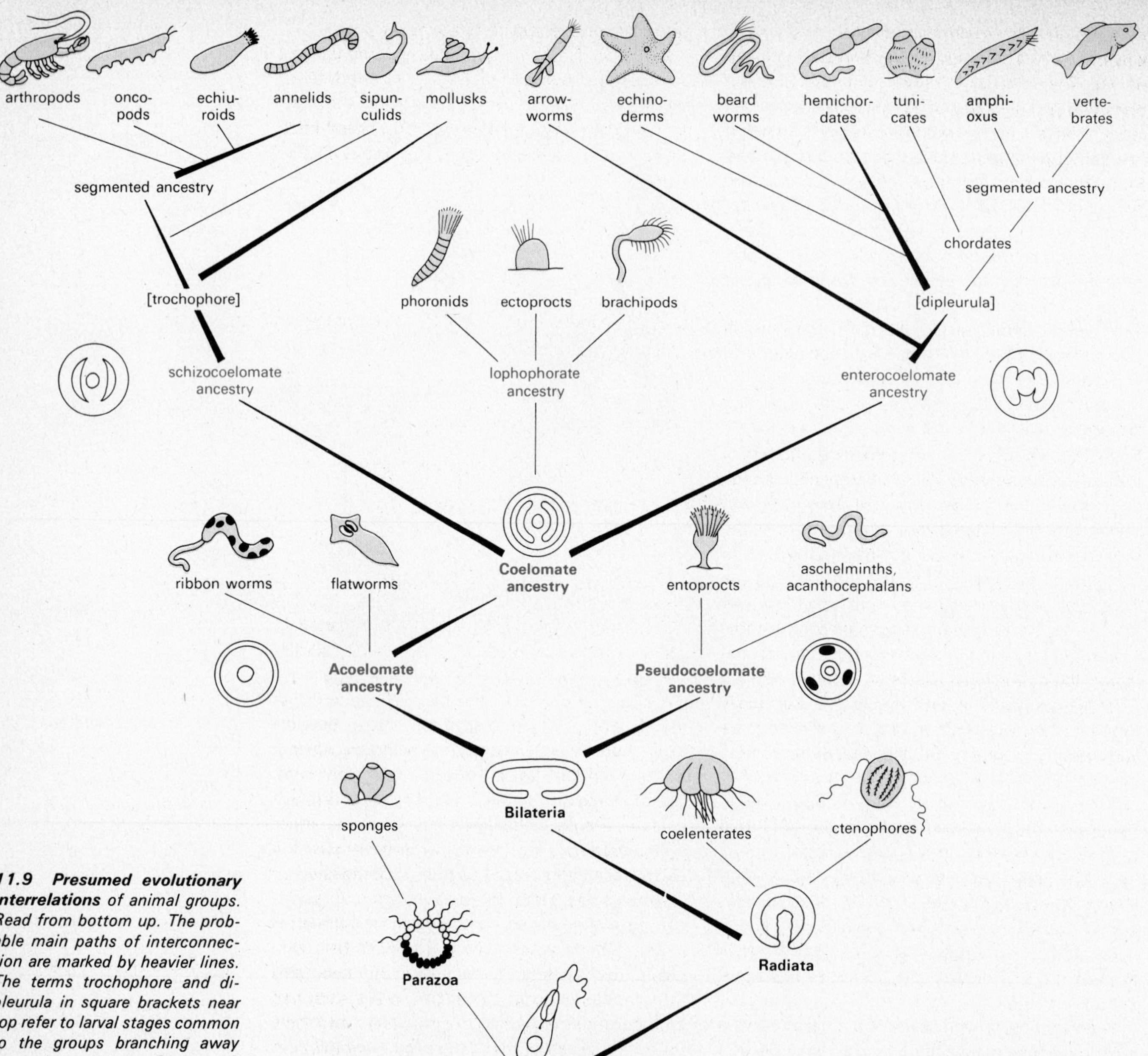

***11.9 Presumed evolutionary interrelations** of animal groups. Read from bottom up. The probable main paths of interconnection are marked by heavier lines. The terms trochophore and dipleurula in square brackets near top refer to larval stages common to the groups branching away in each case (see Chaps. 12 and 13).*

derm arises as a pair of lateral pouches that grow out from the endoderm. These pouches later separate away from the endoderm as closed sacs, but their inner portions still remain adjacent to the alimentary system and their outer portions come to lie along the body wall. The final condition is quite similar to that in schizocoelomates. But since the mesoderm and the coelom here are derived from the future gut (''enteron''), the body cavity is called an *enterocoel;* and animals with such cavities are known as *enterocoelomates.*

In a third subgroup or superphylum, various other, largely unique patterns of coelom formation occur. In one, for example, loose mesoderm cells migrate and eventually arrange themselves as a continuous peritoneal layer (see Fig. 11.8).

Coeloms developed in this and various similar ways have not been given any special technical names. The animals in this group include brachiopods (lamp shells) and other so-called *lophophorates.* The ancestors of this group might have been among the most ancient coelomate animals, from which both the schizocoelomate and the enterocoelomate superphyla later evolved.

Partly on the basis of the developmental patterns just outlined, a number of presumed, tentative evolutionary interrelations among the main animal groups have been inferred. These inferences are summarized diagrammatically in Fig. 11.9.

Branch Parazoa animals at or below tissue level of organization; body tissues not homologous to primary germ layers of other animals; *Porifera*

Sponges

Phylum Porifera "pore-bearing" animals; mostly marine, some in fresh water; adults sessile, often in colonies; alimentation by means of channel system with flagellate collar cells; without nerve cells; 5,000 species

Class Calcarea chalk sponges

Class Hexactinellida glass sponges

Class Demospongiae horny sponges

The larvae of sponges are globular, flagellate, free-swimming organisms composed of two cell layers. When they settle and metamorphose they undergo a curious inversion: the flagellate cells of the outer layer move to the interior, and the cells of the originally interior layer move to the outside (Fig. 11.10). Jelly-secreting cells later come to lie between the outer and inner layers; hence an adult sponge basically has a three-layered construction. However, because of the earlier inversion the three layers are not equivalent to ectoderm, mesoderm, and endoderm. This circumstance is one of the main reasons why sponges are regarded as representing a whole separate taxonomic branch, distinct from all other animals.

The outer layer of a sponge typically forms a covering epithelium (Fig. 11.11). At numerous places in this epithelium are small pores (*ostia*) that lead to the interior of the body and admit food-bearing water. The middle layer contains not only jelly-secreting cells, but also others that form, for example, reproductive cells and skeletal *spicules.* These needlelike secretions have a variety of shapes, and their composition is the basis of sponge classification; spicules consist of calcium salts in chalk sponges, of silica in glass sponges, and of organic substances in horny sponges.

The inner layer of a sponge contains flagellate *collar cells* (or *choanocytes*), remarkably similar to the protozoan collar flagellates. The flagella are directed into the central cavity of the sponge, which communicates with the pores on the surface. Water is drawn through the pores into the cavity by the beat of the flagella, and a common stream of water then leaves the sponge through an *osculum,* a larger opening from the inner cavity. Food present in water that flows past the collar cells is trapped by them and digested in food vacuoles.

In the simplest (or *asconoid*) sponges the inner cavity is a wide, straight-walled chamber, with collar cells lining the entire wall. In more complex (or *syconoid*) types the central cavity is extended into numerous deep side chambers, and only these contain collar cells. The most complex (or *leuconoid*) sponges have a highly branched network of narrow channels throughout the body. Collar cells here occur only in small chambers spaced out along the channels (see Fig. 11.11).

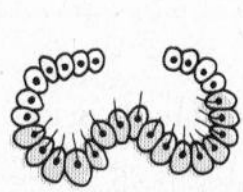

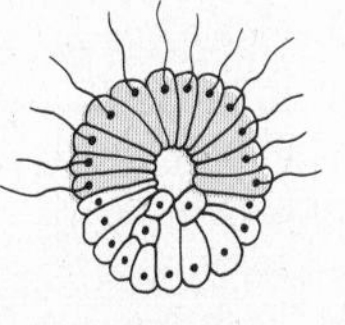

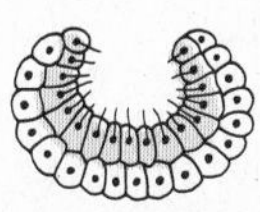

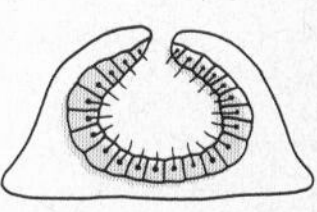

11.10 Sponge development. *1, blastulalike embryo. 2, inversion (embryo turns inside out through opening in nonflagellated half, resulting in exteriorized flagella). 3, amphiblastula larva. 4, invagination of flagellated half into nonflagellated half. 5, larva settles and becomes adult sponge.*

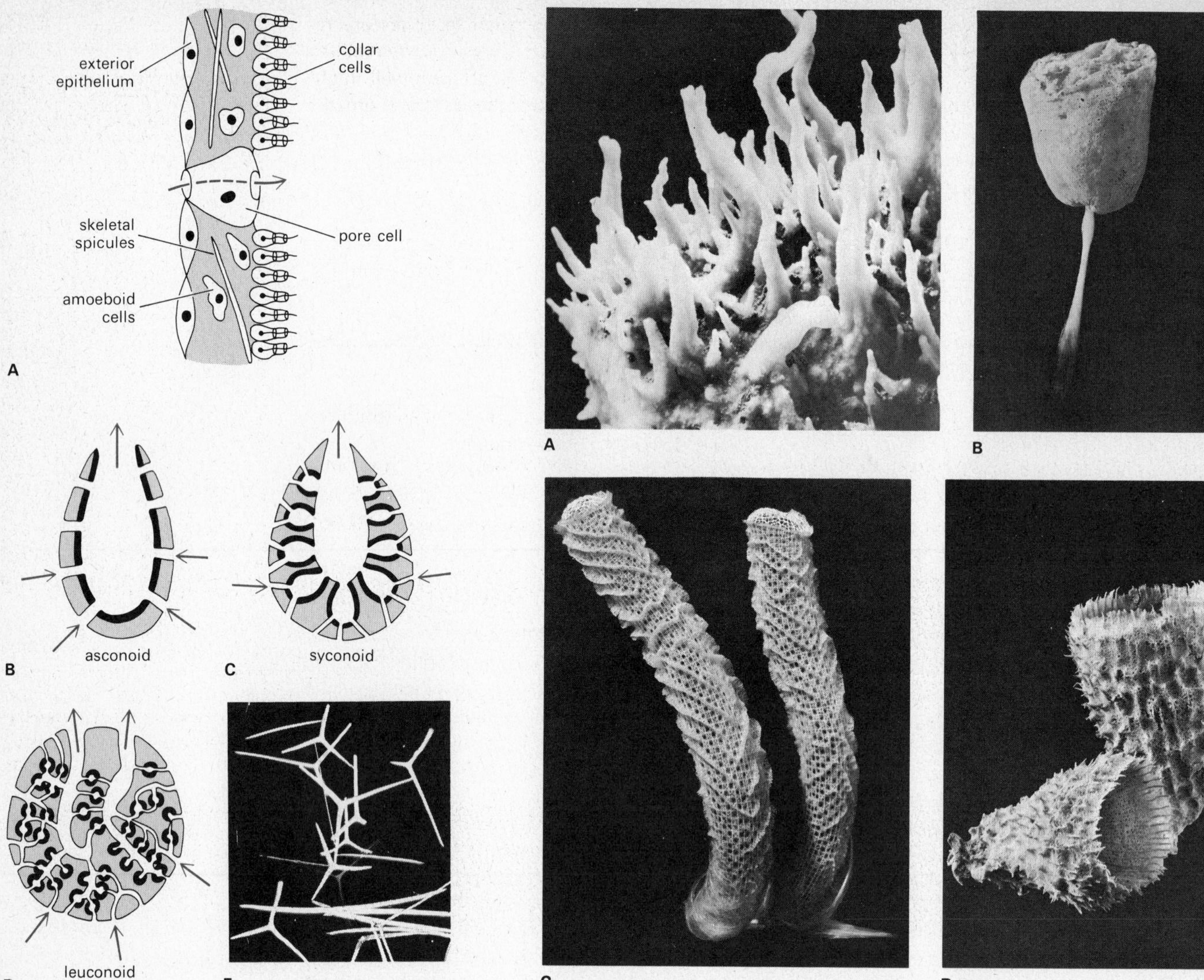

11.11 ***Sponge structure.*** *A, composition of the body wall of a sponge such as that shown in B. B, C, D, the three levels of structural complexity of sponges. The black layers indicate the position of the collar cells. Arrows show direction of water flow. Openings where water enters sponge are ostia, and the exits where water leaves are oscula. E, isolated skeletal spicules of a calcareous sponge (courtesy Carolina Biological Supply Company.)*

11.12 ***Sponge types.*** *A, a calcareous type. B, a glass sponge. The ropy tuft anchors the animal to the sea floor. D, a horny sponge. To this group also belong the bath sponges. C, Venus flower basket, one of the glass sponges.*

Calcareous sponges include all three of these structural types; glass and horny sponges are largely leuconoid (Fig. 11.12).

Apart from propagating through sex cells sponges can also reproduce by *budding,* and freshwater species can form *gemmules* under unfavorable conditions. A gemmule is an encapsulated group of cells that can form a new sponge when circumstances are again appropriate. Sponges can also be fragmented and each piece usually regenerates as a complete individual. Indeed a sponge can be decomposed into a suspension of loose cells, and these cells then migrate together and rebuild themselves into an intact whole.

Because of their unusual developmental patterns, their alimentary water channels, and their primitive level of organization, sponges are regarded almost universally as an independent line of metazoan evolution. The animals well might be descendants of protozoan or more broadly protistan ancestors.

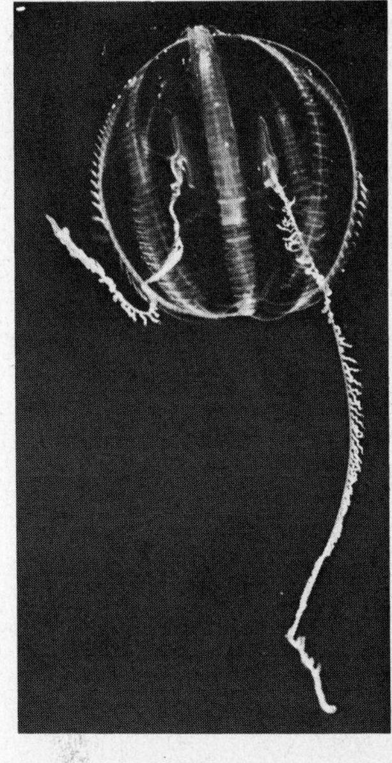

11.13 **Ctenophores.** *The animal shown is Pleurobrachia, photographed from life. Note locomotor comb plates in rows on globular body; fringed (adhesive-cell-containing) tentacles; and position of sensory balancing organ at top of animal.*

Branch Eumetazoa animals above tissue level of organization; adult body formed from embryonic ectoderm, mesoderm, and endoderm; *Radiata, Bilateria*

Radiates

Grade Radiata animals attaining organ level of complexity; typically with adult radial symmetry

Phylum Cnidaria coelenterates; mostly marine, some in fresh water; tentacle-bearing radiates with *cnidoblasts* containing *nematocysts;* body saclike, with single alimentary opening serving as mouth and anus; polymorphic, with medusas and/or polyps; with *planula* larvae; 10,000 species

Phylum Ctenophora comb jellies (Fig. 11.13); all marine; medusalike construction; locomotion by eight meridian *comb plates;* tentacles if present with adhesive cells; 100 species

Of these two phyla of radiate animals, the first is of major evolutionary and ecological significance. Early coelenterates might have been the ancestors of all other eumetazoan animals, comb jellies included; and coelenterates living today, particularly the builders of coral reefs and atolls, are important members of the marine environment.

Coelenterates

Phylum Cnidaria

Class Hydrozoa *Obelia, Hydra, Physalia*

Class Scyphozoa jellyfishes

Class Anthozoa sea anemones, corals

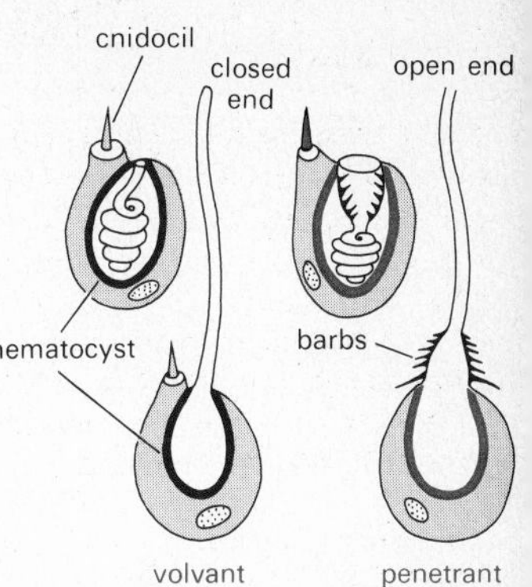

11.14 **Cnidoblasts,** *undischarged and discharged. Numerous variants of each of the two basic types shown here are known.*

The phylum name is derived from the stinging cells, or *cnidoblasts,* found around the mouth, on the tentacles, and elsewhere in these carnivorous animals. Each cnidoblast contains a horny *nematocyst,* a stinging capsule with a coiled, hollow filament inside (Fig. 11.14). Appropriate stimuli cause explosive discharge of the nematocyst, a process in which the filament turns inside out and entangles prey. Some types of nematocysts also secrete a paralyzing toxin.

Coelenterates occur in two basic structural forms, *polyps* and *medusas* (Fig. 11.15). In polyps the main body axis is long in relation to the diameter, and in the umbrella- or bell-shaped medusas the main axis is short. Polyps are sessile, medusas are free-swimming and sexual. Both types or either one only can occur in a given life cycle.

The body of any coelenterate, whether polyp or medusa, typically consists of three layers (see Fig. 11.14). The outside layer is an ectodermal *epidermis,* which, in many polyps, secretes an exoskeleton. Such secretions are often little more than thin, transparent layers of chitin, but they

11.15 Coelenterate structure. *A, the oral-aboral axis is long compared with the body diameter in a polyp, whereas the reverse holds true in a medusa. Both polyp and medusa are variants of a single common body pattern. B, some cell types in the three body layers, as in jellyfishes and sea anemones. In these animals the inner ends of the epidermal and gastrodermal cells are pseudopodial, as shown, but in Hydrozoa the bases of these cells are T-shaped and contain contractile myofibrils. Correspondingly, Hydrozoa are without separate muscle cells. Cells in the mesogloea secrete jelly, considerable amounts of it in medusas. Nerve cells are part of the epidermis, gastrodermis, or both.*

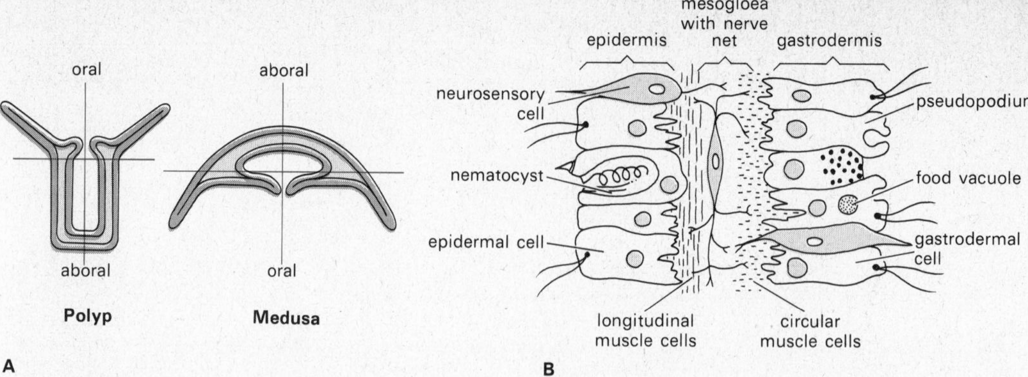

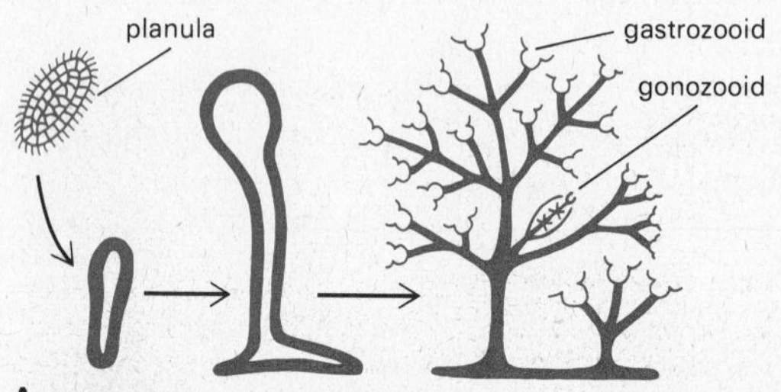

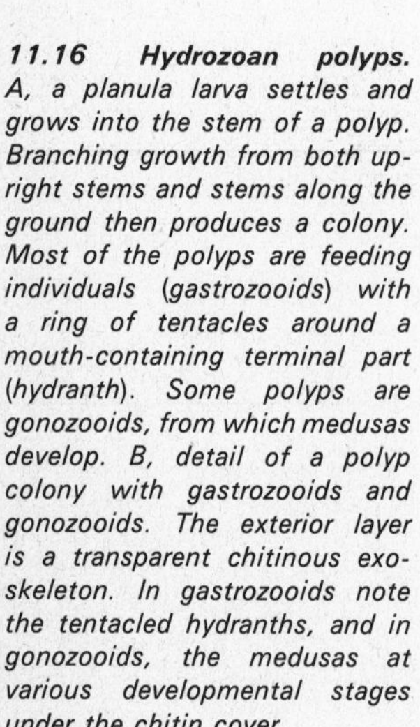
11.16 Hydrozoan polyps. *A, a planula larva settles and grows into the stem of a polyp. Branching growth from both upright stems and stems along the ground then produces a colony. Most of the polyps are feeding individuals (gastrozooids) with a ring of tentacles around a mouth-containing terminal part (hydranth). Some polyps are gonozooids, from which medusas develop. B, detail of a polyp colony with gastrozooids and gonozooids. The exterior layer is a transparent chitinous exoskeleton. In gastrozooids note the tentacled hydranths, and in gonozooids, the medusas at various developmental stages under the chitin cover.*

can also be massive accumulations of calcareous stone, as in the reef-forming corals. The inside layer is an endodermal *gastrodermis,* which lines the alimentary cavity and contains flagellate and amoeboid digestive cells. Between epidermis and gastrodermis is a mesodermal *mesogloea,* a layer containing jelly-secreting cells and varying amounts of connective tissue fibers. In polyps the amount of jelly is generally small; it is absent altogether in *Hydra.* But in medusas the jelly becomes extensive and forms the bulk of the animal. Embedded in the mesogloea is a simple nerve net that innervates both the epidermis and the gastrodermis. Scyphozoa and Anthozoa also have distinct muscle cells. Hydrozoa are without them, but most of their epidermal and gastrodermal cells contain contractile fibrils.

Coelenterate development typically includes an oval, two-layered *planula* larve (Fig. 11.16). This ciliated, free-swimming form eventually settles and gives rise to the polyp phase of a life cycle. In many Hydrozoa the planula grows into a highly branched colony of polyps that contains a continuous, interconnecting alimentary cavity. Most of these polyps are feeding individuals, or *gastrozooids.* Each of them terminates in a *hydranth,* a flower-shaped body part in which a wreath of tentacles surrounds the alimentary opening. At various locations in such a colony develop reproductive polyps, or *gonozooids,* which give rise to medusas by budding. The medusas swim free, and at maturity they develop sex organs. Fertilized eggs then become new planula larvae.

In Hydrozoa such as *Obelia,* the polyp and medusa phases play roughly equally important roles (Fig. 11.17). In other hydrozoan groups one or the other phase is reduced or omitted altogether. For example, in *Gonionemus* the only polyplike stage is a larval form (called *actinula*) that develops from the planula and that does not become attached. Later it transforms directly into a free-swimming medusa, which represents the

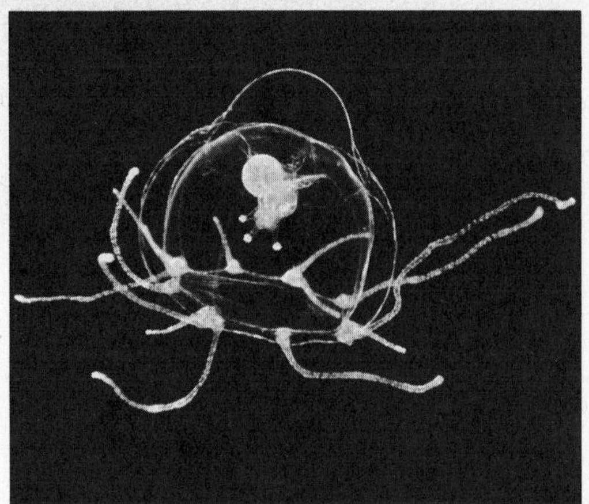
A

B

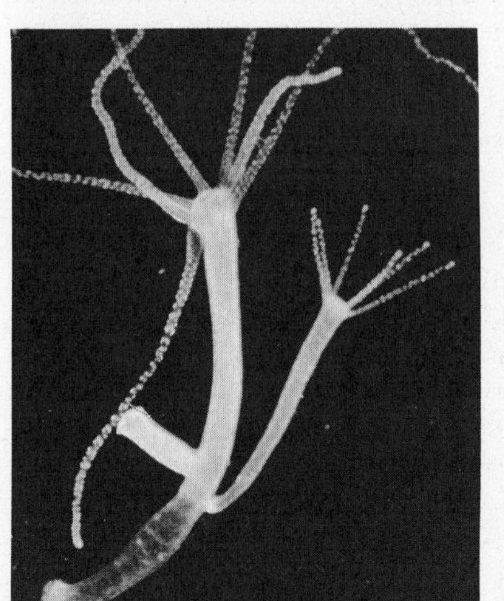
C

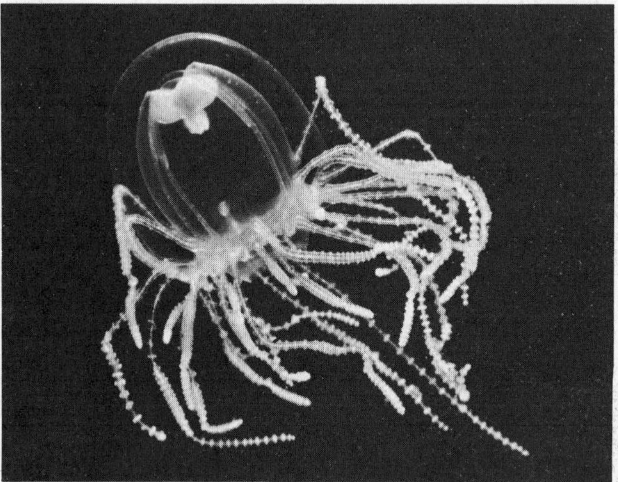
D

11.17 Hydrozoan polyps and medusas. *A, a hydrozoan medusa, from life. Note mouth-containing manubrium in center of deep bell, smooth bell margin, and tentacles. B, calcareous deposit of a millipore coral, a hydrozoan in which the polyp phase is dominant. C, a fresh-water Hydra, from life, with two budded offspring individuals still attached to the parent. Hydras are without medusas. D, Gonionemus (from life), a hydrozoan in which polyps are lacking from the life cycle. See also Color Fig. 15.*

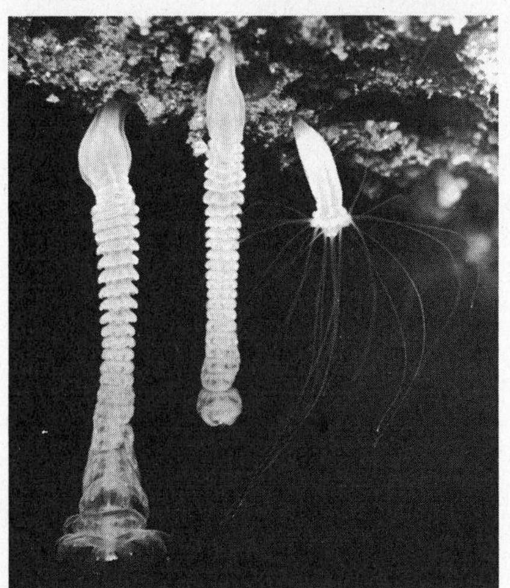
A

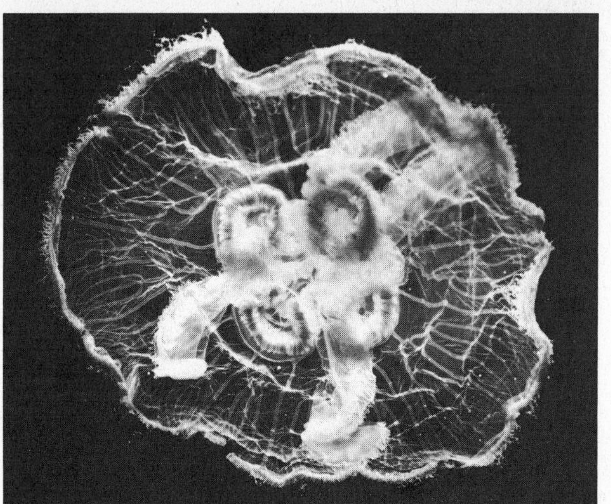
B

11.18 Scyphozoa. *A, larvae of the jellyfish Aurelia hanging from the underside of a rock. At right is a young larva, at center and left are older ones in process of cutting off young medusas successively. A nearly liberated medusa is seen in lower left corner. B, the common jellyfish Aurelia. Note the tentacle-bearing lappets around the bell margin, the canal system in the bell, the four horseshoe-shaped gonads near the center, and the mouth-bearing manubrium, curving from center to lower left. See also Color Fig. 16. (B, courtesy Carolina Biological Supply Company.)*

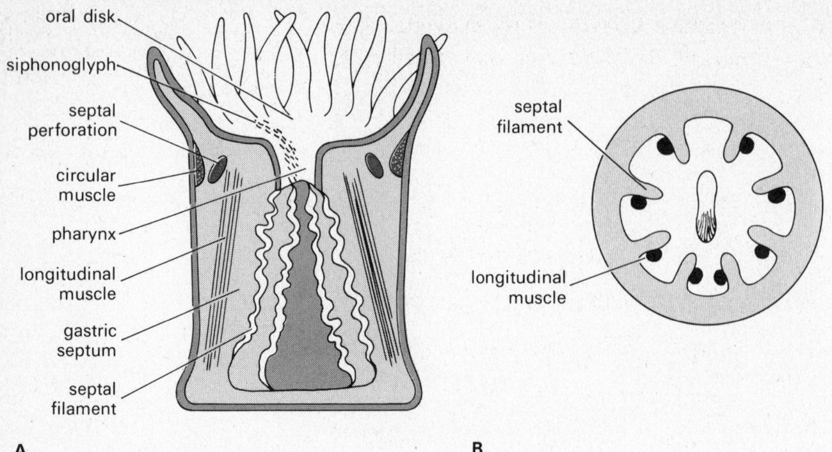

11.19 ***Anthozoan structure.*** *A, cutaway section through a sea anemone. The siphonoglyph is a band of flagella that aids in circulating water into and out of the gastrovascular cavity. Note the partitions (gastric septa) in this cavity. The septal filament contains batteries of stinging cells. B, cross section through an anthozoon. Note bilateral arrangement of the longitudinal muscles and the central mouth opening (with position of siphonoglyph indicated).*

entire adult phase of the life cycle. By contrast, the life cycle of the freshwater *Hydra* does not include a medusa phase. Instead the solitary parent polyp develops sex organs itself and gives rise to new polyps directly. Polyps are similarly dominant in the Portuguese man-of-war *Physalia,* in which several polymorphic types of polyps collectively form a floating colony (Color Fig. 15 and see Fig. 6.5).

In the class Scyphozoa, the planula settles and forms a *scyphistoma,* a solitary attached reproductive polyp (Fig. 11.18). From the free end of this polyp are then budded off a series of medusas; these jellyfishes later acquire sex organs and represent the dominant phase of the life cycle. Jellyfishes are structurally similar to hydrozoan medusas. Among several differences, however, an easily recognizable one is that the margin of the "umbrella" is even in the Hydrozoa but is scalloped into lappets in Scyphozoa (Color Fig. 16 and see Fig. 11.18).

In Anthozoa it is the medusa phase that is absent. The sessile adult is a feeding polyp with sex organs, and planula larvae grow directly into new polyps. Such polyps are structurally quite complex. For example, the mesogloea is a true connective tissue that contains very little jelly, and the digestive surface of the alimentary cavity is enlarged by the presence of tissue folds (Fig. 11.19). Some Anthozoa are solitary (sea anemones, for example); most of them are colonial and include the majority of the builders of coral reefs and atolls (Color Fig. 17).

Coelenterates as a whole are widely believed to represent the most primitive Eumetazoa. If this view is correct, the Bilateria would all be descended from ancestral coelenterates. An alternative possibility is that coelenterates, and Radiata generally, are an independent line of eumetazoan evolution, and that Bilateria evolved separately from an early protistan source. This issue cannot be resolved from the data now available.

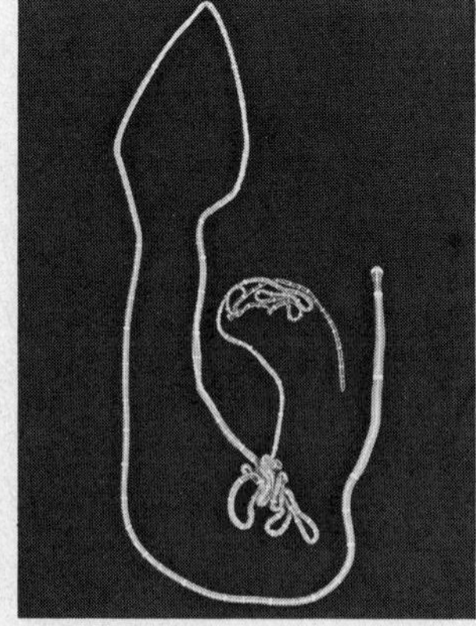

11.20 ***Nemertines.*** *The proboscis worm Tubulanus is shown.*

Bilateral Forms

Grade Bilateria animals attaining an organ-system level of complexity; typically with adult bilateral symmetry; *Acoelomata, Pseudocoelomata, Coelomata*

Acoelomates

Subgrade Acoelomata animals without internal body cavities; protostomial (first embryonic opening of alimentary cavity becomes mouth); skeletal or breathing systems absent; nervous system basically a nerve net with localized thickenings

Phylum Platyhelminthes flatworms; freshwater and marine, some terrestrial; alimentary system with single opening; vascular system absent; 10,000 species

Phylum Nemertina (Rhynchocoela) proboscis worms, ribbon worms (Fig. 11.20); largely marine, some freshwater, a few terrestrial; alimentary system with separate mouth and anus; vascular system present; 600 species

As a group, flatworms are believed to represent the most primitive Bilateria. Thus, early stocks of flatworms might have been ancestral to the proboscis worms and, directly or indirectly, to all other bilaterial phyla as well.

Flatworms
Phylum Platyhelminthes

Class Turbellaria planarians; free-living

Class Trematoda flukes; bulk-feeding parasites

Class Cestoda tapeworms; fluid-feeding parasites

Among the free-living flatworms the members of the order Acoela are generally believed to be the most primitive (and thus the closest link to the ancestors of all Bilateria). An acoel worm is often no more than ½ mm long; it consists of a single-layered epidermis and an inner mass of mesoderm and endoderm cells (Fig. 11.21). A single opening in the epidermis on the underside of the flattened body is the sole component of an alimentary system; the interior endoderm cells

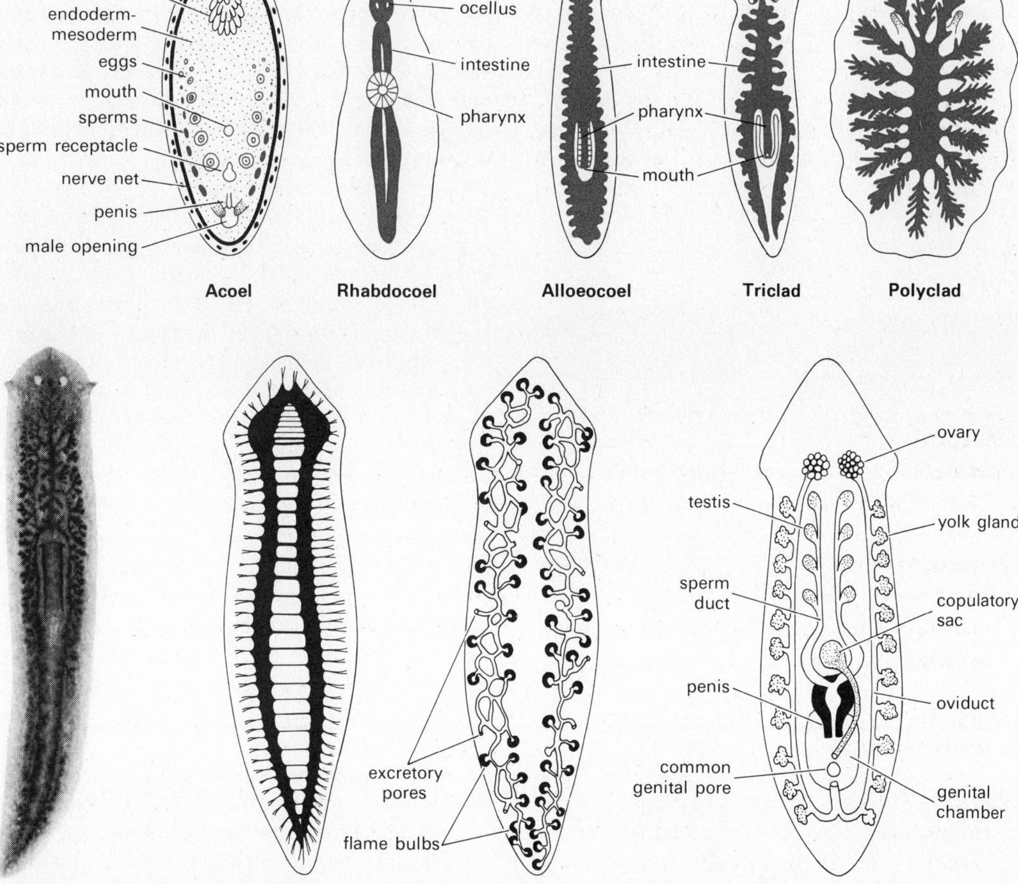

11.21 Free-living flatworms. *The major orders are illustrated. Note variations in the structure of the alimentary system.*

11.22 Planarian structure. *A, the free-living planarian Dugesia. Note eyes, pointed lateral lobes (auricles) at level of eyes, pharynx in middle of underside, and darkly stained parts of the alimentary system. One main branch of the tract passes forward from the pharynx, two other main branches pass backward. All three branches have numerous side branches and pockets. The pharynx can be protruded and retracted. B, the ladder-type nervous system. C, the excretory system. Flame bulbs are cup-shaped cells with flagella inside the cups. They filter the body fluids, and urine passes through a system of ducts that opens to the outside at several excretory pores. D, the reproductive system. Each worm contains both a male and a female system.*

digest food intracellularly. All other free-living orders possess a definite alimentary system composed of mouth, pharynx, and blind-ended intestine. These organs form a straight saclike tube in one order (*rhabdocoels*), a straight tube with lateral pouches in another (*alloeocoels*), a three-branched system with lateral pouches in a third (*triclads*), and a many-branched system in a fourth (*polyclads*).

The triclad planarians are the most familiar. Such a worm is up to $\frac{1}{2}$ in. long and has a roughly triangular head end with a pair of conspicuous dorsal eyes (Fig. 11.22). The epidermis is ciliated ventrally and secretes a slime track on which the cilia propel the animal in a gliding form of locomotion. Muscle layers underneath the epidermis also permit the worm to swim by undulations of its body. The nervous system contains a concentration of nervous tissue in the head, called the *brain ganglion.* A pair of ventral *nerve cords* leads from this ganglion posteriorly. Transverse nerve connections between the cords give the system a ladderlike appearance.

The mouth-anus opening is at the tip of a midventral tubular pharynx that can be protruded and retracted. The pharynx leads to three interconnected intestinal pouches, one of which points anteriorly, the other two, posteriorly. The lining of these pouches contains flagellate and amoeboid cells; food is digested intracellularly, as in coelenterates. The space between the body wall and the intestine is filled solidly with connective tissue, in which are embedded the excretory and reproductive systems.

Excretion is accomplished by a so-called *flame-bulb* system (see Fig. 11.22). A flame bulb is a single cup-shaped cell with a tuft of flagella pointing into the cavity of the cup. On its outside surface the cell filters the body fluids, and the filtrate is then propelled by the flagella into a duct with which the flame bulb connects. The ducts of numerous flame bulbs join and lead to the exterior through several excretory pores. The reproductive structures include both male and female systems in the same worm, Each system consists of numerous pairs of sex organs and of ducts leading to a genital chamber. In mating each partner inserts a copulatory organ into the genital chamber of the other. Sperms are stored temporarily in a copulatory sac (see Fig. 11.22). Fertilized eggs are shed, and in triclads the eggs develop directly into miniature worms; in the marine acoels and polyclads ciliated swimming larvae are formed first.

The exclusively parasitic flukes are structurally like free-living flatworms in most respects, but they exhibit three traits that appear to be direct adaptations to their parasitic way of life (Fig.

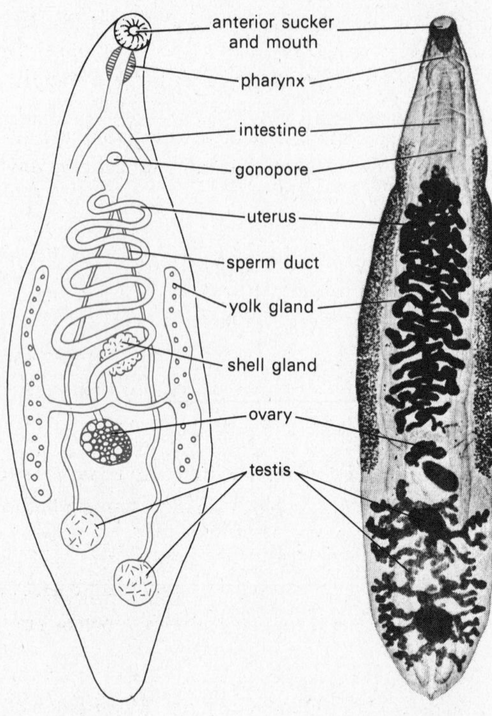

11.23 ***Trematodes.*** *The structure of Clonorchis sinensis, the Chinese liver fluke, is shown. See also life cycle in Fig. 6.21.*

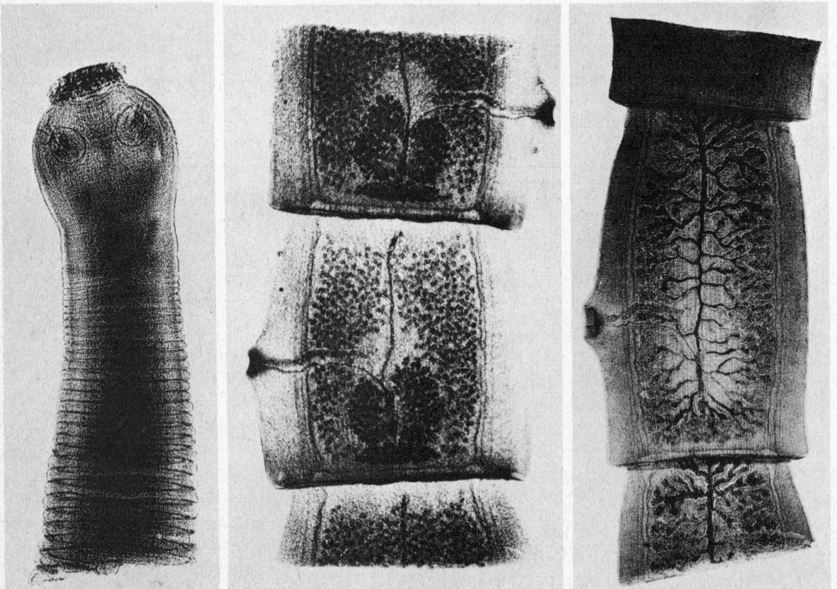

11.24 (*Below*) ***Tapeworms.*** *A, head, or scolex, with hooks and suckers. B, segmental sections, or proglottids, near middle of body. C, proglottids near hind end of body. Tree-shaped structures in B and C are reproductive organs. Note testes filling proglottids in B and genital pores opening on the sides. In C, the uterus filled with eggs is conspicuous.*

11.23). First, flukes lack an epidermis, the exterior layer being a tough and resistant horny cuticle secreted by mesenchyme cells. Second, eyes and other sense organs are reduced or lacking. And third, flukes have one or more muscular suckers, hooks, or other adhesive devices with which they hang on to host tissues. The life cycles are complex and usually require one or more intermediate hosts (see example of Chinese liver fluke, Chap. 6 and Fig. 6.21).

The tapeworms are intestinal parasites lacking an alimentary system of their own; they absorb molecular nutrients directly through their body surfaces. These worms likewise have an exterior cuticle instead of an epidermis. The body consists of a head equipped with hooks and suckers, a neck, and an up to 50-ft-long series of sex-organ-containing *proglottids* that are formed continuously behind the neck (Fig. 11.24). Life histories again usually involve intermediate hosts (see example of beef tapeworm, Chap. 6 and Fig. 6.20).

Both flukes and tapeworms are believed to have evolved from ancestral rhabdocoel turbellarians.

Pseudocoelomates

Subgrade Pseudocoelomata animals with mesoderm locally accumulated in a body cavity that is bounded by ectoderm and mesoderm; protostomial (first embryonic opening of alimentary cavity becomes mouth); skeletal, vascular, or breathing systems absent

Phylum Aschelminthes sac worms; marine, freshwater, and terrestrial; body often segmented superficially; cells or nuclei constant in number and arrangement for each species; musculature typically not in layers; pharynx elaborate; 15,000+ species

Phylum Acanthocephala spiny-headed worms; parasitic in vertebrates; with hook-bearing proboscis; alimentary system absent; with flame bulbs or excretory system absent; nuclear constancy in adult; 600 species

Phylum Entoprocta entoprocts; very largely marine; stalked and sessile, solitary and colonial; with mouth and anus inside a circlet of ciliated tentacles; 60 species

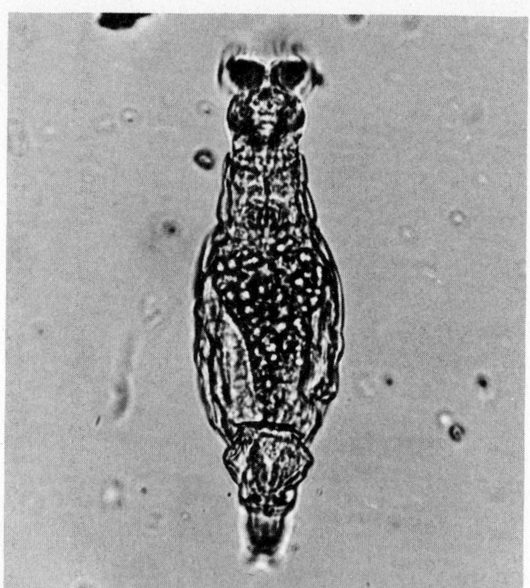

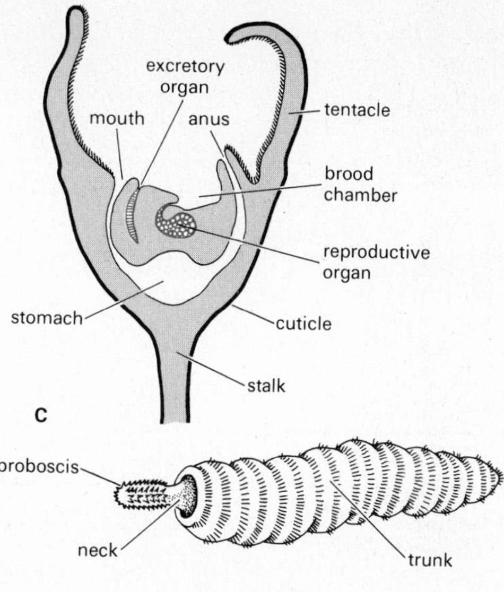

11.25 Pseudocoelomates. *A, a rotifer, representative of the phylum Aschelminthes. B, external features of a member of the Acanthocephala; the proboscis is shown extended in these parasitic worms. C, sectional view of an individual of the Entoprocta. The stalked cup-shaped body has a wreath of ciliated tenctacles, a U-shaped alimentary system, and an anus that opens inside the tentacle ring. The animals also typically form colonies.*

The sac worms and spiny-headed worms have vague evolutionary affinities to each other, and both phyla could be related very distantly to flatworms (Fig. 11.25). These animals are syncytial, the boundaries between cells disappearing during development. Moreover, each member of a given species is constructed from exactly the same number of embryonic cells. Thus all adults in a species are structurally identical, and their architecture can be mapped out precisely, nucleus for nucleus. Many of these animals also exhibit a superficial exterior segmentation that permits a telescoping of the body.

Entoprocts are the only pseudocoelomates that are not wormlike. They are microscopic and sessile, often colonial, each with a circlet of tentacles used in straining minute food particles out of water.

Sac Worms
Phylum Aschelminthes

Class Rotifera rotifers; 1,500 species

Class Gastrotricha gastrotrichs; 200 species

Class Kinorhyncha kinorhynchs; 100 species

Class Priapulida priapulids; 5 species

Class Nematoda roundworms; 12,000+ species

Class Nematomorpha hairworms; 80 species

This phylum encompasses a heterogeneous collection of types which are usually grouped into classes as above but which could be regarded equally well as separate phyla. Only the rotifers and roundworms are sufficiently abundant to warrant consideration here.

The body of a rotifer is usually organized into a *head,* a *trunk,* and a tapered *foot* (Fig. 11.26 and see Fig. 11.25). The head bears an anterior *wheel organ,* a wreath of cilia used in swimming locomotion and in the creation of food-bearing water currents. At the end of the foot are two *toes,* each with a *cement organ.* In the fluid that fills the pseudocoelic body cavity are mesenchyme cells, and the muscle cells do not form layers but crisscross in small bundles through the

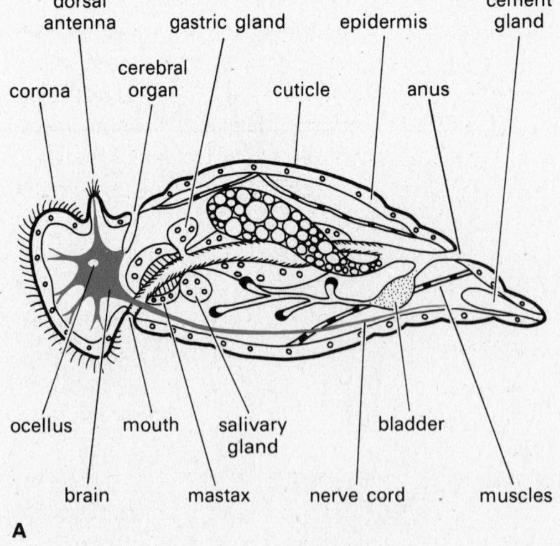

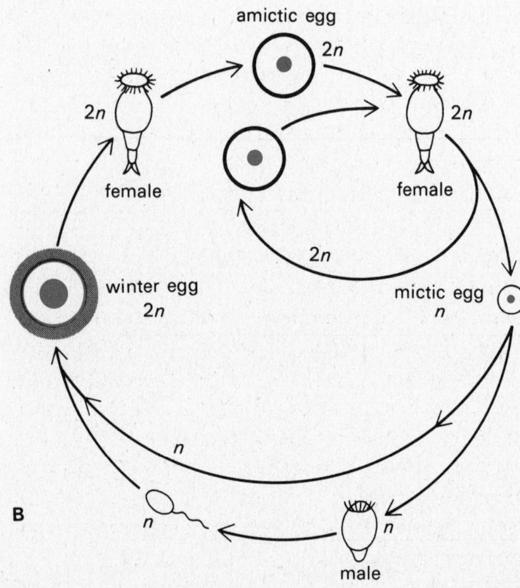

11.26 Rotifer structure and development. *A, diagram of animal seen from the side. B, the life cycle. Amictic eggs are produced in spring and summer and develop without fertilization into new generations of females. Smaller mictic eggs are formed in fall and develop without fertilization into simplified males. If these males then fertilize mictic eggs, encysted winter eggs result. The latter develop into new females the following spring. The symbols n and 2n signify the presence of one or of two sets of chromosomes per cell, respectively.*

body cavity. The alimentary tract begins at the mouth ventral to the wheel organ and leads to a *mastax,* a complex muscular pharynx that contains horny jaws studded with teeth. The remainder of the tract is ciliated internally and terminates in the region between the toes.

From a brain ganglion dorsal to the pharynx lead two main ventral nerve cords. Most rotifers contain an eyespot directly on the dorsal surface of the brain ganglion. Particularly characteristic of these animals is a *dorsal antenna,* a small surface projection dorsal to the brain ganglion. The precise function of this innervated and ciliated organ is obscure. The excretory system consists of a single pair of flame bulb clusters in the body cavity, with ducts opening in the hind part of the intestine.

During spring and summer, female rotifers produce eggs that develop into new females without being fertilized. These females in turn reproduce without fertilization, and many generations of females succeed one another in this manner (see Fig. 11.26). In the fall the females lay some eggs that are smaller than the rest. These hatch as small males, structurally simplified individuals that lack digestive systems but are capable of producing sperms. Fertilization can then occur. The resulting eggs have thick hard shells and can resist unfavorable environments for months or years. Under suitably favorable conditions, as in the following spring, the shelled eggs develop into females. In some types of rotifers males are unknown altogether, the species being propagated exclusively by unfertilized eggs. This phenomenon of egg development without fertilization, or *parthenogenesis,* occurs also in other animal groups (for example, social insects; see Chap. 23).

Roundworms are possibly among the most abundant of all animals, both in numbers of individuals and in numbers of species. New species are being described at an average rate of one per day. Vast numbers of plants and nearly all animals harbor at least one and often more than one type of parasitic nematode, and these parasites are usually implicated when an animal is said to suffer from "worms." Moreover, free-living types are so abundant that a spadeful of garden earth is likely to contain up to a million tiny worms. Informed guesses place the number of existing nematode species at about 500,000, which would make the class the second largest group of organisms after the insects.

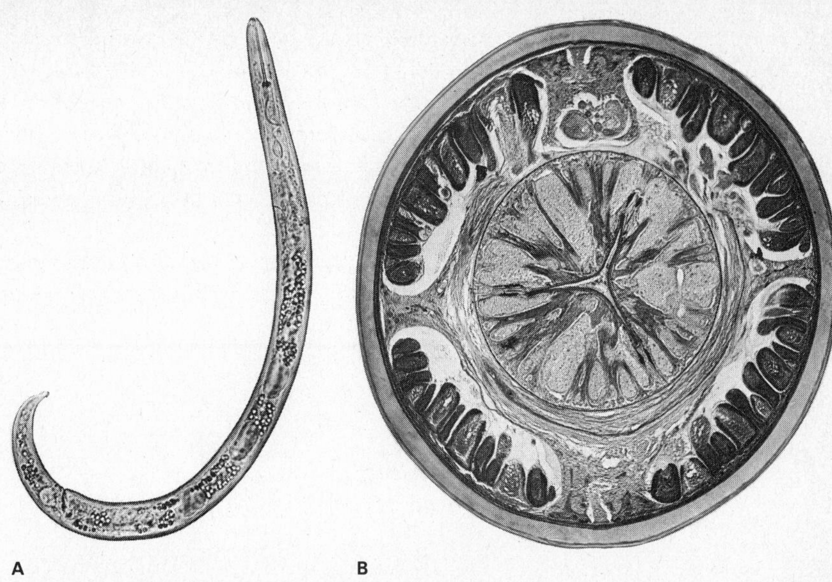

11.27 Nematodes. *A, whole view of a mature female of the nematode Paratylenchus, which causes disease in plants. B, cross section through the pharyngeal region of Ascaris. Note exterior cuticle, muscle quadrants, and thick central pharynx with triangular interior canal.* (*B, courtesy Carolina Biological Supply Company.*)

The mouth and anus of a nematode are at the tapered ends of the cylindrical body (Fig. 11.27). A resistant exterior cuticle is produced by a syncytial epidermis, which is thickened on its inner surface into four longitudinal *chords,* one dorsal, one ventral, and one on each side of the body. The two lateral chords are marked externally as faint lines. Longitudinal muscle cells lie in each body quadrant between the chords. The nervous system includes a nerve ring around the pharynx and a series of nerve cords connecting with this ring. The well-developed pharynx is a long muscular tube, often expanded along its length as one or more bulbous enlargements. The interior canal of the pharynx has a highly characteristic, three-cornered cross section. The excretory structures are unique. They consist of a pair of large cells, the *ventral glands,* situated under the pharynx. The necks of these cells lead forward to excretory pores.

Male nematodes are usually smaller than female ones and have curled posterior ends. During their larval development nematodes typically molt their cuticles, and enlargement of the larvae takes place at these molting stages. In the free-living types the larvae develop directly as new free-living adults. In parasitic types an infective stage is reached at a given point in development or during the adult phase. Up to that point the

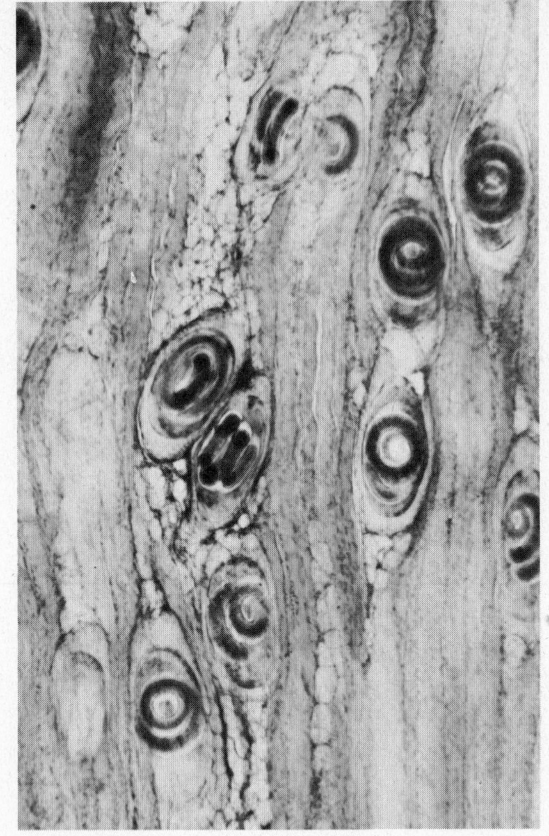

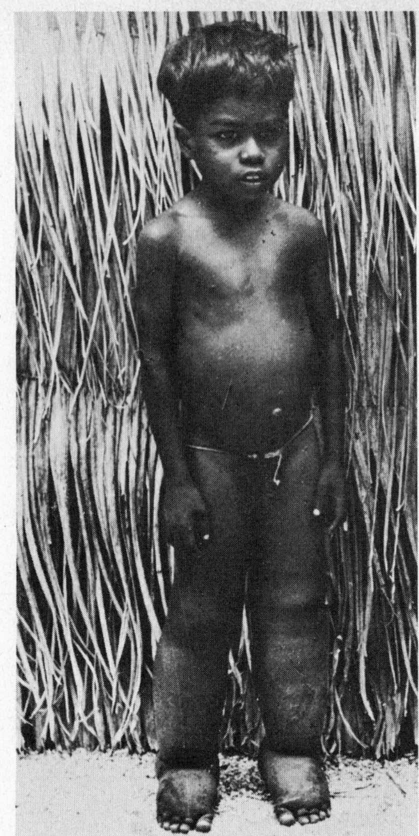

11.28 ***Parasitic roundworms.*** *A, trichina worm larvae, encapsulated in pig muscle. If infected pork is cooked improperly, the larvae are digested out in the intestine of the host, and the worms then invade the host tissues. B, elephantiasis of legs and feet, caused by filaria worms.*

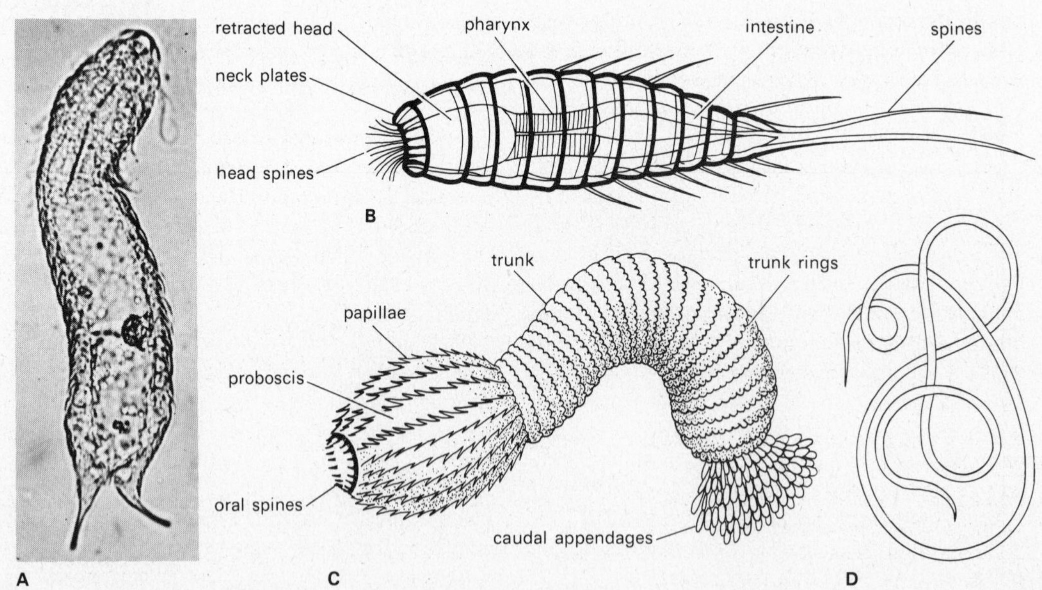

11.29 ***Sac worms.*** *A, gastrotrich. B, kinorhynch, with some structural details. C, priapulid, external features. D, hairworm outline. (A, courtesy Carolina Biological Supply Company.)*

worms are free-living, and when they become infective they must enter a specific plant or animal host within a short time or perish. Numerous nematodes require one or more intermediate hosts.

Man is a host of some 50 species of roundworms. Most of these, including for example the common intestinal nematode *Ascaris,* are fairly harmless. Those that are not include the *trichina worms,* introduced into the human body through insufficiently cooked pork (Fig. 11.28); the *hookworms,* which live in soil and infect man by boring through his skin (see Fig. 6.18); the *guinea worms,* which form ulcerating blisters in human skin and from which the larvae of the next generation are released; and the *filaria worms,* which are transmitted by mosquitoes, block up lymph vessels, and cause the immense swellings of the disease *elephantiasis.*

The remaining groups of sac worms have many features that occur also in rotifers, nematodes, or both (Fig. 11.29). Gastrotrichs resemble rotifers in the organization of the body wall, and the exceedingly elongated hairworms are generally like nematodes. Gastrotrichs and kinorhynchs contain rotiferlike flame-bulb systems, and in both classes as well as in the priapulids the pharynx is structured remarkably like that of nematodes. Kinorhynchs further have roundwormlike epidermal chords, they molt their larval cuticles, and they contain an adult nervous system nearly identical with that of priapulids. But each group also exhibits its own special traits; for example, surface spines and bristles in gastrotrichs, conspicuous superficial segmentation in kinorhynchs, a body having a bulbous, warty forward region in priapulids, and a reduced or absent alimentary system in the parasitic adults of hairworms. The shared traits thus suggest a reasonably close interrelation of these groups, but the unshared traits also suggest that the interrelation is probably not too close.

---

review questions

1 What structural and functional features distinguish most Metazoa from most Metaphyta? In what architectural respects are moving animals generally different from sessile ones?

2 Show in some detail how holotrophic nutrition and the requirement of locomotion determine and influence the characteristics of all other aspects of animal nature. As far as you can, contrast such typically animal attributes with those generally considered to be characteristic of plants.

3 Name the branches, grades, and subgrades of animals. What criteria define each of these ranks? What animals are included in each? Draw up a comprehensive diagram indicating the presumed evolutionary interrelations of all major animal groups.

4 Define Protostomia, Deuterostomia, Bilateria, Parazoa, coelom, schizocoel, enterocoel, mesoderm, germ layer, peritoneum, mesentery, teloblast.

5 Show how Bilateria are subdivided taxonomically according to different patterns of mesoderm and coelom formation. What is the adaptive advantage of a coelom? Does a pseudocoel offer equivalent advantages?

6 Define the phylum Porifera taxonomically. Describe some of the cell and tissue types of sponges, and indicate the function of each. Describe the three architectural variants of sponges. What is the pattern of sponge development?

7 Which phyla are included among the Radiata, and what diagnostic features distinguish these phyla? Name the classes of coelenterates, and describe the life cycles characteristic of each. Distinguish between polyps and medusas.

8 Describe the structural and functional characteristics of cnidoblasts. What cell types occur in the coelenterate epidermis, gastrodermis, and mesogloea?

9 Describe the structure of a hydrozoan polyp colony. How do polyps of *Obelia* form medusas? Describe the structure of a hydrozoan medusa, and outline also the structure of a jellyfish and a sea anemone.

10 Which phyla are included among acoelomates? Name the classes of flatworms, and describe the main structural features of planarians. What are some of the differences between the orders of Turbellaria? Where do planarians live?

11 Review the life cycles of flukes and tapeworms. What are some of the structural differences between free-living and parasitic flatworms? How do various groups of flatworms feed? Move? Describe the anatomy of the nervous, excretory, and reproductive systems of flatworms.

12 Give taxonomic definitions of pseudocoelomates generally and aschelminths specifically. Name the classes of aschelminths. Where do these various groups live?

13 Describe the structure and life cycle of a rotifer. What is meant by cell constancy in these animals?

14 What is the structure of a nemotode? What are longitudinal chords? Name nematodes found in man. Describe the appearance of aschelminths other than rotifers and nematodes.

15 Ascertain (*a*) the species numbers and (*b*) the habitats of the animal phyla studied in this chapter, and indicate the special ecological role, if any, of given phyla.

---

collateral readings

Berrill, N. J.: "Growth, Development, and Pattern," Freeman, San Francisco, 1961. Several chapters of this valuable book (particularly Chaps. 8 and 9) deal specifically with the growth and development of coelenterates (including the formation of polymorphic variants). Other sections analyze growth processes in various invertebrate groups.

Best, J. B.: Protopsychology, *Sci. American,* Feb., 1963. A review of the interesting research on learning and memory in whole and regenerating planarians.

Brien, P.: The Fresh-water Hydra, *Am. Scientist,* vol. 48, 1960. A detailed examination of this common but atypical coelenterate.

Buchsbaum, R.: "Animals without Backbones," University of Chicago, Chicago, 1948. A beautifully illustrated introductory account of invertebrates, including types studied in the present chapter.

Chitwood, B. G.: Nematoda, in "McGraw-Hill Encyclopedia of Science and Technology," vol. 9, 1960. A concise, informative article by one of the foremost students of roundworms.

Lane, C. E.: Man-of-war, the Deadly Fisher, *Nat. Geographic,* March, 1963. A well-illustrated article on *Physalia.*

Lansing, A.: Experiments in Aging, *Sci. American,* Apr., 1953. A review of experiments showing that the longevity of a rotifer is determined by how old its parent was when the latter produced the egg that gave rise to the animal.

Moore, D. V.: Acanthocephala, in "McGraw-Hill Encyclopedia of Science and Technology," vol. 1., 1960. A good, short description of the biology of these worms.

Wilson, H. V., and **J. T. Penney**: Regeneration of Sponges from Dissociated Cells, *J. Exp. Zool.,* vol. 56, 1930. An account on the original experiments showing that loose sponge cells can migrate together and reconstitute a whole sponge.

chapter 12 coelomate groups: protostomes

category	branch	grade	subgrade	phylum	subphylum	class
metazoa	parazoa					
	eumetazoa	radiata				
		bilateria	acoelomata			
			pseudocoelomata			
			coelomata	phoronida		
				ectoprocta		
				brachiopoda		
				mollusca		amphineura
						gastropoda
						scaphopoda
						pelecypoda
						cephalopoda
				sipunculida		
				annelida		polychaeta
						archiannelida
						oligochaeta
						hirudinea
				echiuroida		
				oncopoda		
				arthropoda	chelicerata	xiphosurida
						pantopoda
						arachnida
					mandibulata	crustacea
						chilopoda
						diplopoda
						insecta
				chaetognatha		
				pogonophora		
				hemichordata		
				echinodermata		
				chordata		

Grade Bilateria

Subgrade Coelomata animals with true coelom, formed in various ways as a body cavity lined entirely by mesoderm

As pointed out in the preceding chapter, three groups of coelomates can be distinguished (see Fig. 11.8). In one, probably the most primitive, coeloms develop in various, largely unique ways. These animals also have a characteristic food-catching structure, a lophophore, and can therefore be referred to collectively as *lophophorates.* In a second group the coelom arises by a splitting of mesoderm into outer and inner portions. Animals with such *schizocoelic* body cavities comprise the *schizocoelomates.* In a last group the coelom consists of the spaces in the mesoderm sacs that grow out from the endoderm. Such animals with *enterocoelic* body cavities represent the *enterocoelomates.*

Lophophorates and schizocoelomates are the subject of this chapter. Like all the Bilateria discussed earlier these animals are again protostomial, with the mouth derived from the first embryonic opening.

Lophophorates

Phylum Phoronida phoronids; marine; wormlike tube dwellers; with horseshoe-shaped lophophore; excretion through metanephridia; with circulatory system; 16 species

Phylum Ectoprocta moss animals; marine and freshwater; microscopic, colonial, and often polymorphic; anus of U-shaped alimentary tract opens outside tentacle crown of lophophore; without circulatory or excretory systems; exoskeleton present; 5,000 species

Phylum Brachiopoda lamp shells; marine; with dorsal and ventral shell, often clamlike in appearance; with circulatory system, excretion through metanephridia; 300 species

The animals in these three phyla are sessile or sedentary *filter feeders;* they strain microscopic food organisms from their aquatic environment by means of ciliated tentacles (Fig. 12.1). These grow out in a row from a *lophophore,* a ridge of the body wall that curves around the mouth. The alimentary tract is U-shaped, as is common in sedentary animals, and the anus opens outside the lophophore region. None of these animals has a clearly distinct head region. The body is simply marked into a lophophore-bearing forepart and a trunk, each enclosing a portion of the coelom. In many cases a pair of fine, coiled ducts leads from the coelom to the body surface. Known as *metanephridia,* these

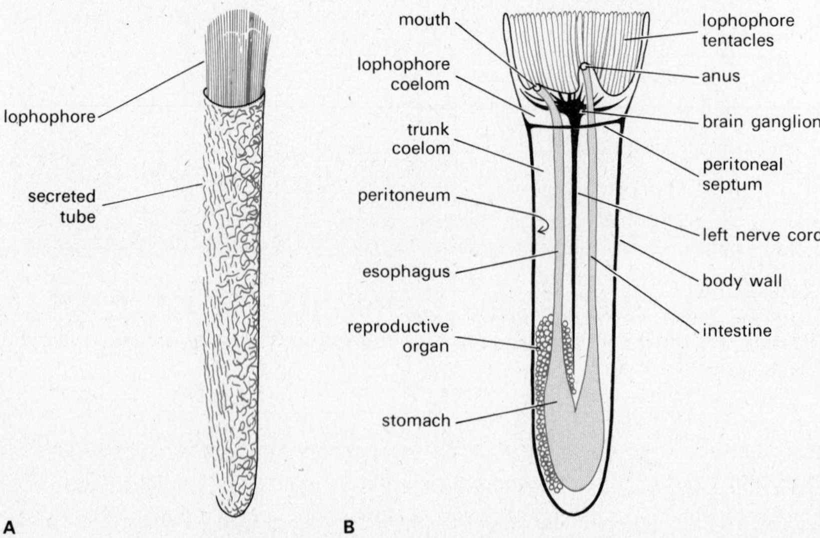

12.1 Phoronids. *A, the secreted tube of a phoronid, with the lophophore projecting at top. B, sagittal section through a worm, simplified. Note the two parts of the coelom separated by the peritoneal septum.*

__15. Physalia,__ the Portuguese man-of-war. Each tentacle suspended from the gas-filled float represents a portion of a single coelenterate individual. The several different types of tentacle here indicate the high degree of polymorphism exhibited by such colonies.

color figure 16

16. Cyanea, *a scyphozoan jelly fish.*

17. Anthozoan coelenterates. *A, top view of two sea anemones* (Actinia). *B, portion of a stony coral* (Astrangia), *with expanded polyps. C, skeleton of organ-pipe coral* (Tubipora). *D. skeleton of a sea fan* (Gorgonia). (*B, C, D, courtesy Carolina Biological Supply Company.*)

color figure 18

A

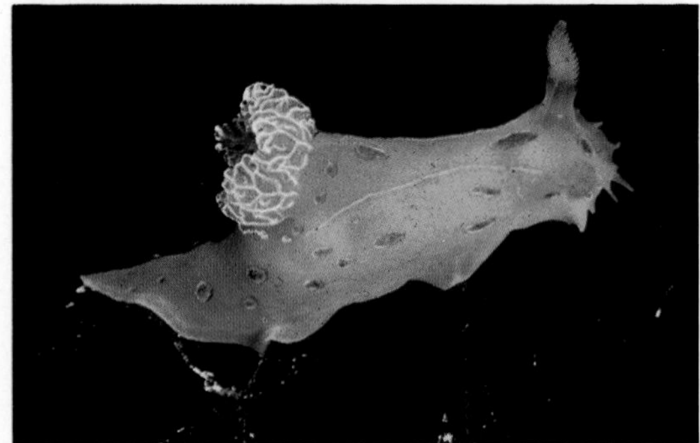

B

C

18. Snails. *A, a nudibranch* (Dirona). *B, a nudibranch sea slug* (Polycera). *Note the breathing rosette dorsoposteriorly. C, an edible, air-breathing land snail* (Helix pomatia). *(A, courtesy Carolina Biological Supply Company.)*

19. ***Mollusks.*** *A, a scalloplike clam* (Chlamys). *Note the small, light-blue ocelli on the fringed mantle along the shell edge. B, a rock-boring clam* (Pholadidea), *positioned in rock.*

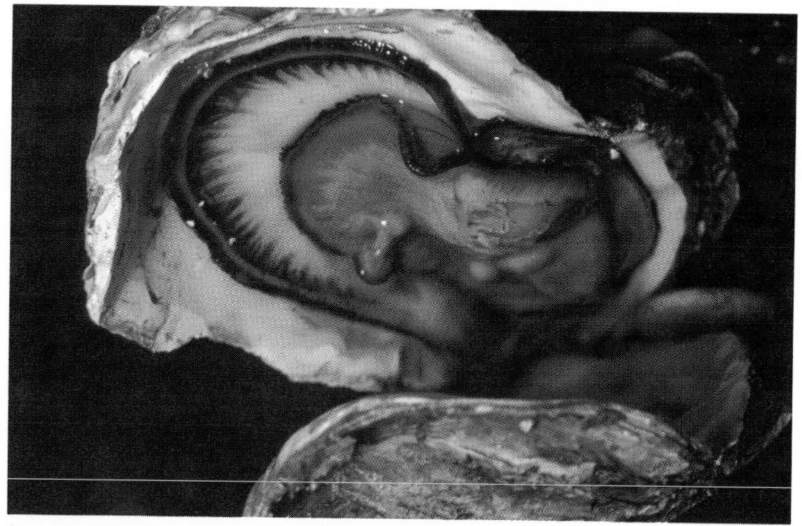

A

B

color figure 20

A

B

20. Polychaete annelids. *A, a clamworm* (Nereis) *at the breeding stage. The egg-filled heteronereis portion is the reddish part of the worm. B, anterior part of a palolo worm* (Leodice). *The animal swarms to the ocean surface at a particular night once a year and bursts, releasing its sperms or eggs. See also Color Fig. 13 for illustration of another polychaete. (A, courtesy Carolina Biological Supply Company.)*

A

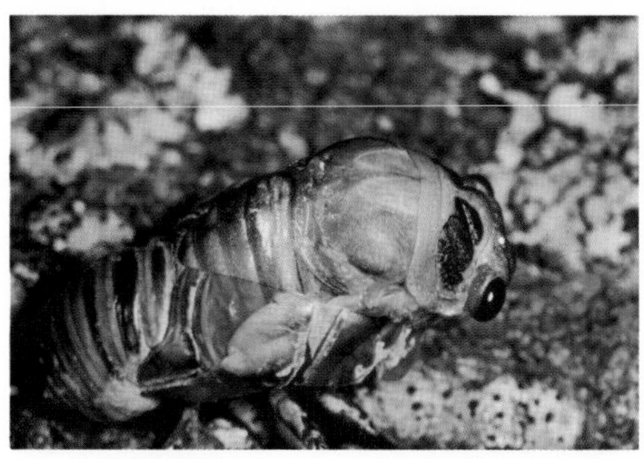

B

C

21. Molting, *as in a cicada, an exopterygote insect of the order Homoptera. A, larva with skin beginning to split along dorsal midline. B, adult emerging from larval skin. C, adult and discarded larval skeleton. (Courtesy Carolina Biological Supply Company.)*

color
figure
22

A

B

C

D

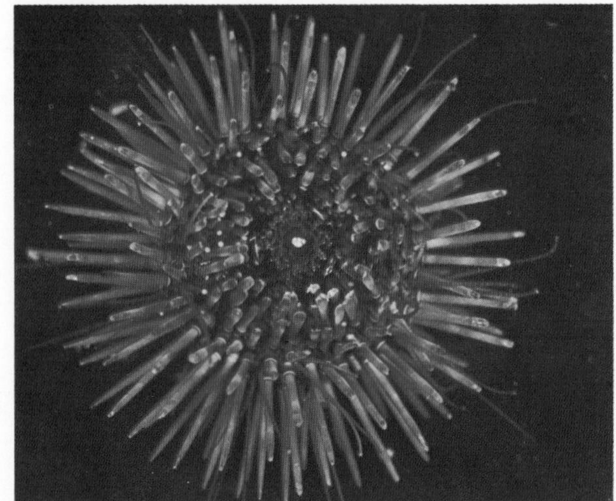

E

22. Echinoderms. *A, a crinoid feather star. B, a holothuroid sea cucumber. C, an asteroid prickly starfish. D, an ophiuroid brittle star. E, an echinoid sea urchin.*

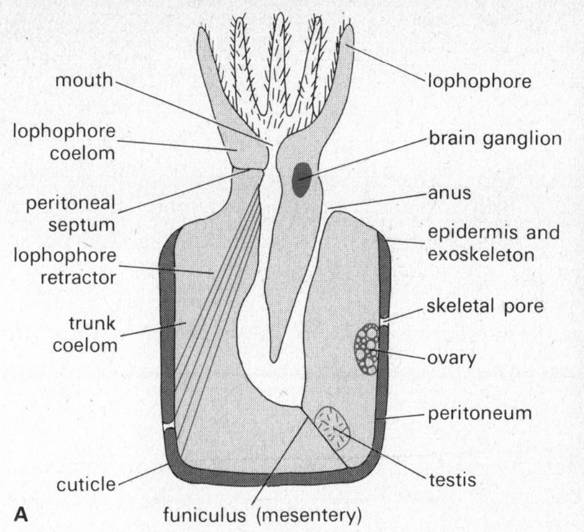

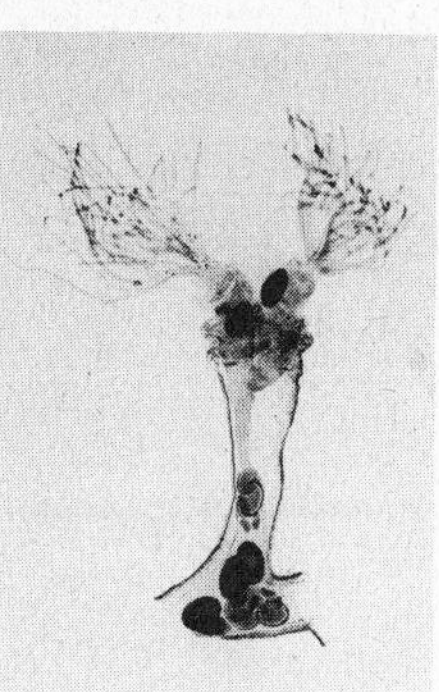

12.2 Ectoprocts. *A, diagrammatic section through a marine ectoproct with extended lophophore. The exoskeleton is calcareous. Note anus opening outside tentacle ring of lophophore. B, a colony of marine ectoprocts on algae. Each small oval represents a single individual as in A. C, a freshwater ectoproct. The exoskeleton is gelatinous. Note lophophore at top. The black oval bodies are statoblasts, reproductive cysts capable of developing into new individuals.*

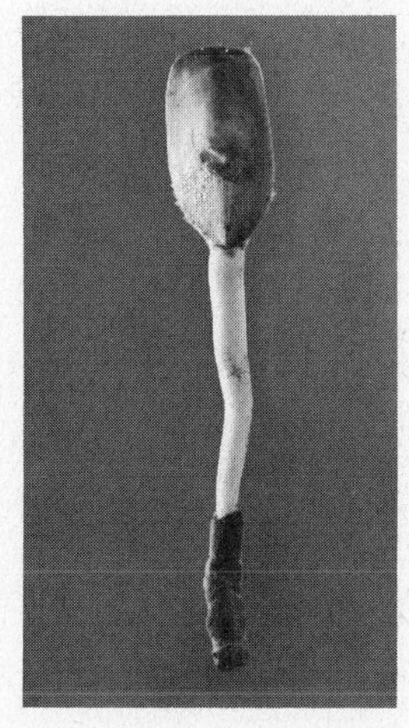

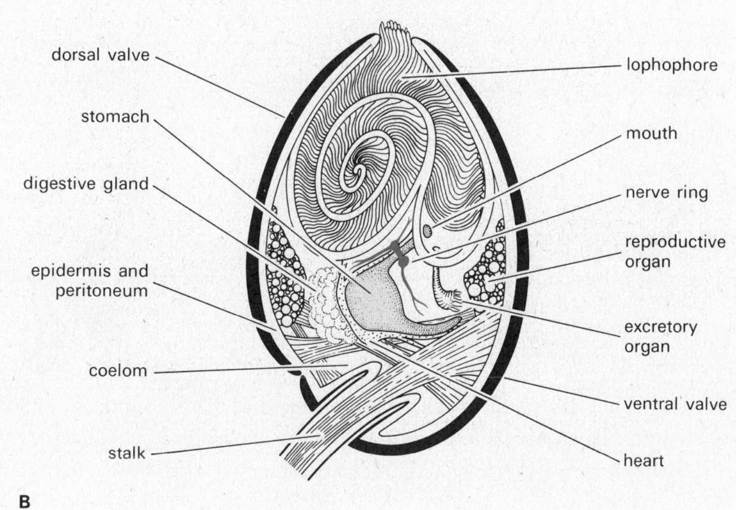

12.3 Brachiopods. *A, a specimen of Lingula. The stalk is normally buried vertically in sandy sea bottoms. The lophophore is under the shell (valve). B, sagittal section through a brachiopod. Note blind-ended intestine.*

are excretory channels (that often also serve as reproductive ducts). Lophophorates are without specialized breathing systems. Development includes free-swimming, ciliated larvae, of distinct types for each of the phyla.

Phoronids live in upright parchmentlike tubes, with the lophophore projecting from these housings. Ectoprocts (also called *Bryozoa*) have a superficial resemblance to ectoprocts. Marine types secrete boxlike calcareous exoskeletons and grow in extensive colonies on seaweeds, wharf pilings, and other solid objects. Freshwater ectoprocts secrete massive gelatinous housings (Fig. 12.2). Lamp shells resemble clams superficially (but the two shells are dorsal and ventral, not lateral as in clams). The lophophore tentacles can be protruded between the shells (Fig. 12.3). Each of the lophophorate phyla appears to represent a distinct evolutionary line, not obviously or closely related to any other coelomates. All three phyla were far more abundant in the past, and phoronids and brachiopods today have the status of evolutionary relics.

Schizocoelomates

Phylum Mollusca mollusks; marine, freshwater, and terrestrial; soft-bodied animals usually composed of *head,* ventral *foot,* and dorsal *visceral hump;* hump covered by a *mantle* and typically an *exoskeleton;* alimentary system with *radula* and digestive glands; breathing by gills; circulatory system with chambered heart and extensive blood spaces in body; excretion through renal organs; trochophore larvae followed in many cases by *veliger* stages; 50,000 species

Phylum Sipunculida peanut worms; marine; body with retractible forepart and trunk; alimentary tract recurved and coiled, anus anterodorsal; circulation rudimentary or absent; excretion metanephridial; 250 species

Phylum Annelida segmented worms; marine, freshwater, and terrestrial; typically with chitinous bristles; coelom and organs arranged segmentally; circulatory system usually closed; excretion metanephridial; 15,000 species

Phylum Echiuroida spoon worms; marine; segments in larva but unsegmented as adults; with proboscislike forepart; bristles few, coelom not partitioned; excretion metanephridial; 60 species

Phylum Oncopoda segmented claw-bearing animals; mostly terrestrial; 500 species

Phylum Arthropoda segmented jointed-legged animals; marine, freshwater, and terrestrial; with chitinous exoskeleton and compound eyes in most cases; circulatory system open; excretion various; 1 million species

Although they include adult types as different as clams, earthworms, and houseflies, the schizocoelomates basically exhibit very similar patterns of development. The mesoderm typically proliferates from endoderm-derived *teloblast* cells, and later the mesoderm splits into an outer layer along the body wall and an inner layer surrounding the alimentary tract. A schizocoelic body cavity forms in this manner. The basic larval form in all groups is a *trochophore* (Fig. 12.4). This stage can be either a ciliated, free-swimming larva or a late phase in the development of the embryo. Other larval forms often succeed the trochophore before the adult is produced.

Two main series of schizocoelomates appear to have evolved. An earlier one remained unsegmented and is represented by the first two phyla listed above. In a later series, represented by the last four

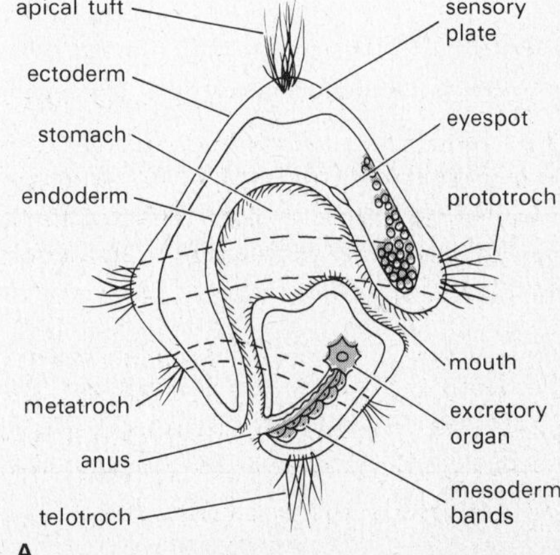

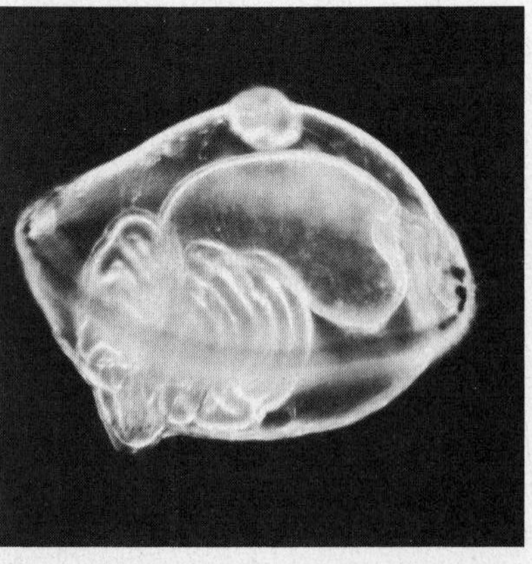

12.4 The trochophore larva, *sagittal section. Mesodermal structures in color. The prototroch and metatroch are circlets of long cilia (indicated by broken lines). A metatroch or telotroch is not necessarily present in all types of trochophores. B, late trochophore, from life; the mouth is toward the right.*

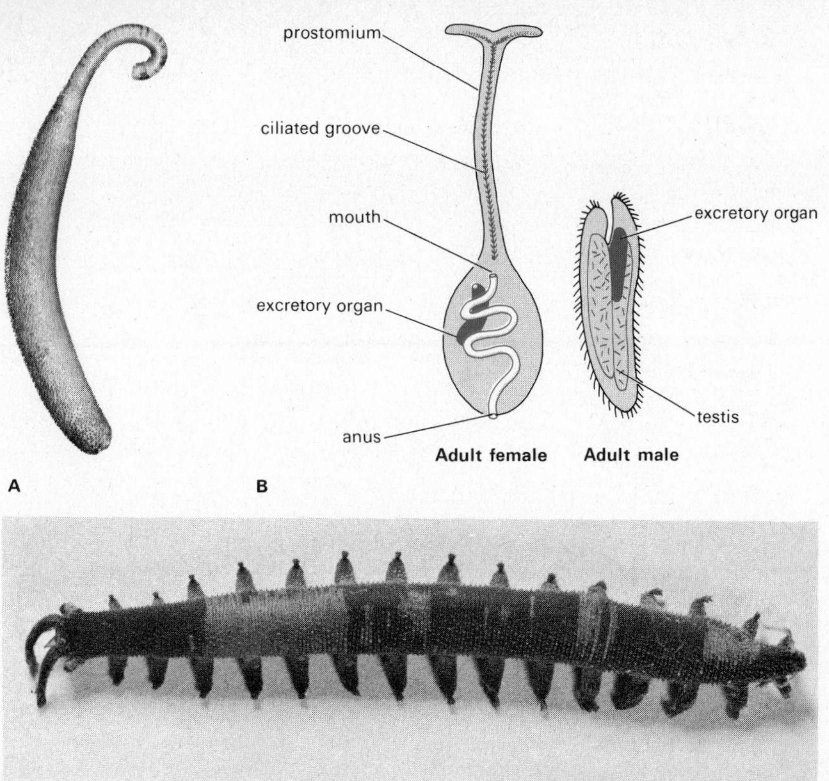

12.5 ***Various schizocoelomates.*** *A, a peanut worm, phylum Sipunculida. The curved tubular part is the so-called introvert, at the front end of the body. The mouth is at the tip. B, the spoonworm Bonellia, phylum Echiuroida. In the female the prostomium is a proboscis-like food-catching extension. Note the simplified structure of the parasitic male. It lives permanently inside the excretory organ of the female. C, Peripatus, of the phylum Oncopoda. The traits of this animal are transitional between those of annelids and those of arthropods. (A, courtesy Carolina Biological Supply Company.)*

phyla, body segmentation became more or less highly elaborated. The mollusks of the first series and the annelids and arthropods of the second are today among the most successful of all groups of living organisms (Fig. 12.5).

Mollusks

Phylum Mollusca soft-bodied animals

Class Amphineura chitons; marine; head reduced, without eyes or tentacles; 700 species

Class Gastropoda snails; marine, freshwater, and terrestrial; visceral hump typically coiled, with torsion or various degrees of detorsion; usually with shell; head with eyes and one or two pairs of tentacles; 35,000 species

Class Scaphopoda tusk shells; marine; shell tubular, open at both ends; foot a burrowing organ; 200 species

Class Pelecypoda clams; marine and freshwater; laterally compressed, with dorsally hinged shells; head rudimentary, foot usually tongue-shaped and burrowing; radula absent; gills usually expanded to ciliary feeding organs; 12,000 species

Class Cephalopoda squids, octopuses; marine; head with tentacles; shell either external and chambered or internal and reduced; nervous system exceedingly well developed; with cartilaginous endoskeleton; 500 species

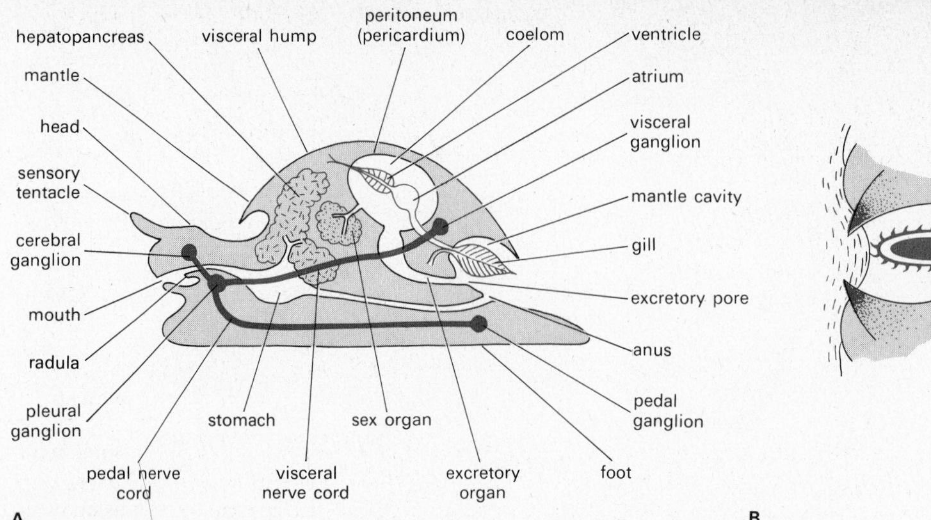

12.6 Mollusks: structural characteristics. *A, presumed structure of hypothetical ancestral mollusk in sagittal section. Of paired organs, only those on one side are indicated. Arteries from the ventricle lead to the blood sinuses in all parts of the body, and blood from there returns to the heart via the two excretory organs, the two gills, and the two atria of the heart. B, the molluscan radula, as in a squid. The radula is a horny band with recurved teeth and is moved back and forth by muscles around a cartilaginous supporting prop (dark oval). Unlike most mollusks, a squid also has horny jaws, as shown here.*

Ancestral mollusks that gave rise to the groups now in existence can be hypothesized to have had the following characteristics (Fig. 12.6).

The body consisted of a *head,* which may have borne a pair of sensory tentacles; a broad, ventral, muscular *foot* that functioned in a creeping form of locomotion; and a dome-shaped, dorsal *visceral hump,* which contained most of the organ systems. The body wall of the dome was a *mantle* that extended as an overhanging rim around the sides of the body, particularly at the posterior end. The space under this posterior rim represented a *mantle cavity.* Projecting into it were a pair of feathery or leaflike *gills.* The mouth led to a pharynx equipped with a *radula,* a horny band studded with recurved teeth. Muscles moved this band back and forth over a cartilaginous supporting rod in the pharynx. Protruded through the mouth, the radular apparatus served in rasping pieces of tissue from plant or animal food organisms. From the pharynx food passed through an esophagus to a stomach, which connected with a conspicuous digestive gland, or *hepatopancreas.* The intestine opened posteriorly into the mantle cavity.

The nervous system consisted of a nerve ring around the esophagus, thickened in places as *ganglia.* From this ring emanated two pairs of nerve cords, one pair (*pedal cords*) to the foot, another (*visceral cords*) to the dorsal hump. Ganglia were present at the ends of these cords. The ancestral mollusk probably had a circulatory system that contained a heart with one ventricle and two posterior atria, as well as vessels from and to the gills. Additional vessels passed to all other body regions and opened into free spaces, or *blood sinuses,* that permeated all organs. Such a system was an *open* circulation, blood here flowing in great part outside vessels. The coelom was largely reduced to a *pericardial cavity* around the heart. Leading to this coelomic space were the ducts of the sex organs, located anteriorly, and passing posteriorly were a pair of excretory (basically metanephridial) ducts. These led from the pericardial coelom to exit pores in the mantle cavity near the anus. Sex cells reached the outside through the excretory ducts.

This ancestral organization is still preserved to varying degrees in the mollusks now in existence.

Chitons
Class Amphineura

Chitons have deviated least from the ancestral construction. However, the head has become reduced, and tentacles and eyes are absent (Fig. 12.7). Eight overlapping shell plates secreted by

A

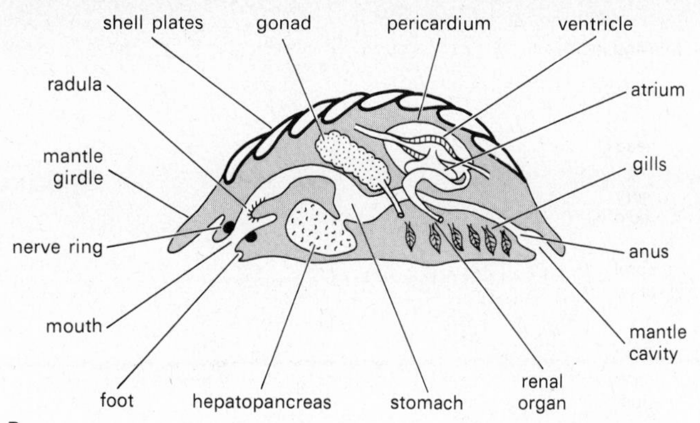

B

12.7 ***Chitons.*** *A, dorsal view. Note the eight shell plates in the mantle. B, sagittal section showing some of the internal structures.*

the mantle form an exoskeleton. A narrow groove circling the animal under the mantle rim represents the mantle cavity, and into it project many pairs of small gills. In conjunction with the head reduction the nervous system has become simplified, and the only other notable deviation from the ancestral pattern is the presence of separate reproductive ducts to the outside. This condition is characteristic also of all other mollusks, as is the elaboration of the excretory ducts as complex *renal organs.*

Chiton larvae are typical trochophores. They develop a foot between mouth and anus and then settle with the foot directed downward.

Snails
Class Gastropoda

In snails the ancestral construction is again largely preserved, but two innovations have evolved in the larval stages that give a snail its characteristic organization.

First, the trochophore develops into a *veliger,* a larval form equipped with an elaborate ciliary girdle used as a swimming organ (Fig. 12.8). The dorsal side of the veliger enlarges greatly and the developing visceral hump thus pushes up in a dorsal direction. This upward growth occurs unequally on the left and right sides, however, resulting in a spiral coiling of the visceral hump and the shell covering it. The upward growth also has the effect of pulling the alimentary tract to a U shape, until the anus comes to lie quite close to the mouth.

The second innovation is *torsion;* the whole visceral hump of the veliger rotates 180° relative to the rest of the body, usually in a counterclockwise direction (Fig. 12.9). As a result the mantle cavity comes to lie anteriorly above the head; the gills are anterior; the anus, excretory pores, and reproductive openings all are anterior, in the mantle cavity; the alimentary tract is twisted from a U shape to a loop; and the heart is turned around, the atria coming to lie in front of the ventricle.

In snails such as limpets and abalones, the left-right inequality of early growth is not too great and the internal organs then develop in pairs despite the coiling and later torsion (Fig. 12.10). But in periwinkles and whelks, for example, larval growth on the left side is suppressed to such an extent that the left organs fail to develop alto-

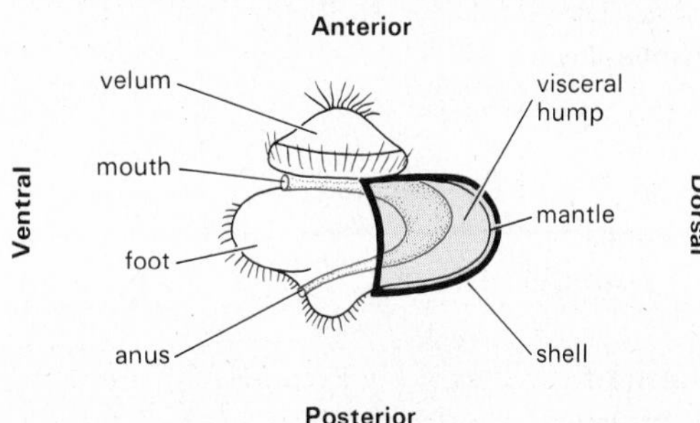

A

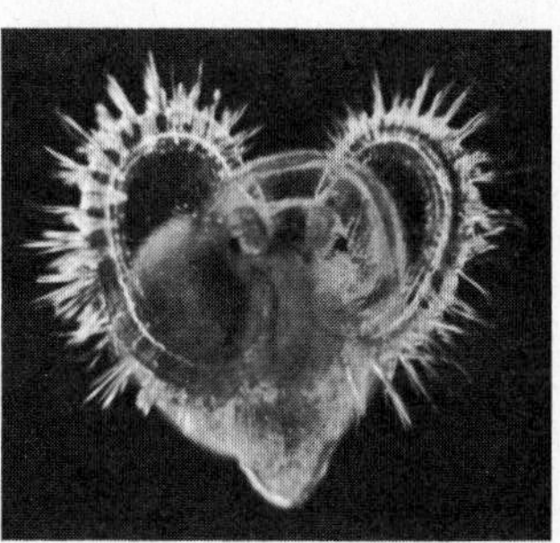

B

12.8 ***The veliger larva.*** *A, a mature veliger. Remnants of the earlier trochophore stage are still discernible anteriorly. The dorsal visceral hump has enlarged greatly, producing a U loop in the alimentary tract. B, veliger of a marine snail, from life. The view is from the anterior end, with the velum nearest and the dorsal visceral hump behind.*

12.9 ***Torsion and detorsion.*** *A, sagittal view of veliger after torsion. The alimentary tract is now coiled, with the anus shifted to same (anterior) side as mouth; compare with Fig. 12.8A. B–D, top views: B, original condition before torsion. Paired organs present, anus posterior. C, after torsion (comparable to A). Only right members of paired organs present (on left side), anus anterior, visceral cords form figure eight. D, 180° detorsion. Pattern resembles A, but only right members of paired organs are present.*

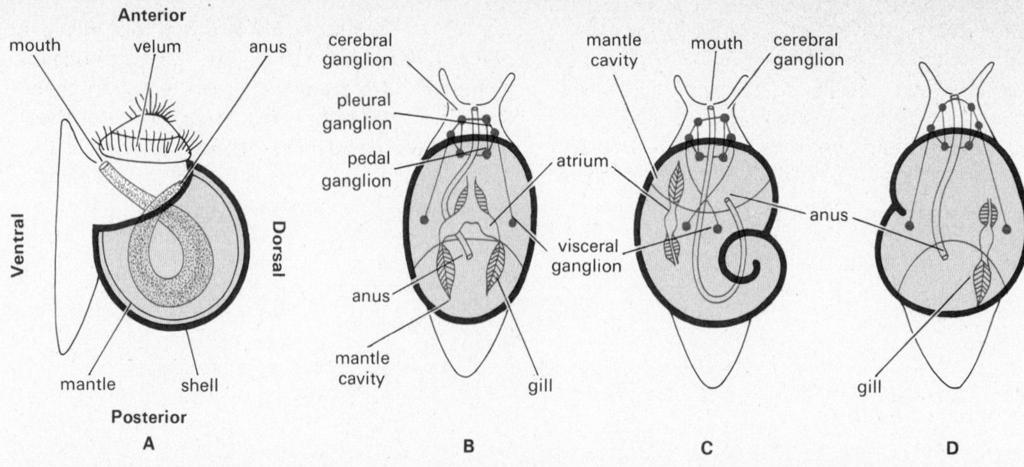

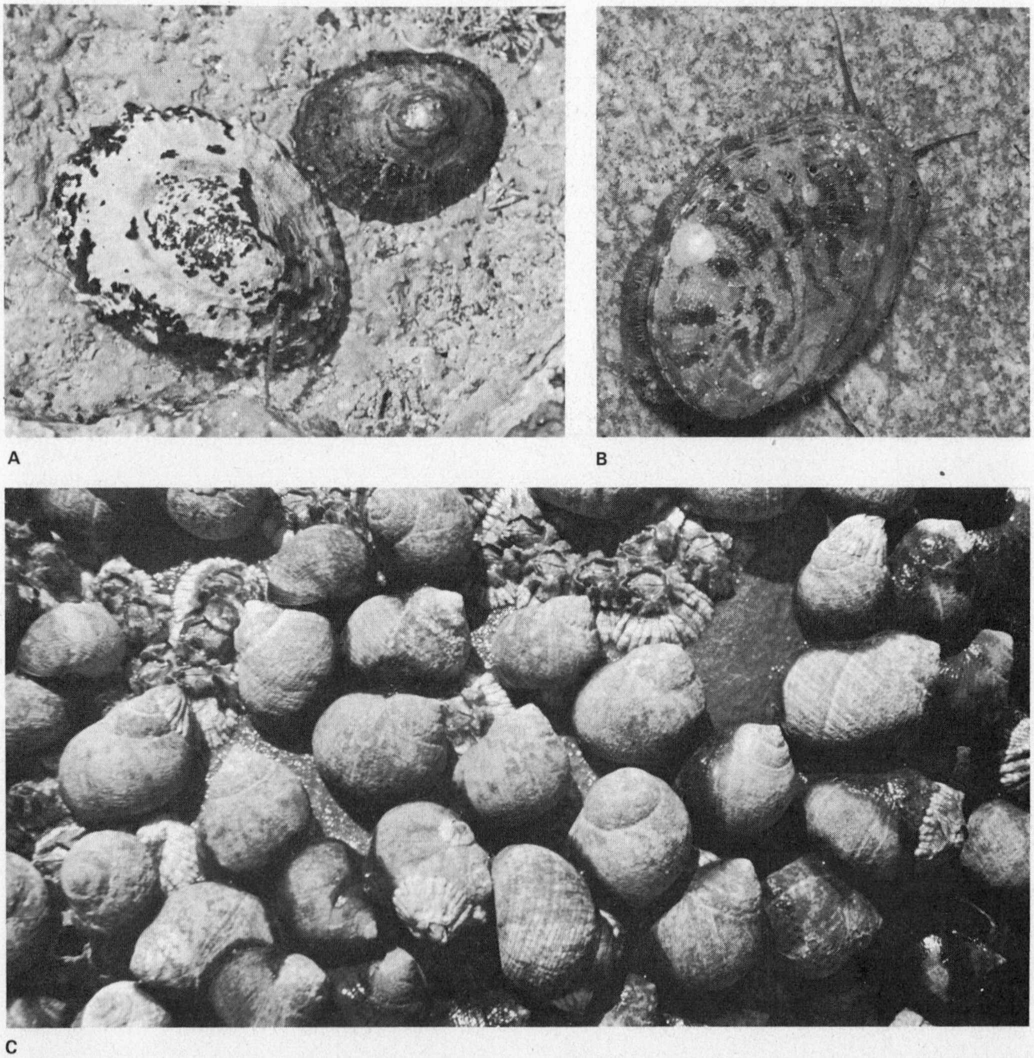

A

B

C

12.10 ***Snails.*** *A, limpets. The shell is hardly coiled. B, abalone. Shell coiling slight. Note row of shell perforations for excurrent water. C, periwinkles. Shell coiling pronounced. These snails live in tidal zones. See also Color Fig. 18.*

gether. Such snails have only one gill, one atrium, and one kidney, located on the left side after torsion. In some snails, notably the *nudibranchs,* shells are reduced or completely absent (Color Fig. 18). Development here includes a *detorsion* that brings the visceral hump back partly or wholly to its original larval position (see Fig. 12.9). In the land snails (a group that includes the edible garden snail *Helix*), the mantle cavity is modified from a gill chamber to a lung chamber, and such snails breathe air. Some of these types have adapted secondarily to aquatic life, but they are still lung-breathers and must surface periodically for air.

Tusk Shells
Class Scaphopoda

Like snails, the tusk shells have similarly elongated in a dorsal direction, but a coiling has not taken place. The scaphopod shell is tapered and tubular, giving the animals a tusklike appearance (Fig. 12.11). From the wider, ventral end of the shell projects a muscular conical foot, which serves as a digging organ. Also protruding from the ventral end is a reduced proboscislike head, to which are attached numerous prehensile tentacles.

12.11 A scaphopod, *as positioned in a sand burrow. Note tusklike shell, open at both ends. From the lower end projects a bulbous burrowing foot and a small head that bears prehensile tentacles.*

Clams
Class Pelecypoda

In clams the ancestral body has become flattened from side to side, the head has disappeared, and the gills have expanded to ciliary food-collecting organs that also retain a breathing function (Fig. 12.12).

The visceral mass of a clam is suspended from the dorsal midline. Continuous ventrally with the visceral mass is the foot, which in many cases can be protruded between the shells. Projecting into the mantle cavity are two pairs of large, platelike gills. These continue posteriorly as a horizontal partition that divides the hind region of the mantle cavity into a dorsal compartment and a ventral main compartment. Both open to

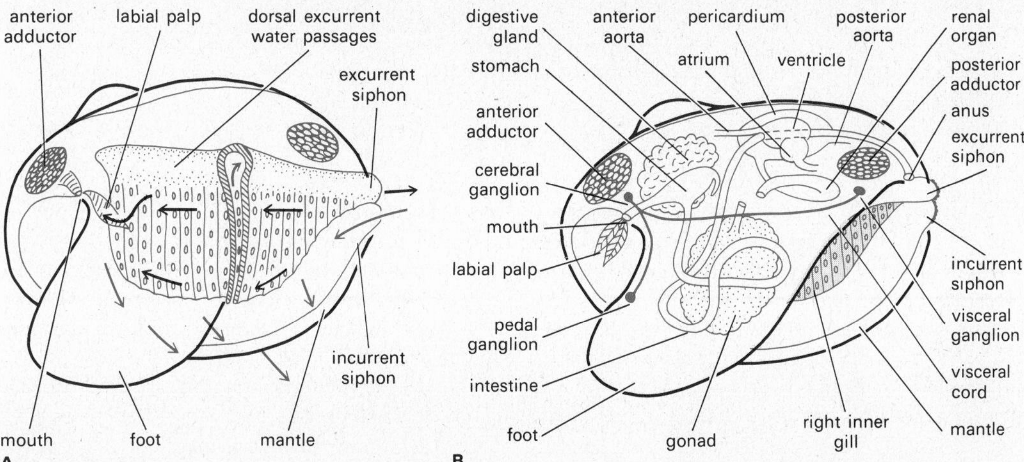

12.12 Clam structure. *A, the gills of the left side, the outer gill shown as a cutaway. Black arrows indicate ciliary paths of food particles toward mouth and of water into excurrent siphon via dorsal gill passage; colored arrows show paths of heavy particles not adhering to gill. B, some of the internal organs in sagittal view. The excretory and reproductive openings exit into the excurrent water passages.*

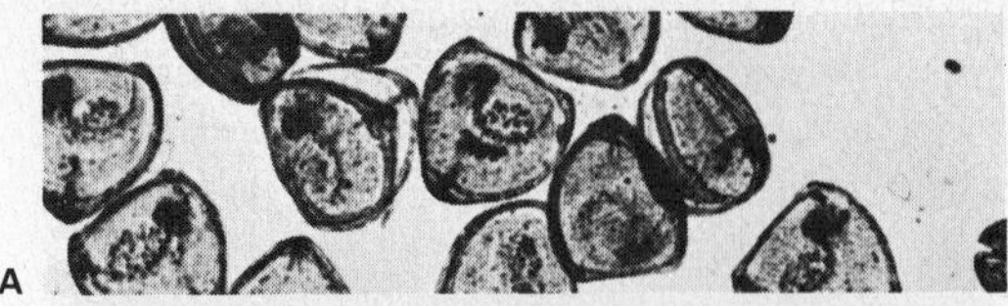
A

B

C

12.13 ***Clams.*** *A, glochidia larvae of a freshwater mussel. B, an adult freshwater clam. Note conspicuous burrowing foot. C, Tridacna, a giant clam. See also Color Fig. 19.*

the outside along the posterior shell edges, the dorsal chamber forming an *excurrent siphon,* the ventral one, an *incurrent siphon.* In some clams these siphons are extended as long retractile tubes that project beyond the valves.

Cilia on the gills draw food-bearing water through the incurrent siphon. Food caught up in mucus on the gills then passes forward to *labial palps,* tissue flaps that conduct food into the mouth. Water passes through the gills and leaves via the excurrent siphon. Clams lack a radula, a superfluous structure in a filter-feeding animal. The alimentary tract passes through the pericardial coelom, coils through the visceral mass, and opens to the excurrent siphon.

In conjunction with the reduction of the head, the nervous system is also reduced to some extent. Paired excretory organs lead from the pericardial coelom to the outgoing water current. The circulation is open. A ventricle in the pericardial coelom surrounds the intestine, and arteries from there pass to open blood sinuses in all body parts. The blood collects in veins, which carry it through the kidneys and gills, and oxygenated blood then returns from the gills to two atria of the heart.

The sex organs are formless masses around the intestinal coils. Reproductive ducts discharge into the outgoing water current. Marine clams develop via free-swimming trochophore and veliger larvae. Freshwater types produce highly modified veligers called *glochidia.* These larvae perish unless they can attach themselves within a short time to fish gills or fins, where they live parasitically until they become independent adults (Fig. 12.13).

Most clams are semisedentary, partly or wholly buried in mud, with the siphon protruding up to clear water. Some are permanently attached, as for example oysters and also giant clams, which can be 2 yd wide and weigh $\frac{1}{4}$ ton (Color Fig. 19).

Squids, Octopuses
Class Cephalopoda

These animals exhibit the most pronounced departures from the ancestral construction. Early cephalopods elongated in a dorsal direction (like snails), but growth remained equal on both sides and the visceral hump therefore formed a flat coil. Also, the covering shell became partitioned into progressively larger compartments as the animal grew, and only the last, largest compartment was occupied by the animal. All earlier compartments were filled with air (Fig. 12.14). Cephalopods thus had considerable buoyancy, which permitted them to adopt a free-swimming existence. In conjunction with this new mode of life the foot became modified partly to muscular prehensile tentacles, which also equipped the animals as predatory carnivores. The chambered nautilus today still exemplifies this early stage of cephalopod evolution. In other evolutionary lines the shells became reduced greatly or were lost altogether, and the nervous and sensory systems became highly developed in conjunction with rapid, swimming locomotion. The result was the emergence of modern squids and octopuses.

In a squid, a thick muscular mantle surrounds the visceral mass (Fig. 12.15). Under this mantle on the upper side lies a horny, leaf-shaped *pen,* the remnant of the shell. The forward edge of the mantle, or *collar,* fits over a midventral tubular *funnel* that leads to the mantle cavity. On contraction of the mantle muscles the collar clamps tightly around the funnel, and water is forced from the mantle cavity out through the funnel tube. In this manner a squid jet-propels in the opposite direction.

A squid has 10 tentacles. One long pair catches prey, and the others hold the prey while powerful horny *jaws* in the mouth bite chunks out of it. A radula is also present. The alimentary tract is U-shaped and includes a stomach to which a large digestive gland is connected. The anus opens anteriorly into the mantle cavity. An *ink sac* discharges into the mantle cavity via the anus. Expelled through the funnel, a cloud of ink probably distracts an enemy while the squid makes its escape.

In the highly developed nervous system several fused pairs of ganglia form a complex brain, which is surrounded by a cartilage capsule. Located between the eyes, the brain represents the dorsal part of a nerve ring that encircles the esophagus. From the ring elaborate tracts of nerves lead throughout the body. The eyes of squids are as complex as those of vertebrates. Breathing is accomplished by a pair of feathery gills in the mantle cavity. The circulation is closed—blood flows entirely inside vessels. A heart ventricle pumps blood throughout the body, and returning blood passes first through the kid-

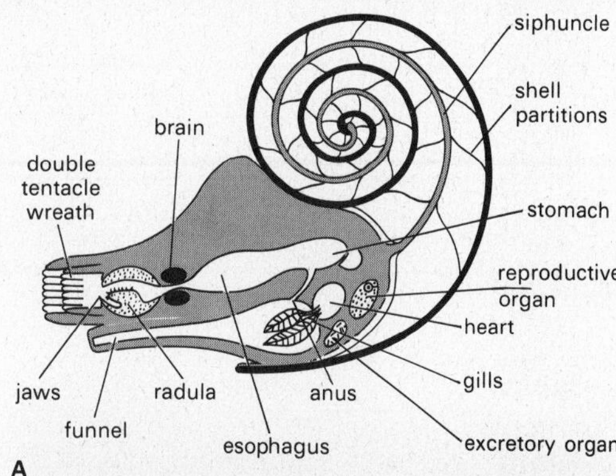

12.14 The chambered nautilus. *A, sectional view showing position of some of the organs. Note double circlet of tentacles and absence of ink sac. Gills shown on one side only. B, section through shell. Note partitioned compartments and the siphuncle, a gas-filled channel.*

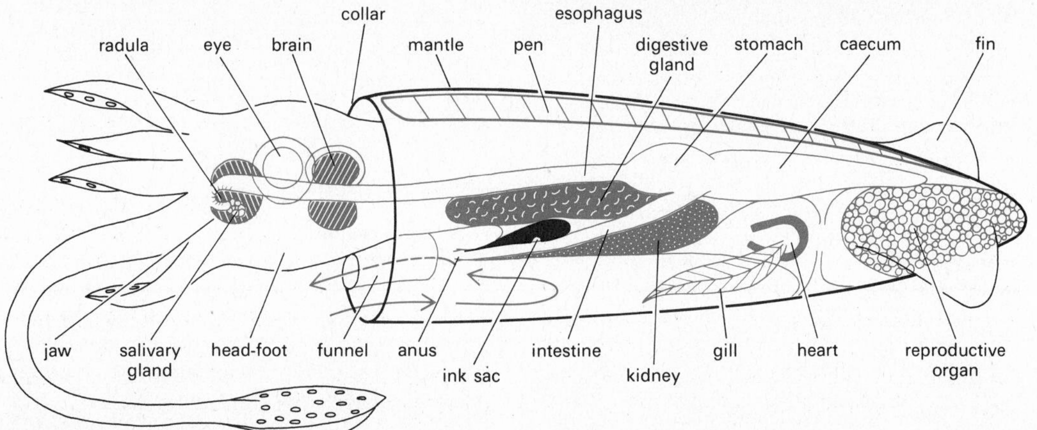

12.15 Squid structure. *Tentacles are shown on left side only. Arrows indicate path of water into and out of mantle cavity, resulting in jet propulsion backward. Note that the head-foot end is anatomically ventral, the hind end, dorsal; the side where the pen is located is anterior, the opposite side, posterior.*

A

B

12.16 ***Squids and octopuses.*** *A, a cuttlefish. B, an octopus. Note funnel below right eye.*

neys and then through *gill hearts* to the gills. Oxygenated blood circulates from the gills back to the main heart. The coelom is spacious and occupies the hind part of the visceral mass. A single sex organ and a pair of kidneys in the coelom open through separate ducts into the mantle cavity.

Cephalopods are without larvae; encased fertilized eggs are shed and develop directly into miniature adults. Squids are all active swimmers, and the up to 60-ft-long giant squids are the largest invertebrate animals. Octopuses, many of which lack an internal shell entirely, lead a semisedentary life. Most of them are quite small, but the largest have an arm spread of about 30 ft (Fig. 12.16).

Annelids

Phylum Annelida segmented worms

Class Polychaeta clamworms, tube worms; largely marine; with segmental parapodia, numerous bristles; with trochophore larvae

Class Archiannelida marine, some parasitic; structurally simplified; without external segmentation; parapodia and bristles generally absent; with epidermal ciliation

Class Oligochaeta earthworms; terrestrial and freshwater; head reduced; parapodia absent, few bristles; without larvae

Class Hirudinea leeches, mostly freshwater parasites; parapodia and bristles absent; number of segments fixed; without larvae

The segmentation of the annelid body affects all organ systems except the alimentary tract, and the coelom too is partitioned segmentally by peritoneal membranes (*septa*). Best seen in polychaetes, the most primitive annelids, segmental development begins with a marked posterior elongation of the trochophore larva (Fig. 12.17). This extension is accompanied by a forward growth of the mesodermal teloblast band on each side. The bands produce a series of paired cell clusters (*somites*), which later hollow out and become segmental coelom sacs. Segments mature in anteroposterior succession, the anterior segments being the oldest. In each larval segment ventral ingrowths from the ectoderm give rise to segmental portions of the nervous system and to metanephridia. Laterally the ectoderm and mesoderm fold out as a *parapodium,* a flap of body wall one each side. Stiff chitinous bristles (*setae*) later develop on the parapodia. Blood vessels, muscles, and sex organs form from parts of the peritoneal mesoderm.

In an adult polychaete such as *Nereis,* the common clamworm, the first segment is the head, or *prostomium,* which bears eyes and paired sensory tentacles (Fig. 12.18). The second segment is a *peristomium,* which contains the mouth and often additional sensory tentacles. The mouth leads to an eversible pharynx armed with chitinous jaws. Behind the pharynx an esophagus with digestive glands continues as an intestine, and the tract terminates at the anus in the last segment of the body.

With the exception of the head and anal segments, all others are more or less alike (Fig. 12.19). Each bears a pair of parapodia, and the bristles on these fleshy lobes serve mainly as locomotor levers and holdfast spikes. Internally, the nervous system is ladderlike. A nerve ring around the pharynx is thickened dorsally as brain ganglia, and ventrally a pair of longitudinal cords passes to the hind end of the body. The cords have lateral branches and thickened ganglia in each segment. In the blood circulation, a longitudinal dorsal and ventral vessel are interconnected in each segment by transverse systems that include capillary nets in the alimentary tract, the parapodia, and the other segmental organs. Blood flows forward dorsally by wavelike contractions of the dorsal vessel, backward ventrally. Breathing occurs through the epidermis, particularly in the parapodia, which move back and forth and thereby circulate water around the body. The segmental metanephridia open near the bases of the parapodia.

Polychaetes generally spend most of their time in sand or mud burrows or they live in secreted tubes (Fig. 12.20 and see Color Fig. 13). During the breeding season the hind portions of many polychaetes develop enlarged parapodia and long swimming bristles, and the coeloms in these segments fill with sperms or eggs. On certain fixed nights, determined in part by environmental factors such as the amount of moonlight in a particular month of the year, the posterior sexual parts of the worms (called *heteronereis* in clamworms) became detached and swarm to the surface of the sea. There they burst, and the released sex cells participate in fertilization. The nonswarming body parts soon regenerate the lost regions (Color Fig. 20).

Archiannelids are a small group of simplified worms in which many larval traits are retained in the adult. Such permanently trochophoral traits include, for example, absence of external seg-

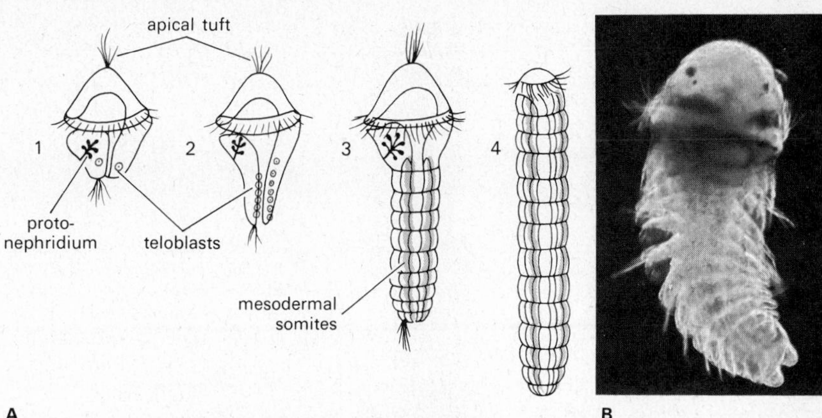

12.17 (*Above*) **Annelid development.** *A1, trochophore. 2, posterior elongation, proliferation of teloblastic mesoderm bands. 3, mesodermal somites forming. 4, later stage in segmental development, reduction of larval head structures. B, larva of marine annelid, corresponding roughly to stage 3 in A.*

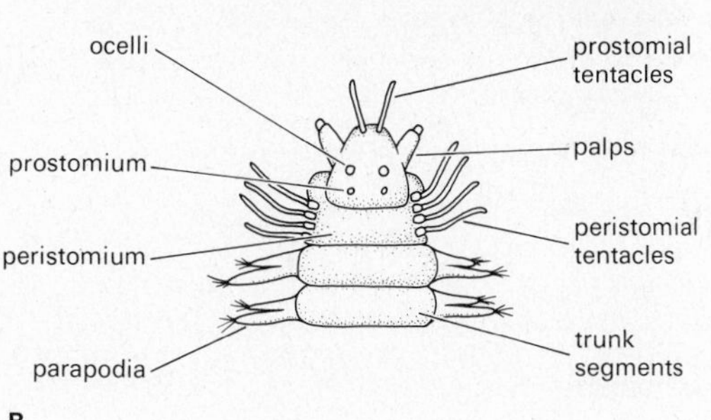

12.18 ***Nereis,*** *the clamworm, external features. A, whole animal. B, head region, dorsal view, pharynx retracted and not visible. See also Color Fig. 20.*

mentation, parapodia, or bristles. Internal segmentation is well developed, however. The group undoubtedly represents an offshoot from polychaete ancestors.

Similarly derived from early polychaetes are the earthworms. These burrowing, detritus-feeding animals are without eyes, head, appendages, or parapodia, and the segmental bristles are reduced to four pairs (Fig. 12.21). In the alimentary tract, an esophagus behind the pharynx carries paired *lime glands,* which regulate the calcium balance between swallowed earth and blood. Behind the

12.19 Polychaete structure. *A, schematic cross section through trunk segment. Parapodium shown only on one side. Note the blood-vessel pattern, with capillary beds in the parapodia and the intestine. Blood flows from the dorsal to the ventral vessel in the anterior segments, in the reverse direction in the posterior segments. B, scheme of the anterior portion of the (ladder-type) nervous system.*

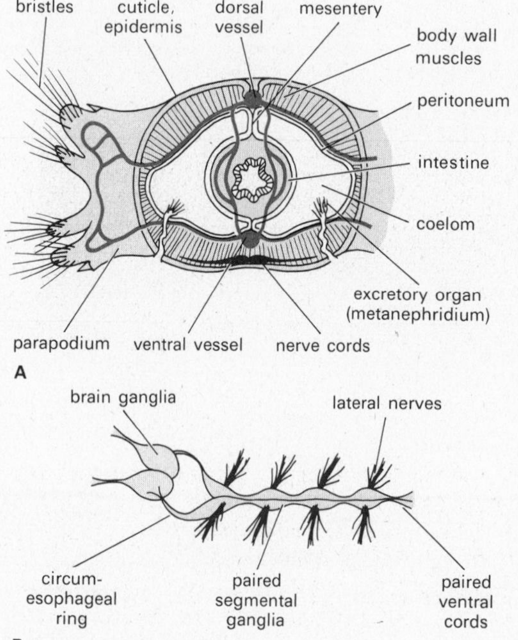

12.20 Tube-secreting polychaetes. *Shown here is a model of a section through the tube of the parchment worm Chaetopterus. The head of the animal is at left. Note the greatly elaborated parapodia. Between the arms of the U tube is a sipunculid. Tube dwellers are illustrated also in Color Fig. 13.*

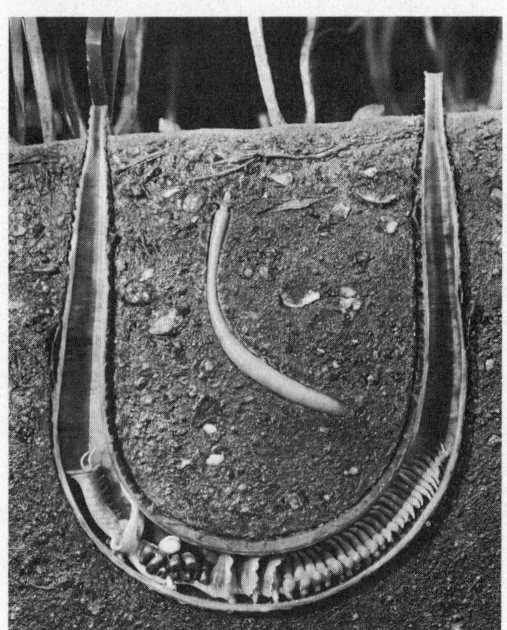

12.21 *(Below)* **Earthworm structure.** *A, cutaway diagram of anterior body region, segments numbered. Segment 12 and all segments behind it contain on each side a transverse vessel (shown in cutaway view) that interconnects the dorsal and subneural longitudinal blood vessels. B, cross section through an earthworm. Note the epidermis, the body wall muscles, the intestine with the deep, dorsal typhlosole fold, the dorsal blood vessel just above it and the ventral vessel below it, and portions of the metanephridial tubes in the coelom to each side of the intestine.*

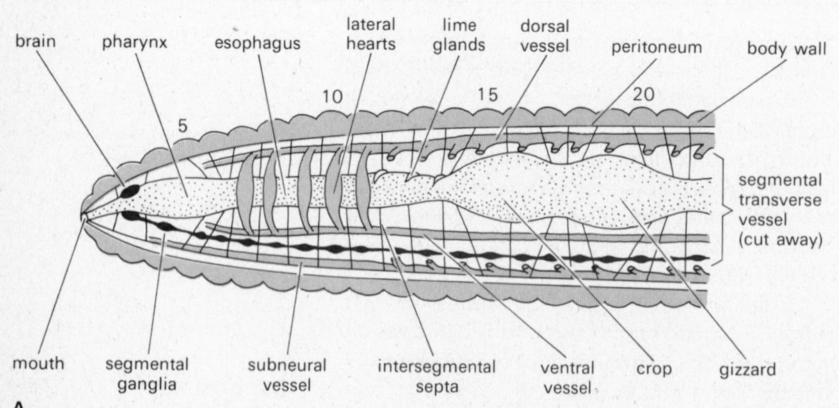

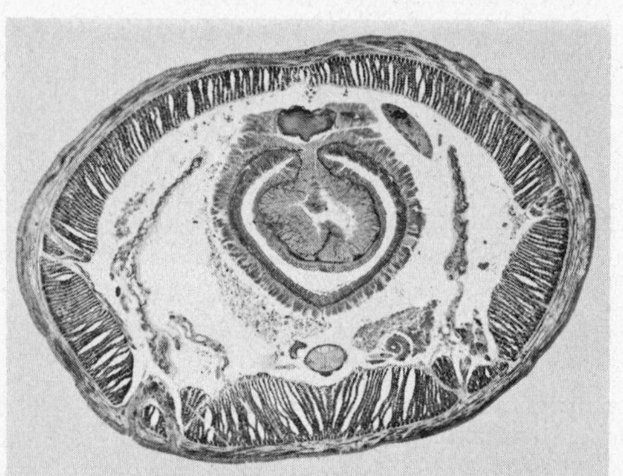

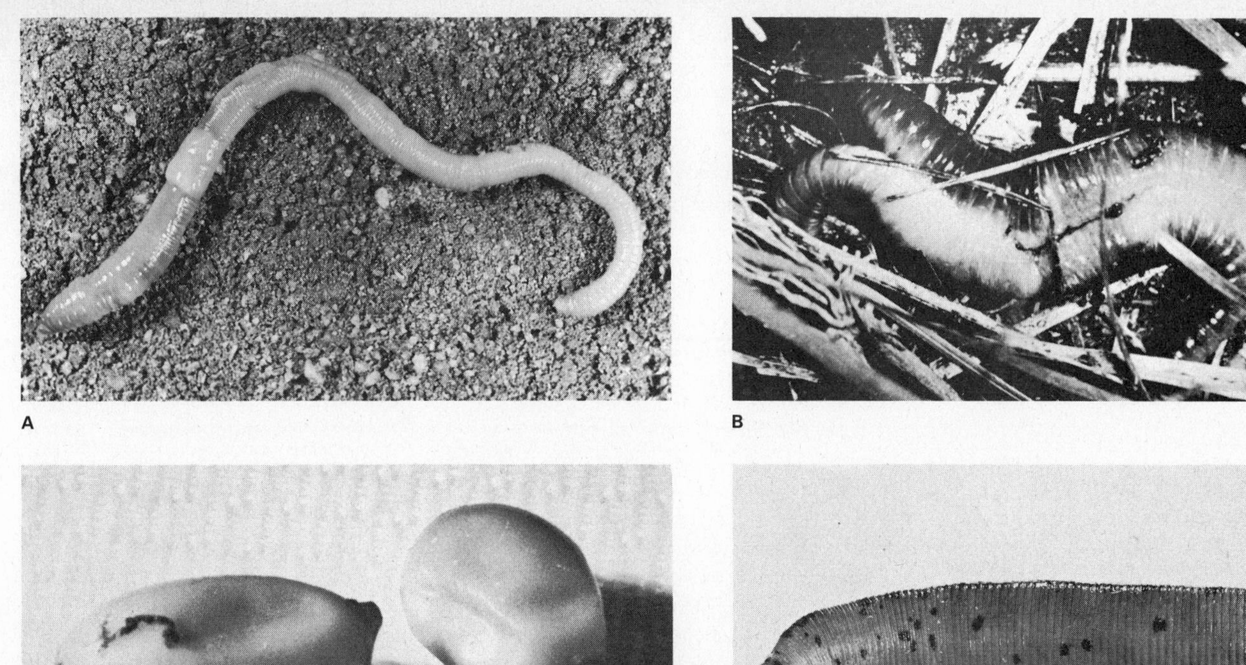

esophagus is an earth-storing *crop,* and behind it a muscular *gizzard* grinds swallowed earth. In the intestine a dorsal fold (*typhlosole*) increases the nutrient-absorbing area. The blood circulation is maintained by five pairs of contractile vessels ("hearts") that join the dorsal and ventral main vessels (in segments 7 to 11). In addition to segmental metanephridia, earthworms also contain excretory *chloragogue* cells in the peritoneum and the coelomic fluid. Such cells are carried to the body wall, where the excretion products are deposited as pigments.

Unlike polychaetes, each earthworm contains both male and female reproductive systems, and the animals mate by copulation. Shed sperms and eggs become encased in a mucus cocoon secreted by the *clitellum,* a thickened glandular band in the epidermis of each animal (in segments 31 to 37). Fertilized eggs in such cocoons then develop without free larval stages directly into new worms (Fig. 12.22).

Leeches are probably evolutionary offshoots of ancestral earthworms. In most leeches bristles are absent, suckers typically occur at both ends of the body, and the number of internal segments is fixed at 34. Externally the body surface exhibits ringlike creases that are more numerous than, and do not correspond to, the true internal segments. Most leeches are blood suckers of fishes and other vertebrates. In such an ectoparasite the alimentary tract contains numerous side branches that can hold up to 10 times as much blood as the weight of the leech itself. An animal can survive as long as 9 months from a single feeding. The worms feed by cutting through host skin with sawlike mouth structures. As blood is then ingested, *hirudin* is secreted into the wound, and this anticoagulant prevents blood from clotting. Many of the blood suckers normally survive carnivorously on worms and other small invertebrates. Some leeches actually are nonparasitic altogether.

12.22 Annelid types. *A, an earthworm. Note unsegmented clitellum at roughly one-third the length from the anterior end. During mating the clitellum secretes mucus, which comes to surround fertilized eggs as an egg cocoon. B, two earthworms in copulation. C, cocoons of earthworms. D, a leech. Note sucker at each end and the external transverse creases of the body. These are more numerous than the true internal segments. (C, D, courtesy Carolina Biological Supply Company.)*

Arthropods

Phylum Arthropoda jointed-legged animals

Subphylum Chelicerata body with cephalothorax, generally unsegmented, and abdomen, either segmented or not; cephalothorax typically with six pairs of appendages; first pair *cheliceras,* second pair *pedipalps,* last four pairs *walking legs;* jaws or antennae not present; *horseshoe crabs, sea spiders, arachnids*

Subphylum Mandibulata body with cephalothorax and abdomen, or head, thorax, and abdomen, or head and trunk; cephalothorax or head unsegmented externally; thorax, abdomen, or trunk segmented; head with one or two pairs of *antennae,* one pair of jaws (*mandibles*), two pairs of *maxillae; crustaceans, centipedes, millipedes, insects*

More arthropod types are known than all other living types combined. In the class of insects the order of beetles alone includes 300,000 species, which makes this order larger than any other *phylum* of organisms. According to one estimate some 10 million insect species may actually exist; about 7,000 new ones are described every year.

The unrivaled success of the phylum is a consequence of the basic arthropod construction, of which the essential features are the segmental organization and the chitinous exoskeleton. In all probability the ancestors of arthropods were early stocks of polychaete annelids, and during their evolution in the arthropod direction the segments of different body regions became elaborately specialized in different ways (Fig. 12.23). The arthropod body now consists of a *head,* a *thorax,* and an *abdomen,* and in many cases head and thorax are fused as a *cephalothorax.* The whole is covered by a chitinous armor that is molted periodically during larval growth or throughout life. The ancestral parapodia became distinct *segmental appendages* of a wide variety of forms and functions, the chitin cover here providing rigidity as well as joint connections.

Chitin also contributed to the development of the unique *compound eyes,* in which numerous complete visual units are grouped together as large composite structures. Each visual unit contains its own chitinous lens and light-sensitive cells. Arthropods in addition have *simple eyes,* in each of which a single lens covers a group of light-sensitive cells (Fig. 12.24).

Internally, the alimentary tract consists of foregut, midgut, and hindgut (Fig. 12.25). The first and last portions have a chitin lining continuous with the exoskeleton, and only the midgut functions digestively. Large digestive glands usually open to the midgut. Breathing is accomplished by *gills, book gills, book lungs,* or *tracheal systems,* all chitinous and segmentally arranged outgrowths or ingrowths from the body surface. Gills, characteristic of crustaceans, are feathery extensions from legs and other segmental appendages. Book gills of horseshoe crabs and book lungs of spiders and scorpions are chambers containing chitinous breathing plates resembling the pages of a book, the gills operating in water, the lungs in air. And tracheal systems, as in centipedes and insects, are interconnecting air ducts that lead from the body surface to all interior body parts (see below).

Segmental coelom sacs arise in the embryo but disappear later, leaving an unlined body cavity that represents a blood sinus; a dorsal tubular and open-ended heart is the main and often the only blood vessel. Excretion takes place mainly through two kinds of organs. Aquatic arthropods excrete through (variously named) tubular organs that open at the bases of certain segmental appendages—for example, at the antennal bases

12.23 Arthropod structure. *Lateral view of a wasp showing general segmental structure. Head is externally unsegmented and bears antennae, eyes, and mouth parts. The thorax, consisting of three segments in insects, bears three pairs of legs (one per segment) and two pairs of wings (on the second and third thoracic segments). The abdomen in insects typically consists of 11 segments and is without appendages. Numbers of segments and types of appendages vary considerably for different arthropod groups, but sets of mutually different segments are present in all.*

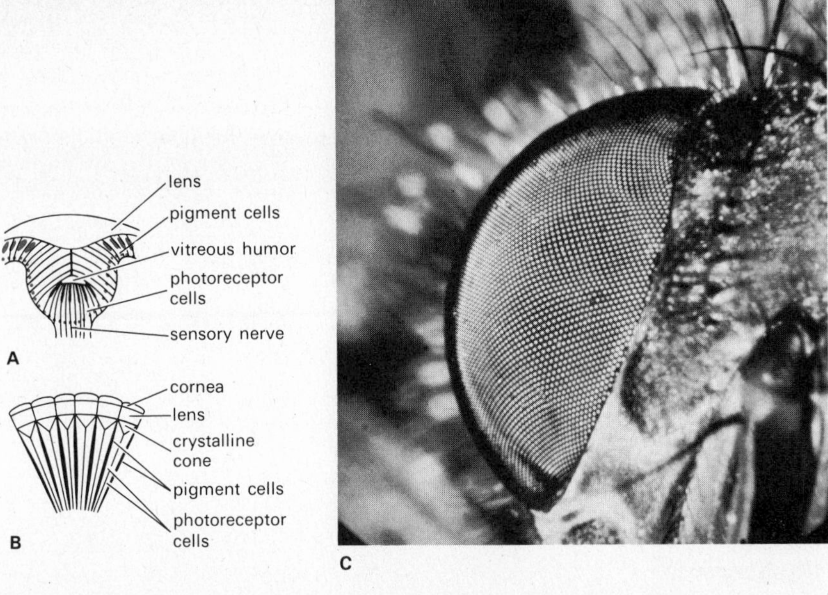

12.24 Arthropod eyes. *A, schematic section of a simple eye. B, several visual units (ommatidia) of a compound eye. One of these units is labeled; hundreds of them are usually present in a whole compound eye, as shown in C.*

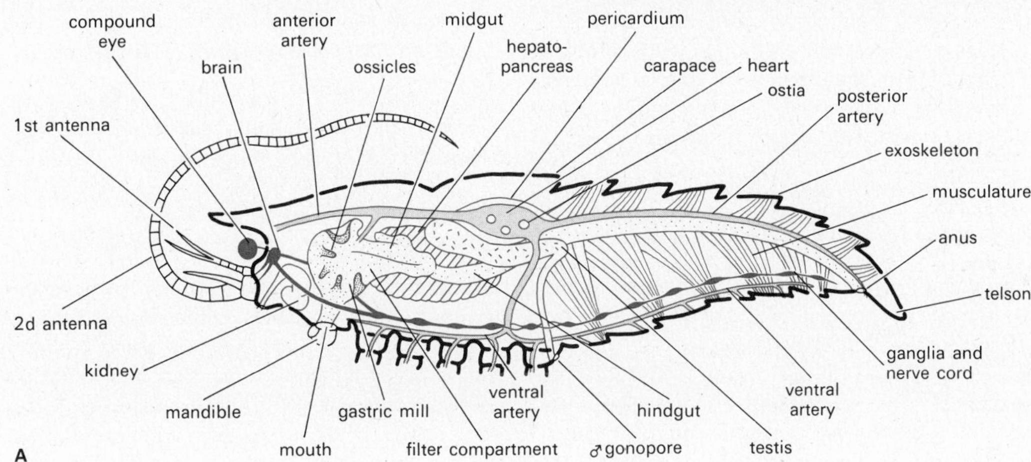

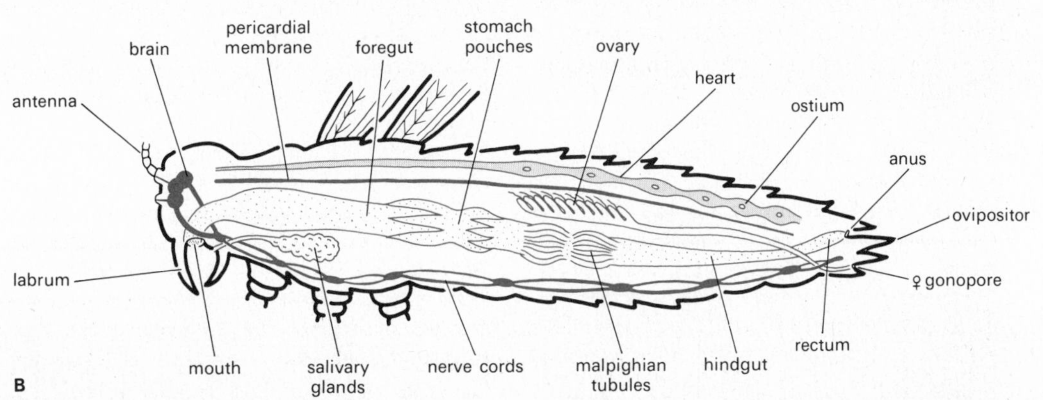

12.25 Internal arthropod structure. *A, lobster. B, grasshopper. In the lobster stomach, chitinous teeth in the gastric mill grind coarse food. A filter compartment then passes finely divided food through the short midgut into the digestive gland (hepatopancreas) for absorption.*

in lobsters. Terrestrial types have *Malpighian tubules* attached to and opening into the hindgut.

The nervous system is basically of the ladder type and annelidlike. Arthropods also have endocrine systems that consist of hormone-secreting cells in the brain and a number of glands near the eyes and in the thorax. The hormones play a major role in, for example, control of molting and development. Arthropod embryos typically pass through annelidlike, wormlike phases, and in some cases even larvae (caterpillars) or adults (centipedes) are still wormlike. Other groups produce larvae of a variety of types.

Two main evolutionary lines of arthropods are in existence today, each with aquatic and terrestrial representatives. One line, the subphylum Chelicerata, includes the aquatic horseshoe crabs and sea spiders and the terrestrial arachnids. The second line, the subphylum Mandibulata, comprises the aquatic crustaceans and the terrestrial centipedes, millipedes, and insects. (A third and most ancient evolutionary line, the aquatic trilobites, has been extinct for 200 million years; see Chap. 29).

Chelicerates
Subphylum Chelicerata

Class Xiphosurida (Merostomata) horseshoe crabs; marine; cephalothorax with carapace hinged to fused abdomen; telson a spine; breathing by book gills; with compound eyes; development with larvae; 5 species

Class Pantopoda (Pycnogonida) sea spiders; head and thorax with long, thin legs; abdomen reduced; compound eyes absent; egg-carrying legs on head of both sexes; 500 species

Class Arachnida scorpions, spiders, ticks, mites; terrestrial, some secondarily aquatic; usually carnivorous, predatory; compound eyes absent; breathing by book lungs, tracheae, or both; 35,000 species

The few surviving species of horseshoe crabs, structurally unchanged for 200 million years, are "living fossils" found along sandy ocean shores, where they lead a burrowing, semisedentary existence. The exceedingly long-legged sea spiders are largely deepwater-bottom forms. Spiders are the most abundant members of the arachnid class of chelicerates, and in addition to scorpions this class also includes a variety of spiderlike groups (daddy longlegs, for example) as well as the ectoparasitic mites and ticks (Fig. 12.26).

The structure of three representative chelicerates is indicated in Table 9 and Fig. 12.27. The head and thorax form a fused cephalothorax developed from eight segments, and the body frequently bears a *telson,* a terminal piece behind the abdomen. On the cephalothorax the appendages include *cheliceras* and *pedipalps,* which are food-handling and sensory structures, as well as four pairs of walking legs. The ends of these appendages either are pincer-equipped (*chelate*) or they terminate in claws. In the absence of jaws, chelicerates chew food with the spiny bases of their anterior appendages and generally suck up the fluid contents. With the exception of horseshoe crabs chelicerates lack compound eyes; spiders have up to eight simple eyes and some scorpions are eyeless. Behind the legs in horseshoe crabs is a pair of *chilaria,* small appendages without known function.

On the abdomen the first segment of horseshoe crabs bears an *operculum,* a flat movable plate that covers and protects the plates of the book gills behind. The reproductive ducts open on the operculum (*gonopores*). A small operculum is present in scorpions, but spiders lack such a structure. Scorpions also have a pair of *pectines,* comblike appendages that brush over the ground and serve as important touch organs in these largely nocturnal animals. Four segments behind the pectines bear paired spiracles, slits that lead

A

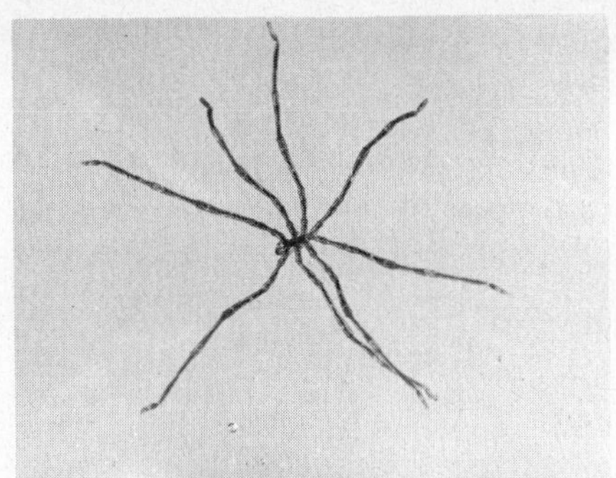

B

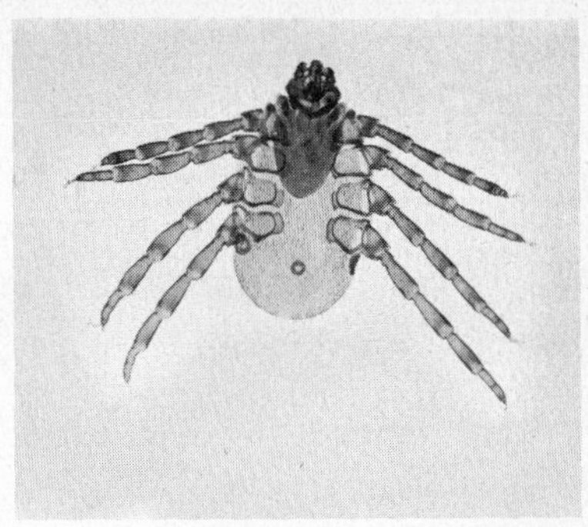

C

D

E

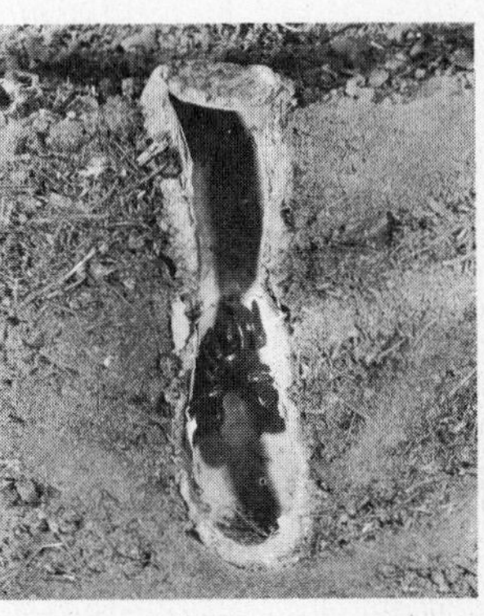

F

***12.26* Chelicerate arthropods.** *A, horseshoe crabs. B, a sea spider. C, a mite (see also Fig. 6.18). D, a scorpion. E, a tarantula. Note vertical fangs (chelicerae). F, a trap-door spider in sectioned silk-lined burrow.*

Table 9. Segments and appendages in chelicerate arthropods

		horseshoe crab	*scorpion*	*spider*
1	cephalothorax	embryo only	embryo only	embryo only
2		chelicerae (chelate)	chelicerae (small)	chelicerae (fangs)
3		pedipalps (chelate)	pedipalps (large)	pedipalps (tactile)
4		walking legs (chelate)	walking legs (clawed)	walking legs (clawed)
5		walking legs (chelate)	walking legs (clawed)	walking legs (clawed)
6		walking legs (chelate)	walking legs (clawed)	walking legs (clawed)
7		walking legs (chelate)	walking legs (clawed)	walking legs (clawed)
8		chilaria	embryo only	embryo only
9	abdomen	operculum, gonopores	operculum, gonopores	embryo only
10		gill books	pectines	lung books/tracheae
11		gill books	lung books	lung books/tracheae
12		gill books	lung books	spinnerets
13		gill books	lung books	spinnerets
14		gill books	lung books	14–18, embryo only
		telson	15–20, "tail" without appendages	
			telson	

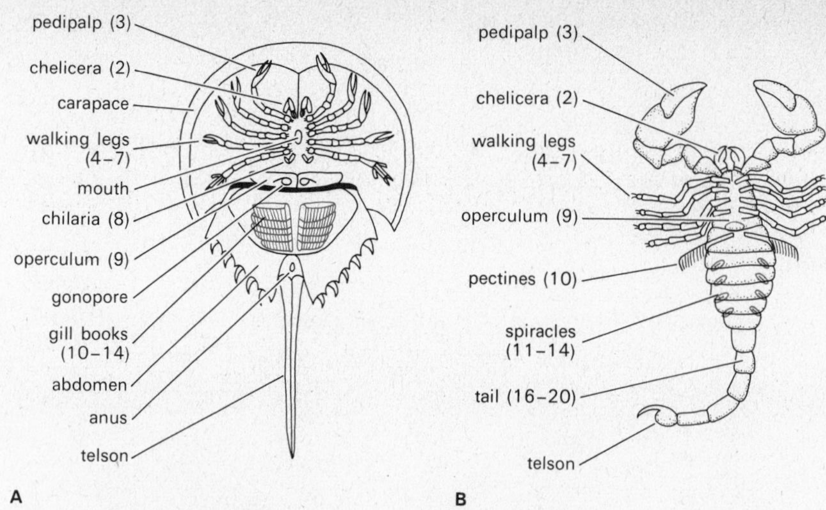

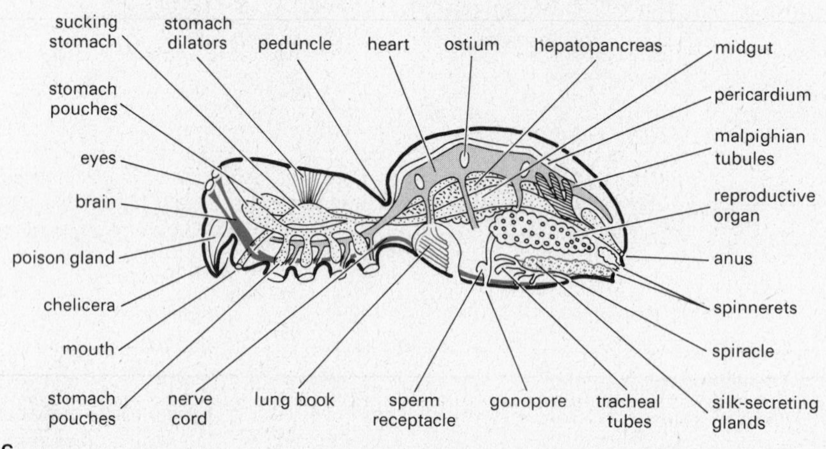

12.27 Structure of chelicerates. *A, ventral view of the horseshoe crab Limulus. Segments numbered according to sequence in embryo. The operculum is drawn turned forward to show the reproductive openings (gonopores) on its underside and to expose the book gills. B, ventral view of a scorpion. Segments are numbered according to sequence in embryo. C, sagittal section showing the internal structure of a spider. The peduncle is the ''waist'' between cephalothorax and abdomen.*

to chambers in which the book lungs are located. The most posterior abdominal segments of a scorpion form a narrow ''tail,'' and at the end of it the telson is a poison sting. In horseshoe crabs the telson is represented by a long spine hinged to the abdomen.

Spiders lack a telson, but these animals have *spinnerets,* appendages that provide outlets for *silk glands* in the abdomen. All spiders produce silk, but not all construct webs. Silk is also used, for example, to spin egg cocoons, burrow linings, hinged trap-doors over burrows, binding thread for prey, draglines, and free-floating gossamer on which a spider rides air currents. The cheliceras of spiders are fangs, with poison glands opening at the tips. Food animals (mostly insects) are killed with the poison fangs, are chewed and torn with the spiny bases of the pedipalps, and are predigested externally for an hour or more by saliva. The food juices are then sucked up, suction being produced by the stomach.

The pedipalps of male spiders also serve as sperm-transferring organs. In some species the female spiders kill and eat their mates after sperm transfer. Batches of fertilized eggs are usually laid into spun cocoons, in which offspring develop without larval stages.

Mandibulates
Subphylum Mandibulata

Class Crustacea crustaceans; marine and freshwater, some terrestrial; head and thorax or cephalothorax, often with carapace; two pairs of antennae; usually with compound eyes; breathing through gills; excretion through antennal or maxillary glands; typically with *nauplius* and other free larval stages; 30,000 species

Class Chilopoda centipedes; carnivorous, predatory; trunk with one pair of poison-claw-containing prehensors and 15 or more pairs of walking legs; eyes compound or simple or absent; 3,000 species

Class Diplopoda millipedes; herbivorous, scavenging; first four trunk segments single, rest double and fused; eyes simple; 10,000 species

Class Insecta (Hexapoda) insects; terrestrial, some secondarily aquatic; head six segments; thorax three segments, typically with three pairs of legs, two pairs of wings; abdomen typically eleven segments, without locomotor appendages; eyes compound and simple; 800,000+ species

Crustaceans
Class Crustacea

The characteristics of this highly diversified class are well exemplified by a lobster (Fig. 12.28 and Table 10). The head and thorax are covered dorsally and along the sides by a carapace, an exoskeletal shield. As in all mandibulate arthropods, the head itself consists of six fused segments. On it are a median simple eye (reduced in lobsters) and a pair of compound eyes (stalked

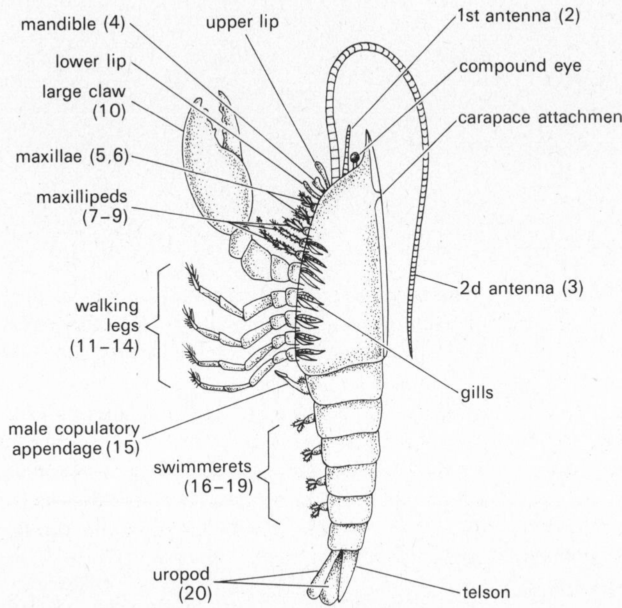

12.28 Lobster appendages. *Segmental appendages in A are numbered according to sequence in embryo. The diagram also shows which of the thoracic appendages bear gills. The carapace is attached at the third head segment (which also bears the second antennae ventrally). Note that the eyes and the upper and lower lips are not segmental appendages but extensions of the body wall.*

Table 10. Segments and appendages in mandibulate arthropods

	lobster	*centipede*	*insect*
1			
2	antennae	antennae	antennae
3	antennae		
4	mandibles	mandibles	mandibles
5	maxillae	maxillae	maxillae
6	maxillae	labium (maxillae)	labium (maxillae)
7	maxillipeds	prehensors	legs
8	maxillipeds	legs	legs, wings (spiracles)
9	maxillipeds	legs	legs, wings (spiracles)
10	chelate legs	legs	(spiracles)
11	legs	legs	(spiracles)
12	legs (female gonopore)	legs	(spiracles)
13	legs	legs	(spiracles)
14	legs (male gonopore)	legs	(spiracles)
15	reproductive	legs	(spiracles)
16	swimmerets	legs	(spiracles)
17	swimmerets	legs	(spiracles), female ovipositor, male copulatory organ
18	swimmerets	legs	
19	swimmerets	legs	(anus)
20	uropods	legs	(anal cerci)
21	telson	legs	
22		legs (gonopores)	
		telson	

in lobsters). At the bases of the short first antennae are balancing organs (*statocysts*), and at the bases of the long second antennae are the openings of the excretory *antennal glands* of lobsters. The mandibles on the third segment are the chewing jaws, which lead to the mouth. Two pairs of maxillary appendages on the head pass bits of food toward the mouth.

In the eight segments of the thorax, the first three carry *maxillipeds,* appendages that aid in macerating food and in passing it to the mouth. At the bases of the second and third maxillipeds are feathery gills. The remaining five segments bear legs, of which the first pair is large and terminates in crushing and cutting pincers. At each leg base is also a gill, normally hidden from view by the covering carapace.

In the abdomen, the reduced appendages of the first segment have functions associated with mating, and in many female crustacea they form brood pouches or other egg-holding structures (see Fig. 12.30). Lobsters have egg-holding *swimmerets* on the second to fifth abdominal segments. The last abdominal appendages are flat, platelike *uropods,* which together with a terminal telson form a tailfan.

Lobsters are scavenging animals, and their stomach has two compartments well adapted to handle the great variety of ingested foods (see Fig. 12.25). An anterior "gastric mill" equipped with chitinous teeth and other hard outgrowths grinds coarse food. A posterior filter compartment then sorts food: coarse particles are returned to the gastric mill; fine particles pass to the intestine; and liquefied food is conducted to a capacious hepatopancreas ("liver") of the midgut, where the bulk of digestion and absorption occurs. In other respects the internal structure of the animals is typically arthropod. A few large, open-ended blood vessels lead away from the heart to various body regions, and blood reenters the heart through three pairs of openings in its wall (*ostia*). In other crustacea the heart is often more distinctly tubular and contains a pair of ostia in each segmental portion.

Crustacea have a well-developed endocrine system. Its components include an *X-organ,* located in each eyestalk, and a *sinus gland* near the base of each eyestalk. This gland appears to be mainly a storage site for hormones produced in the X-organ. Another endocrine component is a *Y-organ* situated in the head. Hormones of the X-organ can be shown to regulate expansion and contraction of epidermal pigment cells and to control the secretions of the Y-organ. Hormones produced by that organ promote growth of the reproductive system, and they also inhibit or accelerate molting. Crustacea molt throughout life, quite frequently during larval growth but progressively less often as adults.

The characteristic larval form of crustacea is the *nauplius,* which as yet contains only some of the head appendages and is still unsegmented (Fig. 12.29). Segments then develop in anteroposterior succession during the course of later larval stages (which are often distinct enough to have special names: for example, *metanauplius, zoaea*). In many crustacea some or all of these later stages are part of the embryonic phase, and free larval phases are reduced or absent. Lobsters, for example, hatch in nearly adult form.

Crustacea are predominantly microscopic, and many, particularly *copepods* and *krill,* are important members of the marine plankton (Fig. 12.30). Copepods are also abundant in fresh water, as are water fleas (*daphnias*). Barnacles are sessile types, and quite a few crustacea live in fairly unusual environments, including subterranean wells, hot springs, glacial waters, salt lakes, and others. Sow bugs, slaters, and woodlice are

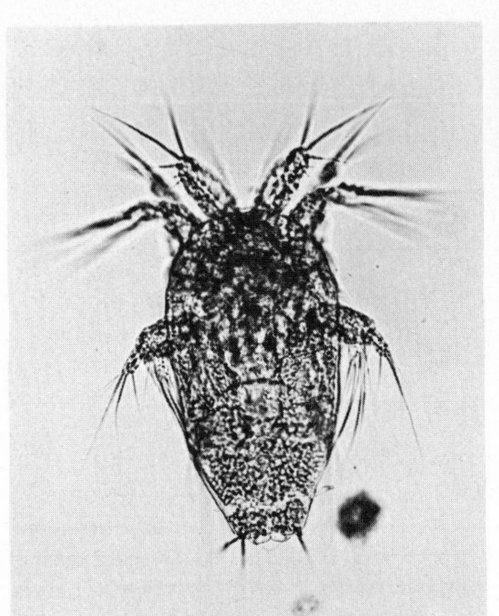
A

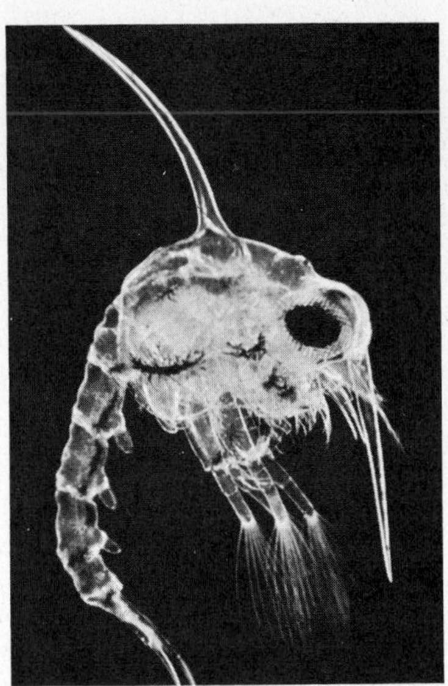
B

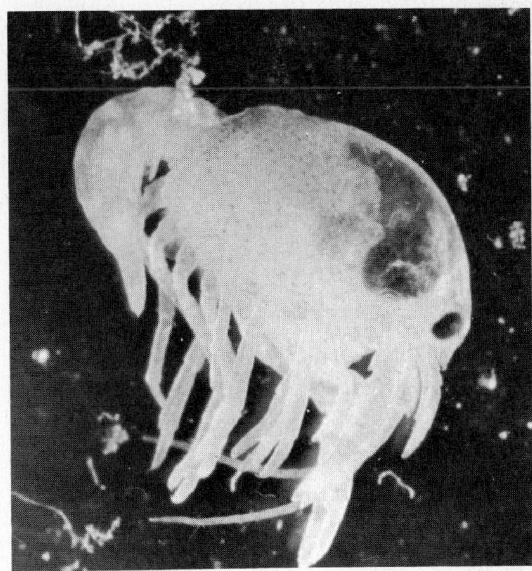
C

12.29 Crustacean larvae. *A, a nauplius of a copepod. B, a zoaea of a shore crab. C, a late zoaea of a prawn.*

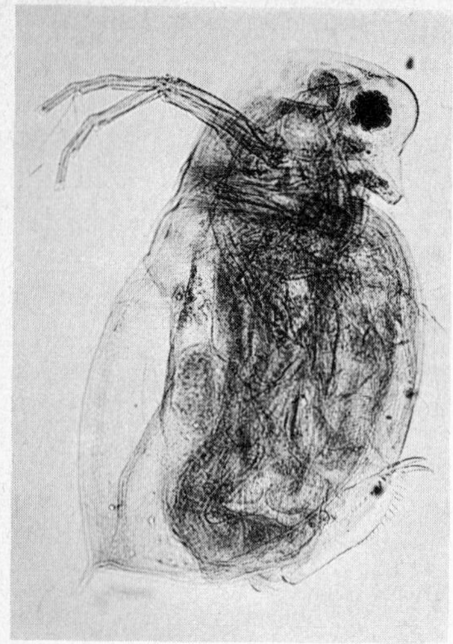
A

B

C

D

E

F

***12.30* Crustacean types.** *A, Daphnia, a water flea. A carapace (with posterior spine) covers most of the body and locomotion is carried out by the second antennae. The abdomen is reduced to a conical, claw-bearing structure near the hind end. B, Cyclops, a freshwater copepod. Note the brood pouches. C, Balanus, the rock barnacle. The legs are modified for food gathering. D, Ligia, a slater, one of a number of terrestrial crustaceans. Some of their posterior appendages have thin surface areas where air breathing takes place. E, Leander, a prawn. Eggs are carried in brood pouches. F, a land crab.*

terrestrial forms that breathe air through thin areas on their abdominal appendages. The class also includes a number of parasitic types, including *Sacculina,* which infects crabs and spreads through such hosts like a malignant tumor. The largest crustacea (and largest of all arthropods) are the giant crabs, which can have a leg span of 12 ft, and the American lobsters, which can weigh well over 40 lb.

Centipedes and Millipedes
Class Chilopoda
Class Diplopoda

The head and the internal structure of these animals is generally like that of insects, but the exterior of the trunk is clearly wormlike (Fig. 12.31 and see Table 10). Millipedes lack compound eyes; centipedes may or may not possess them. The first trunk segment of centipedes bears poison-gland-containing, fanglike *prehensors.* Each leg-bearing segment usually contains a pair

A

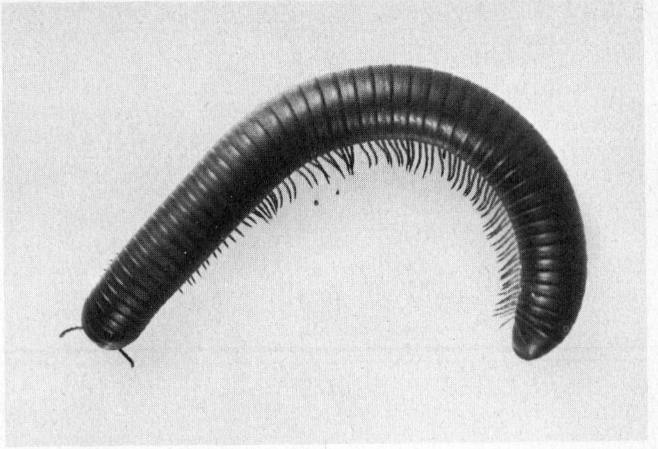

B

12.31 ***Myriapods.*** *A, a centipede. The head is at left. B, a millipede. Note two pairs of legs in most trunk segments. (Courtesy Carolina Biological Supply Company.)*

of *spiracles,* openings leading to the tracheal breathing tubes. The animals are predators and rapid runners. During the day they shun exposure, and at night they leave their crevices and crannies in search for earthworms, insects, and snails. Millipedes carry *two* pairs of legs on most trunk segments, each of which is actually a fused double segment. But these animals are poor runners despite their large number of legs. They are herbivores, and rapid locomotion is not essential. They too are retiring in habit, and when exposed they tend to roll up as a ball.

Insects
Class Insecta

Subclass Apterygota (Ametabola) primitively wingless; without metamorphosis

Subclass Pterygota (Metabola) with wings and metamorphosis

Superorder Exopterygota (*Hemimetabola*) wing growth external on larva; metamorphosis gradual; compound eyes already present in larvae

Superorder Endopterygota (*Holometabola*) wing growth internal in larva; metamorphosis abrupt; larval stages are caterpillars and pupae; compound eyes not present in larvae

Insect evolution has produced three levels of specialization. In the primitive Apterygota the hatched young are miniature wingless adults, and larvae and metamorphosis are essentially absent. Springtails and bristletails (''silverfish'') are included in this smallest group (Fig. 12.32). A second level is represented by the Exopterygota, in which the larvae resemble the adults. Early larvae still lack wings, however, and wing buds on the outside of the body grow progressively larger in a series of molting steps until winged adults are formed (see below). Included in this group are grasshoppers, termites, lice, dragonflies, mayflies, bugs, locusts, aphids, and very many others (Fig. 12.33).

The third and most specialized level comprises

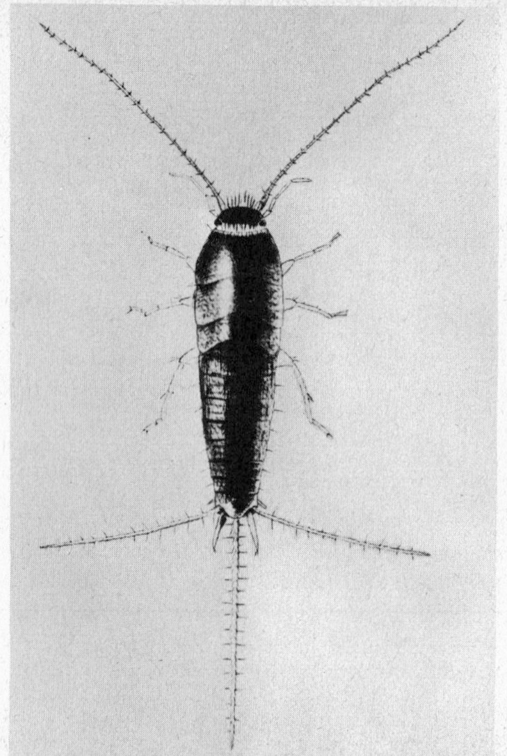

12.32 ***Silverfish*** *(order Thysanura), a primitively flightless apterygote insect.*

the Endopterygota, in which the larvae are caterpillars or caterpillarlike. After a series of molts a caterpillar transforms to a *pupa,* in which the wings and other adult structures develop from internal buds (see below). To this largest group belong moths, butterflies, flies, mosquitoes, fleas, beetles, bees, ants, wasps, and numerous others (Fig. 12.34).

The head of an insect consists of six fused segments, of which four bear appendages (Fig. 12.35 and see Table 10). The mandibles and first maxillae lie lateral to the mouth, and an upper lip, or *labrum,* protects the mouth anteriorly. The second maxillae form an underlip, or *labium.* Primitively, labrum, mandibles, maxillae, and labium function as *biting-and-chewing* mouth parts. Most Exopterygota have oral structures of this type. More advanced forms are variously equipped with *sucking, licking,* or *piercing-and-sucking* mouth parts. In a butterfly, for example, the maxillae are drawn out as elongated sucking tubes. These are rolled up at rest but can be extended deep into a flower for nectar. Flies, mosquitoes, bees, and many other Endopterygota likewise have mouth parts modified and adapted in special ways.

12.33 ***Exopterygote insects.*** *A, praying mantis (order Orthoptera). B, human body louse (order Anopleura). C, damsel fly (order Odonata). D, mayfly (order Ephemeroptera). E, bedbug (order Hemiptera). F, 17-year locust (order Homoptera). See also Color Fig. 21. (A, courtesy Carolina Biological Supply Company.)*

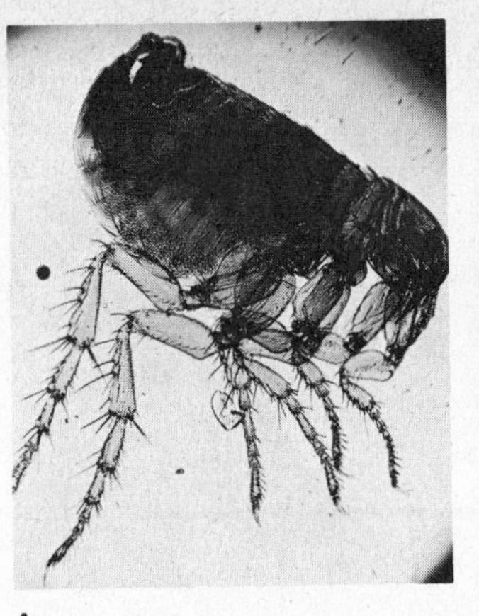

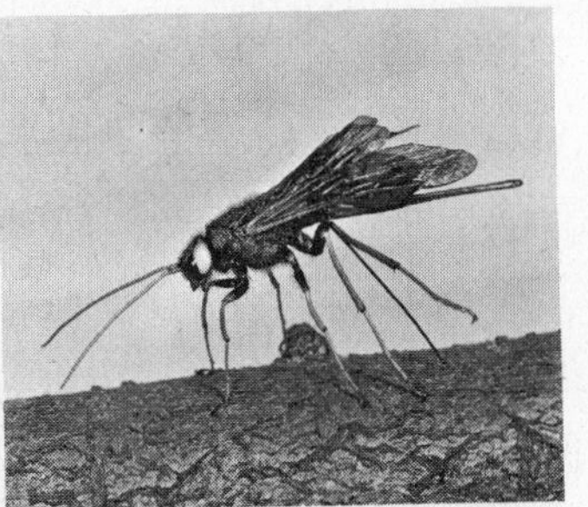

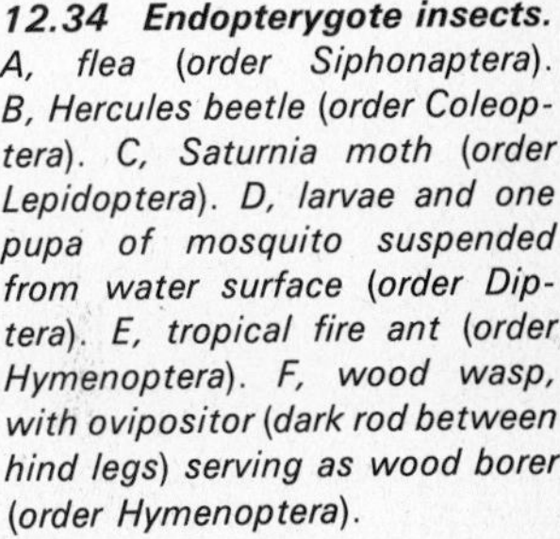

12.34 Endopterygote insects. *A, flea (order Siphonaptera). B, Hercules beetle (order Coleoptera). C, Saturnia moth (order Lepidoptera). D, larvae and one pupa of mosquito suspended from water surface (order Diptera). E, tropical fire ant (order Hymenoptera). F, wood wasp, with ovipositor (dark rod between hind legs) serving as wood borer (order Hymenoptera).*

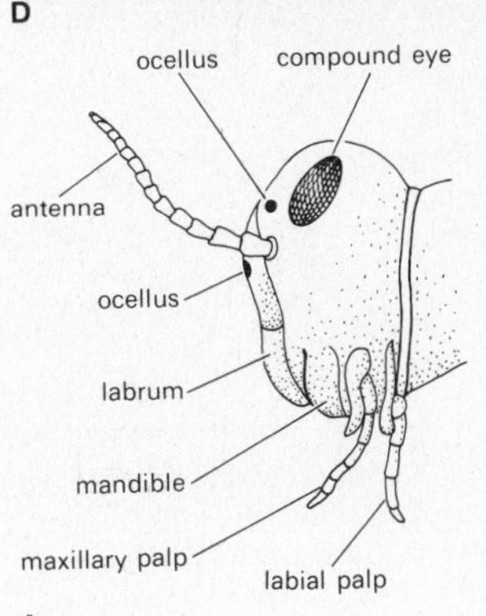

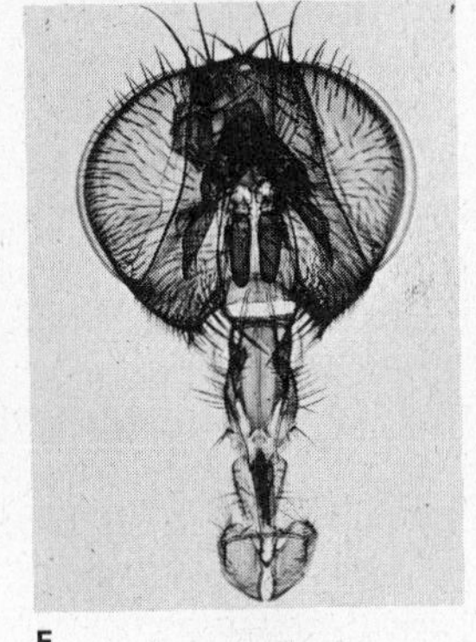

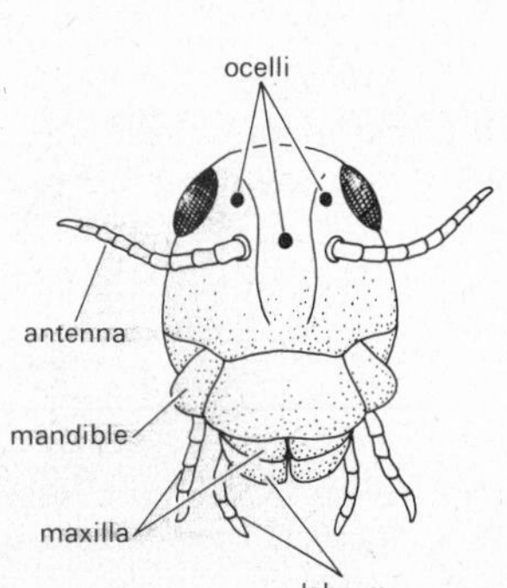

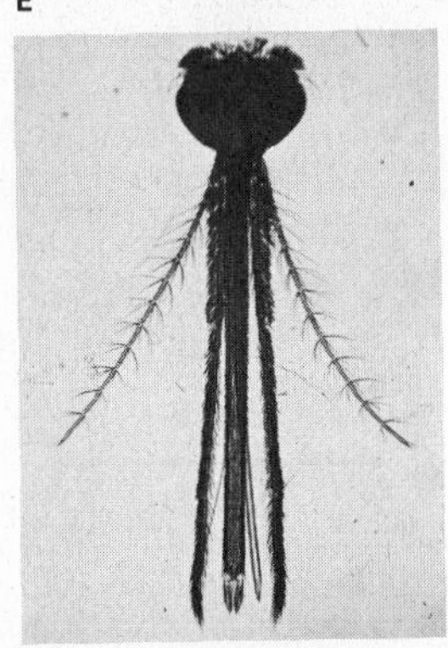

12.35 Insect head structure and mouth parts. *A, B, C, views of grasshopper head, biting mouth parts. Note mandibles in C. D, head of cabbage butterfly, showing sucking proboscis extended. The proboscis is a double tube formed from the pair of maxillae. It rolls up toward the head when not in use. E, front view of the proboscis apparatus of a housefly. Here the proboscis is a highly elaborate underlip (labium). F, head and sucking structures of a female mosquito. The sucking tube in the center is formed by long extensions of the upper lip (labrum) and the floor of the mouth. The dark bristly structures along each side of the central tube are the mandibles, and the shorter extensions on the outside are maxillae. (E, F, courtesy Carolina Biological Supply Company.)*

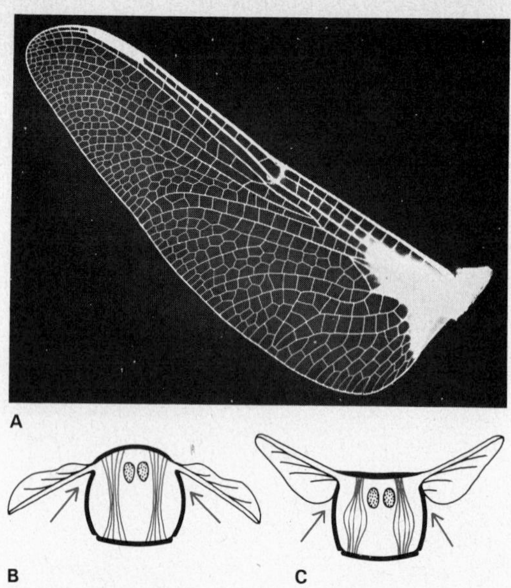

12.36 ***Insect flight.*** *A, a dragonfly wing, showing veins. B and C indicate the indirect, flight-producing wing musculature in the thorax. Arrows point to the fulcrums of the wings. In B, the vertical muscles are relaxed, the longitudinal muscles are contracted, and the wings move down. In C, the converse, with wings moved up.*

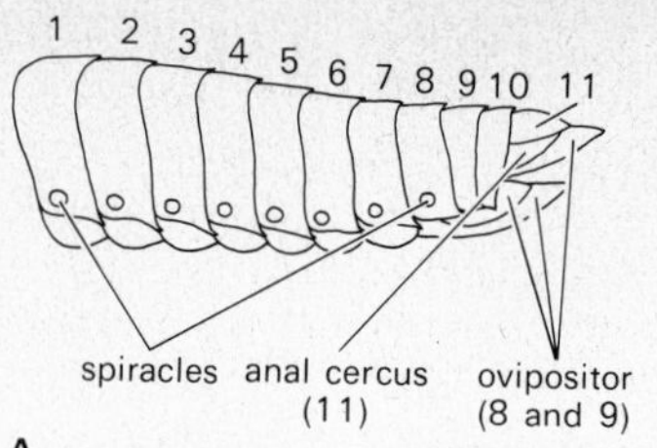

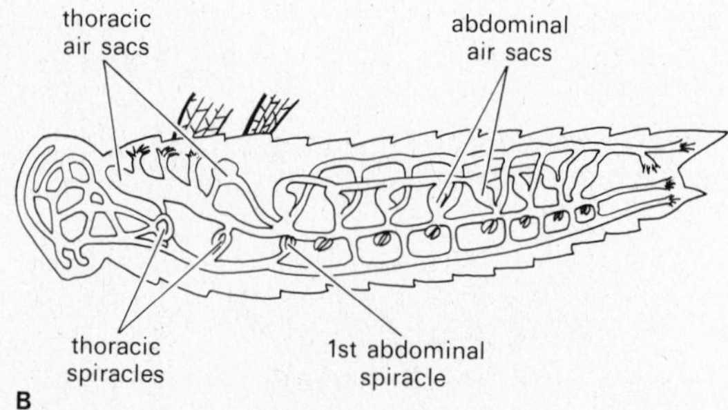

12.37 ***Insect abdomen and breathing.*** *A, side view of abdomen as in grasshopper; numbers refer to segments. B, the main tracheal tubes and air sacs in the breathing system of a grasshopper. C, a spiracle (center) and the systems of the tracheal tubes leading away from it.*

Each of the three segments of the thorax carries a pair of legs, and the second and third each typically also bears a pair of wings. A wing is a flattened fold of the chitinous exoskeleton, with air-filled, tubular spaces forming supporting veins (Fig. 12.36). Muscles attached to a wing directly move the appendage to a flying or rest position. Actual flying motions are produced indirectly, by muscles between the dorsal and ventral parts of the body wall of the thorax. As these muscles alternately flatten and arch the thorax, the wings, locked on the body wall in fixed position, are moved up and down.

Either pair of wings is often modified. For example, the hind wings are reduced to knobbed stumps (*halteres*) in flies and mosquitoes (and the vibrations of halteres during flight produce the buzzing sounds made by these insects). The forewings are hardened as protective covers in grasshoppers, earwigs, and beetles. In fleas and many members of other groups, both pairs of wings are secondarily absent.

In the abdomen the first seven segments lack appendages (Fig. 12.37). The eighth and ninth segments of most female insects bear *ovipositors,* appendages modified to aid in egg laying (but serving as stings in bees and as saws and piercers in related groups; see Fig. 12.34). The appendages of the ninth segment in males form copulatory organs, and the anus is in the tenth segment in most cases. These posterior segments also carry the openings of the reproductive system. The eleventh segment, if present, is often extended as *anal cerci,* projections that form the "forceps" of earwigs, for example.

The last two thoracic and the first eight abdominal segments typically bear paired *spiracles* that lead to the tracheal breathing system. Such a system consists of interconnecting longitudinal tubes, air sacs, and branching air ducts (*tracheae;* see Fig. 12.37). Contraction of muscles attached to the dorsal and ventral skeletal plates of the body produces exhalation, and relaxation of these muscles permits recoil of the skeletal plates and thus inhalation. Such breathing motions of the abdomen can be observed readily in a quiescent fly.

Internally, the nervous system is basically of the ladder type, but in many insects (as also in many other arthropods) various numbers of ventral ganglia are concentrated in single units. The elongated heart has paired ostia (see Fig. 12.25), and it lies dorsal to a usually well-developed pericardial membrane. Excretion occurs through Malpighian tubules that open to the hindgut.

With very few exceptions fertilization takes place by copulation, and the fertilized eggs are laid (with the assistance of the ovipositors). In the embryos, appendage buds arise in anteroposterior succession (Fig. 12.38). In Apterygota and Exopterygota, such buds develop into adult appendages. Thus, when apterygotes hatch they are essentially miniature adults; and when exopterygotes hatch they are larvae (often called *nymphs*) that resemble adults greatly though the wings are still lacking. Exopterygote larvae then develop wings in the course of successive molting steps, during which external wing buds form from folds of chitin and become progressively larger (Fig. 12.39 and Color Fig. 21).

In Endopterygota the embryos hatch in a less fully developed condition, as annelidlike caterpillars. They undergo successive molts and grow, and eventually pockets arise in the body wall in which *imaginal disks* begin to develop. These disks are internal buds from which adult appendages such as wings, legs, and new mouth parts will later form. The transformation of caterpillar to adult occurs in the *pupa.* At this stage the pockets that contain the imaginal disks open out, and the adult appendages then make their first external appearance (Fig. 12.40).

The larval and pupal molts are under precise hormonal control. Three types of glands have been shown to play a role: groups of *neurosecretory cells* (NS) in the brain ganglia; a pair of *corpora allata* (CA) in the mandibular segment; and a pair of *prothoracic glands* (PT) in the first thoracic segment. The NS cells rhythmically secrete a hormone that stimulates the PT glands. These then secrete a hormone that acts on the body tissues and induces molting (Fig. 12.41). The nature of the molt is governed by whether or not hormones are secreted by the CA glands. If CA hormones are being produced, the next molt will transform a larva to a later larva. But if CA hormones are not secreted, then PT hormones acting alone transform the larva to an adult in the case of exopterygotes. In endopterygotes, a first molt induced by PT hormones alone changes a larva to a pupa, and a second molt establishes the adult.

The class of insects as a whole contains some two dozen orders, many of them representing a

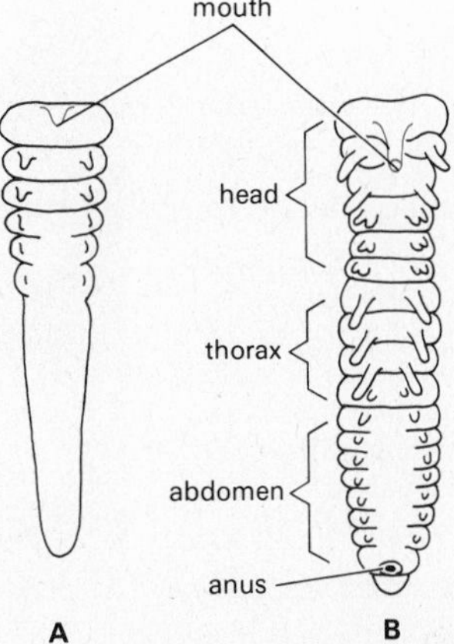

12.38 Early insect development. *A and B are ventral views of two embryonic stages showing gradual anteroposterior formation of segments and segmental appendages. Note movement of mouth backward. Note also general annelidlike structure.*

12.39 *(Below)* ***Exopterygote development.*** *A grasshopper larva (nymph), with wings at early growth stages.*

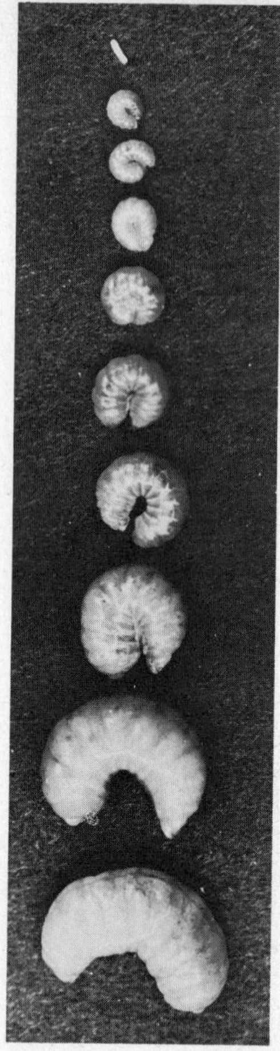
A

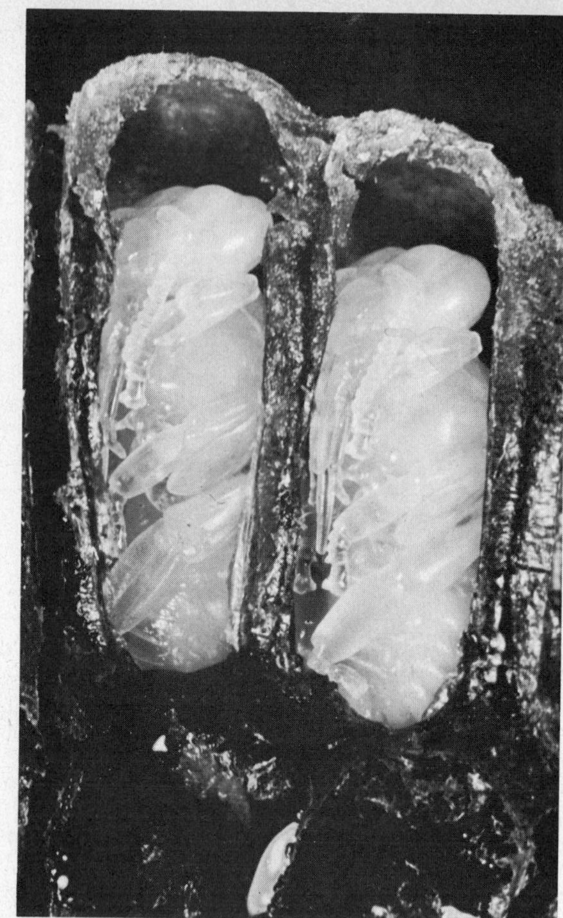
B

12.40 Endopterygote development. *A, B, honeybee. A, egg and series of larvae, each one day older than the previous one. B, pupae developing in (cutaway) brood cells of honeycomb. Legs already well formed. C–F, silkworm moth. C, caterpillar spinning pupation cocoon. D, fully formed cocoon, with pupa seen inside by translucent illumination. E, emergence of adult, wings still uninflated. F, some minutes later, wings attaining mature size.*

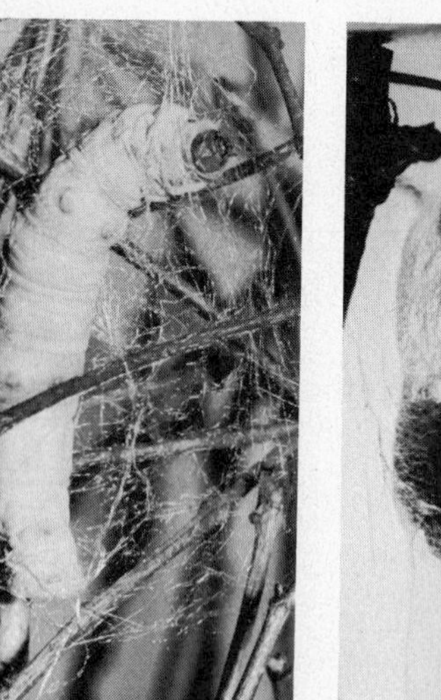
C

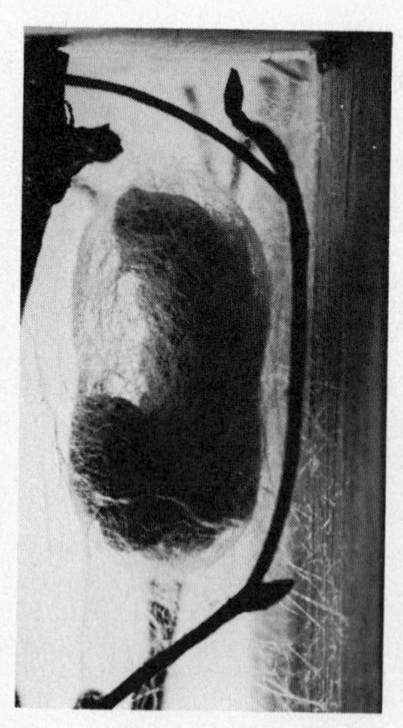
D

E

F

very wide range of ways of life. For example, the order of beetles includes parasites, commensals, carnivores, herbivores (including wood-, wool-, and glue-eaters), omnivores (including rock-borers), aquatic types, subterranean types, arboreal types, diurnal and nocturnal types, and dozens of others, each adapted to a particular, often highly specialized mode of existence. Five of the orders, all endopterygotes, encompass fully two-thirds of all described insect species: *Coleoptera,* the weevils and beetles, with 300,000 species; *Lepidoptera,* the butterflies and moths, with 125,000 species; *Hymenoptera,* the bees, wasps, and ants, with 110,000 species; and *Diptera,* the flies and mosquitoes, with 100,000 species. Next in abundance are the exopterygote orders *Hemiptera,* the true bugs, with 40,000 species; *Homoptera,* the plant lice and scale insects, with 30,000 species; and *Orthoptera,* the grasshoppers, locusts, crickets, and cockroaches, with 25,000 species.

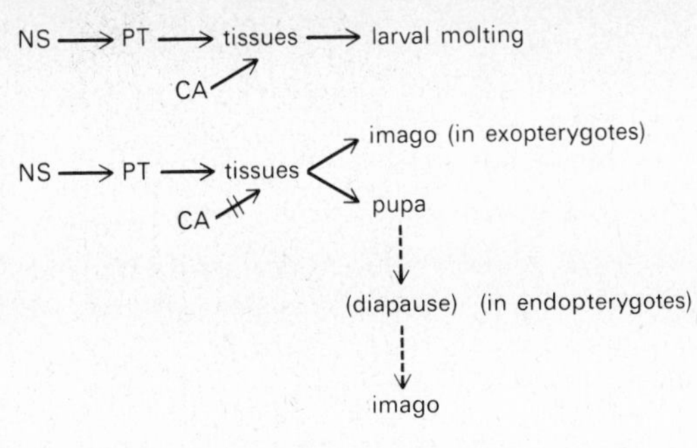

12.41 Hormonal controls in insect development. *Neurosecretory cells from the brain (NS) stimulate production of prothoracic gland hormone (PT), which in conjunction with corpora allata hormones (CA) determines larval molting (step 1). After CA ceases to become available (step 2), the next PT-induced molt produces the adult in exopterygotes, the pupa in endopterygotes. The pupa often passes through a dormant phase, the diapause, and the following PT-induced molt then yields the adult.*

review questions

1 Give difinitions of coelomates, protostomial coelomates, lophophorates, and schizocoelomates. Which phyla are included in each of these groups? What is a lophophore? How does a lophophorate animal feed?

2 Give taxonomic definitions of the phylum of mollusks and of each of the molluscan classes. Describe the structural traits of the hypothetical molluscan ancestor, and show in what ways living mollusks still exhibit the ancestral body construction to greater or lesser degree.

3 Review the development and adult structure of a representative of each of the molluscan classes. What are torsion and detorsion? What is a glochidium? A radula? Which mollusks develop via (*a*) trochophores, (*b*) veligers, (*c*) neither?

4 Give taxonomic definitions of annelids and of each of the annelid classes. Describe the development of a segmented body organization from a trochophore larva. Then describe the segmental structure of an adult polychaete. What are the basic adaptive advantages of body segmentation?

5 Describe the nervous, circulatory, and excretory systems of *Nereis.* How is breathing accomplished? What is a heteronereis? In what respects do oligochaetes differ from polychaetes?

6 Describe the structure of an earthworm, and contrast it with that of *Nereis.* What are typhlosole, crop, and lime glands and what are their functions? Show how mating and fertilization occur in earthworms. Contrast the structure of a leech with that of an earthworm.

7 Characterize the phylum Arthropoda taxonomically, and name the subphyla and classes. How are these subgroups presumably interrelated historically? Compare the species numbers of the various groups.

8 How have the chitinous exoskeleton and the body segmentation contributed to the broad diversification of the arthropod phylum? Describe the basic exterior structure of the arthropod body and the general organization of the 10 organ systems. Review the structure of arthropod eyes.

9 Review the segmental structure of the chelicerate cephalothorax and the structure and function of the appendages of that body division. Describe the structure of a horseshoe crab, a scorpion, and a spider.

10 Distinguish between the chelicerate and mandibulate subphyla. Describe the segmental structure of the crustacean head, thorax, and abdomen. Where is the sinus gland located, and what is its function?

11 Name and state the functions of the appendages of a lobster. Describe the internal anatomy of a lobster. In the process review the organization of every organ system.

12 Review the nature of the larval stages of crustacea. Name crustacea (*a*) that live on land, in fresh water, and in the ocean, (*b*) that are parasitic, (*c*) that are sessile, (*d*) that are planktonic.

13 Describe the segmental structure of centipedes and millipedes, and contrast the external anatomy of these animals. What features are similar to those of insects?

14 Define insects taxonomically. Describe the segmental structure and the internal anatomy of an insect. Review the structure of insect mouth parts. What is the structure of an insect wing, and how is flight motion produced? How do insects breathe?

15 Show how insect development differs according to the subclass or superorder. What are imaginal disks? What developmental events occur in a pupa? Describe the specific role of hormones in the control of molting and metamorphosis.

---

collateral readings

Boycott, B. B.: Learning in the Octopus, *Sci. American,* March, 1965. Tests before and after brain surgery indicate that an octopus may have short-term and long-term memory.

Buchsbaum, R.: ''Animals without Backbones,'' University of Chicago, Chicago, 1948. All invertebrate groups are examined in elementary fashion, including those discussed in this chapter; well illustrated.

Comstock, J. H., and **W. J. Gertsch**: ''The Spider Book,'' 2d ed., Doubleday, Garden City, N.Y., 1940. Must reading for those interested in spiders.

Green, J.: ''A Biology of Crustacea,'' Quadrangle Books, Chicago, 1961. Well worth consulting for more detailed background information.

Jacques, H. E.: ''How To Know the Insects,'' William C. Brown, Dubuque, Iowa, 1947. Valuable in identifying and characterizing different types of insects.

Johnson, C. G.: The Aerial Migration of Insects, *Sci. American,* Dec., 1963. Seasonal migration patterns are described.

Jones, J. C.: The Sexual Life of a Mosquito, *Sci. American,* Apr., 1968. An account on the reproduction of the mosquito that transmits yellow fever.

Metcalf, C. L., W. P. Flint, and **R. L. Metcalf**: ''Destructive and Useful Insects,'' 4th ed., McGraw-Hill, New York, 1962. The ecologic and economic biology of insects is examined thoroughly in this book.

Morton, J. E.: ''Mollusks,'' Hutchinson, London, 1958. Strongly recommended for further reading on this phylum.

Murphy, R. C.: The Oceanic Life of the Antarctic, *Sci. American,* Sept., 1962. The article pays particular attention to krill, a fundamentally important shrimplike crustacean.

Petrunkevitch, A.: The Spider and the Wasp, *Sci. American,* Aug., 1952. On the nearly symbiotic relationship between the tarantula and a giant wasp.

Roeder, K. D.: Moths and Ultrasound, *Sci. American,* Apr., 1965. The article shows how moths perceive and interpret the ultrasonic pulses of bats (which prey on moths).

Rothschild, M.: Fleas, *Sci. American,* Dec., 1965. On the remarkable adaptations of these insects.

Savory, T. H.: Daddy Longlegs, *Sci. American,* Oct., 1962. An interesting account on a familiar arachnid related distantly to spiders.

———: False Scorpions, *Sci. American,* March., 1966. The biology and behavior of arachnids related to scorpions are examined.

Smith, D. S.: The Flight Muscles of Insects, *Sci. American,* June, 1965. The functional aspects of insect flight are examined.

Snodgrass, R. E.: Arthropoda, in ''McGraw-Hill Encyclopedia of Science and Technology,'' vol. 1, 1960. A short but thorough synopsis of the biology of the phylum.

Van der Kloot, W. G.: Brains and Cocoons, *Sci. American,* Apr., 1956. Neurosurgery on insect pupae reveals some relations between the nervous system and behavior.

Williams, C. M.: The Metamorphosis of Insects, *Sci. American,* Apr., 1950. An interesting account on some of the original experiments that have led to our present understanding of the subject.

———: Insect Breathing, *Sci. American,* Feb., 1953. The structural and functional aspects of the tracheal system are discussed.

Wilson, D. M.: The Flight-control System of the Locust, *Sci. American,* May, 1968. On the nervous and genetic regulation of flying behavior.

chapter 13 coelomate groups: deuterostomes

category	branch	grade	subgrade	phylum	subphylum	class
	parazoa					
		radiata				
			acoelomata			
			pseudocoelomata			
				phoronida		
				ectoprocta		
				brachiopoda		
				mollusca		
				sipunculida		
				annelida		
				echiuroidea		
				oncopoda		
				arthropoda		
				chaetognatha		
metazoa				**pogonophora**		
	eumetazoa					
		bilateria		**hemichordata**		
			coelomata			**crinoidea**
						holothuroidea
				echinodermata		**asteroidea**
						ophiuroidea
						echinoidea
						ascidiacea
					urochordata	**thaliacea**
						larvacea
					cephalochordata	
				chordata		
						agnatha
						chondrichthyes
						osteichthyes
					vertebrata	**amphibia**
						reptilia
						aves
						mammalia

As noted in Chap. 11, deuterostomial animals are those in which the first opening of the embryonic alimentary cavity becomes the anus and the later second opening forms the mouth (see Fig. 11.6).

Deuterostomes also happen to be enterocoelomates; their coeloms arise as cavities in mesoderm sacs that grow out from the gut- (or "enteron-") producing endoderm (see Fig. 11.8).

Enterocoelomates

Phylum Chaetognatha arrowworms; marine, planktonic; head with chitinous grasping spines and covering hood; trunk with lateral and tail fins; coelom subdivided into three compartments; without circulatory, breathing, or excretory systems; development without larvae; 50 species

Phylum Pogonophora beard worms; deep-sea, tube-dwelling; with anterior tentacles; alimentary system absent; circulatory system closed; without breathing system; body marked into three parts (*protosome, mesosome, metasome*) and coelom correspondingly divided (*protocoel, mesocoel, metacoel*); 25 species

Phylum Hemichordata acorn worms; marine; colonial in secreted housings or solitary in sand burrows; body marked into three parts (*protosome, mesosome, metasome*), and coelom correspondingly divided (*protocoel, mesocoel, metacoel*); mostly with gill slits; typically with larvae; 100 species

Phylum Echinodermata spiny-skinned animals; marine; larvae bilateral, with protocoel, mesocoel, and metacoel in early stages; adults pentaradial; with calcareous endoskeleton and coelomic water-vascular system; 6,000 species

Phylum Chordata chordates; all environments; with notochord, pharyngeal gill slits, and dorsal hollow nerve cord in preadult stages or throughout life; with tailed *tadpoles* or without larvae; 50,000 species

Developmental and structural evidence suggests that arrowworms probably are not related very closely to the other enterocoelomates. Also, the presence of chitin in this phylum is unique for entero-

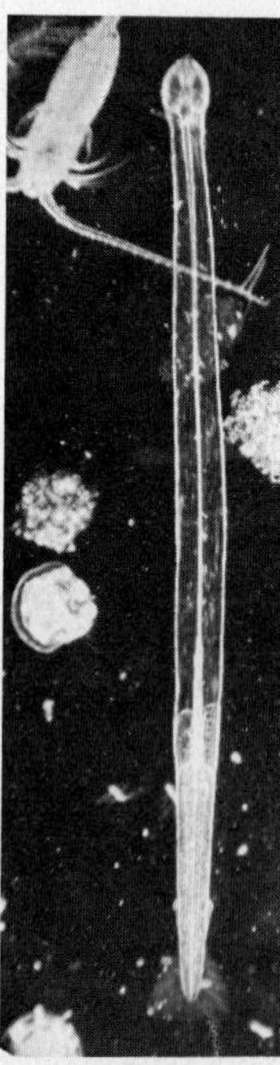
A

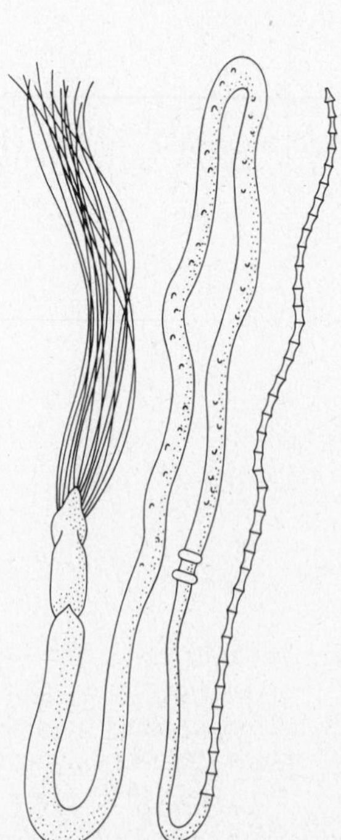
B

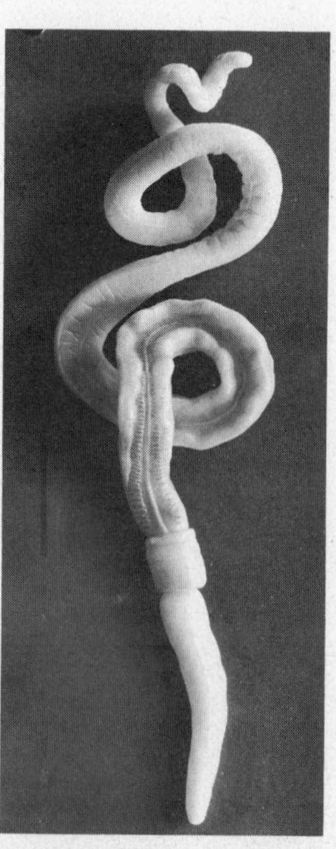
C

13.1 Enterocoelomates. *A, an arrowworm (in plankton, from life). B, external features of a beard worm. The tentacles emanate from a short front region (protosome). Behind this region is a collar section (mesosome), and the rest of the body represents the trunk (metasome). C, model of an acorn worm, dorsal view. Note proboscis (protosome), conspicuous collar (mesosome), and row of paired gill slits along anterior portion of trunk (metasome).*

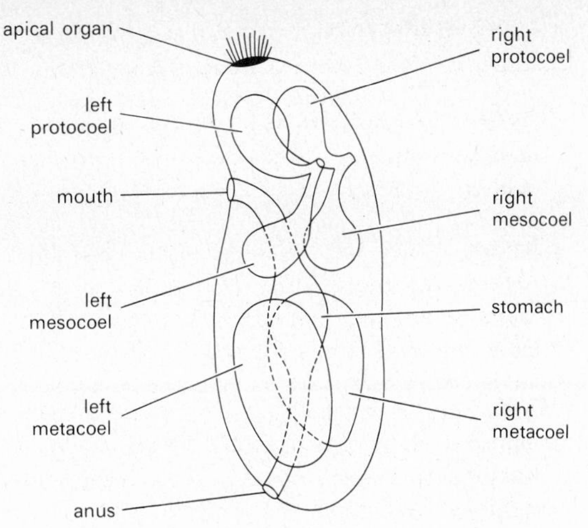

***13.2 The dipleurula.** This hypothetical ancestor of deuterostomes resembles certain actual embryonic and larval stages of hemichordates and echinoderms.*

coelomates. The other phyla do appear to represent a more or less broadly interrelated group. Hemichordates could be closest to an ancestral enterocoelomate line, and beard worms, echinoderms, and chordates could have evolved from it as branch lines (Fig. 13.1 and see Fig. 11.9).

Among unifying features exhibited with varying degrees of similarity in the last four phyla are, for example, the tendency to secrete a celluloselike compound (*tunicin*) as a body covering; the tendency of passing through a so-called *dipleurula stage* during the embryonic or larval phase (Fig. 13.2); the tendency of the coelom to form three paired subdivisions (*protocoel, mesocoel, metacoel*), with corresponding anatomic divisions of the body as a whole (*protosome, mesosome, metasome*); and, at least in hemichordates and chordates, the formation of endodermal pharyngeal gill pouches that develop into gill slits.

The most familiar enterocoelomates are the echinoderms and the chordates, each probably related more to the hemichordates than to each other. Chordates of course are also of special interest, for they include vertebrates and man. Enterocoelomates arose as unsegmented animals, but segmentation did evolve later in two of the three chordate subphyla.

Echinoderms

Phylum Echinodermata spiny-skinned animals

Class Crinoidea sea lilies, feather stars; body cup-shaped, free or attached; endoskeleton limited to aboral side, oral side membranous; arms branched, with open ambulacral grooves; tube feet food-catching

Class Holothuroidea sea cucumbers; secondarily bilateral; mouth region with tentacles; ambulacral grooves closed; endoskeleton reduced to ossicles; oral-aboral axis horizontal

Class Asteroidea starfishes, sea stars; star-shaped; ambulacral grooves open; tube feet locomotor and projecting between endoskeletal plates

Class Ophiuroidea brittle stars, basket stars; star-shaped, with long, highly flexible arms; ambulacral grooves closed, tube feet reduced; madreporite on oral side; without intestine or anus

Class Echinoidea sea urchins, sand dollars; spherical to disk-shaped, without arms; ambulacral grooves closed; endoskeleton fused, nonflexible, with pores for tube feet and with movable spines

Echinoderms develop bilateral, free-swimming (dipleurulalike) larvae, and fossils show that the earliest echinoderms were bilateral also as adults. Later descendants retained the bilateral larvae but became sessile and secondarily radial as adults. They evolved a starlike shape, with arms that could serve as feeding tentacles. Moreover, the entire body became clothed with endoskeletal plates that could protect the attached, vulnerable animal. However, such an endoskeleton must have restricted the mobility and food-catching capacity of the arms. This problem could be solved by the evolution of a *water-vascular* system that contained small, mobile branch tentacles, or *tube feet,* on the armor-plated arms. Also, furrows between rows of tube feet along the arms, so-called *ambulacral grooves,* could serve in passing food from the tube feet to the mouth, located in the center of the star-shaped body (Fig. 13.3). The unique water-vascular system of echinoderms thus may be interpreted as a modified tentacular system, evolved in response to a sessile way of life and a skeleton-induced body rigidity. Crinoids, the most primitive living echinoderms, still exhibit these ancient characteristics in large measure.

Once a tube-foot system for feeding had evolved, it could become modified also for locomotion. Some of the early echinoderm groups relinquished the stalked, attached mode of life and became motile, with the oral side directed downward. Tube feet, and in some cases also endoskeletal spines and the arms themselves, could function in propulsion. The animals thus could move to food actively, use the mouth directly, and no longer needed to depend on what the arms could strain out of the water. The ambulacral grooves then largely ceased to be of importance, and they are actually closed over by folds of the body wall in all living echinoderms except the crinoids and asteroids.

The basic traits of echinoderms as a whole are well illustrated in the asteroids, which combine primitive and advanced traits of the phylum (Figs. 13.4 and 13.5). The body of a common starfish consists of a central *disk* and, typically, five *arms.* Some genera have as many as 20 or more arms. Under the epidermis is an endoskeleton, composed of knobby calcareous plates held together by connective tissue and muscle. In numerous places the body wall folds out as microscopic fingerlike projections, the *skin gills.* The spaces in these breathing organs are extensions of the coelom between adjacent skeletal plates. Also on the body surface are microscopic *pedicellariae,* muscle-operated pincers that protect the skin gills and the epidermis as a whole.

A water-vascular system operates through a series of coelomic, sea-water–filled ducts and serves in locomotion and feeding. The system communicates with external sea water through a reddish *madreporite,* a sieve plate on the upper, or *aboral,* side of the animal, near the angle between two of the arms. From the madreporite a calcified *stone canal* conducts water to a *ring canal* in the body, and from this channel in turn emanate five *radial canals,* one to each arm. There each radial canal gives off short lateral branches, and each of these bifurcates into a saclike *ampulla* in the arm and a muscular *tube foot* that pro-

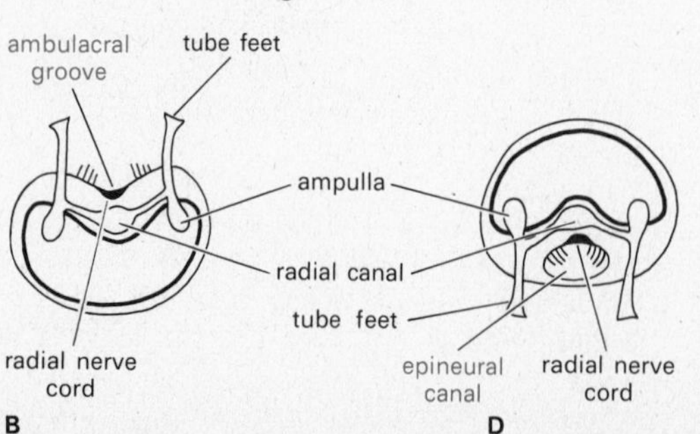

13.3 Echinoderm body plans. *Left, the crinoid pattern, with vertical oral-aboral axis, mouth and tube feet pointing up (A), and open ambulacral groove (B). Right, the ophiuroid-echinoid pattern, with mouth and tube feet pointing down (C), and with ambulacral groove closed in as an epineural canal (D). Asteroids correspond to pattern C, but they have open ambulacral grooves.*

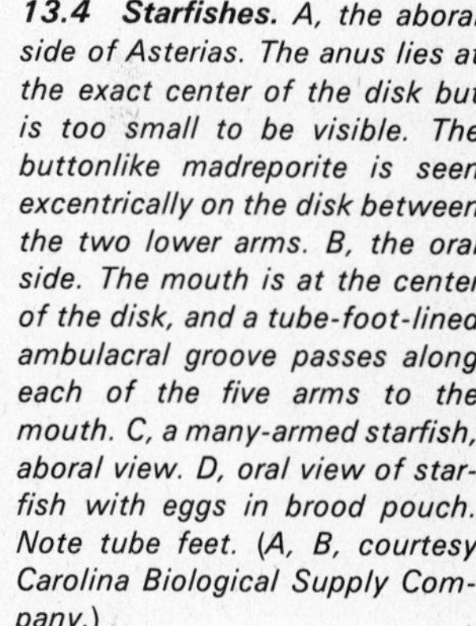

13.4 Starfishes. *A, the aboral side of Asterias. The anus lies at the exact center of the disk but is too small to be visible. The buttonlike madreporite is seen excentrically on the disk between the two lower arms. B, the oral side. The mouth is at the center of the disk, and a tube-foot-lined ambulacral groove passes along each of the five arms to the mouth. C, a many-armed starfish, aboral view. D, oral view of starfish with eggs in brood pouch. Note tube feet. (A, B, courtesy Carolina Biological Supply Company.)*

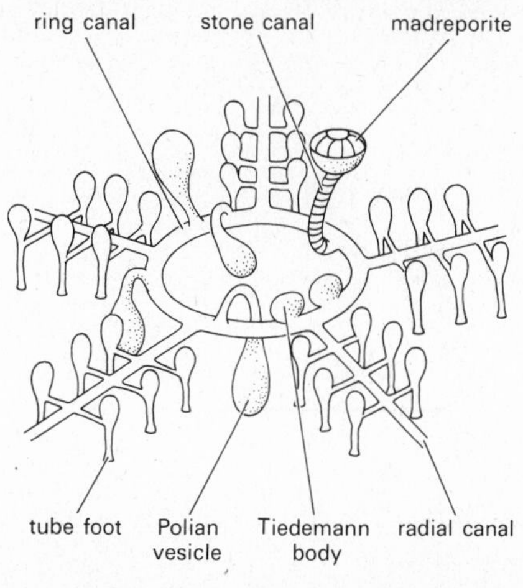

13.5 Starfish structure. *A, cross section of an arm. B, the water-vascular system. Polian vesicles are absent in the common starfish Asterias.*

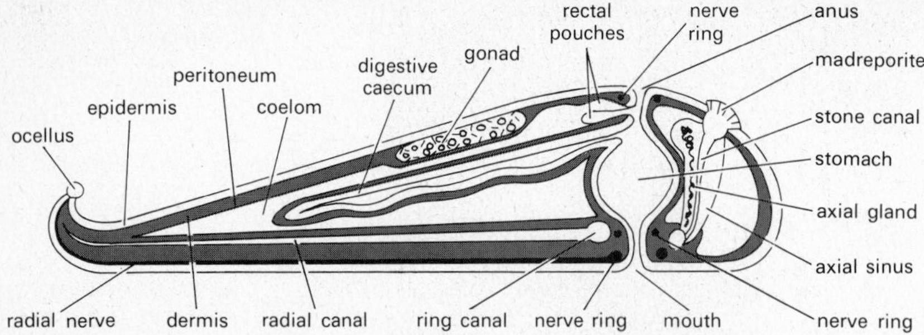

13.6 Starfish structure. *Section through the disk and one arm, simplified.*

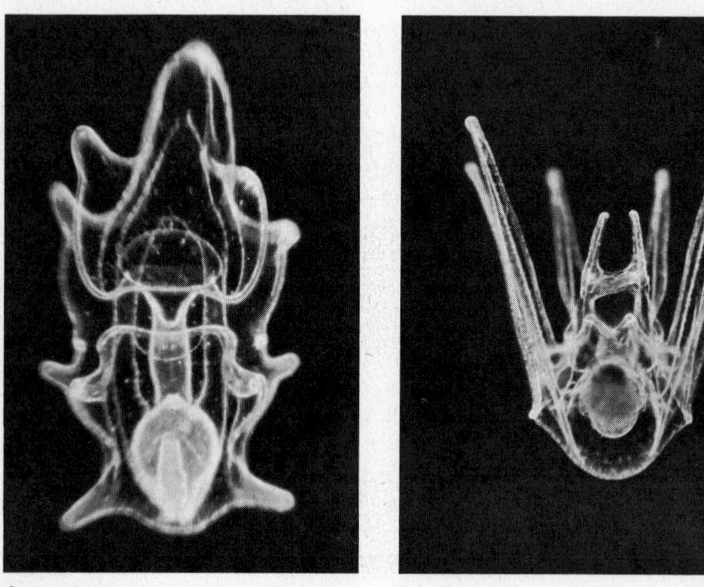

13.7 Echinoderm larvae. *A, bipinnaria larva of a starfish. Note alimentary tract internally and lobes with ciliary bands externally. The larva as a whole resembles a dipleurula. Sea cucumbers have similar larvae. B, pluteus larva of a sea urchin. The ciliated arms, supported internally by skeletal rods, increase buoyancy and swimming surfaces. Brittle stars have quite similar larvae.*

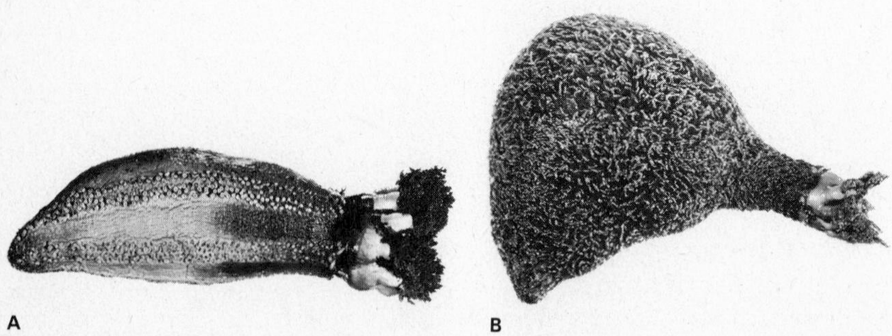

13.8 Sea cucumbers. *A, Cucumaria, a sea cucumber in which tube feet are arranged in five distinct double rows (two of them visible here). B, Thyone, a sea cucumber in which tube feet are not arranged in any orderly pattern. (A, B, courtesy Carolina Biological Supply Company.)*

trudes from the underside of the arm. Stiffened by water pressed into them from the ampullas, tube feet can be used as tiny walking legs. They also serve as suction disks when they are pressed against a solid surface and their end plates are lifted away. By such means the tube feet of a starfish can exert enough steady pull on the shells of a clam to tire the clam and force its shells open.

The tube feet along each arm are arranged in rows that border an *ambulacral groove,* a furrow leading to the mouth in the center of the underside, or *oral* surface. The mouth connects via a short esophagus to a large stomach that can be everted through the mouth into the soft tissues of a clam (Fig. 13.6). Small food particles and fluid foods pass to a short intestine and then to five pairs of large digestive glands (*pyloric caeca*), one pair occupying most of the free space in each arm. The alimentary system terminates at a small anal pore in the center of the aboral surface. Encircling the esophagus and situated close to the ring canal is a *nerve ring,* from which emanate five *radial nerves,* one to each arm. These nerves run along the bottom of the ambulacral grooves (see Fig. 13.5), and they terminate at an eye spot at the tip of each arm. The circulatory system consists of a series of coelomic blood channels, some of them contractile (axial gland and sinus, see Fig. 13.6). Moreover, the fluid that fills the coelom carries out a significant amount of internal transport, too. Excretion is achieved partly by diffusion through the body surface, partly by amoeboid cells in the coelomic fluid. These cells absorb excretory waste and carry it to the exterior through the skin gills.

Starfishes contain five pairs of sex organs, one pair per arm. In most cases fertilization occurs in open water, and development includes a free-swimming, bilateral *bipinnaria* larva (Fig. 13.7). This larva eventually undergoes a very complex metamorphosis into a young radial adult. Such a developmental pattern is generally typical also in the other echinoderm classes, though the larvae differ slightly in appearance and are named differently.

The crinoid class comprises the stalked, sessile sea lilies and the unstalked, gracefully swimming feather stars (Color Fig. 22). The body of these animals is cup-shaped, and the greatly branched arms are attached to the rim of the cup. Sea cucumbers have a horizontal oral-aboral axis, retractile branched tentacles around the mouth, and a leathery body wall that contains micro-

A

B

13.9 ***Brittle stars.*** *A, a whole animal. B, close-up of the disk of Ophiothrix. See also Color Fig. 22.*

A

B

C

13.10 ***Echinoids.*** *A, a sea urchin. B, the skeleton of a sea urchin, showing fused dermal plates with rows of openings for the tube feet. C, sand dollars, aboral (left) and oral (right) views. See also Color Fig. 22.*

scopic endoskeletal *ossicles.* The water-vascular system is simplified, and in many cases functional tube feet are absent (Fig. 13.8). Brittle stars resemble starfishes to a certain extent, but their long and highly mobile arms are marked off sharply from the central disk and serve in serpentine fashion for locomotion. Functional tube feet are again absent, and the animals also lack an intestine or an anus, the stomach being a blind sac. The mouth is armed with five muscle-operated toothlike jaws that serve well in a primarily carnivorous way of life (Fig. 13.9).

Sea urchins are identified readily by their long, movable spines, which are outgrowths from the endoskeleton. This skeleton is fused together as a rigid, globular shell, with rows of pores through which the tube feet protrude (Fig. 13.10). Sea urchins are scavenging omnivores, and they too possess a toothed mouth and a highly complex chewing organ that operates the teeth. Sand dollars have a greatly flattened body and movable spines that are quite short, but in most other respects these animals are similar to sea urchins.

Chordates

Phylum Chordata notochord-possessing animals

Subphylum Urochordata tunicates, sea squirts; marine, sessile or free-swimming, often colonial through budding; with secreted external cellulose envelope (*tunic*); unsegmented; gill slits used in breathing and ciliary filter feeding; circulatory system open; 2,000 species

Subphylum Cephalochordata amphioxus, lancelets; marine, in sand; notochord and dorsal nerve cord throughout life; head or brain absent; segmented; filter-feeding, with numerous gill slits; circulation open, without heart; 30 species

Subphylum Vertebrata vertebrates; segmented, with head, trunk, and tail; endoskeleton with skull enclosing brain; embryo with notochord, adult with notochord and/or vertebral column; with pharyngeal gills or lungs; circulation closed, with heart; blood with white blood cells and hemoglobin in red blood cells; with lymph system; liver present; endocrine system elaborate; 50,000 species

Since this phylum includes man and the animals most directly important to man, it is unquestionably the most interesting from almost any standpoint.

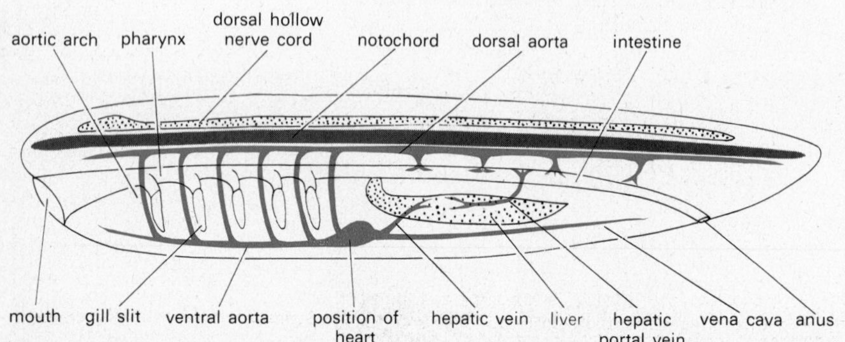

13.11 Chordate characteristics, *particularly as exemplified in vertebrates. Dorsal nerve cord, notochord, and pharyngeal gill slits are diagnostic of all chordates. In the circulatory pattern, blood flows forward through the ventral aorta, up through the aortic arches where oxygenation takes place, and backward through the dorsal aorta. Intestinal blood passes to the liver through the hepatic portal vein and from the liver back to the general circulation through the hepatic vein. The vena cava collects blood from all other hind regions of the body. The gill slits are primitively ciliated and strain food particles from water that flows through mouth, pharynx, and out via the gill passages. Such food then reaches the intestine.*

Chordates are so named because all have a *notochord,* a flexible skeletal supporting rod formed in the embryo from dorsal mesoderm (Fig. 13.11). In vertebrates this rod later becomes surrounded by vertebral components of cartilage or bone, and in most cases the notochord then degenerates. Chordates are identified also by a dorsal hollow nerve cord and paired gill slits, either or both of which are sometimes present during early life-cycle stages only. Gill slits are passages between the pharynx and the sides of the body. The slits serve in breathing; water entering the mouth returns to the outside through the gill slits, where oxygen is absorbed into the blood circulation. In tunicates and amphioxus the slits also have a feeding function. Microscopic food in the water is strained out by cilia around the slits and is passed to the esophagus and stomach. Vertebrates ingest bulkier food, and in fishes the gill slits still serve in breathing but no longer in feeding. In lung-breathing vertebrates, man included, the gill apparatus begins to form in the embryo but it does not develop very far and never becomes functional.

Tunicates
Subphylum Urochordata

Class Ascidiacea sea squirts, ascidians; larvae if present are nonfeeding tadpoles, with notochord and dorsal nerve cord in tail; adults without tail, sessile, colonial through budding or solitary; gill slits numerous; alimentary tract U-shaped

Class Thaliacea chain tunicates; larvae if present with notochord and dorsal nerve cord in tail; adults without tail but free-swimming, locomotion by "jet" propulsion; gill slits few to numerous; polymorphic, with colonial stages budded in chains

Class Larvacea appendicularians; tail with notochord and nerve cord permanent throughout life; adults larvalike, free-swimming; tunic forms complex housing used with tail in feeding; one pair of gill slits

Adult ascidians are not obviously recognizable as chordates, but their tadpole larvae are. Indeed it is believed that tadpoles of ancestral tunicate stocks have given rise to all other chordates. A tunicate tadpole has a conspicuous muscular *tail* supported by a notochord (Fig. 13.12). Above

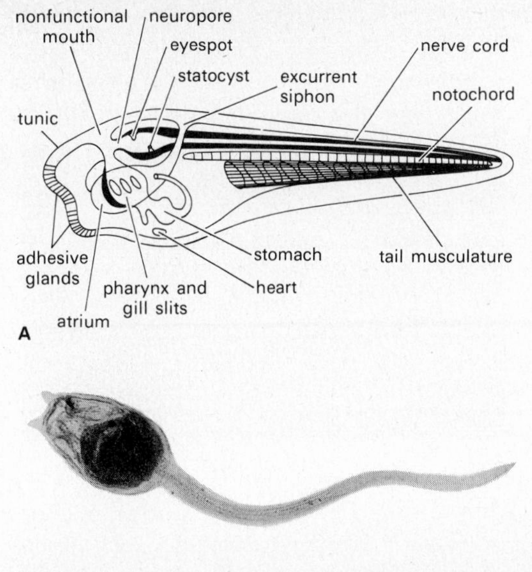

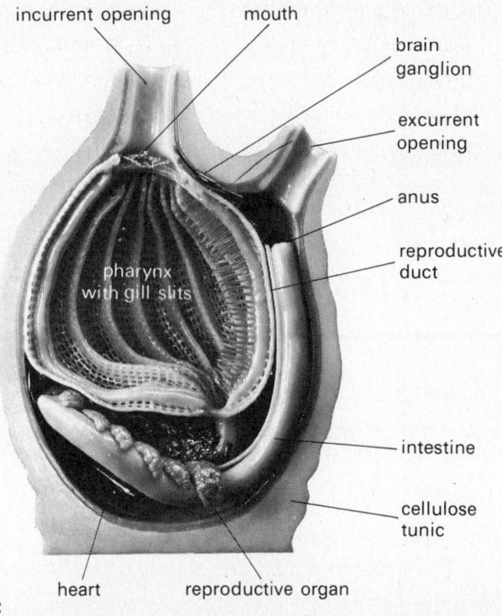

13.12 Tunicate structure. *A, section through a tadpole. B, a whole tadpole. C, cutaway model of adult. Food-bearing water is drawn into the pharynx through the incurrent siphon. Food passes to the U-shaped alimentary tract, and water flows to the outside through gill slits, atrium, and excurrent siphon.*

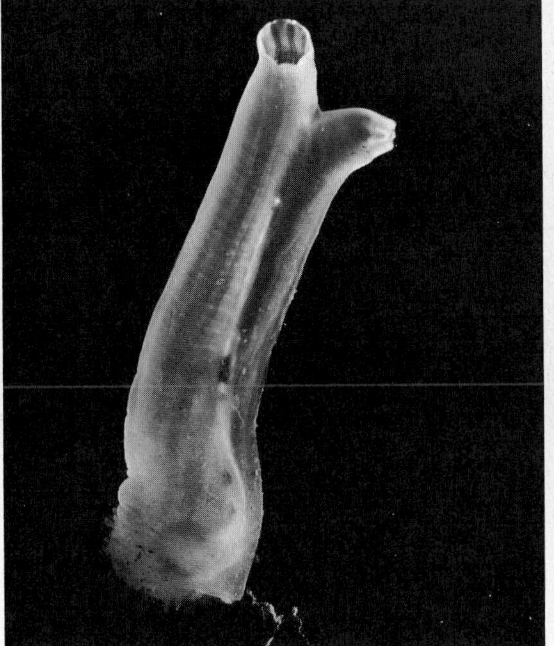

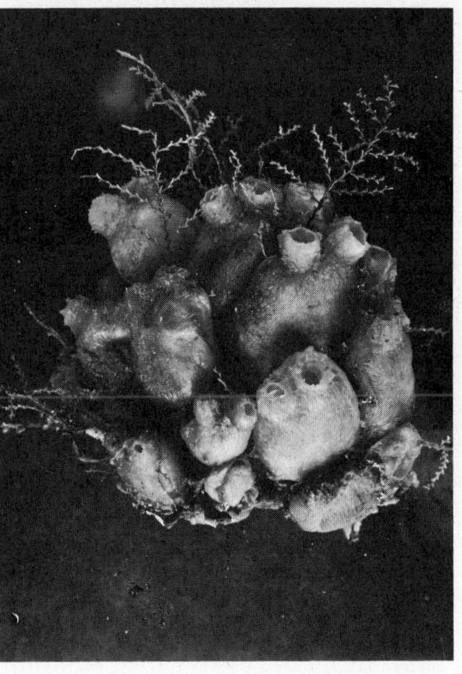

13.13 Ascidians. *A, Ciona, a solitary type. The incurrent siphon is at top, fully open. B, Ascidia, a colonial type. See also Color Fig. 16.*

the notochord lies a hollow nerve cord, which extends forward and widens to a brain. A roughly U-shaped alimentary system is present, and both the gill slits and the anus open into an *atrium,* a chamber that surrounds the pharynx and leads to the outside at an excurrent *atrial siphon.* However, this opening as well as the mouth are covered over by the cellulose tunic that envelops the whole larva. Thus the tadpoles cannot feed. Usually within a few hours after being formed such tadpoles attach to a solid surface at their front ends and transform to adults.

During this metamorphosis the entire tail degenerates, the notochord and dorsal nerve cord disappear, and the brain is reduced to a single ganglion. Also, the alimentary system becomes

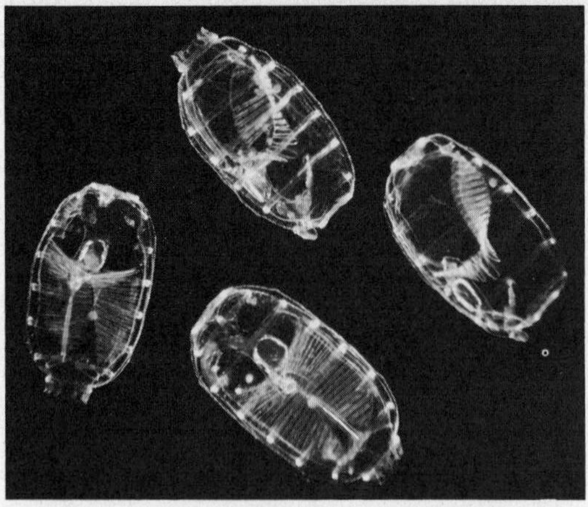

A

B

13.14 ***Tunicates.*** *A, Doliolum, a member of the class Thaliacea, in plankton, from life. Note muscle hoops around barrel-shaped body, siphons at opposite ends of body, and gill baskets inside. B, Oikopleura, a member of the class Larvacea, in plankton, from life. Note long undulating tail, cellulose "house" at base of tail.*

shifted until both mouth and atrial siphon point away from the attached front end of the larva. The tunic over these openings is resorbed, and the animal then begins its sessile adult existence. In many species the adults remain solitary; in others colonies are formed through budding (Fig. 13.13).

Tunicates in the two other classes do not become sessile, but their larvae metamorphose into more or less elongated, still fairly tadpolelike, free-swimming adults (Fig. 13.14). Chain tunicates are barrel-shaped, and the alimentary system is straight, not U-like. Cilia in the gill apparatus propel water through the body from one end of the "barrel" to the other, and the animal thereby jets in the opposite direction. Long chains of linked individuals form by budding. In the class of appendicularians the larval tail persists permanently. The animal is enclosed in a complex "house" developed from the tunic, and the long tail is tucked under the body of the animal along the floor of this house. Undulations of the tail draw food-bearing water through the house and also propel the animal.

It is believed that, like chain tunicates and appendicularians, cephalochordates and vertebrates too could have evolved through retention of larval, tadpolelike features to the adult stage.

Amphioxus
Subphylum Cephalochordata

Amphioxus is slender, laterally compressed, and pointed at both ends (Fig. 13.15). It lies in sand of shallow coastal waters, with only its anterior end sticking out of its burrow. The animal contains a permanent notochord and nerve cord, both extending over the whole length of the body, but there is no brain and a head is absent. The mouth leads to a long ciliated pharynx with 60 to more than 100 pairs of lateral sloping gill slits. Water passing through these emerges in a ventral atrium, which opens to the outside at a posterior *atriopore*.

Amphioxus is a segmented animal. The body musculature forms lateral V-shaped segmental bundles; as in vertebrates these are innervated by paired segmental nerves from the nerve cord. Excretory and reproductive organs likewise have a segmental arrangement. Although a heart is absent and the blood vessels are open-ended, the anatomic pattern of the circulation greatly resembles that of vertebrates. A contractile ventral aorta below the pharynx pumps blood forward and then up through *aortic arches* between the gill slits (see Fig. 13.11). Blood collects above the pharynx in

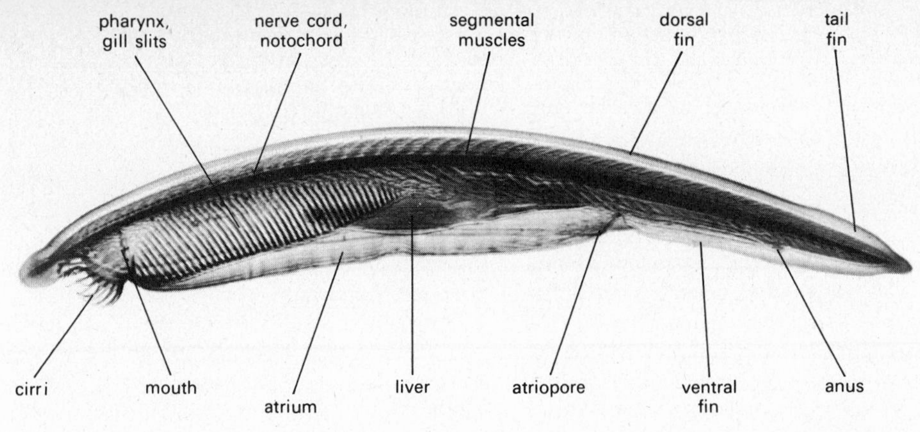

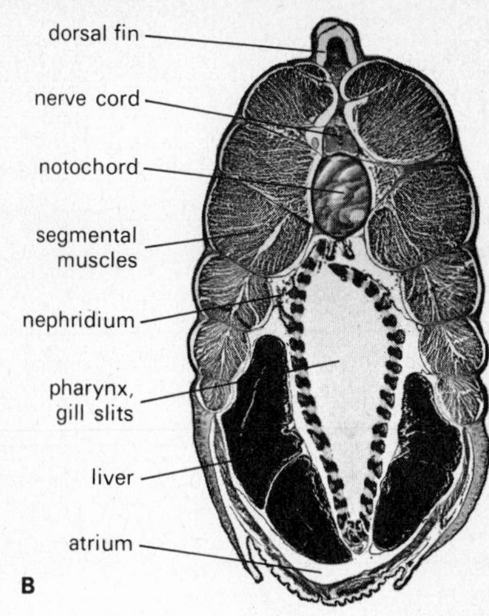

13.15 ***Amphioxus,*** *the lancelet. A, side view. Notochord and nerve cord are not visible separately in this photo. B, cross section near hind end of pharynx. Note segmental nephridia. (A, B, courtesy Carolina Biological Supply Company.)*

a dorsal aorta, which passes backward and gives off branches to the tissues. Veins from the tissues return blood to the beginning of the ventral aorta, where the heart would be located in a vertebrate.

The coelom arises from segmental coelomic sacs in the embryo. Excretion occurs through flame-bulb-like nephridia, located near the dorsal end of each gill slit, where they filter blood from vessels in the coelom lining. The presence of nephridia in a chordate is interesting and puzzling; most biologists regard them as a good example of independent, parallel evolution.

Amphioxus evidently is specialized in many respects, but in others it does suggest in a rather distant way what ancient vertebrates might have been like.

Vertebrates
Subphylum Vertebrata

Class Agnatha jawless fishes: lampreys, hagfishes; freshwater and marine; with notochord throughout life and cartilage skeleton; sucking mouth; paired fins absent; heart two-chambered; excretion pronephric in larva, mesonephric in adult; 50 species

Class Chondrichthyes cartilage fishes: sharks, rays, skates; marine; notochord is reduced but persists in adult; skin with dermal denticles; heart two-chambered; excretion mesonephric; 600 species

Class Osteichthyes bony fishes; freshwater and marine; notochord does not persist in most; skin with dermal scales; with lung or swim bladder; heart two-chambered; excretion mesonephric; 25,000 species

Class Amphibia amphibians: salamanders, newts, toads, frogs; freshwater and terrestrial; paired appendages with legs; skin without scales; breathing via gills, lungs, skin, and mouth cavity; heart three-chambered; 10 pairs of cranial nerves; fertilization mostly external, development mostly via tadpole larvae; 3,000 species

Class Reptilia reptiles: turtles, lizards, snakes, alligators; terrestrial and secondarily aquatic; skin with epidermal scales; breathing by lung; heart four-chambered; 12 pairs of cranial nerves; excretion metanephric; fertilization internal, eggs with shells, larvae absent; 6,000 species

Class Aves birds; skin with feathers; forelimbs are wings; with horny beak, teeth absent; heart four-chambered; body temperature constant; 12 pairs of cranial nerves; excretion metanephric; fertilization internal, eggs with shells, larvae absent; 10,000 species

Class Mammalia mammals; skin with hair; teeth in sockets, heart four-chambered; red blood corpuscles without nuclei; coelom divided by diaphragm; body temperature constant; 12 pairs of cranial nerves; excretion metanephric; fertilization internal, development in uterus in most cases, born young nourished by milk from mammary glands; 5,000 species

Ancestral vertebrates probably invaded the freshwater rivers as segmented, tailed derivatives of tunicate antecedents. Their tadpole larvae had strongly muscled tails that could propel them upriver, and their adults must have been pharyngeal filter feeders like their marine forebears. Also, they evolved a new kind of kidney that could eliminate the large amounts of water drawn into the body osmotically.

This kidney, still formed today in fish larvae, was a *pronephros* (Fig. 13.16). In each of the anterior body segments developed a *nephron,* composed of a double-layered cup (*nephric capsule*) and a ball of blood capillaries (*glomerulus*) that projected into the capsule. Water filtered from glomerular blood into the capsule, and a (*Wolffian*) duct from there joined other such ducts from nephrons in neighboring segments and led to the exterior near the anus. In later vertebrates many more nephron units developed in the segments of the middle and hind regions of the body, and the original anterior nephrons actually degenerated. Such a kidney is a *mesonephros;* it occurs today in the adults of all fishes and in amphibia.

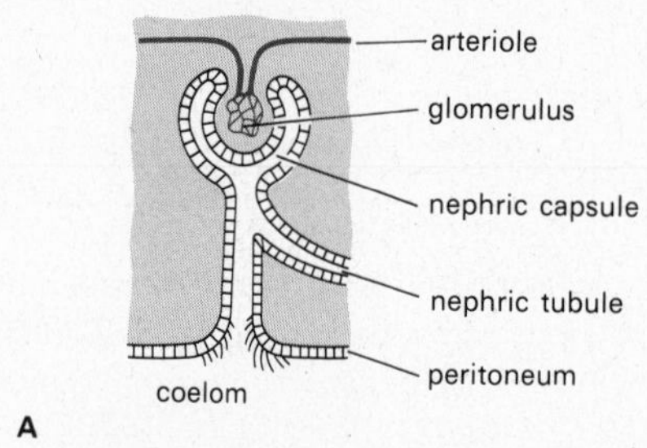

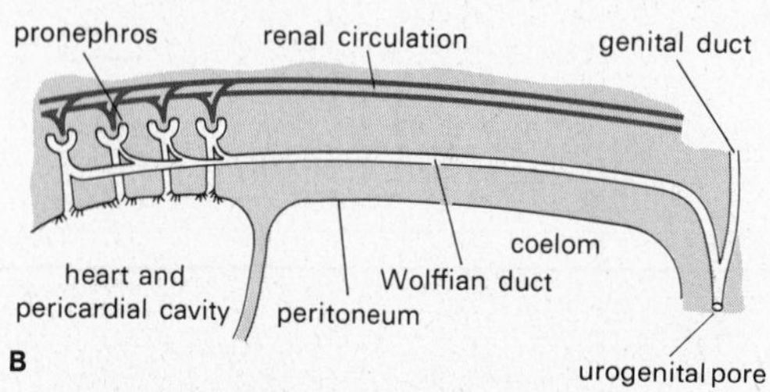

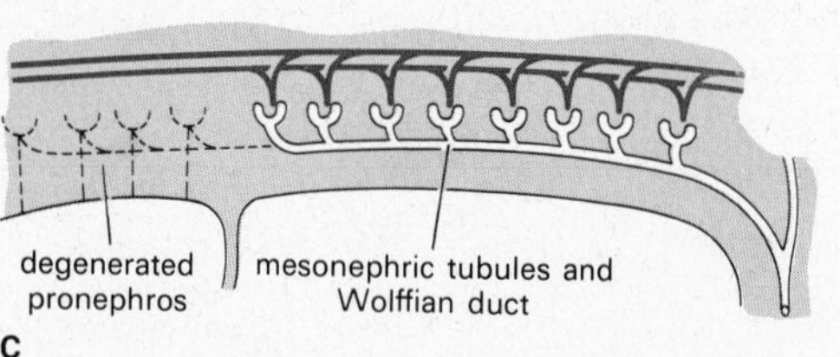

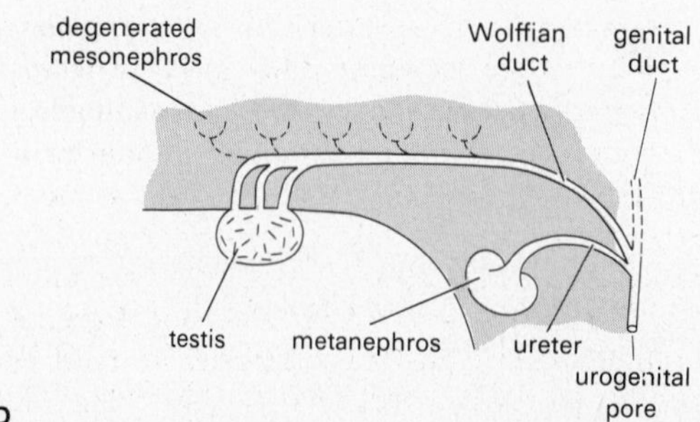

13.16 The vertebrate kidney. *A, a primitive nephron unit. Note ciliated funnel opening to coelom. B, the pronephric kidney. Note ciliated openings into the pericardial (coelomic) cavity. More nephron units actually occur than sketched here. C, the mesonephric kidney. The pronephros has degenerated, and new nephrons have developed along the Wolffian duct. Note absence of ciliated openings to coelom. D, the metanephric kidney. Mesonephric nephrons have degenerated, and a new large collection of nephrons has developed from the hind part of the Wolffian duct. In males this duct also makes new connections with the testes and becomes the sperm duct. In females the Wolffian duct degenerates, too, but the old genital duct becomes the egg channel from the ovaries to the outside.*

Like their ancestors, the most primitive living vertebrates still are pharyngeal filter feeders; in the larvae of Agnatha the cilia of the pharynx suck in water with small food particles through a round jawless mouth (Fig. 13.17). Even in the ectoparasitic adult lampreys, food consists of body fluids and tiny tissue fragments rasped off the host. In all other evolutionary lines of vertebrates, however, the main food-collecting organ is no longer the pharynx but the mouth itself, which has become equipped with jaws and true teeth. The nature of the food has changed concurrently to bulk nutrients, and the ancestral method of filter feeding has ceased. This change has left the gill slits primarily as breathing structures; and since therefore tiny particles no longer needed to be strained out of water, the number of gill slits could become reduced.

Indeed such a reduction has accompanied jaw development; the skeletal supports of the most anterior gills came to be remodeled as jaw supports (Fig. 13.18). But even though fewer gill slits then remained, these became highly efficient oxygenators; for the circulation became a closed network with extensive beds of capillaries in all body parts, gills included, and a newly evolved two-chambered heart moved blood rapidly

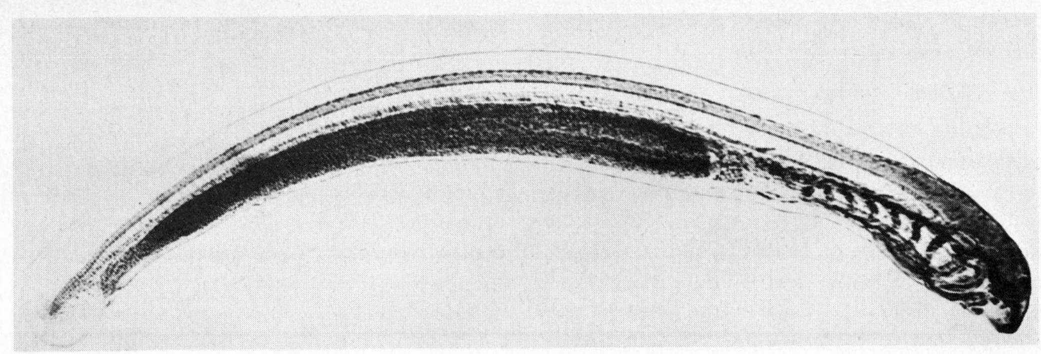

***13.17 Ammocoete larva** of jawless fishes. Note gill slits, nerve cord and brain, and position of notochord just underneath nerve cord. This larva is a pharyngeal filter feeder like the ancestors of vertebrates.*

through this circuit of vessels.

The freshwater environment continued to orient also the later stages of vertebrate evolution. Air sacs that pouched out from the pharynx appear to have been an original trait of bony fishes, in adaptation to occasional periods of drought. Such sacs still function as lungs in the most primitive bony fishes now living, but in most others they have become swim bladders (see Fig. 13.18). From early lung-possessing types then evolved vertebrates with additional adaptations to at first temporary and later permanent terrestrial life: fleshy fins with internal bones, elongated subsequently to legs; very yolky eggs first laid in water but later equipped with shells, laid on land, and developing without larval stages; three and then four chambers in the heart, permitting efficient separation of arterial and venous blood and thus providing enough oxygen for the increased energy requirements on land (see Chap. 20); a distinct energy-saving neck, with a swivel joint for the head; controls for maintenance of constant body temperature in birds and mammals, including insulating surface layers of fat, feathers, and fur; improved breathing and circulatory machinery in mammals, including a diaphragm and highly specialized blood corpuscles; and a new mammalian reproductive mechanism, in which the laying of shelled eggs was replaced by egg development in the uterus of the female, and in which milk was secreted for the newborn.

Furthermore, terrestrial living by reptiles, birds, and mammals came to depend on a new, land-adapted kidney, in which the earlier water-excreting function became reversed to a water-saving function. This new kidney, the *metanephros,* developed as an outgrowth from the hind region of the earlier mesonephros (see Fig. 13.16). Reptiles, birds, and mammals still have a mesonephros as embryos, but in later stages the metanephros arises. Its important new feature in each of the nephrons is a highly elongated, coiled tubule specialized to reabsorb water from urine flowing through it, hence to retain as much water as possible in the body (see Chap. 20). Thus whereas the aquatic vertebrates excrete a dilute, watery urine, the fully terrestrial groups have adapted to the water scarcity on land by excreting a highly concentrated, salty urine.

I II III IV V VI
A ancestral vertebrate

I II III IV V VI
B fishes

I II III IV V VI
C amphibians

***13.18 Vertebrate jaws, gills, and lungs.** A, ancestral vertebrates had six gill slits, six aortic arches (roman numerals), and six skeletal gill supports (the first indicated in black). Also present was a nasal organ and an air sac with a duct from the pharynx. B, development of jaws from the first gill supports was accompanied by a reduction of the first gill slit to a small spiracle (and even that disappeared in later bony fishes), and by a degeneration of the first two aortic arches. The air sac received blood from the sixth aortic arch, and the sac came to function as a lung in lobe-finned fishes and lungfishes but as a swim bladder in all other bony fishes. In many of the latter, moreover, the duct to the pharynx has degenerated. Also, the nasal organ has acquired a connection with the pharynx. C, lobe-finned fishes were the ancestors of amphibia and the later land vertebrates, in which gill slits are absent in the adults and breathing occurs through lungs. Of the aortic arches remaining in these animals, the third forms the carotid artery to the head, the fourth represents part of the aorta to the body, and the lower portion of the sixth is part of the pulmonary artery to the lungs. The heart is three-chambered in amphibians, two-chambered in all earlier vertebrates.*

Jawless Fishes

Class Agnatha

In these roughly eel-shaped animals, the front end of the body is a round funnel-like sucker, equipped with epidermal teeth and a rasping tongue that can be protruded through the central mouth (Fig. 13.19). The skin is smooth and scaleless. Folds of it that extend dorsally and around the tail form low median fins. Paired pectoral or pelvic fins are absent. In lampreys a single dorsal nostril leads to a closed nasal sac. Just behind it lies a functional *pineal eye,* connected with the brain by a nerve as in the lateral eyes. Internally, the persisting notochord is stiffened by incompletely developed segmental cartilage supports, and cartilage also forms the brain case and a capsule around the heart. The pharyngeal gill chamber, ventral to the esophagus, opens to the exterior of a lamprey through seven pairs of gill slits.

A stomach is absent, and the esophagus continues directly as the intestine. The circulation is typically vertebrate, and, as in all fishes, the heart contains one atrium and one ventricle. A single sex organ discharges reproductive cells into the well-developed coelom. Such cells reach the outside through a genital pore in the mesonephric excretory duct, which opens just behind the anus. All lampreys spawn in rivers. Eggs develop into long-lived *ammocoete* larvae, which filter-feed along river bottoms in the ancestral manner (see Fig. 13.17). After metamorphosis young sea lampreys migrate to the ocean, where they lead a mature life as bloodsuckers attached to fish. Adult brook lampreys remain in rivers. They do not feed but spawn within a few days and die. Hagfishes are marine jawless types that develop without larval stages.

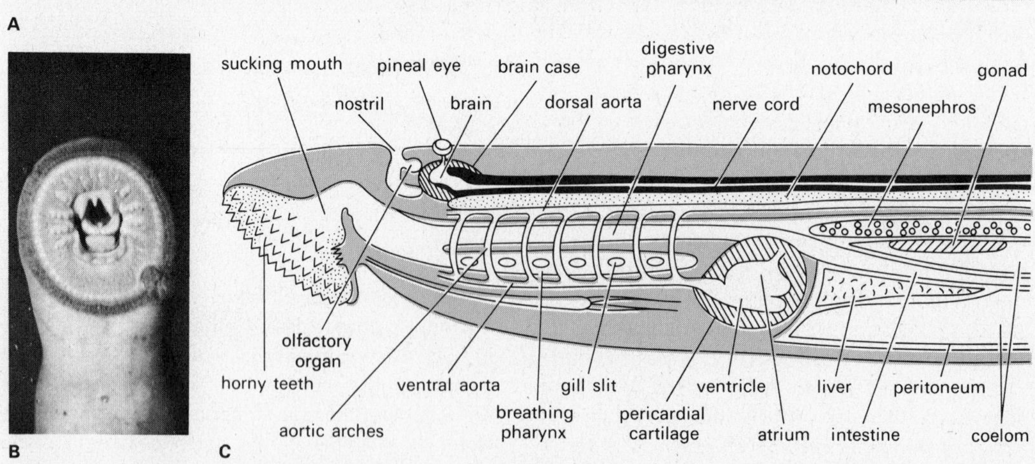

13.19 ***Lampreys.*** *A, side view. Note gill slits, fins. B, the sucker mouth, showing the horny epidermal teeth. C, sagittal section of anterior part of body. (A, B, courtesy Carolina Biological Supply Company.)*

Cartilage Fishes

Class Chondrichthyes

In a shark (Fig. 13.20), the skin is studded with pointed *denticles* that correspond structurally to vertebrate teeth (those of mammals included). In addition to median fins, paired fins are present and are jointed to pectoral and pelvic girdles. As a result of the evolution of jaws the first of the ancestral gill slits has become reduced in sharks to a small opening, the *spiracle* (see Figs. 13.18 and 13.20). Five fully developed gill slits are behind a spiracle. The notochord persists, and it is constricted where the vertebrae surround it. All skeletal components are permanently cartilaginous.

The mouth contains several rows of teeth structured like the surface denticles. The alimentary tract includes a stomach and, opening into the intestine, a large liver and a separate pancreas. In the intestine is a *spiral valve,* a tissue fold that increases the absorptive surface. Separate reproductive and excretory ducts open in a *cloaca,* the terminal part of the hindgut. A salt-secreting *rectal gland* is also attached to the

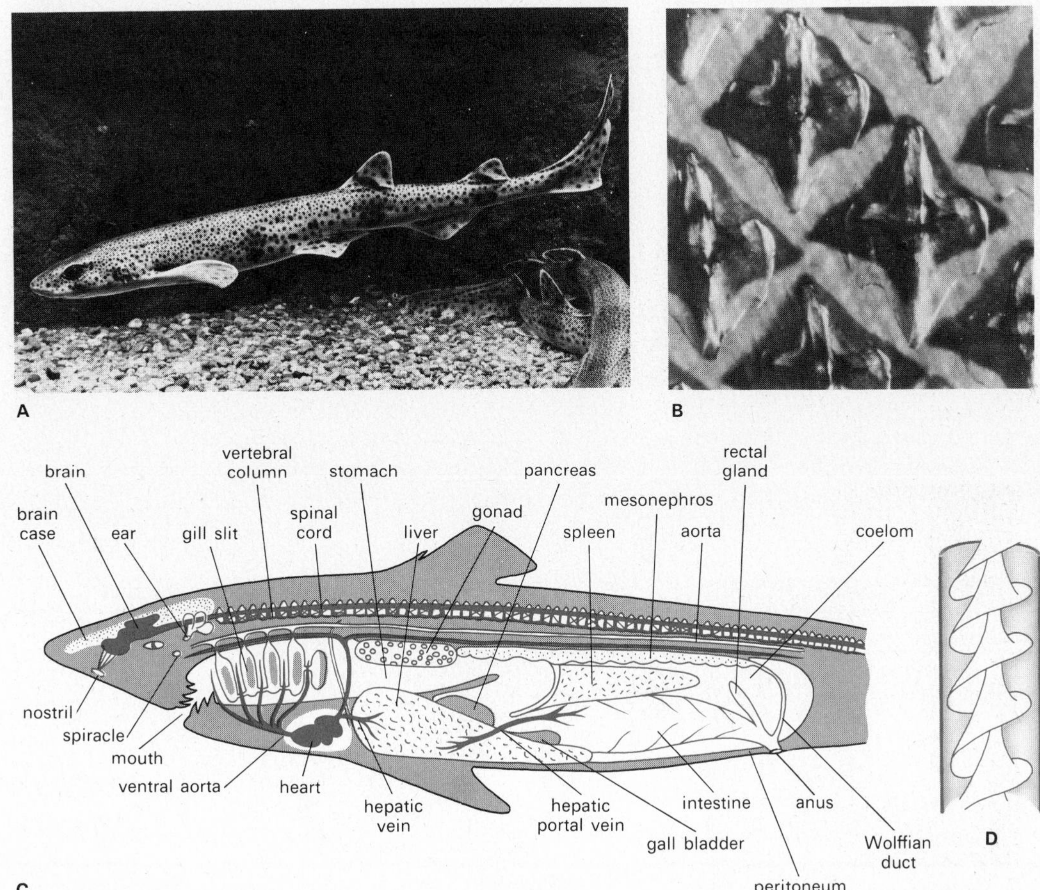

***13.20 Sharks.** A, a dogfishlike type, from life. B, high-power view of skin, showing the toothlike denticles. C, sagittal section of main part of body. D, spiral valve.*

cloaca. Males typically have a pair of copulatory organs (*fin claspers*) between the pelvic fins.

Most sharks are fiercely carnivorous, but the whale and basking sharks are plankton feeders. Basking sharks are the largest of all fishes, attaining lengths of over 50 ft. Many rays and skates exhibit interesting offensive and protective adaptations, among them snouts extended as "saws" in the sawfishes, poison spines at the end of the tail in stingrays, and electric organs lateral to the eyes in the torpedo rays.

Bony Fishes
Class Osteichthyes

This largest vertebrate class comprises two subclasses. In the primitive *flesh-finned* fishes, the pectoral and pelvic fins contain internal bones that correspond substantially to the limb bones of terrestrial vertebrates. Also, the pharyngeal air sac functions as a lung. These fishes are repre-

A

B

***13.21* Flesh-finned bony fishes.** *A, a coelacanth, a rare flesh-finned fish still surviving today. The pectoral and pelvic fins of these lung-breathers have internal bony skeletons. Note the operculum, a bony plate covering the gills. Note also the diamond-shaped enamel-covered (ganoid) scales. B, a lungfish (Protopterus), found today in West Africa.*

A

B

***13.22* Ray-finned bony fishes.** *A, a pike. Note soft-rayed, smooth-contoured fins. B, a perch. Note hard-rayed, spiky fins. See also Fig. 13.24.*

sented today by only four surviving genera, one of *lobe-finned fishes* (*coelacanths*) and three of *lungfishes* (Fig. 13.21). In the *ray-finned* subclass, by contrast, the paired fins are supported by needlelike bony rays, and the air sac is usually a swim bladder (Fig. 13.22).

In both groups, connective tissue in the dermis of the skin gives rise to overlapping bony scales, which are overlain in turn by the epidermis. Gills are usually reduced in number to four pairs, and on each side of the head they are covered by an *operculum,* a bony plate hinged to the skeletal supports behind the jaws. Each gill is a double plate composed of highly vascularized *gill filaments,* and a skeletal arch supports the gill tissue. The inner edges of the gills are often expanded as fingerlike *gill rakers,* which prevent food from passing through the gill slits. Spiracles are absent in most cases (Fig. 13.23).

The largest group of bony fishes comprises the so-called *teleosts,* a superorder of some two dozen orders in the ray-finned subclass. Teleosts exhibit two general structural patterns (Fig. 13.24). In the *clupeiform* pattern, exemplified by fishes such as trout, salmon, and herring, the fin rays are soft, the scales are smooth (*cycloid*), the swim bladder remains connected to the pharynx by a duct, and the pelvic fins are in a primitive abdominal, posterior position. In the *perciform* pattern, exemplified by types such as perch, tuna, and bass, the fin rays are hard and spiny, the scales are rough-textured (*ctenoid*), the swim bladder lacks a duct, and the pelvic fins lie forward, often actually in the head region in front of the pectoral fins. These two patterns are not always sharply distinct, and many teleost groups exhibit mixed and intergrading characteristics.

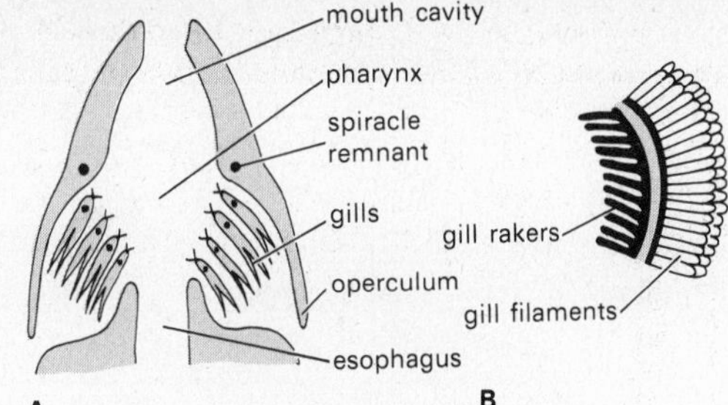

***13.23 Gills.** A, horizontal section through fish head, showing position of the four pairs of gills. B, a left gill in side view, showing double row of gill filaments pointing away from pharynx and gill rakers pointing into pharynx.*

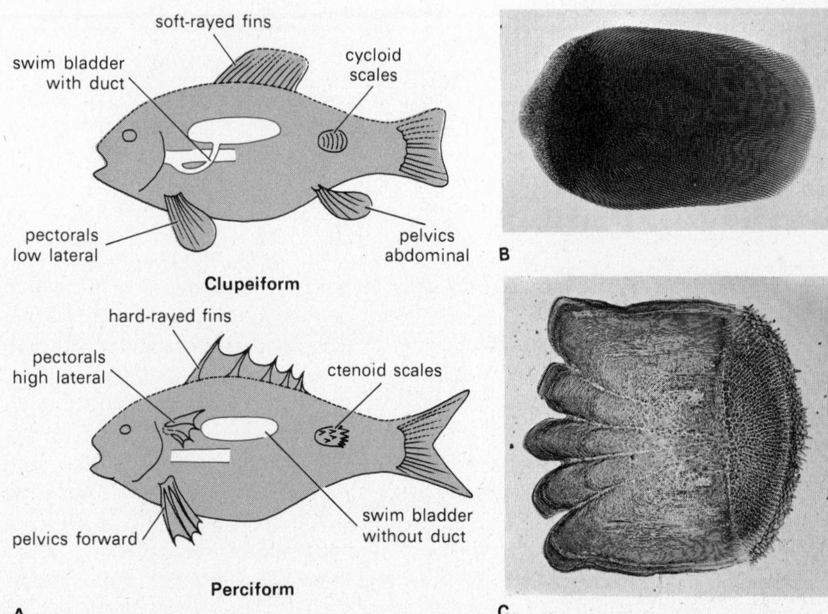

***13.24 Teleost traits.** A, the clupeiform pattern occurs in, for example, herring, goldfishes, or guppies, and the perciform pattern in, for example, perches, basses, or tunas. See Fig. 13.22 for illustrations of fishes exhibiting these two patterns. Many teleosts exhibit a mixture of clupeiform and perciform traits. B, cycloid scales, smooth-textured. C, ctenoid scales, spiny or rough-textured. (B, C, courtesy Carolina Biological Supply Company.)*

Amphibians

Class Amphibia

The most notable traits of amphibians are those that adapt the animals to an at least partly terrestrial life; and most of these traits trace their origin to ancestral lobe-finned fishes, from which amphibia evolved. The paired appendages are legs, each with five (or fewer) toes. Primitive amphibia still live entirely in water, but the majority are air breathers with lungs (Fig. 13.25). Gills still occur in the tadpole larvae and in exceptional cases also in some of the adults. In conjunction with the air-breathing habit, nasal passages open in the pharynx and make breathing possible while the mouth remains closed. The skin is thin and scaleless and serves as an accessory breathing

A

B

13.25 **Amphibia.** *A, Amphiuma, the conger eel, a permanently aquatic type. Note reduced appendages. B, a fire salamander. C, toads copulating. D, Hyla, a tree frog. (A, B, courtesy Carolina Biological Supply Company.)*

C

D

organ. Also adaptive in air breathing is the three-chambered heart, capable to some extent of preventing a mixing of oxygen-rich arterial blood and oxygen-poor venous blood. The two bloods do come together in the single ventricle, but not so much as they do in a two-chambered heart. Thus, with a lobe-finned starting point, the terrestrial amphibian descendant walks and breathes air on a permanent basis. Yet even the most land-adapted amphibian still requires a moist environment, and reproductive and developmental processes actually retain the ancestral fishlike characteristics. Thus, eggs typically must be laid in water, fertilization takes place externally after egg-laying as in fishes, and the tadpoles are clearly fishlike even where the adults are terrestrial (see Color Fig. 12).

Newts and salamanders are tailed throughout life, frogs and toads are tailless as adults. Most of these are lung-breathers, and most frogs and toads also have eyelids, another adaptation to life out of water. In frogs and toads the hind legs are far longer and stronger than the forelegs, and in conjunction with this specialization as jumpers the animals are squat, foreshortened, and without neck. The tongue can be hurled out of the mouth at an insect, posterior end first. Toads are toothless; frogs have teeth on the upper jaw and the roof of the mouth.

Reptiles

Class Reptilia

The first fully terrestrial vertebrates, reptiles have a dry, impervious skin covered with epidermal scales (which are developmentally equivalent to feathers and hair). The limbs raise the body off the ground more than in amphibians. The breathing system contains a trachea (windpipe) and bronchial tubes to the lungs, as in birds and mammals. Also as in birds and mammals, the heart is four-chambered, completely so in crocodiles, nearly so in the other reptiles; it keeps arterial and venous blood separated. And the adult excretory system is metanephric, capable of producing a highly hypertonic, water-conserving urine.

The single most essential adaptation to land life is the shelled egg, about which more will be said in Chap. 26. All reptiles lay eggs on land, even if the adults are secondarily aquatic. And fertili-

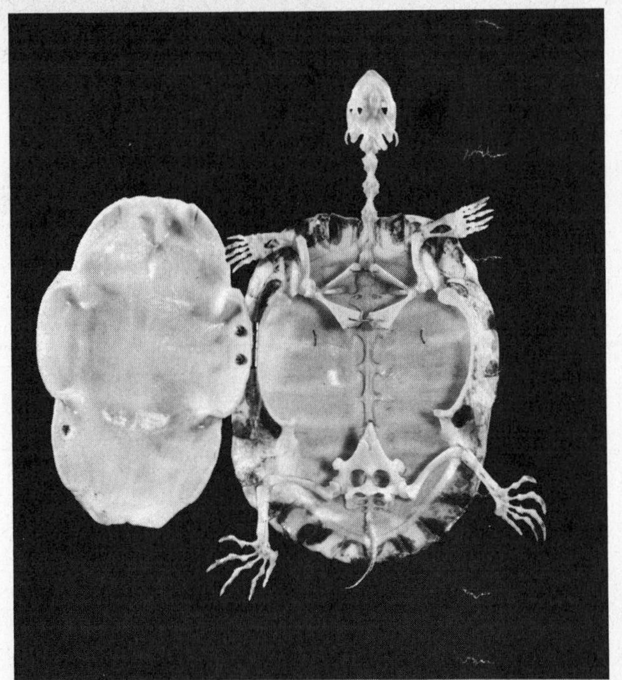

A

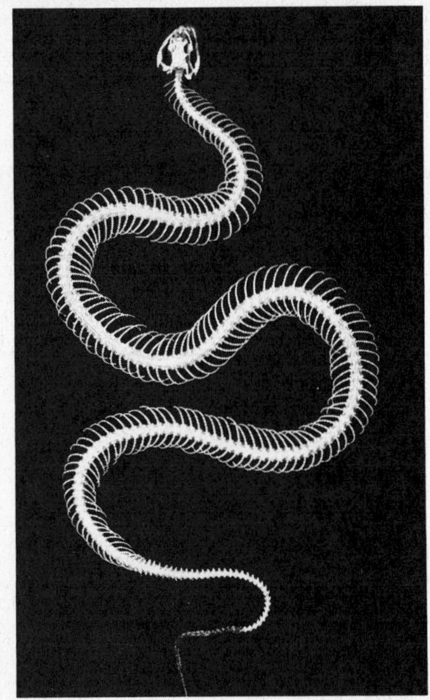

B

13.26 Skeletons of reptiles. *A, the turtle skeleton. The ventral part (plastron) is cut away and hinged back, showing the limb girdles underneath the dorsal part (carapace) formed by the rib cage. B, the snake skeleton. Note numerous vertebrae and absence of limbs, limb girdles, and breastbone. (A, courtesy Carolina Biological Supply Company.)*

13.27 Reptiles. *A, Sphenodon, the lizardlike tuatara of New Zealand. B, the lizard Chamaeleon, catching grasshopper with tongue.*

A

B

zation is always internal; it occurs by copulation as in mammals and birds.

In turtles the body is protected by a bony dome (*carapace*) formed from broadened, fused ribs and by a lower plate (*plastron*) formed from the bones of the pectoral and pelvic girdles (Fig. 13.26). The whole bony casing is covered by skin, which in many cases develops an epidermal shell of hard horn. In sea turtles the legs are modified as flippers.

Some 95 percent of reptile species now living comprise lizards and snakes. Though specialized in many ways, snakes could be characterized as limbless lizards. In snakes the left and right halves of the lower jaws are not fused together but are joined by ligaments. As a result the mouth can be distended greatly; a snake can ingest an animal several times wider than its own diameter. Snakes are without external ear openings, but they "hear" vibrations transmitted from the ground through the skeleton. Eyes are lidless but can be covered by a transparent (*nictitating*) membrane. Vertebrae often number up to 400. Limb girdles and limbs are generally absent, though vestigial remains of pelvic girdles persist in pythons and related types (see Fig. 13.26).

The tuatara of New Zealand is a lizardlike evolutionary relic with a functional pineal eye like a lamprey (Fig. 13.27). Crocodiles and alligators are the closest living relatives of dinosaurs on the one hand and of birds on the other. Among adaptations of these reptiles to a semiaquatic existence are closable nostrils; webbed hindfeet; ear openings that can be covered by flaps of skin; a long palate that separates the mouth and nasal cavities and permits breathing even when the mouth is submerged; and a powerful tail that serves in swimming as well as in offense and defense. Crocodiles and gavials have narrow jaws, and the fourth pair of teeth on the lower jaw remains exposed when the mouth is closed. Alligator and caiman jaws are broader and rounded anteriorly, and teeth are not exposed after mouth closure.

Birds
Class Aves

The earliest birds already flew and had feathers; flightless birds such as ostriches and kiwis today are descendants of flying ancestors (Fig. 13.28).

Flying birds consume much food to provide the energy and high operating temperature for flight. Feathers are the important heat regulators and also the means of flight. They are horny outgrowths from the epidermis, corresponding to the hairs of mammals. Flight feathers on the wings (and the tail) are maintained in overlapping position when a wing moves down. On the upstroke the feathers are canted by muscles like Venetian

13.28 ***Birds.*** *A, an emu, one of the flightless types. B, an Australian lyre bird. C, a shoebill stork.*

A

B

C

blinds, letting air pass through with minimum drag. The short, heat-regulating down feathers retain a layer of insulating dead air between the skin and the environment. The same muscles that produce ''gooseflesh'' in man can erect the down feathers and permit cooling of the body.

The flight-adapted skeleton is light and delicate, the head is rounded and streamlined, and the skull bones are fused. Jaws form a toothless bill or beak and are covered with a layer of epidermal horn. Eardrums are recessed deeply, and the animals are without external earlobes or other projections that might disrupt smooth air flow over the head. The neck vertebrae provide extreme head mobility, but these vertebrae lock to one another firmly during flight. In flying birds, the prominent keel of the breastbone serves as attachment surface for the powerful flight muscles (the ''white meat'' in a chicken). A remarkable breathing system provides the large quantities of oxygen needed in flying. From the lungs extend several large air sacs that occupy much of the space between the internal organs of the body. Some of the sacs extend forward to the neck, where they often play an added role in distending the neck during courtship activities.

The reproductive pattern too is adjusted to the condition of flying. External genitals are absent (except in male ostriches, which have a penis). This lack, perhaps another adaptation for maintenance of smooth body contours, necessitates strong cooperation during mating, for the cloaca of the male must be apposed precisely against that of the female. Exercise of such cooperation is prepared for by courtship rituals, and these are based at least in part on colorful display plumage and color vision (see Chap. 26). Thus color vision in birds and absence of a penis in males in a sense appear to go together.

The largest group of birds comprises the perching birds, in which a system of tendons in the legs assures that body weight alone can keep the toes curled tightly around a tree branch. The attention required for perching therefore is minimal. Perching birds include all the songbirds, which typically build elaborate nests. Song and brilliant mating plumage are usually characteristic of males only.

Mammals

Class Mammalia

Subclass Prototheria egg-laying mammals; adults with horny bill; testes in abdomen; nipples absent, numerous ducts of mammary glands open individually

Subclass Metatheria pouched, marsupial mammals; nipples in ventral abdominal pouch (*marsupium*), where immature young complete development, attached to nipples

Subclass Eutheria placental mammals; in male, ducts from bladder and testes join and form single duct through penis, opening at common urogenital orifice (see Chap. 26); in females, urethra and vagina open at separate urinary and reproductive orifices; young develop in uterus, attached to and nourished through placenta

The primitive platypuses and spiny anteaters (*Prototheria,* Fig. 13.29) lay shelled eggs like the reptilian ancestors, but in all other mammals the offspring develop inside the female parent. In marsupials such as kangaroos and opossums (*Metatheria,* Fig. 13.30) the young are born in immature condition and complete development in a skin pouch on the abdomen of the female. In all other mammals (*Eutheria*) the offspring are born fully developed. These placental mammals comprise 16 orders representing four parallel evolutionary series (Fig. 13.31). One includes insectivores (shrews, moles), bats, anteaters, and armadillos, and particularly primates (lemurs, tarsiers, monkeys, apes, and men). A second series comprises rabbits and all rodents. The third is exemplified by whales, dolphins, and porpoises. And the fourth includes all carnivores such as dogs and cats, as well as elephants and all hoofed, or *ungulate,* mammals: horses, pigs, cattle, sheep, and many others.

Evolution in each of these series has been

A

B

C

13.29 ***Egg-laying mammals.*** *A, duck-billed platypus. B, nest and eggs of a platypus. C, an echidna, or spiny anteater.*

A

B

13.30 ***Pouched, marsupial mammals.*** *A, opossum, the only marsupial surviving in North America. B, koala bear, native to Australia.*

marked by rather similar adaptive trends. First, body size has tended to increase, an advantage in searching for food and in avoiding becoming food. Second, the number of teeth has tended to decrease; and instead of all teeth remaining alike, as in the reptilian ancestors, the fewer teeth have become different in parallel with specializations in the types of food eaten. Third, the legs have tended to become longer and stronger, the body and often also the heels being lifted off the ground more and more. As a result locomotion has not only improved but has also diversified in kind, in line with the alimentary specializations. Fourth, in conjunction with new modes of locomotion, diverse environments and ecological niches could be occupied. And finally, partly as a result of the increase in body size, partly in conjunction with the improved motility, the size of the brain has increased; in the course of evolutionary time mammals of all kinds have become more intelligent.

Thus the insectivore-primate group (Fig. 13.32) now actually includes the most intelligent of all animals, and locomotor diversifications to flying (as in bats) and bipedal walking (as in man) are in evidence as well. Moreover, primates are comparatively very large animals; and a man has only 32 teeth, of several types, whereas a mole, for example, has 44. The rabbit-rodent group is characterized particularly by its adaptation to a wide variety of habitats, and again by high intelligence (as in rats) and by locomotor and dental specializations (for example, leaping and continuously growing incisors, as in rabbits). In the whale series body sizes have increased more than anywhere else, a drastic change to swimming locomotion and marine existence has occurred, and tooth reduction is maximal in whalebone whales, where baleen plates replace teeth altogether. Moreover, the remarkable mental prowess of types such as porpoises is well known.

In the carnivore-ungulate series a running way of life on the plains has been exploited most. In several subseries within the group, the heel has lifted off the ground, the foot has elongated, and the animal walks on its toes, like cats or gazelles. Concurrently the toes have become increasingly hoofed, and the number of toes has become reduced. For example, carnivores are five-toed

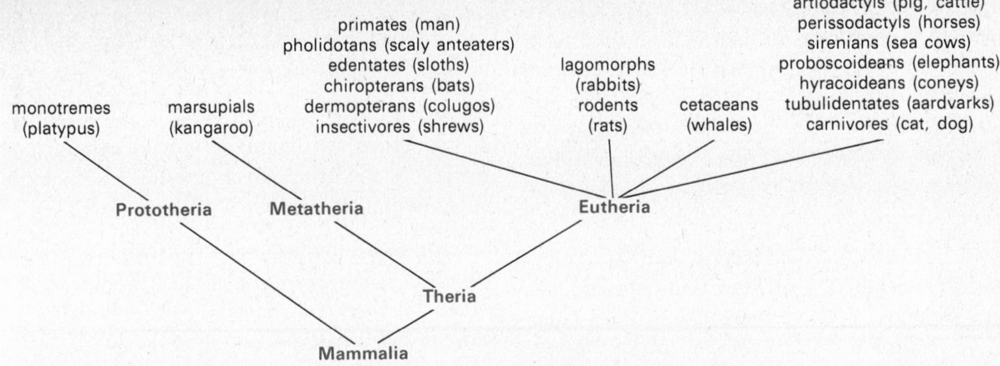

13.31 The orders of mammals, *arranged according to their main evolutionary groupings. Read from bottom up. A representative type is indicated for each order. The four eutherian series represent the placental mammals.*

A

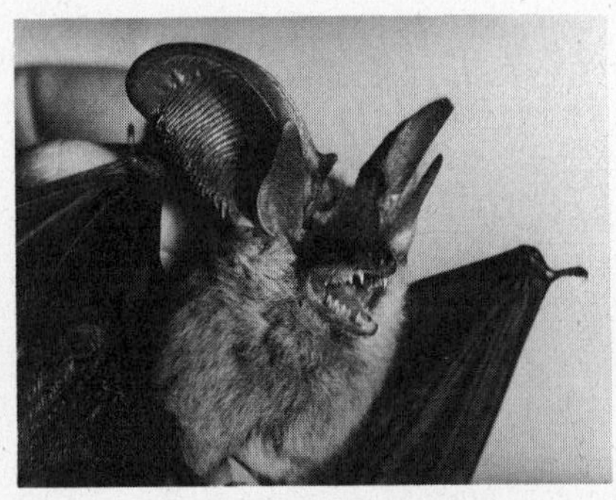
B

C

13.32 Mammals of the insectivore-primate group. *A, a hedgehog. B, a bat. Note highly elaborate ears for sound reception. C, a pangolin, or scaly anteater, native to India. See also Chap. 30 for illustrations of other insectivores and primates.*

and still nonungulate; elephants have small nail-like hoofs on each toe; and a fully ungulate condition (with variously reduced toe numbers) is found in the horse group and the deer-cattle group. With regard to tooth specializations, teeth are pointed and adapted for tearing in carnivores, and the canines form long fangs. But in herbivorous ungulates, incisors are adapted for cutting, molars are adapted for grinding, and canines are often absent. Body size has increased independently several times—bears, horses, elephants, and cattle all have evolved from far smaller ancestors. And intelligence likewise has reached high levels more than once; types like bears, dogs, and elephants clearly are brainy animals.

Such fairly parallel results show well that if ecological opportunities are similar, organisms similar in many respects can evolve several times independently. At the root of these evolutionary trends in mammals actually have been just two basic and related adaptive forces: feeding and the requirement of finding food. Indeed these are the very same that have also shaped the nature of all other organisms since the first primeval cell types appeared in the ocean.

review questions

1 Give taxonomic definitions of deuterostomial coelomates as a whole and of each of the phyla. Discuss the possible evolutionary interrelations of the phyla and the evidence from which such possibilities are deduced. What is a dipleurula?

2 What traits characterize the echinoderm phylum, and what are the classes? What adaptive factors appear to have led to the evolution of water-vascular systems in echinoderms?

3 What are tube feet, ambulacral grooves? Describe the structure of echinoderm skeletons. What are the protocoel, mesocoel, and metacoel of enterocoelomates?

4 Review the structure of a starfish and the

organization of every organ system. What is the function of the water-vascular system, and how are such functions performed? How and on what does a starfish feed? Name representatives of each echinoderm class, and show generally how their structure differs from that of starfishes. What is the general course of echinoderm development?

5 Give taxonomic definitions and structural characteristics of the phylum Chordata and the three subphyla. Indicate the known species number of each of these groups, and name the five largest animal phyla in terms of species numbers.

6 Describe the structure of an ascidian, and show how the adult emerges during metamorphosis. What is the probable evolutionary significance of the tunicate tadpole?

7 Describe the structure of an adult ascidian, and review the organization of every organ system. What are the general characteristics of the other tunicate classes?

8 Describe the structure of amphioxus, and outline the organization of every organ system. What factors probably contributed to keeping cephalochordates in a marine environment whereas vertebrates could become freshwater forms?

9 Show how most of the basic vertebrate traits are direct adaptations to a life in fresh water. What changes in vertebrate anatomy were associated with the change from ancestral filter feeding to bulk feeding by mouth?

10 What were the main steps in the evolution of the vertebrate breathing system, circulatory system, and excretory system? Characterize each vertebrate class taxonomically.

11 Describe the general structure and way of life of (*a*) a lamprey, (*b*) a shark, (*c*) a bony fish. What are ammocoetes? Spiracles? Outline the structure of a fish gill.

12 Distinguish between flesh-finned and ray-finned fishes. What are clupeiform and perciform fishes? Contrast the structure of their fins and scales. Which group of fishes was probably ancestral to the amphibia?

13 Show in what respects amphibia are basically aquatic and in what respects they are terrestrial. What prevents amphibia from being fully terrestrial?

14 Review the biological characteristics of reptiles, birds, and mammals. Name some of the adaptive specializations of (*a*) snakes, (*b*) crocodiles. Show how birds are adapted to flying.

15 List the evolutionary groups of (*a*) mammals, (*b*) placental mammals, and describe the specializations characteristic of each.

collateral readings

Applegate, V. C., and **J. W. Moffett:** The Sea Lamprey, *Sci. American,* Apr., 1955. The biology and economic harmfulness of this parasitic vertebrate is examined.

Berrill, N. J.: "The Origin of the Vertebrates," Oxford, Fair Lawn, N.J., 1955. A masterful documentation of the probable evolution of vertebrates from ascidian ancestors.

Bogert, C. B.: How Reptiles Regulate Their Body Temperature, *Sci. American,* Apr., 1959. Some of the "cold-blooded" reptiles can nevertheless maintain high internal temperatures by behavioral devices.

Brett, J. R.: The Swimming Energetics of Salmon, *Sci. American,* Aug., 1965. On how these fishes sustain their long migrations upstream at spawning time.

Frieden, L.: The Chemistry of Amphibian Metamorphosis, *Sci. American,* Nov., 1963. The article describes the controlling role of hormones in the metamorphic process.

Gilbert, P. W.: The Behavior of Sharks, *Sci. American,* July, 1962. The senses of sharks and their role in feeding behavior are examined.

Gray, J.: How Fishes Swim, *Sci. American,* Aug., 1957. Experiments on the mechanics of locomotion in fishes and other aquatic vertebrates.

Griffin, D. R.: The Navigation of Bats, *Sci. American,* Aug., 1950.

———: More about Bat "Radar," *Sci. American,* July, 1958. Description of experiments on the ultrasonic mechanisms by which bats fly and steer even in the dark.

Hildebrand, M.: How Animals Run, *Sci. American,* May, 1960. An article on the adaptations that permit many vertebrates to move far faster than, tor example, man.

Jensen, D.: The Hagfish, *Sci. American,* Feb., 1966. The article describes the adaptations and some of the remarkable internal functions of this jawless vertebrate.

Johansen, K.: Air-breathing Fishes, *Sci. American,* Oct., 1968. The modern ancestors of ancient lung-breathers are discussed.

McVay, S.: The Last of the Great Whales, *Sci. American,* Aug., 1966. On the effects of overhunting of these largest of all animals.

Storer, J. H.: Bird Aerodynamics, *Sci. American,* Apr., 1952. On the mechanics of bird flight and comparisons with airplanes.

Warden, C. J.: Animal Intelligence, *Sci. American,* June, 1951. Psychological tests measure the comparative intelligence of various vertebrates.

Welty, C.: Birds as Flying Machines, *Sci. American,* Mar., 1955. A sequel to the article by Storer listed above.

Young, J. Z.: "The Life of Vertebrates," 2d ed., Oxford, Fair Lawn, N.J., 1962. A large and highly recommended volume on the biology and evolutionary history of vertebrates.

unit 2
the operations of life

unit 2
the operations of life

part 5
metabolism

part 6
steady states

part 7
reproduction

part 8
adaptation

Up to this point our main concern has been the "what" of living matter: what are the characteristics and forms of the living material, and what kinds and groupings of living units are known? We shall continue to heed the what, but from here on our main concern will be the "how": how is the living world maintained, how are the structures developed, and how are the functions carried out? In short, our preoccupation will be less with the organizational *and more with the* operational *nature of living material.*

All operations of living matter can be considered under the general headings of metabolism and self-perpetuation. Metabolism comprises those processes that permit an otherwise inactive system to remain active and living. Self-perpetuation includes the processes that control the active, living system and thereby ensure its continuance in time. The four parts of this unit deal with these operational characteristics of living matter.

part 5
metabolism

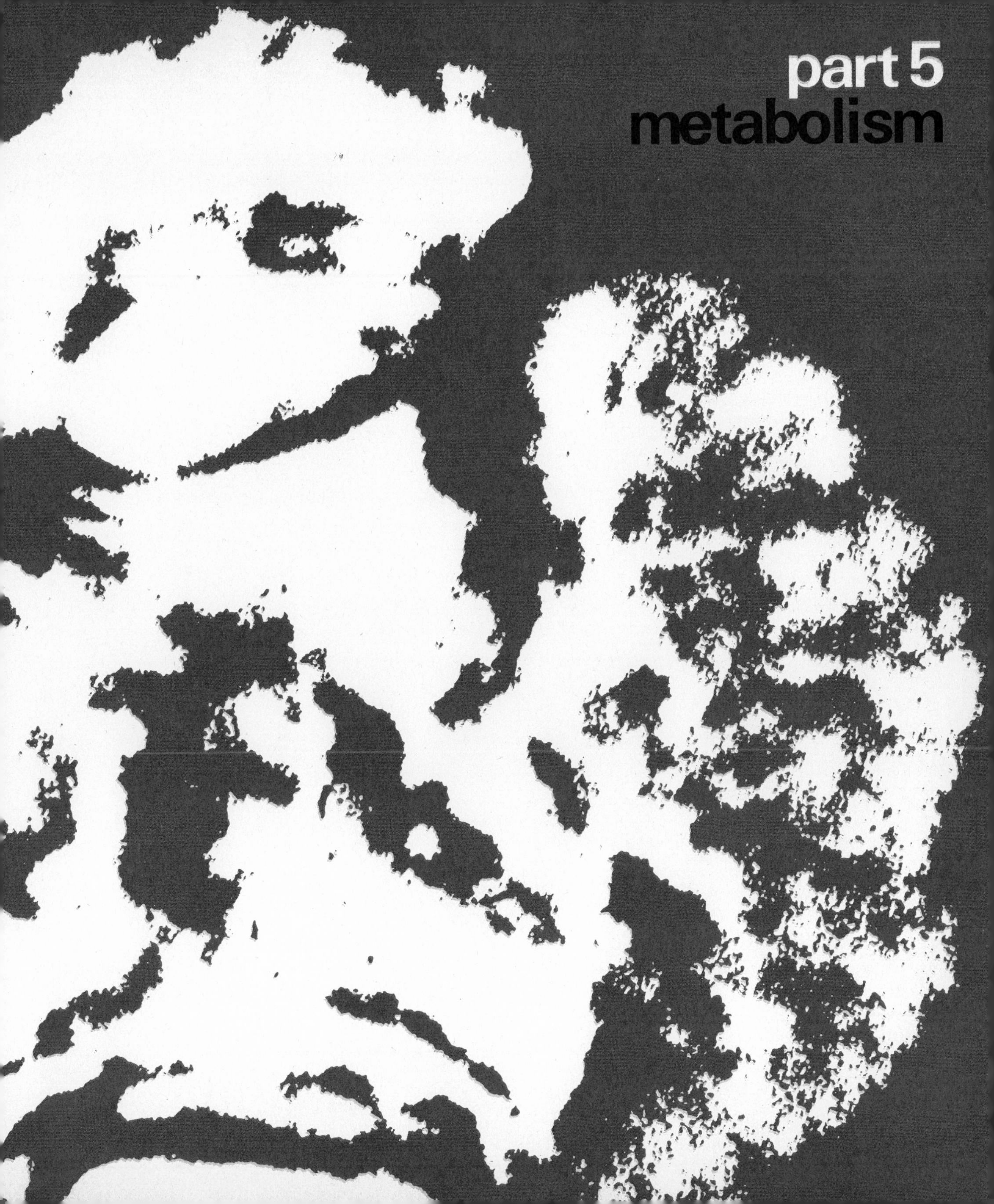

part 5
metabolism

chapter 14
nutrition

chapter 15
respiration

chapter 16
synthesis

chapter 17
genetic codes, physical functions

Metabolic processes include chiefly nutrition, *which supplies raw materials;* respiration, *which liberates energy in usable form from some of the raw materials; and* utilization *of both raw materials and energy in chemical activities such as synthesis and often also in physical activities such as movement.*

The nature of these processes is examined in the following four chapters.

chapter 14 nutrition

Nutrition in all organisms includes *intake* and internal *distribution* of raw materials to all cells; every cell must be nourished if the organism as a whole is to be nourished.

Raw materials that play a role in metabolism as a whole are called *metabolites,* and those that serve in nutrition specifically are *nutrients.* As already noted in Chap. 2, the term *food* is customarily restricted to *organic* metabolites or nutrients; inorganic nutrients are without a special collective name.

patterns

forms of nutrition

All organisms obtain inorganic nutrients directly from the physical environment. Such nutrients are water, mineral ions, and some of the aerial gases. With respect to organic nutrients, an organism is either an *autotroph* or a *heterotroph.*

Autotrophs (also called *lithotrophs,* or "mineral feeders") manufacture all required foods from inorganic nutrients. The basic food produced from such inorganic supplies is a carbohydrate, usually a sugar or sugar derivative, and from it all other required organic substances are then manufactured. The specific inorganic raw materials for sugar synthesis are environmental carbon dioxide, CO_2, the source of carbon and oxygen, and water, the usual hydrogen source. The oxygen of water becomes a byproduct that returns to the environment:

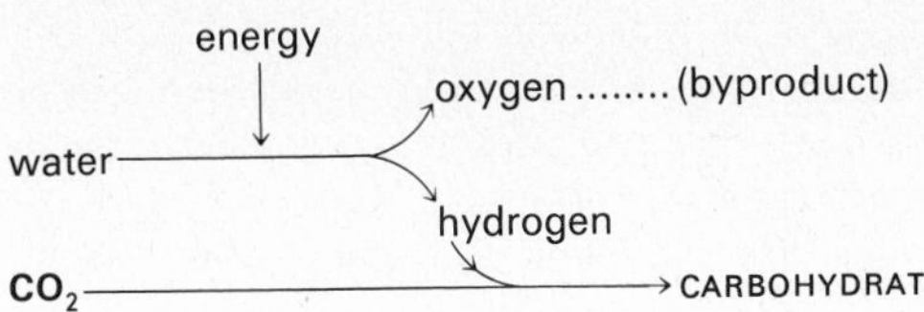

This process of carbohydrate manufacture requires energy. In the majority of autotrophs the primary energy source is light, and one or more varieties of chlorophyll serve in trapping the energy of light. Such organisms are *photosynthesizers* (or *photolithotrophs*; Figs. 14.1 and 14.2). They include all plants, algae, and two groups of bacteria (purple and green sulfur bacteria, which contain unique forms of *bacteriochlorophyll* and in which the hydrogen source is not water but H_2S; the byproduct then is sulfur, S_2, not oxygen).

In a second group of autotrophs the primary energy source for carbohydrate synthesis is certain environmental chemicals that the organisms absorb as inorganic nutrients. Inside the organisms these chemicals are combined with oxygen, yielding inorganic byproducts and energy; and this energy then makes carbohydrate production possible. Organisms of this type are *chemosynthesizers* (or *chemolithotrophs;* see Figs. 14.1 and 14.2). All of them are bacteria, and they include mainly the *sulfur bacteria.* They are named according to the chemicals they use as energy sources, and they usually live in very restricted environments where such chemicals abound. However, the nitrifying bacteria are cosmopolitan and are important participants in the global nitrogen cycle. For them the starting chemical is ammonia, NH_3, and they gain energy by converting it to nitrites and nitrates, NO_2^- and NO_3^-. Nitrates then serve as essential nitrogen sources for other organisms (see Chap. 7).

Heterotrophs (also called *organotrophs,* or "food users") cannot survive in an exclusively inorganic environment. In addition to inorganic supplies they must obtain preexisting foods, hence they ultimately depend on autotrophs. One interesting group of heterotrophs comprises the *purple bacteria,* which are photosynthetic yet require organic raw materials nevertheless. In the presence of light the organic supplies cannot be used as foods directly but serve instead as hydrogen sources. The hydrogen so obtained and CO_2 then participate in carbohydrate production, a photosynthetic process made possible by the energy of light (and bacteriochlorophyll). Purple bacteria can therefore be classified as *photoorganotrophs* (see Fig. 14.1).

All other heterotrophs are *chemoorganotrophs,* or food-requiring organisms in which the primary energy sources are the food chemicals, not light. In this category are *holotrophic, saprotrophic,* and *symbiotic* types. Holotrophs are bulk feeders, largely animals with alimentary systems, but also unicellular protists that ingest food in amoeboid fashion or through gullets. Saprotrophs comprise the slime molds and very many fungi and bacteria. They subsist on anything nonliving that contains organic materials. Such organic matter is decomposed by the organisms, and the resulting food molecules are absorbed.

	autotrophs *food manufactured from inorganic source*	***heterotrophs*** *food absorbed from preexisting organic source*
photosynthesizers *primary energy from light source*	**photolithotrophs** purple sulfur bacteria green sulfur bacteria algae plants	**photoorganotrophs** purple bacteria
chemosynthesizers *primary energy from chemical source*	**chemolithotrophs** sulfur bacteria iron bacteria hydrogen bacteria nitrifying bacteria	**chemoorganotrophs** bacteria fungi slime molds protozoa animals } holotrophs, saprotrophs, symbionts

14.1 Energy sources and food. *Classification of organisms on the basis of their energy sources and methods of food procurement.*

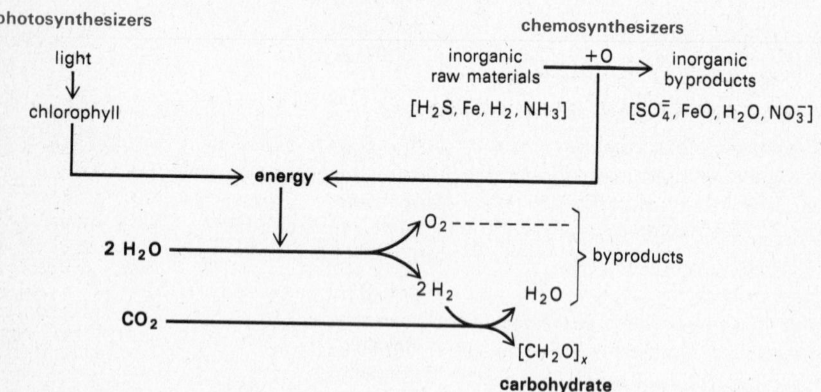

14.2 The autotrophic pattern. *Photosynthesizers and chemosynthesizers obtain energy in different ways, but both use this energy in similar fashion in producing carbohydrate foods from water and CO_2 raw materials.*

Saprotrophs thereby bring about *decay,* which makes them vital components in the global water, oxygen, and carbon cycles (see Chap. 7). Moreover, saprotrophs also include some of the denitrifying and nitrogen-fixing bacteria of the nitrogen cycle. Among the symbiotic organisms a few are holotrophic, but most, parasites in particular, absorb molecular nutrients directly from their living hosts.

processes of nutrition

The basic function of nutrition is to funnel nutrients to every cell of an organism; and at the level of the cell, the chief process of nutrition is *absorption.* It brings about a transfer of compounds from the exterior to the interior of a cell through the cell surface. At least three kinds of events occur in absorption: water is absorbed in part by *osmosis;* compounds dissolved in water are absorbed in part by *diffusion;* and water and all dissolved materials are absorbed in addition by energy-consuming *chemical work* done by a cell, or *active transport.*

Whenever the concentration of dissolved materials is greater inside a cell than outside, the cell will absorb water osmotically. A good example is the uptake of soil water by the root-hair cells of vascular plants (Fig. 14.3). Normally a root-hair cell contains a higher concentration of dissolved particles than soil water, and osmotic pressure therefore moves soil water into the root hair.

Conversely, if the soil is made to contain a higher concentration of dissolved particles than the root-hair cell—for example, by "salting" the soil—then the plant should *lose* water to the soil. Yet under such conditions the roots still take up water, though less than before. Evidently, an absorptive force other than osmotic pressure plays a considerable role. This force results from active, energy-consuming *absorptive work* by the cell. Poisoned nonmetabolizing cells do not absorb water by this means, though purely physical, osmotic absorption can still take place. Thus, in ways that are actually understood only poorly as yet, a living root cell can actively *pump* water into itself.

A very similar combination of osmosis and active transport appears to govern water absorption not only in root cells but also when *any* cell absorbs water, whether from an adjacent cell or from sap or blood or from an aquatic external environment.

Minerals and foods dissolved in water can be absorbed into a cell by *diffusion,* but only if the concentration of dissolved particles outside the cell is greater than inside. The opposite is usually the case, however. Consider again a root-hair cell, in which the internal concentration is normally far greater than the concentration of soil minerals outside. The cell should therefore lose ions to the soil, yet it does not. On the contrary, ions migrate from the soil *into* the root, *against* the prevailing diffusion gradient (see Fig. 14.3). Here, too, the living root cell evidently performs active, energy-consuming, absorptive work; such work cannot take place in a metabolically poisoned cell.

This pattern again applies to *any* cells that absorb materials dissolved in water, and it applies not only to mineral absorption but also to food absorption.

Indeed in the case of at least one food, glucose, something of the detailed chemistry of "living" absorption is known. When a glucose molecule is absorbed through the surface of any cell, it usually must be *phosphorylated,* or combined chemically with a phosphate group (Fig. 14.4). The ultimate sources of such groups are mineral phosphates absorbed by cells as inorganic nutrients. The immediate source in phosphorylation is ATP (adenosine triphosphate), produced in respiration. This compound is also the source of the energy required for phosphorylation. The terminal third phosphate group of ATP is split off, and the energy made available by this decomposition serves in attaching the phosphate group to glucose. The result is glucose-phosphate. Formed at or in the cell surface, this compound then diffuses to the cell interior. (In vertebrates, proper glucose phosphorylation at cell surfaces depends on the presence of the pancreatic hormone *insulin.* Thus if the insulin supply is deficient, as in diabetes, the cells starve of glucose while this sugar accumulates uselessly in blood and is eventually excreted.)

Various cell-surface reactions probably take place also in the absorption of noncarbohydrate foods, but in many of these instances the details are still obscure. Sometimes specific transferring enzymes (*permeases*) are known to promote the uptake of particular metabolites into the interior of a cell.

In unicellular and simply constructed multicellular organisms, absorption through the whole body surface generally represents a major part and most often actually all of nutrition. In complex multicellular organisms, nutrient intake occurs only at limited specialized regions—through root and leaf surfaces in plants, through an alimentary system in animals. Internal distribution of nutrients then follows, in part by direct short-distance transfer from one cell to immediately adjacent cells, in part by long-distance transfer through the vascular tissues—xylem and phloem in plants, blood and lymph vessels in animals.

Absorption plays a critical role in all these processes, as does *secretion,* the reverse of absorption. Thus, cell-to-cell transfer involves secretion of nutrients from one cell and absorption by an adjacent one. Similarly, long-distance transfer requires secretion from nutrient-supplying cells to the vascular channels and absorption by receiver cells at the delivery points along the channels. Evidently, *cellular* nutrition is basically absorptive in all organisms; and although the elaborate organs and systems that in most multicellular organisms serve in procurement and transport are essential, they nevertheless have only auxiliary roles in this key process: nutrient absorption by individual cells.

How these auxiliary procurement and transport

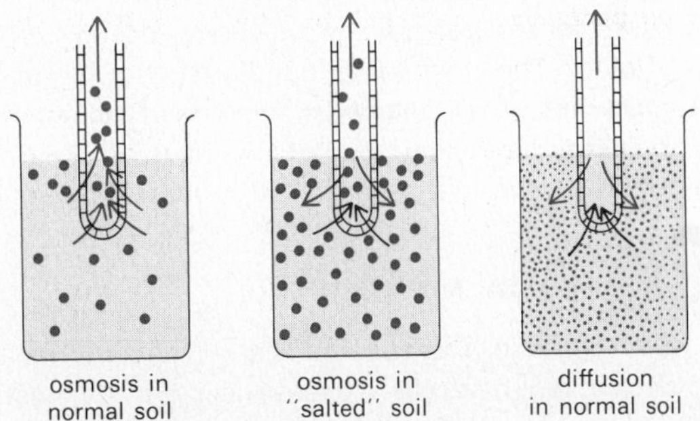

14.3 Osmosis and diffusion in roots. *Left, osmosis. Particle concentrations are greater in root cells than in soil; hence more water moves to root cells from soil than in the reverse direction. Middle, the effect of "salting" the soil. Even if the particle concentration in soil is made greater than in the root, water still moves to the root (black arrows), against the osmotic gradient (colored arrows). This indicates that osmosis is not the only factor in water absorption; active absorption by living root cells is also important. Right, diffusion. Because root cells contain a higher concentration of mineral ions than soil, ions should be expected to diffuse out of roots (colored arrows). Yet ions actually migrate from soil to roots (black arrows), against the diffusion gradient. This indicates that active absorption as well as diffusion is responsible for ion uptake by living root cells.*

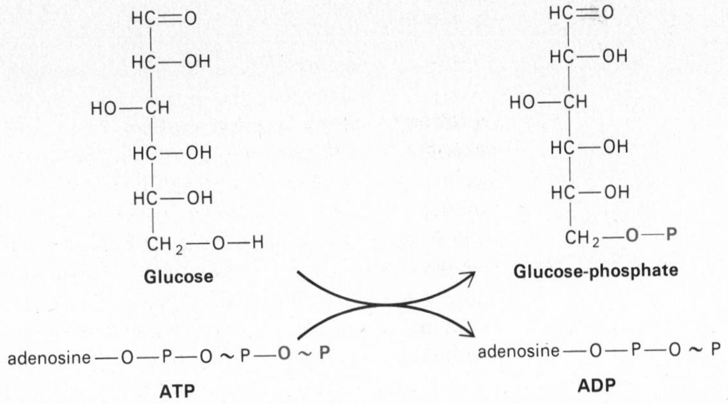

HC═O
HC—OH
HO—CH
HC—OH
HC—OH
CH_2—O—H
Glucose

HC═O
HC—OH
HO—CH
HC—OH
HC—OH
CH_2—O—P
Glucose-phosphate

adenosine—O—P—O ~ P—O ~ P
ATP

adenosine—O—P—O ~ P
ADP

14.4 The phosphorylation reaction. *Glucose reacts with ATP, resulting in phosphorylated glucose and ADP. Note that ATP serves both as energy and phosphate donor. The —O—H at one end of the glucose molecule is replaced by —O~P of ATP (color), and in the process the energy of the high-energy bond is used up; a low-energy bond is left in glucose phosphate (P stands for —PO_3H_2 here and in following illustrations).*

functions take place in multicellular organisms is outlined in what follows.

plants: absorption and conduction

All divisions of the plant body participate in nutritional activities. Leaves and green stems acquire aerial gases and manufacture foods; roots absorb water and dissolved minerals and gases; and stems conduct nutrients of all kinds from leaves to roots and vice versa. Xylem and phloem serve as the long-distance vertical conductors and to some extent also as short-distance lateral conductors. The chief lateral conductors are the parenchyma cells in the cortex and pith of root-stem systems, the xylem and phloem rays of woody plants, and also the mesophyll tissues of leaves.

roots, leaves, and xylem

Soil nutrients are absorbed largely by the epidermal root-hair cells, for these cells provide most of the surface available for absorption. After being absorbed the inorganic supplies are transported by direct cell-to-cell transfers to the xylem at the root core. The vertical tracheids and vessels present there reach uninterruptedly from root tip to leaf tip and serve as channels for upward conduction.

When a root-hair cell absorbs water and materials dissolved in it, the most immediate effect is that the excess water tends to dilute the interior of the cell. However, the cell does not swell up to any appreciable extent, for most of the absorbed substances are secreted from the cell almost as soon as they enter. Such secreted materials are absorbed by cortex cells immediately adjacent to the root epidermis. These cells then tend to swell up, but excessive swelling is prevented by the rigid cellulose cell walls. Instead, water is secreted again and is absorbed by the next inner layer of cortex cells (Fig. 14.5).

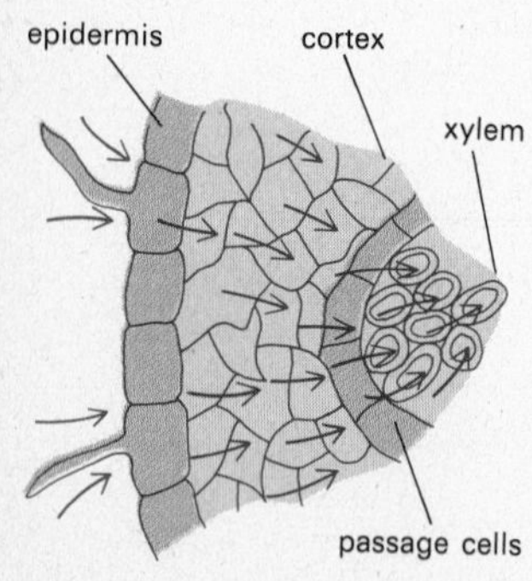

14.5 Absorption paths in a root. *Water and dissolved minerals are absorbed by successively deeper layers of cells. In this manner supplies eventually reach the xylem.*

In this manner water and minerals are drawn progressively from cell layer to cell layer toward the core of the root. Some of these nutritional supplies are retained by the cells along the way, but the bulk soon reaches and passes through the root endodermis. In this tissue active transport by the specialized *passage cells* usually facilitates the movement. Water and dissolved materials then pass through the layers of the pericycle and from there to the xylem.

This water stream from soil to xylem is continuous and uninterrupted. It is maintained by an appreciable *root pressure,* an active push generated by the combined osmotic pressure and the combined absorptive and secretive forces of all root cells. Root pressure drives water forcefully to the xylem tubes at the root core, and it also drives the water upward in the xylem as sap (Fig. 14.6).

In a healthy plant xylem is never empty of water. Even before a xylem channel becomes functional, water already fills the interior; and as the plant grows in length, each new xylem component formed at the top adds a water-containing segment to the column below. In this manner water "grows" up as the plant grows up. Continuous uninterrupted water columns therefore range from every root hair through root cortex, pericycle, and xylem to every mesophyll cell in the leaves. Upward "transportation" then consists of adding water at the bottom of such columns and withdrawing an equivalent amount from the top, minus the fraction that living tissues incorporate. Root pressure is one force, and often the main one, that pushes the water columns up. It alone suffices to drive water right to the top of a tree—as in early spring, for example, before leaves have matured.

Accompanying and reinforcing this lift from below, a second force generates "pull" from above. This force is *transpiration,* or evaporation of water from leaves (see Fig. 14.6). As water vaporizes from a mesophyll cell the concentration of cellular particles tends to increase. This osmotic change will bring about a withdrawal of water from neighboring cells, and *these* cells now tend to develop a water deficit. Osmotic equilibrating pull is propagated back in this manner along cell paths leading to xylem terminals. As in roots, osmotic pull is accompanied here by active cellular absorption. The combined osmotic and absorptive action of leaf cells then pulls water up through the xylem, in quantities equivalent to the amount evaporated. The effectiveness of this pull from above is quite familiar. An isolated leaf or a flower with a stub of stem and a few leaves survives for a considerable time when put into a glass of water; as water transpires from exposed plant tissues, fluid is pulled up from below.

If the water columns in xylem should become discontinuous, water transport from root to leaf would cease. The circumstance that the transport fluid is water rather than another medium greatly aids in maintaining the continuity of the columns, for water has a high degree of *cohesion.* Individual molecules attract one another strongly, and a column therefore "hangs together" with appreciable tenacity. Where xylem includes both vessels and tracheids, the membranes of tracheids present no barrier to continuous water flow. Indeed the pits along the side walls of tracheids even permit a measure of *lateral conduction* and equilibration of flow pressure between adjacent columns of water.

On occasion water droplets are exuded from leaf surfaces, a process known as *guttation.* The water appears at so-called *hydathodes,* which in many cases are modified stomata incapable of closing (Fig. 14.7). Root pressure then can force water from xylem through mesophyll cells and out at hydathodes. In other cases hydathodes are distinct glands that actively secrete water from the interior of a leaf. Through guttation plants can eliminate water when the roots absorb more than the leaves can transpire, as under conditions of high environmental humidity, for example.

The important point about xylem transport is that the power source lies in living roots and leaves. The nonliving xylem channels are passive, in roughly the same way that a pipeline between two pumping stations is passive. Conduction through phloem is different in this respect, for here the power source appears to be spread out all along the transportation route.

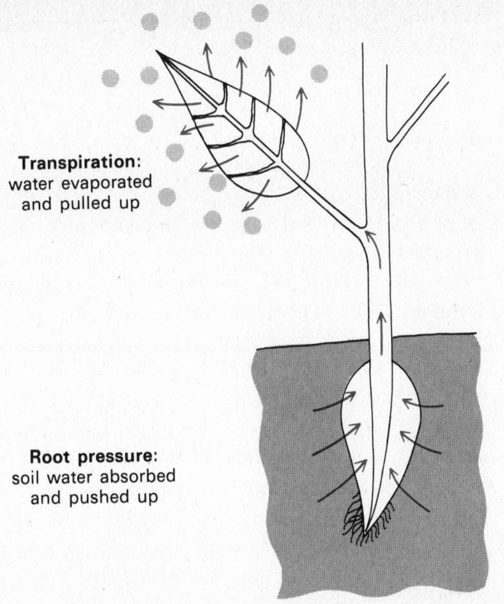

14.6 Xylem transport. *Xylem vessels contain continuous columns of water. Root pressure adds more water at the bottom, and transpiration removes water at the top through evaporation. Water in xylem is transported upward in this fashion.*

leaves, stems, and phloem

Plants are so constructed that most living cells are in direct or nearly direct contact with the external environment. Gas exchange thus can take place in correspondingly direct fashion.

Most of the atmospheric oxygen, carbon dioxide, and water vapor used by a plant enters through the stomata in leaves and green stems. Such gases then diffuse through the cell surfaces and dissolve in cellular water. Carried to the phloem channels along with water, they can supply stem and root tissues as well. Gases dissolved in soil water also enter the plant through the roots. Some of these supplies reach xylem vessels, and stem and leaf tissues therefore can obtain gases by that path. If the stem is woody, lenticels and any crack in the bark provide addi-

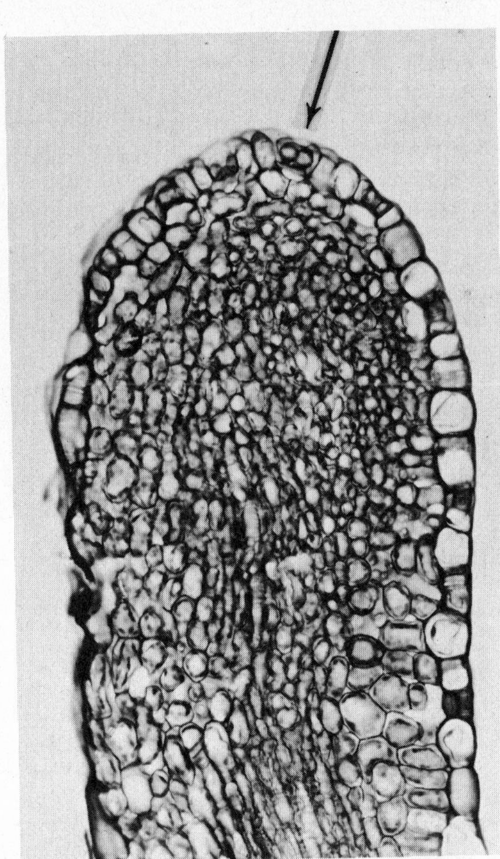

14.7 Hydathodes. *Column of cells forms a water-conducting channel. Arrow points to permanently open stoma of hydathode.*

tional entry points for air. Finally, inasmuch as green tissues produce oxygen during photosynthesis and all tissues produce CO_2 during respiration, plants also have their own internal sources of aerial gases.

Conversely, excess gases in a plant can diffuse to the environment either directly from exposed cells or through phloem, xylem, and stomata. In effect, exchange of gases in plants can be accomplished without specialized breathing systems; gas diffusion to and from individual cells and a certain amount of transport by xylem and phloem suffice. Since much of the deeper substance of a vascular plant is nonliving supporting and conducting material in any case, the gas requirement in such regions is zero.

Food transport is a more specialized activity, and the sieve tubes of phloem are the specific conducting channels of organic nutrients: photosynthesis-derived foods migrate from leaves and green stems downward, and stored foods travel from roots and stem upward. Lateral conduction of organic supplies can take place by cell-to-cell transfer all along the phloem channels.

Unlike the xylem channels, sieve tubes evidently are two-way paths. Downward conduction in sieve tubes has long been known to occur: many roots store foods photosynthesized only in leaf or stem. The occurrence of upward conduction has come to light through grafting experiments. For example, a stem of a tobacco plant grafted to a root of a tomato plant develops normal tobacco leaves, but these lack nicotine. Conversely, a tomato stem transplanted to a tobacco root produces tomato leaves, but these are full of nicotine. The first graft indicates that only the roots of a tobacco plant synthesize nicotine; the second graft, that the drug is transported upward. And since xylem channels are virtually free of nicotine, upward conduction must occur largely in phloem (Fig. 14.8).

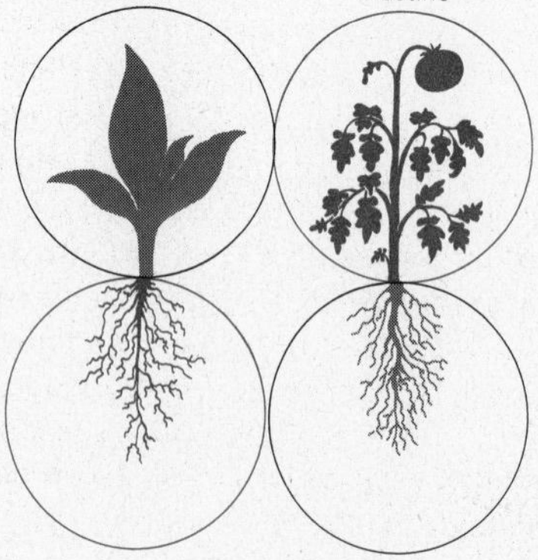

14.8 Phloem transport. *Experiments show that tobacco leaves grafted to tomato roots will not contain nicotine (left). This indicates that nicotine is formed in the roots but not in the leaves of tobacco plants. If tomato leaves are grafted to tobacco roots, the leaves will eventually contain nicotine (right). This experiment shows that nicotine is manufactured only in the tobacco roots and is transported upward by the phloem. The phloem channels evidently carry organic materials up as well as down.*

The main driving force in phloem appears to be diffusion, the same process that brings about internal transport in any cell. In a sieve tube the vertical direction of conduction is usually imposed by the anatomic arrangement. Thus, absorption of food by sieve-tube cytoplasm and secretion from it can probably be accomplished most easily at the top and bottom perforations, where the barriers are minimal (Fig. 14.9).

The two-way nature of phloem conduction becomes intelligible on this basis. Mesophyll cells in the leaf photosynthesize and thereby acquire relatively high concentrations of food molecules. Terminal sieve-tube cells in the vicinity do not photosynthesize, hence their food content is lower. Diffusion will then tend to equalize the concentrations, and the terminal sieve-tube cells will absorb some of the mesophyll-produced foods. Their own food content will therefore increase in relation to that of lower sieve-tube cells next in line along the conduction path. These lower cells will then absorb from units above them, and in this fashion nutrient conduction will continue downward under the influence of the concentration gradient from leaves to roots.

Conversely, organic materials can be carried upward if the concentrations of such materials are high in the roots and lower above. This is the case, for example, in winter and early spring, when leaves are absent and photosynthesis does not take place. Foods stored in the roots during the preceding summer then travel upward to the food-requiring regions of the stem and the crown.

Phloem conduction, up or down, is slow compared with xylem conduction. Also, phloem does not contain a flowing sap as in xylem vessels. Instead the sieve-tube cytoplasm only flows and shifts inside its cellulose walls and does not pass beyond these boundaries. Nutrient molecules alone move from one unit to the next. Such conduction in phloem therefore is often spoken of as *translocation.*

All absorptive and transporting activities in plants not only contribute to but indirectly also depend on photosynthesis. For it is this most essential nutritional activity that permits a whole plant, including roots, leaves, and transport tissues, to be formed at all. Since photosynthesis is a creative process, it will be discussed in detail in Chap. 16 in the specific context of synthesis.

animals: alimentation and circulation

Nutrients are obtained in most animals by ingestion through a mouth, digestion in stomach and intestine, and egestion of unusable remains through an anus. Usable supplies resulting from digestion are then absorbed through the wall of the alimentary system into surrounding tissues or, in complexly structured animals, into the circulatory system. In such a system nutrient transport to all cells of the body occurs in part indirectly through a *liver,* as in vertebrates, and in part directly from intestine to other tissues.

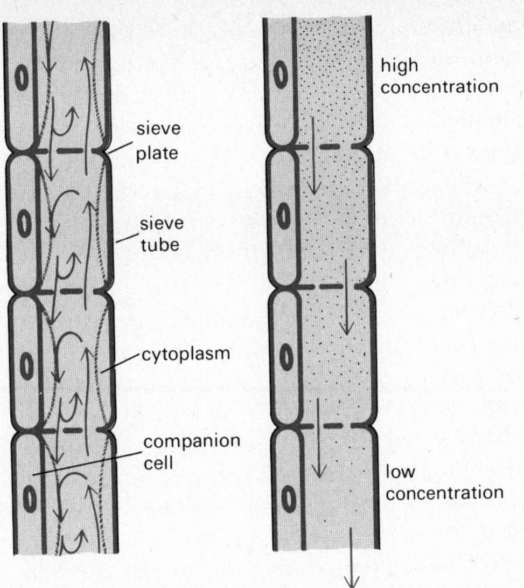

14.9 Conduction in phloem. *Left: materials in the sieve tubes are kept circulating by cyclosis, and concentration differences determine whether or not a given substance will pass through sieve plates. Right: if a given nutrient is highly concentrated at one end of a phloem channel and less highly concentrated at the other, as shown, then a diffusion gradient will point from the high to the low concentration. The nutrient will therefore be translocated in that direction.*

nutrients and ingestion

Survival of a plant cell depends on supplies of water, minerals, and organic carbon in the form of carbohydrates. From these three categories of chemicals a plant cell can construct all the other components of its substance. But if an animal cell is given only these three types of nutrient it soon dies; for it requires four additional types of material that, unlike the plant cell, it cannot manufacture on its own.

First, usable organic nitrogen is required for the construction of, for example, proteins and nucleic acids. The simplest form of organic nitrogen is the amino group ($—NH_2$), and plants are able to make $—NH_2$ out of mineral nitrates (see Chap. 7). Animals, too, have access to nitrates, but they cannot convert these ions to $—NH_2$. Their cells therefore must be supplied with preexisting $—NH_2$ or other forms of usable organic nitrogen. Other animals or ultimately plants must be the source of supply.

Second, plants can convert organic starting materials into all the vitamins they require. Animals cannot do likewise. Most animals do manufacture at least some of their own vitamins, although in many cases only in inadequate quantities (see Chap. 18). Specific abilities here vary with the species, but no species is as self-sufficient in this regard as a green plant. Missing vitamins consequently must be supplied in prefabricated form, and plants again are the ultimate source of supply.

Third, unlike plants, animals are unable to convert organic starting materials into all 23 kinds of amino acids needed for protein synthesis. Depending on the species, 8 or 10 kinds, so-called *essential* amino acids (an unfortunate term since all amino acids are ''essential''), must be supplied in prefabricated form, and plants are the ultimate suppliers here as well.

Last, again unlike plants, many animals are unable to convert organic starting materials into all necessary kinds of fatty acids. Accordingly, various ''essential'' fatty acids must be obtained ready-made from plants.

The minimum supplies to an animal cell therefore must include at least seven types of nutrients: *water, minerals, organic carbon, organic nitrogen, vitamins, essential amino acids,* and *essential fatty acids.* Animals evidently cannot survive without plants, which provide five of these seven items (Fig. 14.10).

This reduced manufacturing ability of animal cells undoubtedly is a result of mutation and evolution. In all probability the ancestors of animals—as of plants—were able to synthesize all needed cellular compounds on their own. In the course of time random mutations must have led to the loss of various synthesizing abilities in different organisms. If the affected organism was photosynthetic it must have become extinct, for it could not have obtained the missing ingredients in any other way; and plants surviving today still must synthesize all needed ingredients on their own. But if the affected organism was an animal, it could survive readily, for as a heterotroph it could obtain any missing compound from plants or other animals by way of food. That mutations often do abolish cellular capacities of synthesizing certain compounds can be demonstrated experimentally.

In most cases nutrients are available to animals

only in more or less bulky masses of plant or animal matter, living or dead. The basic function of an alimentary system, then, is to separate bulk nutrients into individual ions and molecules directly usable by cells. The first step is ingestion.

Most animals eat whenever food is obtainable; hunger is virtually permanent. In a few animals, man most particularly, hunger and food intake usually tend to be intermittent. The brain here plays an important role in controlling the rate and amount of food consumption. According to an early popular hypothesis, the stomach was believed to regulate the quantities of food eaten. Muscular contractions of an empty stomach were thought to control the sensations of hunger, and a hungry animal was assumed to eat until its stomach was filled. Such filling was believed to stop hunger pangs and food intake. But this hypothesis turned out to be untenable long ago, for even after surgical removal of the entire stomach hunger sensations nevertheless continue to come and go as before. Moreover, a ''stomach hypothesis'' of hunger control does not account for chronic overeating or undereating.

A better explanation emerged after experiments had indicated that the mammalian brain contains two special eating-control centers. One is a *hunger center.* When this center is stimulated, it sends out nerve impulses to various parts of the body that prompt the animal to eat. The other is a *satiety center,* which, when stimulated, prompts the animal to refuse food. Tiny electrodes can be used to stimulate one or the other of these centers in, for example, test rats. Animals so treated either overeat and become extremely obese or undereat and starve despite a plentiful food supply. Evidently, the amount of food a mammal normally eats is determined primarily by the commands that the hunger and satiety centers send to the body.

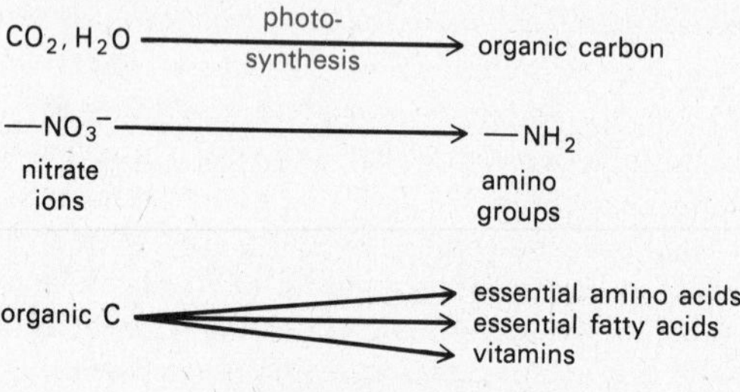

14.10 Animal dependence on plants: *five classes of compounds that green plants can synthesize and that the cells of most animals cannot synthesize. Animals depend on green plants for these products.*

satiety center
hunger center
S
H
high blood-glucose level
low blood-glucose level
digestion
no digestion
eating food
stop food intake
start food intake
not eating food

14.11 Control of food intake. *Desire or lack of desire for food is governed by the satiety (S) and hunger (H) centers of the brain, which in turn respond differentially to the glucose concentration in blood.*

How do these centers determine whether to send a command ''eat'' or a command ''do not eat''? Experiments show *blood glucose* to be the critical agent that stimulates one or the other of the two centers. Glucose circulating in the blood is a very sensitive indicator of the hour-by-hour nutritional state of the body. Shortly after a meal the glucose concentration in blood tends to rise. Long after a meal this concentration tends to fall. If blood reaching the brain contains a high glucose level, the satiety center probably responds selectively to this level and issues the command ''do not eat.'' Conversely, low glucose levels probably stimulate the hunger center selectively and result in the command ''eat'' (Fig. 14.11).

Thus, any condition that directly or indirectly influences glucose delivery to the brain or affects the operation of the brain centers is bound to affect food intake. Dozens of such conditions actually do so. Proper glucose delivery depends, for example, on normal digestive processes, normal liver function, normal blood circulation, normal hormone balances, and normal nervous activities. All these factors affect glucose metabolism profoundly. And if through disturbances in any of these functions the brain receives consistently inappropriate information about the actual glucose supplies in the body, then consistent overeating or undereating can result. Evidently, the seemingly simple decision whether or not to eat is actually determined by a multitude of interconnected processes. It is therefore not surprising that, as is well known, practically *any* disturbance of *any* body function has an effect on food intake.

digestion and egestion

After food is ingested, digestion in different parts of an alimentary tract is achieved by *mechanical* and *chemical* means. Mechanical digestion, carried out for example through chewing by teeth and muscular grinding by a stomach, achieves a progressive physical subdivision of ingested materials to fine particles suspended in water. Chemical digestion then reduces these particles to molecular dimensions. In the process usable ions and molecules become separated out and more complex molecules are broken up into smaller, usable ones. In this chemical dissolution of foods, *digestive enzymes* secreted by *digestive glands* play important roles.

No matter where it occurs or what food is involved, every chemical digestion is an *enzymatic hydrolysis*—a decomposition reaction in which *water* is the active dissolving agent. A generalized digestive reaction can be written

$$\textbf{food} + H_2O \xrightarrow{enzyme} \textbf{food components}$$

In most animals digestive enzymes are *extracellular;* they are produced inside cells, but they are secreted and function outside. This puts them into a special category, for virtually all other enzymes in organisms are intracellular and function within cells. Moreover, digestive enzymes are relatively unusual also in that many of them can act on entire categories of chemicals. For example, digestive *lipase* promotes the decomposition of fat to fatty acids and glycerin:

$$\textbf{fat} + H_2O \xrightarrow{lipase} \textbf{fatty acids} + \textbf{glycerin}$$

The lipase here can be effective with any kind of fat, regardless of what specific types of fatty acid a fat is composed of. Similarly, certain protein- and carbohydrate-digesting enzymes decompose many *different* kinds of proteins and carbohydrates, respectively. By contrast, intracellular enzymes are highly specific, and each is effective only in reactions of one particular type of molecule.

The reason for this broad effectiveness of many digestive enzymes is that the particular chemical bond on which each such enzyme acts occurs widely in a given class of food molecules. Thus the fatty acid–glycerin bond for which lipase is specific occurs in practically all fats. Similarly, the peptide bonds between amino acids for which digestive proteinases are specific occur in all proteins. As in other cases, however, enzymatic decomposition depends primarily on *water,* the actual decomposing agent; enzymes only increase reaction rates. Like other enzymes, also, digestive ones operate best at particular temperatures and pH. Appropriately acid, alkaline, or neutral conditions actually are maintained in the digestive juices and the alimentary organs in which enzymes occur.

Animals with specialized feeding habits are correspondingly specialized in their digestive enzymes. For example, blood feeders among worms and insects secrete large amounts of digestive proteinase but only little carbohydrase. Clothes moths, which eat nothing but the protein in sheep hair (wool), likewise produce digestive proteinases almost exclusively. By contrast, flour beetles and boll weevils secrete an abundance of carbohydrases. Similar specializations occur in silk-, glue-, or wood-eating animals. Also, numerous parasitic animals are fairly narrowly specialized in their digestive capacities. The broadest assortment of digestive enzymes is usually found in free-living omnivores, which can survive on nearly any kind of food. Many mammals, man included, are in this category.

In a mammal, enzymatic digestion occurs mainly in *mouth, stomach,* and *small intestine.* At each of these sites specialized digestive glands secrete one or more digestive juices into the alimentary channel (Fig. 14.12 and Table 11). The salivary glands produce *saliva,* which acts in the mouth and, carried along by food, also in the stomach. Contact of food with the tissues in the mouth stimulates nerve endings that transmit impulses to the brain, and impulses from there to the salivary glands then bring about secretion of saliva. As is well known, smell, sight, or mere thought of food can start the flow of saliva: pleasant past experiences with food here have the same effect as actual food in the mouth (conditioned reflexes; see Chap. 21).

From the mouth food passes through the *pharynx,* where the food channel crosses the air channel that leads from the nasal passages to the windpipe (Fig. 14.13). During swallowing the upper end of the windpipe (larynx) is raised against a flap of tissue, the *epiglottis.* The air channel is thereby closed off, and food is forced to pass from the pharynx to the *esophagus* that leads to the stomach. Wavelike muscular contractions in the wall of the esophagus (*peristalsis*) push a ball of food along. (The direction of peristalsis is reversed in, for example, vomiting.)

The stomach completes mechanical digestion by its muscular grinding action, and it continues chemical digestion through *gastric juice* secreted from the stomach lining. Sight, smell, and

Table 11. The composition and action of digestive juices

	saliva	*gastric juice*	*intestinal juice*	*pancreatic juice*	*bile*
source	salivary glands	stomach wall	duodenal wall	pancreas	liver, gall-bladder store
pH	neutral	highly acid	alkaline	alkaline	alkaline
secretion started by	food in mouth reflex; thought of food	food in mouth; emotions; food in stomach ⟶ gastrin hormone, stimulates stomach wall	food contact in duodenum	secretin hormone from intestinal juice	secretin hormone from intestinal juice
carbohydrases	amylase, for polysaccharides maltase, for maltose		amylase, for polysaccharides disaccharases (maltase, sucrose, lactase), for disaccharides	amylase, for polysaccharides	
lipases		lipase (brought in from duodenum)	lipase	lipase	
proteinases		prorennin $\xrightarrow{HCl}$ rennin ⟶ curdles milk protein (caseinogen ⟶ casein) pepsinogen ⟶ pepsin, for proteins	amino-peptidases, for products of partial protein breakdown (polypeptides)	trypsinogen ⟶ trypsin,* for proteins chymotrypsinogen ⟶ chymotrypsin,* for proteins carboxy-peptidases, for products of partial protein breakdown (polypeptides)	
other components (all contain water, mucus, mineral ions)		HCl, macerates food, activates gastric proteinases	enterokinase, activates trypsinogen, chymotrypsinogen* secretin hormone, stimulates pancreas and liver secretions		bile salts, emulsify fats into colloidal drops bile pigments, excretion products from hemoglobin breakdown in liver

*The pancreatic proteinases are secreted in inactive form, which protects pancreatic tissues from being digested. Enterokinase from intestinal juice converts trypsinogen to active trypsin. The latter then transforms more trypsinogen to trypsin, and it also converts chymotrypsinogen to active chymotrypsin.

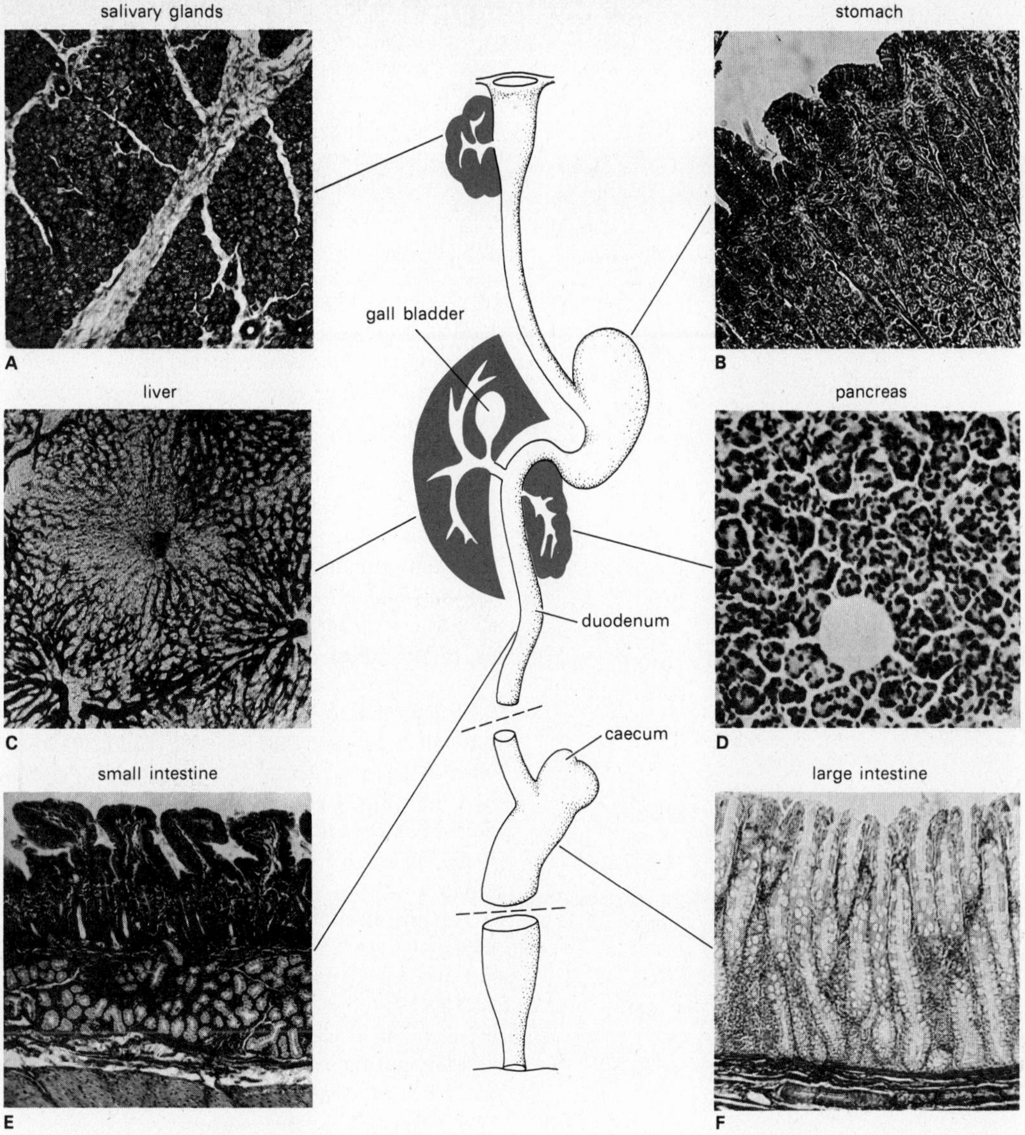

14.12 The mammalian alimentary tract. *Photo insets: A, section through a salivary gland. Note the connective tissue stroma (light areas in photo) traversing the gland and binding groups of gland cells together. Note also the several small salivary ducts (dark rings). B, section through a portion of stomach wall. Note folded mucosa near top of photo. C, section through liver, showing parts of a few lobules injected to reveal the blood channels (dark). Blood brought by the hepatic portal vein to a lobule passes to the hepatic vein in the center of the lobule (see also Fig. 5.31). D, section through pancreas. The large round space is a branch of the pancreatic duct. E, section through the wall of the duodenum. The cavity of the gut is toward the top. Underneath the folded inner surface tissues note the glandular layer. Its secretion is discharged to the gut cavity and contributes to the composition of intestinal juice. F, section through a mucosal fold of the large intestine. Note the many mucus-secreting goblet cells in the mucosal lining. (F, courtesy Carolina Biological Supply Company.)*

thought of food, which can start salivary secretion, can at the same time initiate gastric secretion. Moreover, stomach cells in contact with food release *gastrin,* a hormone, which is distributed by blood throughout the body. When some of this hormone returns to the stomach and reaches the specialized cells capable of manufacturing gastric juice, these cells are activated (see Table 11).

Gastric juice contains strong *hydrochloric acid,* which through its decomposing action contributes to the physical subdivision of food. Also present is *pepsinogen,* an inactive molecule that in the presence of hydrogen ions from HCl becomes the active proteinase *pepsin.* This enzyme catalyzes the breakdown of proteins to free amino acids. Another enzyme of gastric juice is *rennin* (which is similarly secreted as inactive *prorenin* and becomes activated by hydrogen ions). Rennin acts specifically on the milk protein caseinogen and splits it to *casein* and *whey.* In the presence of calcium ions (from milk, for example) casein coagulates, and this protein curd can then be digested by pepsin. The rennin mechanism, unique

14.13 Food and air channels. *In the pharynx the air path (from nasopharynx to glottis) crosses the food path (from mouth cavity to esophagus).*

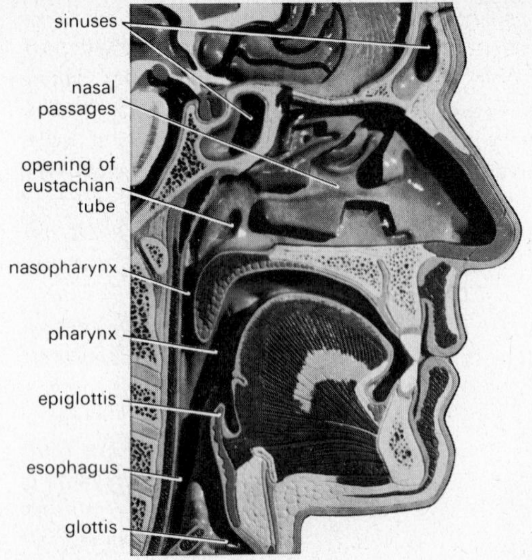

14.14 Digestion summary. *Polypeptides are products of partial protein breakdown. Bile salts act physically, not chemically; they emulsify fats and thereby reduce large fatty masses to tiny droplets of colloidal dimensions.*

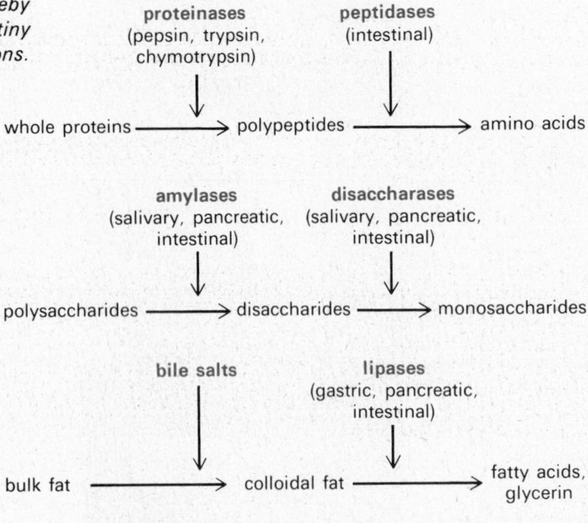

to mammals, is particularly useful in the young, in which milk is the only food for some time; in curdled, solidified form milk stays in the stomach longer than it would as a liquid, and pepsin digestion can therefore proceed for a longer period.

Carbohydrate and fat digestion occurs in the stomach only to the extent that saliva is carried in from the mouth and that lipase regurgitates from the intestine. The small intestine, particularly the section next to the stomach (*duodenum*), is the organ in which the most thorough chemical digestion of all foods takes place. Here *intestinal juice* is secreted by the gut wall, and ducts carry in *pancreatic juice* from the pancreas and *bile* from the liver. The composition and action of these fluids are indicated in Table 11.

In the course of intestinal digestion, carbohydrates not yet fully acted on become decomposed to monosaccharides such as glucose and fructose. Proteins are broken up to individual amino acids. Fats are subdivided physically into colloidal fat droplets through the emulsifying action of bile salts, and substantial numbers of such droplets are then also decomposed chemically to fatty acids and glycerin (Fig. 14.14).

When digestion is completed, therefore, the intestine contains water and dissolved mineral ions, monosaccharides, amino acids, fatty acids, glycerin, and vitamins (which have not been affected by digestion). Also present are colloidal fat droplets, as well as undigested or indigestible materials (including cellulose, for example, or any other compounds that cannot be decomposed by the enzymes present). Such unprocessed substances will be egested, and most other materials will be absorbed.

The food solution in the intestine is continuously agitated by peristaltic contractions of the gut wall, a process that mixes and remixes food with the digestive juices. Churning also brings the food solution into thorough contact with the mucosa, the tissue layer along the interior surface of the gut (see Fig. 5.32). This layer is highly folded and in addition is studded with millions of near-microscopic *villi.* These fingerlike projections give the mucosa a velvety, carpetlike texture and an exceedingly large surface area (see Fig. 14.12). Moving back and forth continuously, the villi also aid in stirring the food solution and in circulating it thoroughly over the mucosal lining.

In man, food stays in the small intestine from 4 to 8 hr. During this time the organ absorbs most of the minerals and organic nutrients but comparatively little water. On the contrary, by pouring digestive juices into the gut cavity the small intestine actually adds water to food. Water is absorbed mainly in the large intestine, or *colon.* The first portion of the colon is the *caecum,* a blind pouch that in man and a number of other mammals carries a terminal fingerlike extension, the *appendix* (Fig. 14.15 and see Fig. 14.12). At its far end the colon joins the *rectum,* a short tube opening at the *anus.*

So called because of its wider diameter, the large intestine has a dual function. First, it is an *absorbing* and *excreting* organ. During the 10-

to 12-hr stay of materials in the colon, most of the water and the remaining inorganic nutrients are absorbed. At the same time, excess amounts of many metabolic wastes and inorganic substances present in the body are excreted from blood to the colon cavity. Thus, by absorbing from and adding to the materials in the gut cavity, the large intestine aids in maintaining a properly balanced internal composition of the body. That the colon actually does contribute to the regulation of, for example, the internal water balance is indicated by the familiar upset conditions of diarrhea and constipation.

Second, the indigestible and unabsorbable materials undergo decay in the large intestine. This action is brought about by dense, permanent populations of saprotrophic bacteria that live in the gut as symbionts. The microorganisms obtain food from many of the materials that the host cannot digest or absorb, and as a result of such bacterial activity the substances in the colon undergo rapid decay. Frequently the bacteria release byproducts of their own metabolism, and some of these can be nutrients usable by the host. Vitamins are among them. Mammals actually obtain an appreciable fraction of their vitamin supply from the intestinal bacteria.

After food has passed through the large intestine chiefly *roughage* is left: tough fibers, gristle, pieces of cellulose, unmacerated plant tissue, all suspended in more or less reduced quantities of water. Mixed with this are bile pigments, colon excretions, bacteria and bacterial products, and whatever else may have been added or left over in the passage of food through the gut. These *feces* are in a more or less advanced state of decay, and they are ultimately egested as semisolid masses.

absorption and distribution

Transfer of usable nutrients to the circulating blood and lymph is achieved by absorption. A few substances—alcohol, for example—can be taken up through the stomach wall, but most foods are absorbed through the intestine. Nutrients here pass through the mucosa to the deeper tissues of the gut wall, where blood and lymph vessels are situated.

That the absorptive work done by mucosal cells is selective is well illustrated by the different rates with which foodstuffs are taken up. For example, the sugars glucose, galactose, and fructose all have the same molecular size and atomic composition, $C_6H_{12}O_6$. Yet galactose is absorbed most rapidly, fructose least rapidly. Moreover, sugar molecules containing only three, four, or five carbon atoms, though smaller than the three 6-carbon sugars just referred to, are generally absorbed much more slowly, if at all. Mucosal cells evidently "recognize" and select among the substances in digested food (see also discussion of membrane selectivity in Chap. 4).

As elsewhere, uptake of glucose is accompanied by *phosphorylation* (see Fig. 14.4). When sugar is later secreted from the mucosa to the deeper tissues of the gut wall, the phosphate groups are removed again and free sugar then enters the blood stream. Water, minerals, amino acids, and vitamins diffuse through the mucosa unchanged. Similarly, collodial fat droplets as well as fatty acids and glycerin are passed without change through the mucosa and reappear on the other side. Here some of the fatty acids and glycerin often recombine immediately as whole fats, a process that increases the amount of colloidal fat transported away from the gut.

14.15 Abdominal dissection, man. *Portions of the large intestine are shown at left and toward top. The rounded termination of the large intestine near left bottom is the caecum, a blind pouch. Attached to it is the appendix (arrow).*

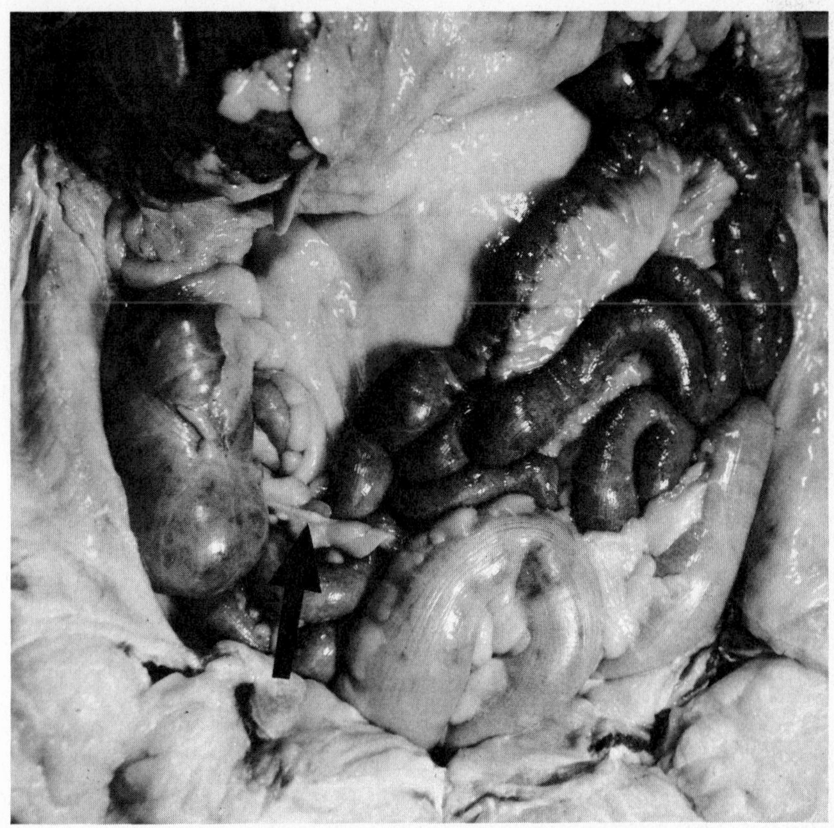

Each villus of the intestinal wall contains capillaries of the blood circulation (Fig. 14.16). Blood is pumped to the intestine through a few large arteries, which then branch out in the gut wall as extensive networks of microscopic capillary vessels (see Fig. 13.11). These capillaries pick up most of the nutrients absorbed through the intestinal mucosa—water, minerals, vitamins, monosaccharides, amino acids, and fatty acids and glycerin.

Food-laden blood now leaves the intestine. The capillaries in the gut collect as larger vessels, these join and rejoin, and a single large channel eventually emerges from the whole intestine. This vessel, the *hepatic portal vein,* leads directly to the *liver* (see Fig. 13.11). Whatever nutrients are not or cannot be transported to the liver in this fashion are collected by the *lymph* system. Among such nutrients are mainly the colloidal droplets of whole fat, which are enormously larger than molecules. But the lymph also receives water, minerals, and variable quantities of other substances that have escaped transport by blood.

The lymph system (Fig. 14.17) returns to blood any fluid lost from the blood circulation. As blood flows in its closed network of vessels, a certain amount of fluid normally passes through the thin walls of the capillaries. This escaped fluid, or lymph, is responsible for the moist condition of all body tissues, and it is through lymph that the cells of the body are ultimately supplied with water and all other necessary supplies. Lymph lost from the blood circulation eventually returns to the circulation through the lymph system. Microscopic lymph capillaries originate in all parts of the body, intestine included, and they pick up any free fluid in the tissues. Lymph capillaries then join as progressively larger, progressively fewer ducts until a single large channel is formed. This channel empties into a vein in the left shoulder region and returns to the blood all the lymph lost originally.

The lymph capillaries originating in the intestine are called *lacteals* (see Fig. 14.16). One lacteal is situated in each villus, and it is here that colloidal fat droplets and some other nutrients enter the lymph system. After reaching the blood circulation the fat droplets are transported to the fat-storing regions of the body and in effect bypass the liver. But other nutrients conducted by the lymph system eventually do circulate via blood to the liver, where they join those already carried in by the hepatic portal vein.

In the liver, the hepatic portal vein breaks up into an extensive network of unlined blood channels (*sinusoids;* see Figs. 14.12 and 5.31). This arrangement brings every liver cell into direct contact with incoming blood. The cells absorb blood-borne nutrients, process them, and return the finished products to the blood. All such blood ultimately leaves the liver through a single large *hepatic vein,* which carries liver-processed foods to the general body circulation. In this manner nutrient supplies reach all parts of the body (see Fig. 13.11).

Representing the largest gland of the vertebrate body, the liver has been estimated to carry out some 200 separate functions. The most important of these will be discussed in the course of later chapters. Many liver functions are not concerned directly with nutrient transport, but the many that are make the liver the main receiving station,

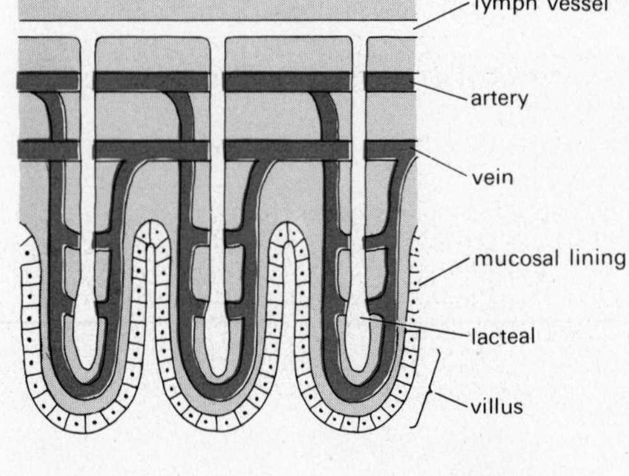

14.16 Intestinal villi. *Colloidal whole fat enters the blind-ended lymphatic lacteals, passes from there to the lymph circulation of the body, and so bypasses the liver. All other organic nutrients from the intestine are absorbed directly to the blood circulation of the villi and are transported from there to the liver. The vessel pattern to and from the liver is indicated in Fig. 13.11.*

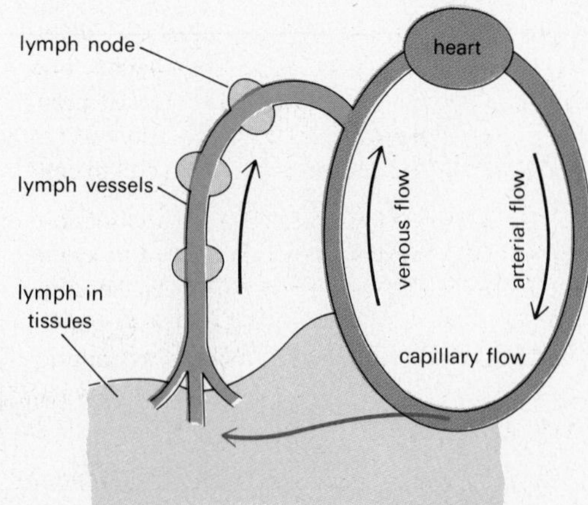

14.17 Lymph circulation. *Fluid (lymph) escapes from the blood capillaries into the tissues of the body (colored arrow) and returns via lymph vessels to the venous part of the blood circulation. Along the path of larger lymph vessels are lymph nodes, which produce some types of blood cells and purify lymph (see Fig. 20.4).*

processing plant, warehouse, distributing organ, and traffic control center, all rolled into one. Whereas the metabolism of other animals reaches peaks just after food has been eaten, the metabolism of the liver-possessing vertebrates can remain at a continuously steady level regardless of the daily pattern of eating. For liver cells regulate what kinds and what quantities of nutrients are sent out to body tissues. The cells carry out numerous chemical transformations of incoming materials and serve as storage depots for some of them. Through such quartermastering activities the liver plays a major role in the maintenance of optimal working conditions throughout the body.

The liver actually can be regarded as one side of a nutritional balance. The other side is the remainder of the body, and blood serves as carrier, signal mechanism, and general connecting link between the two sides (Fig. 14.18). Nutrients coming or not coming from the gut to the liver can shift the balance one way; and nutrients used up or not used up by the body tissues can shift it the opposite way. As will become clear in later contexts, these balancing processes operate through chemical equilibria. They normally adjust in such a manner that the original balance is maintained or, if upset, reestablished.

Among the nutrients delivered from the liver to individual animal cells are glucose; all different kinds of amino acids; fats, fatty acids, and glycerin; water and mineral ions; vitamins; and also various special organic compounds. Receiving such supplies in appropriate amounts, the animal cell, like the plant cell, then can carry out the main business of metabolism: *liberation of energy* on the one hand and *construction of new living matter* on the other.

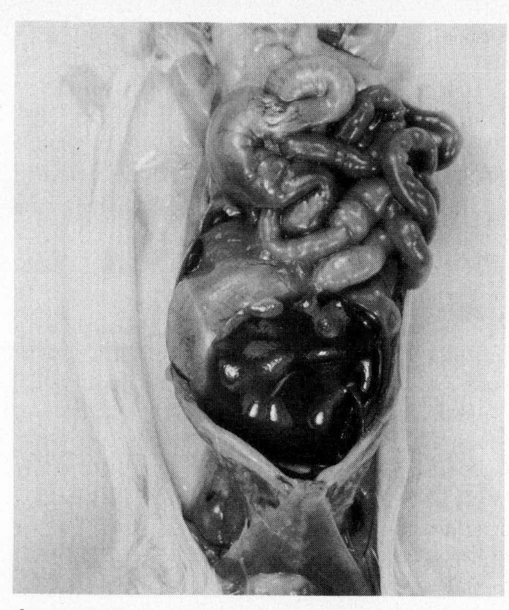

A

nutrient supply from intestine ⟶ liver $\underset{}{\overset{\text{blood}}{\rightleftarrows}}$ body tissues ⟶ nutrient utilization in cells

B

14.18 ***The liver.*** *A, abdominal dissection of a mouse showing the position and gross external appearance of the liver (large dark organ). Internal liver structure is illustrated in Figs. 5.31 and 14.12. B, generalized summary of the food-distributing role of the liver.*

review questions

1 Define nutrition. What are the major nutritional processes of organisms? Define autotroph, heterotroph, photolithotroph, photoorganotroph, chemolithotroph, chemoorganotroph. Which groups of organisms belong to each of these categories?

2 Review the general patterns of food procurement in the various groups of autotrophs and heterotrophs. Review the different nutritional patterns of (*a*) purple sulfur bacteria, purple bacteria, and sulfur bacteria, (*b*) nitrifying bacteria, denitrifying bacteria, and nitrogen-fixing bacteria.

3 Where and through what processes do different groups of organisms obtain (*a*) water, (*b*) other mineral substances, (*c*) molecular foods, (*d*) atmospheric gases? What is phosphorylation, and what role does it play in nutrition? What processes bring about short-distance transport of nutrients inside individual cells and from cell to cell?

4 Describe the mechanism of xylem conduction. What kinds of nutrients are transported in xylem and in which direction? What is (*a*) root pressure, (*b*) transpiration? How are these forces generated? What roles do they play in xylem conduction? What is the importance of cohesion of water in xylem conduction?

5 What forces bring about phloem conduction? What kinds of nutrients are carried in phloem and in which direction? Describe the processes that bring about upward translocation of a given nutrient.

6 If a cut length of stem bearing some leaves were put upside down into a glass of nutrient-rich water, how would (*a*) xylem conduction and (*b*) phloem conduction be affected? How has it been proved that phloem can transport in both directions?

7 Contrast the nutrient requirements of plants and animals. For which materials are animals dependent on plants and why? What is the basic function of an alimentary system?

8 What role does the brain play in hunger control among mammals? What roles do enzymes play in digestion, and how are digestive enzymes distinct from others?

9 What is the composition of saliva and how is salivary secretion initiated? What mechanical and chemical digestive processes occur in the mouth? Through what processes is food transferred to the stomach?

10 What is the composition of gastric juice, and by what processes is secretion of this fluid controlled? Review the mechanical and chemical events of gastric digestion. What are the specific functions of HCl, pepsin, and rennin? What are the results of gastric digestion?

11 Which digestive fluids are added to food in the duodenum, and what is the composition of these fluids? Where are the fluids manufactured, and what processes stimulate their secretion? What is enterokinase, and what is its function?

12 Review the specific course of protein, carbohydrate, and fat digestion in the intestine. What enzymes are involved in each case? What are the results of these digestive processes? What are intestinal villi, and what are their functions? How and in what form are different categories of food absorbed by the intestinal wall?

13 What are the functions of the large intestine? What is the role of the intestinal bacteria? Do these symbionts live mutualistically, commensalistically, or parasitically? If pure glucose were eaten, where would it be digested? Why are eaten vitamins or orally administered medicines not digested in the alimentary tract?

14 Describe the blood circulation through the intestine. Which food materials are carried away from the intestine by blood? Describe the pattern of the lymph circulation in the body as a whole. What is the arrangement of the lymph vessels in the intestine?

15 By what pathways do foods reach the liver? What are the pathway and destination of colloidal fat? By what pathways do processed foods leave the liver? What is the general function of the liver, and what is the adaptive advantage of such an organ?

---

collateral readings

Biddulph, S., and **O. Biddulph**: The Circulatory System of Plants, *Sci. American,* Feb., 1959. The article describes experiments with radioactive tracers on xylem and phloem transport.

Clayton, R. K., and **M. Delbruck**: Purple Bacteria, *Sci. American,* Nov., 1951. An interesting account on these photoorganotrophs.

Crafts, A. S.: "Translocation in Plants," Holt, New York, 1961. A small book containing detailed descriptions of all circulatory functions in plants.

Galston, A. W.: "The Life of the Green Plant," 2d ed., Prentice-Hall, Englewood Cliffs, N.J., 1964. This paperback contains a section on plant nutrition, including xylem and phloem functions.

Greulach, V. A.: The Rise of Water in Plants, *Sci. American,* Oct., 1952. A good discussion of the forces playing a role in the ascent of sap.

Holter, H.: How Things Get into Cells, *Sci. American,* Sept., 1961. A good general discussion of processes and forces of cellular nutrition.

Mayer, J.: Appetite and Obesity, *Sci. American,* Nov., 1956. A noted nutritionist discusses the control of food intake in man.

Mayerson, H. S.: The Lymphatic System, *Sci. American,* June, 1963. The functions of this system are described.

Postgate, J.: The Sulphur Bacteria, *New Biol.,* vol. 17, 1954. A case study of chemolithotrophs.

Prosser, C. L., and **F. A. Brown, Jr.**: "Comparative Animal Physiology," 2d ed., Saunders, Philadelphia, 1961. Chapters 4 and 5 of this text contain detailed discussions of alimentary functions in various animal types.

Salisbury, F. B.: Translocation, in "Plant Biology Today," Wadsworth, Belmont, Calif., 1963. A strongly recommended chapter on the movement of nutrients and other metabolites in plants.

——— and **R. V. Parke**: "Vascular Plants: Form and Function," Wadsworth, Belmont, Calif., 1964. This paperback includes a shorter account of translocation similar to the preceding entry.

Solomon, A. K.: Pores in the Cell Membrane, *Sci. American,* Dec., 1960. The mechanical aspects of cellular absorption are reviewed.

———: Pumps in the Living Cell, *Sci. American,* Aug., 1962. A discussion of active transport, specifically for sodium ions.

Steward, F. C.: "Plants at Work," Addison-Wesley, Reading, Mass., 1964. In this paperback a short chapter on mineral nutrition of plants is included. Recommended.

Zimmerman, M. H.: How Sap Moves in Trees, *Sci. American,* March, 1963. The activities of certain insects represent natural experiments on the transport processes of plants.

chapter 15 respiration

Respiration is a *cellular* process, an activity performed in each cell of an organism. Apart from depending on nutrient raw materials, respiration is associated also with an exchange of atmospheric gases; oxygen is usually a required raw material, and carbon dioxide is always a byproduct. As noted in earlier contexts, plants and many animals are so constructed that most of their living cells are in direct or nearly direct contact with the external environment. Gas exchange here takes place in correspondingly direct fashion. Specialized breathing systems occur only in the most complexly constructed coelomate animals. Such systems usually operate in conjunction with circulatory systems, and they serve not only in gas exchange but also in excretion and other functions of internal chemical control (refer to Chap. 20).

the pattern

Respiration can be defined as a conversion of the chemical energy of organic molecules to energy usable in living cells. The specific organelles in a cell where most respiration occurs are the mitochondria; and the process itself consists of a series of exergonic, energy-yielding decomposition reactions: respiration is a form of burning, or combustion, in which chemical bonds in nutrient molecules are broken and the bond energy becomes available for metabolic work.

If respiration is equivalent to combustion, why does it not produce the high temperatures of a fire? For two reasons. First, a fire is an *uncontrolled* combustion, in the sense that all the bonds in a fuel molecule may be broken simultaneously. A maximum amount of energy can then be released all at once. Such sudden, explosive release generates the high temperatures of a fire. But respiration is a *controlled* combustion; energy is obtained from one or a few bonds at a time. If a nutrient fuel is respired completely, the total energy yield is the same as if it were burned in a furnace, but in respiration the energy is removed bit by bit, bond by bond. Temperatures therefore stay low.

Second, the energy produced in a fire is dissipated largely as heat and to some extent as light. But in respiration only some of the available energy escapes as heat and practically none as light. Instead, much of it is "packaged" directly as new *chemical* energy. This energy-packaging process, already referred to in Chap. 4, is represented by the reaction that converts adenosine diphosphate (ADP) to adenosine triphosphate (ATP):

$$\text{ADP} + \text{phosphate} + \text{energy} \longrightarrow \text{ATP}$$

Energy from a fuel molecule becomes incorporated in ADP and phosphate, and ATP is thereby produced. Thus, fuel energy creates *new* chemical bonds in the form of ATP, and it is in this form that metabolic energy is used in cells. Since chemical bonds are not "hot," temperatures stay low during respiration.

The actual fuels in cells are organic compounds that contain bond energies—in effect, *any* organic constituent of cells: carbohydrates, fats, proteins, nucleotides, their various derivatives, vitamins, other special compounds, and indeed all the innumerable substances that together make up a cell. Like a fire, respiration is no respecter of materials. However, under normal conditions a cell receives a steady enough supply of external foods to make *them* the primary fuels rather than the structural parts of a cell. Nevertheless, the formed parts of a cell, including even those that make up the decomposing apparatus itself, *are* decomposed gradually. A cell therefore can remain intact and functioning only by continuous construction of new living components. Destructive energy metabolism (*catabolism*) and constructive synthesis metabolism (*anabolism*) are normally in balance, and foods serve as both fuel for the one and building materials for the other. The components of a cell in effect are continuously "turned over," existing parts being replaced by new ones, and the living substance consequently is never quite the same from instant to instant.

Just how is energy released from a fuel molecule? Since respiration involves energy-yielding decomposition reactions, the endproducts will contain less energy and will therefore be more stable than the starting fuels. As noted in Chap. 3, reactions tend to proceed in such a way that the least energetic, most stable states are attained. It is this basic thermodynamic circumstance that ultimately "drives" all respiratory processes. The energy liberated in respiration comes from the carbon bonds in food molecules, and different carbon bonds have different stabilities. The least stable, hence most energy-rich, carbon bonds generally occur in *hydrocarbon* groups, atomic groupings that contain only carbon and hydrogen. These exist in organic molecules in forms such as CH_4, $—CH_3$, $—CH_2—$, $=CH—$. On the other hand, the most stable carbon combination is CO_2, a so-called *anhydride,* or hydrogen-free grouping. In general, therefore, usable respiratory energy will result from conversions of hydrocarbons to anhydrides, or from the replacement of H atoms bonded to carbon by O atoms.

Removal of hydrogen, or *dehydrogenation,* actually is the important energy-yielding event in respiration. Through dehydrogenation a hydrocarbon-containing starting fuel is decomposed to CO_2, and energy and hydrogen are released in the process. The energy is then used in converting ADP to ATP. The hydrogen does not remain free either but combines with a *hydrogen acceptor.* Of several substances serving as hydrogen acceptors in cells, the most essential usually is oxygen. That is why this gas must be supplied to all cells as a respiratory raw material. Hydrogen combines with oxygen, and water then becomes one of the endproducts of respiration.

Respiration as a whole thus consists of three interrelated processes (Fig. 15.1). First, a nutrient fuel molecule is decomposed by dehydrogenation. Smaller fuel fragments generally form, which can be decomposed in turn until the original food molecule has been degraded completely to CO_2. This phase of respiration can be termed *fuel decomposition.* Second, as a result of fuel decomposition hydrogen is freed. It becomes attached to an appropriate acceptor, and if the acceptor is oxygen water forms. This phase of respiration can be referred to as *hydrogen transfer.* Third, as a further result of fuel breakdown, energy is released. Some of this energy escapes as heat, but much of it is harvested by the ADP/ATP system. ATP then represents the main product of respiration. This phase can be called *energy transfer.*

In the following sections each of these phases is examined in greater detail.

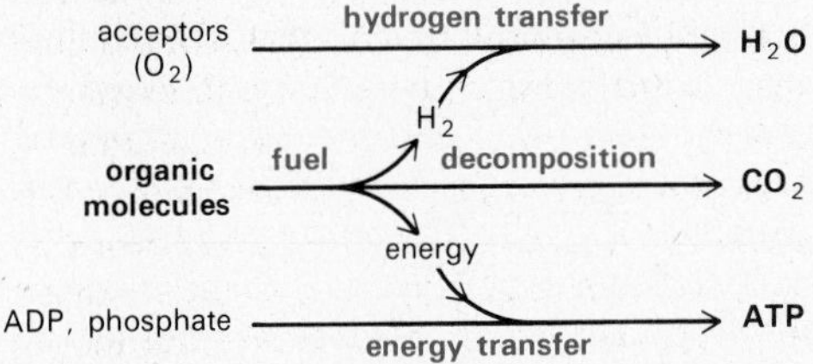

15.1 The three-phase pattern of respiration: *breakdown of fuel, hydrogen transfer from fuel, and energy transfer from fuel.*

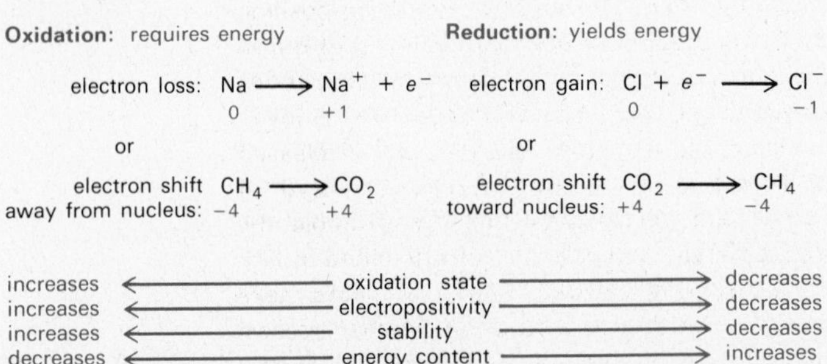

15.2 Oxidation and reduction. *The properties of these two types of reaction are summarized.*

decomposition: oxidation

Dehydrogenations are instances of so-called *oxidation-reduction,* or *redox,* reactions. Every such reaction can be considered to consist of two subreactions, one being an oxidation, the other a reduction.

An oxidation fundamentally is any process that makes an atom more electropositive and thereby endows it with a higher oxidation state (Fig. 15.2). In electron-transfer reactions, for example, an atom that loses electrons becomes oxidized. Thus, a neutral sodium atom is oxidized when it becomes an ion; the ion is more electropositive and has a higher oxidation state (+1) than the neutral atom. Oxidation need not involve an outright loss of electrons, however. If electrons merely shift farther away from an atom, resulting in decreased attraction between the electrons and the atomic nucleus, such changes represent oxidations, too. For example, as pointed out in Chap. 3, the electron pairs that are shared between C and H of methane (CH_4) are attracted strongly by the C nucleus and actually lie much nearer to that nucleus than to the H atoms. In CO_2, by contrast, it is the oxygen atoms that attract the shared electron pairs more strongly than the C atom. Hence if CH_4 is converted to CO_2, the carbon atom becomes oxidized; its electrons shift farther away, the atom becomes more electropositive as a result, and its oxidation state increases (from −4 to +4 in this case; see Fig. 15.2 and Chap. 3). This shift is why removal of hydrogen from carbon compounds, as in respiration, actually represents an oxidation; dehydrogenation makes the carbon atoms more electropositive.

Conversely, a reduction is a process that makes an atom more electronegative and thus lowers its oxidation state. Reductions can occur through outright gains of electrons or through shifts of electrons closer to atomic nuclei (see Fig. 15.2). Oxidations and reductions always occur together, because every redox process requires both an electron donor (which becomes oxidized) and an electron acceptor (which becomes reduced). Thus if a redox process involves hydrogen, as in respiration, a hydrogen-donor compound becomes dehydrogenated and thereby oxidized, and a hydrogen-acceptor compound must be present to bond with the removed hydrogen and thereby become reduced.

In the context of respiration the important point is that every redox change is accompanied by energy changes. Since electrons are energy carriers, oxidation leads to an energy *loss* in the atom being oxidized, inasmuch as electrons are shifted away or removed. Conversely, reduction results in an energy *gain* in the atom being reduced, inasmuch as electrons are gained. In line with the second law of thermodynamics, a lower energy content signifies greater stability, and a higher content, lesser stability. Accordingly, oxidation tends to increase the stability of a chemical unit, reduction, to decrease it. A complete redox change therefore includes an energy transfer: energy is released by a unit that is being oxidized and made more stable, and some or all of this energy is accepted by another unit that is reduced and made less stable. The units that are reduced usually cannot become quite as unstable as those that are oxidized; as in respiration, for example, the endproducts are more stable than the starting materials. A redox change then leads to a net release of some energy to the environment: of the energy resulting from an oxidation, a portion is transferred to the accompanying reduction and the rest becomes free and potentially available for other uses. It is this energy remainder that is the direct source of all the respiratory energy later harvested as ATP. Moreover, it is because energy is released in this fashion that respiratory redox reactions continue to take place unidirectionally rather than reach equilibrium.

Consider, for example, the complete redox decomposition of methane:

$$\mathbf{CH_4} + 2\ \mathbf{O_2} \longrightarrow \mathbf{CO_2} + 2\ \mathbf{H_2O} + \text{energy}$$

Here the endproducts CO_2 and water are more stable and collectively poorer in energy than the starting materials methane and oxygen; the energy difference appears free in the environment.

	Oxidation			Reduction
1	$H_3C{-}H + H{-}OH$ (C: −4) methane	$\longrightarrow$	$H_3C{-}OH + H_2$ (C: −2) methyl alcohol	$- - \rightarrow H_2 + O \longrightarrow H_2O$ + energy
2	$H_2C{-}OH$ (C: −2) methyl alcohol	$\longrightarrow$	$H_2C{=}O + H_2$ (C: 0) formaldehyde	$- - \rightarrow H_2 + O \longrightarrow H_2O$ + energy
3	$H_2C{=}O + H{-}OH$ (C: 0) formaldehyde	$\longrightarrow$	$HC(OH){=}O + H_2$ (C: +2) formic acid	$- - \rightarrow H_2 + O \longrightarrow H_2O$ + energy
4	$HC(OH){=}O$ (C: +2) formic acid	$\longrightarrow$	$O{=}C{=}O + H_2$ (C: +4) carbonic anhydride (CO_2)	$- - \rightarrow H_2 + O \longrightarrow H_2O$ + energy

Sum of oxidations

$$CH_4 + 2H_2 \longrightarrow CO_2 + 4H_2$$

Sum of reductions

$$4H_2 + 2O_2 \longrightarrow 4H_2O + \text{energy}$$

Net reaction: $CH_4 + 2O_2 \longrightarrow CO_2 + 2H_2O$ + energy

15.3 Stepwise decomposition of methane. *In each of the four steps an oxidizing half-reaction liberates* H_2. *The hydrogen then combines with oxygen in a reducing half-reaction, yielding water and energy. The whole reaction sequence is exergonic; it liberates more energy than it requires, and the endproducts are more stable than the starting materials (net reaction at bottom).*

To symbolize the simultaneous oxidation and reduction separately, we can write:

$\mathbf{CH_4} + \mathbf{O_2} \longrightarrow \mathbf{CO_2} + 2\ H_2$	*oxidation of carbon*
$2\ H_2 + \mathbf{O_2} \longrightarrow 2\ \mathbf{H_2O}$	*reduction of oxygen*
$\mathbf{CH_4} + 2\ \mathbf{O_2} \longrightarrow \mathbf{CO_2} + 2\ \mathbf{H_2O}$	*net redox change*

Methane is the hydrogen donor, and the carbon of methane is oxidized to CO_2. At the same time oxygen is the hydrogen acceptor, and oxygen is reduced to H_2O. For convenience we can refer to the whole process simply as an "oxidation." This is actually common practice in discussions of respiration reactions, which are often called "biological oxidations." Notwithstanding the incomplete name, however, every oxidation implies and is accompanied by a reduction.

As noted earlier, a respiratory decomposition does not take place in a single large step but in several small ones; a *series* of consecutive redox reactions occurs, in which hydrogen is removed from fuel bit by bit, in which energy is released bit by bit, and in which the oxidation level of carbon atoms increases in steps. For example, the stepwise oxidation of methane is outlined in Fig. 15.3. Four consecutive redox reactions take place, in which methane is transformed successively to methyl alcohol, formaldehyde, formic

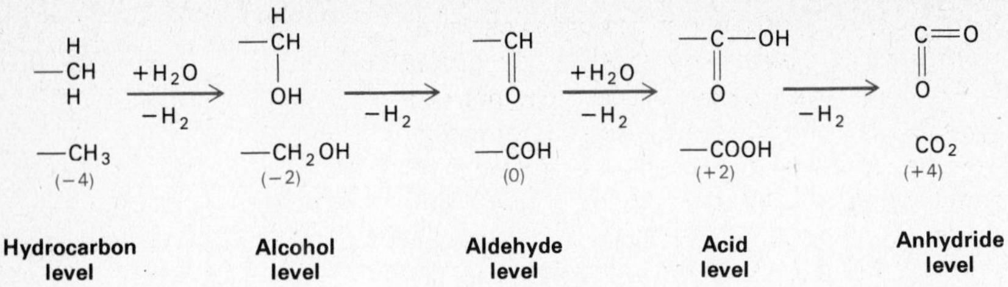

	Hydrocarbon level		Alcohol level		Aldehyde level		Acid level		Anhydride level
	$-CH_3$ (H—CH—H)	$\xrightarrow[-H_2]{+H_2O}$	$-CH(H)OH$	$\xrightarrow{-H_2}$	$-CH{=}O$	$\xrightarrow[-H_2]{+H_2O}$	$-C(=O)-OH$	$\xrightarrow{-H_2}$	$C{=}O$ (=O)
	$-CH_3$		$-CH_2OH$		$-COH$		$-COOH$		CO_2
oxidation state	(−4)		(−2)		(0)		(+2)		(+4)

15.4 Foods and oxidation levels. *Carbon groups in food molecules (symbolized in two ways, top and bottom rows) are at one of the oxidation levels shown, and during respiration these groups are transformed to the successively more oxidized levels indicated. At each step the oxidative event is hydrogen removal, and the resulting level is more stable than the preceding one. Combination of the hydrogen with oxygen in reducing half-reactions (not shown) then yields a net energy gain, as in Fig. 15.3.*

acid, and carbon dioxide. Each of the four oxidative subreactions yields H_2, and in the accompanying reducing subreactions the hydrogen pairs are accepted by oxygen and form water. Each of these four redox processes also yields energy. If the four redox reactions are then added together, we end up with the same final equation and the same net energy yield as in a single-step oxidation of methane.

Stepwise oxidation occurs generally in the respiration of all foods. Indeed, although methane itself is a poison, not a food, the oxidation steps for actual foods are nevertheless the same as those outlined for methane: *the carbon groupings of food molecules are transformed successively from hydrocarbon to alcohol to aldehyde to acid to anhydride.* Moreover, the oxidation states of carbon here change successively from −4 to −2 to 0 to +2 to +4 (Fig. 15.4).

energy transfer

An appreciable fraction of the energy released in biological oxidations dissipates free into the environment, largely in the form of heat, and respiration actually is the most important source of internal heat in all organisms (see also Chap. 17). However, a valuable fraction of the energy from respiratory oxidations does not become "free;" instead, as noted earlier, respiration includes a transfer of energy from chemical bonds in fuel to the chemical bonds of ATP. But if fuel energy already exists in the form of chemical bonds, what is the point of respiration if it only creates other chemical bonds?

Some bonds contain more energy than others, and we can distinguish between *high-energy bonds* and *low-energy bonds.* To create the first kind, a relatively large amount of energy must be expended. A correspondingly large amount then becomes available when such a bond is broken. However, most bonds in organic molecules are of the *low*-energy type. Thus the carbon-carbon, carbon-hydrogen, or carbon-oxygen links in fuel compounds are low-energy bonds. If one of these is broken only a comparatively small amount of energy becomes available. Yet much more concentrated packets of energy are required in metabolic work. An energy-*concentrating* process is therefore needed, one that will pool the many low-energy packets of a fuel molecule in the form of a smaller number of high-energy packets.

Respiration does just that. Through fuel oxidation, the bond energies of fuel become concentrated in one or more high-energy bonds. Atomic groupings containing these bonds are then transferred from fuel to ADP, and ATP results. Respiration therefore accomplishes more than the mere making of new bonds out of old ones; it makes high-energy bonds out of low-energy bonds. The creation of high-energy from low-energy bonds is achieved essentially by *internal reorganizations* of a fuel molecule. In the course of stepwise oxidation, the bond energies of a fuel become redistributed in such a way that one of the bonds comes to hold a great deal of energy, whereas others hold less than before. In effect, a high-energy bond is created at the expense of several low-energy bonds.

The chief atomic groupings in cells in which high-energy bonds can be created are phosphate groups. If we symbolize such a group as —O—P, as on earlier occasions, then the bond that joins O and P is a *phosphate bond.* A bond of this type can be of either the low-energy or the high-energy variety; its properties are such that it can join —O and —P weakly or strongly. In the latter case the phosphate bond can be considered to contain *extra energy* and to represent a high-energy bond. To indicate such a bond, we use the symbol ∼. Thus, a low-energy phosphate bond is symbolized as —O—P, and a high-energy phosphate bond, as —O∼P.

The energy-harvesting phase of respiration can now be symbolized as follows:

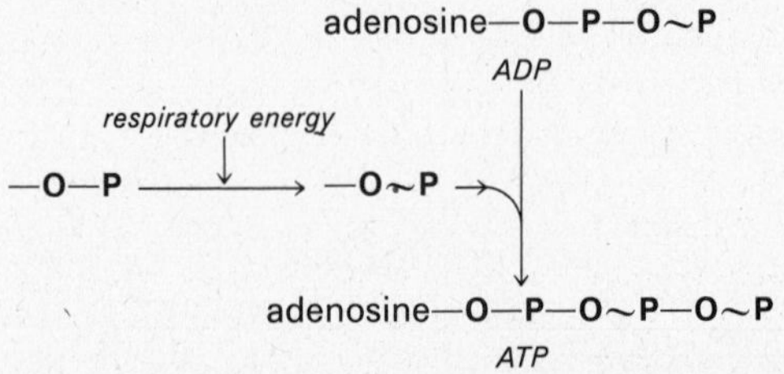

adenosine—O—P—O∼P
ADP

—O—P —(*respiratory energy*)→ **—O∼P** → (joins ADP)

adenosine—O—P—O∼P—O∼P
ATP

This scheme clearly implies that before —O∼P groups can be transferred to ADP to form ATP, such groups must first be created. They are indeed created in respiration. Two general events take place: (1) in a preparatory process a fuel molecule is phosphorylated; a phosphate group (—O—P) is attached to it; (2) this phosphorylated fuel is oxidized by dehydrogenation. The process yields energy, but inasmuch as an —O—P group is now part of the fuel molecule, a major part of this energy is not released as heat. Instead it becomes redistributed in the fuel molecule and —O—P is transformed to —O∼P. The latter is then transferred to ADP (Fig. 15.5).

The ultimate source of the phosphate groups required in these (and other) phosphorylations is the external environment, which supplies inorganic phosphates as mineral nutrients. However, the immediate phosphate source in cells usually is ATP itself. As noted in Chap. 14, for example, glucose uptake by a cell requires an accompanying phosphorylation, and ATP is the phosphorylating agent (see Fig. 14.4). In this and all similar instances, the terminal high-energy phosphate of ATP is split off (and ATP thus becomes ADP), but an ordinary low-energy phosphate is added to the fuel molecule:

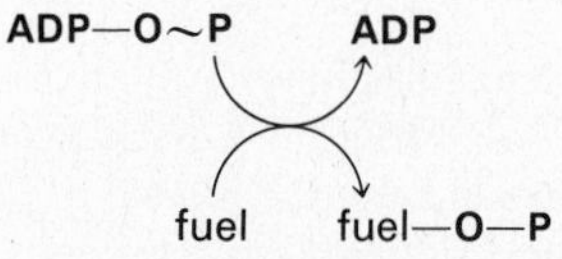

ADP—O∼P → **ADP**

fuel → fuel—**O—P**

ATP here supplies more than enough energy to produce a phosphorylated compound, and any energy excess dissipates unavoidably as heat. Evidently, some of the endproduct of respiration, ATP, is needed at the starting point for preliminary phosphorylations; prior respiration is a necessary condition for further respiration.

The amount of ATP that can be formed in respiration varies with the nature of the fuel, or more specifically, with the number of possible oxidation steps in the fuel. In a fatty acid, for example, the carbon in the —COOH group is at the acid level, the other carbons are at the hydrocarbon level; a sugar such as glucose contains one carbon at the aldehyde level, five others at the alcohol level (Fig. 15.6). Oxidations of individual carbon groups here will proceed stepwise from any given starting level until the anhydride stage is attained. Correspondingly, the energy yields will differ according to how many oxidation steps are still possible for each carbon group.

Moreover, every oxidation step does not necessarily yield enough energy for ATP formation. Conversion of ADP to ATP requires on the average 7 kilocalories (kcal, see Chap. 3) per gram-molecular weight (mole) of ADP. A mole is an amount of a substance equal in grams to the molecular weight. Thus, a mole of ADP weighs 406 g. In effect, 7 kcal represents a kind of minimum energy packet in metabolism, and any oxidation that yields less than that will not result in ATP formation. In fuel oxidations the energy yields range from about 5 to about 11 kcal, with an average of about 8 kcal, per mole of fuel oxidized. Most of such oxidations do result in ATP formation (and any energy excess dissipates as heat). But in certain oxidations the energy yield is less than 7 kcal, and in such cases ATP cannot be formed (see also below).

hydrogen transfer

Hydrogen removal from fuel molecules is an enzymatic process; a specific *dehydrogenase* is

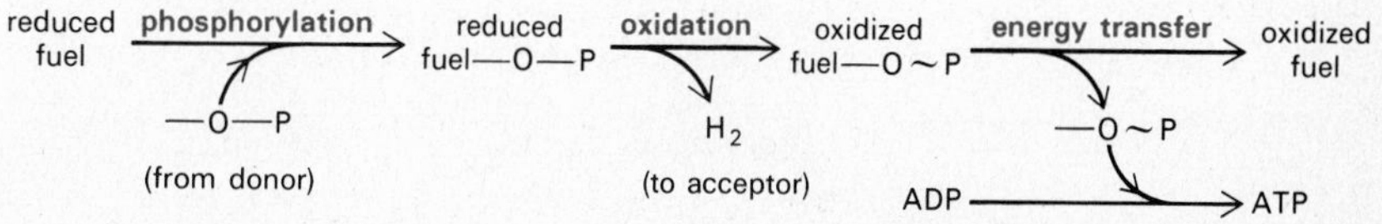

reduced fuel —**phosphorylation**→ reduced fuel—O—P —**oxidation**→ oxidized fuel—O∼P —**energy transfer**→ oxidized fuel

—O—P (from donor); H_2 (to acceptor); —O∼P; ADP → ATP

15.5 (*Above*) ***High-energy bonds.*** *The general pattern of their creation by phosphorylation and oxidation, and the transfer of such bonds to ADP.*

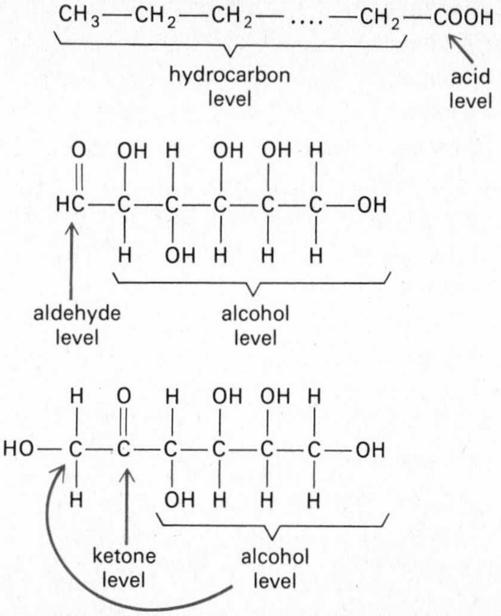

CH_3—CH_2—CH_2— .... —CH_2—COOH

hydrocarbon level; acid level

O=HC—C(OH)(H)—C(H)(OH)—C(OH)(H)—C(OH)(H)—C(H)(H)—OH

aldehyde level; alcohol level

HO—C(H)(H)—C(=O)—C(H)(OH)—C(OH)(H)—C(OH)(H)—C(H)(H)—OH

ketone level; alcohol level

15.6 Oxidation levels of carbon groups. *In fatty acid (top), glucose (middle), and fructose (bottom), the amount of further oxidation still possible for each group depends on its particular oxidation level in the intact molecule. A ketone group (—C=O) has the same oxidation level as an aldehyde group (—HC=O).*

required at each oxidation step. As already noted, moreover, dehydrogenation also requires the presence of a hydrogen acceptor, and the final acceptor in cells usually is oxygen. However, hydrogen from cellular fuels does not combine with oxygen directly. Instead such hydrogen is first passed along a whole succession of intermediate *hydrogen carriers,* and only the last of these finally releases hydrogen to oxygen:

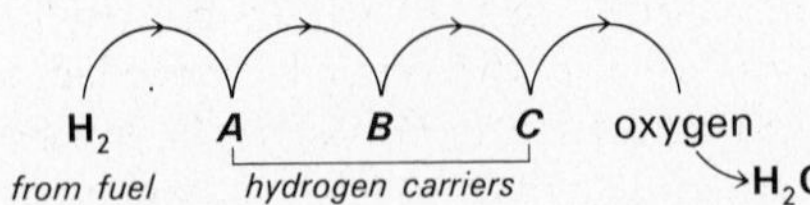

The combination of hydrogen and oxygen is an energy-yielding process. This is well demonstrated by the observation that when mixed in the right proportions in the test tube, the two gases combine explosively; the energy is released as a single large packet and dissipates almost entirely as heat. Most probably, therefore, H transfer to oxygen in cells occurs stepwise through a succession of carriers for exactly the same reasons that fuel decomposition to CO_2 occurs in small steps; smaller, more numerous energy packets can become available for metabolic use.

Indeed, like fuel decomposition to CO_2, each step in a serial hydrogen transfer is itself a complete redox process. A given hydrogen carrier becomes oxidized when it passes on H_2 to the next carrier in the series, and it becomes reduced when it accepts H_2 from the preceding carrier:

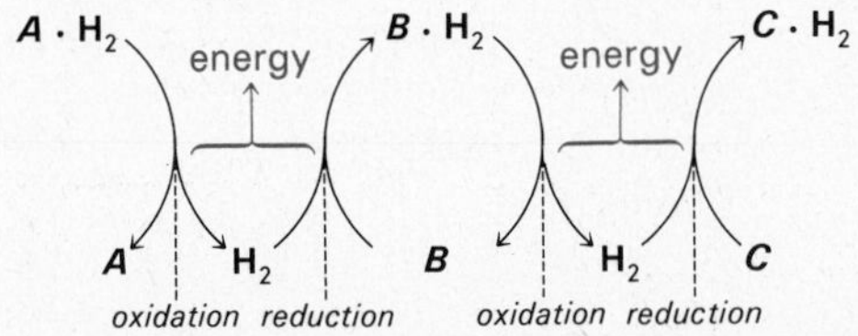

Hydrogen carriers operate cyclically and are alternately reduced and oxidized; and $C \cdot H_2$ above is more stable than $B \cdot H_2$, which in turn is more stable than $A \cdot H_2$. The most stable compound appears at the last transfer, when hydrogen combines with oxygen and forms water.

As indicated in the scheme above, H transfer by carriers yields energy at each transfer step. It has been shown that at three of these steps enough energy is released to suffice for ATP formation. Thus, for every H_2 transferred by carriers from fuel to oxygen, a net total of 3 ATP is formed. High-energy phosphates again play a role here, but it is not yet fully known just how the energy is actually trapped in such phosphates. In any case it is clear that there are *two* kinds of ATP sources in respiration. One is fuel decomposition by dehydrogenation; the other is creation of ATP during hydrogen transfer from fuel to oxygen. Of these two sources, the second is often the more important—hydrogen transfer in many cases yields more ATP than that gained through fuel decomposition (Fig. 15.7).

The actual intermediate H carriers are some of the coenzymes already discussed in Chap. 4. Figure 15.7 indicates their names and the sequence in which they function. In this sequence, NAD (or NADP) and FAD are vitamin B–derived coenzymes (see Fig. 4.12). *Q* is a coenzyme that has not been completely identified as yet, and the cytochromes consist of a family of at least four slightly different coenzymes that operate in succession. Cytochromes are red, iron-containing compounds, structurally quite similar to the iron-containing portion of hemoglobin in red blood cells (see Fig. 4.6).

aerobic and anaerobic transfer

Because H transport requires atmospheric oxygen as the final hydrogen acceptor, this pattern of transfer is said to define an *aerobic* (with air) form of respiration. It is the standard, universal form in the vast majority of organisms.

If any one of these aerobic transport reactions were stopped, the whole transfer sequence would become inoperative and the energy it normally supplies would remain unavailable. Reaction blocks can actually occur in a number of ways. For example, *inhibitor* substances of various kinds can interfere specifically with particular transport reactions. Thus, cyanides specifically inhibit the cytochromes, and this is why cyanides are poisons. Another form of reaction block is produced if one of the hydrogen carriers is in deficient supply. For example, inasmuch as riboflavin (vitamin B_2) is a structural part of the FAD molecule (see Fig. 4.12), a consistently riboflavin-deficient diet would soon impair the reactions in which FAD participates.

Although cyanide poisoning and vitamin B deficiencies are not particularly common hazards, all organisms quite frequently do have to contend with inadequate supplies of atmospheric oxygen. Lack of oxygen is a reaction block of the same sort as cyanide poisoning or vitamin deficiencies, with the consequence that respiration as a whole stops. Whenever hydrogen transport to oxygen is blocked for some reason, organisms can respire in a way that does not require oxygen. This *anaerobic* (without air) respiration, or *fermentation,* then becomes a substitute or auxiliary source of energy.

The principle of anaerobic hydrogen transport is relatively simple. With the path from NAD to oxygen blocked, another path, from NAD to another hydrogen acceptor, must be used. Such an alternative path is provided by *pyruvic acid,* one of the compounds normally formed in the course of carbohydrate respiration (see below). If enough oxygen is available, pyruvic acid is merely one of the intermediate steps in the decomposition of carbohydrates to CO_2. But pyruvic acid has the property of reacting readily with hydrogen, and if NAD cannot use its normal hydrogen outlet to FAD and oxygen, pyruvic acid is used instead. The acid then ceases to be a fuel and becomes a hydrogen carrier.

When pyruvic acid reacts with hydrogen, the result in plants and most microorganisms is the formation of alcohol and CO_2, and in animals and certain bacteria, the formation of lactic acid (Fig. 15.8). Either reaction completes anaerobic respiration; alcohol or lactic acid accumulates in a cell and eventually diffuses to the outside.

The energy gained through fermentation suffices to maintain the life of organisms such as yeasts, many bacteria, and other *anaerobes,* or organisms that must or can live in the absence of oxygen. But the vast majority of organisms are *aerobes,* in which fermentation energy by itself is insufficient to sustain life. If such organisms lack oxygen, the energy normally harvested by H transfer to oxygen cannot be obtained. Moreover, fuel oxidation has stopped at the pyruvic acid stage, and the potential energy still contained in this acid therefore remains untapped and locked in alcohol or lactic acid. Fermentation actually yields only about 5 percent of the energy obtainable by aerobic respiration (see below). This is too little to maintain the life of plants or animals; as is well known, such organisms die within minutes if oxygen is completely absent.

Even so, fermentation can nevertheless *supplement* the aerobic energy gains. Whenever energy demands are high, as during intensive muscular activity in animals, the oxygen supply to the cells tends to become insufficient despite faster breathing. Under such conditions of *oxygen debt,* fermentation can proceed in parallel with aerobic respiration and provide a little extra energy. Lactic acid then accumulates in the muscles. Eventually fatigue becomes so great that the animal must cease its intensive activity. During the later rest period faster breathing at first continues and the oxygen debt is thereby being repaid. Lactic acid is carried by blood from the muscles to the liver, where it is converted to glucose. Returned to muscles, glucose is transformed to glycogen. And with extra oxygen now available, glycogen can be oxidized completely to CO_2. In this indirect way the potential energy still present in lactic acid can be recovered, and fatigue then gradually decreases.

the process

In the course of being decomposed progressively, fuel molecules lose their carbons one at a time, until sooner or later the entire molecule is converted to C_1 fragments, or CO_2. If we follow the

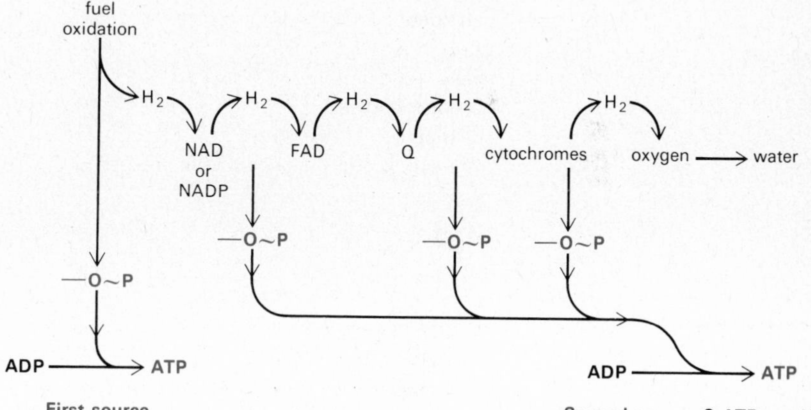

15.7 Coenzymes, hydrogen transfer, and energy sources. *Among the coenzymes in respiratory hydrogen transfer from foods, Q is a still poorly known hydrogen carrier and the cytochromes are a series of five successive carriers. Of the two sources of ATP, one is fuel oxidation itself and another is H_2 transfer to oxygen. The latter source yields three high-energy phosphates as shown, hence 3 ATP for every H_2 transferred.*

NAD[H_2] → NAD

H_2

$CH_3CO\mathbf{COOH}$
pyruvic acid

CH_3CH_2OH + $\mathbf{CO_2}$
alcohol

$CH_3CHO\mathbf{HCOOH}$
lactic acid

15.8 Anaerobic respiration. *Pyruvic acid accepts hydrogen from NAD and becomes either alcohol and CO_2 in plants and most microorganisms or lactic acid in animals and certain bacteria. Different enzymes in these two sets of organisms account for the different results.*

decomposition sequence backward, the next-to-last stage in fuel breakdown should be a 2-carbon C_2 fragment. This is the case; every fuel molecule sooner or later appears as a 2-carbon fragment, specifically *acetyl* ($CH_3C{=}O$), a derivative of acetic acid. Acetyl does not exist by itself but is attached to a carrier coenzyme called *coenzyme A,* or CoA (see Fig. 4.12). Acetyl joined to CoA is *acetyl CoA,* which can be symbolized as $CH_3CO{-}CoA$.

The manner in which the acetyl CoA stage is reached differs for different types of fuel. For example, many carbohydrates are first broken up to 3-carbon compounds. Complex carbohydrates often are built up from 3-carbon units, and their carbon numbers then are whole multiples of 3. This holds, for example, for glucose and all other 6-carbon sugars, for 12-carbon disaccharides, and for polysaccharides such as starch and glycogen. When any of these is used as respiratory fuel, the original 3-carbon units reappear in the course of breakdown. All such C_3 units are eventually converted to *pyruvic acid,* the common 3-carbon stage in respiration. Pyruvic acid then loses one carbon in the form of CO_2 and is converted to acetyl CoA. Fatty acids and related molecules do not break up to 3-carbon units but become 2-carbon units directly, and these eventually appear as acetyl CoA. Amino acids break down partly to pyruvic acid (which subsequently becomes acetyl CoA), partly to acetyl CoA directly. This holds also for many other substances that may happen to be used as fuel.

Thus, the overall pattern of aerobic fuel combustion can be likened to a tree with branches or to a river with tributaries (Fig. 15.9). A broad main channel is represented by the sequence pyruvic acid → acetyl CoA → carbon dioxide. Numerous side channels lead into this sequence, some funneling to the C_3 pyruvic acid step, others to the C_2 acetyl CoA step. In the end the flow from the entire system drains out as C_1 carbon dioxide. It is best to discuss this common last step first.

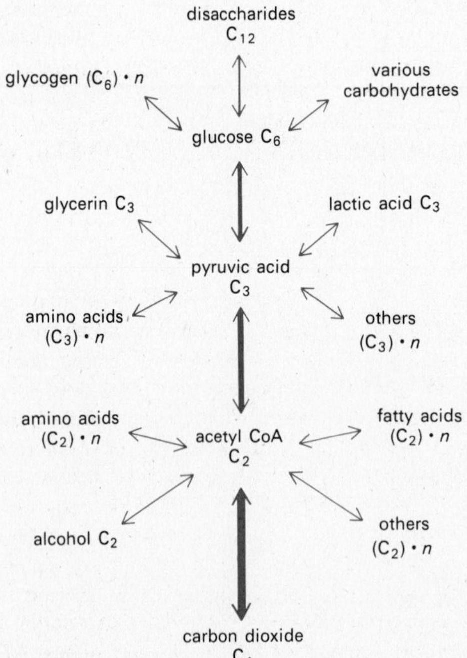

15.9 Pathways in respiration. *Pyruvic acid, acetyl CoA, and carbon dioxide form a main sequence that other pathways join, like branches of a tree.*

formation of CO_2

The breakdown of the C_2 acetyl fragment in the mitochondria of cells takes the form of a *cycle* of enzymatic reactions. Acetyl CoA is funneled in at one point of the cycle, two carbons emerge at other points as CO_2, and the starting condition is eventually regenerated. The whole sequence is known as the *citric acid cycle,* after one of the participating compounds, or as the *Krebs cycle,* after its discoverer.

A simple, condensed representation of the cycle is given in Fig. 15.10. The figure shows that acetyl CoA first interacts with water and with *oxaloacetic acid,* a C_4 molecule normally present in the mitochondria of a cell (step 1 in Fig. 15.10). The result is the formation of free CoA and the C_6 compound *citric acid.* In a following series of reactions (step 2), this acid loses 1 H_2 and 1 CO_2 and becomes *ketoglutaric acid,* a C_5 compound. The hydrogen loss here is oxidative: carbon 5 is at a hydrocarbon level in citric acid and at a level equivalent to an aldehyde in ketoglutaric acid. In a further series of reactions (step 3), ketoglutaric acid loses CO_2 in its turn, yielding the C_4 compound *succinic acid.* This step, too, yields H_2 and is oxidative: carbon 5 has become oxidized to the acid level in succinic acid. Through a final sequence (step 4), succinic acid eventually becomes rearranged to oxaloacetic acid, the same C_4 compound that started the cycle. This segment yields 2 H_2 and oxidizes carbon 4, from a hydrocarbon level in succinic acid to a level equivalent to an aldehyde in oxaloacetic acid.

In the whole sequence, the raw materials are one molecule of acetyl CoA and three molecules of water. The endproducts are 2 CO_2 (which represent the two carbons fed into the cycle at the start as acetyl), free CoA, and 4 H_2. These hydrogen pairs are accepted as soon as they appear by NAD (and also NADP), and are then transferred via FAD and the cytochromes to oxygen. In these transfers ATP is created, three molecules for every H_2. Thus the citric acid cycle yields a net total of 12 ATP. In summary:

$$CH_3CO \cdot CoA + 3\,H_2O \longrightarrow 2\,CO_2 + CoA \cdot H + 4\,H_2$$

to oxygen: 4 H_2O, 12 **ATP**

As pointed out earlier, acetyl groups generally form by respiratory decomposition of various original foods. How do such foods become acetyl, and how are they thereby funneled to the citric acid cycle?

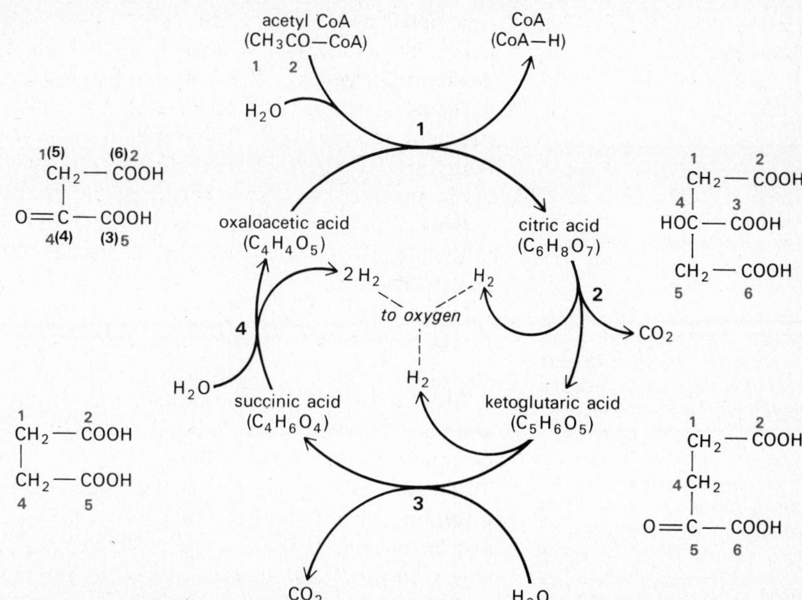

15.10 The citric acid cycle. *The nine actual steps are condensed and simplified here as four. In step 1, citric acid is formed by combination of acetyl CoA and oxaloacetic acid (small black numbers marking carbon positions in oxaloacetic acid correspond to colored numbers in citric acid). In step 2, carbon 3 is oxidized from an acid level (—COOH) to an anhydride level (CO_2) and H_2 is released. Also, carbon 5 is oxidized from a hydrocarbon (—CH_2—) to a ketone (—C=O), equivalent to an aldehyde level. In step 3, carbon 6 is oxidized from an acid to an anhydride level and H_2 is again released. In step 4, carbon 4 converts from a hydrocarbon to a ketone, 2 H_2 are released, and oxaloacetic acid is regenerated. In this acid the carbons now assume new positions for the start of the next turn of the cycle (colored numbers change to black numbers). Note therefore that the carbons 1 and 2 of acetyl fed into the cycle in one turn do not become oxidized (as carbons 5 and 6) until the following turn.*

carbohydrate respiration

Carbohydrate fuels are first converted to pyruvic acid, a common C_3 stage as already noted. In this conversion, often called *glycolysis,* polysaccharides such as starch or glycogen are initially split up and phosphorylated by ATP to glucose-phosphate. If free glucose is used as fuel, it, too, becomes glucose-phosphate through phosphorylation by ATP. Glucose-phosphate is therefore a common early stage of glycolysis. Its further transformation to pyruvic acid is outlined in Fig. 15.11.

This figure shows that the (enzyme-requiring) reaction sequence includes, first, a series of additional phosphorylations; —O—P groups become attached at *each* end of the C_6 chain of glucose-phosphate. Then the chain splits into two C_3 chains (step 3 in Fig. 15.11), and more —O—P groups become attached to the free ends of these C_3 compounds. Next, in successive oxidations, all —O—P groups now present are transformed to —O~P groups. And last, these high-energy phosphates are transferred to ADP. What is then left of the original fuel is a C_3 compound, pyruvic acid. Note that the carbon atoms of the original C_6 fuel are largely at an *alcohol* level of oxidation (see Fig. 15.6), and that the reactions of glycolysis yield first *aldehydes* and then *acids*. Thus the oxidation sequence follows the general stepwise pattern of respiratory decomposition.

If free glucose is considered to be the original raw material, glycolysis includes four phosphorylations, two by H—O—P (phosphoric acid) and two by ATP. Each of the four added phosphates eventually becomes a high-energy phosphate. And of the four ATP molecules then formed, two "pay back" for the two expended at the start of glycolysis, while two represent the net gain. The fate of the atoms in glucose is described by the equation

$$C_6H_{12}O_6 \longrightarrow 2\,C_3H_4O_3 + 2\,H_2$$

The net loss of atoms from glucose therefore amounts to 2 H_2, and these are accepted by NAD.

If respiration occurs under anaerobic conditions, the pyruvic acid formed must now serve directly as the final hydrogen acceptor. Carbohydrate oxidation in this case stops with the formation of alcohol or lactic acid, and the two ATP molecules gained represent the net energy yield of the entire process. But if conditions are aerobic, two advantageous consequences follow. First, the 2 H_2 held by NAD can be passed on to oxygen, a transfer that yields three additional ATP molecules per H_2, or a total of six ATP

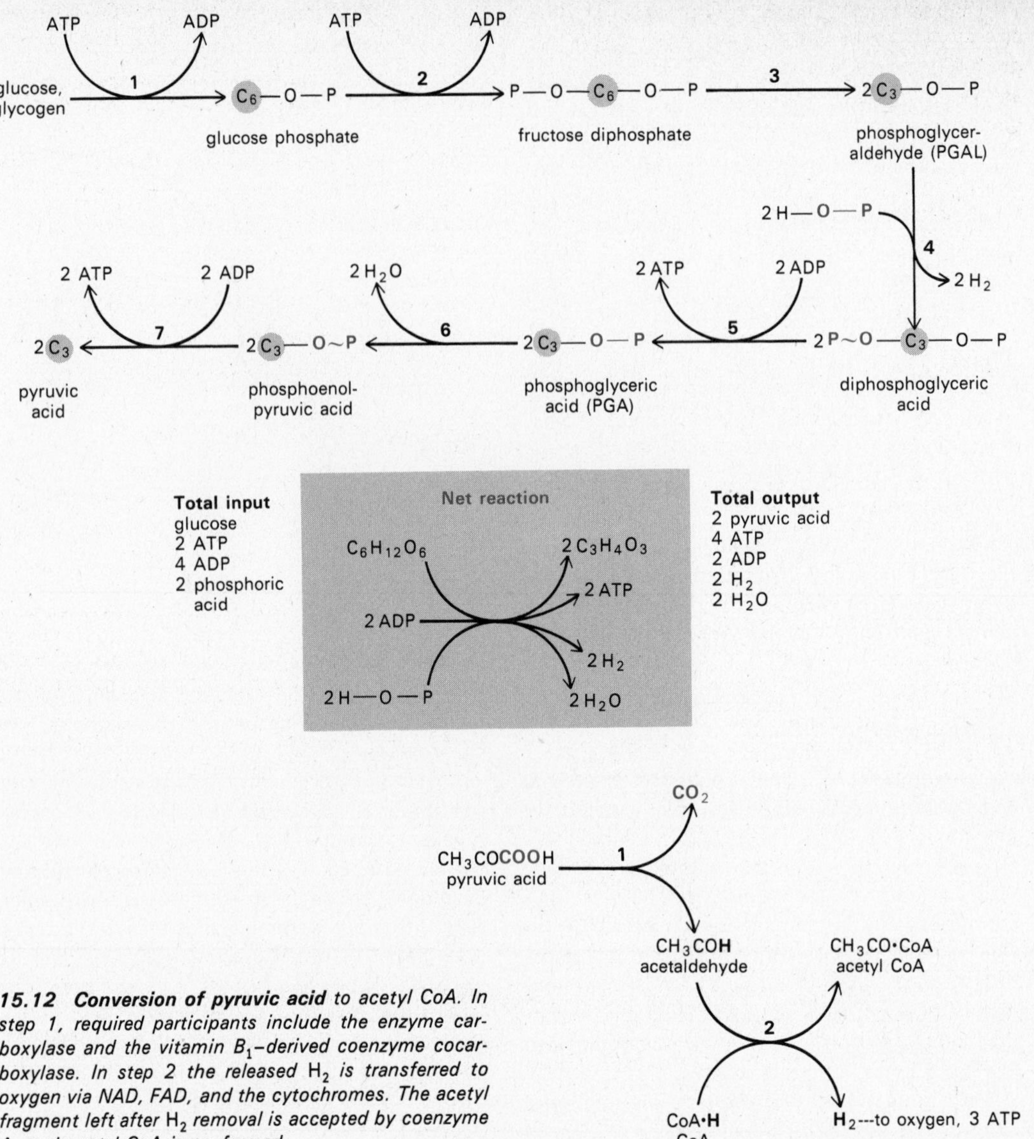

15.11 ***Glycolysis.*** *The nine actual steps are shown here simplified and abbreviated as seven, and the structure of the participating compounds is indicated only in the form of carbon numbers. In step 4, the —O—P added by phosphoric acid becomes a high-energy phosphate, which is then transferred to ATP (step 5). Step 4 also yields 2 H_2, which is transported by carriers to oxygen. Through steps 4 and 5 an aldehyde (PGAL) becomes an acid (PGA). In step 6 oxidative removal of water produces another high-energy phosphate, transferred again to ATP (step 7). In these two reaction steps an alcoholic carbon group (in PGA) is oxidized to a ketone group (in pyruvic acid). The summary below the reaction sequence assumes that free glucose is the starting fuel and that 2 ATP must therefore be expended in the preliminary phosphorylations (steps 1 and 2) for every 4 ATP gained at the end.*

15.12 ***Conversion of pyruvic acid*** *to acetyl CoA. In step 1, required participants include the enzyme carboxylase and the vitamin B_1–derived coenzyme cocarboxylase. In step 2 the released H_2 is transferred to oxygen via NAD, FAD, and the cytochromes. The acetyl fragment left after H_2 removal is accepted by coenzyme A, and acetyl CoA is so formed.*

molecules. Second, since pyruvic acid need not serve as a hydrogen carrier, it can be oxidized further and more of its chemical energy can become usable.

Pyruvic acid transforms to acetyl CoA through a series of enzymatic reactions in which both hydrogen and CO_2 are removed from pyruvic acid (Fig. 15.12). Removal of CO_2 takes place first, and this step requires (apart from enzymes) a coenzyme called *cocarboxylase.* It is a derivative of *thiamine,* or vitamin B_1, and it serves as a kind of carrier of CO_2. Through CO_2 removal pyruvic acid is converted to *acetaldehyde,* a compound that is next dehydrogenated. In this step NAD must be present as a hydrogen acceptor (and transfer of H_2 to oxygen then yields 3 ATP). Another required ingredient is CoA, which serves as the carrier of what is left of acetaldehyde after H_2 has been removed. This remnant is acetyl, and acetyl CoA arises in this manner. In the sequence as a whole, pyruvic acid is transformed first to an *aldehyde* and then to the *anhydride* CO_2, again in line with the general pattern of oxidative decomposition.

Acetyl CoA later can be respired via the citric acid cycle, and we already know that 12 ATP are gained from one acetyl group. If it is therefore assumed that the original starting fuel is free glucose and that it is respired completely to CO_2, then the aerobic energy yield can be shown to total 38 ATP, as outlined in Fig. 15.13. Such a net gain contrasts sharply with an anaerobic yield of only 2 ATP, or about 5 percent of the aerobic yield.

As pointed out earlier, one mole of ATP represents energy equivalent to about 7 kcal, on the average. Glucose respiration produces 38 ATP, hence 38 moles of ATP amount to an energy gain of 266 kcal per mole of glucose respired. If one mole of glucose is burned in a furnace, it releases energy equivalent to about 686 kcal. Thus carbohydrate respiration has an average efficiency of $^{266}/_{686}$, or about 40 percent. In other words, some 40 percent of the potential fuel energy is actually harvested as ATP, and the remaining 60 percent escapes as heat. A "burning" efficiency of 40 percent is comparable to that of the best fuel-using engines man can construct.

Where glycogen is the chief carbohydrate fuel, as in muscle, carbohydrate respiration occurs almost entirely via glycolysis and the citric acid cycle, as described. In many animal tissues, however, the main carbohydrate fuel may be—and in brain must be—glucose, not glycogen. In plants, similarly, glucose as such is often a primary fuel. In such cases an important alternative way of carbohydrate respiration exists that involves neither glycolysis nor the citric acid cycle, nor indeed even the mitochondria. Known as the *hexose shunt,* this oxidation process occurs in the free cellular cytoplasm, and it too has the form of a complex cycle of reactions.

It is summarized in highly condensed manner in Fig. 15.14. The raw materials are water, NADP, and glucose-phosphate, the latter representing the starting fuel. The endproducts are CO_2, free phosphate, H_2 held by NADP, and one less molecule of glucose-phosphate than the number present at the start. In effect, one glucose-phosphate has become decomposed to CO_2 and H_2, and the 12 hydrogen pairs are passed on to oxygen via NADP. This hydrogen transfer yields 36 ATP, of which one must "pay back" for the ATP used up in the conversion of free glucose to glucose phosphate. Thus the net energy yield is 35 ATP per molecule of glucose—only slightly less than the 38 ATP obtainable via glycolysis.

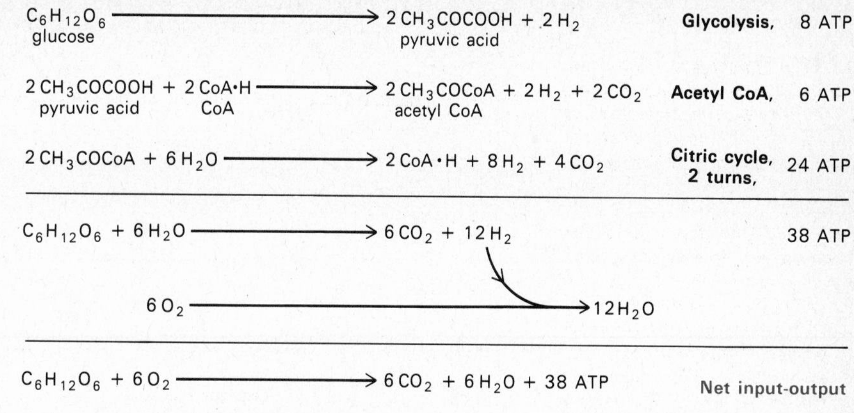

15.13 Glucose respiration summary.

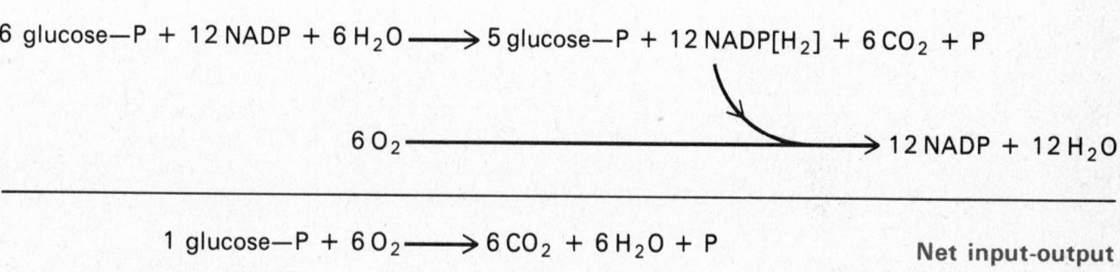

15.14 The hexose shunt, *summary. In a cyclical reaction sequence one out of six glucose-phosphate molecules is oxidized to* CO_2 *and* H_2O.

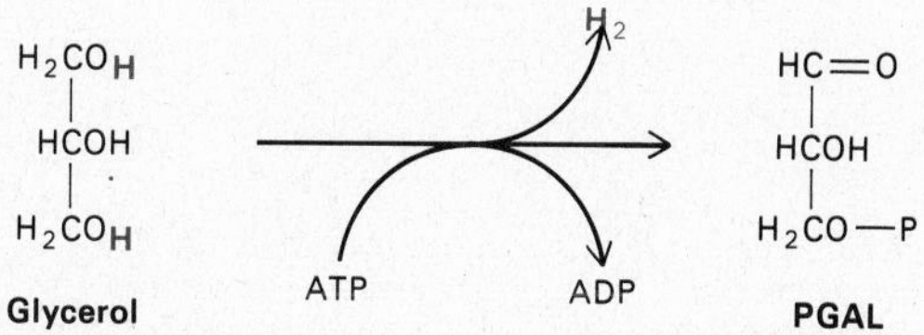

15.15 Conversion of glycerol to phosphoglyceraldehyde.

lipid respiration

A first step in the respiration of a fat molecule is decomposition to glycerol and fatty acids, with lipase as the specific enzyme. This process occurs inside a cell and is equivalent chemically to digestion in animal alimentary systems. Glycerol can then be phosphorylated by ATP and oxidized to phosphoglyceraldehyde, PGAL (Fig. 15.15). This reaction requires 1 ATP for the phosphorylation but yields 3 ATP in the transfer of H_2 from NAD to oxygen. PGAL, a normal intermediate in carbohydrate decomposition (see Fig. 15.11), can then be respired by glycolysis and the citric acid cycle, processes that yield 20 ATP per molecule of PGAL. Complete aerobic respiration of one

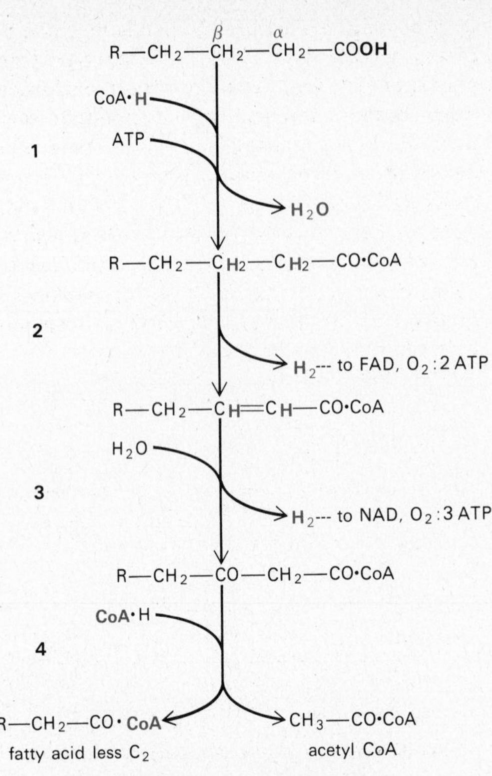

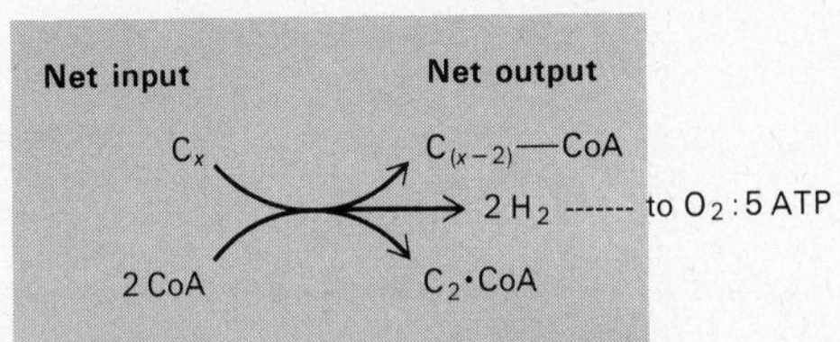

***15.16** **β-oxidation of fatty acids.** In step 1 a fatty acid is activated by combination with CoA and concurrent removal of water. Step 2 is dehydrogenation, FAD being the* H *acceptor. Step 3 is an addition of water and represents the actual β-oxidation; the carbon group, originally at a hydrocarbon oxidation level, becomes a ketone group (—CO—). In step 4 the 2-carbon fragment acetyl is split off, resulting in acetyl CoA and a fatty acid shorter by two carbons than the original one. The summary shows that 5 ATP are gained through* H *transport to oxygen.* C_x *here stands for a fatty acid with x numbers of* C *atoms.*

molecule of glycerol thus produces a total net gain of 22 ATP.

The decomposition of fatty acids is known as *β-oxidation;* the second, or β, carbon of the acid (counted after the —COOH group) undergoes oxidative changes. Figure 15.16 summarizes the main steps. In a first reaction CoA becomes linked to the acid end of the fatty acid, with the aid of energy from ATP. A dehydrogenation occurs next, one H atom being removed from each of the α and β carbons. The hydrogen is accepted by FAD (and NAD is bypassed here). In a third step another dehydrogenation takes place, in this case at the β carbon. This hydrogen is carried by NAD. Finally, another molecule of CoA is added, at the β carbon in this instance. Two fragments are thereby produced. One is acetyl CoA, and the other is a CoA-carrying fatty acid that is two carbons shorter than the original acid. This shorter acid can now undergo β-oxidation in turn, and consecutive acetyl CoA units can be cut off in this way.

Hydrogen transfer from FAD to oxygen yields 2 ATP (not 3, since NAD is bypassed), and transfer from NAD to oxygen yields 3 ATP. Thus 5 ATP are gained for every acetyl CoA unit formed. If, for example, an actual starting fuel is assumed to be stearic acid, a C_{18} fatty acid very common in animal fats, then β-oxidation of this acid can occur successively eight times, yielding acetyl CoA each time and leaving a ninth acetyl CoA as a remainder. At 5 ATP per β-oxidation, the yield is $5 \times 8 = 40$ ATP, minus 1 ATP expended in the first reaction of the stearic acid starting molecule. One C_{18} fatty acid therefore yields a net of 39 ATP and 9 acetyl CoA. The latter generate 9×12, or 108 ATP in the citric acid cycle, so that the total energy gained from the complete respiration of stearic acid is 147 ATP.

By way of comparison, we already know that one glucose molecule yields 38 ATP. Since stearic acid is a C_{18} compound, whereas glucose is a C_6 compound, the fatty acid might be expected to yield three times as much ATP. However, three glucose molecules yield only 114 ATP, which means that an 18-carbon fatty acid actually produces *more* than three times as much—almost four times as much—ATP than a 6-carbon carbohydrate. Fatty acids evidently are a richer source of usable energy than equivalent quantities of carbohydrates. The reason is that the carbons in a fatty acid still are largely at the hydrocarbon level, whereas those in a carbohydrate are already at the alcohol or aldehyde level of oxidation from the outset (see Fig. 15.6).

The figures above suggest a reason why fats are the chief storage foods in animals and why animal metabolism is highly fat-oriented in general: energy stored in the form of fat *weighs* less than if it were stored in the form of carbohydrate or protein. Fat storage therefore makes for less bulk, important in a moving animal. It is interesting that clams, for example, which move very little, do store their foods largely as carbohydrates, like rooted plants, whereas plant seeds adapted for dispersal through air store foods largely as lipids, like moving animals.

Apart from the greater energy content of fats, the efficiency of fat respiration nevertheless is roughly equivalent to that of carbohydrates. For example, if *tristearin,* a common animal fat, is burned in a furnace, its energy potential can be shown to be about 8000 kcal. Tristearin consists of three C_{18} fatty acids (stearic acid) and one C_3 carbohydrate (glycerol). Its complete respiration in cells will therefore yield 3×147 plus 1×22, or 463 ATP. At about 7 kcal per mole of ATP, the respiratory energy gained will then be about 3241 kcal, and the efficiency of this respiration will be $^{3241}/_{8000}$, or about 40 percent. Fats evidently give rise to the same proportions of ATP and heat as carbohydrates.

amino acid respiration

Amino acids can enter respiratory pathways in two general ways.

One way is made possible by *deamination,* a reaction in which an amino group ($-NH_2$) is removed from an amino acid (Fig. 15.17). In vertebrates this process takes place particularly in liver cells, where any amino acid excess supplied by eaten food is deaminated. In other animals and in plants deaminations can occur in a large variety of cell types. The resulting free ammonia is highly alkaline and therefore toxic, and it is ultimately excreted. Excretion often occurs in the form of unchanged ammonia, as in most aquatic types. Or ammonia can undergo various chemical transformations and be excreted in the form of, for example, *uric acid,* as in insects and birds, or *urea,* as in mammals (see Chap. 16). The other product of deamination is a *keto acid.* In most keto acids the —R groups are chemically similar to carbohydrates or to fatty acids, and a keto acid is then actually respired either like a carbohydrate or like a lipid.

A second pattern of amino acid respiration results from the circumstance that each amino acid has a structurally corresponding keto acid. Conversely, if to any given keto acid an amino group is added, a corresponding amino acid will be formed (see Fig. 15.17). Through such *transamination* reactions, any amino acid can be transformed to any other provided the appropriate keto acid is available. Transaminations can occur in all cells, and they permit any amino acid to be respired via the citric acid cycle. For it happens that certain transaminations produce keto acids that are normal components of the citric acid cycle.

For example, if the amino acid glutamic acid participates in a transamination, this amino acid becomes ketoglutaric acid, an intermediate in the citric acid cycle (Fig. 15.18). Similarly, when the amino acid aspartic acid is transaminated, the corresponding keto acid formed is oxaloacetic acid, another citric acid cycle compound. Moreover, if alanine transaminates with some other keto acid, alanine becomes pyruvic acid. Therefore, any amino acid can, by transamination, become glutamic acid or aspartic acid or alanine, and by a further transamination these three amino acids can become ketoglutaric or oxaloacetic or pyruvic acid, respectively. The last can then participate in the citric acid cycle.

A

$$NH_2{-}C(R)(H){-}COOH + O \longrightarrow NH_3 + O{=}C(R){-}COOH$$

amino acid; ammonia; keto acid

B

$$NH_2{-}C(A)(H){-}COOH + O{=}C(B){-}COOH \longrightarrow NH_2{-}C(B)(H){-}COOH + O{=}C(A){-}COOH$$

amino acid A; keto acid B; amino acid B; keto acid A

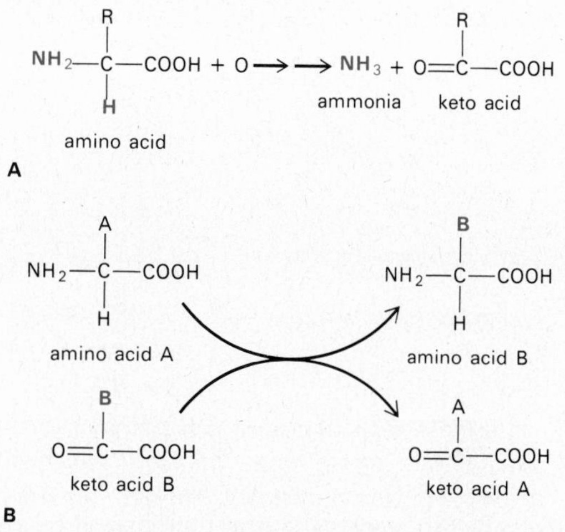

15.17 Deamination and transamination. *A, oxidation of an amino acid yields a free ammonia molecule, which is excreted, and a keto acid, so named for its ketone (—CO—) in place of amino group. B, interaction of an amino acid A and a keto acid B can result in a substitution of the amino group by a ketone group in A and by a reverse substitution in B.*

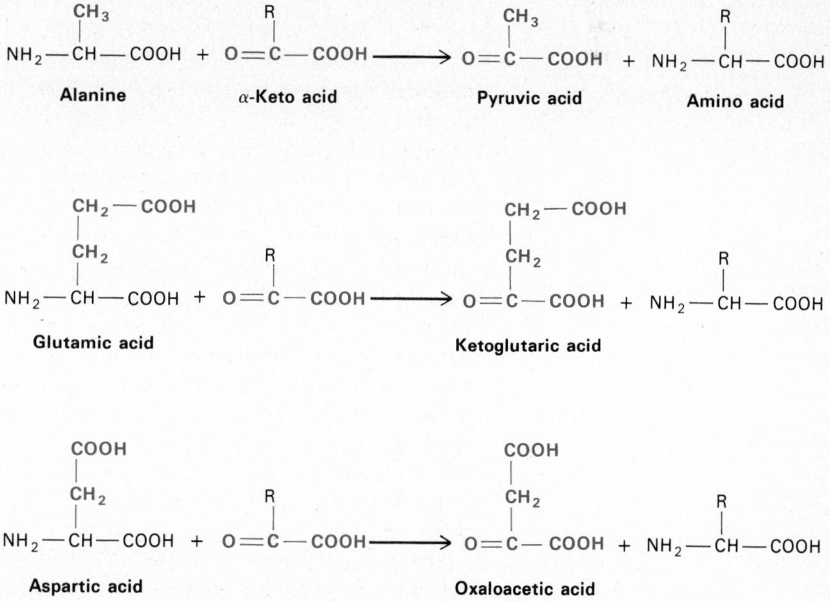

$$NH_2{-}CH(CH_3){-}COOH + O{=}C(R){-}COOH \longrightarrow O{=}C(CH_3){-}COOH + NH_2{-}CH(R){-}COOH$$

Alanine + **α-Keto acid** → **Pyruvic acid** + **Amino acid**

$$NH_2{-}CH(CH_2{-}CH_2{-}COOH){-}COOH + O{=}C(R){-}COOH \longrightarrow O{=}C(CH_2{-}CH_2{-}COOH){-}COOH + NH_2{-}CH(R){-}COOH$$

Glutamic acid → **Ketoglutaric acid**

$$NH_2{-}CH(CH_2{-}COOH){-}COOH + O{=}C(R){-}COOH \longrightarrow O{=}C(CH_2{-}COOH){-}COOH + NH_2{-}CH(R){-}COOH$$

Aspartic acid → **Oxaloacetic acid**

15.18 Three transamination reactions *important in amino acid respiration. The keto acids resulting from transamination happen to be participants in glycolysis and the citric acid cycle. Therefore, through the reactions shown, amino acids can enter the same final respiratory pathways as carbohydrates and fatty acids.*

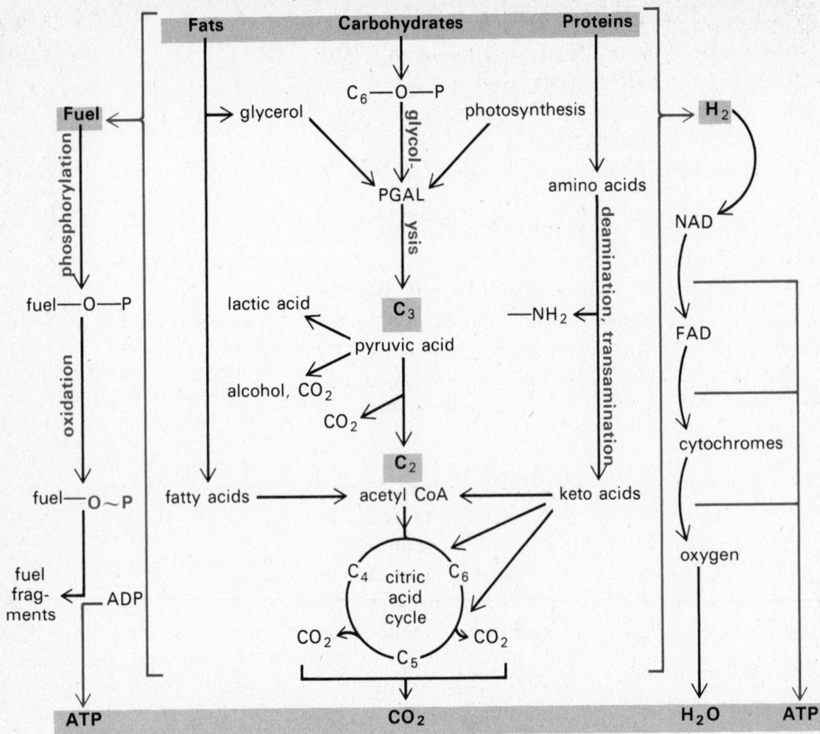

15.19 Respiration: overall summary. *The center panel outlines the main pathways of the respiratory breakdown of carbohydrates, fats, and proteins. The left-hand panel summarizes the general nature of any of the respiratory reactions that occur in the center panel, and the right-hand panel similarly summarizes the process of hydrogen transport. The two sources of ATP gain are also indicated.*

The ATP yields of protein and amino acid respiration vary according to the specific reaction pathways followed, but the efficiency is again roughly 40 percent, equivalent to that of carbohydrate or fat respiration. However, oxidation of proteins, far more than that of carbohydrates or fats, is accompanied by many other energy-requiring and therefore heat-producing reactions. For example, transaminations, deaminations, and urea or uric acid synthesis occur in parallel with amino acid respiration, and many of these processes consume ATP and release heat to the environment. It has been shown that for every 100 kcal supplied by protein, heat to the extent of some 30 kcal is generated by accompanying reactions (as compared with only about 5 kcal for every 100 kcal supplied by fat or carbohydrate). Thus the net usefulness of protein as an energy source is only about 70 percent of its potential value, and this is probably why carbohydrates and fats are the primary energy sources in organisms. The large heat generation accompanying protein degradation is known as the *specific dynamic action* of protein.

An overall summary of respiratory reactions is outlined in Fig. 15.19. These reactions take place exceedingly rapidly in cells. In vertebrates, moreover, respiratory rates are influenced greatly by the thyroid hormone thyroxin, which accelerates respiration in proportion to its concentration. Most organisms are not vertebrates, however, and their respiration is not under thyroxin control. Nevertheless, respiratory decompositions still occur extremely rapidly; a glucose molecule can be respired in less than 1 sec. Very efficient enzyme action is probably one condition that makes such speed possible. Another undoubtedly is the close, ordered arrangement of all required ingredients in the submicroscopic spaces of the mitochondria. Just as a well-arranged industrial assembly line turns out products at a great rate, so do the even better arranged mitochondria.

The fate and function of the chief product of respiration, ATP, is the subject of the next chapter.

review questions

1 Compare and contrast a fire with respiration. What do they have in common? What is different? Which materials are fuels in respiration? What general types of event occur in respiration?

2 What are redox reactions? Define oxidation and reduction. Show how both electron-transfer and electron-sharing reactions can be oxidative. What energy relations exist during redox reactions?

3 Show how progressive changes of oxidation level occur during the transformation of hydrocarbons to anhydrides.

4 What is dehydrogenation? Where does it occur, and what role does it play in respiration? Under what conditions does it take place? How is hydrogen transferred to oxygen? Describe the sequence of carriers and the specific role of each during aerobic hydrogen transport.

5 Distinguish between aerobic and anaerobic respiration. Under what conditions does either take place? How and where can aerobic respiration become blocked? How is alcohol or lactic acid formed? How and under what conditions is lactic acid respired? What is an oxygen debt, and how is it paid?

6 Describe the role of adenosine phosphates in respiration. What is a high-energy bond? How and where are such bonds created in fuels? During H transfer?

7 How much energy is required for ATP formation? Show how ATP is both an endproduct and a specific raw material for respiration. Compare the ATP gain in aerobic and anaerobic respiration.

8 Describe the general sequence of events in the citric acid cycle. Which steps are oxidative, and what changes in oxidation level take place? What is the total input and output of the cycle? How much ATP is gained and through what steps?

9 Review the sequence of events in glycolysis. Which steps are oxidative, and what changes in oxidation level take place? How much energy is obtained? Which classes of nutrients pass through a pyruvic acid stage in respiration?

10 Review the conversion of pyruvic acid to acetyl CoA. What are the functions of carboxylase, cocarboxylase, and coenzyme A? How much energy is gained and where? What classes of nutrients pass through an acetyl CoA stage in respiration?

11 Summarize the events of the hexose shunt. What respiratory role does this process play, and where does it occur? How does the energy gain compare with that of glycolysis?

12 Describe the process of β-oxidation. Which steps are oxidative? How much energy is gained, and where? Distinguish between deamination and transamination. By what metabolic pathways are amino acids respired?

13 How much potential energy does each of the main classes of nutrients contain? What fraction of this energy is actually recovered as ATP during respiration? Calculate the efficiency of respiration for each of the main classes of nutrients.

14 Review and summarize the overall fate of one molecule of glucose during complete respiratory combustion. What is the total net input and output? What happens to the individual atoms of glucose? What is the total ATP gain, and how much is gained during each of the main steps of breakdown?

15 Where in cells does respiration occur? What factors probably contribute to the speed of respiration? Inasmuch as respiratory reactions are reversible, how does it happen that energy continues to be produced?

collateral readings

Baker, J., and **G. Allen:** "Matter, Energy, and Life," Addison-Wesley, Reading, Mass., 1965. A paperback containing good introductions to the chemical aspects of nutrition, respiration, and metabolism in general.

Giese, A. C.: Energy Release and Utilization, in "This Is Life," Holt, New York, 1962. A good, concise review of respiratory processes.

Green, D. E.: The Metabolism of Fats, *Sci. American,* Jan., 1954. An article on the respiration of fats.

———: Biological Oxidation, *Sci. American,* July, 1958. An account on the process as a whole.

Jensen, W. A.: "The Plant Cell," Wadsworth, Belmont, Calif., 1964. This paperback contains a chapter on the course of respiration in plants.

Lehninger, A. L.: Energy Transformation in the Cell, *Sci. American,* May, 1960. The article includes a discussion of respiratory enzymes from both structural and functional standpoints.

———: How Cells Transform Energy, *Sci. American,* Sept., 1961. The photosynthetic role of chloroplasts and the respiratory role of mitochondria are compared.

———: "Bioenergetics," Benjamin, New York, 1965. This paperback contains discussions of the molecular aspects of biological energy transformations, including those of respiration and photosynthesis. Slightly more advanced than the presentation in this chapter, but not difficult. Recommended for those interested in greater detail.

Loewy, A. G., and **P. Siekevitz:** "Cell Structure and Function," Holt, New York, 1963. A paperback containing good accounts on all general aspects of respiratory reactions.

McElroy, W. D.: "Cellular Physiology and Biochemistry," Prentice-Hall, Englewood Cliffs,

N.J., 1961. Like the preceding reference, a paperback that includes a general review of respiration.

Racker, E.: The Membrane of the Mitochondrion, *Sci. American,* Feb., 1968. The inner of the two mitochondrial membranes is taken apart (and then put together again) in studies of respiratory enzymes.

Siekevitz, P.: Powerhouse of the Cell, *Sci. American,* July, 1957. The structure and function of mitochondria are discussed.

Steward, F. C.: "Plants at Work," Addison-Wesley, Reading, Mass., 1964. A good, detailed discussion of respiration is included in this paperback.

Stumpf, P. K.: ATP, *Sci. American,* Apr., 1953. An article on the cellular roles of this energy carrier.

chapter 16 synthesis

Once nutrients and ATP are available, a cell can carry out metabolic *synthesis* activities. Of these, photosynthesis is unquestionably the most fundamental; on this process ultimately depend nearly all other synthesis activities of plant or animal cells. Photosynthesis is therefore considered first.

photosynthesis

the pattern

It is hardly possible to overestimate the importance of the photosynthetic reactions through which *inorganic* CO_2 and H_2O are transformed to *organic* compounds, specifically carbohydrates. These compounds are the primary substances from which virtually the whole organic part of the living world is constructed, and on which therefore virtually all organisms also depend for their food. The only organisms not dependent on photosynthesis are the chemosynthetic bacteria, which together constitute probably less than 0.0001 percent of all the living matter on earth.

It has been estimated that some 200 billion tons of carbon go through the photosynthetic process every year. This makes photosynthesis the most massive chemical event and, after the global water cycle, the second most massive event of all kinds on earth. Carbon dioxide is used up in photosynthesis in such large amounts that without replenishment through plant and animal respiration and other combustion processes, the CO_2 content of the entire atmosphere would be exhausted in a few months and that of the ocean in about 300 years. Oxygen is released through photosynthesis so voluminously that all the O_2 of the present atmosphere could be generated in about 2,000 years, an incredibly short time from a geologic standpoint. Finally, the solar energy harvested annually through photosynthesis in the form of carbohydrates amounts to fully one-fourth of the total energy now available to man from all sources.

Because CO_2 and water are the known raw materials and carbohydrates and oxygen the known endproducts, an overall chemical description of photosynthesis is the equation

$$6\ CO_2 + 6\ H_2O \xrightarrow[chlorophyll]{light} C_6H_{12}O_6 + 6\ O_2$$

But this equation does not describe the details of the photosynthetic process. For example, CO_2 does *not* react directly with water; if it did, the result would be nothing but carbonated water. Research has shown that in photosynthesis CO_2 reacts with the *hydrogen* of water, and the oxygen of water becomes a byproduct. Evidently, a first step in photosynthesis is the decomposition of water molecules to separate hydrogen and oxygen components. It is known that this decomposition is associated with processes involving the green pigment chlorophyll and the energy of light. This first phase of photosynthesis is therefore called *photolysis,* or light-associated water decomposition. In a second phase the hydrogen resulting from photolysis reacts with CO_2, and a carbohydrate is formed. This phase is called *CO_2 fixation,* implying a combination of CO_2 and hydrogen. Unlike photolysis, CO_2 fixation does not require light and can occur in the dark (Fig. 16.1).

Both photolysis and CO_2 fixation take place in the chloroplasts of green cells. A single green cell contains from 1 to about 80 chloroplasts, and the total surface area for light absorption of all the chloroplasts in a mature tree can amount to some 150 square miles. As noted in Chap. 5, a chloroplast contains numerous *grana,* the usual structural units for photosynthesis.

Each granum of a chloroplast is a stack of protein layers, and in the spaces between these layers is the chemical "machinery" of photosynthesis (Fig. 16.2). This machinery includes enzymes, carrier coenzymes for hydrogen and other substances, nucleic acids, lipids, and three kinds of pigments: carrot-red to butter-yellow *carotenoids,* bright yellow to brownish *xanthophylls,* and variously green *chlorophylls.* Some of these molecules appear to be positioned in an orderly, rather crystal-like arrangement.

The green of chlorophyll usually masks the colors of the carotenoids and xanthophylls present. Also, different plant groups contain different pro-

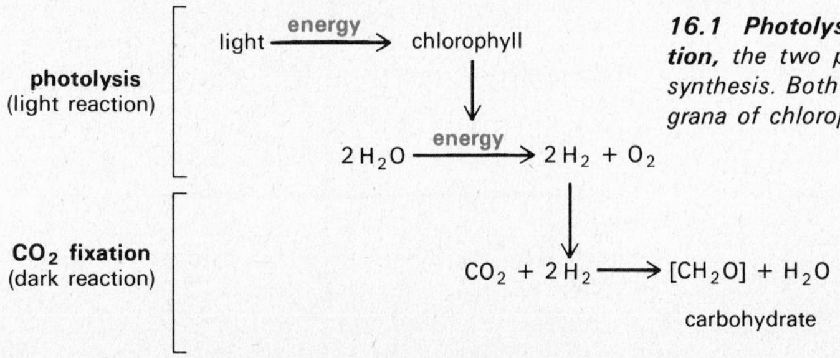

photolysis (light reaction)

light $\xrightarrow{energy}$ chlorophyll

$$2\,H_2O \xrightarrow{energy} 2\,H_2 + O_2$$

CO_2 fixation (dark reaction)

$$CO_2 + 2\,H_2 \longrightarrow [CH_2O] + H_2O$$

carbohydrate

***16.1* Photolysis and CO_2 fixation,** *the two phases of photosynthesis. Both take place in the grana of chloroplasts.*

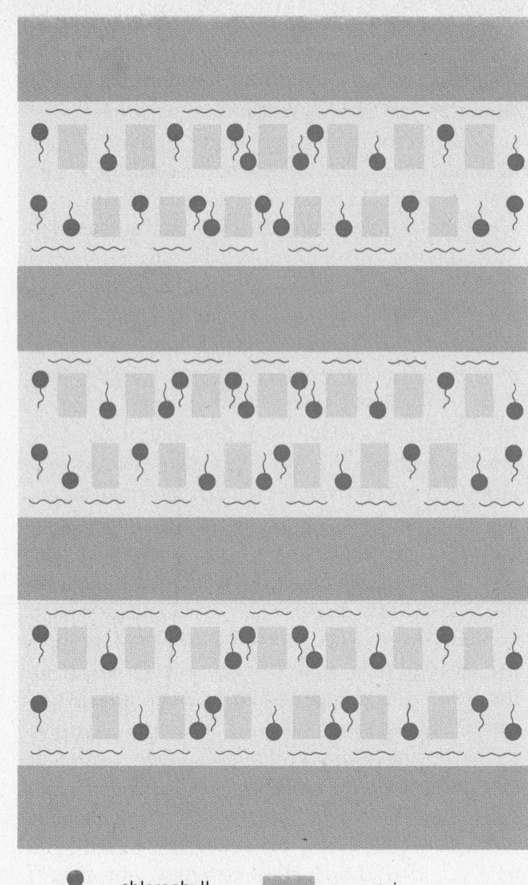

16.2 Internal structure of a granum. *The layered arrangement of the components is also apparent in Fig. 5.8.*

16.3 Chlorophyll, *molecular structure.*

"head"

"tail"

$(C_{20}H_{39})$

$(C_{55}H_{72}O_5N_4Mg)$
Chlorophyll a

portions of these pigments, hence the various lighter and deeper shades of green in a landscape. In many plants production and maintenance of chlorophyll ordinarily depend on exposure to light. A young shoot, for example, does not turn green until it is well above the soil surface; and in a plant grown in a dark chamber chlorophyll soon breaks down and the plant loses its green color. In the fall the chlorophyll of deciduous plants disintegrates in any case, even in light. As a result the more stable carotenoid and xanthophyll pigments are unmasked and become visible as the brilliant colors of autumn foliage. Autumn colors are produced also by red to purple *anthocyanin* pigments, which are manufactured at that season outside the chloroplasts of many plants (and which do not play a role in photosynthesis).

A molecule of chlorophyll consists of a "head" and a "tail" (Fig. 16.3). The head contains four carbon-nitrogen rings that are joined as a larger ring. At the center of this larger ring is a single atom of magnesium. The tail is a chain of linked carbons attached to the head. As shown in Chap. 9, the various phyla of photosynthetic organisms in part contain different structural forms of chlorophyll. Such chemical variants differ mainly in the kinds and arrangements of other atoms attached to the basic head-tail structure. Except for the photosynthetic bacteria, which contain distinct forms of chlorophyll not found elsewhere, all other photosynthesizers contain chlorophyll *a.* Additional chemical variants occur in most algae and in plants (see Chaps. 9 and 10).

The almost universal presence of chlorophyll *a* in photosynthetic organisms suggests, and experimental data actually tend to confirm, that this particular pigment is essential for photolysis. (Photosynthetic bacteria lack chlorophyll *a,* but these organisms also do not photolyze; as shown in Chap. 14, their hydrogen source is not water but compounds such as H_2S, and they therefore do not liberate oxygen either.)

photolysis

When light enters a chloroplast and strikes chlorophyll molecules, the molecules *absorb* some of the light energy. As is well known, ordinary visible light consists of a mixture of different wavelengths which, when unmixed, are seen in the colors of a rainbow—red, orange, yellow, green, blue, and violet. These light waves contain energy; red light has the least energy, violet light the most. When a mixture of wavelengths as in ordinary "white" light falls on a chlorophyll molecule, the molecule absorbs red and violet wavelengths strongly, and orange, yellow, and blue wavelengths somewhat less strongly. The green wavelengths are hardly absorbed at all and are for the most part reflected. This is why an illuminated leaf appears green to the eye; chlorophyll has absorbed all *but* the green wavelengths in light.

Because it absorbs certain light waves, chlorophyll absorbs energy; the molecule contains more energy after illumination than before, and in this state it is said to be "excited." It is not well known what actually happens to the absorbed energy, but its final effect appears to be an *ionization* of the excited chlorophyll molecule: an electron (e^-) can become dislodged from the molecule. In a sense such an electron carries most of the extra energy provided by the light, and we can regard it as a "high-energy" electron. Since the electron is negatively charged, the chlorophyll molecule that loses it would become a positively charged ion. Such a process of *photoionization* of chlorophyll is believed to be the fundamental energy-supplying event in photosynthesis as a whole (Fig. 16.4). All following events seem to serve in converting the energy of the high-energy electron to usable chemical form. In effect, chlorophyll appears to be essential as the critical substance that first traps light energy and that subsequently releases some of the light-derived energy in the form of electron energy.

Some evidence suggests that the carotenoids, the xanthophylls, and perhaps also the accessory variants of chlorophylls might contribute to an efficient utilization of light in chloroplasts. Thus the amount of photosynthesis carried out with a given dosage of light is greater when accessory pigments are present than when chlorophyll *a* is present alone. Like all pigments the accessory ones in chloroplasts absorb light, too, and it is possible that some of the energy of this light might become transferred to chlorophyll *a* molecules and thereby increase their photoionization. Conceivably, therefore, the presence of various accessory pigments could have become a standard evolutionary feature in photosynthetic organisms because such pigments might make possible a more complete utilization of available light.

After photoionization, some dislodged high-energy electrons are apparently recaptured immediately by the same chlorophyll molecules that released them. In the process the electrons give up their extra energy in the form of heat or light. When light is emitted, chlorophyll is

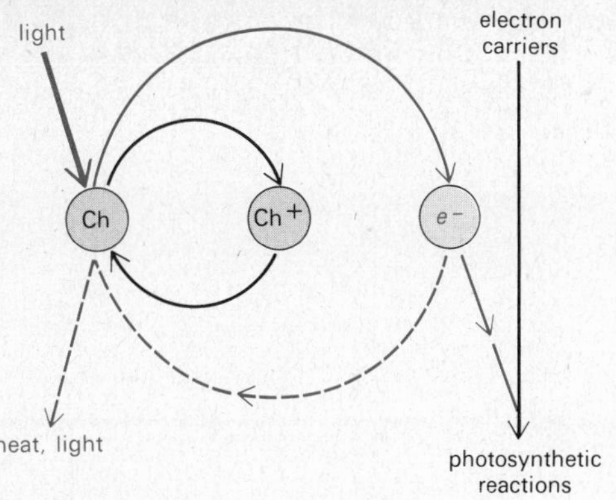

***16.4* Photoionization.** *When light "excites" chlorophyll molecules, high-energy electrons (e^-) become dislodged and chlorophyll thereby acquires a positive charge. Some of the high-energy electrons return to chlorophyll immediately, and the extra energy dissipates as heat or as light (in which case chlorophyll is weakly fluorescent). High-energy electrons are also captured by specific carrier molecules present in chloroplasts, and such electrons participate in photosynthetic processes.*

weakly fluorescent. The energy of all such emitted heat or light simply dissipates. However, many high-energy electrons are captured not by chlorophyll itself but by other electron carriers in the chloroplasts; and such electrons come to play a critical role in photosynthesis (see Fig. 16.4).

The electron carriers in photosynthesis have been found to function in sequence; electrons are transferred successively from one carrier to the next. In such stepwise transfers the electrons give up their extra energy progressively, and some of the released electron energy is harvested as ATP. Just how such ATP creation, or *photophosphorylation,* takes place is still unclear, but it is known that the process resembles ATP formation during hydrogen transfer in respiration. It has also been found that the actual transfer of electrons can occur in two different sequences. One, a *cyclic* sequence, leads to ATP formation only; the other, a *noncyclic* transfer, makes possible ATP formation as well as food manufacture.

In cyclic transfer (Fig. 16.5), one of the electron carriers, possibly the first, appears to be *ferredoxin,* an iron-containing coenzyme normally present in chloroplasts. Other carriers are known to include at least two *cytochromes,* coenzymes similar to those that also function in aerobic respiration. Thus, high-energy electrons appear to pass from chlorophyll to ferredoxin and from this compound to a series of other carriers. Among them are two or more cytochromes as well as several others that are not completely identified as yet. In the end the electrons are again accepted by ionized chlorophyll—the same molecules that lost the electrons to begin with. Chlorophyll then ceases to be ionized and becomes electrically neutral, ready to be photoionized anew.

Evidently, the electrons here travel in a complete cycle, from chlorophyll back to chlorophyll. But at the start the electrons have been brought to a high energy level by light, and at the end they are at a low energy level. The energy difference is harvested as ATP; for every pair of electrons carried through one cycle turn, one or possibly two ATP molecules can be formed from ADP and phosphate.

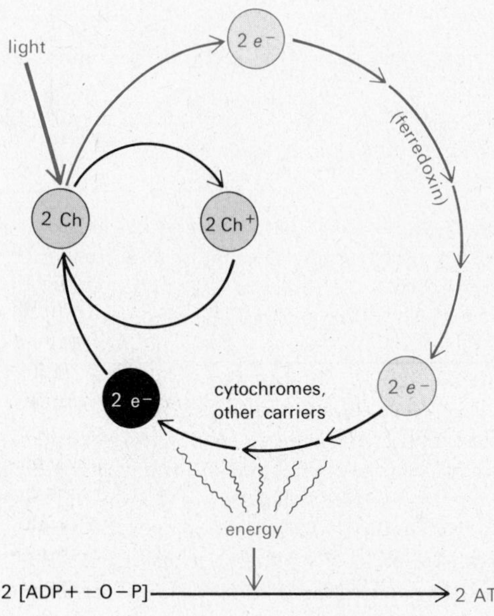

16.5 Cyclic electron transfer. *The same electrons that escape chlorophyll after photoionization again return to chlorophyll. In the course of being transferred by carrier molecules the electrons yield energy for ATP formation. For every two electrons carried through the cycle, 2 ATP can probably be gained. The cycle as a whole requires more energy than it yields and can therefore continue only so long as light is available for ionization of chlorophyll. The net input is light, ADP, and phosphate, and the net output is ATP.*

In the second, noncyclic transfer sequence, high-energy electrons from chlorophyll are again believed to be captured first by ferredoxin (Fig. 16.6). Thereafter, however, the electrons are transferred to NADP, a hydrogen-carrying coenzyme very similar to the respiratory hydrogen carrier NAD (see Fig. 4.12 and also Fig. 15.7). In photolysis the hydrogen that NADP comes to carry is formed from two components, high-energy electrons and hydrogen ions:

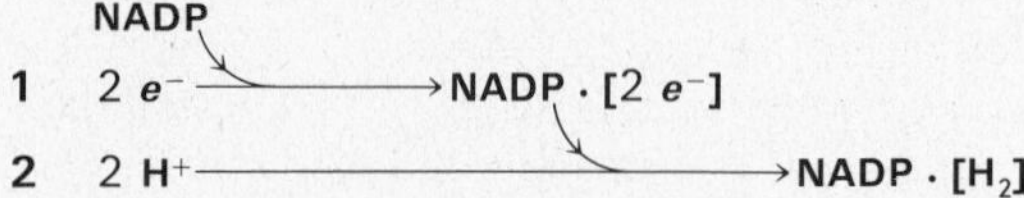

NADP

1 2 e^- ⟶ **NADP · [2 e^-]**

2 2 H^+ ⟶ **NADP · [H_2]**

The high-energy electrons come from chlorophyll, and the source of the hydrogen ions is *water.* In any sample of water a small fraction normally exists in ionized form:

$$2\ H_2O \rightleftharpoons 2\ H^+ + 2\ OH^-$$

If this equilibrium is disturbed by removal of H^+ or OH^-, more water molecules will ionize until the equilibrium is reestablished. In chloroplasts, NADP that carries high-energy electrons is an avid acceptor of the hydrogen ions of water. Thus as chlorophyll continues to be illuminated, NADP

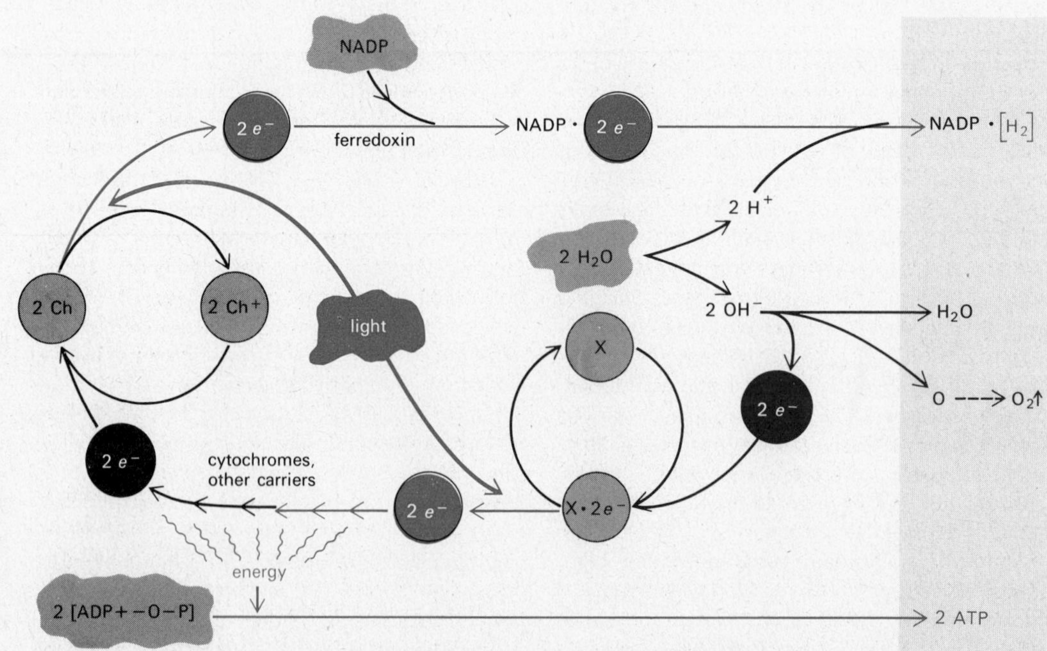

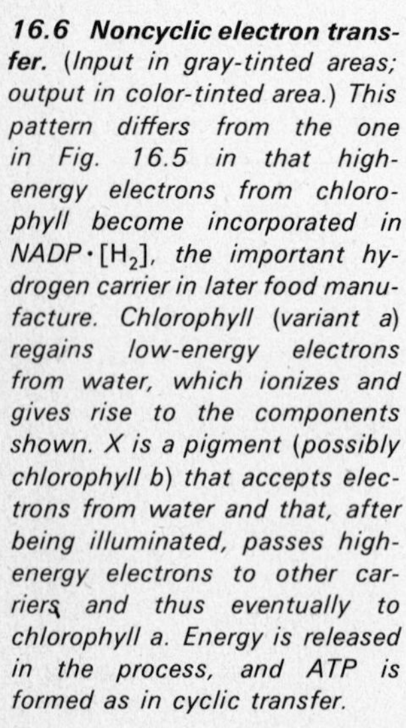

16.6 Noncyclic electron transfer. *(Input in gray-tinted areas; output in color-tinted area.) This pattern differs from the one in Fig. 16.5 in that high-energy electrons from chlorophyll become incorporated in NADP·[H_2], the important hydrogen carrier in later food manufacture. Chlorophyll (variant a) regains low-energy electrons from water, which ionizes and gives rise to the components shown. X is a pigment (possibly chlorophyll b) that accepts electrons from water and that, after being illuminated, passes high-energy electrons to other carriers, and thus eventually to chlorophyll a. Energy is released in the process, and ATP is formed as in cyclic transfer.*

continues to receive high-energy electrons and therefore will continue to remove H^+ from the water medium. More and more water will then become ionized. It is essentially this process that the term "photolysis" refers to: light-associated decomposition of water.

It has been postulated that not only the H^+ ions of water but also the OH^- ions play a role in photolysis. In ways that are still unclear, the hydroxyl ions are believed to become reorganized through several chemical steps and to yield the following products:

$$2\ OH^- \longrightarrow \longrightarrow \longrightarrow \begin{bmatrix} H_2O \\ O \\ 2\ e^- \end{bmatrix}$$

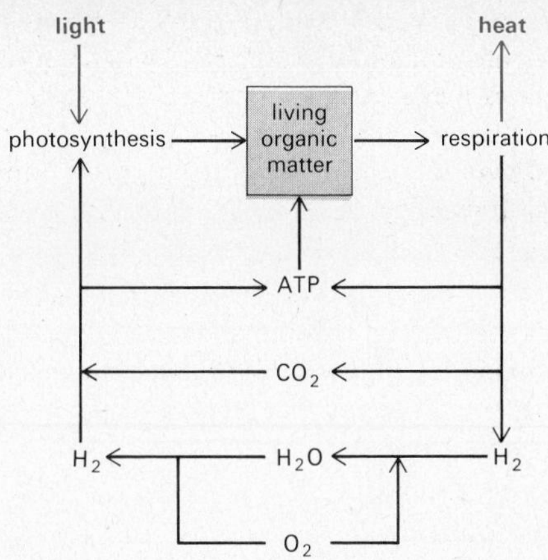

16.7 ***Thermodynamics of life.*** *In a stepwise transformation of energy from light to heat, the energy difference is incorporated in living matter through photosynthesis and is then utilized through respiration. Hydrogen (and the electrons of hydrogen) derived from water serves as the major transferring agent of energy, and oxygen is the main hydrogen carrier.*

The H_2O so produced "pays back" some of the water used up in the initial ionization; the oxygen gas escapes in molecular form, O_2, and accumulates in the environment as a photosynthetic byproduct; and the electrons appear to be accepted by a pigmented carrier molecule. The nature of this carrier is not yet fully established; some investigators believe that, in green algae and plants, it might be chlorophyll *b.* Whatever its precise identity, the available evidence strongly suggests that when this pigment is illuminated, the water-derived electrons it carries are brought to a high energy level. The resulting high-energy electrons then appear to be transferred to the ionized chlorophyll *a* formed at the beginning of the whole sequence; and chlorophyll *a* thereby becomes electrically neutral. The transfer probably involves the cytochromes and the other carriers that also function in the cyclic sequence. In the process, moreover, the electrons again become less energetic and the energy difference is harvested as ATP.

In effect, therefore, the noncyclic transfer sequence appears to contain *two* light-requiring steps (see Fig. 16.6). Through one of them high-energy electrons are removed from chlorophyll *a* at the start, and these pass *without energy loss* to NADP. This compound also accepts hydrogen ions from water and becomes NADP · $[H_2]$. Through the second light-requiring step, electrons derived from water and carried by a pigment are raised to a high energy level. These electrons eventually return to chlorophyll *a,* and in the process they yield their extra energy for ATP formation.

Thus, as in the cyclic pattern, chlorophyll again loses high-energy electrons at the start and gains low-energy electrons at the end. But in contrast to the cyclic pattern, the electrons now gained are not the same as those lost; *water* is the important intermediate compound that supplies electrons to chlorophyll and that also makes possible the formation of NADP · $[H_2]$. The process as a whole is therefore noncyclic, and it runs on the material input from decomposition of water and on the energy input from light. These inputs yield two products that incorporate some of the light-derived energy: the energy appears in ATP in the form of high-energy phosphate bonds, and in NADP · $[H_2]$, in the form of high-energy electrons in hydrogen.

Formation of NADP · $[H_2]$ completes photolysis, for this compound is the immediate hydrogen source in the food manufacture that follows. Production of this particular hydrogen source is also the key event in photosynthesis as a whole. Numerous other hydrogen sources are available on earth, and if these could be used in food manufacture the evolution of photosynthesis would have been unnecessary. But other hydrogen sources do not contain sufficiently energetic electrons. And photosynthesis appears to have evolved as a specialized process in which, through light and chlorophyll, the high-energy hydrogen required in food synthesis actually can be created.

Sunlight and water thus emerge as the critical agents in the energetics of life (Fig. 16.7). First, through photosynthesis, hydrogen from water is energized by light and together with CO_2 then becomes food and the substance of living matter. Oxygen is a byproduct. Later, through respiration, food and living matter are decomposed to the original starting materials, CO_2 and hydrogen, and the hydrogen rejoins with oxygen and forms water again. The energy gained in these decompositions first appears as ATP, which maintains life for a time but is ultimately dissipated entirely as heat. Living matter therefore represents a temporary construction built with the aid of energy from the sun; and this energy rides part of the way within hydrogen that cycles from water back to water and that finally ends up as environmental heat.

CO_2 fixation

The combination of CO_2 with hydrogen from NADP · $[H_2]$ is independent of light and occurs through a cyclic reaction sequence. This so-called *Calvin cycle,* or *carbon-fixation cycle,* consists of three basic steps, each with several substeps and catalyzed by specific enzymes (Fig. 16.8). In a first series of reactions CO_2 enters the cycle as a raw material. In a second series hydrogen from NADP · $[H_2]$ enters as a raw material. And in a last series the carbohydrate endproduct emerges while at the same time the starting point of the cycle is regenerated.

This starting point is *ribulose diphosphate,* RDP for short, a 5-carbon sugar carrying a phosphate group at each end of the carbon chain. It can be shown that the cycle must run completely through three consecutive turns before a single molecule of carbohydrate endproduct is obtained. To condense the description, it is convenient to add the three turns together; and instead of starting with one molecule of RDP and running the cycle three times, we can start with three molecules of RDP and run the cycle just once. Although such an artificial summation does not correspond to the actual reaction pattern, it does portray the sequence of steps adequately, and it is also correct arithmetically.

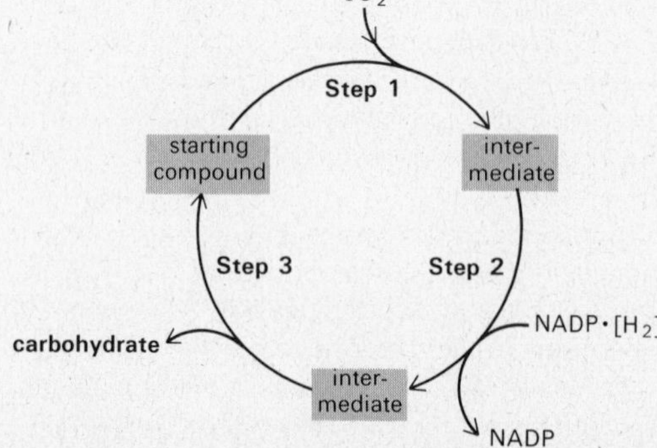

16.8 **CO_2 *fixation,*** *general pattern. In step 1, CO_2 enters the cycle as a raw material, and in step 2 hydrogen enters as a raw material. Step 3 yields the carbohydrate endproduct and also regenerates the starting compound.*

If, then, 3 RDP is taken as the starting point, the first reaction series involves an addition of three molecules of CO_2 and three molecules of H_2O (Fig. 16.9). By acquiring an extra carbon, the C_5 chain of each RDP becomes lengthened to a C_6 chain. But the C_6 molecule so formed is unstable and splits immediately into two molecules of phosphoglyceric acid, PGA. We have already encountered this C_3 compound in the discussion of glycolysis during carbohydrate respiration. Thus the net product of the first step of the Calvin cycle is six molecules of PGA.

In the second step, these 6 PGA are phosphorylated by 6 ATP (produced during photolysis) and then they interact with 6 NADP · $[H_2]$, also formed in photolysis. Byproducts are free NADP, phosphate, and water. The main endproduct is six molecules of phosphoglyceraldehyde, PGAL, again already familiar as an intermediate in glycolysis.

Evidently, photolysis generates not only the hydrogen for the Calvin cycle but also the necessary ATP. Further, the transformation of PGA to PGAL is a chemical *reduction,* through which an acid, PGA, is converted to an aldehyde, PGAL. This is almost the exact reverse of the oxidation of PGAL to PGA in glycolysis. In that respiratory process ATP and NAD · $[H_2]$ are produced (see Fig. 15.11), whereas in carbon fixation ATP and NADP · $[H_2]$ are consumed.

Note, incidentally, that NADP · $[H_2]$ is generated not only through photolysis but also through carbohydrate respiration via the hexose shunt (see Fig. 15.14). This shunt can therefore keep the Calvin cycle going—but only temporarily: the shunt produces NADP · $[H_2]$ by using up already existing carbohydrates, yet if such carbohydrates are to be available the Calvin cycle must first have produced them. Ultimately, therefore, the Calvin cycle depends on photolysis, the only process that creates NADP · $[H_2]$ independently of preexisting foods.

Of the six PGAL molecules formed during the second step of the Calvin cycle, *one* represents the main carbohydrate endproduct of photosynthesis as a whole. Solar energy, grana, chlorophyll, photolysis, CO_2 fixation—all cooperate to yield this final result. The five remaining PGAL molecules undergo a set of final transformations through which 3 RDP, the starting compounds

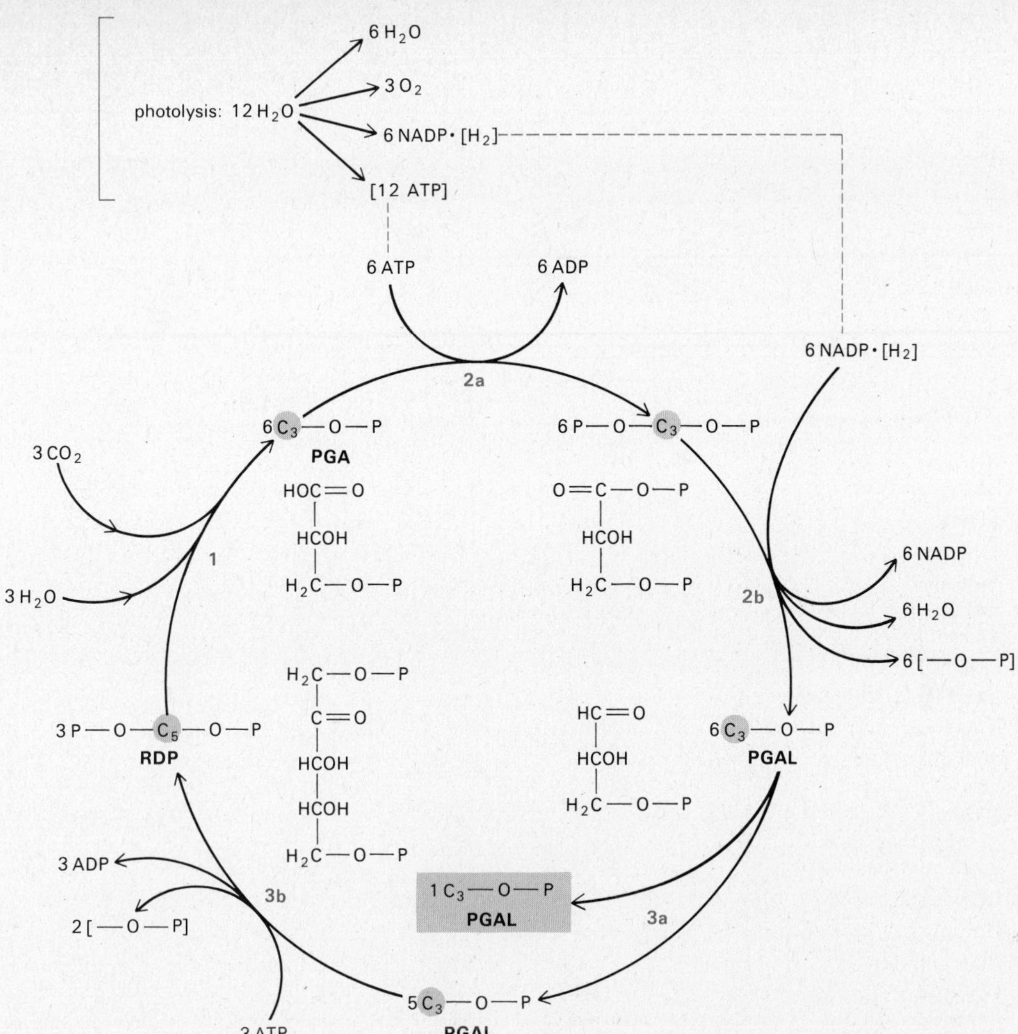

16.9 The Calvin cycle. *The compounds along the main path of the cycle are shown as carbon numbers with phosphate groups; complete structural formulas are alongside. In step 1, addition of CO_2 lengthens the C_5 chain of RDP to a C_6 chain; an extra carbon is interposed between the second and third carbons of RDP. The result is unstable and breaks into two identical PGA chains. The reactions of step 2, in which hydrogen from NADP·[H_2] is added to PGA, results in PGAL. The amount of photolysis necessary to provide the NADP·[H_2] and the ATP for step 2 is indicated at top. One PGAL molecule is the net endproduct, and the remaining 5 PGAL are reconverted to 3 RDP with the aid of more ATP from photolysis. An input-output summary is given in Fig. 16.10.*

of the cycle, are regenerated. Thus five C_3 molecules of PGAL are converted to three C_5 molecules of RDP. In this process more photolysis-derived ATP provides energy and required phosphate groups.

An input-output summary of the Calvin cycle and of photosynthesis as a whole is given in Fig. 16.10. The three *inorganic* carbons supplied by separate CO_2 molecules are now "fixed," or joined together as *organic* carbon in a single molecule of PGAL.

the endproduct

The prime endproduct of photosynthesis, PGAL, is a *food.* A plant nourished artificially with prefabricated PGAL can survive without photosynthesis and without any other organic supplies.

As PGAL forms in the grana it does not accumulate to any great extent, for it is soon used in one of three main ways: it can be used directly as a *nutrient* in the cell that produced it; it can be "packaged" for *export* to other cells; or it can be packaged for *storage.*

As a nutrient PGAL is usable immediately in respiration. It might happen, therefore, that some of the PGAL just manufactured is respired at once to pyruvic acid and through the citric acid cycle. PGAL is also usable directly as a building material; it contributes to the synthesis of any of the innumerable structural components of plant cells, including some of the chemical machinery re-

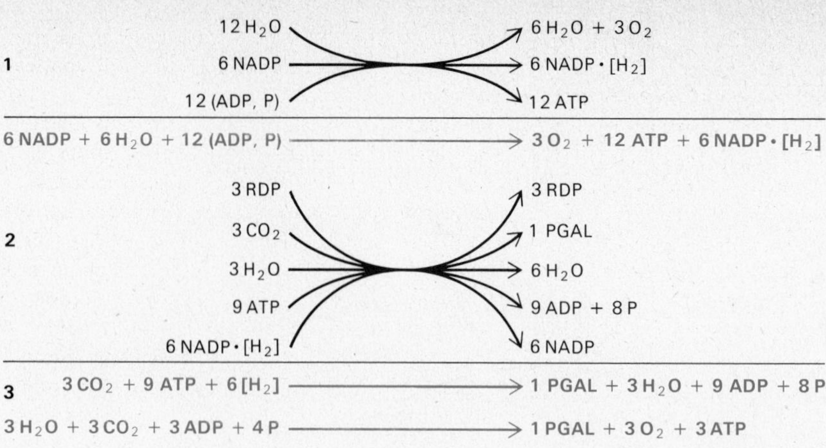

16.10 Chemical summaries of photosynthesis. *(P symbolizes phosphate.) 1, total and (color) net inputs and outputs of photolysis to create 6 NADP • [H$_2$] for the Calvin cycle. 2, total and (color) net inputs and outputs of the Calvin cycle to create an endproduct of 1 PGAL. Of the nine phosphate groups supplied by ATP, one is used in PGAL formation and eight thus appear as free byproduct. 3, net input and output of photosynthesis as a whole, obtained by adding the net inputs and outputs of reactions 1 and 2; this equation summarizes the formation of one PGAL molecule, the net endproduct.*

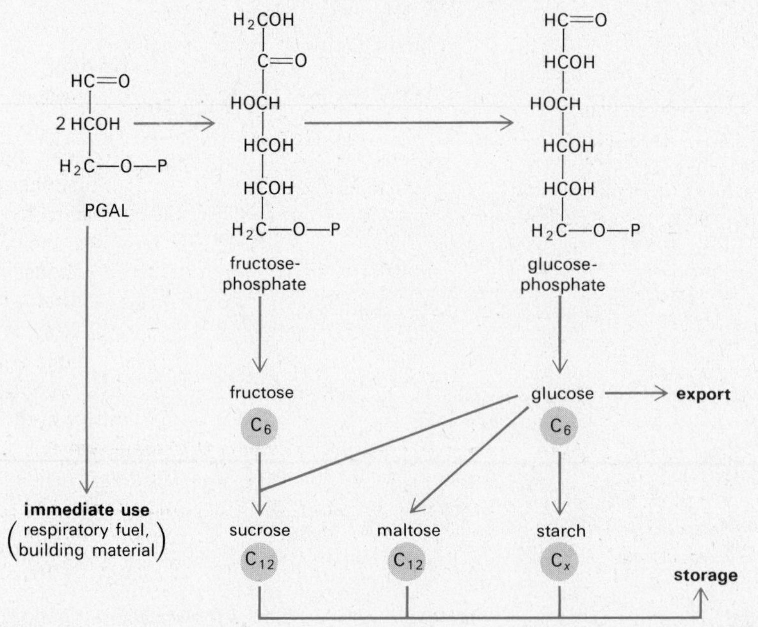

$$6\,H_2O + 6\,CO_2 + 6\,ADP + 8\,P \longrightarrow 2\,PGAL + 6\,O_2 + 6\,ATP \qquad \text{six Calvin cycles}$$

$$2\,PGAL \longrightarrow C_6H_{12}O_6 + 2\,P \qquad \text{glucose formation}$$

$$\left.\begin{array}{l} 6\,H_2O,\ 6\,CO_2 \longrightarrow C_6H_{12}O_6,\ 6\,O_2 \\ 6\,ADP,\ 6\,P \longrightarrow 6\,ATP \end{array}\right\}\text{net}$$

B

16.11 The photosynthetic endproduct. *A, the possible fates of PGAL formed in photosynthesis. The pathway to glucose is substantially the reverse of that in respiratory glycolysis (see Fig. 15.11). B, to produce 2 PGAL for glucose formation, the Calvin cycle must run six times, with an input and output as shown (twice the amounts in reaction 3, Fig. 16.10). P stands for phosphate. The overall net input and output for the photosynthetic production of one glucose molecule is then as shown at bottom.*

quired for PGAL production itself. Indeed it is because PGAL functions as the basic organic construction material that photosynthesis becomes the source of all foods and all organic components of nearly the whole living world.

But a green cell generally manufactures much more PGAL than it requires for its own maintenance. The bulk of this photosynthetic product then becomes available for export to nongreen cells of the organism. However, green cells do not export PGAL as such; it is probably too reactive a material. In transit from leaf to root, for example, it would react with other substances long before it could reach its destination. Green cells instead convert PGAL to less reactive compounds, particularly sugars such as glucose, fructose, and sucrose.

In these conversions two PGAL molecules are joined to form one monosaccharide molecule. The reactions here greatly resemble the reverse of glycolysis, from glucose-phosphate to PGAL. The key steps are given in Fig. 16.11. Since production of sugars (particularly sucrose) and export to other cells is the fate of most of the photosynthesized carbohydrate, sugar is often, though not quite correctly, regarded as the primary end-product of photosynthesis.

The green cells of a plant normally produce enough PGAL not only to meet all current food requirements of the nongreen cells but also to provide appreciable amounts for longer-term storage. Green cells themselves store foods to some extent, and roots and stems are particularly specialized for this function (for example, taproots, tubers). Like export, storage does not involve PGAL as such. In any efficient storage the stored material should take up as little space as possible, and it should also be "out of circulation," or relatively unavailable for rapid utilization. Since PGAL reacts readily with cellular components in its vicinity, it would not remain out of circulation for long. Even glucose, though less reactive, would enter metabolic processes fairly rapidly.

Plants actually condense PGAL molecules to more compact and relatively unreactive packets. For example, sugar cane, sugar beets, and many kinds of fruit owe their sweetness to stored fructose and sucrose. Numerous other plants accumulate carbohydrates in the form of starches. Still other plants manufacture storage fats instead of or in addition to carbohydrate reserves (for example, olive oil, castor oil, peanut oil, coconut oil). Such storage syntheses occur in both green and nongreen cells, and sugars are the usual starting materials (see Fig. 16.11 and also the following sections). In most cases storage molecules are in fact more compact physically than the separate starting units. For example, disaccharides such as sucrose or maltose consist of two C_6 units but contain one water molecule less than two separate monosaccharides. Similarly, a polysaccharide in starch composed of, say, 500 C_6 units contains 499 water molecules less than 500 separate glucose molecules. It is this physical condensation that makes storage synthesis of adaptive value.

Photosynthesis as a whole is a very efficient process. It has been estimated that, under ideal conditions, up to 50 percent of all the light energy absorbed by chloroplasts can be recovered as energy built into carbohydrates. However, a field of wheat absorbs only about 2 percent of the total light energy it receives from the sun; chloroplasts are spread rather thinly over the whole field. Yet this 2 percent of sunlight, produced by thermonuclear reactions 93 million miles away, represents the whole power source that keeps living organisms alive through photosynthesis.

synthesis metabolism

The metabolic link between photosynthesis and finished living matter is a large variety of synthesis reactions. These produce the chemicals that a cell does not obtain directly as prefabricated environmental nutrients or as secretions from other cells. Such missing ingredients include most of the critically necessary compounds for cellular survival: nucleic acids, structural and enzymatic proteins, polysaccharides, fats, and numerous other groups of complex organic substances. In most cases such synthesis reactions are endergonic and ATP-requiring. A cyclical interrelation is therefore in evidence. On the one hand, breakdown of organic compounds leads to a net buildup of ATP through respiration. On the other, breakdown of ATP leads to a net buildup of organic compounds through chemical synthesis (Fig. 16.12).

Synthesis of cellular components and breakdown occur simultaneously, all the time. As pointed out in the preceding chapter, breakdown can affect any cellular component regardless of composition or age. A certain *percentage* of all

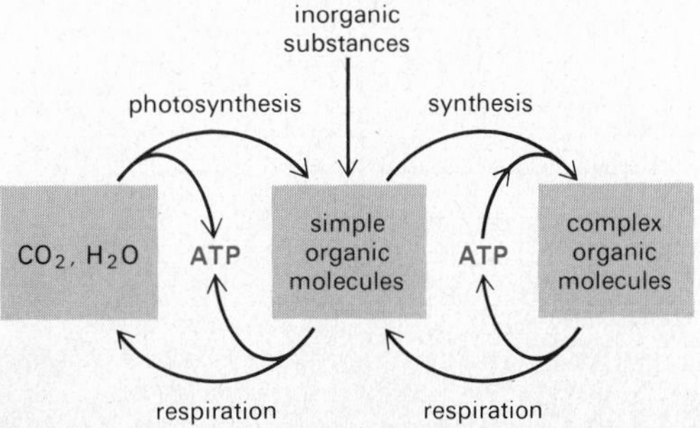

16.12 Metabolic balance. *All synthetic and other creative processes of metabolism are sometimes collectively referred to as "anabolism," and all respiratory and other destructive processes, as "catabolism."*

cellular constituents is decomposed every second, and what particular constituents actually make up this percentage is largely a matter of chance. Such randomness applies also to synthesis. Regardless of the source of materials, a certain percentage of available components is synthesized every second to finished cell substances. If synthesis and breakdown are exactly balanced, the net characteristics of a cell remain unchanged. But continuous turnover of energy and materials occurs nevertheless, and every brick in the building is sooner or later replaced by a new one. Thus the house always remains "fresh."

But even when the two processes are balanced exactly, they cannot sustain each other in a self-contained, self-sufficient cycle. Energy dissipates irretrievably through physical activities and through heat losses in chemical reactions; and materials dissipate through elimination, evaporation, and friction. Just to maintain a steady state, therefore, a cell must be supplied continuously with energy and raw materials. Moreover, the rate of supply must often exceed the rate required for mere maintenance, for net synthesis frequently exceeds net breakdown, as in growth or repair after injury.

In a very general sense, synthesis reverses the result of respiratory decomposition; the products formed at successive steps of respiration can be the starting materials in synthesis. However, only green cells and autotrophic cells generally can reverse the final step of respiration. Only they can "fix" the respiratory endproduct CO_2 and create original PGAL from this inorganic source. But once organic compounds are available, *all* cells, including nongreeen plant cells and the cells of animals, can add CO_2 to these compounds and thereby increase the lengths of carbon chains.

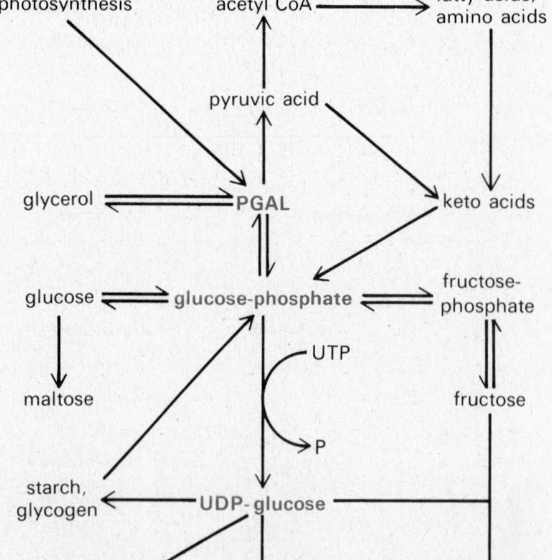

16.13 Main pathways in carbohydrate synthesis. *The compounds shown in color represent key intersections of numerous reaction sequences. UTP is uridine triphosphate, a uracil derivative functionally similar to ATP. UDP-glucose is uridine-diphosphate-glucose. Interconversions occur readily and frequently according to pathways indicated by the arrows. Note that carbohydrate metabolism is interconnected with fatty acid and amino acid metabolism.*

carbohydrates

In any orgainsm most carbohydrates are usually synthesized from glucose. This sugar can itself be formed from C_3 units such as PGAL, as noted (essentially by the reverse of part of the reaction sequence of glycolysis). Alternatively a cell obtains glucose as a prefabricated nutrient, in plants by transport in phloem from storage regions, in animals by transport in blood from gut or liver. After phosphorylation of glucose at the cell surface, glucose-phosphate can then interact inside a cell with UTP, uridine triphosphate, a nucleotide derivative functionally equivalent to ATP. The result of this interaction is a *UDP-glucose* complex, the actual starting material in many glucose-requiring syntheses. For example, UDP-glucose participates in the manufacture of monosaccharides such as galactose, disaccharides such as sucrose, and polysaccharides such as starch, cellulose, and glycogen (Fig. 16.13).

Starches stored in plant cells and glycogen in animal cells are normally the most abundant carbohydrates. They are also the usual starting carbohydrates both in respiration and in other syntheses. When used as fuel, starch or glycogen is phosphorylated by ATP and converted to glucose-phosphate; and when used as building materials, these polysaccharides are reconverted to UDP-glucose. Glucose-phosphate and UDP-glucose are themselves interconvertible, and glucose-phosphate can also be exported from a cell in the form of free glucose. In most organisms a chemical balance is probably maintained between carbohydrates inside cells and free glucose outside them. Such balances are particularly precise in vertebrates, where the liver performs an important carbohydrate-regulating function (Fig. 16.14).

The liver stores incoming carbohydrates as glycogen and releases carbohydrates to the blood as glucose. Moreover, small-scale fluctuations notwithstanding, the liver maintains a fairly *constant* glucose concentration in blood. Whenever

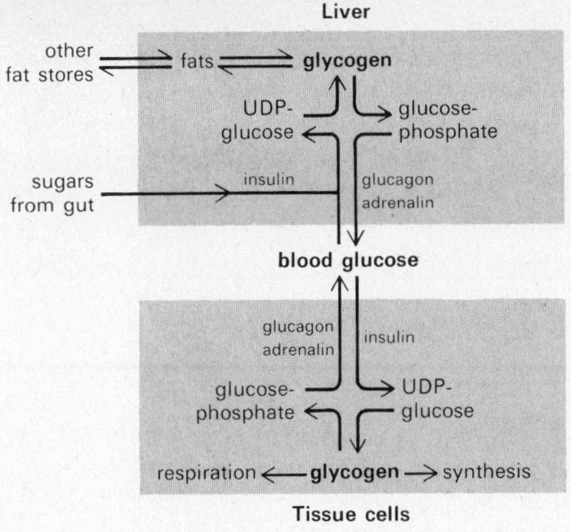

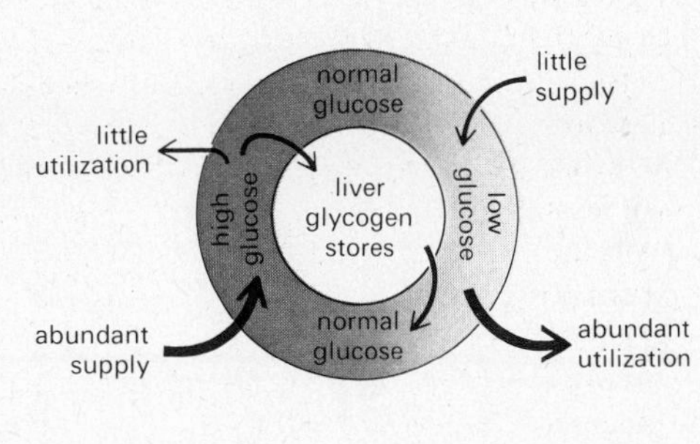

16.14 Carbohydrate balance in vertebrates. *A, the pathways of interconversion between liver glycogen, blood glucose, and tissue glycogen. The hormones promoting given reactions are indicated in smaller type. Any excess liver glycogen can be converted to fat. Tissue glycogen is a main respiratory fuel as well as a starting compound in synthesis. B, the maintenance of blood-glucose balance by the liver. If much sugar is supplied to blood from food and little is used, then the blood-glucose concentration will tend to be high (left). Under such conditions the liver withdraws glucose and stores it as glycogen, thus establishing a normal glucose level (top). But if much glucose is used up and little is supplied, then the blood-glucose concentration will tend to be low (right). The liver then adds glucose to blood from its glycogen stores and so reestablishes the normal glucose level (bottom). By these means the liver maintains a constant blood-glucose concentration.*

the glucose level in blood tends to rise, as after a meal, when large quantities of carbohydrates pass from the gut to the circulation, then liver cells withdraw the excess from blood, produce UDP-glucose, and convert the latter to storage glycogen. Conversely, when blood-glucose levels tend to fall, as during intense body activity, when muscles and other tissues use up carbohydrates rapidly, then liver cells convert stored glycogen to glucose-phosphate and then to free glucose and release that sugar to the blood. These transformations are governed basically by mass action, or changes in the concentration balance between glycogen inside a liver cell and glucose outside it. If blood glucose decreases in concentration, the reaction equilibrium will shift in such a way that liver glycogen is transformed to free glucose; and if blood glucose increases in concentration, the equilibrium shift is such that glucose will be converted to glycogen.

These interconversions are affected greatly by hormones. The pancreatic hormone *insulin* promotes transformation of glucose to glycogen. If therefore insulin production is inadequate, as in a diabetic vertebrate, glucose cannot become glycogen in the tissue cells but will accumulate uselessly in blood. Much of this unusable blood sugar is then excreted in urine though the body tissues suffer from lack of carbohydrates. (Conversely, if too much insulin is present, glucose will be converted to tissue glycogen to such an extent that the blood-glucose level drops drastically. The brain is particularly dependent on glucose, and when the glucose supply in blood becomes abnormally low "insulin shock" and eventual death can ensue.)

The reverse transformation of glycogen to glucose is promoted by the pancreatic hormone *glucagon* and the adrenal hormone *adrenalin* (*epinephrine*). The latter is secreted particularly during emotional or physical stress. Thus, just when the body tissues require a great deal of fuel in combating stress, a rapid large-scale conversion of liver glycogen to blood glucose takes place.

The amount of glycogen the liver can store is not particularly large. When sugars supplied by food exceed the storage capacity, the excess carbohydrates are converted to *fats.* These are stored partly in the liver, partly in other parts of the body. Such fat production explains why even a nonfatty diet can lead to obesity, particularly if for long periods more food is eaten than the body requires.

Conversely, when so few carbohydrates are consumed that glycogen stores are severely reduced, then the fat stores of the body can be converted to carbohydrates. Indeed the liver can maintain normal blood-glucose levels even when the diet is carbohydrate-free, provided eaten food contains compensating amounts of fat (see Figs. 16.14 and 16.15).

One major role of the vertebrate liver thus emerges. The organ ensures that all cells of the body receive an adequate carbohydrate supply regardless of when or how often food is eaten. Invertebrates and all other organisms do not have organs functioning in the same way, and in such

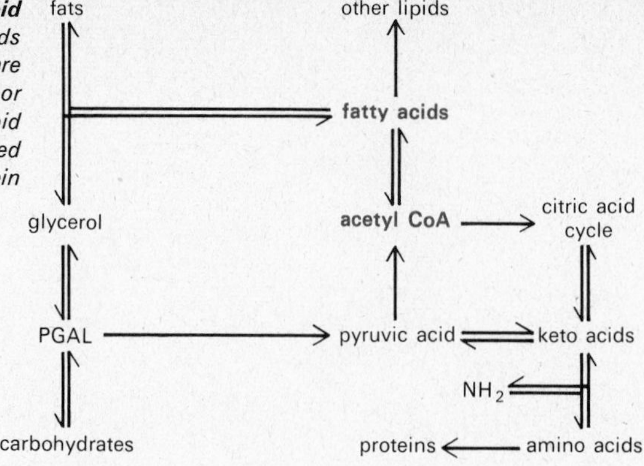

16.15 Main pathways in lipid synthesis. *The key compounds acetyl CoA and fatty acids are interconverted by β-oxidation or its reverse. Note that lipid metabolism is interconnected with carbohydrate and protein metabolism.*

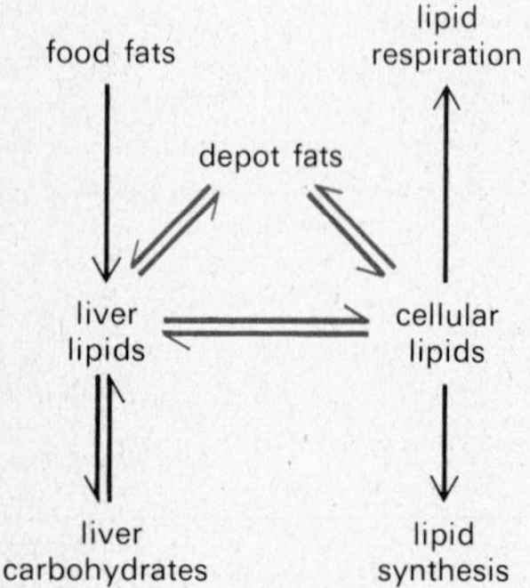

16.16 Lipid balance in vertebrates.

organisms carbohydrate balances are far less regulated.

lipids

In all organisms the simplest starting material in lipid synthesis is the 2-carbon acetyl group (Fig. 16.15). From acetyl CoA can be synthesized, for example, fatty acids of any length. This process is almost exactly the reverse of β-oxidation: successive C_2 groups in the form of acetyl CoA are added to acetyl CoA itself or to already existing longer carbon chains. The main steps can be traced by reading Fig. 15.16 in reverse. Recall here that animal cells are unable to synthesize certain "essential" fatty acids, which must be supplied fully formed in the diet. Acetyl CoA can also enter the citric acid cycle, and various participants of this cycle can then become transformed to pyruvic acid and carbohydrates generally. This is a common pathway in lipid-carbohydrate interconversions.

In the synthesis of fats, fatty acids are one type of required building material, glycerol is the other. Glycerol is usually formed from C_3 compounds such as PGA or PGAL—read Fig. 15.15 in reverse. In fat synthesis, one molecule of glycerol is joined enzymatically to three molecules of fatty acids (see Fig. 4.5). Fatty acids and therefore fats can also arise from carbohydrate starting materials, as already noted, and indeed amino acids can contribute to fat formation as well (see Figs. 16.15 and 16.17). Whole fats are the basic lipid reserves of organisms. Plants frequently store fats as oils in fruits and seeds, and animals contain fat bodies or other specialized regions for fat storage. In vertebrates, for example, fats are deposited under the skin, around the heart and the kidneys, and particularly along the mesenteries, the peritoneal membranes that envelop the intestine.

The liver, too, is an important fat depot, as noted above. Its total fat store is in balance with the reserves in other body regions. If liver fat increases too much, the excess is exported through the circulation to the other depots. Conversely, the other depots make up any deficiency in liver fat. In these redistributions fat is transported largely in the form of fatty acids and glycerol. The nonstoring tissues of the body are supplied either by the liver or by the other fat depots. Fat balance in a vertebrate is therefore maintained by an equilibrium between three groups of compounds, as shown in Fig. 16.16.

amino acids

Amino acid synthesis in cells ordinarily takes place by transamination (see Fig. 15.17). Thus, any amino acid can be formed if an amino group ($—NH_2$) interacts with an appropriate keto acid derived from lipids or carbohydrates:

$$\underset{\text{amino donor}}{NH_2—\underset{|}{\overset{}{X}}H} \quad + \quad \underset{\text{keto acid}}{O{=}\overset{R}{\overset{|}{C}}—COOH} \quad \rightleftarrows \quad \underset{\text{amino acid}}{NH_2—\overset{R}{\overset{|}{\underset{\underset{H}{|}}{C}}}—COOH} \quad + \quad O{=}X$$

Amino groups can be supplied by other available amino acids, but, as noted in Chap. 7, the ultimate source is mineral nitrate, NO_3^-. Microorganisms and plants can convert these ions to $—NH_2$. Animals cannot, and they depend on each other and in the end on plants for their supply of amino groups. Indeed, recall also that plants must supply animals with "essential" amino acids, or, more specifically, those keto acid portions of amino acids that animal cells cannot synthesize on their own.

Plant cells usually synthesize amino acids only in amounts actually required for current construction processes; hence little if any excess or deficiency of amino acids is likely to exist. Animal cells are different in this respect, for their supply of amino acids, particularly "essential" ones, depends on the food intake of the whole animal, a factor not under direct control of an individual cell. Moreover, unlike carbohydrates or fats, amino acids are not stored. If then the supply from the gut is inadequate, an amino acid deficiency will develop. Breakdown of proteins already in a cell or transamination can alleviate such shortages temporarily, but the cell and indeed the whole animal will eventually suffer disease or death if essential amino acids remain unavailable. Animals must therefore consume daily doses of essential amino acids (or the corresponding keto acids).

Normally, however, animal diets actually supply more than immediately needed amounts of amino acids. Requirements are greatest in young, growing animals, in pregnant females, and in animals in which extensively damaged or diseased parts undergo healing. In all such cases large amounts of amino acids are used in protein synthesis. But even then more amino acids are usually eaten than required. In healthy adults growth and structural replacement occur at a much reduced rate, and amino acid requirements are correspondingly reduced. Any excess of amino acids is then degraded, in vertebrates mainly in the liver and in other animals probably in all cells. This degradation takes the form of deamination, as already outlined in Chap. 15 (see Fig. 15.17). The resulting keto acids later participate in carbohydrate or lipid metabolism (see Fig. 16.15), and the ammonia, a toxic alkaline waste product, is excreted.

Most aquatic animals reduce the toxicity of ammonia by diluting it in large amounts of water and excreting a copious urine. Some aquatic forms, and also terrestrial types that must conserve water, convert ammonia to less toxic substances before excretion. Among such substances *urea* and *uric acid* are particularly common. Both are far less toxic, and thus can be excreted in more concentrated form, than ammonia itself.

In the liver cells of mammals, for example, ammonia is combined enzymatically with respiratory CO_2 and urea is produced. The process occurs through a cycle of reactions, called the *ornithine cycle,* after one of the three amino acids that form the "endless belt" of the sequence (Fig. 16.17). The other two amino acids here are citrulline and arginine. For every urea molecule generated, two NH_3 molecules and one CO_2 molecule feed into the cycle.

As indicated in Fig. 16.17, urea also arises in

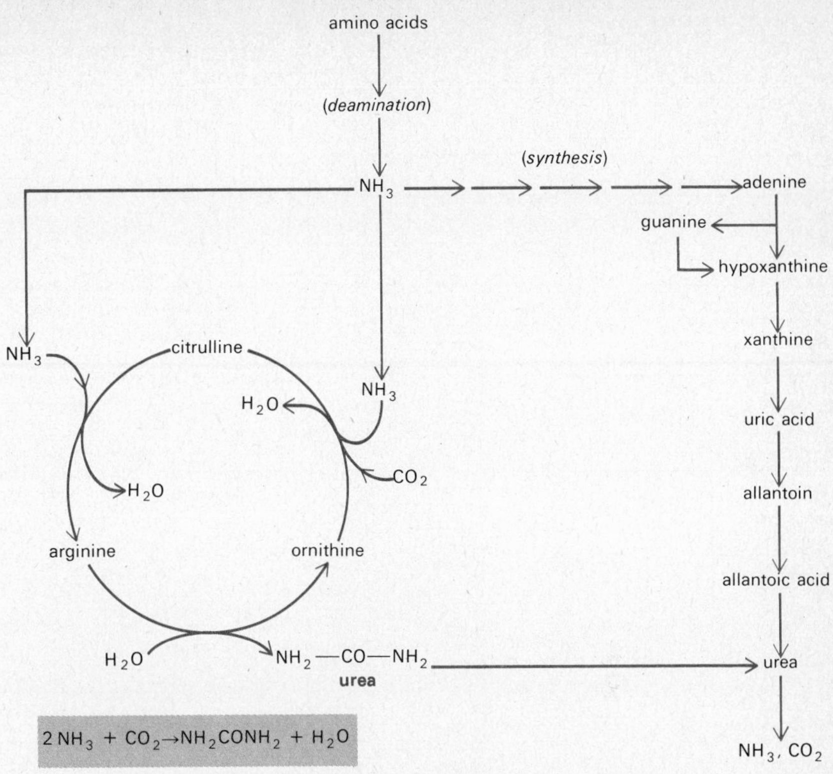

16.17 Metabolism of amino nitrogen. *Urea production through the ornithine cycle in the vertebrate liver is outlined at left. The net input and output are in the color box under the cycle.* NH_3 *is also used in the synthesis of nitrogen bases, and later stepwise degradation of such bases yields the series of excretion products shown in the vertical sequence at right. Uric acid is a major excretory endproduct in, for example, insects, birds, and some reptiles; allantoin, in turtles and some mammals; allantoic acid, in some bony fishes; urea (produced in two ways as this diagram indicates) is excreted in most vertebrate groups not named here; and* NH_3 *is excreted in most invertebrate groups. Animals generally excrete mixtures of various endproducts, but one or the other substance tends to predominate.*

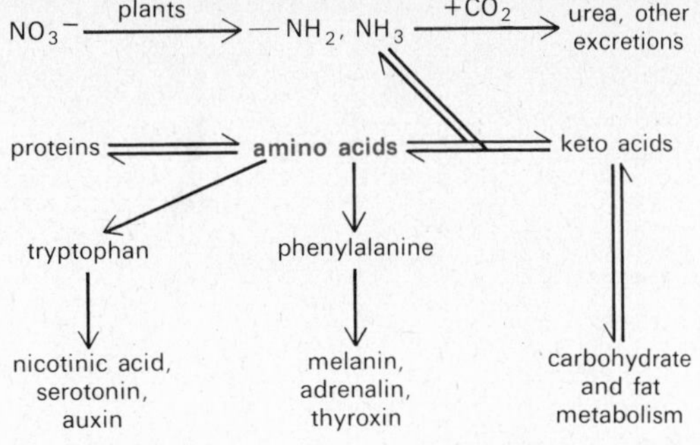

16.18 Main pathways in amino acid synthesis. *Arrows do not necessarily imply single reaction steps. In animals, keto acids for the essential amino acids must be obtained from the diet. Tryptophan, phenylalanine, and thyroxin are amino acids themselves (see Fig. 4.7). Serotonin, auxin, adrenalin, and thyroxin function as hormones, and melanin is a black pigment.*

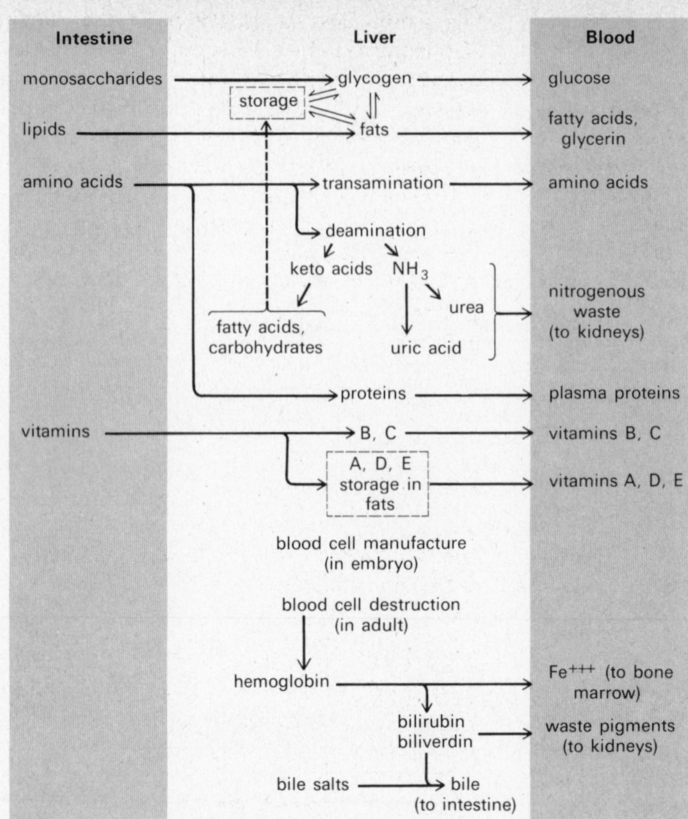

16.19 ***Liver functions,*** *summary.*

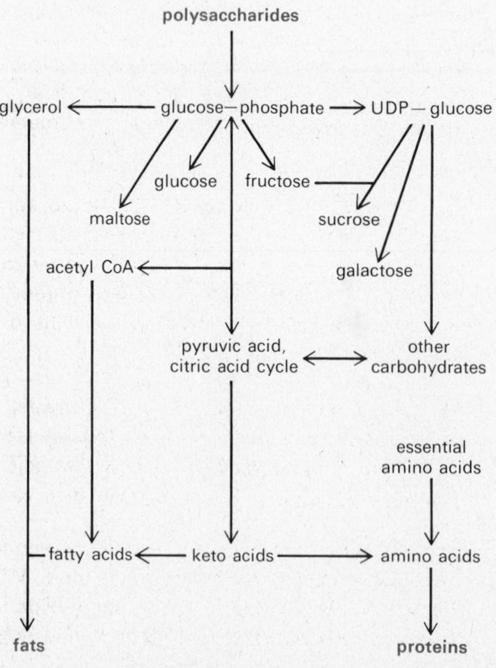

16.20 Synthesis metabolism: *overall summary. Many of the reaction pathways shown here are reversible and can lead either to synthesis or to respiratory degradation.*

the course of normal metabolic breakdown of nitrogen bases such as adenine and guanine. Nitrogen sources like NH_3 or $—NH_2$ originally contribute to the synthesis of these bases, and whenever they break down later they undergo a sequence of enzymatic transformations in which uric acid and urea are two of the intermediate steps. Some organisms have all the enzymes for the complete transformation sequence, and in such cases NH_3 and CO_2 are endproducts of degradation. Other organisms lack the enzymes for some of the later steps of degradation, and breakdown here proceeds to different endpoints in different cases. In insects, birds, and also many plants, uric acid is the chief excretion product. Insects and birds eliminate this compound in a minimum of water as a semisolid urine; and in some plants and animals uric acid is deposited in or on the organism in dry, crystalline form (for example, the powdery material on the wings of many butterflies and moths). In some mammals (man included), a small amount of uric acid likewise appears in urine as a normal component or larger internal deposits may be formed abnormally (as in gout).

Apart from amino acids that are deaminated, all others, either synthesized directly in a cell or supplied to a cell as nutrients, serve as raw materials in a wide variety of manufacturing processes (Fig. 16.18). For example, the amino acid tryptophan is converted to the B vitamin *nicotinic acid,* which in turn contributes to the formation of NAD and NADP. Tryptophan is also a precursor of *serotonin,* a hormone of the nervous system, and of *auxin,* the chief growth hormone of plants.

The amino acid phenylalanine is the starting compound in the synthesis of the common black pigment *melanin* and the animal hormones *adrenalin* and *thyroxin.* But amino acids play their most important role by far as raw materials in protein synthesis, a process associated intimately with nucleic acid synthesis. This topic will occupy our attention in the next chapter.

A comprehensive summary of the main functions of the vertebrate liver is given in Fig. 16.19, and of the main synthesis pathways in cells generally, in Fig. 16.20.

---

review questions

1 What physical processes are implied by the statement, "Chlorophyll is green"? What is the general chemical structure of chlorophyll? What is the internal architecture of chloroplasts?

2 State the general chemical nature and function of photosynthesis as a whole. Review the sources of the carbon, hydrogen, and oxygen atoms that compose photosynthesized carbohydrates.

3 What are the functions of light and chlorophyll in photosynthesis? What are the events of photolysis? Show how water becomes separated into several components. Define photoionization and photophosphorylation.

4 Review the events in cyclic and noncyclic electron transfers. Show how such transfers contribute to (*a*) ATP formation, (*b*) food manufacture. What carrier compounds participate in electron transfers?

5 Write a net input-output statement of photolysis. In what form is hydrogen from photolysis used in food manufacture?

6 Describe the main steps of the Calvin cycle. Which of these steps have some similarity to respiratory reactions? Where and in what form does energy contribute to the cycle? Write a net input-output statement of the cycle, and also of photosynthesis as a whole.

7 What is the main endproduct of photosynthesis? Review the possible fates of this endproduct. What are the chief transportation and storage forms of carbohydrates in plants? By what reactions are these carbohydrates produced from the photosynthetic endproduct?

8 Review patterns of carbohydrate synthesis. How can carbon chains be lengthened in cells? Shortened? What is the role of UDP-glucose, and what compounds can be formed from it?

9 By what processes does the vertebrate liver maintain a constant glucose concentration in blood? Describe several specific situations in which the blood-glucose level tends to change, and show how such tendencies are counteracted by the liver.

10 How do cells synthesize (*a*) fatty acids, (*b*) fats? Describe the interplay between liver, fat depots, and body tissues in animal lipid metabolism.

11 How does a cell synthesize amino acids? What precursors are required? Review the nature and the results of transamination and deamination reactions. In which form do various organisms eliminate nitrogenous wastes? Review the ornithine cycle.

12 Show how the following interconversions could occur: (*a*) carbohydrate to fat; (*b*) fat to carbohydrate; (*c*) carbohydrate to amino acid or vice versa; (*d*) fat to amino acid or vice versa.

13 Suppose that an animal were not given any food for a considerable length of time. What changes would then occur in the body-wide balances of carbohydrates, fats, and amino acids?

14 Could an animal survive if its foods consisted of (*a*) only carbohydrates, (*b*) only fats, (*c*) only proteins, (*d*) carbohydrates and fats only, (*e*) carbohydrates and amino acids only, (*f*) fats and amino acids only?

15 Describe the basic balance between synthesis and breakdown in cells, and explain the meaning of metabolic turnover. Name some compounds synthesized in cells from amino acids. How is chlorophyll synthesized?

collateral readings

Arnon, D. I.: The Role Of Light in Photosynthesis, *Sci. American,* Nov., 1960. The conversion of light energy to chemical energy is discussed.

Bassham, J. A.: The Path of Carbon in Photosynthesis, *Sci. American,* June, 1962. A general account of the Calvin cycle.

Bogorad, L.: Photosynthesis, in "Plant Biology Today," Wadsworth, Belmont, Calif., 1963. A thorough general discussion of the subject; recommended.

Galston, A. W.: "The Life of the Green Plant," 2d ed., Prentice-Hall, Englewood Cliffs, N.J., 1964. A good review of photosynthesis is included in this paperback.

Green, D. E.: The Synthesis of Fat, *Sci. American,* Feb., 1960. The title of this article describes its contents adequately.

Jellinck, P. H.: "The Cellular Role of Macromolecules," Scott, Foresman, Glenview, Ill., 1967. This paperback covers most of the topics of these chapters on metabolism in slightly more advanced form than that presented here. Recommended for further background reading.

Jensen, W. A.: "The Plant Cell," Wadsworth, Belmont, Calif., 1964. A short section on chloroplasts and photosynthesis is included in this paperback.

Lehninger, A. L.: How Cells Transform Energy, *Sci. American,* Sept., 1961. The light-trapping role of chlorophyll is one of the subjects discussed in this article.

———: "Bioenergetics," Benjamin, New York, 1965. The chemical aspects of most metabolic processes are discussed in this paperback, including those of photosynthesis, synthesis, and respiration. Somewhat more advanced than material presented here, hence excellent for follow-up reading.

Loewy, A. G., and **P. Siekevitz:** "Cell Structure and Function," Prentice-Hall, Englewood Cliffs, N.J., 1963. The brief section on metabolic syntheses in this paperback is pertinent to the topics of this chapter.

Rabinowitch, E. I., and **Govindjee:** The Role of Chlorophyll in Photosynthesis, *Sci. American,* July, 1965. An up-to-date account showing how H atoms of water are incorporated in organic materials.

Steward, F. C.: "Plants at Work," Addison-Wesley, Reading, Mass., 1964. This paperback contains a short chapter on the chemistry of photosynthesis.

chapter 17 genetic codes, physical functions

Apart from photosynthesis in green cells, protein and nucleic acid syntheses are the most basic manufacturing processes in all cells. The production of these compounds is examined in the first section below, which rounds out the discussion of the *chemical* aspects of metabolism. Cells use nutrients and ATP also in producing heat, often in generating light and electricity, and particularly in bringing about movement. These *physical* aspects of metabolism are examined in the last sections of this chapter.

genes and protein synthesis

the pattern

The synthesis of proteins is bound to differ in at least one basic respect from the manufacture of other cellular compounds: a cell cannot use just any newly made proteins but only *specific* proteins. For only if newly formed proteins are exactly like those present earlier can a cell maintain its own special characteristics. Such a specificity problem does not arise with most other kinds of compounds. A cellulose molecule, for example, is composed of identical glucose units and is structured like any other cellulose molecule containing the same number of glucose units. But a protein molecule is composed of *different* kinds of amino acid units, and a merely random linking together of such units would make one polypeptide chain quite different from every other. Protein synthesis therefore requires *specificity control;* a ''blueprint'' must provide instructions about the precise sequence in which given numbers and types of amino acids are to be joined as a protein.

Ultimately such specificity control is exercised by the genes of a cell, the DNA of the chromosomes. *The primary function of genes is to control specificities in protein synthesis.* It has been found that the particular sequence of the nitrogen bases in DNA represents a coded chemical message that specifies a particular sequence of amino acids. The different genes in a cell carry different messages, and a cell can manufacture proteins only as these genetic instructions dictate.

Genes are housed in the chromosomes in the nucleus, but the ''factories'' where proteins are actually put together are the ribosomes in the cytoplasm. Genetic instructions are transmitted to the ribosomes by RNA. Chromosomes produce RNA, and in the process the chemical message of DNA becomes incorporated, or *transcribed,* in the structure of RNA. The new RNA molecules then leave the chromosomes and diffuse to the cytoplasm, where they eventually reach the ribosomes. Here amino acids are joined together as proteins in accordance with the genetic instruction supplied by the RNA molecules (Fig. 17.1).

Evidently, genes are essentially passive information carriers. All they do, or allow to be done to them, is to have their code information copied by RNA molecules, which then serve as information carriers in turn. Genes thus can be likened to important original ''texts'' carefully stored and preserved in the ''library'' of the nucleus. There they are available as permanent, authoritative ''master documents'' from which expendable duplicate copies can be prepared. RNA passing to the cytoplasm actually is expendable and comparatively short-lived; soon after it has exercised its function as code carrier it is degraded by respiration. New RNA from the nucleus is then required if repeated protein synthesis is to occur. The genes on the contrary persist and are protected from respiratory destruction by the nuclear boundary. A nuclear membrane therefore appears to be an important evolutionary adaptation that promotes preservation of gene stability. It is advantageous also that the permanent message center and the manufacturing center are at different locations in a cell. If both were in the nucleus together, the manufacturing center might be too distant and isolated from the energy sources and the raw material supplies; and if both were in the cytoplasm together, the message center would be subject to rapid respiratory destruction.

Inasmuch as the RNA formed by the chromosomes carries chemical messages to the ribo-

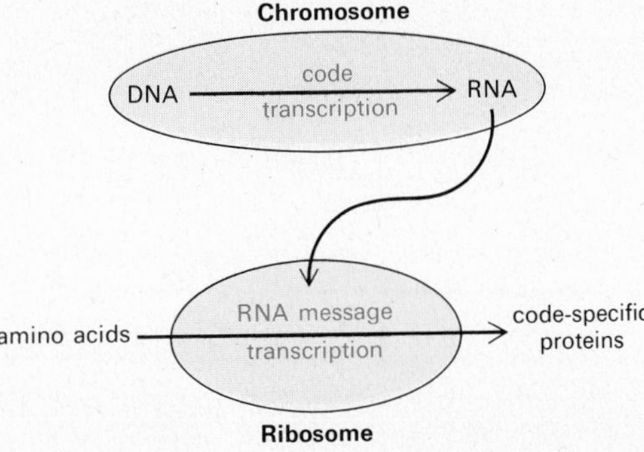

17.1 The pattern of protein synthesis. *The genetic ''message'' in the chromosomal DNA of a cell is transcribed to RNA and from RNA to specific amino acid sequences in proteins manufactured in the ribosomes.*

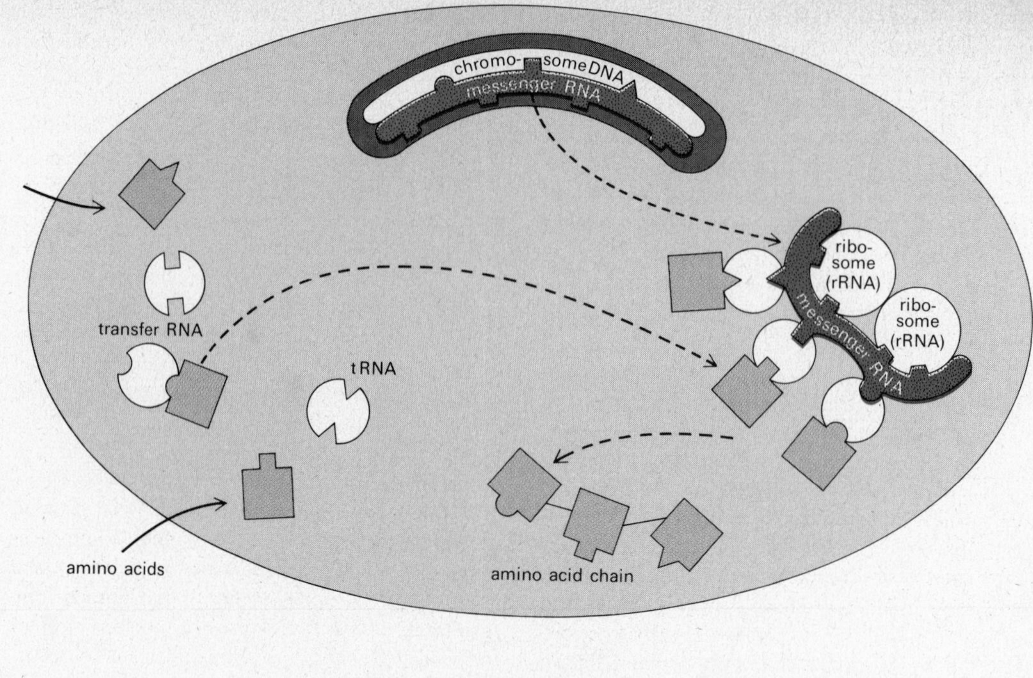

17.2 The pattern of protein synthesis. *Specific messenger RNA (mRNA) manufactured in chromosomes becomes attached at ribosomes (and the rRNA there perhaps aids in the attachment). Amino acids entering a cell as food become joined to specific transfer RNA molecules, and the tRNA–amino acid complexes attach at specific, code-determined sites along the messenger RNA. The amino acids there link together through formation of successive peptide bonds (as in Fig. 4.8). The completed, code-specific amino acid chains then become free.*

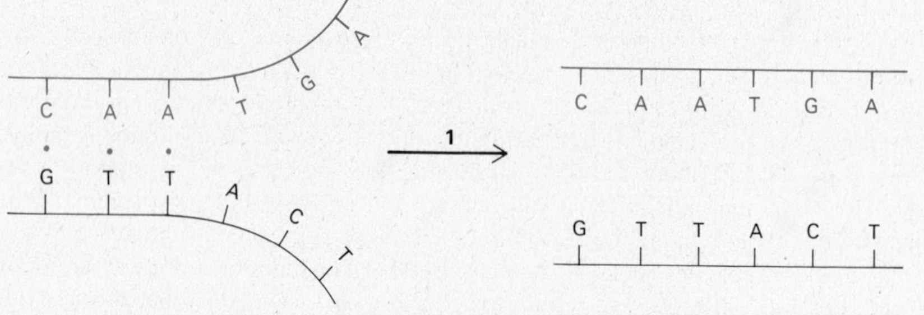

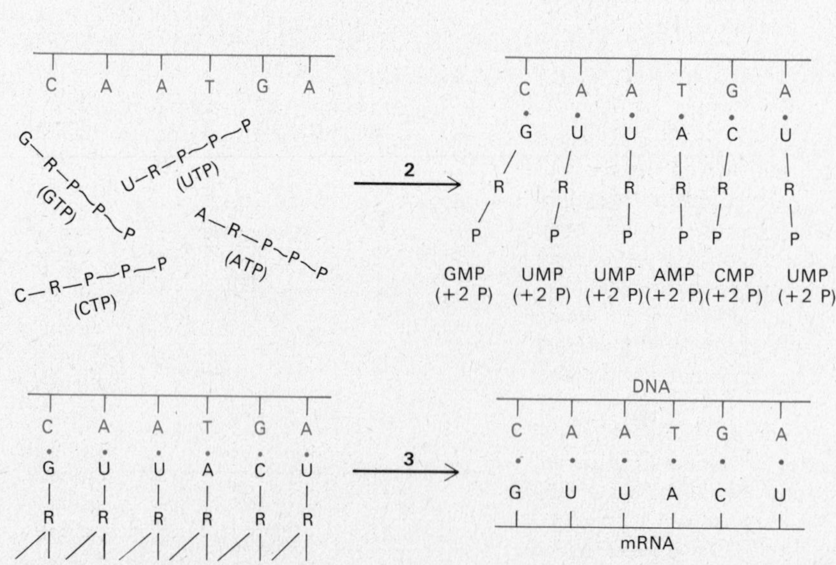

17.3 Code transcription *from DNA to mRNA. (A, T, G, C, U, purine and pyrimidine bases; R, ribose; P, phosphate.) In a first step part of the DNA double chain unzips. In the second step the nucleotide-triphosphate raw materials ATP, GTP, CTP, and UTP become bonded to appropriate nitrogen bases along a single DNA chain (color), and the two terminal phosphates of each of these raw materials split off in the process. In the third step a linked ribose-phosphate chain is formed under the influence of RNA polymerase. The finished mRNA then has a nitrogen-base sequence specifically determined by that of DNA. After mRNA becomes detached from DNA, the spiraled double chain of DNA is re-formed.*

somes, it is called *messenger* RNA, or *m*RNA. Two additional types exist in a cell. One is *ribosomal* RNA, or *r*RNA, a normal structural component of the ribosomes. This type of RNA might be derived from RNA stored in the nucleoli inside a cell nucleus, and nucleoli thus might be assembly sites for ribosomal RNA. The other type is *transfer* RNA, or *t*RNA, which functions as *amino acid carrier.* A cell contains about 60 different kinds of *t*RNA, roughly three times as many as there are different kinds of amino acid. When a particular kind of amino acid is used in protein synthesis, a corresponding kind of *t*RNA becomes attached to the amino acid and carries it to the ribosomes. Here the *t*RNA ''delivers'' its amino acid at a particular place along the *m*RNA chain already present. Other *t*RNA carriers similarly deliver their amino acids at other specific locations along the *m*RNA chain. In this manner large numbers of amino acids become lined up along *m*RNA in a particular sequence. As will become apparent presently, the nature of this sequence has been determined by the chemical message in *m*RNA. The ''correctly'' stationed amino acids then become joined to one another, and a polypeptide chain with a gene-determined specificity results (Fig. 17.2).

code transcription: DNA $\longrightarrow$ protein

We know that DNA is a spiraled double chain of nucleotides (see Figs. 4.13 and 4.14). In it, the genetic information is coded by a four-letter alphabet of nitrogen bases, and in the double chain these bases occur in four pair combinations, $A \cdot T$, $T \cdot A$, $G \cdot C$, and $C \cdot G$. The genetic code then consists of a specific succession of such pairs. If the code of a given segment of a DNA chain is to be transcribed, the first requirement is an unspiraling and ''unzipping'' of this segment of the double chain into two separate single chains. Assume that, as in Fig. 17.3, part 1, the nitrogen-base sequence *CAATGA* of one of the single chains is to be transcribed to RNA.

The first nitrogen base in the DNA sequence to be transcribed is *C,* cytosine. We know that such a base can link up through a hydrogen bond specifically with the nitrogen base *G,* guanine, and form a $C \cdot G$ pair. If therefore the available raw materials in a chromosome include a guanine-containing nucleotide, then such a molecule can bond to the *C* of DNA. The raw material actually required is GTP, guanosine triphosphate ($G—R—P{\sim}P{\sim}P$ in Fig. 17.3, part 2). In the process of bonding enzymatically to the DNA chain, the two terminal phosphates split off as byproduct, the split high-energy phosphate provides bonding energy, and the molecule that then remains attached to DNA is GMP, guanosine monophosphate ($G—R—P$ in Fig. 17.3, part 2). Quite similarly, an *A* of DNA can bond to UMP derived from a UTP (uridine triphosphate) raw material; a *T* can bond to AMP derived from ATP; and a *G* can bond to CMP derived from CTP (cytidine triphosphate). In other words, the DNA sequence serves as a *template,* or mold, along which raw material molecules can become attached in specific sequence. To form RNA it is then necessary only that the attached nucleotides become linked together as a chain (Fig. 17.3, part 3). This last process occurs not all at once but progressively, and it is catalyzed by the enzyme *RNA polymerase:*

$$(\textbf{\textit{N}}\text{-base}—\textbf{\textit{R}}—\textbf{\textit{P}}{\sim}\textbf{\textit{P}}{\sim}\textbf{\textit{P}})_x \xrightarrow{\textit{RNA polymerase}} (\textbf{\textit{P}}{\sim}\textbf{\textit{P}})_x + (\textbf{\textit{N}}\text{-base}—\textbf{\textit{R}}—\textbf{\textit{P}})_x$$

Here x symbolizes the number of ribonucleotide units linked together.

The finished RNA chain is *m*RNA, which separates from the DNA template and eventually reaches a ribosome. Note that the specific DNA code is imprinted in *m*RNA in somewhat the same way that a photographic negative shows light objects as dark areas or that a plaster cast shows elevated objects as depressions. Such ''inverted,'' negative codes in *m*RNA represent the actual working blueprints for protein synthesis.

The particular chromosome regions where *m*RNA is actually synthesized can be seen under the microscope in certain instances. For example, the salivary-gland cells of various insects contain thick giant chromosomes that consist of ordinary chromosome filaments joined together in bundles. It was first demonstrated in such giant chromosomes that *m*RNA synthesis occurs specifically in regions where the chromosomes exhibit conspicuous enlargements, or *puffs* (Fig. 17.4). The puffed regions give the impression that the DNA chains there become separated and loosened like the strands of a frayed string, as if the chains exposed themselves as fully as possible to surrounding raw materials. Puffs wax and wane at any one region, and they appear at different chromosome regions at different times and at different developmental stages of the organism. These observations suggest that not all genes of a cell are active simultaneously in *m*RNA synthesis—as indeed would be expected from what is

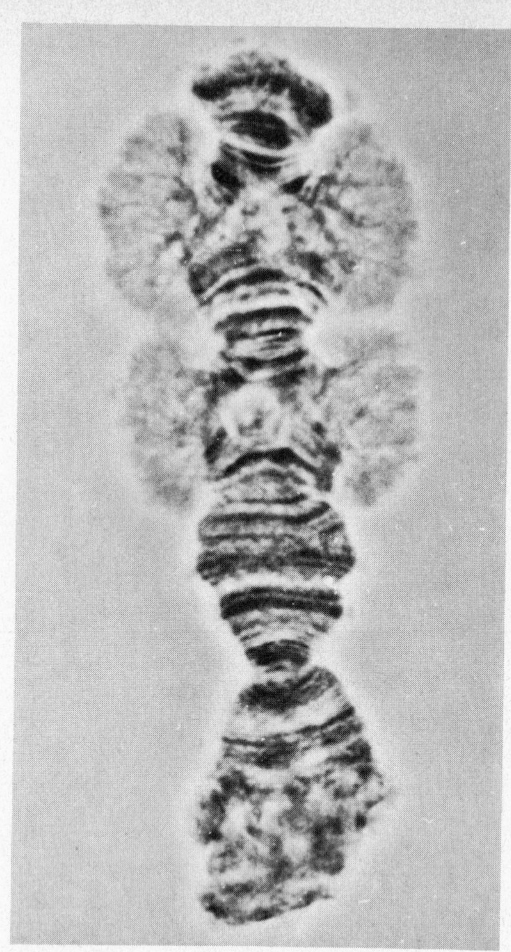

17.4 **Chromosome puffs.** *High-power view of a stained salivary gland chromosome of a midge, with conspicuous puffs in upper part of photograph.*

known about gene function (see Chaps. 18 and 27). That chromosome puffs actually do represent regions of active *m*RNA synthesis is indicated fairly conclusively by various experiments. For example, the antibiotic actinomycin is known to be a specific inhibitor of RNA synthesis—and it has also been found to inhibit the formation of puffs. Similarly, uracil is a nitrogen base that occurs specifically in RNA and is required in RNA synthesis; and if radio-labeled uracil is introduced into a cell, the compound accumulates specifically in the chromosome puffs, indicating that RNA synthesis occurs only there.

Just what does the genetic code in *m*RNA actually say? We know that it must somehow "spell out" in chemical terms an identification of the 23 different amino acids, and that it must do so with a four-letter alphabet. Assuming that nature is as concise as it can be, how are 23 different identifying "words" constructed out of four letters, such that each word contains as few letters as possible? If the code consisted of one-letter words, a four-letter alphabet *A-B-C-D* would allow only four different identifications: *A, B, C, D.* If the code were made up of two-letter words, there could be 4^2, or 16 different letter combinations: *AA, AB, AC, AD, BB, BA, BC,* etc. Yet 16 combinations are still too few to specify 23 words. However, if the code contained three-letter words, there could be 4^3, or 64 different letter combinations, more than enough to spell out 23 words (and roughly as many as there are different kinds of transfer RNA).

On the basis of such reasoning, it was hypothesized and later actually confirmed that the genetic code "names" each amino acid by a sequence of three "letters" or three adjacent nitrogen bases. In such a *triplet code,* 23 triplets would be "meaningful" and would spell out amino acid identities.

Which nitrogen-base triplets identify which amino acids? The answer has been obtained through ingenious experiments. It is possible to extract RNA polymerase from bacteria and to add to this enzyme in the test tube known nitrogen-base raw materials. In the first experiments of this kind, for example, only UTP was added. From such a reaction system could be obtained artificial RNA that consisted entirely of a sequence of uracil-containing nucleotides. To such RNA could then be added a mixture of different amino acids, and a chain of linked amino acids could be synthesized in the test tube. Analysis of these chains showed that they contained only a single kind of amino acid, *phenylalanine.* In other words, the artificial RNA "selected" only phenylalanine from the many different kinds of amino acids available and controlled the formation of a polypeptide chain that consisted of phenylalanine only. From this it could be concluded that the triplet code for phenylalanine must be *UUU.*

In later work many different kinds of artifical RNA could be prepared from various combinations of the raw materials ATP, GTP, CTP, and UTP. Such artificial RNA of known composition could then be employed as above in a search for the triplet codes of various amino acids. These searches have been successful, and the code triplets for all amino acids have been identified (Table 12). The exact sequence of the three bases in each triplet is still not clear in all cases. For example, the code triplet for aspartic acid contains *G, A,* and *U,* but it is not established as yet whether the triplet reads *GAU* or *AGU* or *GUA* or some other sequence of these three bases. Also, it has been found that certain amino acids are coded by more than a single triplet. Leucine, for example, is coded as *AUU, GUU,* and *CUU.* Because of such multiple codings the genetic code is said to be *degenerate.* A limited degree of degeneracy is of considerable adaptive advantage, for despite a change of one code letter—by mutation, for example—the meaning of the whole triplet can still be preserved.

In the sample *m*RNA in Fig. 17.3, therefore, the six-base sequence *GUUACU* consists of two consecutive triplets that could represent the code for the amino acid combination valine-histidine. How does such an *m*RNA code in the ribosomes control the formation of a valine-histidine portion of a polypeptide? To answer this we must turn our attention to *t*RNA.

The linking of an amino acid with its *t*RNA carrier in the cytoplasm represents *amino acid activation.* This process requires ATP as energy donor and a specific enzyme that attaches to the amino acid and then joins the acid to *t*RNA (Fig. 17.5). Each *t*RNA is a comparatively short nucleotide chain in which both ends of the molecule play a critical role. One end may be regarded as the "carrier" region; the amino acid becomes attached there. This carrier end consists of the nitrogen-base triplet *ACC* in all types of *t*RNA, and thus it is nonspecific; all amino acids are joined to and carried by *t*RNA in the same way. However, the other end of *t*RNA functions in amino acid "recognition;" present there is a nitrogen-base triplet that spells out a positive, DNA-like code for a particular amino acid. In the case of valine, for example, the specific *t*RNA would carry the terminal recognition triplet *CAA,* the inverse of *GUU;* and in the case of histidine, the recognition triplet would be *UGA,* the inverse of *ACU.* It is the specific enzyme in the activation reaction that "recognizes" and promotes interaction of a given amino acid and its corresponding *t*RNA. The enzyme ensures that a particular acid is combined with the "correct" type of *t*RNA. More than one type of *t*RNA can be "correct" in this sense for those amino acids that are identified by more than one triplet code.

When a *t*RNA carrier then arrives at a ribosome, the positive recognition triplet of *t*RNA will be able to bond only to a corresponding inverse code triplet along *m*RNA. Thus, as in our exam-

Table 12. Probable triplet codes for amino acids in mRNA (A, adenine; U, uracil; G, guanine; C, cytosine)

amino acid	*code triplet*
alanine	*CCG, CGU*
arginine	*CCG*
asparagine	*CAU, AAU, AAC*
aspartic acid	*GAU, CAA*
cysteine	*GUU*
glutamic acid	*GAU, GAA*
glutamine	*AAC, AGG*
glycine	*GGU*
histidine	*CAU, CAC*
isoleucine	*AUU*
leucine	*AUU, GUU, CUU*
lysine	*AAU, AAA*
methionine	*GAU*
phenylalanine	*UUU*
proline	*CCU, CCC*
serine	*CUU, CCU*
threonine	*AAC, ACC*
tryptophan	*GGU*
tyrosine	*AUU*
valine	*GUU*

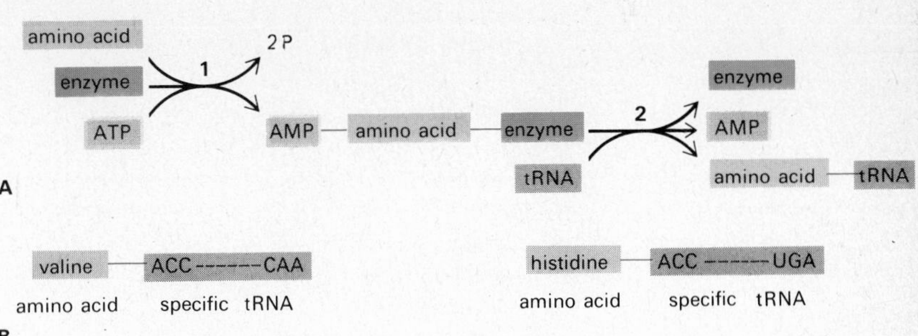

17.5 Amino acid activation. *A, joining of an amino acid and a tRNA specific for that acid. In a first step the amino acid becomes activated by linking to a specific enzyme with the aid of energy from ATP. In a second step tRNA specific for both the enzyme and the amino acid links to the acid, and the enzyme becomes free. B, each tRNA has a nonspecific carrier triplet of nitrogen bases at one end (ACC), where attachment to an amino acid is achieved. At the other end is a specific recognition triplet, CAA in the case of valine-specific tRNA, UGA in the case of histidine-specific tRNA. This triplet will attach to an appropriate nitrogen base along the messenger RNA on the ribosomes (see Fig. 17.6).*

ple, a valine-carrying *t*RNA with the recognition triplet *CAA* will be able to bond to a *GUU* triplet along *m*RNA; and a *t*RNA with the triplet *UGA* can bond to a *ACU* triplet of *m*RNA. In this way amino acids become stationed along *m*RNA in a code-determined sequence (Fig. 17.6).

The final joining of amino acids as polypeptide chains occurs through formation of *peptide bonds* between adjacent amino acids. This bonding requires the participation of energy donors such as ATP and is accomplished enzymatically by removal of one molecule of water from two amino acids (see Fig. 4.8). A finished chain of amino acids disengages step by step from its RNA connections, and then constitutes a protein or a part of a protein built according to gene-determined instructions.

Figure 17.2 may now be consulted again for a summary representation of the whole pattern of protein synthesis. In accordance with this scheme, and with extracts of RNA polymerase, *m*RNA, *t*RNA, and ribosomes from bacterial cells, it has actually been possible to synthesize in the test tube several (enzymatic) proteins that are otherwise manufactured only in living cells. But although formation of a specific primary (polypeptide) structure of a protein can now be explained, little precise knowledge is available as yet of how specific secondary, tertiary, or quaternary structures are determined. If two proteins differed, for example, in tertiary structure but not in primary structure, then the same *m*RNA would provide the code for the primary structure of both. What then governs the higher structural specificities?

Newly formed proteins become part of the structural and functional makeup of a cell. Some proteins might be incorporated in various fibrils, membranes, mitochondria, chromosomes, ribosomes, or indeed any other cellular organelle. Other proteins might, by virtue of their particular specificities, come to function as specific enzymes and thus determine at what rates the reactions in a cell can take place. Each of the many genes present in a cell controls the manufacture of a different kind of protein, and the totality of the proteins formed then determines and maintains the nature of that cell.

17.6 tRNA and mRNA. *The link-up between mRNA and the recognition ends of amino acid–carrying tRNA is shown. Adjacent amino acids then join through peptide bonding (as illustrated in Fig. 4.8).*

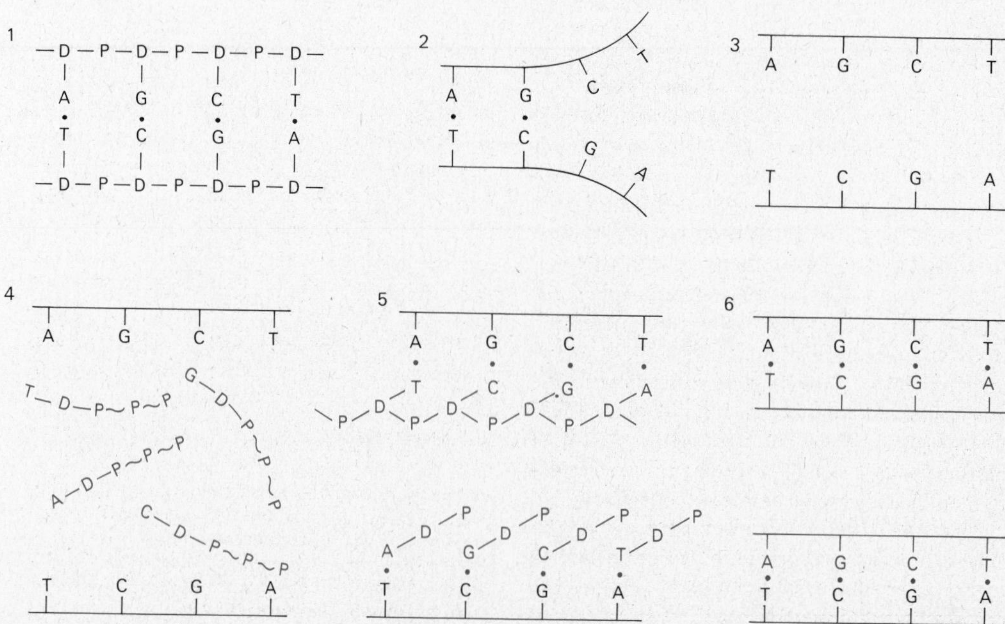

17.7 DNA duplication. *(A, G, C, T, nitrogen bases; D, deoxyribose; P, phosphate.) If a double DNA chain (1) is to be duplicated, it separates progressively (2) into two single chains (3). Nucleotide-triphosphate raw materials (4) then become attached to each free nitrogen base as monophosphates (5, top), and the deoxyribose and phosphate parts of adjacent nucleotides become joined with the aid of DNA polymerase (5, bottom). Two DNA double chains thus result (6), identical to each other as well as to the original parent chain. Note that in each newly formed double chain one single chain served as the code-specific template in the manufacture of the (colored) new single chain. In certain respects this message transcription from DNA to DNA resembles that of transcription from DNA to mRNA (compare with Fig. 17.3).*

code transcription: DNA ⟶ DNA

DNA governs not only the production of proteins but also its own synthesis. Each gene controls the manufacture of new genes exactly like it; DNA is "self"-replicating.

New formation of DNA has many features in common with message transcription from DNA to *m*RNA (Fig. 17.7). A DNA double chain first separates progressively into two single chains, and each such single portion links to itself appropriate nucleotide raw materials. In this case these are deoxyribose nucleotides (*ATP, GTP, CTP,* and *TTP* in Fig. 17.7). After attaching to appropriate places along a single DNA chain (and becoming monophosphates in the process), such nucleotides become joined together as a new chain. The enzyme *DNA polymerase* catalyzes this linking.

Evidently, DNA synthesis is equivalent to DNA *reproduction;* one double chain gives rise to two identical double chains. One of the two single chains in each "daughter" DNA has existed originally in the parent DNA, and the other single chain has been newly manufactured. In this manner the genetic information is inherited by successive DNA generations.

Replication of DNA usually takes place after more or less extended periods of cell growth. Thereafter, some—so far unknown—stimulus brings about a change in chromosome activity: DNA manufactures not only *m*RNA but also new DNA. One set of genes and chromosomes so becomes two sets. Chromosome reproduction then appears to be the trigger—again in an unknown manner—for nuclear division, which is accompanied in many cases by cell division (see Chap. 24).

Genetic DNA is among the most stable of all organic compounds. Indeed, unless it were relatively stable it would be useless as a dependable code carrier. In addition to this inherent stability several other safeguards ensure that the genetic messages of DNA are not lost or altered. One such safeguard is the nucleus itself. The evolution of distinct membrane-bounded nuclei in the early Protista actually can be regarded as an adaptation that shields genes from destructive metabolism of the cytoplasm. Another safeguard is *redundancy;* to ensure that a message is not lost or altered it can be made redundant, or repeated several times. Indeed, the genetic messages are stored in more than one place. First, the cells of many organisms ordinarily contain two complete sets of genes, one set inherited originally from the egg-producing parent, the other from the sperm-producing parent. Second, each cell type is usually represented by many like cells. Even if some cells die, therefore, the DNA of the remaining cells still contains the specific information characteristic of that cell type.

Yet despite inherent stability, protected existence, and redundancy, DNA, like any other material on earth, is subject to structural change nevertheless. As will be shown later, a variety of physical and chemical agents can affect and alter gene structure and therefore gene specificity. Often the change need not involve more than a substitution or switching of nitrogen bases at a single position in a code triplet. Such a *mutation* will be stable and will be transmitted to all duplicates of the affected DNA molecule. Protein synthesis will then be affected correspondingly, and cell traits will become altered as a result. If such cellular changes also influence the larger-scale traits of a whole organism and its progeny, as is sometimes the case, the final result after numerous generations may be an evolutionary change.

In effect, therefore, the crucial significance of genes is not simply that they are inherited. Rather, by governing the synthesis of new genes and of specific proteins, DNA plays so strategic a role that it ultimately controls the whole nature and the very life of every cell in every organism. First, since proteins make up the basic organic framework of cells, DNA determines the fundamental *structure* of every cell (including structural differences between cells and in individual cells at different times). Second, genes determine what kinds of *metabolic processes* are possible in a cell, for virtually all such processes are enzyme-dependent, hence protein-dependent, hence DNA-dependent. Third, DNA is the ultimate maintainer of *steady states,* for through its control over metabolism it also governs all control agents in cells, including DNA itself (see also Chap. 18). Fourth, by governing synthesis generally and production of new DNA specifically, DNA directs growth, development, and the *reproduction* of cells. By being exchanged among cells and pooled in cells, DNA becomes the basis of *sex* (see Chap. 24). By duplicating itself and being inherited by offspring cells, DNA becomes the basis of *heredity.* And through its property of undergoing occasional mutations, DNA becomes the key to *evolution.*

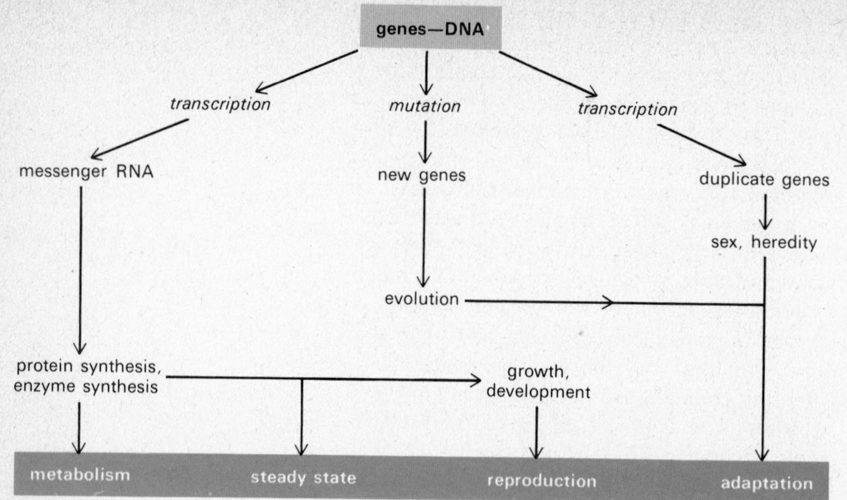

17.8 The pattern of gene action. *Through the fundamental action of transferring their coded specificities, genes control cellular metabolism and all phases of cellular self-perpetuation.*

In summary, therefore, DNA serves in just one primary role: it allows its specificities to be copied. Three indirect secondary roles emerge from this: DNA controls protein specificities; DNA controls the specificities of new DNA; and, to the extent that DNA stability is imperfect, DNA can change its specificities. Through these three secondary activities DNA then has indirect derivative effects that govern every aspect of living. For by controlling all metabolism and all self-perpetuation, DNA governs cell structure, cell function, and cell development. And by controlling the life of cells, DNA governs the life of all organisms, hence the survival of the whole living world. Genes started life, genes still continue it, and, by their failure or absence, genes ultimately end it (Fig. 17.8).

In this context it is worth noting that recent experiments with DNA and RNA have already contributed much toward an eventual test-tube synthesis of living matter. It is now possible, for example, to create in the laboratory a test-tube system in which known nucleotide raw materials give rise to nucleic acids with specific chemical information; in which such nucleic acids, together with added ATP, promote conversion of amino acids to specific proteins; and in which these proteins function enzymatically and catalyze specific chemical reactions. Such a system is still far from being alive, to be sure. But inasmuch as it metabolizes in precisely the same way as a living system, the test-tube system represents a major element of a living unit. Recall, furthermore, that starting materials like amino acids and sugars can be produced artificially from simple materials such as ammonia, methane, and water (see Chap. 8). Thus there does not appear to be any theoretical obstacle to the experimental production of a lifelike metabolizing system from the simplest inorganic starting materials.

Even more dramatic are recent experiments in which artificially prepared nucleic acids have been made to duplicate themselves in the test tube. Another procedure now feasible is the test-tube manufacture of whole artificial genes. For example, the protein insulin consists of 51 known amino acids joined in known sequence (see Fig. 4.7), and the DNA code triplets for each of these amino acids is also known. Hence it is possible to prepare artificial nucleotide triplets corresponding to those of the DNA for insulin and to link these triplets together. The result is an ''insulin gene''—a DNA chain with the exact genetic information for the control of insulin manufacture. Such a laboratory effort is now actually in progress. Capabilities of this sort pave the way for artificial creation of potentially any gene, for incorporation of such genes into cells, and thus for ''genetic engineering,'' or biochemical manipulation of traits directly at the level of the gene. Such a prospect is clearly desirable for medicine, but it can also be alarming considering the many possibilities of social misuse. In any event, we are evidently only a few steps away from being able to create test-tube systems that not only metabolize but also perpetuate themselves, even if only in limited fashion. ''Living'' units of this sort would have roughly viruslike characteristics. It is also clear, however, that experimental creation of complete living cells is still very far in the future. Nevertheless, much of the research now being conducted provides important data, often as an incidental byproduct, for a possible future laboratory synthesis of life.

The chemical metabolism of cells has now been outlined in its main features. To complete this examination of metabolism as a whole, the physical metabolism of cells is considered next.

biophysical metabolism

movement

Probably the most important and widespread physical functions of cells are those that produce movement, resulting in either locomotion of whole organisms or internal motion of parts of organisms. All such movements are ATP-dependent.

Certain nonlocomotor movements occur in all cells. Every cell moves nutrients through its boundaries, and we already know that respiratory energy is expended in the absorption of, for example, glucose. Compounds also move inside cells, partly by diffusion, partly by cyclosis. The role of ATP is less clear here, but that it plays some role, even if very indirectly, seems almost certain; for if respiration stops, cyclosis stops. Just as incompletely understood are the movements of chromosomes during cell division (see Chap. 24), the motions of flagella, cilia, and pseudopodia, and the migrations of cells or cell groups in the course of growth and embryonic development. All that can be said at present is that if ATP becomes unavailable the various movements cease.

Somewhat better known today are the events of *muscular* movement. These are among the most important in animals generally; animals carry out few functions that do not include muscular contraction. Moreover, muscles are often the most abundant tissue of an animal, particularly a vertebrate, and a proportionately large amount of energy must be expended to keep muscles operating. Even during "inactive" periods like sleep, for example, the muscular system maintains not only posture and shape but also vital functions such as breathing, heartbeat, and blood pressure. Mainly because of muscular movement the energy requirements of animals are far greater pound for pound than those of any other kind of organism.

The functional units of muscles are long, thin filaments called *myofibrils* (Fig. 17.9). Each is actually a bundle of many ultrathin, parallel strands, composed mainly of five kinds of materials: water, inorganic ions, ATP, and two proteins called *actin* and *myosin*. Together these form the basic contraction apparatus.

That this is so has been demonstrated dramatically by experiment. With appropriate procedures actin and myosin can be extracted from muscle, and it can be shown that neither actin nor myosin alone is able to contract. But by mixing actin and myosin together artificial fibers of *actomyosin* can be made. If to these are added water, inorganic ions, and ATP, it is found that the fibers contract forcefully. Such contracting fibers can lift up to 1,000 times their own weight, just as a living muscle can do. And it is also found that, in a contracted fiber, ATP is no longer present but low-energy phosphates are present instead.

Experiments of this sort provide clues as to how contraction might be brought about in a living muscle. Muscle activity appears to be at least a two-step cycle involving alternate *contraction* and *extension*. These movements are believed to be a result of a sliding of actin fibers back and forth past stationary myosin fibers (Fig. 17.10). Energy is used up at some point or points in such a cycle.

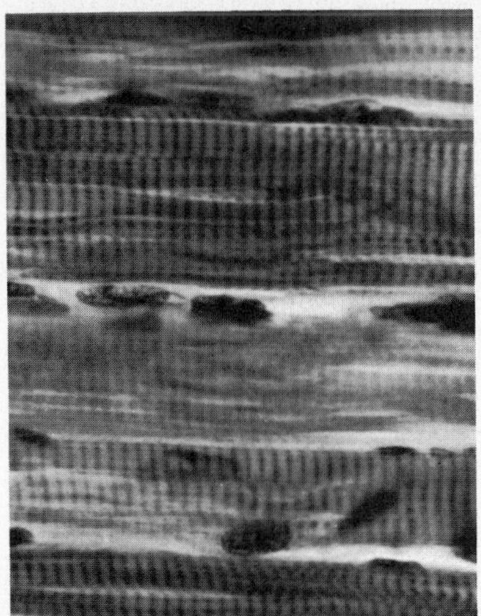

A

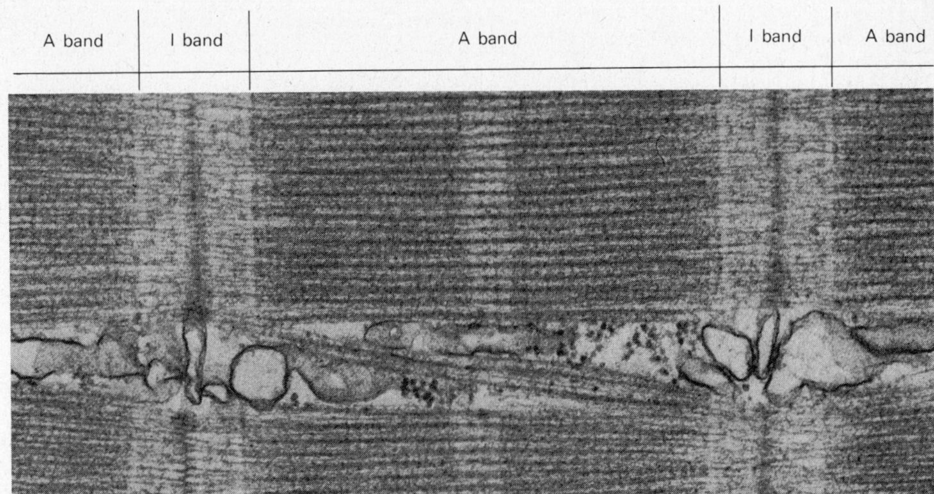

B

17.9 Skeletal muscle. *A, whole muscle fibers. Note the cross striations, the faintly visible internal longitudinal myofibrils, and the nuclei, which appear as dark patches (see also Color Fig. 1). B, electron micrograph of portions of two horizontal myofibrils (in the tail muscles of a frog tadpole), separated by a layer of cytoplasmic material (endoplasmic reticulum). The cross striations seen in A appear here as A and I bands. The distribution of myosin and actin in these bands is shown in Fig. 17.10.*

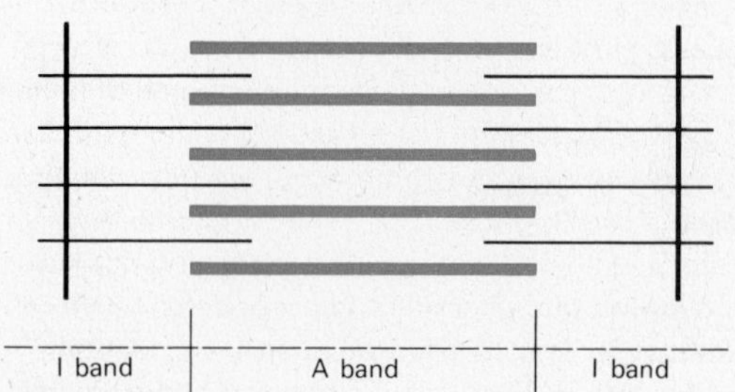

17.10 ***Muscle activity.*** *Myosin, colored bars; actin, black lines. Top, contracted state; bottom, extended state. The A band and the portions of the adjacent I bands of a muscle fiber shown here are intended to represent a working unit repeated horizontally many times in a whole fiber.*

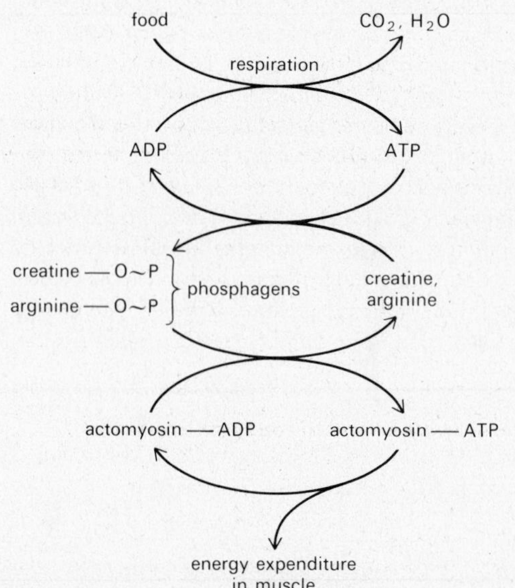

17.11 ***Energy and muscle activity.*** *Respiration supplies energy for muscles via the phosphagen stores.*

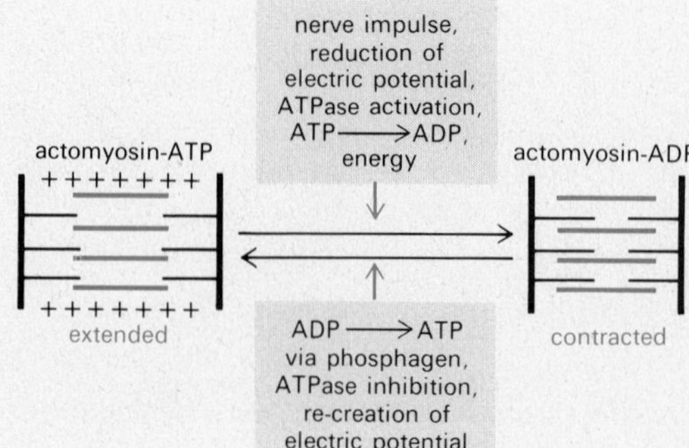

17.12 ***Unit action of muscle,*** *summary of probable events. Processes associated with contraction are listed in the box above the horizontal arrows; processes associated with extension, in the box below the arrows.*

One view is that the energy makes possible the contraction of a muscle, like compressing a spring. Extension then is thought to be essentially an automatic recoil. According to an alternative view, energy must be expended to extend a muscle, as in stretching a rubber band. Contraction would then be automatic. A good deal of evidence appears to favor this second hypothesis, but the first cannot be ruled out. Indeed there are strong indications that muscle could require energy for contraction as well as for extension.

The energy donor in muscle activity is ATP, which, together with actin and myosin, forms a so-called *actomyosin-ATP complex.* During a contraction-extension cycle, the ATP of actomyosin-ATP gives up its energy. To prepare a muscle for a new contraction-extension cycle new energy must be supplied. The characteristic fuel of muscle is glyocgen, and respiration of glycogen is the ultimate source of muscle energy. But glycogen breakdown is not the immediate source; it is far too slow to supply the ATP required by an active muscle. A glycogen molecule can be respired within a second, but in that second the wing muscle of an insect can contract up to 100 times and use up energy far faster than could be supplied directly by fuel oxidation.

Unlike most cells, muscles contain compounds other than ATP that can store relatively large amounts of energy in high-energy phosphate bonds. Among such compounds is, for example, *creatine,* a nitrogen-containing substance found in the muscles of most vertebrates and some invertebrates. The role of creatine can be described as follows:

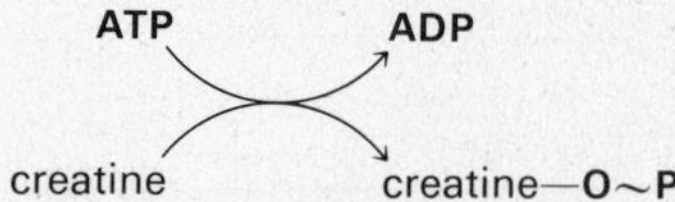

In other words, creatine can accept —O~P from ATP and become creatine-phosphate. Compounds of this type carrying high-energy phosphates are also known as *phosphagens.* The amino acid *arginine* is another of several kinds of compounds that, like creatine, serve as phosphagens in various animals.

Thus, if during rest fuels supply more —O~P than can be harvested as ATP, then ATP "unloads" —O~P to phosphagens and becomes ADP. Phosphagens accumulate in this manner. When a muscle later becomes active and must be reenergized rapidly, the immediate energy source for such "recharging" is the phosphagens.

They give up their —O∼P and are later reenergized themselves by respiration. Respiratory ATP therefore replenishes the phosphagen stores slowly, and these re-create actomyosin-ATP rapidly while a muscle is active (Fig. 17.11).

The specific trigger for the contraction of a muscle is a nerve impulse. Also, it is known that inorganic ions, notably Mg^{++} and Ca^{++}, are attached to or in some other way associated with the actomyosin-ATP complex. By virtue of such positive charges the complex has an electric potential over its surface; and one of the known effects of nerve impulses is to bring about a reduction of electric potentials (see Chap. 21). Like several other tissues, furthermore, muscles contain ATPases, enzymes that promote conversion of ATP to ADP. Muscle ATPase either is identical with myosin itself or is so closely linked with myosin that available techniques are unable to separate the two. In effect, the actomyosin-ATP complex contains not only built-in potential energy in the form of ATP but also the necessary built-in enzyme that can make this energy available. The enzyme remains inhibited in some unknown way before arrival of a nerve impulse; directly or indirectly, the impulse appears to be the necessary stimulus for activation of ATPase.

These considerations provide clues to the sequence of events that might occur during muscle action (Fig. 17.12). At first the actin and myosin components of actomyosin-ATP would be stretched apart and the muscle would be extended. Such a condition might be maintained by the electric charges; since like charges repel each other, contraction of the actomyosin-ATP complex would be prevented by electric repulsion of actin and myosin. But when a nerve impulse arrives, it would reduce the electric potentials and thereby remove the obstacle to contraction. The nerve impulse would also activate the ATPase, ATP would be split, and the potential energy of actomyosin-ATP would become actual. As noted, it is still not clear whether this energy brings about contraction or reextension after contraction. In either event new potential energy is supplied thereafter by phosphagen. In some way reextension of muscle must also be associated with rebuilding of electric potentials, sliding apart of the actin and myosin components, and inhibition of ATPase.

Whatever the actual details of the action cycle may eventually prove to be, cycles of this sort clearly take place fast enough to propel a cheetah, for example, at speeds of 50 mph; and they are powerful enough to permit many animals to lift objects weighing more than the animals themselves.

heat, light, electricity

One source of cellular heat is the external environment, which supplies heat in varying amounts. Another, most important source is food. As shown in Chap. 15, respiration yields up to 60 percent of the energy content of foods directly as heat. A third heat source is phosphorylation; when ATP is used as a donor of low-energy phosphates, any excess energy of —O∼P becomes heat. Still another internal heat source is ATP-energized movement, for friction of moving parts generates heat. Moreover, conversion of chemical energy of ATP to mechanical energy of motion is not 100 percent efficient and is accompanied by a loss of energy in the form of heat. Whatever its source, heat maintains the temperature of an organism and offsets heat lost to the environment by evaporation and radiation. Heat also creates tiny convection currents in cells and thereby assists in diffusion and cyclosis. Above all, heat provides adequate operating temperatures for enzymes and all other functional parts of cells (Fig. 17.13).

In birds and mammals heat production is balanced dynamically against heat loss, and in these "warm-blooded" (or *homoiothermic*) animals a

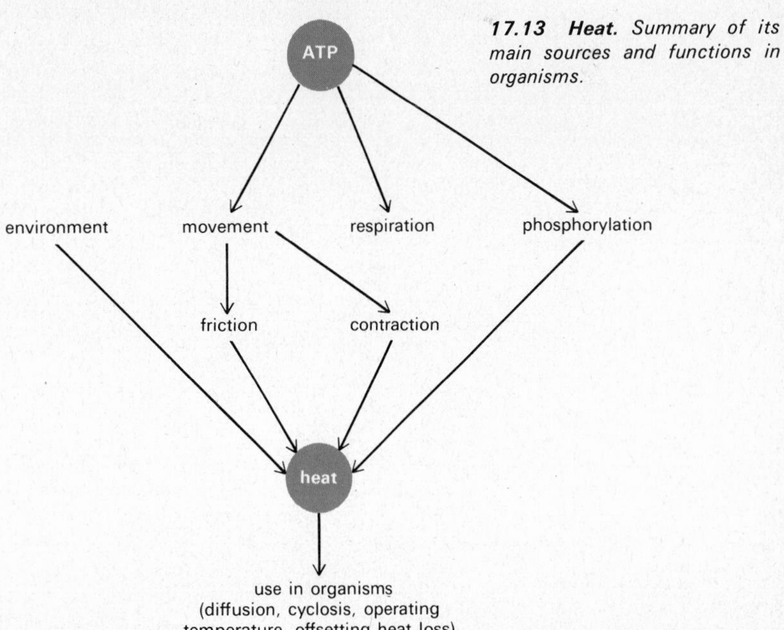

17.13 ***Heat.*** *Summary of its main sources and functions in organisms.*

constant body temperature is thereby maintained. In all other animals, and in other organisms generally, the internal temperature by and large matches that of the external. (Animals of this type are *poikilothermic* and are sometimes referred to as being "cold-blooded"—a poor term since the blood could be hot or cold and since many of these animals lack blood to begin with.) Such organisms cannot survive if the environment is either too cold or too hot. But within these extremes food combustion and ATP create internal heat that to some extent counteracts low external temperatures; and the cooling effect of evaporation reduces internal heat and thereby counteracts high external temperatures.

17.14 Bioluminescence. *A, the pattern of light production in organisms. B, test-tube culture of bioluminescent bacteria. The continuous light they emit is strong enough to illuminate printed words. (B, courtesy Carolina Biological Supply Company.)*

Light can be emitted by some subgroups of virtually all major groups of organisms; most moneran, protistan, and metazoan phyla include marine or terrestrial representatives that are bioluminescent. In all these forms the main components of the light-generating mechanism are two substances called *luciferin* and *luciferase.* They can be extracted from light-producing cells, and they are nonluminous on their own. If ATP is added to luciferin, a luciferin-ATP complex is formed. And if in the presence of oxygen a solution of the enzyme luciferase is now added, the mixture emits light. This light soon disappears, but if then more oxygen and more ATP are added, light is generated again. Light production evidently is an oxygen-requiring, ATP-dependent process (Fig. 17.14).

Bioluminescent organisms emit light either continuously or in intermittent flashes. Light emission in animals depends on nervous stimulation of specialized cells in light-producing organs. The light generated by different organisms can be red, yellow, green, or blue. The actual color of the light is probably determined by the particular chemical makeup of luciferin. Some organisms contain two or more kinds of luciferin and can light up in several colors. Little heat is lost during light production, hence living light is often designated as "cold" light. Also, the intensity of the light is remarkably high; it compares favorably with that of modern fluorescent lamps.

Bioelectricity is a byproduct of all processes in which ions play a part—in other words, virtually all cellular processes. A highly specialized capacity to produce electricity has evolved in certain eels and rays, which have *electric organs* composed mainly of modified muscles. Production of electricity in such organs depends on ATP and a substance called *acetylcholine.* Electricity is generated when acetycholine splits into separate acetyl and choline fractions. The two then recombine as acetycholine with energy from ATP. An electric eel can deliver a shock of up to 400 volts, enough to kill another fish or to jolt a man severely or to light up a row of electric bulbs wired

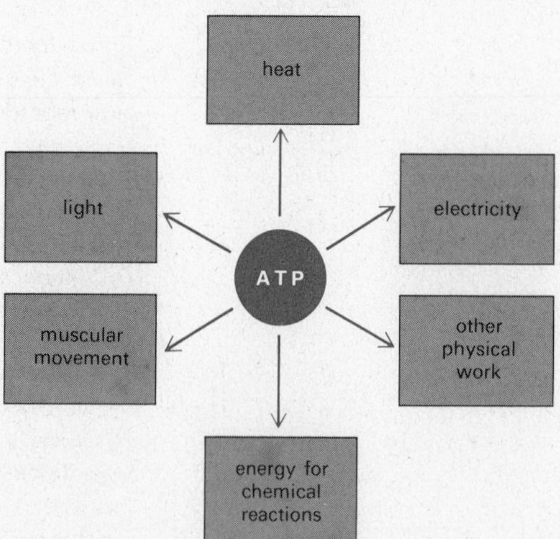

17.15 ATP functions, *summary.*

to the tank that contains the eel. Nervous stimulation of the electric organ triggers the production of electricity.

It is still unknown just how the chemical energy of ATP is actually converted to light or electric energy. But that ATP is the key is clearly established, and this versatile compound thus emerges as the source of all forms of living energy, chemical as well as physical (Fig. 17.15).

metabolic maintenance

The total metabolic effort of a cell can be considered to serve two general functions. One is *interior maintenance,* or activities promoting chiefly the survival of the cell in which the activities take place. Among physical activities here are, for example, heat generation and internal motions. Chemical activities consist of procurement of substances required for survival and putting such substances to use. Collectively all such processes of interior maintenance counteract normal decomposition and wear and tear, make possible the replacement of cellular parts after injury, and permit a cell to grow and reproduce.

The other general function is *exterior maintenance,* or processes contributing chiefly to the survival of other cells or of the organism as a whole. On a physical level, for example, the contraction of a muscle cell is often far less significant for the survival of that cell itself than for the survival of the entire organism. On a chemical level, every cell exports compounds that it produces but that often are waste in its own metabolism—CO_2 or H_2O, for example. Yet what is waste for one cell well might be an essential metabolite in another.

Moreover, many cells manufacture more or less special substances that are exported and that in many cases play special roles in other cells or regions of an organism. For example, such secretions can be *nutritive,* like glucose exported from photosynthetic cells; or *digestive,* like enzymes secreted in alimentary systems; or *supportive,* like cellulose secreted by plant cells or bone substance by animal cells; or *reproductive,* like certain scents secreted by many plants and animals; or *protective,* like irritants and poisons produced by plant and animal cells (including also secreted antibiotics formed by microorganisms). Actually there is hardly any function in any organism in which secretions exported from some cell or cells do not play a role.

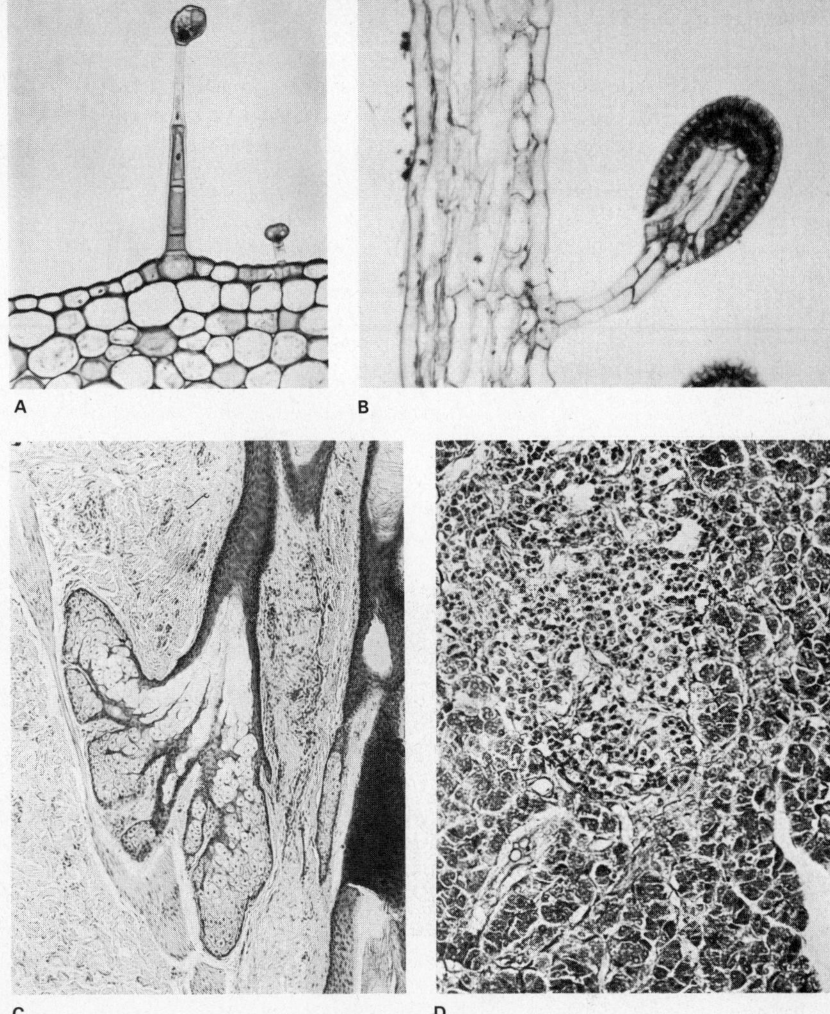

***17.16* Glands.** *A, B, glandular hairs on the surfaces of plants. C, section through a sebaceous gland of man. This is one of the exocrine glands, all of which secrete to a duct or a space. Sebaceous glands occur along hair shafts, and the oily secretion keeps a hair soft and pliable. D, section through mammalian pancreas showing an islet of Langerhans (light-colored tissue). This is one of the hormone-producing endocrine glands, all of which secrete to the blood. The islets produce the hormone insulin. (D, courtesy Carolina Biological Supply Company.)*

Any cell or group of cells *specialized* for the manufacture of secretions can be called a *gland* (Fig. 17.16). Thus, cells are not usually regarded as glands if they merely export water or salts as part of their regular housekeeping metabolism; *all* cells actually carry out such exports. By contrast, the actively water-secreting hydathodes that in some plants are responsible for guttation are distinctly glandular, since these cells are specialized for that function (see Chap. 14, Fig. 14.7). Similarly, certain plants living in salty soil contain distinct salt-secreting glands in the roots. Glands among plants also include, for example, cells in leaves of carnivorous plants that secrete digestive juices; temporary hairs in the young buds of many woody plants that secrete gummy substances for

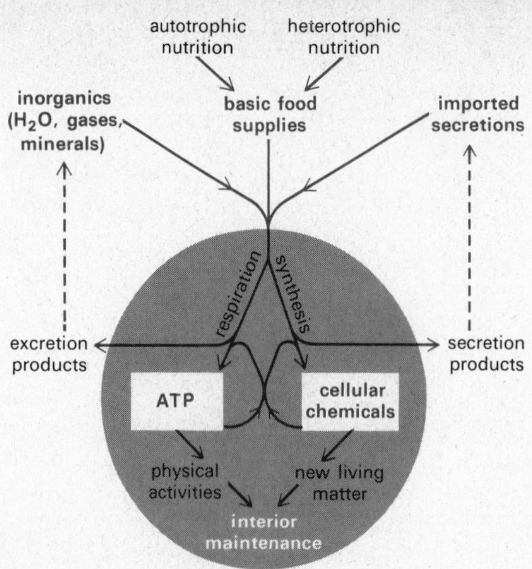

*17.17 **Metabolism,** overall summary of the main processes.*

bud protection during the winter; and numerous others that in particular plants serve particular functions.

Among animals glands are largely of two general types. So-called *exocrine* glands empty their secretions into ducts or free spaces. Included in this category are all the digestive glands already discussed (liver, pancreas, salivary glands); skin glands (sweat-, oil-, and wax-secreting glands); and numerous others associated with reproductive, excretory, and other systems. The second category comprises the *endocrine* glands, which are ductless and secrete into the blood. The characteristic products of these glands are *hormones* (see Fig. 17.16 and Chap. 19).

In summary, therefore, a cell obtains the materials it requires in three general ways. Some components, like water, mineral ions, and in animal cells also a number of organic materials, must come in prefabricated final form from the external environment. Some others, like hormones, must come as prefabricated secretions from other cells in the organism. And all other materials must be synthesized from foods inside the cell itself. Collectively these various chemicals then maintain the body of a cell (Fig. 17.17).

But it must not be imagined that this multitude of ingredients just happens to arrange itself as new living substance. A mere random mixture of such ingredients would only form a complex but lifeless soup. As has long been appreciated, *omnis cellula e cellula*—all cells arise from preexisting cells; new life must arise from preexisting life. New components become living matter only if already existing living matter provides a framework. The house can be added to and its parts can be replaced or modified, but an altogether new house cannot be built. That apparently occurred only once during the history of the earth, when living matter arose originally.

How then can metabolism continue as an ordered, properly functioning series of events rather than as a mere jumble of random activities? The answer is *self-perpetuation:* processes that control, integrate, and coordinate metabolic reactions and thereby convert the merely active system to a living one.

review questions

1 Review the chemical structure of DNA. Review also the structure of RNA and distinguish between *m*RNA, *r*RNA, and *t*RNA. Where in a cell do each of these occur, and what are their functions?

2 What is the genetic code, what are code triplets, and on the basis of what reasoning has a triplet code been postulated for amino acid specification?

3 In what sense is the genetic code "degenerate," and what are the functional consequences of this degeneracy? Describe the mechanism of amino acid activation. How do amino acids along *m*RNA become polypeptides?

4 What is the function of RNA polymerase? What are the raw materials in RNA synthesis? What are chromosome puffs, and what is their apparent significance?

5 How does DNA synthesis take place? What is the role of DNA polymerase? What are mutations, and what are their general effects in a cell? What kind of change qualifies as a mutation?

6 How is the stability of genes safeguarded? What is the importance of gene stability? What is the effect of alterations in gene structure? In what way is genetic information redundant?

7 Review the pattern of gene function as a whole. Which function may be regarded as primary? Which indirect secondary functions derive from this, and which tertiary functions result from the secondary ones in turn?

8 Show how DNA controls all aspects of metabolism and self-perpetuation. Describe the general sequence of the processes that would have to occur in the test tube if a specific, catalytically active enzyme were to be synthesized from inorganic starting materials such as water, ammonia, and methane.

9 Describe the internal fine structure of a muscle cell. What and where is actomyosin? What are the roles of ATP in muscle?

10 In what specific ways is the ATP supply of muscle maintained? Describe the energetics of a unit cycle of muscle activity.

11 Describe the nervous, chemical, mechanical, and electrical events which, according to current hypotheses, could occur during a unit cycle of muscle activity.

12 What different kinds of movements occur in organisms and their cells? What is known about the role of energy in these movements?

13 In what ways does an organism obtain and produce heat? What are the functions of heat in metabolism? How do organisms produce light?

14 How do the properties of light produced by organisms compare with those of light from nonliving sources? How and by what organisms is bioelectricity produced?

15 Name cellular activities that serve in internal and external maintenance. What is a gland, and what roles can glandular secretions play? Review the various ways by which a cell obtains all the ingredients it requires for its survival.

collateral readings

Allfrey, V. G., and **A. E. Mirsky:** How Cells Make Molecules, *Sci. American,* Sept., 1961. The role of DNA in protein synthesis is discussed.

Barry, J. M.: "Genes and the Chemical Control of Living Cells," Prentice-Hall, Englewood Cliffs, N.J., 1964. A recommended paperback, covering all aspects of DNA structure and function and the subject of protein synthesis.

Beerman, W., and **U. Clever:** Chromosome Puffs, *Sci. American,* Apr., 1964. Regional enlargements in giant insect chromosomes probably represent the places were code transcription from DNA to *m*RNA actually occurs.

Clark, B. F. C., and **K. A. Marcker:** How Proteins Start, *Sci. American,* Jan., 1968. On the initiation of polypeptide synthesis.

Crick, F. H. C.: The Genetic Code, *Sci. American,* Oct., 1962. A review of the triplet code by one of the discoverers of DNA structure; see also the later article by Nirenberg cited below.

———: The Genetic Code: III, *Sci. American,* Oct., 1966. A sequel to the earlier article.

Dawkins, M. J. R., and **D. Hull:** The Production of Heat by Fat, *Sci. American,* Aug., 1965. A discussion of heat generation by respiration of various fat deposits in young and hibernating animals.

Fraenkel-Conrat, H.: The Genetic Code of a Virus, *Sci. American,* Oct., 1964. Experimental changes in virus nucleic acids show how protein synthesis might be controlled.

Gamov, G.: Information Transfer in the Living Cell, *Sci. American,* Oct., 1955. The arithmetic from which the nature of the genetic code has been predicted is discussed in this article.

Gorin, L.: Antibiotics and the Genetic Code, *Sci. American,* Apr., 1966. Streptomycin and other drugs can change the genetic code and alter the structure of ribosomes.

Hanawalt, P. C., and **R. H. Haynes:** The Repair of DNA, *Sci. American,* Feb., 1967. The article describes repair processes that restore the integrity of bacterial DNA.

Hayashi, T.: How Cells Move, *Sci. American,* Sept., 1961. The molecular basis of flagellar, amoeboid, and muscular motion is discussed.

Holley, R. W.: The Nucleotide Sequence of a Nucleic Acid, *Sci. American,* Feb., 1966. The first determination of the genetic code of a whole protein is described.

Hurwitz, J., and **J. J. Furth**: Messenger RNA, *Sci. American,* Feb., 1962. A good discussion of the role of this type of RNA. See also the article by Rich, below.

Huxley, H. E.: The Mechanism of Muscular Contraction, *Sci. American,* Dec., 1965. A good review of the fine structure of muscle cells and the function of their operating units.

Ingram, V. M.: How Do Genes Act? *Sci. American,* Jan., 1958. A disease of man resulting from a mutation of a single amino acid in hemoglobin is analyzed.

Kornberg, A.: The Synthesis of DNA, *Sci. American,* Oct., 1968. The test-tube synthesis of artificial but active DNA is described by the Nobel-prize-winning investigator who first achieved such a synthesis.

McElroy, W. D., and **H. H. Seliger**: Biological Luminescence, *Sci. American,* Dec., 1962. A comprehensive review of bioluminescence in various organisms and of the chemistry of the process.

Mirsky, A. E.: The Discovery of DNA, *Sci. American,* June, 1968. A review of the 100-year old history of research on nucleic acids.

Nirenberg, M. W.: The Genetic Code: II, *Sci. American,* March, 1963. Experiments that have uncovered the nature of the triplet code are described by one of the Nobel-prize-winning investigators in the field; a sequel to Crick's first article cited above.

Porter, K. R., and **C. Franzini-Armstrong**: The Sarcoplasmic Reticulum, *Sci. American,* March, 1965. The ultrastructure of muscle is examined by means of high-resolution electron microscopy.

Rich, A.: Polyribosomes, *Sci. American,* Dec., 1963. An analysis of the role of ribosomes in protein synthesis.

Sinsheimer, R. L.: Single-stranded DNA, *Sci. American,* July, 1962. The discovery of DNA consisting of only one nucleotide chain helps to clarify the duplication mechanism of this nucleic acid.

Spiegelman, S. L.: Hybrid Nucleic Acids, *Sci. American,* May, 1964. Experiments with DNA composed of two different but complementary nucleotide chains throw light on information transfer in cells.

Stahl, F. W.: "The Mechanics of Inheritance," Prentice-Hall, Englewood Cliffs, N.J., 1964. This paperback includes a very detailed account of the structure and function of nucleic acids and of protein synthesis. Recommended.

Taylor, J. H.: The Duplication of Chromosomes, *Sci. American,* June, 1958. A description of experiments with radio-labeled chromosomes showing that one of the two strands of just-formed DNA preexisted and that the other strand was newly manufactured.

Watson, J. D.: "The Molecular Biology of the Gene," Benjamin, New York, 1965. A paperback on the nature of the gene and its role in protein synthesis. Strongly recommended.

Yanofsky, C.: Gene Structure and Protein Structure, *Sci. American,* May, 1967. An interesting review of how the correspondence between the genetic code and the amino acid sequence in polypeptides was demonstrated.

part 6
steady states

part 6
steady states

chapter 18
cellular control

chapter 19
hormonal control

chapter 20
intercellular control

chapter 21
nervous control

chapter 22
behavioral control: the individual

chapter 23
behavioral control: the society

We recall that self-perpetuation comprises, first, processes that maintain the steady state *of living units and adjust and coordinate their internal operations; second, processes of* reproduction, *which extend the operations of living units in space and in time; and third, processes of* adaptation, *which mold and fit the long-term characteristics of living units to the characteristics of specific environments.*

All three of these functions are carried out on all levels of the living hierarchy. However, cellular *steady states are the foundation of all steady states and indeed also of self-perpetuation as a whole. Accordingly, this part begins with an examination of the nature of control functions generally and of cellular controls specifically. The steady-state controls of higher organizational levels are considered thereafter.*

chapter 18 cellular control

The general function of all control activities in an organism is to maintain adequate, and as far as possible *optimal*, operating conditions despite changes in the internal and external environment. The net result of control is steady state and, through this, maintenance of life for the longest possible time.

All control devices of living matter operate according to the same fundamental principles. This common *pattern of control* is the subject of the first part of the chapter. The following parts deal with the specific control operations on the cellular level, particularly those performed by *genes, enzymes,* and *vitamins.*

the pattern

Any condition that tends to upset the smooth operations of a system can be regarded as a *stress.* In a living organism stresses are often produced by the environment—enemies, injurious agents, lack of food, change of temperature, and innumerable other physical, chemical, and biological conditions. Internally, stresses arise continuously as a result of the very processes of life—nutrients are used up, concentrations change, parts age and wear out, waste products accumulate. Any change affecting living matter is also a more or less significant stress, and the living system actually is under stress all the time.

The problem of maintaining a steady state, therefore, is to counteract or to relieve stress. Doing so requires, first, ability to *recognize* stress, and second, ability to *react* to stress in self-preserving fashion. Thus if a system can recognize a *stimulus* and can carry out an appropriate *response* to that stimulus, it exercises *control.* And it can then remain intact and functioning despite stresses that would otherwise upset its operations.

control operations

To achieve control a first fundamental requirement is continuous flow of *information* among the parts of a system. Each part must receive signals about the action of other parts, and if a stimulus affects one part, other parts must receive appropriate information about it. Moreover, if the system is capable of responding to a stimulus in more than one way, a second requirement is ability to make *selections.* A simple system that always gives the same response is not required to select. But where several response possibilities exist ability to decide among them is crucial, for choice of inappropriate responses leads to unsteady, not steady, states (Fig. 18.1).

The terms information and selection imply messages or signals of some sort, message carriers, senders, receivers, transmission pathways, relays, switches, channel selectors—in short, all the components of a communications system. Indeed, in one form or another communications systems are found wherever biological steady states are maintained; we find them in cells and between cells, in organisms and between organisms, on all levels of organization. Such systems are control systems.

Living control systems largely operate on a common pattern. An initial stimulus irritates, or *excites,* a receiving device, called a *receptor.* Excitation of this receptor causes the emission of a signal, which is transmitted over a *sensory pathway* to an "interpreting" and response-selecting device. Such a device can be referred to generally as a *modulator.* This component sends out an appropriately chosen command signal over an appropriately chosen *motor pathway.* The signal leads to an *effector,* a device that executes the commands and thereby produces a response to the original stimulus (Fig. 18.2).

The operation of such a system can be illustrated by means of a physical model. Suppose that the water level of a flow tank, as in Fig. 18.3, is to be maintained in steady state; despite possible variations of inflow or outflow the water level is to stay at a predetermined height. This objective can be fulfilled through an automatic regulating device such as that sketched in Fig. 18.3. An air-filled float *R* here is comparable to a receptor; as it moves up or down with the water, it "senses" changes of water level. Any up or down motion of *R* is communicated by a rod *sp,* the "sensory pathway," to the modulator *M.* Here the up or down motion of *sp* is "interpreted" and appropriate commands for response are sent out. Imagine *M* to be so built that any change in the position of *sp* trips electric switches and that each switch causes the flow of an electric current of different characteristics. These electrical impulses are the command signals transmitted over the motor pathways *mp* to the two effectors *E.* The effectors are engines that operate the valves at the inflow and the outflow; at each command signal the valves are moved to a particular position.

Imagine now that for some external reason the

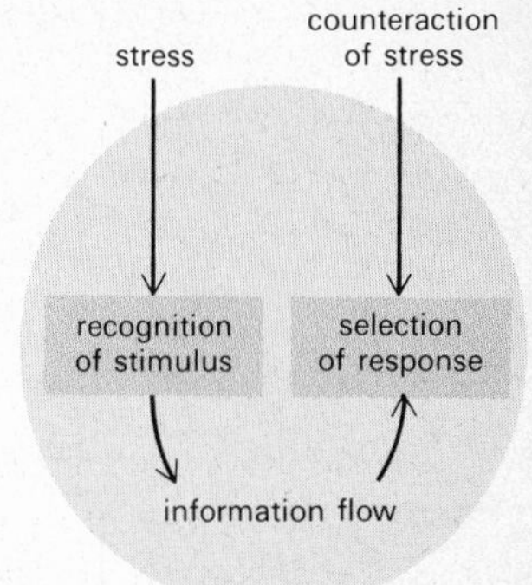

18.1 Steady state: *the general pattern of maintenance and control.*

stimulus
receptor → sensory pathway → modulator → motor pathway → effector
response

18.2 ***Control components*** *in living matter.*

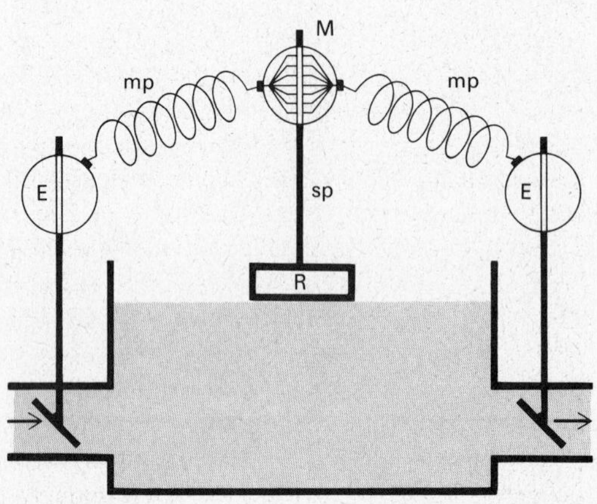

18.3 ***Steady-state maintenance.*** (*R, receptor; M, modulator; E, effector; sp, sensory pathway; mp, motor pathway.*) *If this model is adjusted as described in the text, then any change of inflow or outflow will bring about signals through $R \rightarrow sp \rightarrow M \rightarrow mp \rightarrow E$. Valve positions will then be adjusted so that the valves will counteract the change of inflow or outflow and reestablish the original water level in the tank.*

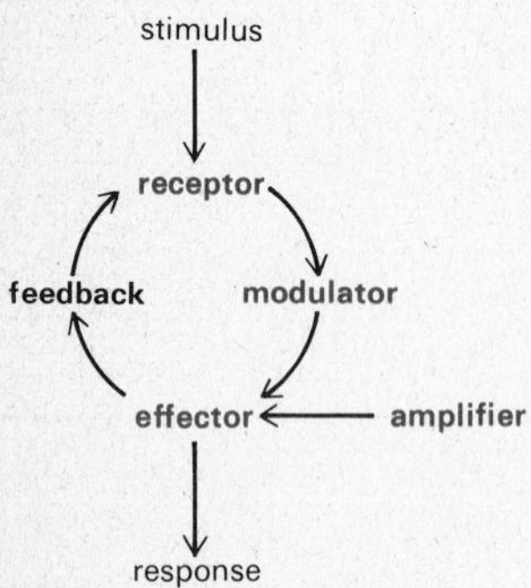

18.4 ***Feedback.*** *The role of feedback in a control cycle is shown. An amplifier provides energy for powerful effector action. ATP serves as amplifier in living control systems.*

water inflow decreases. The water level will begin to drop, but at once the modulator *M* will be informed of this change through *R* and *sp.* Appropriate electric signals will therefore go to the effectors and the inflow valve will open more, the outflow valve close more. As a result, before the water level can drop very far, the net inflow will increase and the water will rise back to normal. This new change of level will again be communicated to the modulator; new signals will go out to the effectors; and the valves will be returned to their original positions. If at this point the inflow is still reduced, the control device will go into action once more, precisely as above. Clearly, by readjusting as often as necessary the device is capable of maintaining a steady state despite changes in the ''environment.''

This model illustrates a number of general features common to control systems, living ones included. First, internal *operating energy* is needed to make the system work. In the model energy is required for the transmission of electric signals and for the motors that move the valves. In living control systems, similarly, small amounts of energy are needed for the transmission of information and comparatively large amounts of energy are required to operate the effectors. All this energy must be supplied by respiration and ATP.

A second common feature of many control devices is that response to a stimulus often is not a sudden, single event, but a stepwise, repeated one. In the model, a small initial change in valve position produces a small initial change in water level. The receptor immediately signals to the modulator that a certain adjustment has been carried out. Accordingly, the modulator then cues the effectors to continue, to stop, or to reverse operations. The resulting effector action is essentially a new stimulus, which again is communicated back through the receptor to the modulator. In this manner continuous information passes from sensory to motor component and from motor back to sensory component. Many such cyclical passages of information, each contributing a small effector action, are usually required before a total response to a stimulus can be achieved. Indeed the regulating device is not at rest even then. For in the absence of environmental stimuli the receptor is stationary, and this absence of motion in effect is equivalent to the signal ''no change.'' The modulator then sends ''no adjustment required'' to the effector, and the effector in turn informs the receptor of ''no operation.''

In such unceasing cyclical passages of information, a response is ''fed back'' to the sensory end of the regulating device as a new stimulus (Fig. 18.4). Such *feedback* is an important element in the operation of a control system; for without feedback the modulator would not become informed about the action of the effector and it would not be able to send out ''correct'' new commands.

Feedbacks and continuous cycles of information account for a third property of many control systems; they function essentially by *trial and error,* by ''hunting'' for the correct equilibrium condition. Refer again to the model. If the water level begins to drop, a few seconds might elapse before the valves are brought to corrective positions. By that time the water level could already be below the correct level. The water then begins to rise, but again there will be a time lag before the effectors return the valves to normal. By that time the water could already have risen somewhat above the correct level. New signals to reverse valve positions a bit will therefore go out, and by the time that action is executed the water could again be below the appropriate level.

Many controls *overshoot* in this fashion, and they undergo hunting oscillations to either side of an equilibrium state. Poorly adjusted controls often produce hunting oscillations that do not subside but increase, in which case "steady" states of course will not be maintained. Good examples are the often erratic paths of organisms that move from dark to light regions or vice versa, or in general from unsuitable to more suitable environments. Such organisms tend to "tack" first to one side, then to the other, in irregular paths. Their internal controls make these organisms "hunt" for regions of progressively greater suitability, in trial-and-error fashion.

A fourth general property of control systems is that they have inherent limits of efficiency. If they are overloaded they must work too fast or too hard, and they can then make *errors* in sensing stimuli or in "interpreting" signals or in selecting and executing responses. Extreme overloading can also cause structural breakdowns. In living organisms such functional or structural failures of control systems result in *disease.* Disease itself is a stress stimulus to other, still intact regulating devices, and repair or circumvention of the diseased condition may follow.

control systems

The regulating devices of living matter form a hierarchy paralleling that of the organizational levels. Molecules and organelles make up the control systems of cells, whole cells are the control components of tissues, tissues in turn form the control apparatus of organs, and so on.

In cells, certain organelles serve as control components by virtue of their other functions. For example, pigment-containing bodies such as chloroplasts or eyespots absorb light and this property makes the organelles receptors of light stimuli. Surface hairs or long internal fibrils are sensitive to displacement and pressure and thus can serve as receptors of mechanical stimuli. Mitochondria, storage granules, and other organelles are sensitive to various classes of chemicals and can therefore function as chemoreceptors.

Modulatorlike organelles are exemplified by, for example, the nucleus, which through its genes directs protein synthesis; and among effectors are motion-producing kinetosomes and flagella as well as Golgi bodies and other organelles that manufacture particular products. Most organelles actually have *multiple* regulating functions. For example, the cell surface can be regarded as a receptor when it distinguishes between two or more different molecules, but as an effector when it allows some of these molecules to pass through. Apart from being a modulator the nucleus is also a receptor, for it receives numerous chemical stimuli from the cytoplasm; and it is an effector as well, for it executes many responses. In short, organelles can serve like receptors in certain instances, like modulators in others, and like effectors in still others. Their roles as control components are as varied as their functioning.

The cellular level is the lowest on which modulators are capable of *selecting* among various possible responses. For example, the cell surface is *selectively* permeable. Functioning as a modulator it can "interpret" the chemical nature of different kinds of molecules in contact with it, and it can "decide" how fast and to what extent each such molecule is to be passed through. Similar selectivity is displayed by other complex control components in a cell, and also by all control systems above the cell level. This crucial capacity of "making decisions" probably results from the circumstance that every organelle contains many different *molecular* control systems, each capable of a single response. Therefore, the number of decisions a complex modulator can make is perhaps related to the number of different molecular unit systems that compose it.

The control activities in a cell collectively form important elements of control on higher levels. Thus if a cell as a whole functions as receptor, its response can represent a sensory signal on the tissue level. Or the cell could serve as modulator, which makes its response a motor signal on the tissue level. Or the cell might act as effector, and its response then could serve as a feedback signal on the tissue level. The response of a cell is propagated to other cells by direct contact or by the internal transport systems—xylem and phloem in plants, blood circulation in animals. If one cell stimulates others in the manner of a chain reaction, a whole tissue or organ or organism can eventually be drawn into a larger response. Steady-state regulation of this kind is still essentially cellular. Although more than one cell is involved, receptors, modulators, and effectors beyond those present in individual cells do not exist.

This form of functional control predominates in plants and also in animals such as sponges. The tissues and organs of these organisms are not specialized mainly or exclusively just for control functions. They carry out many functions and, to a greater or lesser degree, control is generally one of them. In this respect most animals are different, for they have body parts that are spe-

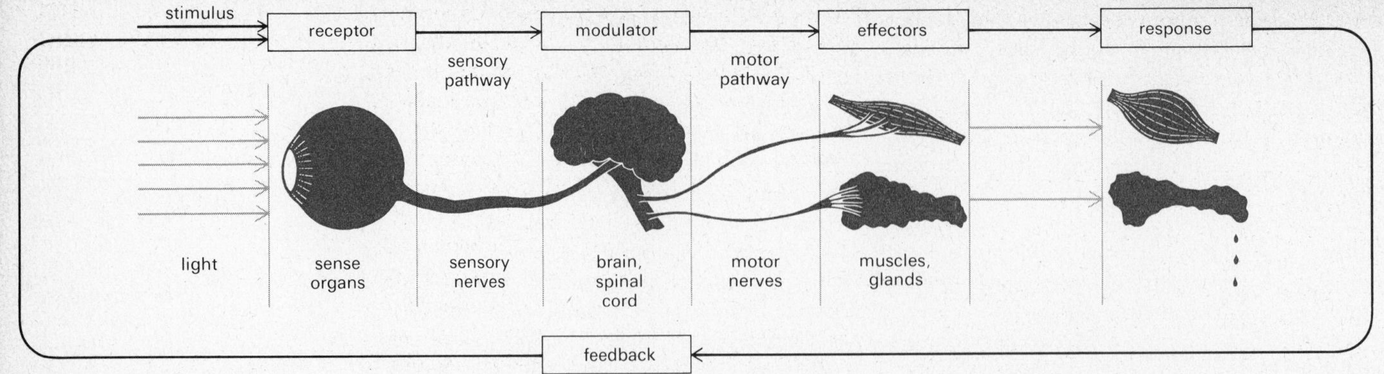

18.5 ***Steady-state control:*** *reflex action. The components of any kind of steady-state-maintaining device are indicated along the top row, those of a nervous reflex, immediately underneath. A stimulus (such as light) will produce a response such as muscle contraction and/or glandular secretion. The response itself then becomes a feedback, or a new stimulus, through which the modulator is ''informed'' whether the response has produced an adequate reaction to the original stimulus. The feedback stimulus then may or may not initiate a new reflex.*

cialized more or less exclusively for control functions—nervous systems, for example. In nervous control, sense organs are receptors, brains or brain ganglia are the chief modulators, muscles and glands are effectors, and nerves serve as sensory and motor paths. Transmission of information through such a sequence of structures constitutes a *reflex,* an important form of nervous steady-state control (Fig. 18.5).

Where present, endocrine systems likewise exercise important control through their hormones. But *every* other organ system actually contributes to regulation as well. For example, the vertebrate liver is not only a digestive gland but also a major regulator in nutrient distribution (see Chap. 16). The circulatory system is not only a series of transport channels but also an important contributor to body defense, to internal chemical regulation, and to other control functions (see Chap. 20). Similarly, the excretory and breathing systems, and indeed most organs and systems of the animal body, participate in many ways in internal regulation.

In effect, every part of living matter is regulated *by* all other parts and at the same time contributes *to* the regulation of all other parts. As a result, ''regulating'' becomes a major component of ''living,'' and without such control life becomes nonlife. Conversely, nonlife became life when the first regulating mechanism came into existence. That probably was the nucleic acid molecule, the gene. All evolution ever since can be regarded as a progressive development of more varied and more efficient control mechanisms. These were capable of counteracting more environmental stresses and thereby made possible an extension of life in any given environment for longer periods.

How do genes, and cellular regulating agents in general, actually exercise their governing functions?

control in cells

DNA and operons

Regardless of how a cell is stressed, the stress stimulus usually affects one or more *metabolic* reactions—particular processes of respiration or synthesis or physical activities such as movement are likely to be speeded up or slowed down. Similarly, regardless of how a cell responds, the response is ultimately produced by metabolic reactions—acceleration back to normal of those that had been slowed down or deceleration of those that had been speeded up.

In short, steady states can be maintained if, in response to particular stimuli, a cell can adjust and readjust the pattern of its chemical reactions. Reaction patterns are determined by enzyme contents, and these in turn depend on protein synthesis. Ultimately, therefore, cells must maintain steady states by *adjusting the rates of protein synthesis.* Since protein synthesis is under gene control, rate changes will occur if the activity of each gene in a cell can somehow be ''turned on and off.''

The means by which genes might actually be turned on or off has been suggested by the chemical phenomena of *repression* and *induction.* It has long been known that in certain reaction sequences in cells, the endproduct of the sequence often tends to inhibit some earlier point of the sequence. For example, in a serial transformation of compound *A* to compound *Z,* the endproduct *Z,* once formed in given amounts, might inhibit some earlier step such as $B \rightarrow C$:

$$A \xrightarrow{enz_1} B \xrightarrow{enz_2} C \xrightarrow{enz_3} \cdots \xrightarrow{enz_z} Z$$

Such "endproduct inhibitions," or repressions (symbolized by the transverse double bar above), prevent more endproduct from being formed.

Conversely, for some reaction sequences in cells it has been found that addition of excess amounts of reactants leads to a rapid formation of excess amounts of specific enzymes. For example, in a serial transformation of *A* to *Z*, an excess of *A* can induce, or lead to an increase in, the amount of enzyme that converts *A* to *B*, hence to a more rapid formation of *Z*:

$$A \xrightarrow{enz_1} B \xrightarrow{enz_2} C \xrightarrow{enz_3} \cdots \xrightarrow{enz_z} Z$$

A classic example of such induction, or "adaptive enzyme formation," is the effect of various sugars that, when added to a cell in excess amounts, stimulate formation of large quantities of the specific enzymes that catalyze the reactions of these sugars (Fig. 18.6).

A recent hypothesis shows how both repressions and inductions might actually operate through a switch mechanism affecting gene activity and thus protein synthesis. This so-called *operon hypothesis* (Fig. 18.7) postulates the existence of two types of gene, *regulator genes* (*RG*) and *structural genes* (*SG*). Regulator genes are thought to control the manufacture of protein products *R*, which specifically affect the activity of structural genes. These are genes that control protein synthesis in general; they transcribe their codes to *m*RNA, and thus they control the synthesis of, for example, enzymes that promote transformation of *A* to *Z*. All the structural genes controlling the successive steps of a particular reaction sequence are thought to be located close to one another on a chromosome. This chromosome region is also postulated to contain an *operator gene* (*Op*), which must be active if the nearby structural genes are to be active. The whole region, including operator and associated structural genes, is said to form an *operon*.

In a repression (Fig. 18.8), the product *R* of the regulator gene is assumed not to affect the operator gene *Op*, which is then active. This permits the structural genes to be active as well, resulting ultimately in the formation of endproduct *Z*. However, *Z* now is believed to combine with *R*, and the complex *RZ* becomes attached to the operator *Op* and thereby inhibits it. The structural genes consequently become inactive, too, transcription ceases, and the reaction sequence *A* to *Z* is soon halted. Endproduct *Z* is then no longer formed. The repression lasts as long as the concentration of *Z* stays above a certain critical level. Thereafter *Op* becomes free again, and formation of *Z* can recur—temporarily.

In an induction (Fig. 18.9), the product *R* of the regulator gene is an inhibitor of *Op*, and endproduct *Z* therefore cannot be manufactured. But if raw material *A* is introduced into the cell,

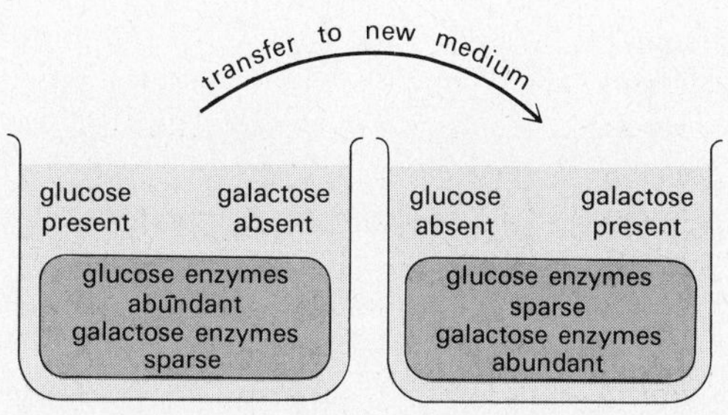

18.6 Adaptive enzymes. *The dark-colored boxes inside the beakers represent bacteria. As the available external nutrients vary in abundance, so the internal bacterial enzymes capable of acting on these nutrients come to vary in abundance, too.*

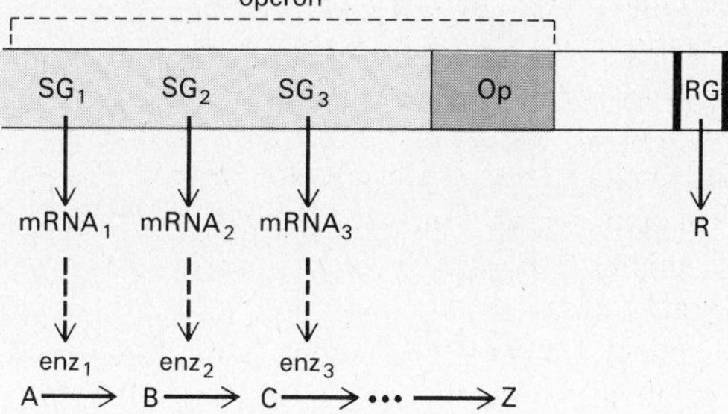

18.7 Operon structure. *SG, structural gene; Op, operator gene; RG, regulator gene; all three of these gene types are located in a chromosome. R, protein product formed by RG and influencing Op in ways to be shown in next two illustrations. A to Z represents a reaction sequence in which a succession of specifically required enzymes (enz) is manufactured under the control of SG and mRNA.*

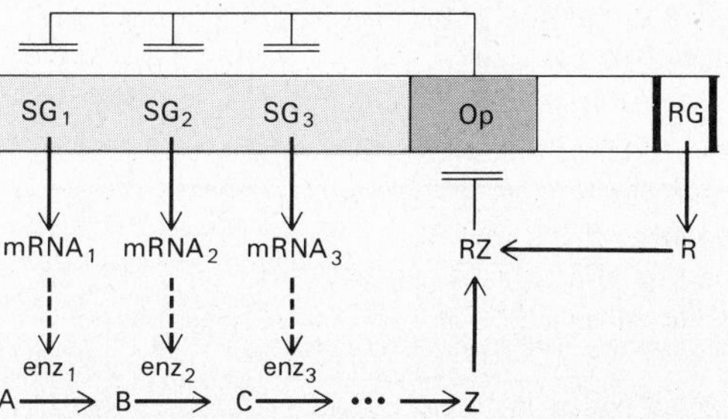

18.8 Operon functioning: repression. *R by itself does not affect Op, but if R combines with reaction endproduct Z, the complex RZ inhibits the operator gene Op (transverse double bar denotes inhibition). As a result, Op also prevents the SG's from functioning, enzymes will not be produced, and the reaction sequence A to Z will cease. Thus the endproduct Z eventually represses the continuation of its own manufacture.*

18.9 ***Operon functioning: induction.*** *R inhibits Op, hence the SG's do not operate and Z is not formed. But if starting material A is introduced into the system, R combines with A and the complex RA inhibits the inhibition exerted by R on Op; in effect, RA permits Op to function again. The SG's then will function, too, enzymes will be formed, and A can be converted to Z. Thus A removes a repression (it derepresses Op), hence it promotes its own conversion to Z.*

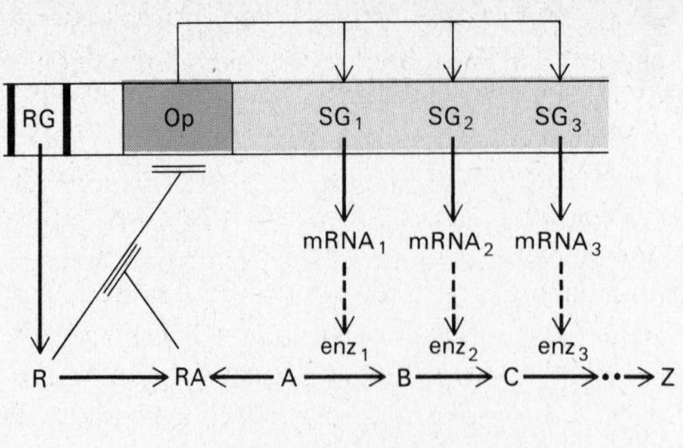

18.10 ***Molecular modulators*** *and their control over steady-state-maintaining metabolic reactions in a cell. Through RNA, enzymes, and control over synthesis reactions, genes also control the nature of the growth factors that can be present in a cell.*

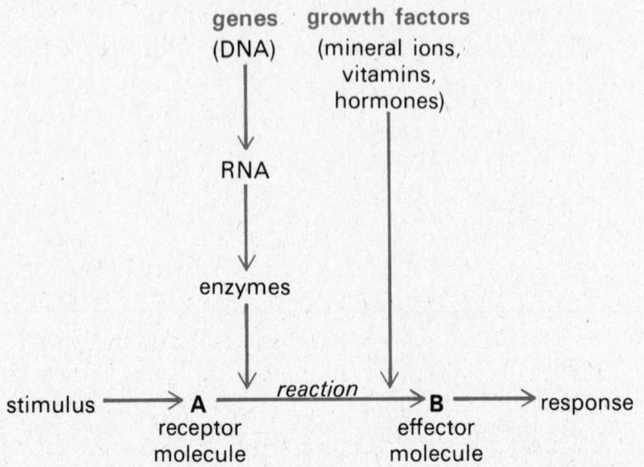

A is believed to combine with *R,* and the complex *RA* is postulated to abolish the inhibition of *Op.* The structural genes would then become active, and *A* could be transformed to *Z.* After all of *A* is used up, *Op* becomes inhibited again, and the enzymes necessary for formation *Z* are no longer synthesized. Induction therefore amounts to removal of a repression, a process that has come to be termed *derepression.*

Clearly, control through operons saves a cell energy and materials in considerable measure. Enzymes are synthesized only when they are actually needed—when raw materials are actually available, and when endproducts are not already present to excess. Quite as important, operon control permits a cell to be responsive to its environment. Compounds entering a cell as food can be the specific stimuli for their own utilization, by enzyme induction; and compounds accumulating as finished products can be the specific stimuli halting their own manufacture, by enzyme repression. Adjusting its metabolic activities in this manner, a cell can exercise effective steady-state control.

enzymes and growth factors

In the language of control systems, the enzymes synthesized in a cell can be regarded as modulators in metabolic reactions, the simplest and most basic kinds of regulating devices. In such molecular systems the starting compounds can be receptors, the endproducts, effectors. For example, in the reversible sequence

$$\text{glucose} \xrightleftharpoons{\text{enzymes}} \text{polysaccharide}$$

the totality of glucose molecules in a cell, or *glucose pool,* can function as a receptor. If additional glucose arrives in the cell as food, this excess can represent a stimulus. By mass action, the reaction to the right will then occur at a higher rate than that to the left, and more polysaccharide will be formed. The polysaccharide pool here is equivalent to an effector, and increase of polysaccharide concentration is the response. For as polysaccharide accumulates at the expense of glucose, the glucose pool decreases to normal levels, and the original stimulus is thereby removed. The extra polysaccharide in turn can be a new stimulus in the cell, initiating other reactions and new responses.

But the designations "receptor" and "effector" are not fixed. If a cell were to acquire additional polysaccharide rather than glucose, then the polysaccharide pool would function as a receptor and the glucose pool as an effector. In either case the function of modulator is performed by the enzyme; it takes a specific enzyme to act on a specific molecular stimulus and to promote a specific molecular response. (Because an enzyme is specific for a particular reaction, it cannot interpret various different stimuli but only one. And it cannot select among several possible responses but must promote the same response every time.)

In addition to DNA- and RNA-dependent enzymes, cells also contain a variety of *growth factors* that function as secondary modulators in metabolic reactions. A growth factor is any controlling agent a cell requires but cannot manufacture on its own. Included in this category are chiefly *minerals, vitamins,* and *hormones.* They are named "growth" factors because they often reveal their action most obviously through particular effects on growth. In this sense genes and enzymes qualify as growth factors, too, but these are produced directly in the cell in which they act.

Like genes and enzymes, growth factors promote metabolic sequences. Mineral ions are required in many reactions; vitamins are starting materials in the production of specific coenzymes; and the participation of hormones in particular reactions has already been noted as well. Actually most reaction sequences analyzed closely have been found to depend on a whole battery of growth factors in addition to enzymes, including mineral ions, vitamin-derived coenzymes, and often also hormones (Fig. 18.10).

All these agents essentially facilitate or accelerate specific reactions; or in the language of control systems, they function as information relays, or modulators. Each shares with enzymes the property of promoting the same reaction response every time, without freedom of choice. Like enzymes, moreover, each is ultimately gene-dependent. Hormones and vitamin-derived coenzymes are synthesized directly under gene control, and indirectly the genes also determine what minerals a cell is capable of acquiring through its surface. Genes therefore exercise control over all other cellular controllers and serve as the final regulators of steady states.

Control of metabolic reactions requires not only acceleration, however, but also deceleration. Ultimately reactions are slowed down by genes, through reduction of the rates of enzyme synthesis. Secondarily deceleration can also occur in at least four other ways. One is a result of the inherent *reversibility* of most metabolic reactions; a reaction in one direction can be inhibited by accelerating the opposite reaction. This principle holds not only on the molecular but also on any other level. Brakes and accelerators are present together and hold one another in mutual check. The net reaction they allow to occur is a compromise between excitation and inhibition. Any change in the concentration of reactants or in the quantity of modulators will change the balance between excitation and inhibition; and the reaction will then speed up in one direction, hence slow down in the other.

In certain cases an acceleration of one reaction inhibits not only the opposite reaction but also some quite different reaction as well. This process is illustrated by certain instances of adaptive enzyme formation, as already discussed earlier (see Fig. 18.6). For example, large amounts of glucose in a cell can, through induction by an operon mechanism, lead to increased synthesis of the enzymes necessary for reactions of glucose. It is found at the same time, however, that enzymes for other sugars—galactose, for example—are manufactured only in greatly reduced amounts. Such sugars are therefore metabolized very little or not at all. But if galactose is then supplied in large amounts and the glucose supply is stopped, galactose-metabolizing enzymes soon increase in quantity whereas glucose-metabolizing enzymes soon decrease. Evidently, glucose metabolism inhibits enzyme formation for galactose metabolism, and vice versa. Such *alternative pathway* effects represent a second way by which certain reactions can be slowed down (Fig. 18.11).

A third way involves *competition among modulators* for reactants. For example, glucose can be transformed either to polysaccharide by synthesis or to CO_2 by respiration, depending on whether synthesis-promoting (M_s) or respiration-promoting (M_r) modulators react with glucose:

$$\text{polysaccharide} \xleftarrow{M_s} \text{glucose} \xrightarrow{M_r} CO_2$$

M_s and M_r here compete for glucose, and the reactions toward one endproduct will necessarily slow down the reactions toward the other. Here again the modulators hold one another in check, and the net reactions are quickly adjusted when any part of the balance shifts.

Last, reactions can be decelerated by *competition among reactants* for modulators. This can occur when two reactions are so alike that the same modulator can promote them. For example, the same lipase could transform different fatty acids (along with glycerin) to either fat *A* or fat *B:*

fatty acids *A* + glycerin		fatty acids *B* + glycerin
↓	⟵ lipase ⟶	↓
fat *A*		fat *B*

The reactants on the *A* side here compete with those on the *B* side for the required enzyme. Accordingly, whenever concentrations or other conditions favor one reaction, the other will be inhibited.

Chemical competition of this sort often is either a cause or a cure of disease. For example, disease can be caused by a poison that competes with either a normal modulator or a normal reactant and thereby inhibits an essential reaction. Cure can then be brought about by reversing the abnormal competition—by supplying normal modulators or normal reactants in sufficient quantities to inhibit the disease reaction (Fig. 18.12).

Control of cellular metabolism can now be envisaged as follows (Fig. 18.13). In a given

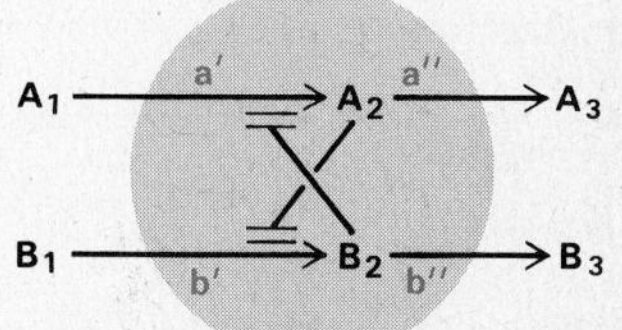

18.11 Alternative pathway switching. *Assume that A_1, A_2, A_3 and B_1, B_2, B_3 are two reaction pathways requiring the enzymes a′, a″ and b′, b″ respectively. Assume also that A_2 has the property of inhibiting b′, and B_2, of inhibiting a′. If then the A sequence is in operation it will inhibit the B sequence; and if the B sequence is in operation it will inhibit the A sequence. Also, if presence of A induces the enzymes a′ and a″ through an operon mechanism, then the B sequence will automatically be inhibited through the effect of A_2 on b′. By such means two or more separate metabolic pathways can exert significant control over one another and thus over the kinds and amounts of materials synthesized in a cell.*

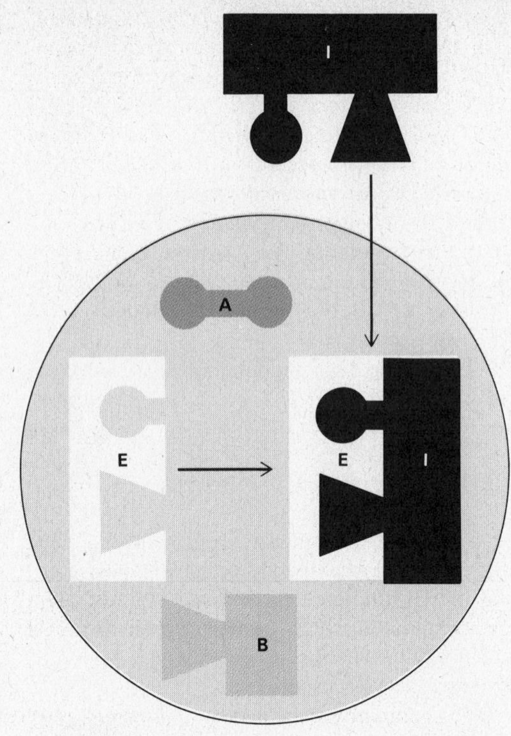

18.12 ***Chemical competition.*** *Suppose that reactants A and B normally require an enzymatic modulator such as E for reaction. If then an inhibitor I is introduced from the outside, E and I could combine preferentially and thus "crowd out" the interaction of A and B. For example, if I is a poison, it can impair a normal process; or if I is a medicinal drug, it can prevent a disease reaction.*

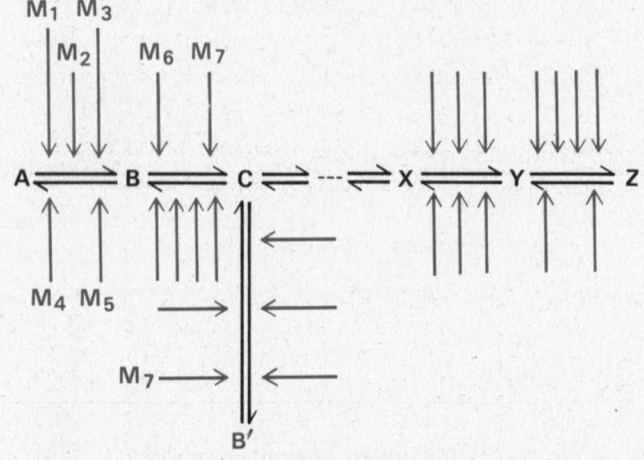

18.13 ***Control of molecular metabolism.*** *A, B, C ··· X, Y, Z symbolize molecular reactants, and M_1, M_2, etc., symbolize molecular modulators. Some of the modulators promote a given reaction in one direction (M_1, M_2, M_3), others promote it in the opposite direction (M_4, M_5). Modulators compete for reactants (M_4, M_6), and reactants compete for modulators (B and B′ compete for M_7). Some modulators are mutually reinforcing in their activity (M_4, M_5). Each step of a reaction sequence is controlled by a battery of modulators, and the net reaction is a resultant of the various modulator effects.*

sequence of reactions each separate reaction is influenced by several modulators of various types—genes and enzymes always, vitamin-derived coenzymes usually, and minerals and hormones in many cases. Some of these modulators reinforce one another and promote a given reaction in one direction or in the opposite direction. Some modulators compete for reactants, some reactants compete for modulators. Depending on the specific balances between all modulators and all reactants at any moment, the whole sequence or parts of it will proceed one way or the other at certain rates. The overall result is a steady state, a dynamic equilibrium. When a stimulus then affects any part of the sequence, the balance between the accelerations and decelerations will shift; and like ripples in a pond traveling away from a center of disturbance, the reaction sequence will be perturbed until a steady state is reattained.

minerals and vitamins

All organisms require mineral substances as growth factors, and all also require vitamins. Minerals serve in two general capacities: in part they are nutrients used as structural components of cells, and in part they are growth factors used in reaction control. In some cases the same mineral contributes to both functions. For example, magnesium is both a structural component (in chlorophyll) and a controlling agent (in respiratory and other reactions). By and large, most organisms require roughly the same kinds of mineral substances.

Vitamins are growth factors mainly in animals, for in most other organisms these substances are synthesized internally, usually directly in the cells in which they act. In such organisms vitamins therefore belong to the same self-manufactured group of control agents as genes and enzymes.

Even animals synthesize at least some vitamins, but generally not enough or not all necessary kinds. For example, insects can synthesize all except the B vitamins. A few rodents, apes, and man cannot manufacture their own vitamin C, but other animals can. Man happens to be a particularly poor vitamin synthesizer, being unable to produce sufficient quantities of any except the D vitamins. Such differences in synthesizing ability between different species probably result from loss mutations. And once an organism loses the capacity of synthesizing a particular vitamin, that vitamin becomes a required growth factor for that species.

More than 30 compounds are known to have the properties of vitamins. They are needed in very small amounts and their prolonged absence from a cell impairs metabolic processes and produces unsteady or diseased states. In this connection, careful distinction should be made between the *biological* and the *clinical* effects of a deficiency. Most and possibly all cells of an organism require most or all vitamins; if a vitamin deficiency exists, some metabolic process in cells will be impaired. This is a biological effect. As noted in Chap. 4, for example, the B vitamin riboflavin is a precursor of the coenzymes FMN and FAD. If riboflavin is in deficient supply, respiratory reactions in cells will be affected. Superimposed on such biological effects are clinical ones. These become evident when the cells of given tissues or organs are more sensitive to a deficiency than other cells. Such sensitive cells then will exhibit symptoms of disease sooner or more pronouncedly than others. For example, riboflavin deficiency in mammals has long been known to lead to loss of hair, to growth failure, and to eye disorders (Fig. 18.14). By themselves, clinical data alone would imply that riboflavin is required specifically in hairs, bones, and eyes. Actually, however, clinical results represent only the large-scale secondary consequences of the deeper biological effects of deficiency, which influence most or all cells.

When they were first investigated, vitamins were given letter designations. Later virtually every vitamin so labeled was found to consist of not one but several, often related substances. Letters with subscripts then came into use. Today the tendency is to refer to a new vitamin by its chemical name only. Many vitamins therefore do not have a letter designation, and some have both letter and chemical labels (Table 13).

Vitamins are partly fat-soluble and partly water-soluble. The first group includes vitamins A, D, E, and K; the latter, vitamins B and C. In vertebrates, fat-soluble vitamins require bile for proper absorption from the gut. Therefore, whenever fat digestion is impaired or when fats are rigidly excluded from the diet, vitamin deficiency can develop readily. Water-soluble vitamins are normally present in the fluids in and around cells and tissues; hence in foods such fluids are nutritionally valuable,

vitamin A group

The several closely related substances so designated are derivatives of the *carotene* pigments synthesized in plastids. Carotenes can therefore be found in leaves, and other rich sources are red-orange-yellow plant parts such as carrots, tomatoes, squash, sweet potatoes. Egg yolk, butter, and cream are among animal products rich in carotene. Spinach contains more carotene than an equal weight of egg yolk. In yellow foods,

A

B

C

D

E

***18.14* Vitamins.** *All rats shown have the same age. A, normal rat, weight about 170 grams. B, vitamin A deficiency: eyes infected, fur rough, weight about 60 g. C, riboflavin deficiency: hair loss, sickly, weight about 60 g. D, thiamine deficiency: lack of muscle coordination. E, vitamin D deficiency.*

Table 13. The main vitamins and their functions

name	food sources	chief cell functions	effects of deficiency
vitamin A	leaves, yellow foods, liver	chemistry of vision; membrane integrity	night blindness; infectious diseases; bone, nerve abnormalities
thiamine (B_1)	grain products, yeast, beans, nuts, liver, eggs, meat	cocarboxylase precursor	beriberi
riboflavin (B_2)		FMN and FAD precursor	hair loss; growth failure
nicotinic acid		NAD and NADP precursor	pellagra
pantothenic acid		coenzyme A precursor	anemia; growth failure; hemorrhages; bone disorders; nerve, skin disorders; infectious diseases
biotin (H)		CO_2-carrying coenzyme precursor	
choline		$—CH_3$-carrying coenzyme	
pyridoxine (B_6)		$—NH_2$-carrying coenzyme	
folic acid		nucleic acid metabolism	
vitamin B_{12}			
vitamin C	citrus fruits, tomatoes, cabbage	aerobic H transfer; synthesis of cell cement	scurvy
vitamin D	liver, fish oils	Ca and P regulation	rickets
vitamin E	most foods	aerobic H transfer	sterility; eye abnormalities; nerve, muscle disorders
vitamin K			failure of blood clotting

depth of color is an index of comparative carotene content.

When a molecule of carotene is split enzymatically in the presence of water, two molecules of vitamin A are formed (see also Fig. 4.6):

$$\underset{\text{carotene}}{C_{40}H_{56}} + 2\ H_2O \longrightarrow 2\ \underset{\text{vitamin A}}{C_{20}H_{30}O}$$

The vitamin is stored in the vertebrate liver, and fish livers and their oils contain particularly large amounts (hence the nutritive value of, for example, cod-liver oil). Fish obtain carotene through food chains originating with algae.

Vitamin A plays an important role in the chemistry of vision; deficiency of the vitamin leads to night blindness (see Chap. 21). Among its other, less clearly understood cellular functions, the vitamin controls proper growth of bones, tooth enamel, and nerve tissue; and it prevents drying and cracking of exposed, normally moist membranes, like those in the eyes, the breathing system, and the alimentary and urogenital tracts. Probably through this action the vitamin reduces the incidence of infectious diseases (vitamin A actually is sometimes called the "anti-infection vitamin," but such a designation applies equally well to many other vitamins).

vitamin B group

These water-soluble vitamins include *thiamine* (B_1), *riboflavin* (B_2), *nicotinic acid* ("niacin"), *pyridoxine* (B_6), *biotin* (H), *vitamin B_{12}*, *pantothenic acid, folic acid,* and *choline.* The substances are not particularly related in chemical structure or biological function. They are grouped together largely because they tend to occur together in plant and animal foods. Most of the vitamins have been identified chemically, and many can be synthesized in the laboratory. The B vitamins occur in natural foods of all types; rich sources are whole-grain products, yeast, peas, beans, and nuts among plant foods, and liver, egg yolk, and meat among animal foods. Intestinal bacteria synthesize many of the B vitamins.

Most of these vitamins are raw materials in the synthesis of cellular coenzymes. Thus, thiamine gives rise to cocarboxylase; riboflavin to FMN and FAD; nicotinic acid to NAD and NADP; and pantothenic acid to coenzyme A (see also Fig. 4.12). Pyridoxine is a precursor of a coenzyme that serves as $—NH_2$ carrier in transaminations, and biotin becomes a CO_2-carrying coenzyme. Similarly, a choline-derived coenzyme carries methyl groups ($—CH_3$) in chemical transformations, and folic acid and vitamin B_{12} are known to participate in nucleotide metabolism specifically.

A more or less well-defined clinical disease is associated with lack of each of the B vitamins. Thus, mild thiamine deficiency produces fatigue, weakness, and lassitude. More severe thiamine starvation over a period of weeks can result in *beriberi,* a disease characterized by muscular paralysis. Riboflavin deficiency leads to hair loss, eye disorders, and stunted growth, as noted; niacin deficiency, to *pellagra,* a disease of the skin and the nervous system; vitamin B_{12} and folic acid deficiencies, to anemia; choline deficiency, to bone deformities (in chickens) and internal hemorrhages; and pyridoxine and pantothenic acid deficiencies, to growth failure, anemia, lowered resistance to infections, and nerve and skin disorders. In all these cases administration of the appropriate vitamin usually relieves the disease.

vitamin C

This compound is *ascorbic acid,* a derivative of monosaccharide sugars. It is widely synthesized in plants, particularly in citrus fruit, cabbage, and tomatoes. As pointed out, most animals—but not man—manufacture it. Ascorbic acid is one of the least stable vitamins. Cooking destroys it, and in fresh and canned foods much of this water-soluble vitamin diffuses out to the food juices.

That vitamin C participates in aerobic hydrogen transfer is known, but it is not yet known which specific reaction the vitamin affects. Like other vitamins participating in respiratory reactions, ascorbic acid is generally found in the mitochondria of cells. Vitamin C also takes part in a phase of synthesis metabolism; it plays a role in the production of the cementing substance that binds tissue cells together. When this function is impaired, *scurvy* results. Blood vessels become abnormally permeable, and hemorrhages can occur in any part of the body. Connective tissues no longer bind efficiently, and teeth, for example, loosen from their sockets. In more advanced stages bones weaken, muscles degenerate, and death ultimately supervenes. Mild deficiencies need not lead to an outright scorbutic condition, but they can impair energy metabolism enough to produce lassitude and to cause fleeting, rheumatismlike pains in limb joints.

vitamin D group

Some ten related compounds are included in this group. Two of them, D_2 and D_3, are particularly potent. In man, precursors of the D vitamins are present in skin. Such precursors are converted to active vitamins by irradiation with ultraviolet light, hence the designation of the D vitamins as "sunshine vitamins." The active vitamins are stored in the liver along with vitamin A in the lipid reserves. Good external sources of D vitamins are fish-liver oils, dairy foods, and, in general, foods rich also in vitamin A.

The D vitamins participate in reactions involving calcium and phosphorus, particularly in the complex processes of bone formation and bone maintenance. In the cells of the gut the vitamins probably balance calcium and phosphorus absorption against excretion to the gut cavity. Through this the vitamins play a part in maintaining an optimum supply of Ca and P in the body, and then they regulate the deposition of these raw materials as bone and tooth substance.

Deficiency of the D vitamins leads to *rickets,* a disease marked by softening and bending of bones, beading of ribs, erosion of teeth, and elimination of calcium and phosphorus in urine. Conversely, continued overdoses of vitamin D can lead to abnormal thickening of bones and some calcification of soft tissues.

vitamin E group

Several chemically identified, closely related compounds are in this category. The vitamins are relatively unstable, but they are so widely distributed in the fatty fraction of both plant and animal foods that a deficiency is not likely to arise on any normal diet. These substances are often called "antisterility vitamins"; deficiency can be shown to lead to permanent infertility in male rats and to death of embryos or to premature births in pregnant female rats. In man, embryos deficient in vitamin E often undergo abnormal eye development. As to its cellular function, vitamin E is known to participate in some way in hydrogen transport during respiration.

vitamin K group

These vitamins are known best for their role in blood clotting; deficiency leads to failure of the clotting mechanism (see Chap. 20). For this reason vitamin K is often administered before surgery, particularly surgery on bile ducts blocked by gallstones. Since vitamin K is dissolved in the fatty portions of food, bile is required for its proper absorption from the gut cavity. If then the bile duct is blocked, an individual is likely to be vitamin K–deficient, and his blood-clotting mechanism will be impaired. Ingestion of the vitamin (along with bile salts) before an operation can therefore forestall hemorrhages.

Like vitamin E, vitamin K contributes to respiratory hydrogen transfer. These two groups of vitamins also resemble each other in chemical structure, in their wide occurrence among foods, and in being synthesized by intestinal bacteria.

review questions

1 What general kinds of processes take place in the execution of control activities? What general function do such controls serve in the maintenance of life? What is the role of information flow in the maintenance of steady states?

2 What are the structural components of every control system in living matter? What specific role does each component play in the maintenance of steady states? Review the functional properties of control systems. How is the energy requirement distributed among control components?

3 What is feedback, and what is its significance in control activities? What is the significance of trial and error in control activities? What happens when control systems are overloaded? Interpret the temperature-regulating action of a home thermostat in terms of a control system, and indicate the specific roles of feedback and of trial and error.

4 In what sense does a molecular reaction constitute a control system? What kinds of substances can serve as molecular modulators? What characteristics do these have in common? What is the relation of genes to control systems?

5 For each organelle usually present in cells, name a cellular activity in which that organelle functions as (*a*) receptor, (*b*) modulator, (*c*) effector, and (*d*) sensory or motor pathway.

6 Review the general pattern of steady-state control on supracellular levels. How do plants and animals differ in this respect? Which parts of an organism do not participate in control activities?

7 Review the processes by which genes control (*a*) cellular metabolism, (*b*) other cellular controllers, including other genes, and (*c*) all aspects of self-perpetuation. What are growth factors?

8 What are chemical repression, induction, operator genes, regulator genes, structural genes? Review the operon hypothesis, and show how it can account for control of cellular operations. In what different ways can metabolic processes become decelerated?

9 Review the general cellular functions of vitamins. How do autotrophs and heterotrophs differ in their vitamin requirements? How, and why, do different heterotrophs differ in their vitamin requirements?

10 Distinguish between clinical and biological effects of vitamin deficiencies. Which vitamins are fat-soluble, and which are water-soluble? Review the food sources and the chemical nature of the principal vitamins. What are the clinical effects of deficiencies of these vitamins?

collateral readings

Barth, L. J.: "Development," Addison-Wesley, Reading, Mass., 1964. Chapter 10 of this paperback contains a brief review of the operon hypothesis.

Benzinger, T. H.: The Human Thermostat, *Sci. American,* Jan., 1961. Temperature regulation in man is discussed as a case study of control systems operations.

Brown, G. S., and **D. P. Campbell:** Control Systems, *Sci. American,* Sept., 1952. A general discussion of the operation of such systems.

Changeux, J. L.: The Control of Biochemical Reactions, *Sci. American,* Apr., 1965. A description of cellular feedback controls governing enzyme synthesis on the one hand and enzyme activity on the other. Very pertinent to the topics of this chapter.

Dowling, J. E.: Night Blindness, *Sci. American,* Oct., 1966. The role of vitamin A in the chemistry of vision is discussed.

Held, R.: Plasticity in Sensory-motor Systems, *Sci. American,* Nov., 1965. The article describes experiments on locomotion-controlling feedback systems in mammals.

Jacob, F., and **J. Monod:** Genetic Regulatory Mechanisms in the Synthesis of Proteins, *J. Mol. Biol.,* vol. 3, 1961. The evidence for regulator genes is discussed by the originators of the operon hypothesis.

Pierce, W. H.: Redundancy in Computers, *Sci. American,* Feb., 1964. The means by which errors can be minimized in computers parallel those found in living control systems.

Spiegelman, S.: Hybrid Nucleic Acids, *Sci. American,* May, 1964. Information flow in a cell is studied by means of artificially prepared DNA.

Tustin, A.: Feedback, *Sci. American,* Sept., 1952. A good account on this component of control operations.

As a general class of growth factors, hormones differ from vitamins and mineral ions in several respects. First, unlike other growth factors, hormones are synthesized by specialized body parts and then exert their effects elsewhere in the organism. Second, it is not completely known as yet just how hormones actually influence metabolic reactions. Some evidence suggests that hormones affect the transcription of the genetic code during protein synthesis. Third, although hormones act primarily in cells, they have effects that often extend well beyond the cellular level; in particular they contribute in major ways to the visible *behavior* of a whole organism. Last, substances known to have hormonal effects differ chemically to a great extent in different groups of organisms and also within single groups.

As in the case of mineral ions and vitamins, the normal control functions of a hormone are usually investigated by deliberately making an organism deficient in that hormone or by supplying an excess of it. In either case abnormal *unsteady* states are induced, and these often give clues about the normal regulating activity of the hormone.

plant behavior

The chief growth hormone of plants are *auxins,* and the most important naturally occurring one is *heteroauxin.* Chemically this hormone is *indoleacetic acid,* IAA for short, a derivative of the amino acid tryptophan (Fig. 19.1). IAA occurs in many Monera, Protista, and Metaphyta, and related compounds without hormonal effects are found also in Metazoa. Two other (synthetic) auxins are naphthaleneacetic acid, or NAA for short, and 2,4-dichlorophenoxyacetic acid, or 2,4-D for short. Still other auxins exist and many can be synthesized in the laboratory.

Actively growing and developing regions of a plant usually produce the largest amounts of auxin. Thus, particularly auxin-rich regions are meristems of all kinds, including shoot tips, root tips, and cambia, as well as young leaves, developing flower parts, and fruits. In such regions auxins bring about an *elongation* of individual cells, and they probably do so by affecting the formation of the cell walls. Auxins apparently induce a cell to synthesize more primary wall material and to deposit this material at the two ends of the cell. Lengthening of the cell follows.

Thus the apical tip of a shoot (or a root) normally produces IAA, which then diffuses to cells farther back. There it brings about cell elongation. If the cross-sectional distribution of IAA is roughly even the shoot will elongate straight up. The growth-promoting effect of auxin is known to be reduced in some way by light, hence an illuminated shoot does not grow as fast as if it were kept in darkness. Plant growth evidently is a compromise between stimulation by light through photosynthesis and inhibition by light through reduced auxin effects (Fig. 19.2).

Apart from auxins the hormones of plants also include the *gibberellins.* These appear to exert their main effects on stem length. In young stems particularly, the hormones increase the length of all the internodes without affecting the number of nodes. The results can be striking. For example, by applying gibberellins to cabbage, normally a low head with closely packed leaves, the plant can be induced to become tall and vinelike (Fig. 19.3). Such results are produced by increases in the rates of cell division, but just how gibberellins actually accelerate cell divisions is not clearly understood as yet. Similarly unclear is the precise action of *kinins,* another group of hormones that also promotes cell division. Kinins appear to be normally present in plants, but to date their effects have been studied mainly by application of man-made kinin preparations.

Through their regulating functions in individual

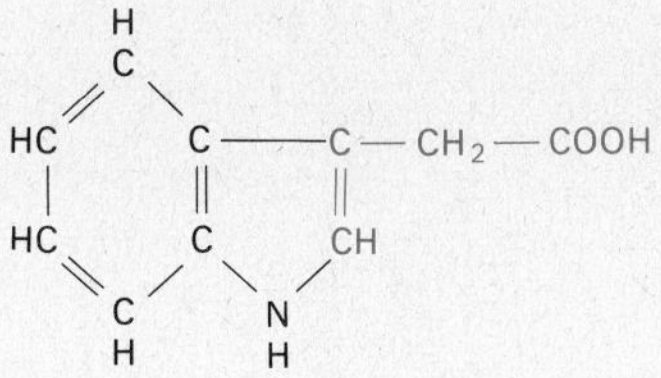

indoleacetic acid (IAA)

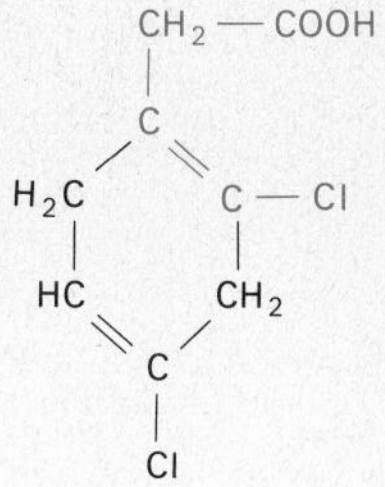

2,4-dichlorophenoxyacetic acid (2,4-D)

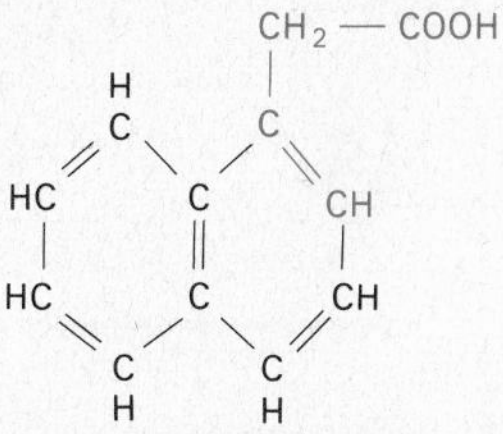

α–naphthaleneacetic acid (NAA)

19.1 Auxins. *Structure of three auxin compounds. Portions of formulas in color emphasize the similar atomic groupings often present in auxins.*

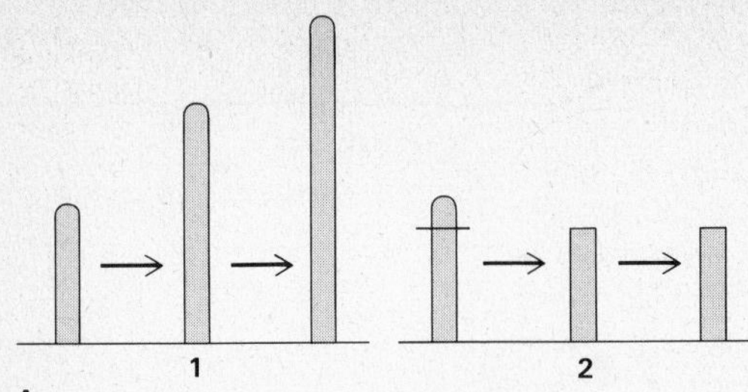

19.2 Auxin effects. *A, that auxin produced by a shoot tip normally promotes elongation of the shoot (1) is proved if the shoot tip is cut off (2); under such conditions elongation does not occur. B, a light-grown (left) and dark-grown (right) specimen of the common bean. The light-grown plant has not grown as much during the same time as the dark-grown plant, indicating that light reduces the growth-promoting effect of auxin.*

19.3 Gibberellin effects. *Left, untreated cabbage. Right, cabbage after gibberellin treatment. Internodes have elongated enormously.*

cells, plant hormones in general and auxins in particular affect the behavior of a whole plant in considerable measure. Such plant behavior is expressed mainly in two ways, by *movement* and by *development.*

motion responses

In response to particular stimuli certain body parts of a fixed plant undergo *growth* movements or *turgor* movements.

Most growth movements occur too slowly to be observable directly, but time-lapse photography reveals them clearly. Among movements brought about by internal—and in part presumably also by external—stimuli, the actual regulating function of hormones is not clearly understood as yet. One such movement is *nutation,* a back-and-forth rocking or nodding motion of the apical shoot tips of certain species (Fig. 19.4). It is caused by alternately changing growth rates on opposite sides of the apical tip. Another motion response is *spiral movement,* a rotational growth of an elongating shoot around its long axis. A common form of spiral motion is *twining,* in which rotational growth of the shoot tip produces a spirally curving stem. A third type of response comprises so-called *nastic movements.* These occur in leaves, petals, and other flattened plant parts in which one surface grows faster than the other. Nastic motions then result either in an opening and folding out of a body part, as in the opening of maturing buds, or in a closing and folding in.

The response-regulating function of hormones is much better understood in growth movements that are induced wholly by external stimuli. Such movements are known as *tropisms,* and several kinds can be distinguished on the basis of the various growth-inducing stimuli: light-induced *phototropism,* gravity-induced *geotropism,* contact-induced *thigmotropism,* chemical-induced *chemotropism,* and others. A given tropic response is said to be positive or negative according to whether a plant part grows toward or away from the stimulus. For example, leaves and stems are positively phototropic and negatively geotropic; they grow toward light and away from the gravitational center of the earth. Roots, on the contrary, are positively geotropic and negatively phototropic (Fig. 19.5).

Phototropic and geotropic responses are known to be under auxin control. As already noted, the apical tip of a shoot produces IAA that promotes elongation of cells behind the tip. If the shoot is illuminated predominantly from one side, auxin on that side is rendered less effective by light and the opposite, shaded side therefore elongates more extensively. The shoot then curves toward the light source as it lengthens. Thus the stem is positively phototropic and behaves as if it were "aware" of the position of the light source (Fig. 19.6).

It has been found that the optimum IAA concentration for elongation of root cells is about 100,000 times less than the optimum for elongation of stem cells. In other words, an IAA concentration that stimulates stem growth is far too high to stimulate root growth. Under such conditions root growth in effect is inhibited and does not take place. Conversely, an IAA concentration that stimulates root growth is so low that it inhibits (or at any rate does not promote) stem growth. Therefore, if a stem-root system in water is illuminated from one side the stem tip will curve toward the light. But any auxin diffusing to the root on the shaded side will be sufficiently concentrated to inhibit root elongation there. As a result, the side of the root that faces the light will grow faster and the root tip will curve away from the light stimulus; hence the negative phototropism of roots (see Fig. 19.6).

The negative geotropism of stems and the positive geotropism of roots (responses that occur in the dark) can be explained by the gradual diffusion of auxin to the lower parts of a plant. It can be shown that, if a plant is placed horizontally, as much as two-thirds of all the auxin in a shoot tip will accumulate on the lower side of this tip. As the auxin then moves back to cells capable of elongating, most of the hormone reaches cells located on the lower side of the stem. These cells therefore elongate more than cells on the upper side, and the stem tip curves upward as a result. When auxin later reaches root cells, the concentration of the hormone is still highest on the lower side, which means that the cells on that side will be inhibited most. Root cells on the upper side therefore elongate to a comparatively greater extent. The root tip thus curves downward (Fig. 19.7).

Changes in hormone distribution and concentration probably play a role in other growth movements and indeed also in turgor movements, the second type of motion response of plants. However, in most of these cases it is still not quite

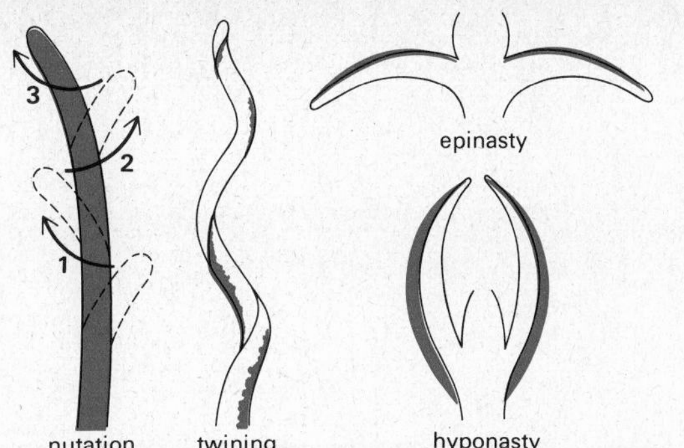

***19.4* Growth movements.** *The plants carry out the movements shown in response to largely internally generated stimuli.*

***19.5* Tropic movements.** *Left, the effect of gravity: geotropic response. Right, the effect of light: phototropic response. The plant is illuminated from the left, and it grows in the direction of the light.*

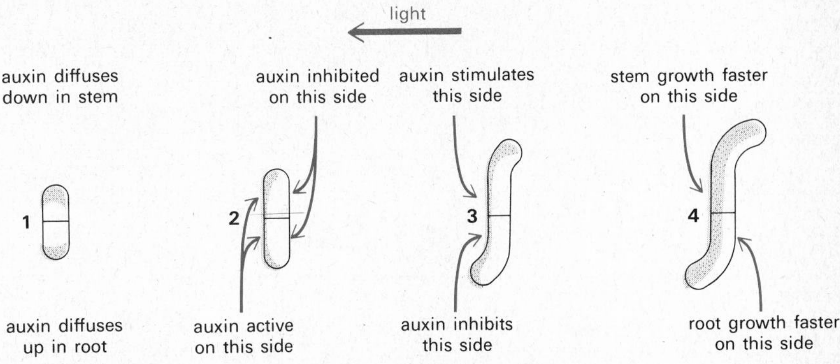

***19.6* Light and auxin** *interact in the control of stem and root growth.*

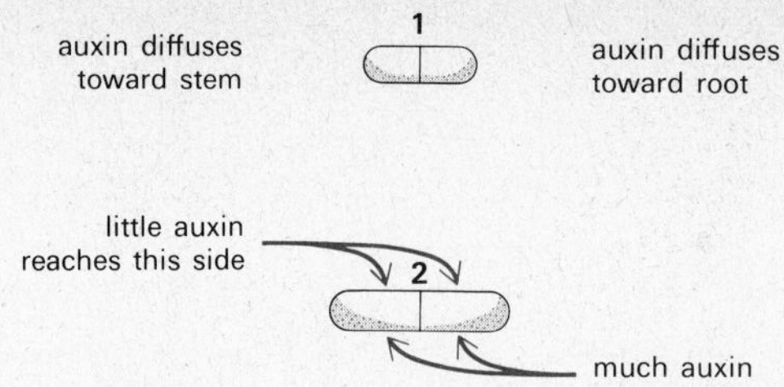

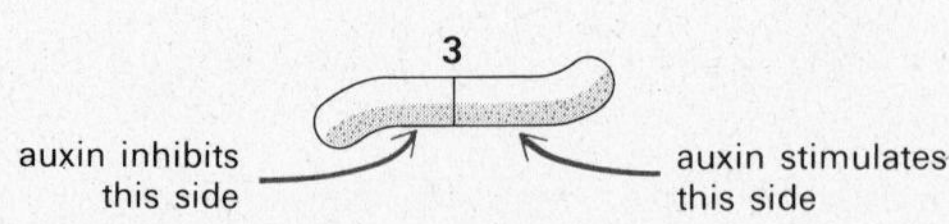

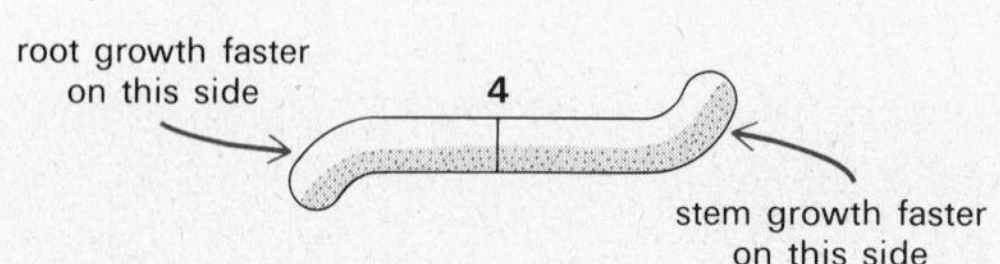

19.7 ***Gravity and auxin*** *interact in the control of stem and root growth. These processes are independent of light and occur also in the dark.*

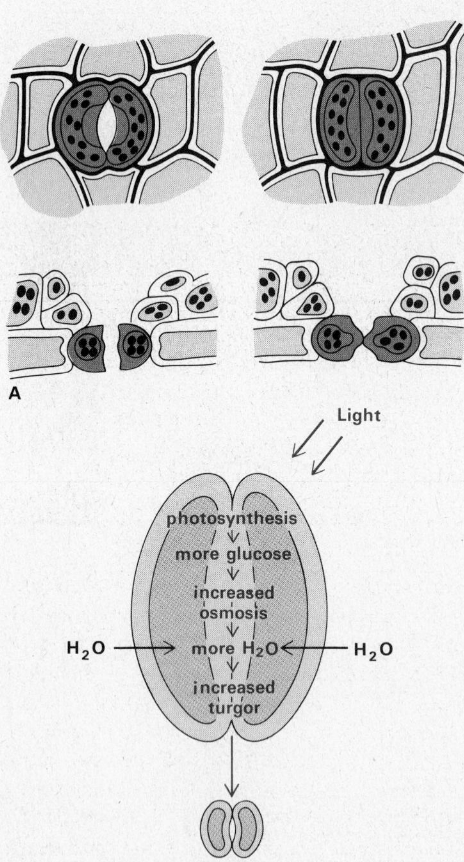

19.8 ***Stomatal action.*** *A, a pair of guard cells in a leaf. Upper figures, surface view; lower figures, cross-sectional view; left figures, stoma open; right figures, stoma closed. B, the osmotic control of guard-cell movements.*

clear how the external stimulus actually brings about particular hormone activities. Turgor movements result from changes in water pressure in cells or cell groups. Unlike growth movements, which are slow and produce more or less permanent results, turgor movements are rapid and repeatable.

The most widespread turgor movements are the opening and closing of the epidermal *guard cells* in leaves and stems. The walls of these crescent-shaped cells are thickest and stiffest on the inner sides, where they form the stomatal pore (Fig. 19.8). This construction permits a stoma to open or close when turgor increases or decreases in the guard cells. Turgor increases when the cells photosynthesize. The carbohydrate concentration then rises, and as a consequence water is drawn osmotically to the guard cells from surrounding epidermal cells. This extra water makes the guard cells swell up, and the thin outer portions of their walls curve out farther under the increased water pressure. The result is that the inner, thicker portions of the walls curve more, too, opening the stoma. Under illumination, therefore, and if other conditions are optimal, stomata will open and permit CO_2 to enter a leaf and O_2 to escape. Conversely, guard cells tend to become less turgid in the dark. Water then leaves the cells, their elastic walls revert to original positions, and the stomata close.

To be sure, lighting is not the only stimulus to which guard cells are sensitive; humidity, temperature, and possibly other environmental conditions affect the cells as well. Indeed it is in their response to combinations of various stimuli that guard cells display perhaps their most important adaptive function. For example, on a dry, hot summer day the stomata usually are almost fully closed despite the ample illumination. The rate of photosynthesis in a leaf is then reduced, inasmuch as not enough CO_2 can enter. But the evaporation of internal water, a problem of more immediate concern, is held down at the same time.

A second category of turgor movements comprises *contact motions,* produced when external agents touch parts of certain plants. For example, the leaves of *Mimosa,* the "sensitive plant," drop down from an erect position almost instantaneously when touched or warmed (Fig. 19.9). Leaves are normally kept erect by large, turgid cells in a swelling (*pulvinus*) at the base of the petioles. A touch or heat stimulus quickly leads to the transmission of a chemical signal—possibly an auxin—from the point of contact to the leaf base, and the cells there lose water rapidly. As a result the whole leaf drops down (and thereby breaks off contact with the irritating stimulus source). A turgid, erect condition is reestablished after some 10 min.

Reversible contact movements also produce the insect-trapping action of the leaves of carnivorous plants such as Venus's-flytrap (Fig. 19.10). The trapping mechanism in this plant is triggered by touch-sensitive hairs on the inner leaf surfaces. Other types of contact movement occur in the flowers of certain plants. In some, for example, the stamens snap to altered positions when an insect touches them, thereby powdering the insects with pollen. In other cases the tip of a pistil forms two joined lobes that snap together when pollen grains touch then. Pollen is trapped in this fashion. Turgor changes and signal transmission by diffusible chemical agents appear to be involved in all such plants, but the details of action are still unknown.

Changes in light intensity are the specific stimuli for so-called *sleep movements* in many plants, legumes in particular. In these turgor-produced motions the leaves assume one position during the day and another during the night. The day position is usually horizontal, the night position usually vertical, either upright or hanging. Here again the mechanism of action is not understood as yet, nor is the possible functional significance of these particular movements.

A

B

19.9 ***Contact movements.*** *Mimosa, the sensitive plant is shown before (A) and after (B) stimulation of leaflets and leaves.*

A

B

C

19.10 ***Contact movements:*** *Venus's flytrap. A, whole plant with traps in various states of closure. Hairs on the inner surfaces of the traps are sensitive to contact with external objects. B, C, one of the traps in action. (A, courtesy Carolina Biological Supply Company.)*

developmental responses: auxin effects

Numerous developmental responses of plants have been shown to be under auxin control. Some of these responses can also be produced artificially, through use of auxin preparations applied to a plant from the outside.

One action of auxin promotes *bud development.* As noted in Chap. 10, lateral stem buds form at the bases of leaves. Buds near the stem tip usually remain dormant, but those farther back along the stem often break dormancy and develop as branch stems. It can be shown that this inhibiting effect of the tip is due to auxin. IAA produced by the tip moves back toward the lateral buds. However, the optimum IAA concentration for bud growth is only about 1/1,000 of the optimum concentration for cell elongation. Therefore, as a high IAA concentration reaches the buds near the stem tip they are inhibited from breaking dormancy. This apical dominance extends backward for considerable distances, until auxin becomes sufficiently dilute to stimulate rather than inhibit bud development. The visible result is the usual tapering growth pattern of the branch system of a plant (Fig. 19.11). One problem remains to be answered: why is the development of the dominant bud not inhibited by the very high auxin concentration in that bud itself?

Auxins also exert developmental control over

19.11 Auxin effects on bud development. *The assumption here is that auxin (dark color) released from a terminal bud is concentrated enough to inhibit the development of the first three buds that produce branches behind the terminal bud. Branch buds farther back receive less than an inhibitory concentration of auxin and thus can break dormancy.*

embryonic tissues such as *cambia.* In woody plants, auxins produced in the spring by actively growing shoots diffuse to the cambia, where the hormones probably activate the cambial tissues and stimulate them to form that season's wood and bark. Developmental effects of auxin are evident also in the formation of *callus* tissue. If the cut surface of a bean stem is covered with a paste containing a large amount of IAA, this external stimulus will lead to the development of a callus, a tumorous mass of cells. Such a callus can be cut off and kept growing indefinitely in tissue culture, provided IAA is continually added to the medium.

Calluslike tissues are formed also in plant tumors known as *crown galls* (Fig. 19.12). When parasitic bacteria of a particular kind infect the tissues of certain plants, these tissues respond by forming crown-gall overgrowths. Bacteria-free portions of such a tumor can be grown in tissue culture, and auxins produced by the tumor then maintain its growth without further external stimulation. Crown galls have some superficial similarity to the malignant tumors of animals, but in such cancers auxin is never responsible for autonomous growth.

19.12 Crown galls. *A callus overgrowth on the stem of a sunflower is shown. Calluses are formed also when high concentrations of IAA are applied on cut surfaces of, for example, bean plants.*

Another important developmental function of auxins is their control of leaf fall and fruit drop. Leaves and fruits separate from a plant at an *abscission layer,* a region of special cells formed where a leaf petiole or a fruit stalk joins the stem (Fig. 19.13). In such a layer the cementing material between adjacent cells eventually dissolves, the cells die, and the leaf or the fruit then drops off. It has been shown that such separations are governed by the relative auxin concentrations on the two sides of the abscission layer. So long as IAA concentrations in a leaf or a fruit are higher than in the stem abscission normally does not occur. This is the case while leaf or fruit growth is under way, when these organs actively produce their own auxins. But after auxin manufacture ceases, as at full maturity or when cold autumn weather slows growth, then IAA concentrations in a leaf or a fruit decrease in relation to the concentrations in the stem. Under such conditions abscission is likely to take place.

Fruit growers make practical use of these relationships. In spring they can spray auxins on the stems, a procedure that raises the hormone concentrations of the stems relative to those of flowers or young fruits. The result will be many premature abscissions and a thinning out of the fruits on a tree. The fewer fruits can then become larger and better, since more food will be available to them. Later in the year auxin spray can be applied to the fruits, a procedure that will delay abscission and permit longer tree-ripening of the fruits.

Auxins play an important role in controlling the development of adventitious roots. As is well known, if a stem piece with an apical bud and some leaves is cut away from a plant and is put in soil or water, then roots will form from the base of the stem piece. It has been shown in these cases that IAA moves from the shoot tip to the vascular regions of the stem base, where it stimulates development of root tissues. Weak solutions of IAA are frequently used to promote root formation in such stem *cuttings,* a common means of propagating mature plants (Fig. 19.14).

Auxins not only aid in making new plants but also in killing old ones. When auxins are applied externally to certain plants, at concentrations much higher than those that normally promote growth, then the hormones interfere drastically with the metabolism and development of the plants. Dicot weeds are particularly sensitive to very high auxin levels, and plant death is a frequent result. Just how auxins exert this lethal effect is not clearly understood, but the effect

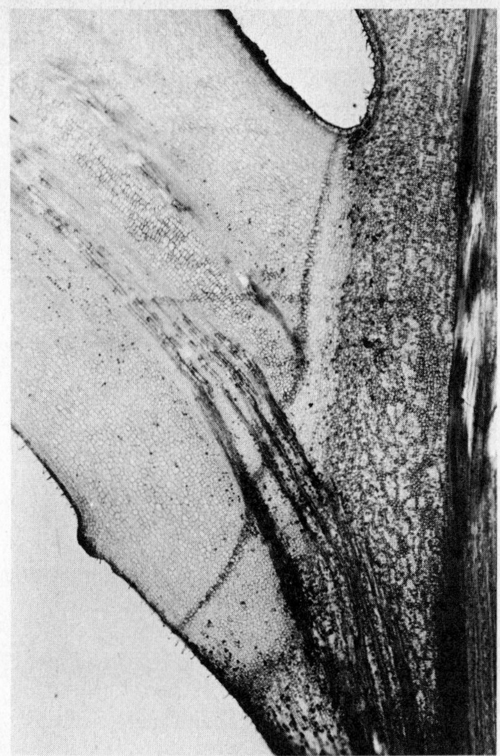

19.14 **Auxin and roots.** *After auxin application the cut stem at left develops roots as at right.*

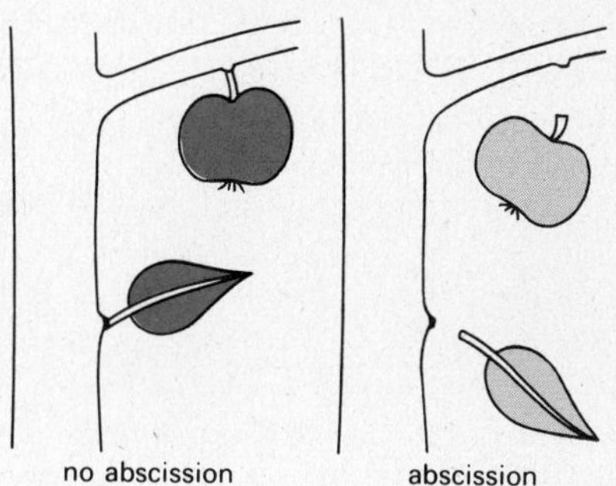

19.13 **Abscission.** *A, section through junction of leaf and stem, showing abscission layer (dark transverse cell layer) across leaf base. B, if auxin concentrations (suggested by depth of color) in leaves or fruits are higher than in the stem, abscission will not occur (left); in the converse situation the abscission cells die and leaves or fruits then drop off (right).*

19.15 *Portion of a cultivated field showing the effect of weed-killing hormones on left side. An untreated section is on the right side.*

itself has become extremely important in weed control, for monocot crop plants such as corn and grain formers are hardly affected by auxin concentrations that kill dicot weeds (Fig. 19.15).

In these various developmental responses, a basic stimulation or inhibition of cell elongation by auxin clearly accounts for many of the results. But others cannot be explained in this way alone.

developmental responses: light effects

A different set of developmental responses is produced by each of the three main attributes of light, *intensity, quality,* and *duration.*

Tomatoes and grasses are among plants that develop best in intense, direct light. In such plants the synthesis of living matter increases with increasing light intensities, up to a maximum corresponding to somewhat less than the full light of the summer sun. By contrast, plants such as violets and ferns develop optimally in dim, diffuse light and are stunted by the direct sun. Still other plants, roses among them, do well both in bright and in diffuse light.

Everything else being equal, plants grown in darkness or in dim light develop taller stems with longer internodes than if the same plants were grown in bright light. Such differences are a result of the reduced effectiveness of auxin in bright light. For the same reason brightly lit outer leaves of a plant often stay smaller than inner, more shaded ones. Where leaf size is of commercial importance, as in lettuce or tobacco, plants can be shielded by light screens or nets to promote development of larger leaves.

Prolonged darkness or exceedingly dim light usually leads to *etiolation* of plants: stems are excessively long and without sufficient supporting fiber tissue, and leaves are whitish, with a greatly reduced chlorophyll content. If light intensity does not increase, death ultimately follows. Conversely, long exposure to excessively bright light stunts plant development abnormally and also leads to death (see Fig. 19.2).

The quality of light depends on its wavelengths, and these, too, can affect plant development. For example, it has been shown that brief exposure to red light retards stem elongation in plants such as oats, peas, beans, or barley. However, these retardations can be reversed and stem growth can be stimulated by then exposing the plants to light close to the limit of visibility, in the far-red region of the spectrum. In leaves, such red–far-red treatment produces opposite effects; far-red light retards leaf development, red light reverses the retardation. The functional significance of these responses is still unclear. It has been found that certain pigmented substances (*phytochromes*) present in cells in minute amounts are the stimulus receptors of the light waves.

The developmental responses of plants to different light durations are described by the term *photoperiodism.* Flower development in particular is affected by various day lengths, or *photoperiods.* Three groups of flowering plants can be distinguished on the basis of the photoperiods they require.

In *short-day plants,* flowers develop only if the plants are illuminated for less than some maximum number of hours. Cockleburs, violets, asters, strawberries, chrysanthemums, and rice are among many plants in this group; and cockleburs, for example, will flower only if their days are shorter than about 15½ hr. If such plants are exposed consistently to light periods of longer duration, their flowering is greatly retarded or they fail to flower altogether. In *long-day plants,* flowers develop only if the daily photoperiod is longer than some minimum of hours. This group includes, for example, henbane, corn, wheat, clover, beets, and lettuce. Thus, henbane will flower only if it is exposed to days longer than about 11 hr. If the photoperiods are shorter the plant will flower late or not at all. A third group of plants is not limited in its illumination requirements; such *indeterminate plants* produce flowers regardless of the length of the daily photoperiod. Tomatoes, corn, cucumbers, cotton, sunflowers, and dandelions are representative of this group.

Some of the factors involved in producing photoperiodic responses are known. First, the receptor organs specifically sensitive to light durations are the leaves. Defoliated plants cannot be made to flower even with proper light treatment. Second, the red portion of the spectrum is a more effective flower-inducing stimulus than the blue portion. Also, the amount of flowering varies with the total amount of light energy received by the leaves. Thus if two plants are illuminated for the same period but one receives light of greater intensity, that plant is likely to flower faster or more extensively.

Third, it has been found that, in short-day plants, for example, the important photoperiodic factor actually is the length of the *night,* not the length of the day. If the dark periods are of less than a certain critical length, flowering will not occur even if the light periods are of appropriate length. Moreover, if an appropriately long dark period is interrupted by even a single brief flash of light flowering will again be suppressed. Evidently, short-day plants can justifiably be called "long-night plants" as well (Fig. 19.16).

Fourth, aerial CO_2 is required to induce flowering. The role of the gas here does not appear to be nutritional, for even a well-nourished plant cannot be induced to flower if CO_2 is not present. It has been suggested that CO_2 might be needed in leaves as a raw material in the manufacture of a special flower-inducing compound. Such a "compound *A*" would be synthesized from CO_2 during the light period. During the following dark period *A* would be converted to another necessary "compound *B*." If therefore, the dark period is too short or is made too short by a light interruption, there may not be enough time for the production of sufficient amounts of *B*. Flowering would then not occur.

Last, compounds *A* and *B* probably cannot be the only substances required for flower induction. *A* and *B* are postulated to be produced in the leaves, but flowers are formed near the shoot tips. It therefore becomes necessary also to postulate the existence of a hormone *C*. This hormone would be manufactured in the leaves from compound *B* and would then migrate to a shoot tip, where it would initiate flowering (Fig. 19.17). The existence of such a flowering hormone, or *florigen,* can actually be demonstrated experimentally. In short-day cocklebur plants, for example, one test individual can be grown under short photoperiods that lead to flowering. Another individual can be kept under long photoperiods, which suppress flowering. If then the two plants are grafted together and if their earlier photoperiods are maintained, it is found that the previously nonflowering plant now begins to flower too. Evidently, a diffusible florigen has moved from one plant to the other and has induced the latter to flower.

All attempts to isolate florigens (or the postulated compounds *A* and *B*) have so far been without success. But the flower-inducing mechanism suggested by the experiments does account for the difference between short-day and long-day plants. In short-day plants, long days would make the nights too short for adequate conversion of compound *A* to *B*. Florigen in sufficient quantity would therefore not be formed, and flowering could not occur. In long-day plants, short days would not provide adequate illumination for formation of enough *A*, again leading to insufficient amounts of florigen and a suppression of flowering. Indeterminate plants would be able to form enough *A, B,* and florigen under any naturally occurring photoperiods. Accordingly, the photoperiodic differences among plants well could be quantitative rather than qualitative.

The global distribution of flowering plants tends to reflect their photoperiodic nature to some degree. Thus the days in tropical and subtropical regions are fairly uniformly short (rarely more than 12 or 13 hr), and many plants in these regions are short-day species. The temperate zone supports both short-day and long-day types. The former flower mainly during the short-day seasons of spring and fall, the latter during the long-day season of summer. In higher latitudes above the temperate zone most plants are long-day species, adapted to the long days and short nights that characterize most of the growing season. Indeterminate plants are distributed widely over all climatic zones.

Knowledge of photoperiodic responses has been turned to horticultural advantage. By artifi-

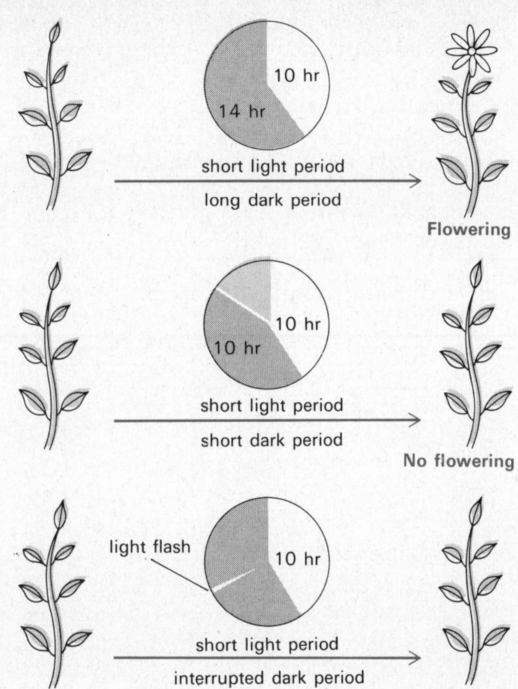

19.16 Photoperiodism. *Importance of the right duration and continuity of the dark period in short-day plants.*

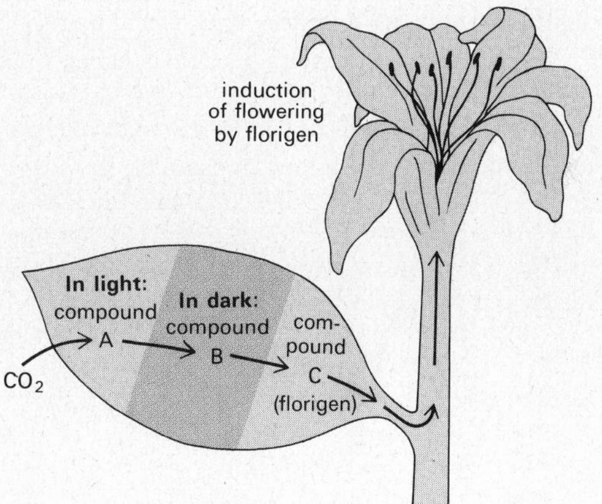

19.17 Flowering hormones. *Hypothetical sequence of events leading to formation of florigen and a photoperiodic response.*

cially extending or reducing day lengths under controlled conditions, commercially important plants can be induced to flower at virtually any season of the year or can be inhibited from developing flowers.

developmental responses: temperature and other effects

Temperature has developmental effects in plants that are probably not due merely to changes in metabolic rates. The most striking developmental results of temperature treatment, or *vernalization,* again are flowering responses.

Whether or not flowering will occur in mature annual plants can be shown to depend on the temperature to which the germinating seeds of such plants had been exposed. For example, seeds of temperate-zone annuals like winter wheat must be exposed to low temperatures if flowering is to occur later in the mature plants. Such seeds are normally sown in the fall and the following winter provides the required low temperature. If the seeds are not vernalized in this manner flowering does not occur. By contrast, seeds of tropical annuals such as rice must be vernalized at high temperatures (80°F or more) if later flowering is to take place (Fig. 19.18).

The receptor of the temperature stimulus in a seed is the embryo. The suggestion has been made that vernalization might permit manufacture of a special hormone that persists as the plant matures and that eventually induces flowering. The name *vernalin* has been proposed for this hormone, but, as in the case of florigen, attempts to extract it have so far been unsuccessful. Experiments do show, however, that a plant must be vernalized first before it will respond to photoperiodic stimuli. Conceivably, vernalin produced early in development could be a prerequisite for the later manufacture of florigen.

Whereas annual plants are normally vernalized in the seed stage as just described, biennial and perennial plants are usually vernalized later, during adult growth. Biennials such as celery, beets, and henbane grow during a first season, and the winter vernalizes the plants. Flowering then occurs during the following season. In perennials such as apples and peaches vernalization usually occurs during each winter after the plants have fully matured (see Fig. 19.18). It follows that if such cold-requiring perennials are raised in tropical or otherwise uniformly warm climates, they will not flower (even though they continue to grow). Similarly, tropical perennials grown at very high latitudes often are not vernalized either and will then not flower.

Whenever vernalization occurs in mature plants, the receptors of the temperature stimulus are the apical buds. That this is so can be demonstrated by grafting experiments. For example, a vernalized apical bud of one plant can induce flower formation in a nonvernalized apical bud of another plant if the two are grafted together. The transmitted signal appears to be quite unspecific, for flower induction occurs even when the graft partners are of different species.

The importance of flowering in the life of plants evidently is fully matched by the complexity of its control. Temperature, light, hormones, and presumably other agents as well, all must exercise their separate effects; the total result then is the development or nondevelopment of a flower. The adaptive value of this complex control probably lies in a saving of energy and materials; a flower is normally formed only under the best possible environmental conditions, when the reproductive effort is most likely to succeed.

Other stimuli affecting plant development include *mechanical* ones, such as the pressure of rocks on roots or the pressure of wind on stems and branches. Plants are able to resist such mechanical constraints to a considerable degree and indeed generate pressure themselves, as when growing roots split rocks and crack pavement. Numerous *chemical* stimuli influence plant development as well. Many of these are toxic and stunt growth or retard development and flowering. The rapid disappearance of vegetation from heavily industrialized regions is probably due as much

19.18 Vernalization. *A, vernalization at the seed stage. B, vernalization at the adult stage.*

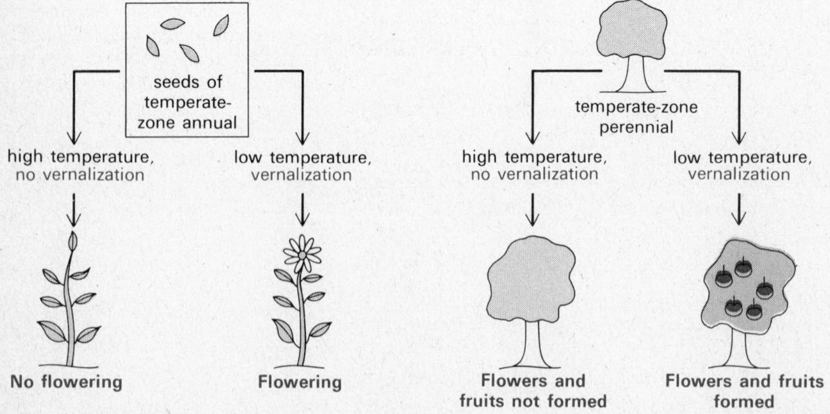

19.19 ***Toxic effects on plants.*** *In the early 1940s, poisonous fumes from the smelter shown here (in the Tennessee Copper Basin) killed off all plants in a surrounding area of about 100 square miles. Today the vegetation is only just beginning to come back, very slowly.*

to pollutants in air, water, and soil as to restrictions of space (Fig. 19.19). Surprisingly also, soil decomposition products of certain plants often tend to be toxic to later individuals of the same species. This circumstance can result in a gradual decline of vigor over successive generations. Crop rotation is beneficial partly for this reason.

Through hormones and other, still unknown controls, plants evidently respond to the multitude of stimuli that affect them, and in many cases these responses are adequate countermeasures to the stimuli. Such controls permit plants to maintain steady states and to remain alive even in a rapidly and complexly changing environment.

endocrine secretions

All animals probably contain chemical agents that after being produced in one body part, have specific regulatory or coordinating effects in other parts. Such substances are generally referred to as *humoral* agents. For example, CO_2 qualifies as a simple humoral agent in mammals; among other effects it exerts a controlling function over breathing (see Chap. 20).

In certain instances humoral agents are distinct hormones, produced by specialized *endocrine* cells and discharged not through ducts but directly to the body fluids. For example, nerve cells are endocrine inasmuch as they secrete hormones at their ends (see Chap. 21). Indeed in some animals all endocrines present are *neurosecretory* cells: modified or unmodified nerve cells that secrete a variety of hormones having a variety of functions outside the nervous system. In other instances endocrine cells are not part of the nervous system and are often components of elaborate endocrine organs. Several such organs and any neurosecretory cells present constitute an endocrine system.

Hormones vary greatly in chemical composition. Some are proteins, a few are amino acids, and the rest are various other simple or complex compounds. A few can be synthesized in the laboratory, a few have known chemical structure, and the remainder are known only through the abnormal effects produced by hormone deficiency or hormone excess.

To date, the presence of endocrine cells has been demonstrated more or less definitely only in animals such as nemertine worms, certain segmented worms, mollusks, most arthropods, and chordates, including tunicates and all vertebrates. Cells of the neurosecretory type occur in all these groups, but nonnervous endocrine cells are conspicuous only in arthropods and vertebrates. The known functions of the endocrine secretions differ greatly among the groups named. In some worms the hormones play a role in growth and regeneration. In squids and octopuses neurosecretory hormones appear to control mainly the expansion and contraction of pigment-containing cells in the skin. By such means the animal can change its coloration to blend with environmental backgrounds or in response to external stimuli (for example, color changes in an "excited" octopus).

Regulation of the activities of pigment cells also is one function of arthropod hormones. Among others are control of breeding and mating behavior and, as noted in Chap. 12, regulation of molting during development. Apart from such specific direct effects on given tissues and processes, the endocrines of arthropods also affect one another; hormones synthesized by particular glands stimulate or inhibit the hormone production of other glands. It is through interactions of this kind that the glands become an integrated endocrine system, even though they are unconnected structurally.

Vertebrate endocrine systems are by far the most complex. In vertebrates the number of glands is much greater than in other animals, and indeed many of these glands are anatomical composites of two or more distinct endocrine organs, each producing its own hormones (Fig. 19.20 and Table 14). In a vertebrate hardly any function occurs that is not influenced at least in part by hormones. Endocrine control usually operates in conjunction with nervous control, and in many instances the nervous system supplies information about the external environment while the endocrine system regulates the internal response to this information.

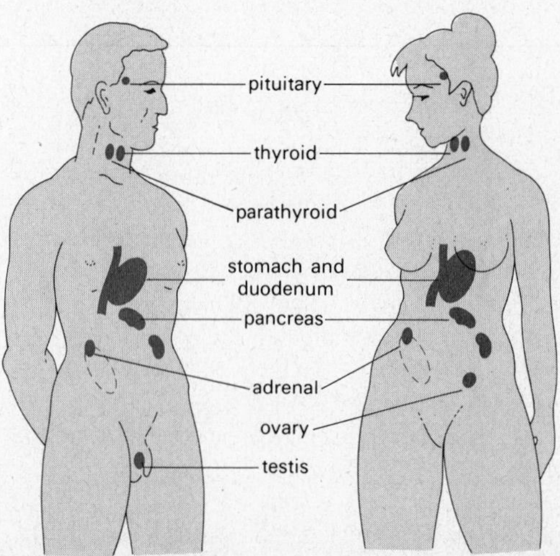

19.20 Vertebrate endocrine organs.

Like vitamins, most vertebrate hormones are required in most or all cells of the body. Accordingly, labels such as "sex hormones," for example, are somewhat misleading. To be sure, sex hormones are manufactured in sex organs and the hormones contribute to the proper functioning of these organs. However, sex hormones also contribute to the functioning of virtually every other organ of a vertebrate. It happens that the effect of deficiency or excess of a given hormone often reveals itself first or most obviously in a particular body part. For convenience the hormone can then be named according to this body part, but it cannot be concluded that the hormone functions only there.

Apart from their other controlling roles in cells, some vertebrate hormones perform an additional special function: like some arthropod hormones, they control each other. Of particular importance in this respect are some of the hormones of the pituitary gland.

pituitary hormones

The pituitary gland consists of an *anterior lobe,* an *intermediate lobe,* and a *posterior lobe* (Fig. 19.21). Each is a distinct endocrine gland that secretes its own hormones. A short stalk from the posterior lobe attaches the whole gland to the underside of the brain.

Through secretion of so-called *tropic hormones,* the anterior lobe exercises control over the thyroid gland, the adrenal glands, and the sex organs. The hormones of these glands inhibit the activity of the pituitary in turn. The result is that the output of each gland is regulated by the output of the others.

For example, the pituitary secretes a *thyrotropic* hormone, TSH for short (see Fig. 19.21). The only known function of this hormone is to stimulate the thyroid gland. Without TSH the thyroid is inactive; with TSH the thyroid is stimulated to secrete its own hormone, *thyroxin.* Apart from influencing respiratory rates thyroxin also has one other function; when its concentration in blood exceeds certain levels, it inhibits a region of the brain called the *hypothalamus* (see Chap. 21). This region in turn signals the pituitary,

Table 14. The main vertebrate endocrine glands and their hormones

gland	*hormones*	*chief functions*	*effects of deficiency or excess*
pituitary, anterior lobe	TSH (thyrotropic)	stimulates thyroid	
	ACTH (adrenocorticotropic)	stimulates adrenal cortex	
	FSH (follicle-stimulating)	stimulates ovary (follicle)	
	LH (luteinizing)	stimulates testes in male, corpus luteum in female	
	prolactin (lactogenic)	stimulates milk secretion, parental behavior	
	growth	promotes cell metabolism	dwarfism; gigantism
pituitary, midlobe	intermedin	controls adjustable skin-pigment cells (for example, in frogs)	
pituitary, posterior	at least five distinct fractions	controls water metabolism, blood pressure, kidney function, smooth-muscle action	increased or reduced water excretion
thyroid	thyroxin	stimulates respiration; inhibits TSH secretion	goiter; cretinism; myxedema
parathyroid	parathormone	controls Ca metabolism	nerve, muscle abnormalities; bone thickening or weakening
adrenal cortex	cortisone, other steroid hormones	controls metabolism of water, minerals, carbohydrates; controls kidney function; inhibits ACTH secretion; duplicates sex-hormone functions	Addison's disease
adrenal medulla	adrenalin, noradrenalin	alarm reaction; for example, raises blood pressure, heart rate, blood-sugar level	inability to cope with stress
pancreas	insulin	glucose $\longrightarrow$ glycogen conversion	diabetes
	glucagon	glycogen $\longrightarrow$ glucose conversion	
stomach	gastrin	stimulates gastric juice secretion	
duodenum	secretin	stimulates bile and pancreatic juice secretion	
testis	testosterone, other androgens	promote cell respiration, blood circulation; maintain primary and secondary sex characteristics, sex urge; inhibit FSH secretions	atrophy of reproductive system; decline of secondary sex characteristics
ovary: follicle	estradiol, other estrogens		
ovary: corpus luteum	progesterone	promotes secretions of oviduct, uterus growth in pregnancy; inhibits LH secretions	abortion during pregnancy

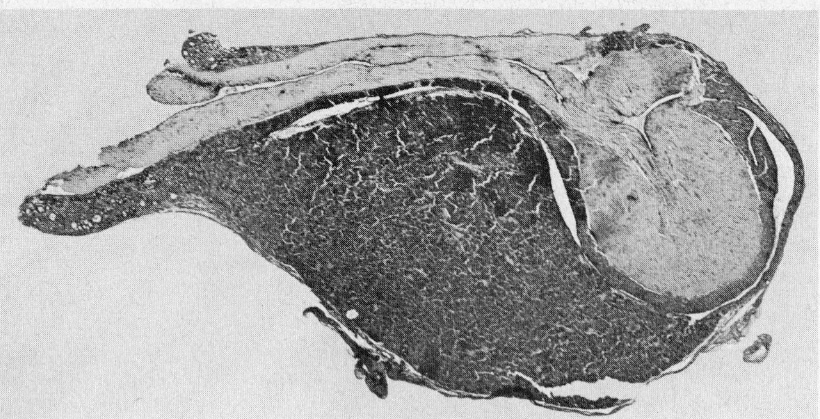

A

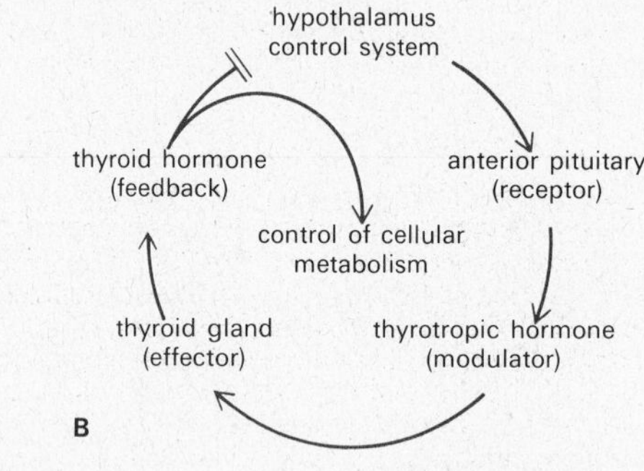

19.21 The pituitary. *A, section through a pituitary gland. The left side of the photo points in the direction of the face. Note the anterior lobe in the left part of the gland and the intermediate and posterior lobes in the right part. The posterior lobe continues dorsally as a stalk that joins the whole gland to the brain. B, the stimulative effect of thyrotropic hormone on the thyroid gland, and the inhibitive effect of thyroid hormone on the hypothalamus and the pituitary. Through such control cycles, the output of tropic pituitary hormones is automatically self-adjusting.*

which is then inhibited from secreting more TSH. Since TSH is required for thyroid activity, a reduced TSH output will be followed by a correspondingly reduced thyroxin output. But the lesser amounts of thyroxin will now have a reduced inhibitory effect on the hypothalamus; hence more TSH can again be produced.

The net result of these successive stimulations and inhibitions is that the hormone output of both the pituitary and the thyroid gland is maintained at fairly steady levels within narrow limits. Indeed the two glands and their two hormones form an automatic, self-adjusting control system with built-in feedback. Similarly controlled interactions occur also between the pituitary and the cortisone-producing adrenal cortex, and between the pituitary and the sex-hormone-producing gonads (see below).

Apart from tropic hormones the anterior lobe also secretes a *growth hormone* that regulates the general growth rates of cells (Table 14). The results of excess and deficiency of this hormone in the young are *gigantism* and *dwarfism*, respectively. Hormone excess in the adult leads to the coarse-featured condition known as *acromegaly,* characterized particularly by overgrowths in parts of the skeleton. Through the growth hormone directly and its tropic hormones indirectly, the anterior lobe has marked effects on carbohydrate, protein, and fat metabolism in cells. Another anterior-lobe secretion is *prolactin,* a hormone responsible for maternal or paternal behavior (see Chap. 26). In mammals the hormone regulates milk production specifically (and is here called *lactogenic hormone*).

All hormones of the anterior lobe are proteins. The intermediate lobe secretes *intermedin,* a hormone that functions primarily in vertebrates with adjustable skin pigmentation. In a frog, for example, the hormone brings about an expansion of pigment cells, and it thereby lightens the skin. Mammals produce intermedin, too, but in the absence of adjustable pigment cells the hormone is probably without function. Evidently, a control agent can persist through evolution even though the target of control is lost.

The posterior lobe secretes several distinct hormones. Some regulate water excretion, a function performed in conjunction with adrenal hormones (see below). Others stimulate contraction of smooth muscles, particularly in the blood vessels and in the uterus. Through these effects on blood vessels and water balance the posterior lobe influences blood pressure decisively. The effect on the uterus probably contributes to the process of childbirth during labor.

thyroid hormones

The thyroid gland lies along the trachea below the larynx. Secreting cells form single-layered hollow spheres, and the spaces in the spheres are storage depots for the secretion of the gland (Fig. 19.22).

This secretion is *thyroglobulin,* composed of a carrier protein (globulin) and *thyroxin,* the actual hormone. Thyroxin ($C_{15}H_{11}O_4I_4N$) is one of the naturally occurring amino acids (see Fig. 4.7). Its potency as a hormone is in some way associated with the four iodine atoms it contains.

Thyroxin functions chiefly in accelerating respiratory rates, as already noted in Chap. 15. If a hormone deficiency develops in early youth the clinical result may be *cretinism.* In this disease growth is stunted, mental development is retarded, sexual development is delayed or does not take place, and body weight increases unduly since little food is respired but much is stored as fat. In the adult, thyroxin deficiency leads to *myxedema,* marked by reduction of mental and bodily vigor, loss of sex drive, loss of hair, and abnormal water accumulation in the skin.

In many cases thyroxin deficiency is counteracted by enlargement of the thyroid gland and secretion of more hormone. Body functions can then become normal, but a *goiter* will be in evidence. Hormone deficiencies (and goiter) can also be relieved by administration of thyroxin from an external source. Under conditions of thyroxin excess, so much heat is generated through respiration that the affected individual feels hot all the time. Despite abundant food intake so much is burned that body weight can decrease. The hyperthyroid individual also is tense and highly irritable and is unable to do sustained work because of lack of fuel reserves.

In amphibians thyroxin plays a critical developmental role during metamorphosis. If thyroid function in an embryo or a young tadpole is in some way inhibited (for example, by excising the thyroid gland), then the animal remains a tadpole permanently. Conversely, if a young tadpole is given an excess of thyroxin, the larva metamorphoses prematurely into a tiny froglet.

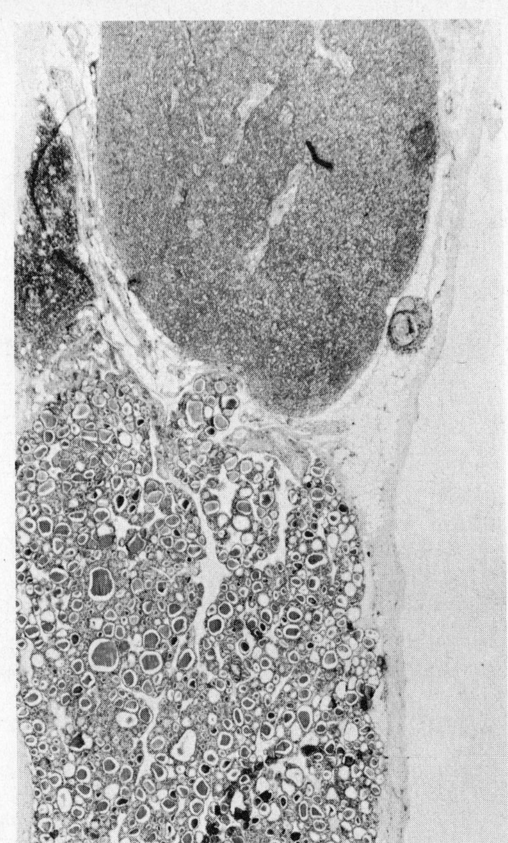

19.22 Thyroid and parathyroid. *A portion of the parathyroid gland is seen at top (darker, denser tissue). In the thyroid section at bottom, the round spaces largely filled with dark material are the regions where thyroxin accumulates before being carried off in blood.*

parathyroid hormones

The parathyroid glands are tiny paired organs located either near or right inside the thyroid. The basic function of the parathyroid hormone (*parathormone*) is control of cellular calcium metabolism and, as a corollary, maintenance of a constant calcium level in blood. If the hormone is in abnormally low supply, blood calcium is deposited in abnormally large quantities in bones. Lack of these ions also makes muscles and nerves hyperirritable; the slightest stimulus can throw the whole body into convulsive twitching. Such attacks are completely exhausting and lead to death very quickly. When parathormone is present in excess, calcium is withdrawn from bones and the skeleton weakens; the blood calcium level rises; and nerves and muscles become hypoirritable, making an individual unresponsive to stimuli.

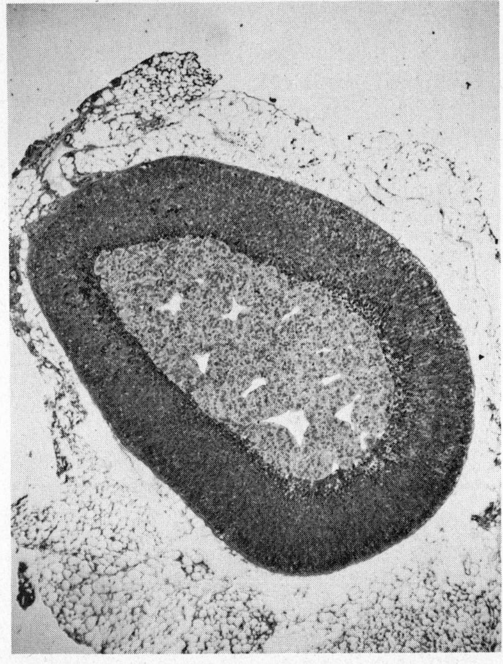

19.23 The adrenal gland. *In this section through a mouse adrenal, note the dark cortex and the inner medulla.*

adrenal hormones

Adrenal glands are paired organs near the kidneys. Each consists of two distinct parts, an outer *cortex* and an inner *medulla,* that produce their own hormones (Fig. 19.23).

All cortical hormones (among which the best

known is *cortisone*) are related steroid compounds. As noted, their secretion is under the control of a tropic hormone from the pituitary (adrenocorticotropic hormone, or ACTH). The main functions of the cortical hormones are regulation of water, mineral, and carbohydrate metabolism in cells. Thus, through control over water balance (exercised in conjunction with hormones from the posterior pituitary), the adrenal cortex affects the excretory activities of the kidneys. There the cortical hormones also promote retention of sodium and chloride ions and excretion of potassium ions, as well as elimination of wastes such as urea. Moreover, the hormones accelerate the conversion of glycogen to glucose in cells (an action paralleling that of the pancreatic hormone glucagon but contrary to that of insulin and thyroxin).

In addition, the adrenal cortex influences the sex organs and in turn is influenced by them. The chemical differences between the hormones of both types of organ are slight (see Fig. 4.6), and some of the cortical hormones actually duplicate the effects of sex hormones to a certain extent. Particularly before puberty, or sexual maturity, many of the sex differences between males and females (other than those in the reproductive systems) are maintained by adrenal hormones. The cortical hormones have still other effects, on membranes in joints and eyes and on the skin and other body parts. Most of these actions are secondary consequences of cortical control over water, ion, and carbohydrate metabolism. By virtue of these widely divergent functions the adrenal cortex is one of the most crucial regulators in the vertebrate body.

The hormones produced by the adrenal medulla are *adrenalin* and *noradrenalin* (also called *epinephrine* and *norepinephrine,* or collectively simply "adrenalin"). These substances are synthesized from the amino acid tyrosine, and they are also formed locally inside the nervous system (see Chap. 21). The connection between the adrenal medulla and the nervous system actually goes even deeper, for both structures develop from embryonic ectoderm and the secretion of the adrenal medulla is under nervous control.

Adrenalin raises blood pressure; increases heart rate; promotes conversion of liver glycogen to blood glucose; inhibits the peristaltic movements of the gut; stimulates the tiny muscles attached to hairs and feathers, which are raised as a result (and produce "goose flesh" in man); dilates the pupils of the eyes; increases muscular power and resistance to fatigue; promotes faster coagulation of blood; and generally promotes faster and sharper responses to external stimuli. Together, most or all of these effects are called the *alarm reaction.* It comes into play during danger or emergency, when an animal is under great emotional or physical stress (see also Chap. 23). Increased secretion of adrenalin then prepares the animal for more intense effort.

other hormones

Male sex hormones, or *androgens,* are secreted by mature testes, and female sex hormones, or *estrogens,* by mature ovaries. The functions of these hormones are discussed in detail in Chap. 26. All sex hormones are steroid compounds, chemically similar to adrenocortical hormones, as noted (see Fig. 4.6). Both sexes in fact produce *both* androgens and estrogens in the sex organs. It is the relative quantitative ratio of hormones, not their absolute amount, that is of importance. Thus so long as a definite balance of male and female hormones is present, regardless of which is more abundant in absolute terms, the cells of a female will respond differentially to estrogens, the cells of a male, to androgens. The sex-hormone balances actually differ slightly for different individuals, which probably accounts for the various degrees of masculinity and femininity widely in evidence.

The roles of the hormones *gastrin* and *secretin* have already been discussed (see Chap. 14), as have the actions of the pancreatic hormones *insulin* and *glucagon.* Unlike pancreatic juice, insulin and glucagon do not have access to the pancreatic duct; blood is their only exit path (see Fig. 17.16). The kidneys produce a hormone called *renin,* which regulates blood pressure. And in Chap. 21 hormones are described that participate in the transmission of nerve impulses.

Many of the hormonal substances of vertebrates are known to occur also in other animal groups and indeed in plants as well. In such organisms the compounds do not *function* as hormones, however, just as auxins do not function as hormones in the many animals in which such compounds are found. Wide occurrence of certain chemicals indicates that they are fairly usual products of metabolism; and during the evolution of certain organisms many of these chemicals happened to prove useful as control agents in newly evolved processes.

In most animals steady-state regulation is achieved not only by hormones and growth factors in general, but also by various tissue- and organ-level control systems without counterparts in plants. These unique animal controls are examined in the following chapters.

review questions

1 Describe the chemical nature of auxins and the effect of these hormones on plant cells and on the growth and development of whole plants. Show how auxins contribute to maintenance of steady states in plants.

2 What are gibberellins and kinins? Describe the effects of these substances on plants and plant cells.

3 What different types of growth movement occur in plants? Describe various tropic responses of plants, and review the role of auxins in producing such responses. What is the importance of different auxin sensitivities?

4 Describe the different types of turgor movement in plants. Review the mechanism of the opening and closing movements of guard cells. Describe the nature of the responses of sensitive plants to touch.

5 Review the role of auxins in controlling developmental responses of plants. What is an abscission layer? How can fruit or leaf abscission be promoted or inhibited by artificial means?

6 What are calluses and crown galls? Describe auxin effects on root growth, cambia, and bud development. Review all the nondevelopmental effects of light on plants.

7 Describe the developmental responses of plants to (*a*) light intensity, (*b*) light quality, (*c*) light duration. What is etiolation? What is a photoperiod? Define short-day, long-day, and indeterminate plants.

8 What factors play a role in the production of a photoperiodic response in plants, and what sort of hypothesis can account for the significance of these factors? What are florigens? What evidence has suggested that such compounds exist?

9 Show how the photoperiodic characteristics of given plants are reflected in the global distribution of the plants. Describe the nondevelopmental and the developmental effects of temperature on plants. What is vernalization, and what is its practical importance?

10 Show how vernalization requirements differ for (*a*) annual and perennial plants, (*b*) temperate-zone and tropical plants. Review the effects of other physical and also of chemical and biological stimuli on plants.

11 Review the specific functions of arthropod hormones. Which animal groups are known to have endocrines? What are humoral agents?

12 Which vertebrate endocrine glands control the activity of other endocrine glands? Make a diagram showing how the activity of the adrenal cortex is regulated by the pituitary and vice versa.

13 What are the specific hormones produced by the various endocrine glands of vertebrates? As far as is known what are the primary cellular functions of each of these hormones? In each case, what are the clinical effects of hormone deficiency and hormone excess?

14 What are the specific metabolic effects of intermedin, glucagon, adrenalin, gastrin, parathormone? What determines whether a medicinal preparation of hormones or other drugs must be injected or can be taken orally?

15 In what respects are the actions of hormones, vitamins, and minerals similar, and in what respects are they different? What defines a control agent as a growth factor? What categories of control agents are usually not growth factors?

collateral readings

Braun, A. C.: Plant Cancer, *Sci. American,* June, 1952. An account on calluses and crown galls.

Butler, W. L., and **R. J. Downs**: Light and Plant Development, *Sci. American,* Dec., 1960. A recommended article on photoperiodism in plants.

Davidson, E. H.: Hormones and Genes, *Sci. American,* June, 1965. Preliminary evidence indicates that hormones probably exert reaction control by influencing the transcription of genetic codes.

Etkin, W.: How a Tadpole Becomes a Frog, *Sci. American,* May, 1966. A description of the feedback system between the pituitary and thyroid glands that controls amphibian metamorphosis.

Funkenstein, D. H.: The Physiology of Fear and Anger, *Sci. American,* May, 1955. A study of the role of adrenalin in human emotion.

Galston, A. W.: "The Life of the Green Plant," 2d ed., Prentice-Hall, Englewood Cliffs, N.J., 1964. Sections on plant growth and growth substances are included in this paperback.

Gray, R. W.: Cortisone and ACTH, *Sci. American,* May, 1950. The role of these hormones in stress and human disease is reviewed.

Greulach, V. A: Plant Movements, *Sci. American,* Feb., 1955. Some of the movements studied in this chapter are examined.

Jacobs, W. P.: What Makes Leaves Fall?, *Sci. American,* Nov., 1955. An account on experiments on abscission and the role of auxins in this process

Levey, R. H.: The Thymus Hormone, *Sci. American,* July, 1964. An organ previously believed to have no endocrine effects has now been shown to secrete substances that play a role in antibody manufacture.

Levine, R., and **M. S. Goldstein**: The Action of Insulin, *Sci. American,* May, 1958. The cellular and general biological role of this hormone is discussed.

Li, C. H.: The Pituitary, *Sci. American,* Oct., 1950. A general examination of this gland and its hormones.

———: The ACTH Molecule, *Sci. American,* July, 1963. The function of this pituitary hormone is outlined in relation to its structure.

Naylor, A. W.: The Control of Flowering, *Sci. American,* May, 1952. Some of the hormonal and other controls are examined.

Overbeek, J. van: The Control of Plant Growth, *Sci. American,* July, 1968. An article describing the most recent knowledge available concerning hormonal stimulating and inhibiting effects on the growth of plants. Recommended.

Rasmussen, H.: The Parathyroid Hormone, *Sci. American,* Apr., 1961. The function of this hormone in man is described.

Salisbury, F. B.: Plant Growth Substances, *Sci. American,* Apr., 1957. A review of growth factors other than auxins.

———: The Flowering Process, *Sci. American,* Apr., 1958. Experiments revealing the functioning of flowering hormones are described.

——— and **R. V. Parke**: "Vascular Plants: Form and Function," Wadsworth, Belmont, Calif., 1964. This paperback contains a section on photobiology, another on biological time, and a third on the flowering process, all pertinent readings in the context of this chapter.

Scott, B. I. H.: Electricity in Plants, *Sci. American,* Oct., 1962. Electric currents in some respects similar to nerve impulses appear to exert certain controlling influences on plant behavior.

Steward, F. C.: The Control of Growth in Plant Cells, *Sci. American,* Oct., 1963. The roles of inhibition and promotion of growth in the transformation of a root cell into a whole plant are described.

———: "Plants at Work," Addison-Wesley, Reading, Mass., 1964. A section on growth in this paperback contains accounts of tropisms, hormones, and responses of plants to various stimuli.

Sweeney, B. M.: The Measurement of Time in Plants, in "Plant Biology Today," **W. A. Jensen** and **L. G. Kavaljian** (eds.), Wadsworth, Belmont, Calif., 1963. A very interesting chapter on rhythmic behavior and biological clocks of plants.

Went, F. W.: Plant Growth and Plant Hormones, in "This is Life," **W. H. Johnson** and **W. C. Steere** (eds.), Holt, Rinehart and Winston, New York, 1962. An excellent review article by the discoverer of auxins. Recommended.

Wurtman, R. J., and **J. Axelrod:** The Pineal Gland, *Sci. American,* June, 1965. Another organ that previously was believed to be without function in mammals has been shown to have some regulatory effects on the sex organs.

Zuckerman, S.: Hormones, *Sci. American,* March, 1957. An interpretive article on the general biological significance of these control agents.

chapter 20 intercellular control

Cells are in steady state relative to their immediate surroundings. In an animal these surroundings are other cells and, in most instances, also body fluids, *blood* and *lymph.* These fill all the spaces between cells and cell layers. Cells and tissues thus reflect the conditions prevailing in blood and lymph, and vice versa.

The attributes of the body fluids are controlled primarily by three systems. The *circulatory* system regulates the physical properties of the fluids it carries, such as pressure, distribution, and rate of flow. And the *breathing* and *excretory* systems govern the chemical properties of the body fluids. Both systems continuously monitor and adjust the composition of the body fluids, and they control the exchange of materials between body fluids and the external environment. In the process they also determine what is or is not a waste product.

blood and lymph

In ancestral animals the internal fluid was probably little different from sea water, and modern animals have inherited a form of "sea water," or *lymph,* as the universal internal medium of their bodies.

Lymph functions chiefly in maintaining *water, salt, pH,* and *osmotic* equilibria between the interior and exterior of cells. Secondarily lymph also provides a medium for the diffusion and transport of foodstuffs, respiratory gases, waste materials, and in some cases hormones, and any other substances that pass from one body region to another. In many animals the body fluids are kept in motion by means of specialized flow channels and pumping organs, or circulatory systems. Any body fluid confined partly or wholly in circulatory channels is *blood.*

As noted in earlier contexts, blood channels in different animals are either open or closed. In an open system blood and lymph are essentially indistinguishable and both body fluids contain the same components. In a closed system most materials in blood pass through vessel walls readily, but blood proteins and blood cells largely do not. All blood components other than the cells form a fluid *plasma,* and the presence of such a medium between blood cells makes blood a tissue.

plasma

The main ingredient of plasma is water. Its source is food and metabolic water exported from cells to the body fluids. The supply of water is carefully adjusted by elimination of excess amounts through the breathing and excretory systems. In this fashion the total water content of the body, hence also blood volume, is maintained constant. The water of plasma influences blood pressure, and it is the transport vehicle of blood cells and numerous dissolved materials.

These dissolved components are of two general types (Table 15). One comprises substances that fluctuate more or less widely in concentration, depending on body activity. In this category are a number of foods, hormones, certain waste products (urea, for example), and many other compounds. In the second group are components normally maintained at constant concentrations. Included here are, apart from water itself, mineral ions, foods such as glucose, and numerous other compounds that are either nutrients in transit to tissue cells or waste products in transit to the excretory organs.

Constancy in the concentration of these substances is achieved by a balance between supply and removal. Supplies are obtained from tissue cells via lymph and from the alimentary system, particularly the gut and the liver. Removal can involve liver storage, elimination through the excretory system, or passage to lymph and later absorption by tissue cells. In each case too high or too low a concentration of a given substance in blood is the critical stimulus for its own removal or replenishment. For example, a moderately high blood-glucose level stimulates liver cells to reduce the concentration by storing the excess as glycogen. A still higher level stimulates storage not only in liver but also in muscle and skin; and a very high concentration leads to glucose excretion from the kidneys.

The mineral ions in plasma are of the same types as those in lymph and in the interior of cells in general. These ions contribute to *salt, pH,* and *osmotic* balance between plasma, lymph, and tissue cells. For example, if through intake of much salt water the mineral concentration of blood should rise, then the tissues would lose water osmotically and would become dehydrated. Conversely, if through intake of too much plain water the ion concentration in blood should fall, the tissues would gain water. Temporary fluctuations of this sort (and accompanying pH changes) can occur frequently; but fairly narrow limits are imposed by the excretory organs, which eliminate any excess material. From hour to hour, therefore, blood has constant osmotic pressure and pH; in

*Table 15. The main components of blood plasma and their functions**

components	functions
1. water	maintains blood volume and pressure; forms lymph; water supply of cells; provides vehicle for other constituents
2. mineral ions	maintain osmotic balance, pH balance; buffer capacity; varied effects on tissue cells
3. plasma proteins	all maintain osmotic and pH balance
fibrinogen	participates in blood clotting
prothrombin	participates in blood clotting
albumins, enzymes	functions obscure
globulins	basis of blood types; act as antibodies
4. glucose, other organic metabolites	in transit to and from cells
5. urea, CO_2, O_2, various foods, hormones, vitamins, and others	in transit to and from cells

*Categories 1 to 4 are maintained at constant concentrations; materials in category 5 occur in variable concentrations.

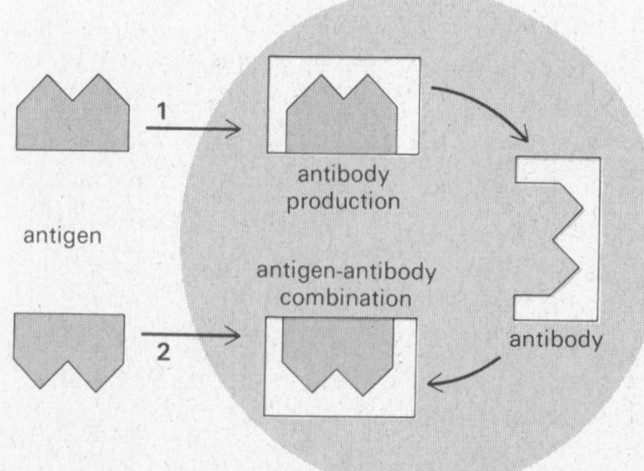

20.1 Antibodies. *A foreign protein introduced into an animal is an antigen. It elicits the formation of antibodies (1), which "fit" precisely the surface configuration of the antigen. If later these same antigens invade the animal (2), the specific antibodies already present can combine with the antigens and render them harmless.*

human blood the pH is normally 7.3 or 7.4.

Plasma differs importantly from lymph in that it contains an appreciable concentration of *blood proteins,* another group of components kept at constant concentrations. In vertebrates these proteins are manufactured largely in the liver, they normally leave the circulation only in very limited amounts, and they serve in a variety of nonnutritional roles. First, like the mineral ions, all these proteins contribute to maintaining the osmotic pressure and pH of blood. Particularly important in osmotic regulation are the *albumins,* blood proteins named after their chemical resemblance to egg white. Second, some of the proteins are ingredients in the *clotting* reaction (see below). Third, many of the proteins are active enzymatically. One of them, *prothrombin,* is a clotting factor. Others are enzymes such as are found in tissue cells generally and even in the intestine. Their catalytic functions in plasma are still largely obscure.

Fourth, proteins called *globulins* are the basis of differences in the *blood types* of animals, a consequence of the general phenomenon of protein specificity (see Chap. 30). And last, some of the globulins also serve as defensive *antibodies,* which destroy or render harmless infective agents such as bacteria. Animals can thereby become *immune,* an important aspect of steady-state control that is ultimately a consequence of protein specificities, too (Fig. 20.1).

Apart from its protein content, plasma in many animals differs from lymph also in another respect, the presence of *respiratory pigments.* However, in a good many animal groups such pigments occur not in plasma but in blood cells.

blood cells

The bloods of most animals contain *nonpigmented* cells of various kinds, and many also contain *pigmented* cells (Fig. 20.2). The nonpigmented cells are usually capable of amoeboid locomotion. Called *white* blood cells in vertebrates, such cells can squeeze in between the cells that form the walls of the smallest blood vessels and leave the circulation in this manner. White blood cells are of two main types, *leukocytes* and *lymphocytes.* In leukocytes the amoeboid habit is developed particularly well. Once leukocytes are out in the body tissues, they can migrate toward sites of infection and engulf the bacteria present there (Fig. 20.3). An accumulation of leukocytes, bacteria, and cellular debris in wounded areas represents *pus*.

Lymphocytes, too, serve in body defense. By transforming to mesenchyme cells and fibrocytes, lymphocytes contribute importantly to wound healing and scar-tissue formation after injury. Lymphocytes also serve as lymph-purifying agents. Particles of dust, smoke, and other materials frequently get into lungs, and lymph then usually carries such particles to the lymph nodes present along the paths of lymph vessels (Fig. 20.4 and see Fig. 14.17). The lymphocytes there engulf the particles and retain them permanently.

A cubic millimeter of human blood normally contains about 8,000 to 10,000 white blood cells, a number that increases greatly during infections. The control system that regulates the number is not fully understood as yet. Lymphocytes are manufactured mainly in the lymph nodes; leukocytes originate in the liver and spleen during embryonic stages but in the marrow of long bones in the adult. Bone marrow is also believed to be the main generating tissue of the *platelets* of vertebrate blood (see Fig. 20.2). These bodies are cell fragments, often without nuclei, and their number, too, is normally constant; a cubic millimeter of human blood contains some 250,000 platelets on the average.

When platelets rupture on the rough edges of torn blood vessels, they initiate blood *clotting*. Broken platelets release an enzymatic substance, *thrombokinase*. This substance interacts in plasma with calcium ions and the blood protein *prothrombin*. The protein is an inactive precursor of the catalyst *thrombin*. In the presence of calcium ions and thrombokinase, prothrombin becomes thrombin. The latter then reacts with *fibrinogen*, another of the blood proteins, yielding fibrin (Fig. 20.5). This insoluble coagulated protein is the blood clot. As noted in Chap. 19, vitamin K participates in some manner in the clotting process.

In pure form a clot is a yellowish-white meshwork of fibers, but pigmented blood cells are usually trapped in this meshwork, hence the clot is normally red. Clotting cannot occur when any of the ingredients are missing or inoperative. For example, fibrinogen can be removed fairly easily from whole blood or plasma, a procedure often used in storing blood or plasma for transfusions. Plasma minus fibrinogen is *blood serum*. Clotting is also inhibited in the absence of calcium or when blood platelets are defective. In one type of (hereditary) disease in man, platelets are not being produced. In another, platelets have thickened

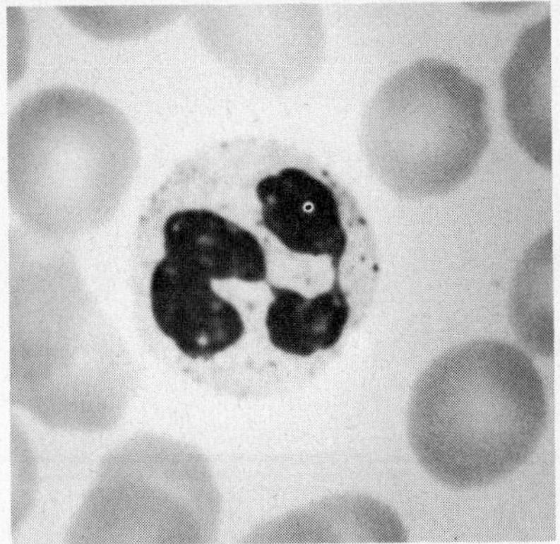

A

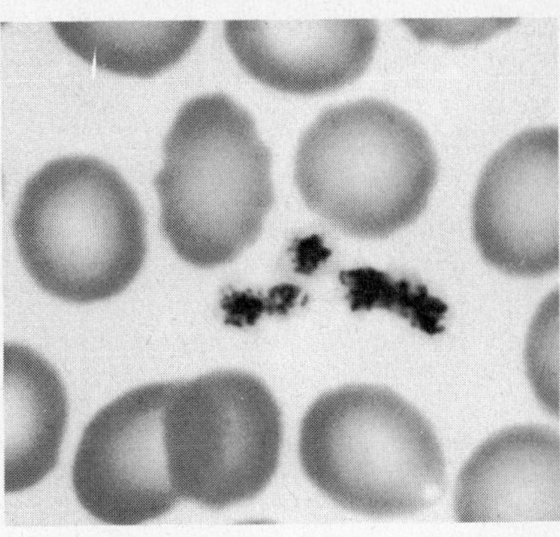

B

20.2 Blood cells. *Human red blood corpuscles are shown in both photos. Note absence of nuclei. A white blood cell (nucleated) is shown in A, center, and a few blood platelets in B, center. See also Fig. 5.1.*

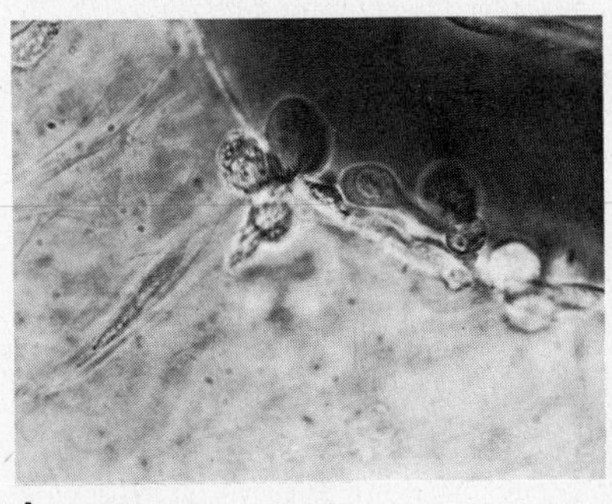

A

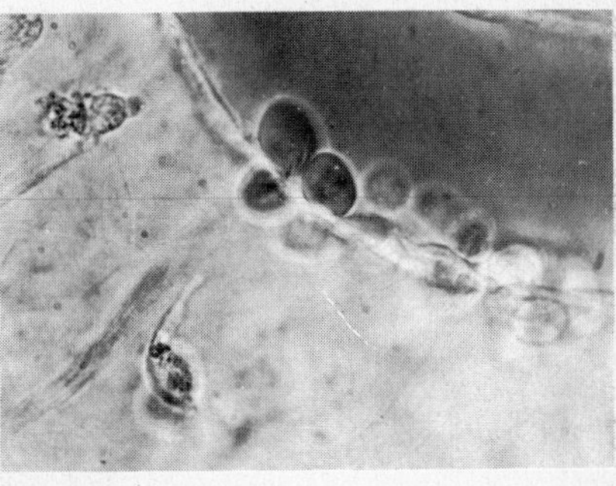

B

20.3 Blood cell migration. *In each photo a blood-filled capillary is in upper right portion. In A two white blood cells have just penetrated through the capillary wall into surrounding tissues. In B the white blood cells have migrated farther into the tissues.*

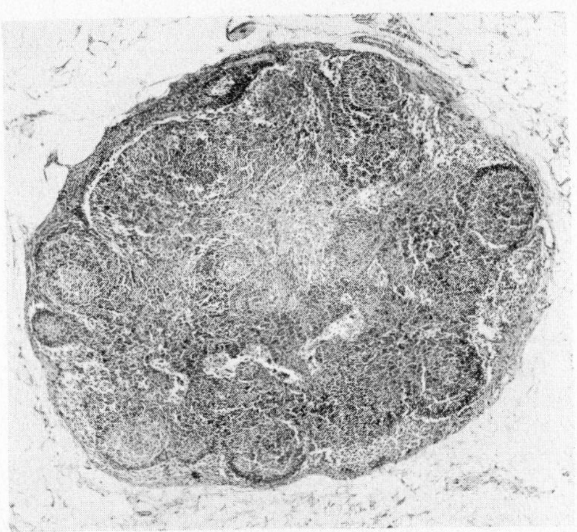

20.4 Lymph nodes. *A section through a node is shown. The position of such nodes in the lymph system is illustrated in Fig. 14.17.*

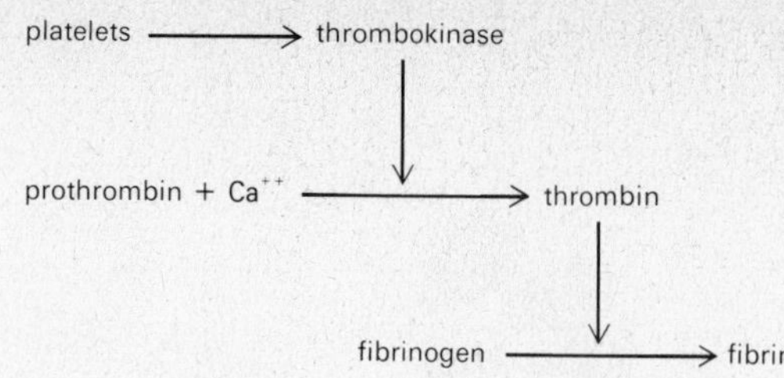

20.5 ***Blood clotting.*** *A simplified reaction sequence is shown.*

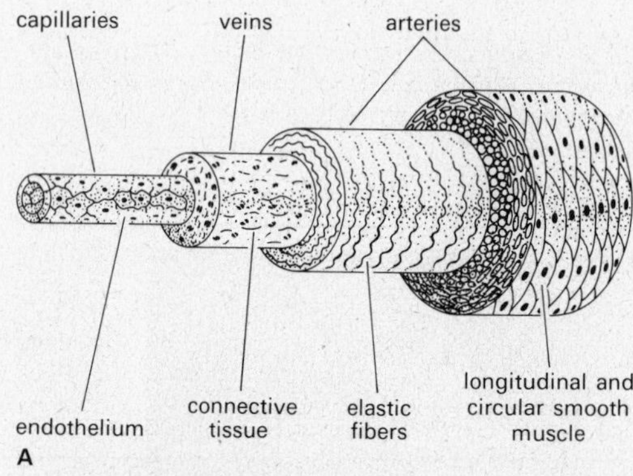

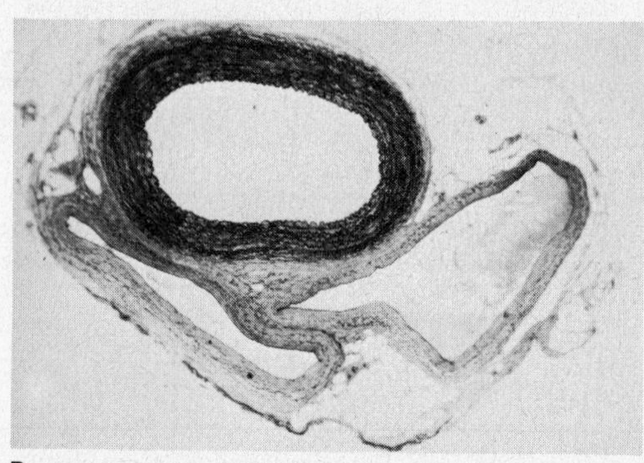

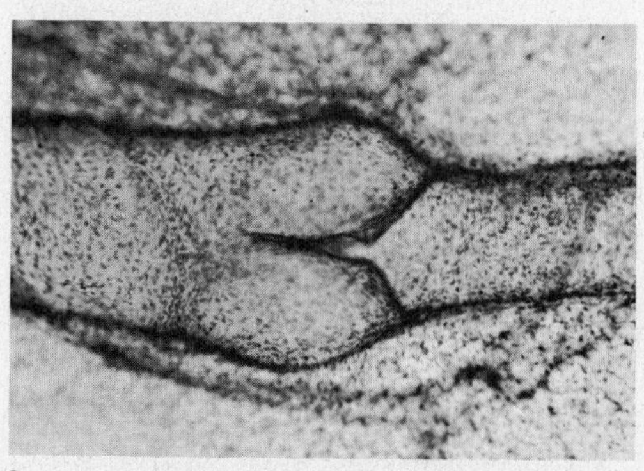

20.6 ***Circulatory vessels.*** *A, diagram illustrating the progressively greater thickness and tissue complexity of capillaries, veins, and arteries. The single cell layer of squamous endothelium is continuous throughout a vessel system. Additional tissues do not necessarily occur in such neat layers as sketched here. B, section through an artery and two veins. Note the thicker wall of the artery and the many elastic fibers (dark wavy lines) in this wall. C, longitudinal section through a lymph vessel showing an internal valve. Such valves prevent backflow. Valves very much like this are present also in the larger veins.*

membranes that do not rupture on contact with obstructions. In either of these *bleeder's diseases* the slightest wound can be fatal.

Pigmented blood cells of vertebrates are manufactured in the liver and spleen of embryos and in the bone marrow of adults. In mammals the nuclei of the cells disintegrate as they mature. The resulting *red corpuscles* remain in the circulation for limited periods only, in numbers that are maintained constant: the spleen and to some extent also the liver destroy corpuscles, while bone marrow manufactures them. The rate-controlling factor here is the amount of oxygen in the environment. A high O_2 content in the air slows the production rate (and increases the destruction rate), whereas a low O_2 content (as at high altitudes) has the opposite effect. It has been estimated that in human blood some 10 million corpuscles are destroyed and just as many are manufactured every *second.* A cubic millimeter of blood normally contains more than 5 million corpuscles, and these therefore represent the most abundant cellular blood components. The spleen of many adult vertebrates (man not included) serves to some extent as a blood-storing organ; when it contracts it squeezes stored blood into the circulation.

Pigmented blood cells derive their color from *respiratory pigments* dissolved in their cytoplasms. The pigments serve primarily in oxygen transport, but CO_2 can be carried to some extent too (see below). Respiratory pigments are largely of four different types: *hemoglobin, hemerythrin, chlorocruorin,* and *hemocyanin.*

Hemoglobin (Hb) is by far the most widespread. Its presence has been demonstrated in all animal phyla except the sponges and the radiates. The compound consists of the iron-containing pigment *heme* (chemically similar to the cytochromes) and of the protein *globin* (see Fig. 4.6). When red blood cells are destroyed in the liver the iron of heme is salvaged for renewed use, and the rest of the heme molecule appears in modified form both in the feces (via bile) and in urine (via blood and kidneys); hence the characteristic colors of these elimination products. Robins deposit the heme remnants in their egg shells, which become blue as a result.

Iron is present also in hemerythrin, a colorless pigment that turns red when combined with oxygen. It occurs only in one group of annelids, in some echiuroid worms, and the brachiopod *Lingula.* Chlorocruorin is a green pigment with

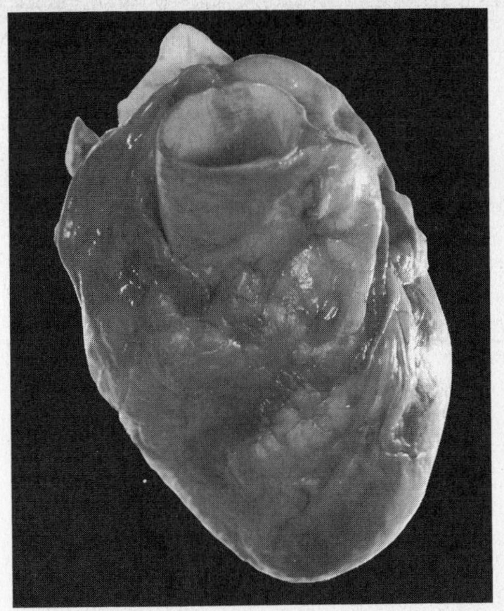

A

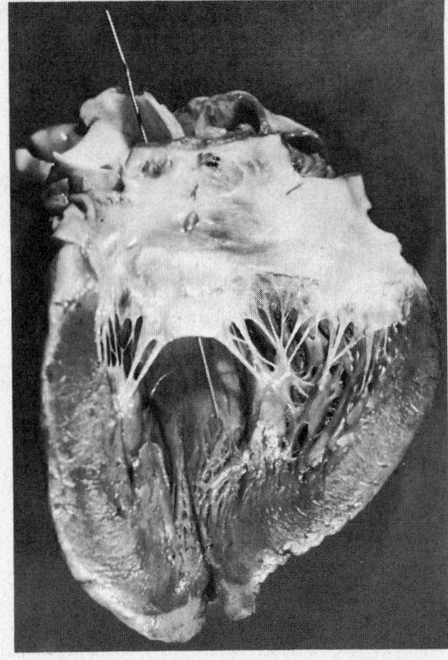

B

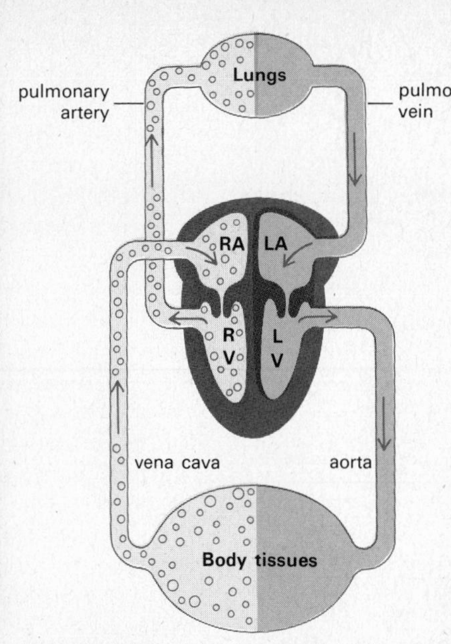

C

20.7 Heart and circulation. *A, the human heart. The large blood-vessel stump is the aorta. The atria (auricles) are partly hidden by the aorta. The size of your fist is very nearly the actual size of your heart. B, the human heart cut open to show the interior of the left ventricle. Note the strands of tissue attached to the two flaps of the bicuspid valve. These strands prevent the valve from opening into the auricle (white area above the ventricle). C, the mammalian blood circulation. Arterial blood is in the left side of the circulatory system (right side of diagram), venous blood in the right side of the system.*

a reddish color in a concentrated state. Like Hb it is an iron-containing heme protein. It is found in certain sedentary marine annelids, where it occurs not in the cells but in the plasma of blood. Hemocyanin likewise occurs in plasma. It is colorless but turns blue in combination with oxygen, and it differs also from the other blood pigments in that it is a copper compound. Hemocyanin is encountered only in mollusks (squids, octopuses, and certain snails) and in arthropods (crustacea most particularly).

By virtue of its various constituents, blood as a whole evidently plays a vital role in steady-state maintenance. For in addition to its many transport functions, blood also functions as a receptor that receives stimuli from all body regions; as a sensory and motor path that interconnects all cells; as a modulator that contributes to optimum operating conditions in all body parts; and, through antibodies, white blood cells, and clotting capacity, as an effector that serves in internal defense. However, all these control functions can be exercised only if blood circulates.

circulation

vessels and heartbeat

The organs of a circulatory system usually are *hearts, arteries, veins,* and in most closed systems also *capillaries.* Blood is carried away from a heart by arteries, toward a heart by veins. Capillaries are vessels of microscopic diameter that interconnect the narrowest arteries and veins. A capillary consists of a single layer of flat epithelial cells, and it is through them that the all-important material exchanges occur between blood and the exterior lymph and tissue cells (Fig. 20.6).

Vessels with larger diameters have additional tissues on the outside, mainly layers of connective tissue and muscle. Arteries, which carry blood under the greatest pressure, have thicker walls than veins. At frequent intervals along the larger veins there are internal *valves* that open toward the heart and prevent backflow of blood. The lymph vessel systems of vertebrates consist mainly of *lymph capillaries* and *lymph veins* (see Fig. 14.17). Such vessels are thinner than blood veins and contain a greater number of internal valves. Along the course of lymph vessels are *lymph nodes,* as noted.

In most animals, hearts generally consist of two types of chamber, *atria* that receive blood and *ventricles* that pump blood out. The mammalian heart contains two of each, a right and left atrium (here also called *auricle*), and a right and left ventricle (Fig. 20.7). The atria are comparatively thin-walled, but in the ventricles the walls are quite thick. Oxygen-poor venous blood from all body regions enters the right atrium through a large vessel, the *vena cava.* Blood then passes from the right atrium to the right ventricle through the *tricuspid valve.* The three tissue flaps of this valve prevent blood from flowing in the opposite direction. From the right ventricle blood leaves through the *pulmonary artery,* a vessel that leads to the lungs. In the lungs blood is oxygenated, and oxygen-rich arterial blood then flows through the *pulmonary vein* to the left atrium.

A *bicuspid* (*mitral*) *valve,* equipped with two tissue flaps, separates the left atrium and ventricle. Like the tricuspid on the right side, the bicuspid opens to the ventricle only. Both valves are known as auriculoventricular, or *AV,* valves. Blood leaves the left ventricle through the large, thick-walled *aorta,* a vessel that sends branches to all parts of the body. Valves are present where the aorta and the pulmonary artery leave the heart.

A heartbeat starts with the full distension of both atria by incoming blood. Atrial contraction then forces blood to the ventricles (Fig. 20.8). As the ventricles now distend, the atria relax and slowly distend again in preparation for the next beat. Fully distended ventricles contract in their turn. Blood is thereby forced against the AV valves, and the flaps of these valves snap together and prevent backflow to the atria. The impact of blood against the valve flaps produces a *first heart sound,* which can be heard as "the" heartbeat.

Blood can then leave the ventricles only through the aorta and the pulmonary artery. These vessels dilate as blood rushes through them, but their elastic walls snap back and add to the forward pressure of blood. Blood also tends to be pressed backward, but this back pressure snaps the exit valves shut and blood therefore cannot return to the ventricles. The impact of blood against these exit valves generates a *second heart sound,* fainter than the first.

The whole beat lasts about 0.8 sec (Fig. 20.9). Atria contract during the first tenth, ventricles, during the following three tenths. At all other periods the chambers are relaxed, and thus even the ventricles rest more than half the time. When contraction does occur, it is primarily the pressure generated by heart muscle that determines the position of the heart valves, hence the path that blood can take.

Arterial blood flows in rhythmic spurts according to the rhythm of the heart. As each spurt of fluid impinges on the walls of arteries, it gives rise to *pulse* vibrations. With increasing distance from the heart the arterial flow becomes more nearly continuous. By the time blood has passed through capillary vessels and has reached veins, it no longer spurts but flows in a continuous, even stream. The heart here produces very little push. Venous blood keeps moving by the push of blood from behind and by contraction of skeletal muscles that squeeze the veins. In lymph vessels the pressure of lymph is even lower than that of blood. Here again pressure of lymph from behind and muscular activity provide the major forces that return lymph to the blood circulation.

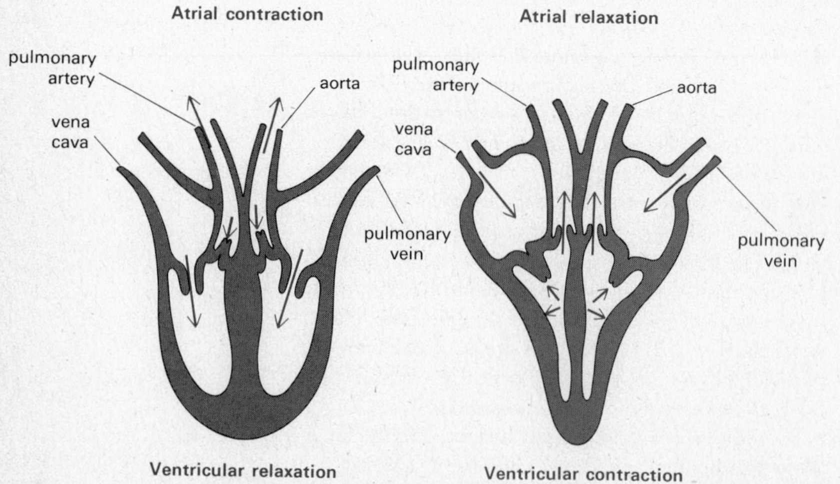

20.8 Heart action. *When atria contract (left), they force blood into the relaxed ventricles. The auriculoventricular valves are open, but the pressure of blood closes all other exits. When ventricles contract (right), they force blood into the pulmonary artery and the aorta. The atria are relaxed at the same time and fill with blood in preparation for the next beat.*

heart rate and blood pressure

The mammalian heart contains a built-in signal-generating system that can initiate successive beats. In the wall of the right atrium lies a *pacemaker,* or *sinus node,* a specialized patch of modified heart muscle (Fig. 20.10). This structure emits periodic impulses, each of which produces a wave of contraction that spreads over both atria. Atrial contraction in turn stimulates a second patch of modified muscle, the *AV node,* located in the median partition of the heart. At this node originates a so-called *bundle of His,* a set of specialized muscle strands that conduct impulses through the walls of both ventricles. Such impulses lead to ventricular contraction. The time required for impulse transmission from pacemaker to AV node ensures that the ventricles contract a fraction of a second *after* the atria.

By virtue of these nodes and conducting structures, the heart has an *intrinsic beat* that can be maintained even when the organ is separated from the body. But in the body the beat is under close nervous control; nerve impulses from the brain to the pacemaker override the intrinsic beat and impose a variable, adjustable heart rate.

A *heart-rate center* is located in the hindbrain, in a region called the *medulla oblongata* (see Fig. 20.10). Two pairs of nerves lead from there to the pacemaker. One pair travels part of the way through the spinal cord, and impulses through these nerves accelerate the heart. The second pair forms part of the large *vagus nerves,* the 10th cranials, which travel through the neck alongside the windpipe (see Chap. 21). Impulses through these decelerate or inhibit the heart. Variable degrees of inhibition have been shown to be more important in heart-rate control than acceleration. Thus the heart speeds up mainly when the impulse frequency through the vagus nerves decreases; a faster beat results more from reduced braking action than from stepped-up acceleration. Similarly, a slower beat is produced primarily by increased braking action through the vagus nerves.

The heart-rate center sends out brake or accelerator signals in response to sensory nerve impulses that affect it. Such impulses can reach it from anywhere in the body. As is well known, heart rate is influenced greatly by environmental changes communicated through vision, hearing, and other senses. Emotions, too, affect heart rate, and so do internal body activities. For example, suppose that strenuous work is started. Muscles become active and compress many veins vigorously, and much blood returns to the heart as a result. This more abundant flow distends the vena cava greatly and initiates a *stretch reflex* (see Fig. 20.10): sensory nerves in the walls of the vena cava are stimulated and impulses are conveyed to the heart-rate center. This center then sends impulses to the heart that increase the rate of beat. The heart will thus beat faster just when the tissues require more fuel and oxygen and when more incoming blood must be pumped out. This increased outflow now dilates the walls of the aorta. Stretch reflexes originate in this vessel, too, but these *slow* the heart; they prevent the heart from beating *too* rapidly. Through such controls the heart rate is automatically adjusted to the volume of blood the heart must handle. Moreover, any excessive speedup produces signals forcing a slowdown and vice versa.

Heart rate is regulated also by nonnervous means, through stimuli acting directly on the heart muscle or the pacemaker. For example, higher temperatures accelerate the heart, lower temperatures decelerate it. Heart rate is also increased by a lower pH, particularly when increased respiration during intensive body activity raises the CO_2 content of blood: CO_2 reacts with the water of blood and becomes carbonic acid, which lowers blood pH temporarily. Increased CO_2 concentrations also speed up breathing (see below), hence a fast heart and fast breathing usually go together. Hormones, too, have marked effects on heart rate; as already noted earlier, for example, adrenalin accelerates the heart during conditions of stress. At any given moment, therefore, the actual rate of the heart is a net response to numerous stimuli.

Adequate circulation requires not only an appropriately controlled rate of blood flow but also

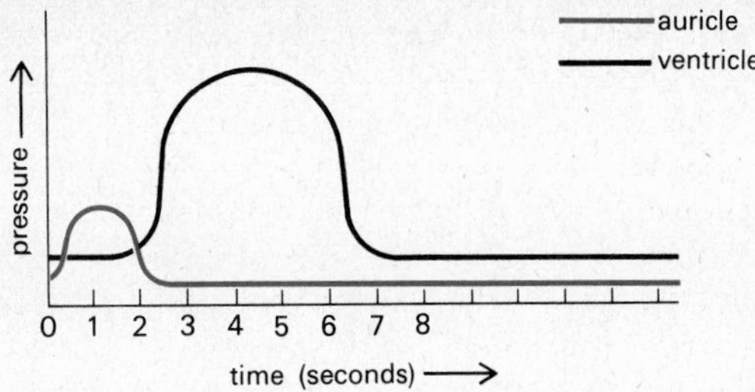

20.9 Heartbeat. *The atria contract and generate pressure when the ventricles are relaxed, and vice versa. The whole heart is relaxed for half the time of a beat.*

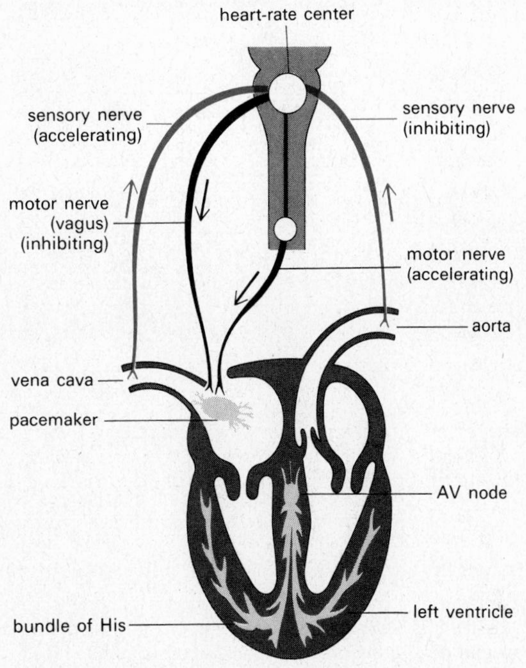

20.10 Innervation of the heart. *The heart-rate center receives messages through many sensory nerves. Some of them originate in the vena cava and the aorta. Such messages can initiate a stretch reflex: the center can send command signals to the pacemaker via motor nerves that either inhibit or accelerate the heart. Note that sensory impulses from the vena cava lead to accelerating motor signals, and impulses from the aorta lead to inhibiting motor signals. Impulses from the pacemaker then stimulate the atria (which contract as a result) and then the AV node, which in turn sends contraction signals to the ventricles through the bundle of His.*

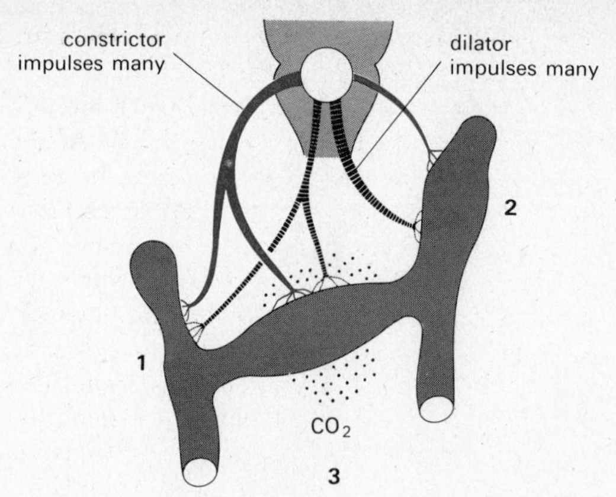

20.11 ***Vasomotion.*** *Vasoconstriction as at 1 occurs when a blood vessel receives many constrictor impulses and few dilator impulses from the vasomotor center. Vasodilation as at 2 occurs when constrictor impulses are few and dilator impulses are many. Locally produced CO_2 as at 3 can override the vasoconstriction ordered by the vasomotor center and can bring about a local vasodilation.*

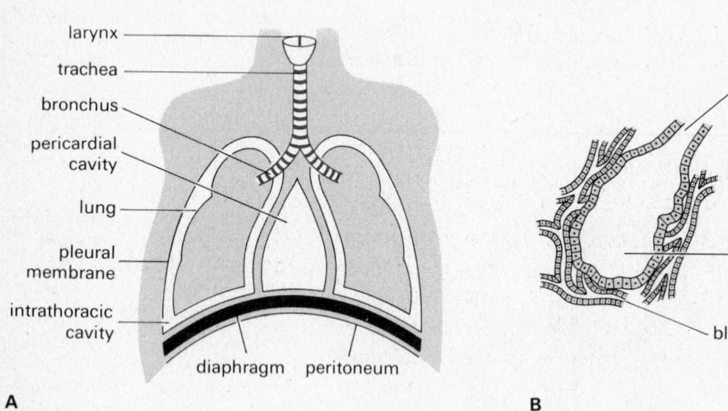

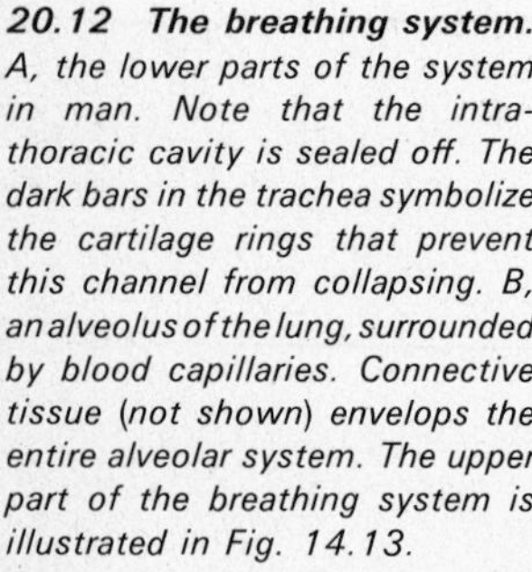

20.12 ***The breathing system.*** *A, the lower parts of the system in man. Note that the intrathoracic cavity is sealed off. The dark bars in the trachea symbolize the cartilage rings that prevent this channel from collapsing. B, an alveolus of the lung, surrounded by blood capillaries. Connective tissue (not shown) envelops the entire alveolar system. The upper part of the breathing system is illustrated in Fig. 14.13.*

a properly regulated blood pressure. This pressure depends mainly on three factors: the *force* generated by heart-muscle contraction; the total *volume* of blood in the circulation; and the size of the blood *space* inside the vessel system. The first two of these conditions can change to some extent, but blood pressure is controlled chiefly by nervous regulation of the amount of space that the blood vessels provide. Near the heart-rate center in the medulla oblongata is a *vasomotor center.* Nerves from it lead to the smooth muscles in the walls of arteries, and nerve impulses to different sets of arterial muscles initiate either *vasoconstriction,* a narrowing of vessels, or *vasodilation,* a widening of vessels (Fig. 20.11).

Simultaneous vasoconstriction in all parts of the body raises overall blood pressure, and vasodilation lowers it. Vasomotion can also occur in limited body regions and lead to a constriction of vessels in one region and a dilation in another. Less blood will then flow through regions with constricted vessels and more through regions with dilated ones. Vasomotion thus adjusts not only the pressure but also the *distribution* of blood in the body.

These adjustments are initiated by the vasomotor center, which, like the heart-rate center, acts in response to nervous and chemical cues from all parts of the body. Almost any sensory nerve impulse reaching the brain is likely to have an effect not only on the heart-rate center but on the vasomotor center as well. For example, pain, emotions, and stresses in general all tend to affect both heart rate and vasomotion, hence blood pressure. If an animal sustains a wound, the internal response normally includes increases in heart rate and overall blood pressure. The faster circulation will then provide improved capacity to cope with the external stress that produced the wound. At the same time the blood vessels in the wounded area will dilate, permitting more blood to flow to that region. More nutrients and oxygen become available there as a result, and more water becomes available to dilute and carry off any toxic substances.

Like the heart-rate center, the vasomotor center is sensitive to the CO_2 content of blood. Low CO_2 concentrations lead to vasodilator impulses throughout the body, hence to a fall in blood pressure. Conversely, high CO_2 concentrations initiate a general rise in blood pressure. Thus whenever CO_2 accumulates in blood, as during intense activity, the gas promotes its own rapid elimination: increased blood pressure and heart rate raise the rate of CO_2 collection and transport, and faster breathing raises the rate of exhalation through the lungs. At the same time these changes also bring more nutrients and oxygen to the tissues.

In body regions where much CO_2 is produced, the gas has a local vasodilator effect, distinct from its effect on the vasomotor center (see Fig. 20.11). After a meal, for example, the active alimentary tract produces large amounts of CO_2. Locally this gas brings about vasodilation, hence increased blood flow to the region. As noted above, however, the gas also acts on the vasomotor center, which initiates vasoconstriction elsewhere in the body. Blood flow will then decrease in, for example, the head and the skeletal muscles. This flow pattern is reversed when muscles are active and the alimentary system is empty. Such blood distributions explain why an animal is disinclined to undertake physical activity immediately after a heavy meal, or, conversely, why eating is best avoided just before strenuous muscular exertions.

breathing

the apparatus

The basic component of any breathing system is a *breathing surface,* where O_2 can diffuse in and CO_2 can diffuse out. As shown in Chaps. 12 and 13, such surfaces are provided by skin, gills, tracheal tubes, lungs, or modifications of such organs. In each case the breathing surface permits exchange of respiratory gases between the external environment and either the circulating body fluids or the tissue cells directly.

In mammals the breathing apparatus contains an air channel that leads to and from the lungs through the nose and the mouth (see Fig. 14.13). The air path between nose and lungs passes *across* the food path between mouth and esophagus, the region of intersection being the pharynx. The nasal channels connect through openings with a series of *head sinuses,* paired air-filled cavities in some of the skull bones. Also leading to the nasal passages are the *tear ducts,* which collect the lymphlike fluid secreted continuously by tear glands in the outer corners of the eyes. Near the connection of the nasal channels with the pharynx are the openings of the *eustachian tubes,* a pair of ducts leading to the middle-ear cavities (see Figs. 21.17 and 14.13). These tubes permit equilibration of air pressure between the external atmosphere and the middle ear on each side of the head. The eardrums prevent air from reaching the middle ears directly. In the nasal passages themselves, some of the ciliated lining cells are specialized as odor receptors. Nerves lead from them to the nearby brain, where impulses are interpreted as smell.

The pharynx connects with the lungs through the windpipe, or *trachea* (Fig. 20.12). At the upper end of the trachea is the *larynx,* or voice box. It is formed from a number of cartilage plates that are held together by membranes and can be moved by muscles. After air enters the larynx through an upper slit, the *glottis,* it passes through the opening left between the *vocal cords,* two horizontal fibroelastic ligaments. The tension of these cords and the size of the opening between them can be changed by the muscles attached to the laryngeal cartilages. Sounds are produced when the cords are made to vibrate by exhaled air (Fig. 20.13).

The shape of the glottal opening and, as in a violin string, the tension of the vocal cords determine tone pitch. The volume of the sound produced depends on the force of the air blast and on the amplitude with which the cords vibrate. A third characteristic of voice, tone quality, is influenced by the size and shape of the resonating cavities: chest, pharynx, mouth, and nasal passages. That tone quality changes as the position of lips, tongue, jaws, and cheeks is changed is quite familiar. During puberty in males, the chest cavity and larynx enlarge and the vocal cords lengthen. The voice then "breaks" as the individual learns to control his modified sound equipment.

During swallowing the whole larynx moves upward and is pressed against the *epiglottis,* a cartilaginous flap that comes to lie over the glottis and thereby prevents food from entering the air channel (see Fig. 14.13). The larynx and trachea are lined with a ciliated, mucus-secreting epithelium. Also in the wall of the trachea are C-shaped cartilage rings that prevent this air channel from collapsing.

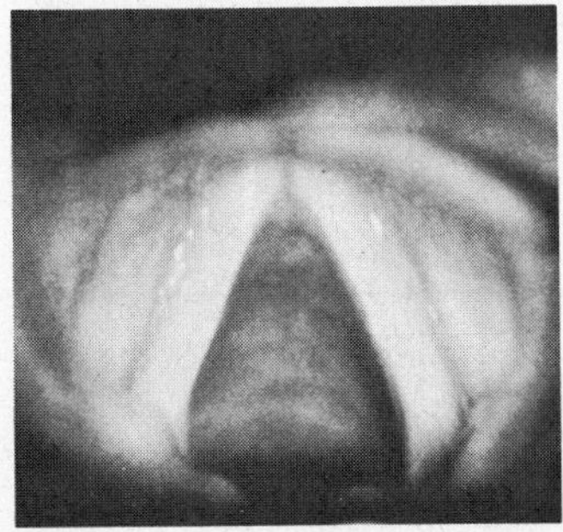
A

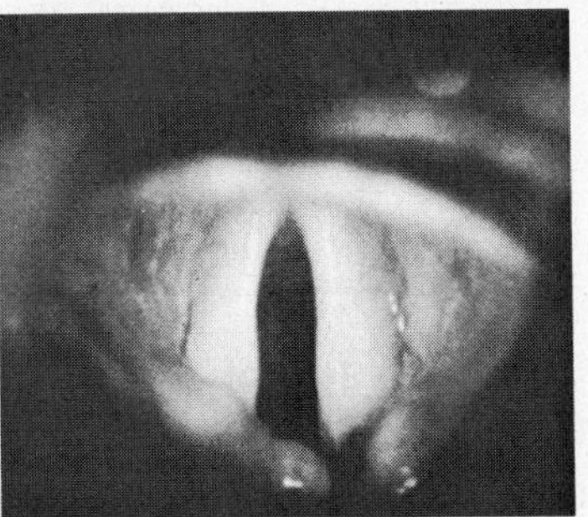
B

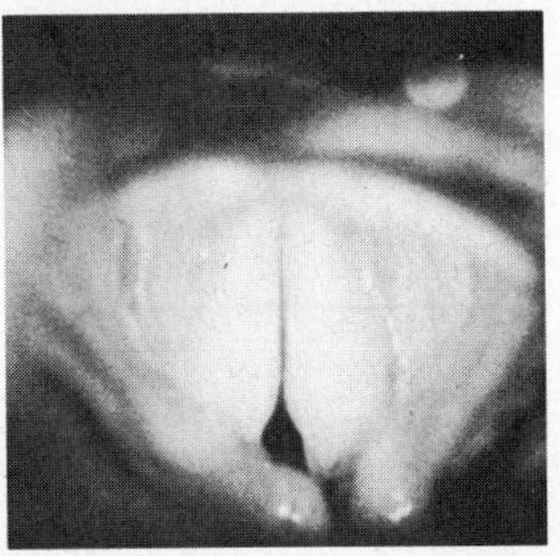
C

***20.13* Vocal cords.** *The view is from above, looking into larynx and trachea of man. From left to right, sequence of vocal-cord positions during the transition from quiet breathing to voicing.*

At its lower end the trachea divides into a left and right *bronchus*, and after some distance each of these subdivides into *bronchioles*. Each of them then branches repeatedly in turn. The diameters of these channels become progressively smaller and their walls become thinner. Only the ciliated lining layer and some connective tissue continue to the microscopic terminations of the branch system. Each such terminus is an *alveolus*, a raspberry-shaped sac. The sum of all alveoli represents a lung. A thin layer of connective tissue around the alveoli carries nerves and a dense network of blood capillaries (see Fig. 20.12).

The lung on each side lies in an *intrathoracic cavity* that is sealed off from the rest of the coelom by a muscular partition, the *diaphragm*. Dome-shaped at rest, the diaphragm flattens out on contraction and enlarges the chest cavity. The suction thereby generated enlarges the lung alveoli, and external air rushes into them. Relaxation of the diaphragm then permits elastic recoil of the lungs and expulsion of air (Fig. 20.14). Inhalation and exhalation can also be brought about by the *rib muscles* present between successive ribs. When these muscles raise the rib cage, the chest cavity enlarges and an inhalation occurs. Conversely, a lowering of the rib cage leads to exhalation. This principle is used in the various procedures of "artificial respiration" and in iron lungs, by means of which air is forced into and out of the lungs intermittently.

the process

Breathing is under nervous and chemical control. A *breathing center* in the medulla oblongata, located near the heart-rate and vasomotor centers, sends motor impulses to the diaphragm and the rib muscles. This nerve center is spontaneously active; it generates rhythmic motor impulses with a basic frequency that is ultimately determined genetically. When an impulse arrives at the diaphragm or the rib muscles, these contract and produce an inhalation (Fig. 20.15). As a result the lungs become inflated and stretched, and this stretching in turn stimulates sets of sensory nerves in the walls of the lungs (stretch receptors). Impulses from there then temporarily *inhibit* the breathing center from sending more signals to the breathing muscles. These consequently relax and exhalation occurs. As the lungs now recoil, the stretch receptors there cease to be stimulated, and the breathing center therefore ceases to be inhibited. At this point the center sends out motor impulses again, and a new cycle starts.

As already pointed out earlier, the rate of breathing tends to be higher the greater the CO_2 concentration in blood. Thus, breathing becomes faster during intense physical or emotional activity, when CO_2 levels in blood tend to be high. The gas here hastens its own removal through the lungs, and faster breathing at the same time increases the oxygen supply, just when the tissues require more oxygen. Recall also that CO_2 speeds up the heart, which aids further in accelerating gas exchange. If an animal holds its breath deliberately, the accumulating CO_2 soon stimulates the center so strongly that breathing *must* be resumed, even against the most intense will; the automatic controls ensure that breathing does not occur too slowly.

Conversely, breathing slows down during rest or sleep, when respiration and CO_2 production are minimal. The extreme is the *hyperventilated* condition, produced, for example, when breathing is intentionally made as deep and as rapid as possible. Carbon dioxide is then exhaled so fast that its concentration in blood becomes abnormally low. In that case the breathing center usually ceases to operate temporarily, a "blackout" ensues, and breathing will remain stopped until the CO_2 concentration has again built up to a normal level.

Fresh inhaled air contains some 20 percent oxygen and 0.03 percent carbon dioxide. Exhaled air includes only 16 percent oxygen but as much as 4 percent carbon dioxide. A fifth of the available oxygen thus is retained in the body, and more than 100 times the amount of CO_2 is expelled. This exchange is governed by differences in gas pressures between blood and lung. Venous

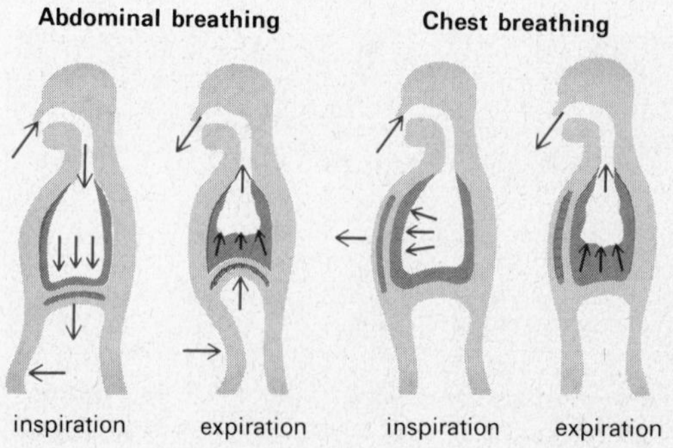

Abdominal breathing — Chest breathing

inspiration — expiration — inspiration — expiration

20.14 Breathing movements.

blood flowing to the lungs from the body is comparatively oxygen-poor, but air in the lungs is oxygen-rich. A pressure gradient therefore leads from the lungs *to* blood, and more oxygen diffuses into the blood capillaries than in the reverse direction (Fig. 20.16). At the same time, venous blood coming to the lungs is almost saturated with CO_2, whereas the air in the lungs contains a far lower concentration of this gas. A pressure gradient here leads *out* of the blood capillaries, and more CO_2 diffuses to the lungs than in the opposite direction. As a result blood ceases to be venous, and the incoming oxygen makes it arterial.

As in the lungs, gas exchange between blood and the body tissues is likewise governed by pressure gradients. Tissue cells use up oxygen, and the higher pressure of this gas in blood therefore drives oxygen into the cells. Blood then ceases to be arterial. At the same time respiration in cells builds up a higher CO_2 pressure than in blood, and CO_2 therefore diffuses out of the cells. Blood here becomes venous (see Fig. 20.16).

In blood itself, small amounts of the respiratory gases (and indeed of all aerial gases) are dissolved physically in plasma. Thus if the environmental pressure should drop suddenly, as in too rapid ascents from great depths or to high altitudes, then the dissolved gases can bubble out of blood like gases fizzing out from an opened bottle of soda. The results often are internal blood clots and dangerous "bends."

The bulk of the respiratory gases is carried in blood by chemical means. Oxygen combines reversibly with the respiratory pigments. If the pigment is hemoglobin, as in the red blood cells of vertebrates, *oxyhemoglobin* forms:

$$\mathrm{Hb} + \mathrm{O_2} \rightleftharpoons \mathrm{HbO_2}$$

Governed by mass action, this reaction shifts to the right in the lungs, where oxygen enters the blood in quantity. HbO_2 is then transported to the body tissues. There the reaction proceeds to the left, liberating free O_2 to the oxygen-poor cells. Hemoglobin can also combine with carbon monoxide, CO, and indeed this union takes place more easily than that with oxygen. Carbon monoxide is therefore a poison, for formation of HbCO in preference to HbO_2 prevents or severely impairs the transport of oxygen.

Hemoglobin normally also transports a small amount of CO_2, but most of this gas interacts with the water of plasma and is carried in the form of bicarbonate ions:

$$\mathrm{CO_2} + \mathrm{H_2O} \underset{\text{in breathing system}}{\overset{\text{in body tissues}}{\rightleftharpoons}} \mathrm{H^+} + \mathrm{HCO_3^-}$$

This reaction proceeds to the right in the tissues, where cellular CO_2 enters the blood continuously, and to the left in the lungs, where CO_2 passes to the air.

The breathing system eliminates not only CO_2 but also water, which saturates expired air, and often vapors of other volatile compounds as well. Through these functions the system contributes significantly to the *excretory* activities of an animal.

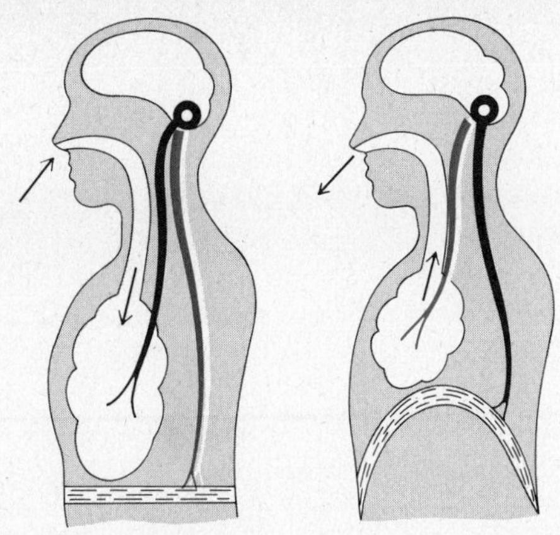

20.15 Breathing control. *Left, the breathing center sends motor impulses to the diaphragm, leading to inhalation. Right, sensory impulses from the inflated lung inhibit the breathing center, resulting in exhalation.*

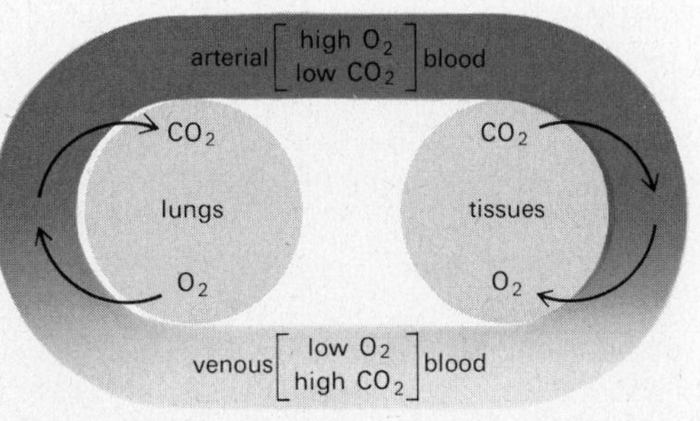

20.16 Gas exchange *between lungs and blood and between body tissues and blood. Oxygen enters blood in the lungs and leaves in the tissues. Carbon dioxide enters in the tissues and leaves in the lungs.*

excretion

Excretory systems are not named very adequately, for elimination of wastes is only one of their functions; they also retain and adjust. Indeed

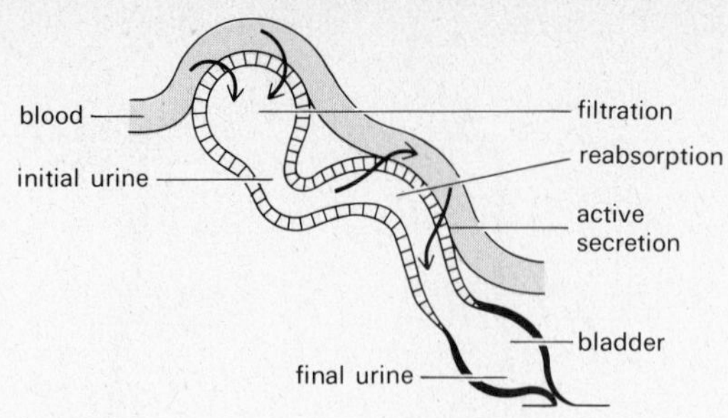

20.17 Excretory processes. *In an excretory system a filtrate of blood (or lymph) forms initial urine, from which some materials are reabsorbed and to which other materials are secreted. These functions are performed by the cells lining the system. Final urine is the ultimate product.*

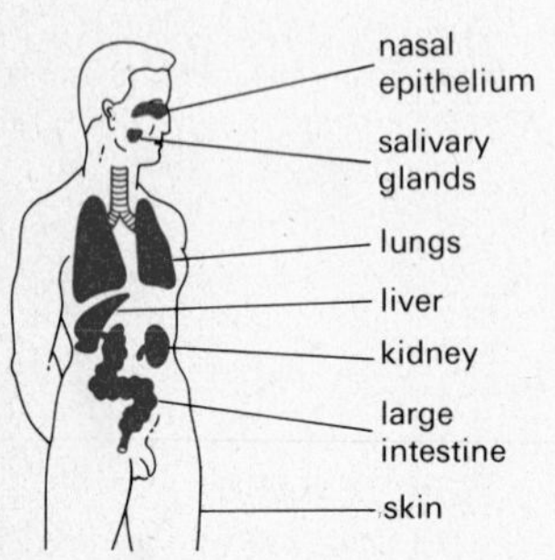

20.18 Vertebrate excretory organs.

what is or is not "waste" at any given moment is precisely what an excretory system must determine. The basic wastes are excess water, excess salts, ammonia and other nitrogenous byproducts of metabolism, and CO_2. In the case of water and salts, however, the difference between waste and nonwaste is a difference of amount, not kind. In most animals ammonia and its derivatives are toxic wastes in almost any amounts; and CO_2, excreted mainly through the breathing surfaces, is largely waste.

Excretory systems carry out their functions through three kinds of processes, *filtration, reabsorption,* and *secretion* (Fig. 20.17). Filtration takes place between the body fluids and the interior of an excretory structure. The pressure of the fluids—blood pressure in vertebrates, for example—supplies the force necessary for filtration. Cells and proteins in blood normally cannot pass through the filter, but most other components can. Thus the filtrate that collects in the excretory structure is essentially lymph, here called *initial urine.* A separation of waste from nonwaste then occurs when initial urine flows through another region of the excretory system on its way to the outside. Reabsorption takes place there: excretory cells in contact with initial urine remove substances "judged" to be valuable and return them to the body fluids. When salts or other dissolved materials are reabsorbed, the remaining urine becomes more dilute, or hypotonic to the body fluids; when water is reabsorbed, the remaining urine becomes hypertonic and more concentrated than the body fluids.

The third process, secretion, can take place either in the same general region of the excretory system or in another body part altogether (gills, for example). Secretion transfers materials from the body fluids to urine or the external environment directly. Secretion and reabsorption therefore operate in opposite directions, but the substances reabsorbed often differ greatly from those being secreted. The fluid then present, *final urine,* is discharged to the outside either continuously or, after accumulating in a *bladder,* intermittently. In many cases the excretory system opens directly to the outside. In others it empties to the hind region of the alimentary tract (*cloaca*) or to the outgoing ducts of the reproductive system.

The organs that contribute to excretion in mammals are shown in Fig. 20.18. Evidently, all organs with access to the outside of the body either directly or through the alimentary system play an excretory role. But the kidneys exercise the main excretory control; if they should become inoperative, death would soon follow. Each kidney (*metanephros;* see Fig. 13.16) consists of an outer *renal cortex* and an inner *renal medulla* (Fig. 20.19). Located partly in the cortex and partly in the medulla are many thousands of *nephrons,* the functional units of a kidney.

A nephron is composed of a *glomerulus,* a tiny ball of blood capillaries; a double-layered, cup-shaped *nephric capsule* around the glomerulus; and a long *nephric tubule* that leads away from the capsule. Such a tubule contains two highly coiled (*convoluted*) regions, interconnected by an extended, U-shaped *loop of Henle.* At its far end the nephric tubule opens to a *collecting duct* that receives the output of many other such tubules. The numerous collecting ducts in a kidney eventually join and form a wide vessel, the *ureter.* This channel carries urine to the *urinary bladder.* As urine accumulates the bladder distends, and at a certain stage it contracts reflexly and discharges to the outside through the *urethra.*

A large artery enters the kidney where the ureter leaves and branches out repeatedly. One of the capillary branches forms the glomerulus in a nephron, and blood from there passes to a dense capillary bed that envelops all parts of a nephric tubule. Blood then drains through progressively larger and fewer veins and eventually leaves the kidney through a single large vessel.

In each nephron blood is filtered from the glomerulus to the interior space of the nephric capsule. Initial urine then flows through the nephric tubule, where reabsorption and secretion take place. Note here that it is the great length of the nephric tubules that specifically makes the entire metanephric kidney adaptively useful to land vertebrates: the whole tubule and particularly the long loop of Henle represent the water-reabsorbing and therefore water-conserving

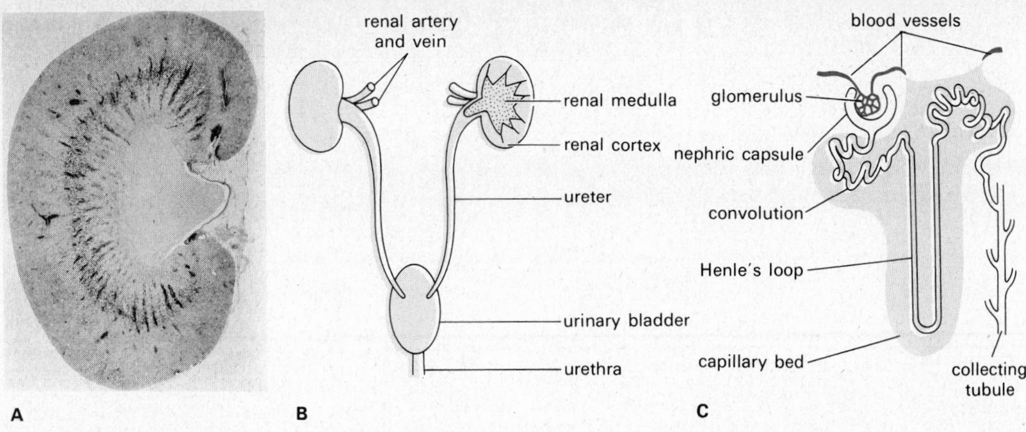

20.19 Kidney structure. *A, section through rat kidney. Note outer renal cortex, inner renal medulla. B, the kidneys, their ducts, and the bladder (kidney on right in section). C, a nephron unit, showing the convoluted portions of the tubule and Henle's loop. The capillary bed that envelops the coiled parts of a nephron is indicated as the tinted area.*

structures. Water is in fact the most abundant of the substances that are filtered out from blood and later returned to it. The two kidneys of man, for example, filter the equivalent of about 160 qt of blood plasma a day, but only about $1\frac{1}{2}$ qt of fluid is actually released as final urine; some 99 percent of the water in the blood filtrate is reabsorbed by the nephric tubules, and especially by the loops of Henle.

Among substances normally reabsorbed completely is glucose. Initial urine contains glucose in the same concentration as in blood. But all this glucose tends to be returned to the blood, and none normally escapes in final urine. Other materials undergoing more or less complete reabsorption include amino acids, lipids, vitamins, hormones—in short, all the essential nutrients and other usable supplies in transit to cells. Such materials are said to be *high-threshold* substances; they are reabsorbed entirely unless their concentrations in blood are excessively high (Fig. 20.20).

So-called *low-threshold* substances on the contrary are not reabsorbed by the cells of the nephric tubules. Among these substances are nitrogenous byproducts such as urea, pigmented blood-breakdown products, and other materials the tubule cells "determine" to be outright wastes. They become highly concentrated as water is withdrawn from initial urine. For example, final urine contains some 70 times more urea than an equal volume of initial urine. As a result of such increases in concentration the osmotic pull of urine becomes greater. But despite this force, which tends to draw water *from* blood *to* urine, tubule cells nevertheless continue to transport more water from urine to blood. In counter-

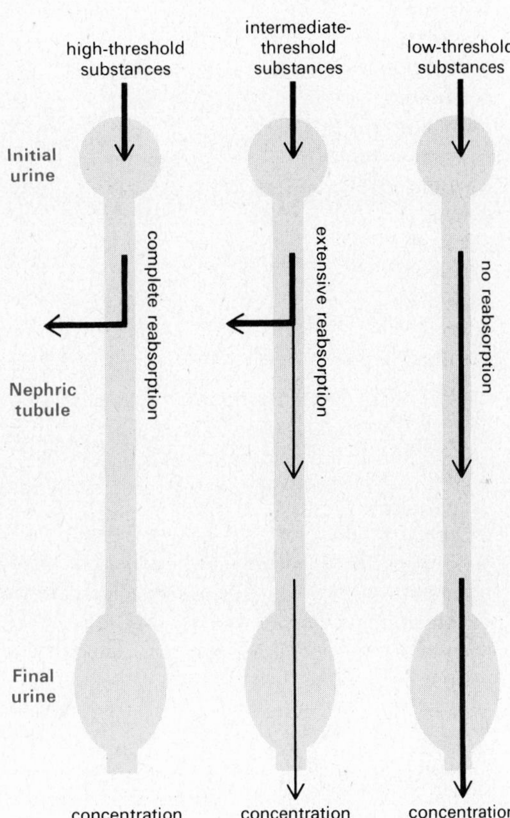

20.20 Selective excretory action *of the cells of a nephric tubule. The color areas symbolize nephric capsules, tubules, and bladders of excretory systems. High-threshold substances like glucose are reabsorbed more or less completely (left). Low-threshold substances like urea are not reabsorbed at all (right). And intermediate-threshold substances like water and many mineral ions are reabsorbed in part, depending on the amounts already present in blood (center).*

acting this prevailing osmotic gradient tubule cells expend large amounts of energy.

A third group of materials comprises *intermediate-threshold* substances. They are or are not absorbed depending on whether or not their blood concentrations are at optimal levels. Mineral ions belong to this category. For example, if blood already contains normal concentrations of sodium chloride, then additional salt intake with food will be followed by salt excretion. But if the internal supply is low, the tubule cells will reabsorb salt and will not reduce the concentration in blood any further. Water itself qualifies as an intermediate-threshold substance.

Evidently, kidneys serve not merely as excretory organs but as "retention" organs as well. It can therefore be appreciated why examination of urine will reveal not only how well the kidneys function, but also how well chemical steady states are maintained in the body as a whole.

review questions

1 Define lymph and blood. What are the basic functions of blood and lymph? Distinguish between open and closed circulations. Review the composition of blood plasma and the functions of each group of components.

2 What are antibodies, and how do they function? What cellular components occur in blood, and what are the functions of each? By what processes is the number of red corpuscles maintained relatively constant? Review the reaction pattern of blood clotting.

3 What organs are the main components of a circulatory system? A lymph system? How do arteries differ from veins and capillaries (*a*) structurally, (*b*) functionally?

4 Name the main parts of the mammalian heart and the main blood vessels, and review the general course of the blood circulation. What functions do lymph nodes have in internal steady-state regulation?

5 Review the events during a complete heartbeat, with attention to pressure patterns, valve positions, direction of blood flow, and heart sounds. How is blood moved through veins and lymph vessels?

6 Describe the nervous controls of the heart. How are control signals transmitted through the heart itself? Which motor signals accelerate the heart and which decelerate it? Describe stretch reflexes that accelerate and decelerate the heart.

7 Through what specific processes is the heart (*a*) speeded up when physical exercise is begun and (*b*) slowed down during rest or sleep? What nonnervous agencies affect heart rate?

8 What three major factors control blood pressure, and what governs each of these factors? Describe the action of the vasomotor center. What nervous and chemical agencies affect this center and how?

9 Suppose that physical exercise is begun; describe the specific processes that lead simultaneously to (*a*) increased heart rate, (*b*) increased breathing rate, (*c*) increased blood pressure, (*d*) redistribution of blood in the body.

10 Describe the anatomy of the breathing system in man. How is sound produced, and how can sound be varied in pitch, volume, and quality? What is an alveolus, and what is its relation to the lung? What chest structures surround the lungs?

11 Describe the pressure changes in the body associated with inhalation and exhalation in (*a*) abdominal breathing and (*b*) chest breathing. How are inhalation-exhalation cycles controlled and maintained automatically? Review here the roles of CO_2 and the brain.

12 Describe the processes through which breathing rate increases when physical exercise is begun and decreases at the onset of sleep. What is overventilation, and what is its effect?

13 Interpret the automatic alternation of inhalation and exhalation in terms of control activity. What parts of the breathing system serve as receptors, modulators, effectors, and transmission paths, and what are the stimulus, the feedback, and the response?

14 How are the respiratory gases transported in blood? What reactions occur in the lungs and the tissues? Why is carbon monoxide a poison? Why is breathing difficult (*a*) in an unventilated room, (*b*) at high altitudes?

15 What is the basic structure and function of an excretory system? What does it excrete? Distinguish between excretory filtration, secretion, and reabsorption.

16 Show how the pattern of water and salt excretion varies according to whether an animal lives in a marine, a freshwater, or a terrestrial environment. Describe the structure of the vertebrate pronephros, mesonephros, and metanephros. How do they differ functionally?

17 What organs compose the mammalian excretory system, and what is the specific excretory role of each? Describe the general structure of the mammalian kidney and its associated ducts.

18 Describe the structure of a nephron, its ducts, and its blood circulation. Where is the loop of Henle, and what is its significance?

19 Review in detail the process of urine formation in man. What are the roles of filtration and reabsorption; where and how does each occur? What are high-threshold substances? Give examples.

20 Construct a table showing how final urine differs from blood and initial urine with respect to (*a*) the kinds of substances present and (*b*) the concentrations of substances present.

---

collateral readings

Adolph, E. F.: The Heart's Pacemaker, *Sci. American,* March, 1967. Recommended reading for further background.

Botelho, S. Y.: Tears and the Lacrimal Gland, *Sci. American,* Oct., 1964. A study of the secretion of the tear glands and of the functions of tears.

Burnet, M.: How Antibodies Are Made, *Sci. American,* Nov., 1954. A hypothesis regarding this still unsolved problem is described.

———: The Mechanism of Immunity, *Sci. American,* Jan., 1961. The article examines the antibody-antigen interplay in immune reactions.

Chapman, C. B., and **T. H. Mitchell**: The Physiology of Exercise, *Sci. American,* May, 1965. The adaptive changes that occur in the breathing and circulatory systems during exercise.

Comroe, J. H., Jr.: The Lung, *Sci. American,* Feb., 1966. A recommended review of the biology of this organ.

Hong, S. K., and **H. Rahn**: The Diving Women of Korea and Japan, *Sci. American,* May, 1967. The breath-holding capacity of these divers is examined.

Irving, L.: Adaptations to Cold, *Sci. American,* Jan., 1966. The circulatory redistributions of blood in the body play an important role in counteracting external temperature changes.

Kilgour, F. G.: William Harvey, *Sci. American,* June, 1952. The life and work of the discoverer of the blood circulation are described.

Kylstra, J. A.: Experiments in Water-breathing, *Sci. American,* Aug., 1968. How air breathers can obtain adequate amounts of oxygen under water.

Mayerson, H.: The Lymphatic System, *Sci. American,* June, 1963. A good account on the biology of this system.

McKusick, V. A.: Heart Sounds, *Sci. American,* May, 1956. The production and meaning of these sounds are examined.

Nossal, G. J. V.: How Cells Make Antibodies, *Sci. American,* Dec., 1964. Experiments on single cells in culture show how genes appear to control antibody production.

Perutz, M. F.: The Hemoglobin Molecule, *Sci. American,* Nov., 1964. An account on the detailed configuration of the four polypeptide chains that compose hemoglobin.

Ponder, E.: The Red Blood Cell, *Sci. American,* Jan., 1957. A discussion of the significance of red corpuscles in circulation and breathing.

Porter, R. R.: The Structure of Antibodies, *Sci. American,* Oct., 1967. The chemistry of this class of proteins is examined.

Schmidt-Nielsen, K.: Salt Glands, *Sci. American,* Jan., 1959. An examination of specialized glands in marine birds and reptiles that play an important role in maintaining the salt balance of these sea-water-drinking animals.

Scholander, P. F.: The Master Switch of Life, *Sci. American,* Dec., 1963. The article describes the vasomotor mechanism of blood distribution in relation to the oxygen-carrying role of blood.

Smith, H.: The Kidney, *Sci. American,* Jan., 1953. A recommended article on the function of the mammalian kidney.

Speirs, R. S.: How Cells Attack Antigens, *Sci. American,* Feb., 1964. The role of defensive cells in protecting against antigens is described.

Surgenor, D. M.: Blood, *Sci. American,* Feb., 1954. A good general discussion.

Wiggers, C. J.: The Heart, *Sci. American,* May, 1957. The structure of the heart muscle and the quantitative work of the human heart are described.

Wood, J. E.: The Venous System, *Sci. American,* Jan., 1968. An excellent article on the structure and functions of these vessels.

Wood, W. B., Jr.: White Blood Cells vs. Bacteria, *Sci. American,* Feb., 1951. A good account on the infection-combating activity of white cells.

Zweifach, B. J.: The Microcirculation of the Blood, *Sci. American,* Jan., 1959. An examination of the steady-state functions of the capillary circulation.

chapter 21 nervous control

Like all other control operations, nervous activity is based on structural components that can function as receptors, sensory pathways, modulators, motor pathways, and effectors. The neural receptors are specialized *sensory cells* that in many cases are parts of sense organs. Sensitive to environmental or internal stimuli, receptors initiate nerve inpulses that convey information related to the stimuli. These impulses are transmitted over *sensory nerve fibers* to modulators such as ganglia, nerve cords, and brains. Modulators "interpret" sensory impulses, often store incoming information as memory, and send out motor impulses that usually are in some way associated with the incoming information. Such impulses pass through *motor nerve fibers* to effectors, which are either *muscles* or *glands.* These then carry out responses that normally bear some more or less direct relation to the original stimuli and that in the long run usually tend to preserve steady states. Many of these responses contribute to recognizable forms of *behavior.*

neural pathways

In vertebrates the two main cell types of nervous systems are *neuroglia cells* and *nerve cells* (Fig. 21.1). Neuroglia are believed to perform a variety of nutritive and other housekeeping functions in nerve tissue, and nerve cells, or *neurons,* are the impulse-generating and impulse-conducting units proper. Each neuron typically consists of a nucleus-containing *cell body* and of one or more filamentous outgrowths, or *fibers,* that extend away from the cell body. Impulses usually originate at the terminals of fibers called *dendrites,* which then carry the impulses toward the cell body. Impulses travel away from a cell body through fibers called *axons.* Many dendrites and axons are short, but others have lengths of over a yard (for example, axons from the base of the spinal cord to the toes in man).

The long axons and dendrites are enveloped by a *Schwann sheath,* a single layer of thin flat cells that supplies nutrients to a fiber and that also provides a pathway when a cut fiber regenerates. In certain cases the cells of a Schwann sheath wind around the nerve fiber several times, and the fatty contents of these wrapping layers then form a *myelin sheath.* A myelin wrapping is believed to serve as a kind of insulation, comparable perhaps to an insulating rubber envelope around an electric wire (see Fig. 21.1).

The fibers of two adjacent neurons are not in direct contact; their terminals come close together at a *synapse,* a microscopic space through which impulses are carried by chemical means (Fig. 21.2). In crude terms a whole nervous system can be envisaged as an intricate network of neurons, with fibers interconnecting functionally at numerous synapses. Many pathways in such a network form *reflex arcs,* composed of a sequence of neurons with specific functions. Thus, *sensory* (or *afferent*) neurons in such an arc transmit impulses from a receptor to a modulator, and *motor* (or *efferent*) neurons transmit from a modulator to an effector. Neurons in a modulator are *interneurons.* Groups of nerve fibers frequently traverse a body region as a single collective fiber bundle, or *nerve.* Nerves are designated as sensory, motor, or mixed, depending on whether they contain sensory fibers, motor fibers, or both.

The most primitive type of neuron arrangement known is a *nerve net* (Fig. 21.3). Representing the only neural structures in, for example, certain coelenterates, such nets also form at least part of the nervous system of most other animals. In vertebrates, for example, nerve nets occur in the walls of the alimentary tracts. Most animals in addition contain *nerve cords,* condensed regions of nets, and *ganglia,* dense accumulations of neurons and fiber terminals. Ganglia can be sensory, motor, or mixed according to the kinds of fibers they connect with. Large ganglia usually contain functional subdivisions called *nerve centers,* specialized groups of interneurons that regulate specific activities. Very large ganglia usually also store information as memory and control intricate forms of behavior. Large ganglia or groups of ganglia that integrate the main sensory inputs and motor outputs of animals constitute *brains.*

By far the most complex nervous systems are those of vertebrates. The main parts develop from a hollow dorsal *neural tube,* formed in the embryo as an ingrowth from the ectoderm (see Chap. 26). The anterior portion of the tube enlarges as a *brain,* the posterior portion becomes the *spinal cord,* and nerves grow out from both. The fluid-filled space in the tube forms brain *ventricles* anteriorly and a *spinal canal* posteriorly. In the mature brain the major divisions are the *forebrain,* the *midbrain,* and the *hindbrain* (Fig. 21.4).

Of two main subdivisions of the forebrain, the more anterior one is the *telencephalon.* It contains paired *olfactory lobes,* the centers for the sense of smell. In birds and mammals the telencephalon

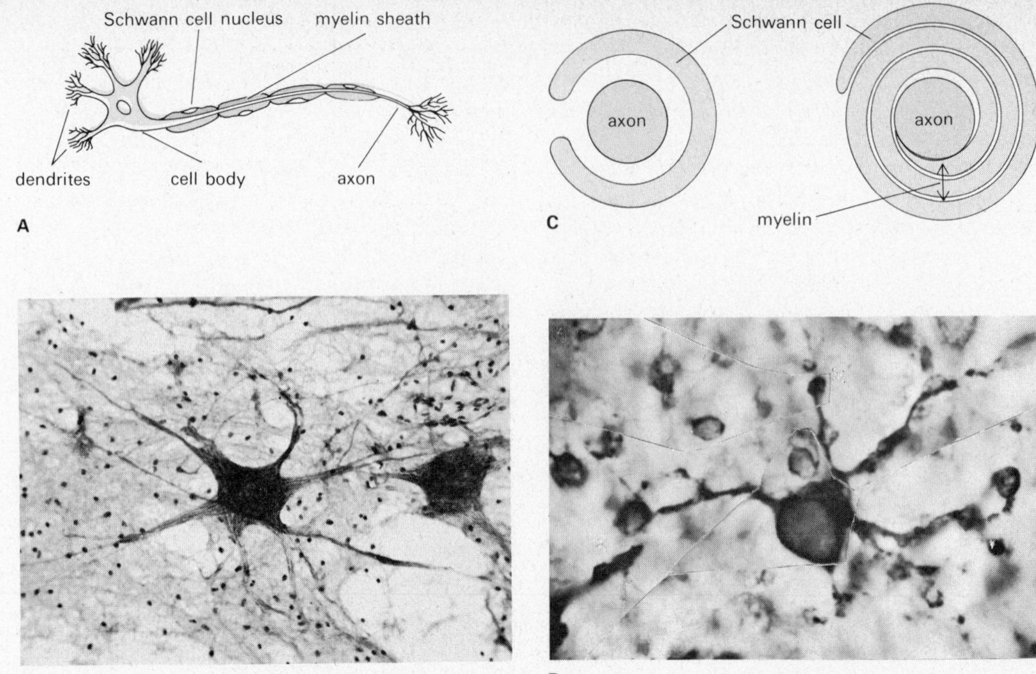

21.1 Nerve tissue. *A, general structure of a neuron with a myelinated axon. B, micrograph of a stained (multipolar) motor neuron. C, nonmyelinated and myelinated fibers. Left, cross-sectional view of a fiber without myelin, showing a Schwann cell surrounding an axon almost completely. Right, cross-sectional view of a developing myelinated fiber. A myelin sheath grows as an extension of the Schwann cells, each of which wraps around the axon several times (more often than shown) and forms an envelope of many layers. The inner layers collectively represent the myelin sheath. D, high-power view of a single neuroglia cell. Note the elongated extensions from the main part of the cell (×1,500).*

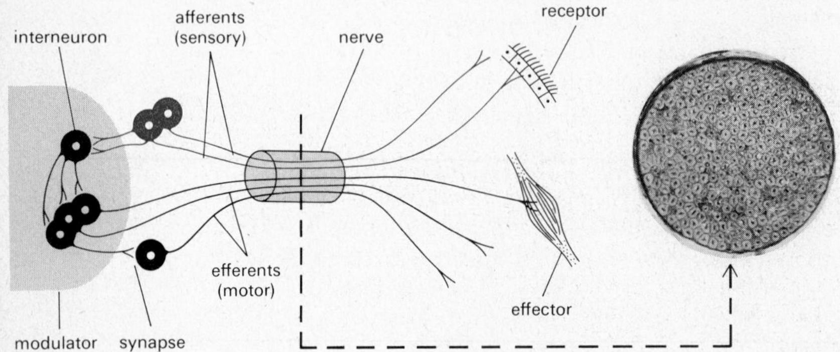

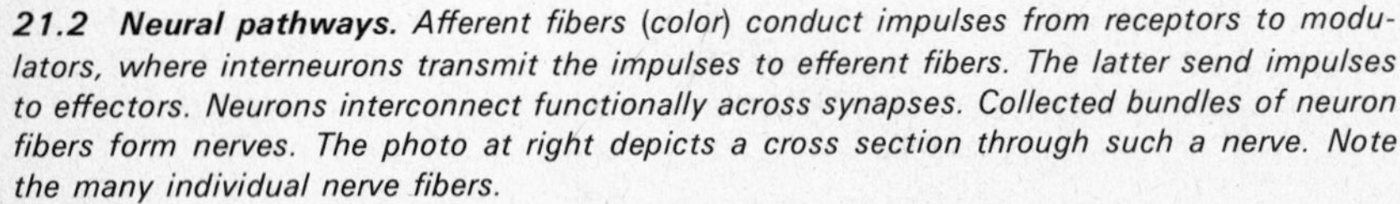

21.2 Neural pathways. *Afferent fibers (color) conduct impulses from receptors to modulators, where interneurons transmit the impulses to efferent fibers. The latter send impulses to effectors. Neurons interconnect functionally across synapses. Collected bundles of neuron fibers form nerves. The photo at right depicts a cross section through such a nerve. Note the many individual nerve fibers.*

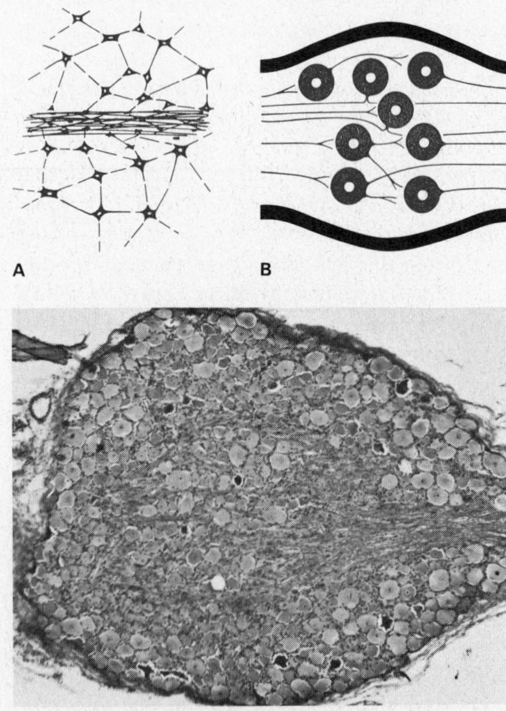

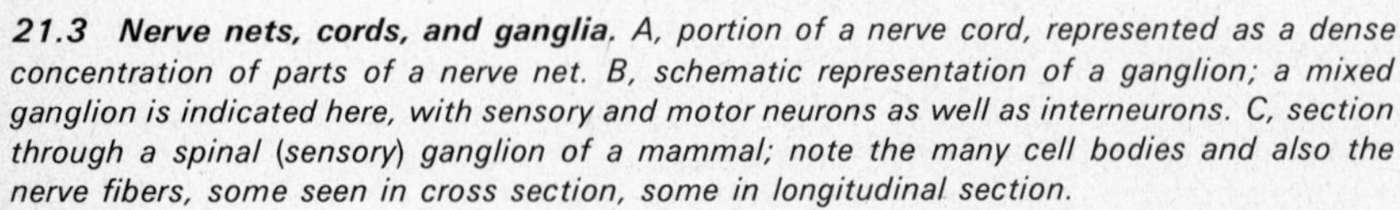

21.3 Nerve nets, cords, and ganglia. *A, portion of a nerve cord, represented as a dense concentration of parts of a nerve net. B, schematic representation of a ganglion; a mixed ganglion is indicated here, with sensory and motor neurons as well as interneurons. C, section through a spinal (sensory) ganglion of a mammal; note the many cell bodies and also the nerve fibers, some seen in cross section, some in longitudinal section.*

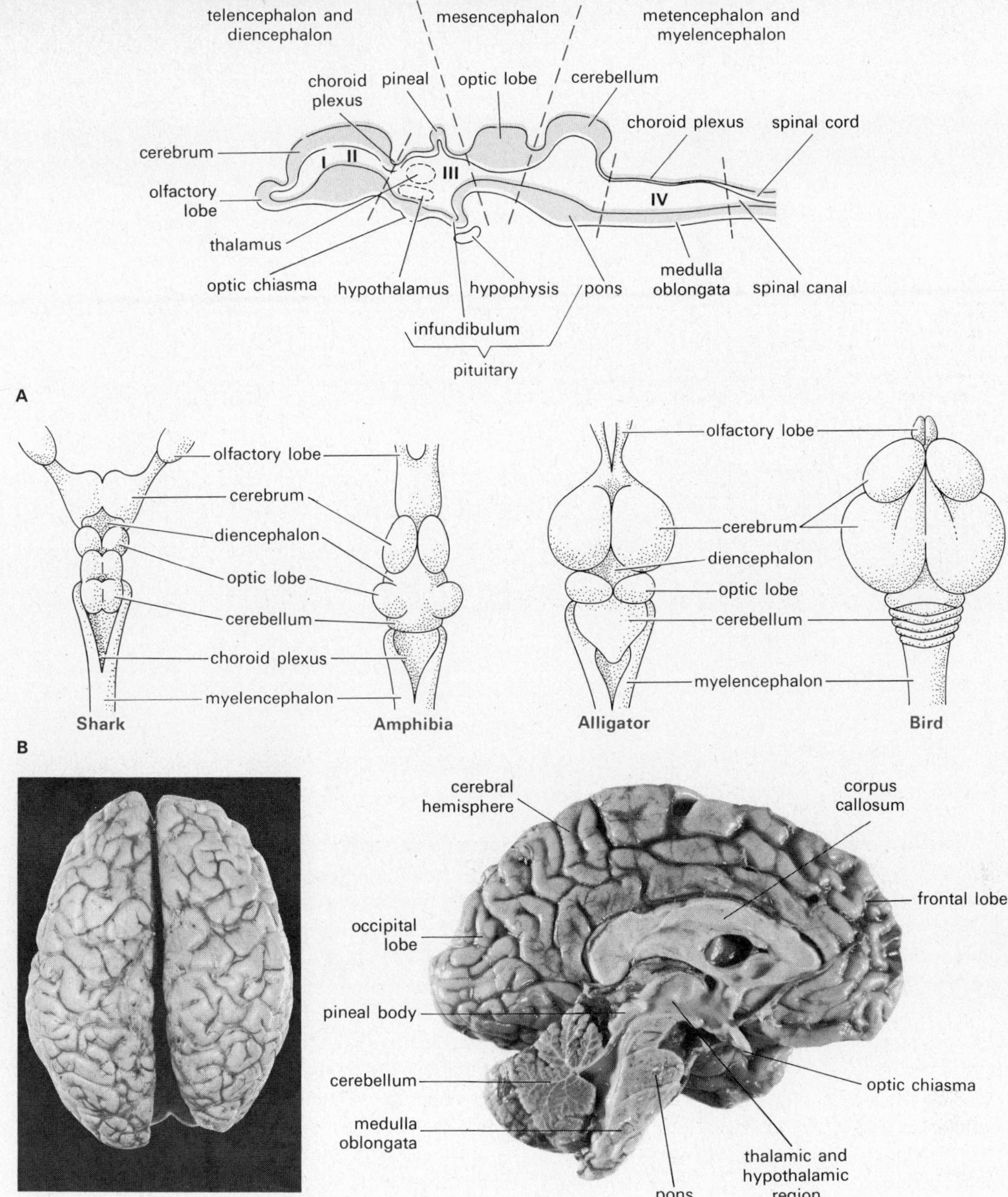

21.4 The vertebrate brain. *A, median section through primitive vertebrate brain (as in fishes), showing basic structural plan. Roman numerals refer to ventricles. Thalamus and hypothalamus regions are indicated in light broken lines, since these brain parts lie on each side of the median plane (as do ventricles I and II). The hypophysis forms as an outpouching from the roof of the mouth cavity; it becomes the anterior lobe of the pituitary, the infundibulum becoming the posterior lobe. The two choroid plexi are membranous regions in which blood vessels are carried. B, dorsal views of brains in different vertebrate classes. Note the proportionate progressive enlargement of the cerebrum in a posterior direction (and the parallel reduction of the olfactory lobes). C, dorsal view of human cerebrum. The left cerebral hemisphere is slightly larger than the right, as it usually is in right-handed persons. D, median section through human brain. The cerebrum is so large that, in dorsal view, it covers the cerebellum posteriorly.*

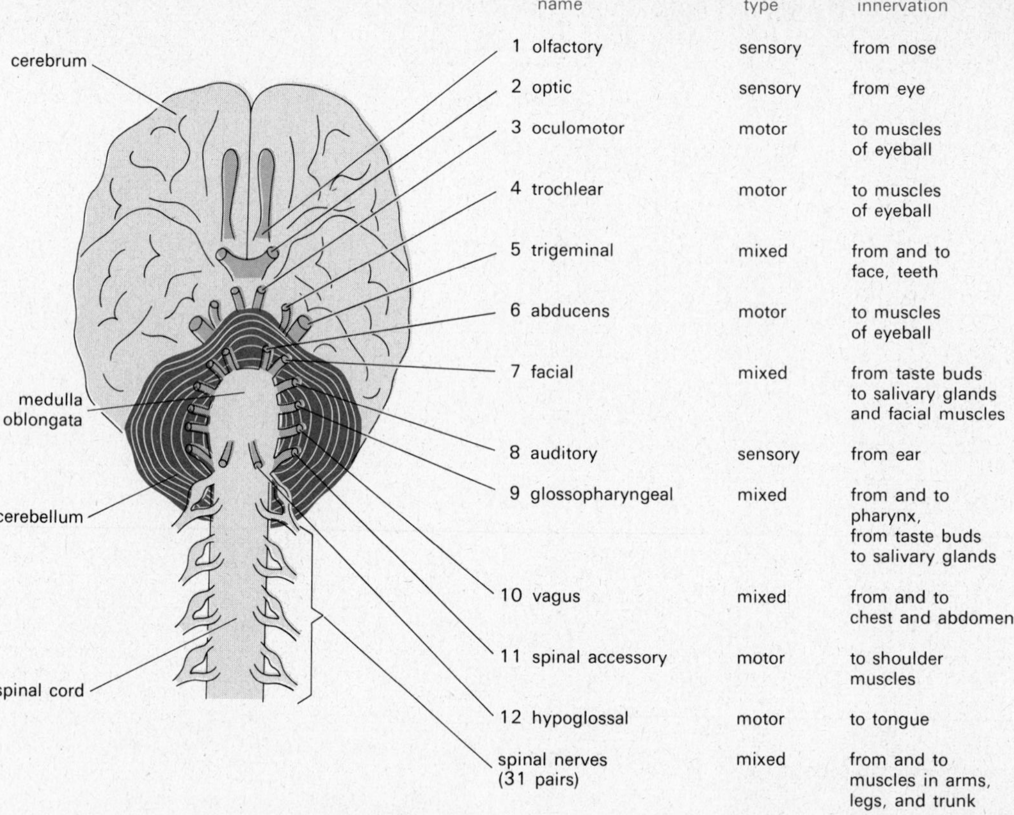

Cranial and spinal nerves in mammals

name	type	innervation
1 olfactory	sensory	from nose
2 optic	sensory	from eye
3 oculomotor	motor	to muscles of eyeball
4 trochlear	motor	to muscles of eyeball
5 trigeminal	mixed	from and to face, teeth
6 abducens	motor	to muscles of eyeball
7 facial	mixed	from taste buds to salivary glands and facial muscles
8 auditory	sensory	from ear
9 glossopharyngeal	mixed	from and to pharynx, from taste buds to salivary glands
10 vagus	mixed	from and to chest and abdomen
11 spinal accessory	motor	to shoulder muscles
12 hypoglossal	motor	to tongue
spinal nerves (31 pairs)	mixed	from and to muscles in arms, legs, and trunk

***21.5* The main nerves.** *Left, underside of brain and part of spinal cord of man, showing the origin of cranial and spinal nerves. The names and functions of these nerves are given in the tabulation at right. In the spinal nerves, the dorsal roots (with ganglia) are sensory, the ventral roots, motor.*

is enlarged greatly as a pair of *cerebral hemispheres,* which cover virtually all the rest of the brain. These hemispheres contain the centers for the most complex sensory integration and for voluntary motor activities, and they also play the key roles in the control of memory and intelligence. A conspicuous set of nerve tracts, the *corpus callosum,* interconnects the two hemispheres.

Behind the telencephalon, the (unpaired) *diencephalon* contains the *thalamus* and *hypothalamus.* These lateral regions control numerous involuntary activities, and they also affect consciousness, sleep, food intake, and emotional states (see Chap. 23). Ventrally the *pituitary* gland and dorsally the *pineal body* project from the diencephalon. The pineal body forms a third eye on the top of the head in lampreys and tuataras but is hidden under the cerebral hemispheres in birds and mammals.

The midbrain, or *mesencephalon,* contains dorsally located *optic lobes.* In all vertebrates except the mammals these lobes contain the centers of vision, and the nerve tracts from the eyes terminate there. In mammals the optic nerve tracts continue to visual centers located posteriorly in the cerebral hemispheres. The original optic lobes here are little more than relay stations for visual nerve impulses.

The hindbrain consists of two subdivisions, an anterior *metencephalon* and a posterior *myelencephalon,* or *medulla oblongata.* Dorsally the metencephalon includes the *cerebellum,* a comparatively large lobe that coordinates muscle contractions as smoothly integrated movements. For example, locomotion and balancing activities are regulated from this lobe. Ventrally the metencephalon contains a conspicuous bulge, the *pons,* in which the nerve tracts between brain and spinal cord cross from the left side to the right side. Because of this crossover the left side of the brain controls activities on the right side of the body and vice versa.

The medulla oblongata, which contains the nerve centers controlling heartbeat, vasomotion, and breathing, continues posteriorly as the spinal cord. Twelve pairs of *cranial nerves* (only 10 pairs in fishes and amphibia) emerge from the brain, and most of them lead away from the medulla oblongata (Fig. 21.5). The spinal cord gives rise to segmental *spinal nerves* (31 pairs in mammals), which pass to the trunk and the appendages. In each spinal nerve sensory fibers from the body enter the dorsal part of the spinal cord, and motor fibers leave from the ventral part. The cell bodies of the sensory fibers lie just outside the spinal cord, in *spinal ganglia* (Fig. 21.6 and see Fig. 21.5).

Vertebrates also have a well-developed *autonomic* subdivision of the nervous system (ANS, distinct from the remainder, called the *central* subdivision, or CNS). Controlling all involuntary activities and containing only nonmyelinated nerve fibers, this autonomic system has its nerve centers in the spinal cord and the brain and in a series of small peripheral ganglia. Sensory nerve fibers lead to these centers from all body parts that are not under voluntary control. (Among such fibers are, for example, those that form the stretch receptors in the large blood vessels near the heart; see Chap. 20).

From the autonomic centers lead away *two* functionally different sets of *autonomic motor fibers* (Fig. 21.7). Fibers from the brain and the most posterior part of the spinal cord represent

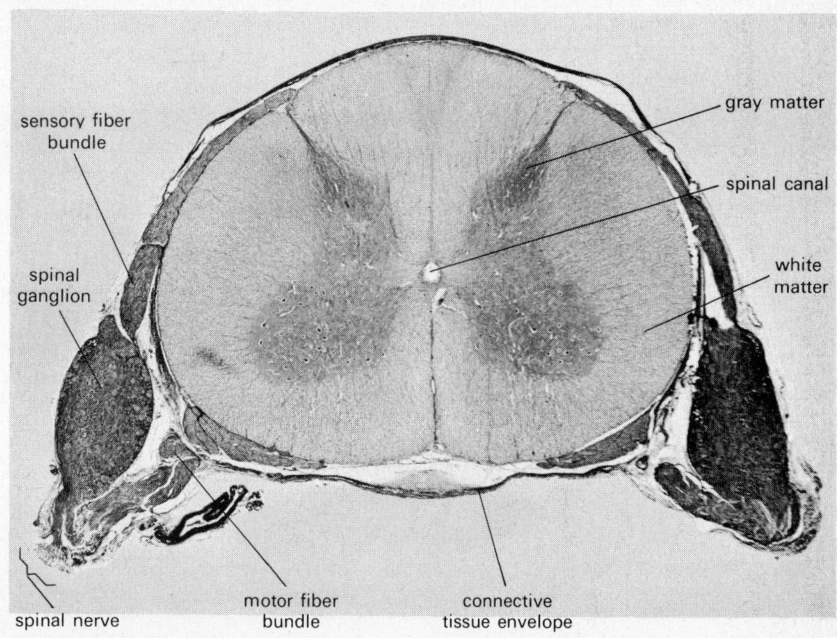

21.6 The mammalian spinal cord, *cross section. Note the spinal nerves, each dividing into two fiber bundles. The motor bundle connects with the cord ventrally, and the sensory bundle passes through a spinal ganglion and connects with the cord dorsally. The spinal cord itself is a dense meshwork of neurons, the cell bodies of which are aggregated around the center and form so-called gray matter. The axons and dendrites of these neurons form white matter around the gray matter. The central spinal canal contains lymphlike spinal fluid.*

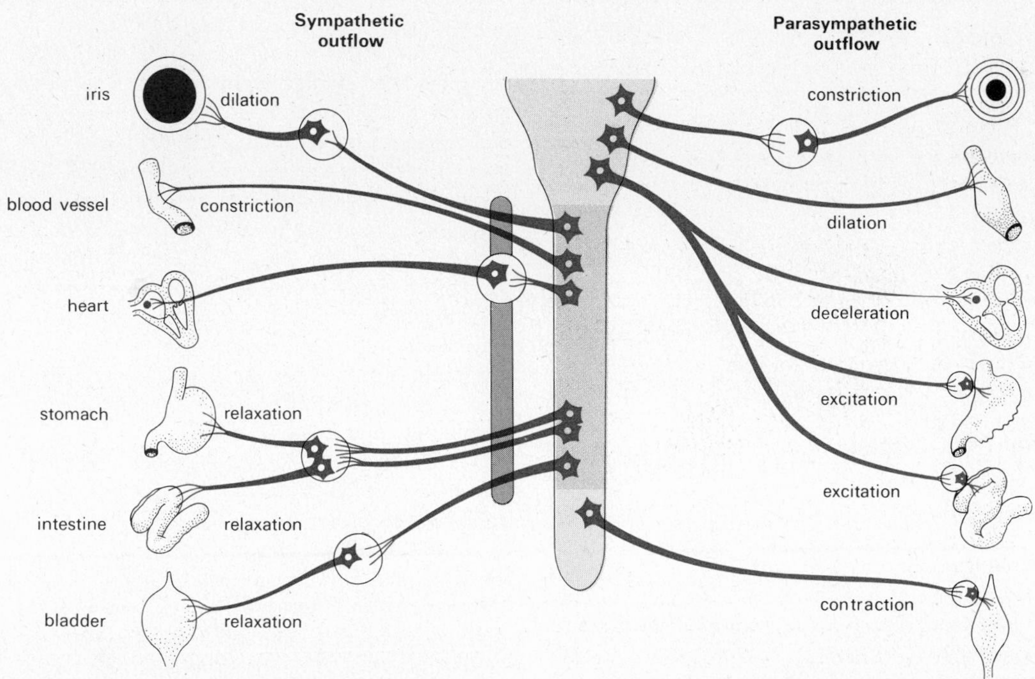

21.7 Autonomic nervous system: *some of the motor pathways. In spinal cord (center), parasympathetic centers are shown in light gray, sympathetic centers are darker. The column to the left of spinal cord represents the sympathetic ganglion chain on that side. Each neural path shown occurs pairwise, one on each side of the body. For simplicity only one side is indicated in each case, but every organ is innervated by both sympathetic and parasympathetic nerves.*

a *parasympathetic outflow* of the autonomic system; and fibers from the midportion of the spinal cord form a *sympathetic outflow.* Each organ of the body that is not under voluntary control receives fibers from both outflows, and these generally have opposing effects. If parasympathetic fibers inhibit a particular organ, sympathetic fibers stimulate it; or vice versa. For example, the inhibitory fibers to the pacemaker of the heart (which travel in the cranial vagus nerves; see Chap. 20) are part of the parasympathetic outflow, and the accelerating fibers to the heart belong to the sympathetic outflow. Similarly, vasodilator fibers to blood vessels are parasympathetic, and vasoconstrictor fibers are sympathetic. All other organs that function involuntarily are likewise equipped with both braking and accelerating controls.

Each autonomic motor path to a given organ consists of at least two consecutive neurons, which synapse in an *autonomic ganglion* located somewhere along the path to the organ. The nerve fiber leading to this ganglion is said to be *preganglionic,* and the fiber from the ganglion to the organ is *postganglionic.* In the sympathetic outflow the autonomic ganglia lie just outside the spinal cord, and on each side of the cord they are interconnected as an *autonomic chain* (Fig. 21.8). These chain ganglia also have interconnections with the spinal ganglia. Parasympathetic ganglia are more dispersed and are not arranged as chains.

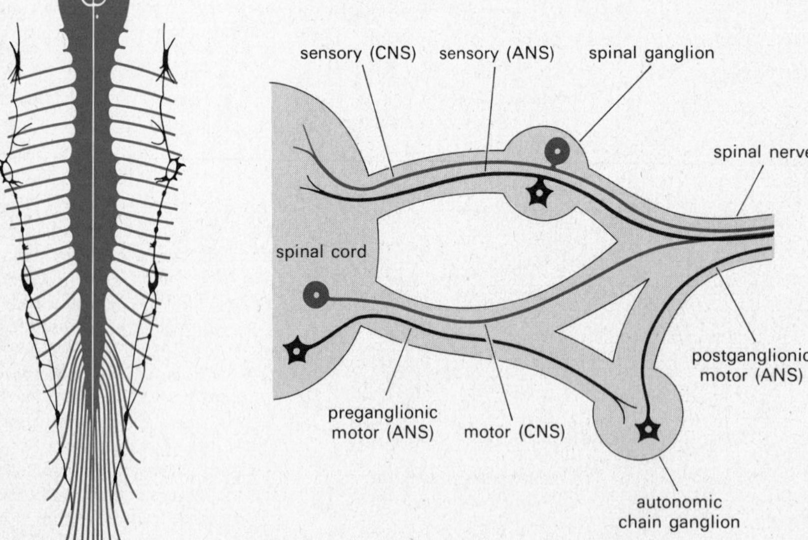

21.8 Autonomic chains. *A, spinal cord and nerves in color, autonomic chains black. B, interconnections of autonomic chain ganglia and spinal ganglia. CNS neurons in color, ANS neurons black. The cell bodies of all sensory ANS neurons lie in the 31 pairs of spinal ganglia that also contain the cell bodies of sensory CNS neurons. Sensory fibers of all kinds enter the spinal cord dorsally; motor fibers of all kinds leave ventrally.*

The involuntary operations of the ANS are interrelated closely with the voluntary ones of the CNS. For example, within certain limits a man can alter his breathing rate voluntarily through CNS control, even though this rate is basically under involuntary ANS control. Conversely, numerous autonomic changes affect voluntary behavior—for example, ANS-controlled hiccoughing limits CNS-regulated speaking.

neural impulses

A nerve impulse consists of a sequence of electrochemical reactions; during the passage of an impulse a *wave of electric depolarization* sweeps along a nerve fiber. After an impulse has passed the reaction balance returns to the original state, readying the fiber for a new impulse.

A resting, nonstimulated neuron is electrically positive along the outside of its surface membrane and electrically negative along the inside. These electric charges are carried by ions that are part of, or are attached to, the two sides of the cell membrane of the neuron. This membrane is so constructed that in the rest state it prevents the positive and negative ions from coming together. As a result an *electric potential* is maintained through the cell membrane; the membrane is said to be *polarized* electrically. When an impulse sweeps along a nerve fiber, the permeability of the membrane changes at successive points along the fiber. As this happens at any one point, an avenue is created through which the positive and negative ions of an adjacent point can pass, thus depolarizing that region. In other words, one depolarized region drains electric charges from adjacent parts of the membrane, causing depolarization there, too (Fig. 21.9). In this manner the impulse itself produces the necessary conditions that allow it to advance farther, and it travels wavelike along a fiber. Some short time after an impulse has passed a given point the membrane at that point reacquires both its original permeability state and its polarization.

If fine wires and electric measuring equipment are connected to a nerve, the passage of an impulse is recorded in such equipment by a flow of current of certain characteristics. By studying these action currents, or *action potentials,* of different nerves, it has been found that impulses differ in speed, strength, and frequency. In some nerve fibers, like those from the heart-rate center to the heart, impulses are fired continuously in rapid succession. Adjustment of heart rate occurs through frequency modulation: heart rate changes with alterations in impulse frequency. In motor fibers to many glands, by contrast, the fibers are normally at rest and carry impulses only when secretions are to be produced. Each type of fiber has its own characteristic pattern of impulse transmission, and it has been found also that impulse speeds tend to be directly proportional to the thickness of a nerve fiber. Moreover, speeds are influenced by the presence or absence of myelin sheaths. Myelinated CNS fibers conduct impulses at speeds up to 100 yd per sec, whereas nonmyelinated ANS fibers of comparable thickness conduct at about 25 yd per sec at most.

How does an impulse get across a synapse? In certain cases it can be shown that when an impulse reaches an axon terminal, the terminal acts as an endocrine structure and secretes minute amounts of a hormonal transmitter substance. This hormone diffuses through the synapse, and some reaches dendrite terminals of adjacent neurons. There the hormone can depolarize the dendrites in such a way that new impulses are initiated in them (Fig. 21.10).

Four hormonal substances that function in this manner have been identified in vertebrates: *serotonin, acetylcholine, adrenalin,* and *noradrenalin.* One or the other of the last two is secreted by sympathetic postganglionic fibers, and probably also by at least some of the interneurons in brain and spinal cord (for example those in the ANS centers of the hypothalamus). All such neurons are said to be *adrenergic.* Serotonin or acetylcholine is produced by sympathetic preganglionic fibers, all fibers of the parasympathetic system, and probably also by CNS fibers and CNS centers in brain and spinal cord. Such neurons are *cholinergic.*

The secretion pattern of these hormonal substances in the brain is not yet known very precisely, largely because of the so-called *blood-brain barrier,* a selective metabolic block between blood capillaries and nerve tissue. Probably maintained by neuroglia cells that surround the capillaries, this barrier lets only oxygen and basic nutrients such as glucose and amino acids pass into the brain, and it lets only waste products leave. The hormonal transmitter substances normally cannot diffuse in or out, hence investigation of their activity in the brain has proved difficult. Even so, through research done in conjunction with tranquilizers and drugs such as LSD, it has been found that the hormonal transmitters play a key role in regulating moods and emotional states, both normally and in mental illness. Thus, elevated moods and feelings of well-being are associated directly with high levels of noradrenalin and serotonin in the brain, whereas depressed states are associated with low concentrations of these substances. Some findings further suggest that normal and certain abnormal changes in mental state might result from internally generated alterations in the chemical reaction patterns through which the transmitter substances are manufactured in the brain.

Synaptic impulse transmission by chemicals also has important consequences outside the brain. For example, nerve fibers as such rarely fatigue, but their transmitter-secreting terminals "tire" fairly easily. Moreover, since only axon terminals secrete hormones and only dendrite terminals are sensitive to these substances, impulse conduction becomes unidirectional.

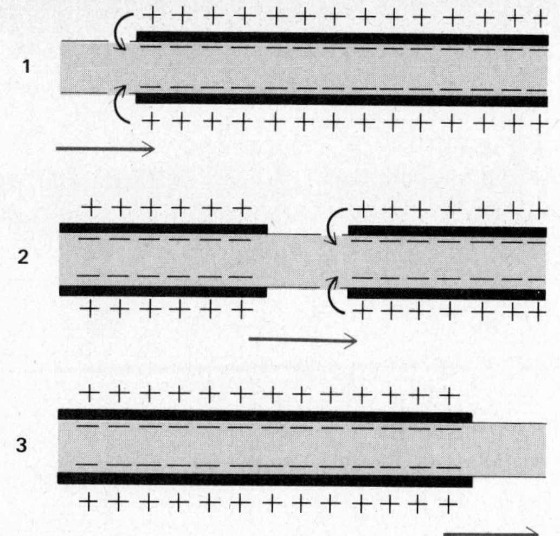

21.9 The nerve impulse. *Passage of an impulse through a nerve fiber involves local depolarization of the fiber membrane, an effect that is propagated like a wave through successive portions of the fiber. After an impulse has passed a given region, the original polarization is reestablished.*

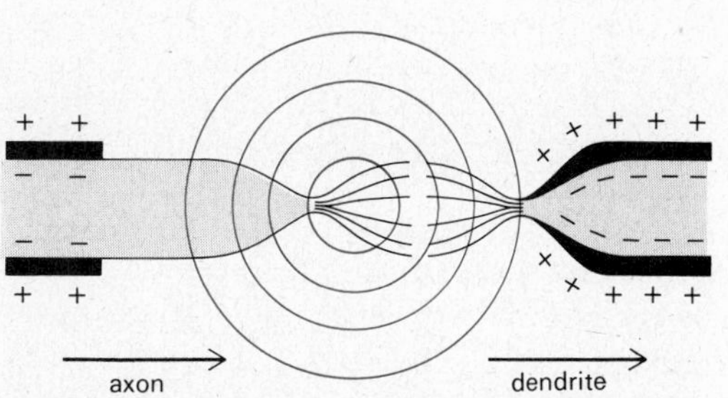

21.10 Chemical impulse transmission. *In a neural synapse, hormonal transmitter substances are released and spread locally (colored rings) from the axon terminal of one fiber to the dendrite terminal of another. Impulses are transmitted across synapses by such chemical means.*

21.11 **Modulator activities.** *Black lines symbolize passage of impulses. 1, simple reflex relay. 2, suppression of impulse conduction. 3, augmentation of outgoing impulse by summation of weak incoming impulses. 4, channel selection. 5, in certain cases information is believed to be stored by continued impulse conduction in an oscillator (cyclical) circuit.*

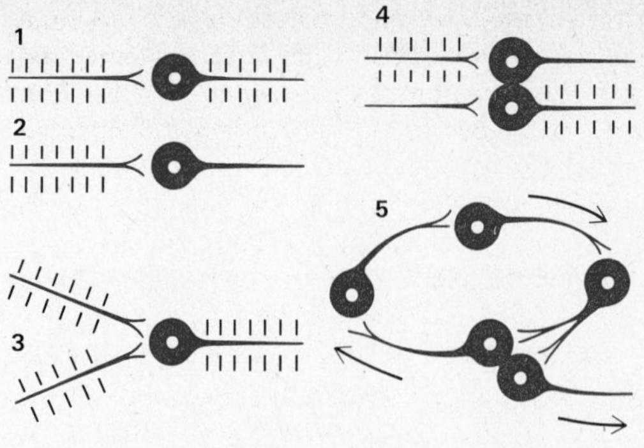

neural centers

In general, the activity of all types of neural modulator is based on two kinds of information: genetically inherited information and newly acquired information obtained through the sensory system.

Certain genetically determined neural pathways and patterns of neural activity are already established once an animal has completed its embryonic development. Even in a just-formed nervous system, therefore, relatively simple sensory inputs to the modulators often can evoke fairly complex outputs to the effectors, and behavior can be correspondingly complex. In many cases, indeed, sensory inputs are not required at all: neural centers are often spontaneously active. This is particularly true for those that control the most vital rhythmic processes of an animal. For example, as already pointed out in the preceding chapter, the breathing center in the medulla oblongata sends out rhythmic motor impulses spontaneously. This rhythm can be shown to persist even if the center is isolated surgically. Similarly spontaneous activity takes place in the heart-rate center and in many—possibly most—other neural control centers as well.

In effect, the genetic endowment ensures that, as soon as an animal is completely developed, it has fully functional neural controls for at least those motor activities that are basically necessary for survival. To the extent that these activities are spontaneous, neural operations evidently do not involve complete reflexes; receptors and sensory paths do not participate directly.

To a greater or lesser degree, however, inherited neural activity is usually modified by sensory experience. Information about the current status of the external and internal environment is acquired by receptors and is transmitted to the neural centers in the form of more or less complex sensory impulses. In such instances nervous activity is based on complete reflexes. But here the modulating centers do not merely relay incoming sensory impulses to outgoing motor paths; even the simplest modulators are usually capable of *reflex modification.* The nature of this modification depends in some cases on inherited factors, in others on information acquired through past experience and stored as memory.

Among the simplest and most basic forms of modification are *suppression* and *augmentation* of reflexes. Suppression occurs when certain neurons inhibit others. Some synapses are so organized that, when impulses arrive in incoming nerve fibers, the production of impulses in outgoing fibers becomes harder rather than easier. The opposite effect, *augmentation,* can be brought about by a *summation* of impulses. In a synapse receiving many incoming impulses, each impulse individually might be too weak to produce an impulse in an outgoing fiber. However, the small quantities of chemical transmitters produced by the many incoming fibers can add together and become sufficiently powerful to initiate impulses in an outgoing fiber (Fig. 21.11).

A more complex form of modulator activity, based largely on summation and inhibition, is *channel selection.* Even a simply organized modulator selects among many possible outgoing fibers and sends out impulses only over certain specifically chosen paths. Normally only *appropriate* effectors will then receive motor commands. As a result the effector response of an animal can be adaptively useful and can actually contribute to steady-state maintenance. Little is known as yet about the mechanism by which certain neural channels are selected in preference to others. In most cases preferred circuits become established during the embryonic development of the nervous system. Thereafter given sets of sensory impulses to a modulator result in more or less fixed, predictable sets of motor impulses to effectors. Such neural activities are among those that have a largely genetic basis, and they govern most of the internal operations of most animals.

Preferred channels include, for example, sets of interneurons that are arranged as *oscillator circuits,* in which an impulse travels continuously over a circular route. Each time such an impulse passes a given synapse, a motor impulse to an effector might be initiated. The rhythmic heartbeat of an insect is controlled by an oscillator circuit of this type, in which nine circularly arranged neurons are embedded directly in the heart. Many other rhythmic, automatic activities are known to be governed by oscillator circuits.

A modulator often reacts to an incoming sensory impulse by sending out not just one but several selected motor commands. Here a simple external stimulus can lead to the completion of several or many simultaneous responses, all occurring as a single, integrated pattern of activity, or *programmed behavior.* A good example is the startle response in man. An unexpected blow directed at the head leads to a closing of the eyes, a lowering of the head and assumption of a crouching stance, and a raising of hands to the face. These several dozen separate reflexes occur simultaneously, as a unified "program." Most programs of this type are largely inherited, and in most animals, invertebrates in particular, behavior is very largely programmatic in this sense. Moreover, the execution of such programs involves most of the neurons present in the nerve centers. In comparatively large-brained animals, the majority of neurons again probably form fixed inborn circuits, yet substantial numbers seem to remain available for the later development of new or modified circuits and new or modified programs. Such animals, notably (but not only) cephalopod mollusks, arthropods, and vertebrates, are capable of *learning* and of storing learned experiences as memory.

The simplest form of learning is probably *habituation,* or progressive loss of responsiveness to repeated stimulation. For example, most animals carry out avoidance or escape activities in response to mild stress stimuli. However, if such stimuli are repeated many times in succession the response can gradually subside and ultimately often disappear. It is not well known as yet how such habituation comes about. (Indeed, organisms without nervous systems can habituate to environmental stimuli, too, hence learning of this type probably operates on an intracellular, chemical level.)

A more complex form of learning depends on *conditioned reflexes.* In so-called *classical conditioning,* two or more stimuli are presented to an animal simultaneously and repeatedly, until the animal learns to execute the same response to either stimulus. For example, if bright light is directed into the eyes the pupils will contract reflexly. If the light stimulus is given repeatedly and is accompanied each time by food, sound, or some other stimulus, then pupillary contraction can eventually be made to occur by such a stimulus alone, without the bright light. Evidently, the animal now associates the second stimulus with light, and it comes to have not only the inherited neural circuit to the eyes but also an additional one acquired by learning through experience. Either one alone or both together can then produce the pupillary response.

Indeed, pupillary retraining in man is probably possible even if the second stimulus is no more than a single spoken word, and if this word is spoken by the test subject himself. The stimulus word might not even need to be spoken but could be merely an unvoiced thought. Such a self-conditioned individual would then be able to contract his pupils at will. The occasionally recorded feats of human self-control over pain and other normally nonvolitional responses are undoubtedly based on self-conditioning of this sort.

Learning can also occur through *operant conditioning,* which differs from the classical type in that the animal participates actively and deliberately in the learning process. Thus if a certain activity at first happens to be carried out by chance and if this activity happens to have desirable consequences, then the animal can recreate these consequences by deliberately repeating the activity. Learning by this means becomes particularly effective if it is "reinforced," that is, if repetition of an activity entails material or psychological rewards. Much of the learning of vertebrates—mammals and man in particular—is based on operant conditioning of this sort (see Chap. 22).

Undoubtedly the most complex modulator activities are those that are involved in intelligence, personality, ability to think abstractly, and capacity to manipulate and control the environment. Depending extensively on memory and learning, such functions are developed to any notable degree only in the most advanced mammals. But note again that, regardless of their relative complexities, all modulators depend on adequate *information;* apart from whatever built-in, inherited information they have available, modulators can act only on information that the neural receptors supply in the form of sensory impulses.

neural receptors

Receptor cells are either *epitheliosensory* or *neurosensory* (Fig. 21.12). The first type is a specialized, nonnervous epithelial cell that receives

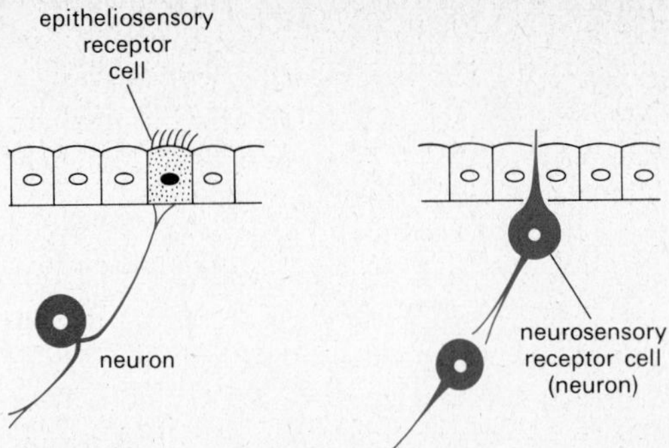

21.12 ***Receptor cells.*** *The two kinds are shown.*

stimuli at one end and is innervated by a sensory nerve fiber at the other. The second type is a modified sensory neuron that carries a dendrite-like stimulus-receiving extension at one end. At the other is an axon that synapses with other neurons. Both types of receptor cell can occur in clusters and together with accessory cells form *sense organs.* All receptor cells of invertebrates are of the neurosensory type. Vertebrates contain both neurosensory and epitheliosensory receptors.

Nerve impulses generated by receptors become perceptions only in the neural centers. In effect, eyes do not see and ears do not hear; eye-brain complexes are required for seeing, ear-brain complexes for hearing. In some instances the perceptions become conscious, but more often they do not. When nerve impulses reach the brain from a blood vessel, for example, sensing takes place, but in this case the sensation does not become conscious.

Environmental change as such is known to be an important factor in the production of sensory impulses by receptor cells. For when a given stimulus persists unchanged for a time, a sense dulls, or "adapts." For example, we soon become relatively insensitive to the pressure of clothes, to a persistent odor, or to a taste. Pain is most difficult to adapt to, but odor perception dulls very easily. We cannot judge our own body odors, for example, since we live with them constantly and adapt to them continuously.

Different kinds of sense perceptions depend not so much on differences in impulses to the brain as on the different *central connections* of sensory fibers in the brain. For example, if a fiber from a heat receptor and a fiber from a cold receptor could be cut and the cut ends were allowed to reinnervate the sense organs in switched order, then the animal would feel hot when the cold receptor were stimulated and cold when the heat receptor were stimulated. In other words, the quality of a perception depends on which of various brain centers receives signals.

Furthermore, correct *localization* of a stimulus similarly depends on the central connections. The anatomical distribution of receptors throughout the body is matched virtually point for point in the anatomical distribution of neural centers. So long as these structural relations are preserved, impulses will be correctly interpreted as coming from particular body regions and particular receptors. That this is actually so has been demonstrated through experimental rearrangements of neural pathways.

One qualification should be added here, however. It is a fairly common experience that pain originating in an internal organ is often sensed as if it originated at some other region. For example, pain stimuli actually affecting the liver can be felt as pain in the shoulder region; and an ache in one tooth is often thought to come from the whole side of the head. In such cases of *referred pain,* pain fibers that originate in different body regions lead to the same general area in the brain. Impulses through one of the fibers can then stimulate a greater or lesser portion of that area. Pain sensations can be diffuse as a result, as if impulses actually arrived over more than one pain fiber.

chemoreceptors

These receptors give information about environmental *chemicals.* They include receptors that mediate the senses of *smell* and of *taste.* In most animals the receptor structures are located in the skin, and they are usually free sensory nerve endings that can be stimulated directly by particular chemicals. The ability to sense common environmental chemicals has particular significance for many invertebrates, aquatic ones especially. This sense permits such animals to detect the presence of irritants or poisons and the chemical exudates of enemies, prey, food, and mates.

Smell is mainly a distance sense. Aquatic animals smell traces of chemicals in solution, terrestrial types smell vaporized chemicals or traces of chemicals that adhere to the ground. In vertebrates the smell receptors are parts of the ciliated epithelium that lines the upper nasal passages (Fig. 21.13). Sensory fibers from there lead to the olfactory lobes of the forebrain, relatively small in man but large in many other vertebrates (see Fig. 21.14). It is difficult to classify odors adequately into basic categories, and it is also not well established if or to what extent smell-receptor cells form different functional classes. They are structurally more or less alike in any given animal.

The sense of taste conveys information mainly about the general chemical nature of potential food substances. Insects such as flies and moths taste with their legs and mouth parts, the receptors being in bristles on these appendages. In mammals the taste receptors are *taste buds,* clusters of elongated ciliated cells located in depressions in the tongue (Fig. 21.14). Given chemicals stimulate buds in different regions of the tongue and different taste sensations are then perceived. The four primary tastes are *sweet, sour, salty,* and *bitter.* Stimulation of buds near the tip of the tongue produces sweet tastes; those at the back, bitter tastes; and those along the tongue edges, sour and salty tastes.

Numerous composite chemical perceptions are built up from different combinations and intensities of the four basic tastes, from smell, and from the other sense perceptions initiated in the mouth. For example, both a hot meal and a cold meal affect the same taste buds if the two meals are alike chemically. But the hot meal vaporizes more and therefore smells more, and it also stimulates heat receptors in the lining of the mouth and on the tongue. The hot and the cold meals consequently "taste" different.

Chemical perceptions of all kinds are subjective sensations, not objective properties of chemicals. For example, sugar is not inherently sweet; it merely has the property of stimulating particular taste buds. Sweetness and all similar sensory qualities then are purely subjective interpretations. Thus the same chemical that might be pleasant to one animal or at one region of the tongue can be distinctly less pleasant or repugnant to another animal or at another region of the tongue. At least one substance is known (*phenylthiocarbamide*) that one person might not taste at all but that tastes sweet to another, bitter to a third, salty to a fourth, and sour to a fifth. Individual differences of this sort trace back to differences in heredity.

mechanoreceptors

These structures register stimuli of touch and of mechanical pressure generally. The receptors are often free nerve endings, which in many cases are highly branched or elaborated as meshworks. Such receptors occur abundantly in the skin and in muscles, tendons, and most connective tissues. The skin of vertebrates also contains distinct nonnervous touch-registering organs innervated by sensory fibers (Fig. 21.15).

Mechanoreceptors are stimulated by mechanical displacement or by changes in the mechanical

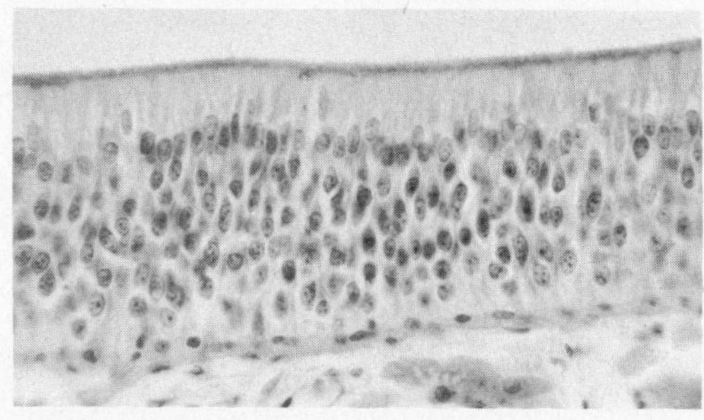

21.13 Chemoreceptors. *A section through the epitheliosensory nasal epithelium of vertebrates is shown.*

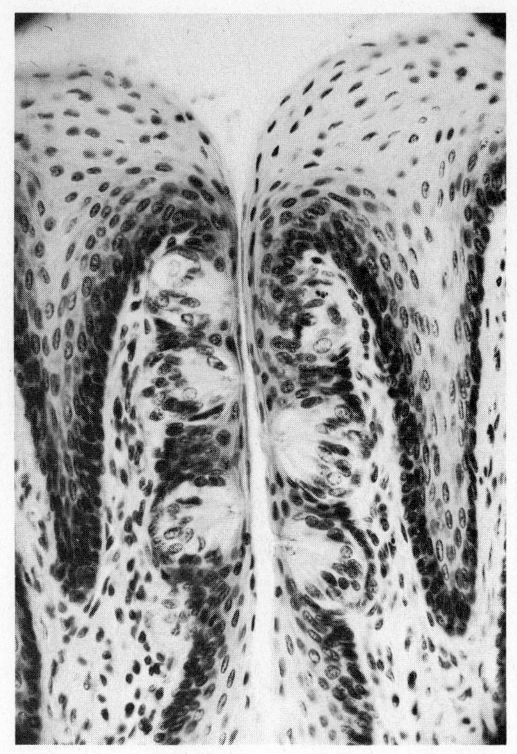

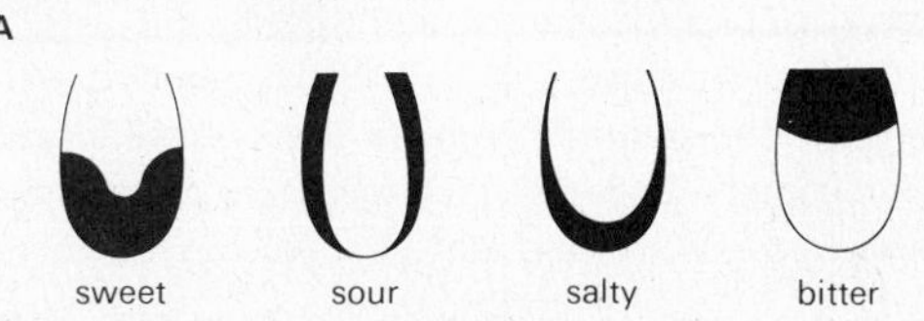

21.14 Chemoreceptors. *A, section through tongue showing taste buds; the buds are located along the deep narrow channel leading into the tongue from the surface. B, the distribution of taste buds for the four taste sensations.*

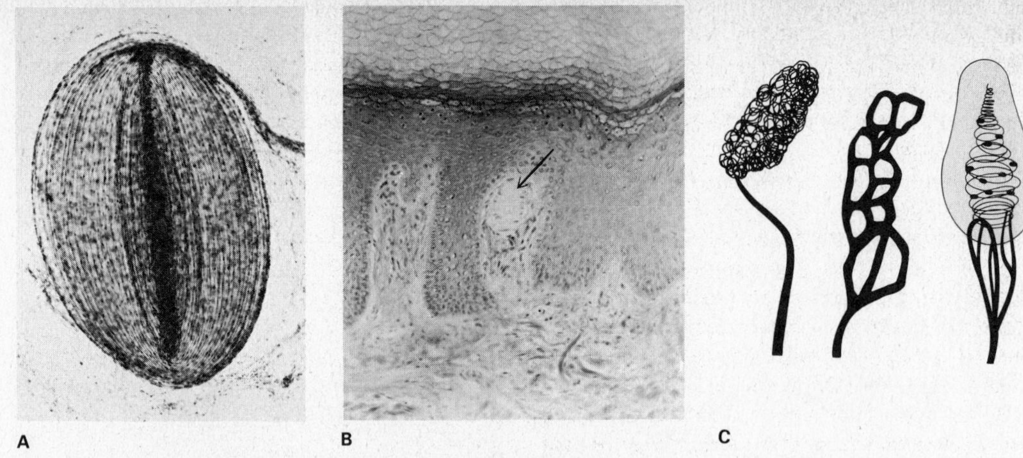

21.15 ***Mechanoreceptors.*** *A, section through a Pacinian corpuscle, a pressure receptor in mammalian skin. B, the location of a Pacinian corpuscle in the skin. C, left, organ of Ruffini, a pressure receptor consisting largely of a ball of nerve endings; center, touch receptor nerve net surrounding a hair; right, Meissner's corpuscle, another type of touch receptor organ in the skin. (A, courtesy Carolina Biological Supply Company.)*

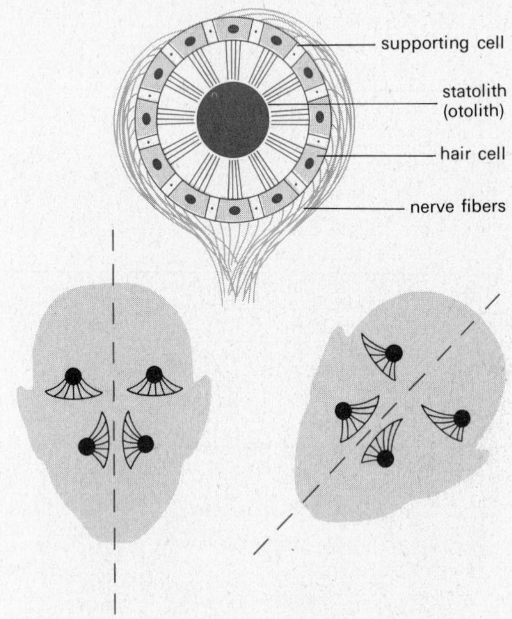

21.16 ***Statoreceptors.*** *The statocyst at top shows how hair cells support an ear stone (statolith) in the center of the cyst. Lower figures show position of the receptor organs in relation to the head, and the effect of tilting the head.*

stresses that affect surrounding parts. For example, a bending or stretching of part of the skin or of an internal organ usually results in receptor stimulation. An animal thereby receives information both about contacts with external objects and about movements of any body part. In mammals the base of each hair is surrounded by a meshlike terminal of a mechanoreceptor fiber, and a nerve impulse is initiated if a hair is touched even lightly. The action of some of the internal mechanoreceptors, called *stretch receptors* (or also *proprioceptors*), has already been discussed in the accounts on breathing and circulation. Stretch receptors in muscles are moderately complex sense organs. They contribute to the control of the relative positions and movements of body parts and thus play an important role in maintaining posture and balance.

statoreceptors

Present in many invertebrate groups and in all vertebrates, these organs are special types of mechanoreceptor for the sense of body orientation in relation to gravity (Fig. 21.16). Most commonly a statoreceptor is a small, fluid-filled sac, or *statocyst,* that contains a cluster of ciliated *hair cells.* Attached to or resting against the hairs is a *statolith,* a grain of hard, often calcareous material. When an animal moves the statolith shifts position under the influence of gravity and its own inertia, and it then presses against a somewhat different set of hair cells. Such a change in the pressure pattern produces a corresponding change in the pattern of nerve impulses traveling away from the sensory cells. In this manner the brain receives information about altered orientations or accelerations of the body. Body position is also sensed independently by information from mechanoreceptors, as noted, but the statoreceptors must function if an animal is to maintain normal orientation in relation to gravity.

In most animals statoreceptors are located in the head or in head appendages such as antennae. In vertebrates they are part of the inner ear. Indeed, the vertebrate ear has evolved primarily as a statoreceptor and only secondarily as an organ of hearing. Hair cells with statoliths (*ear stones*) are located at several places along the walls of two inner-ear chambers, the *saccule* and the *utricle* (Fig. 21.17). These receptors are organs for *static* body balance. They give information about head positions and permit perception of up, down, side, front, and back, even when visual stimuli and sensory data from muscles fail to provide such information. A blindfolded mammal with inoperative ear-stone receptors has difficulty in remaining upright, and when its position is abnormal it does little to correct this position.

Vertebrates also have *semicircular canals,* which provide information about head movements and through this about the *dynamic* balance of the body. Three semicircular canals in each ear loop from the utricle back to the utricle. The canals are placed at right angles to one another in three planes of space (Fig. 21.18). At one end of each canal is an enlarged portion, or *ampulla,* which contains a cluster of hair cells. When the semicircular canals move as the head is moved, the fluid in the canals "stays behind" temporarily as a result of its inertia and "catches up" only after the head has stopped moving. This delayed fluid motion bends the hairs of the receptor cells. Different impulse patterns then reach the brain according to the direction and intensity of fluid motion in the three pairs of canals.

Sudden accelerations, particularly in a vertical direction, or rapid spinning, or also uneven warming or cooling of the fluid in the semicircular canals, initiate reflexes through the receptors of dynamic balance that often lead to well-known symptoms of dizziness, nausea, and gastric upsets. Seasickness has the same cause, as does the discomfort produced by jerky motions of elevators and airplanes.

phonoreceptors

These organs are sensitive to pressure vibrations in water or air. Organs of hearing are particular kinds of phonoreceptors.

Receptors for nonauditory vibrations, largely free nerve endings and hair cells, are located in or near the body surface. Most aquatic vertebrates have highly specialized phonoreceptors in the head and trunk skin. These regions contain so-called *lateral-line systems,* essentially series of water-filled canals that communicate through pores with the external medium (Fig. 21.19). Movement of the water in the canals produces nerve impulses in hair cells. The lateral-line system is capable of detecting water turbulence created by moving objects or by a fish itself, and in a sense the system is comparable to the "listening" component of submarine sonar.

A distinct sense of hearing is restricted to some

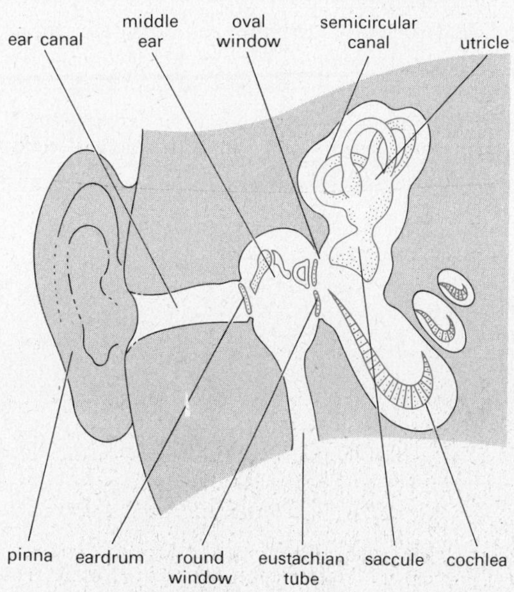

21.17 Phonoreceptors: *the mammalian ear. Note ear bones in the middle-ear cavity and attachment of semicircular canals to utricle. Statoreceptors are in the utricle and the saccule.*

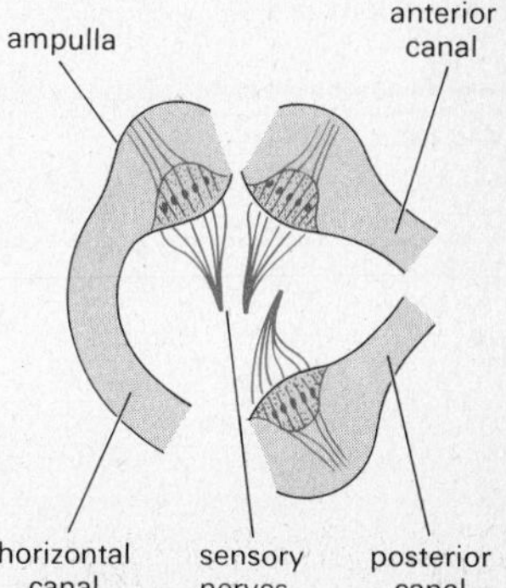

21.18 (*Above*) ***Semicircular canals*** *of the left ear. Top of diagram is anterior, right side is toward median plane of head. The three canals are set at right angles to one another; hence only the horizontal canal reveals its curvature in this view. Both ends of each canal open in the utricle. The hair cells in the ampullas function as receptors for the sense of dynamic balance. When the head is moved, fluid in the canals bends the hair cells, thereby initiating sensory nerve impulses.*

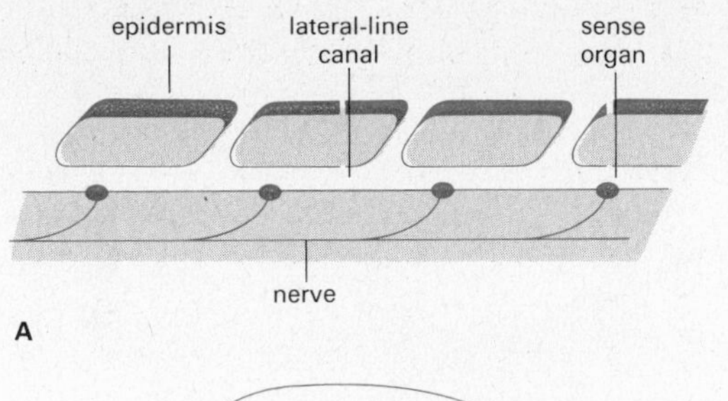

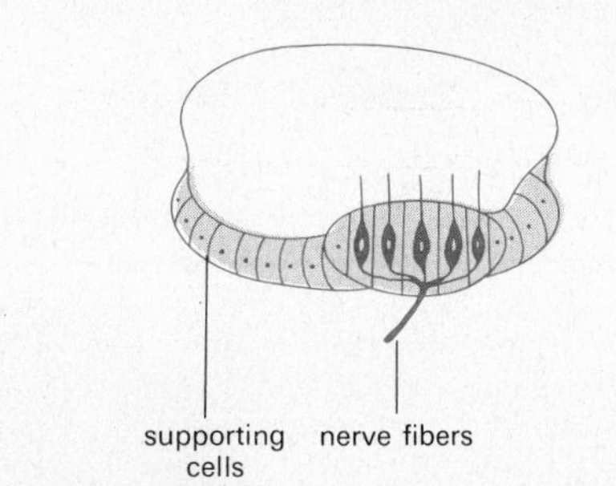

21.19 Phonoreceptors: *the lateral-line system. A, general plan of the system in relation to the body surface of fishes. B, schematic cross section through a lateral-line canal, showing supporting cells and sense organ, the latter with phonoreceptive hair cells embedded among supporting cells.*

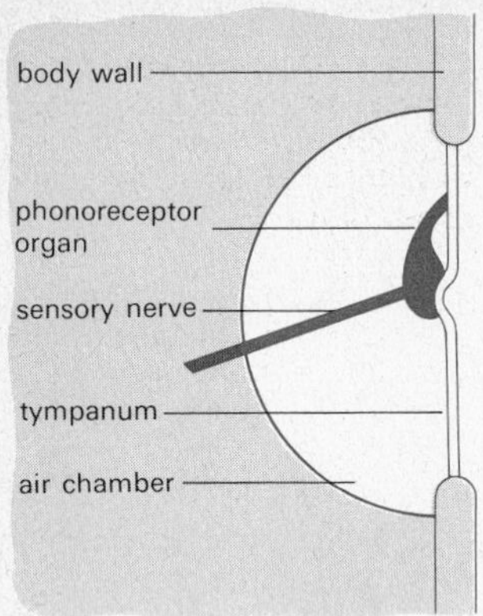

21.20 (*Above*) ***Phonoreceptors:*** *the arthropod ear. An organ of this type is found, for example, on grasshopper legs. The tympanum corresponds functionally to the eardrum of mammals.*

arthropods (certain crustacea, spiders, and insects) and to vertebrates; by and large only animals that make sounds can also hear them. In arthropods the receptor organs are located in various body regions. For example, mosquitoes hear with their antennae, and a male mosquito can best hear the sounds that have the same frequency as those produced by the wings of flying females (Fig. 21.20).

In terrestrial vertebrates, an *outer ear* carries sound to the *eardrum,* a membrane that closes off the cavity of the *middle ear* (see Fig. 21.17). As pointed out in Chap 20, this cavity connects with the pharynx through a eustachian tube.

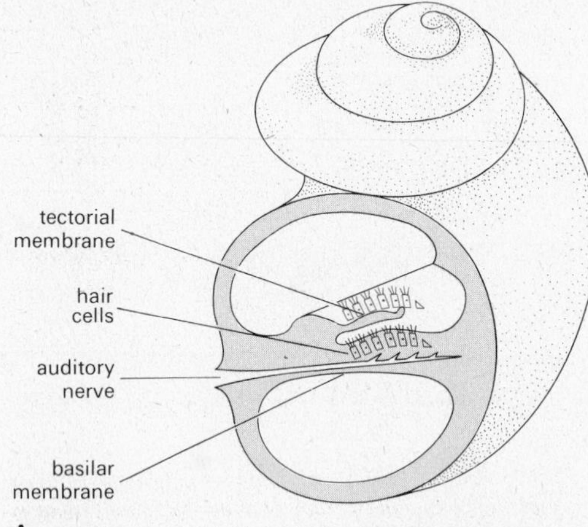

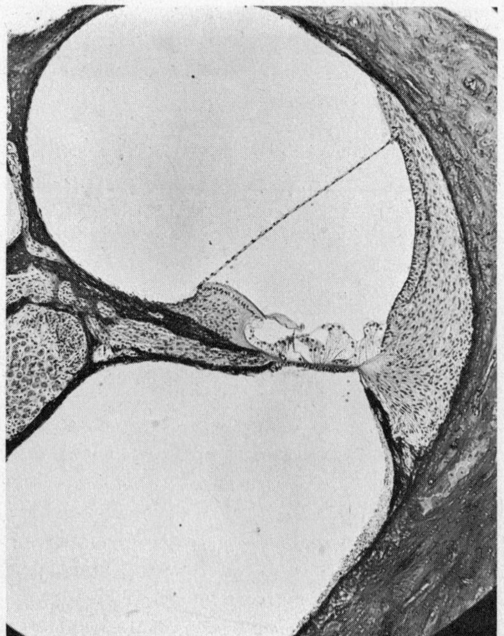

21.21 ***The cochlea.*** *A, the coils of the cochlea and a cochlear cross section with the parts of the organ of Corti. B, section through the organ of Corti.*

Three tiny middle-ear bones, *hammer, anvil,* and *stirrup,* form an adjustable sound-transmitting bridge from the eardrum across the middle-ear cavity to the inner ear. Two membranes, the *round window* and the *oval window,* close off the middle-ear cavity from the inner ear. The stirrup bone is anchored on the oval window.

The inner ear is an intricate system of interconnected canals and spaces, all surrounded by bone and filled with lymphlike fluid. Apart from the saccule and the utricle already referred to above, the inner ear also contains a *cochlea,* a coiled, very elaborate receptor organ for the sense of hearing (Fig. 21.21). It contains a *basilar membrane* with fibers of graded lengths stretched across the cochlear tube (an arrangement similar to that of the strings of a piano). Attached to these fibers are innervated hair cells, and each fiber–hair-cell complex is selectively sensitive to a particular vibration frequency. Sound waves transmitted to the cochlea produce fluid vibrations of given frequencies, and the fibers that are sensitive to such frequencies move up and down as a result. As the hair cells attached to the fibers now move up and down, too, they come into contact with an overhanging *tectorial membrane.* It is presumably these contacts that initiate nerve impulses. Impulses from defferent sets of hair cells are interpreted in the temporal lobes of the brain as sounds of different pitch. Basilar membrane, hair cells, and tectorial membrane together represent an *organ of Corti.*

Mammals probably have the best sense of hearing. Man can perceive sound frequencies ranging from 16 to 20,000 cycles per sec. Dogs are sensitive to frequencies up to 30,000 cycles per sec, and bats and some insects, to frequencies up to 100,000 cycles per sec. The ear of man is probably unsurpassed in distinguishing tones of only slightly different pitch and widely different quality. As an interpretive sense and as an important adjuster of speech, hearing has acquired a human importance second only to vision.

photoreceptors

The light-sensitive receptors of animals are cellular organelles that contain special *photopigments.* These pigments are chemically quite similar in all animals, and each consists of two joined molecular parts. One is a variant of *retinene,* a derivative of vitamin A; the other is a variant of *opsin,* a protein. Light splits retinene from opsin, and in the process light energy is in some way converted to chemical energy. Further chemical and electrical reactions then produce nerve impulses in the nerve fibers. At the same time retinene is rejoined to opsin through a series of ATP- and enzyme-requiring reactions, and the photopigment is thereby regenerated (Fig. 21.22).

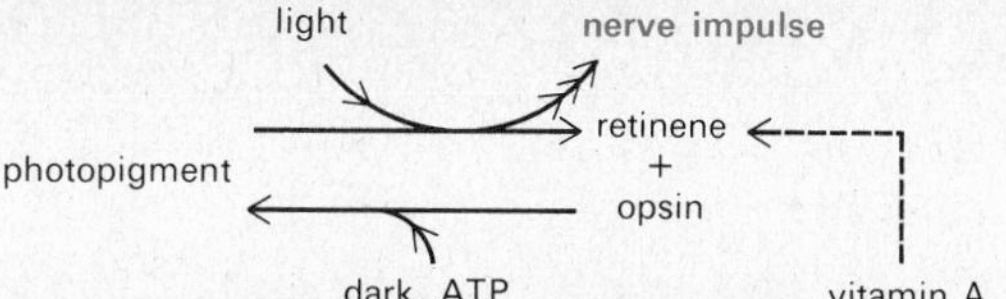

21.22 ***Photoreception.*** *The photopigment is iodopsin in cone cells, rhodopsin in rod cells. Note that vitamin A can replenish the supply of retinene.*

Numerous invertebrate groups and all vertebrates have photopigments in elongated receptor cells that enable the animals to perceive different black-white intensities of light. Such cells serve mainly as illumination and motion detectors. In vertebrates these cells are called *rods,* and their photopigment is "visual purple," or *rhodopsin.* In addition, a few animal groups, notably some insects, some reptiles, most birds, and monkeys, apes, and man, also have receptor cells that detect color. In vertebrates with color vision, these cells, called *cones,* are structurally different from rods and their photopigments are various kinds of *iodopsin,* combinations of retinene and forms of opsin that are different from those in rhodopsin. Functionally cone cells appear to be of three kinds, sensitive respectively to red, blue, and yellow wavelengths of light. Since all colors are produced from combinations of these three primary colors, the three kinds of cones together can detect and analyze light of any color.

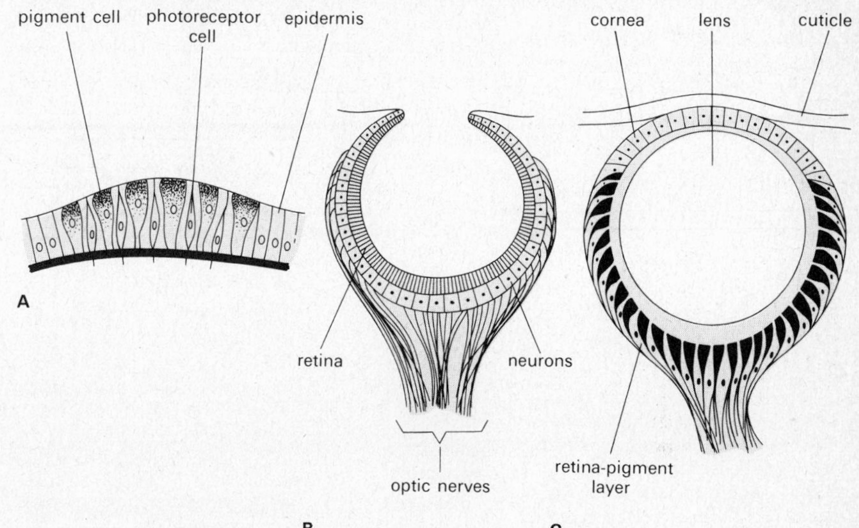

21.23 (*Above*) ***Eyes.*** *A, eye spot, as in coelenterates. B, eye cup, as in chambered nautilus. C, vesicular eye, as in snails and annelids. In all these eyes light reaches the retina directly, without first passing through neuron layers.*

Clusters or layers of photoreceptor cells form *retinas,* the main components of seeing organs. Some of these organs are relatively simple constructed *eyespots,* flush with the body surface. Others are *eyecups,* and the most complex are more or less spherical *eyes.* Most types of eyes are usually equipped with various accessory structures, including light-screening pigment layers and transparent, light-concentrating lenses (Fig. 21.23 and see also Fig. 12.24).

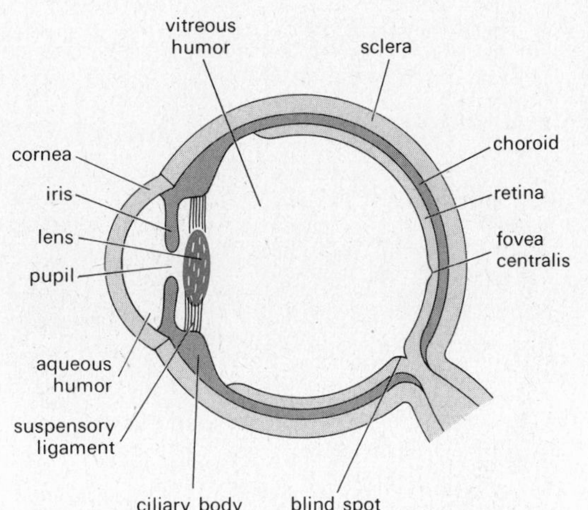

21.24 ***Eyes.*** *The structure of the mammalian eye is shown.*

In the vertebrate eye the retina is the innermost of three coats (Fig. 21.24). The outer coat is the *sclera,* fibrous in man, cartilaginous in many other mammals. The middle coat is the *choroid,* a black-pigmented light-screening layer that also carries blood vessels to and from the eye. (In many vertebrates a thin film of crystalline light-screening material coats the choroid, which makes the eyes of these animals shine in near-darkness.) In the front of the eye these coats are modified structurally. The sclera merges with the transparent *cornea.* The choroid coat continues as the sometimes pigmented *iris,* which encloses the *pupil.* Just behind the iris is a ring-shaped muscle, the *ciliary body,* to which the *lens* is attached by ligaments. The spaces between lens and cornea are filled with a lymphlike *aqueous humor;* and the space between lens and retina contains a jellylike *vitreous humor.*

Functionally the eye resembles a photographic camera. The pupil, corresponding to the diaphragm of a camera, narrows or widens and thereby regulates the amount of light admitted to the eye. Intense light initiates a reflex through the retina, the autonomic nervous system, and a set of circularly arranged muscles in the iris (see Fig. 21.7). These muscles contract, the pupil

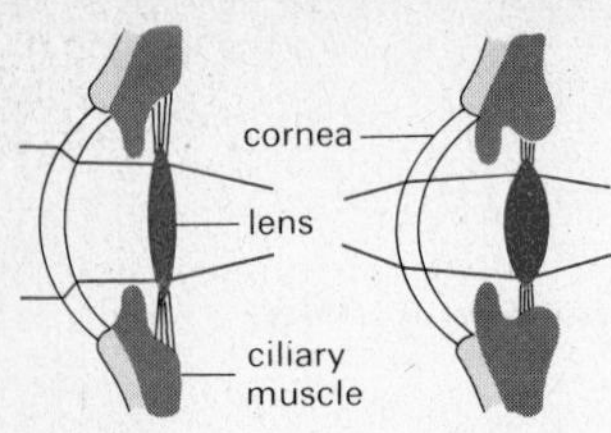

***21.25* Focusing.** *Left, far object, flat lens. Right, near object, curved lens. Lens curves out when the muscles of the ciliary body contract.*

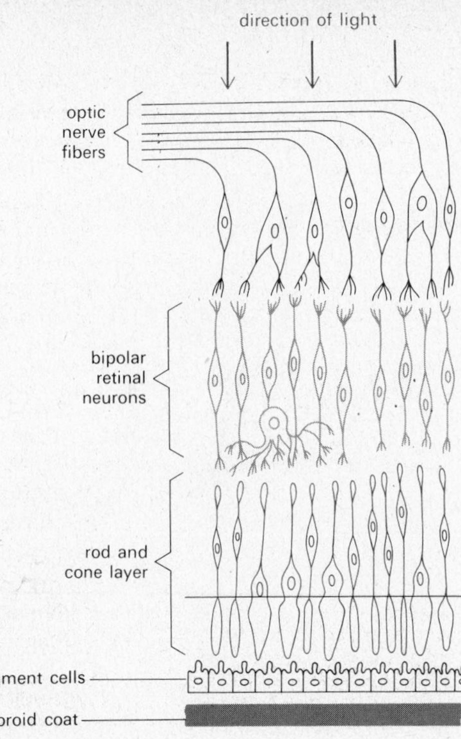

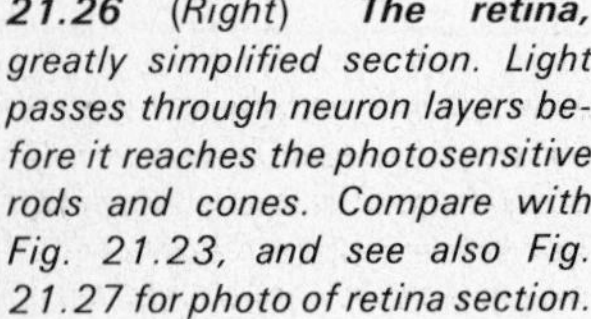

21.26 (*Right*) **The retina,** *greatly simplified section. Light passes through neuron layers before it reaches the photosensitive rods and cones. Compare with Fig. 21.23, and see also Fig. 21.27 for photo of retina section.*

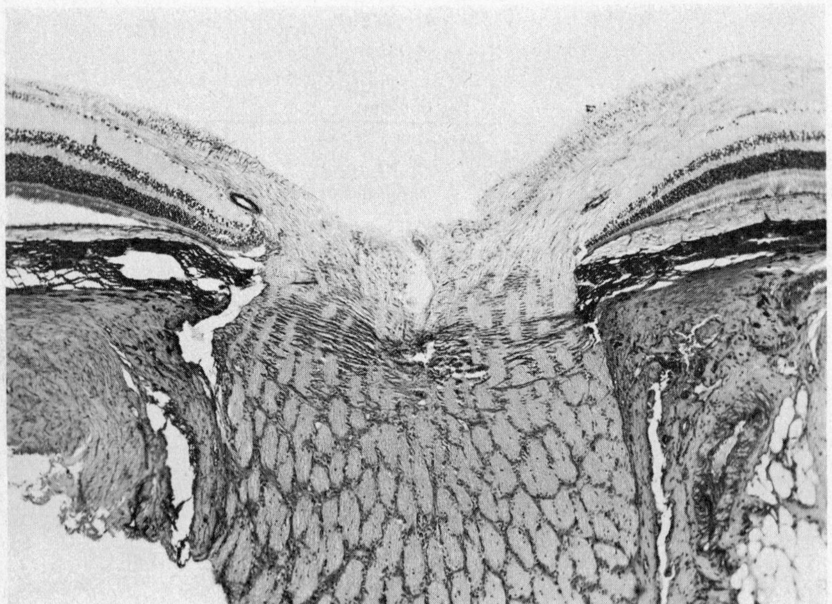

***21.27* Retina, blind spot, and optic nerve.** *Note the neuron layers at the surface of the retina (top of photo) and the merging of the neuron fibers at the depression of the blind spot, forming the optic nerve (leading down in the photo).*

narrows, and less light is admitted. Conversely, low light intensity results in reflex signals to a set of iris muscles arranged like the spokes of a wheel. When these contract the pupil enlarges and permits more light to enter.

The lens focuses an object on the retina by changing shape according to the distance of the object (Fig. 21.25). Lens shape is controlled by the ciliary body. When this muscular ring is relaxed the lens ligaments relax, the elastic lens assumes a bulging shape, and near objects are focused. A blurred image on the retina probably leads to reflex impulses to the ciliary body, which then contracts or relaxes until the image is no longer blurred.

The retina consists of several layers of neurons that innervate one layer of rod and cone cells adjacent to the choroid coat (Fig. 21.26). Light therefore must pass through the neuron layers before it reaches the rods and cones. The fibers of the neuron layers collect as a thick optic nerve that leaves the hind part of the eye at one point, somewhat off-center. At this *blind spot* the layer of rods and cones, the choroid coat, and the sclera are interrupted (Fig. 21.27). The concentration of rod cells is greatest at the periphery of the retina and decreases toward the optical center of the eye. Thus the retinal periphery is particularly efficient in detecting movement and in black-and-white vision. Conversely, the concentration of cone cells increases toward the optical center of the retina, and this central area is therefore best adapted for reception of sharp, stationary images and for color vision. Indeed, only cones occur in the *fovea centralis,* a tiny depression at the very optical center of the retina. Rods are absent here, as are overlying neurons; hence the cones are exposed to light directly. The fovea is the receptor for the most acute vision.

An external object is "pictured" on the retina as a series of points, like the points of a newspaper photograph. Each point corresponds to a rod or a cone. Impulses from these points are transmitted to the optic lobe in each cerebral hemisphere according to the pattern illustrated in Fig. 21.28. Each optic lobe thus receives impulses from *both* eyes, and normally the visual interpretations of both lobes give a simple, smoothly superimposed picture of the external world. Sometimes a smooth superimposition fails to occur (under the influence of alcohol, for example), in which case one "sees double."

The image of an external object is projected on the retina in an inverted position, just as an image is inverted on the film of a camera. But such images are not perceived inverted because the optic centers in the brain give visual experiences correct orientations. Space orientation actually depends not only on vision but also on perception of gravity through the statoreceptors; and the brain apparently interprets orientations in the visual world in accordance with its interpretation of gravity stimuli.

It is known also that visual interpretations in the optic lobes are assisted by the retinal neurons, which carry out a considerable amount of "data processing" before impulses are sent to the brain. It has been found, for example, that the retina of a frog generates four distinct sets of impulses to the brain. One set provides the animal with a black-and-white "outline drawing" of the stationary content of the visible world. A second set similarly provides an outline drawing, but only of illuminated objects that move across the visual field. A third set informs of objects that blot out illumination in part of the visual field and that become rapidly larger—undoubtedly indicating the approach of potentially dangerous animals. And a fourth set informs of moving objects that blot out illumination but that remain small—probably an insect-detecting device of special importance to a frog. These four sets of impulses are neatly superimposed in the brain and appear to be interpreted as a single "picture." A frog evidently sees the world in a unique, subjective manner, and a similar conclusion undoubtedly holds for light-sensitive animals of all kinds.

The human visual apparatus probably registers color at least as well as that of any other animal, and human eyes, like those of flies, are about as light-sensitive as eyes can possibly get. Moreover, the eyes probably initiate more behavioral activities than any other receptors, and it is that which makes the sense of vision so important to man.

other receptors

Numerous animal groups contain *temperature receptors.* Separate heat and cold receptors occur in, for example, vertebrate skin. The skin and all other parts of the body also contain *pain receptors,* usually free nerve endings. Collectively the receptors for pain, pressure, touch, and temperature in the skin represent the *cutaneous receptors.* The human skin is estimated to contain some 4 million pain receptors, $\frac{1}{2}$ million mechanoreceptors, 150,000 cold receptors, and 16,000 heat receptors.

Apart from the senses here described (and they obviously add up to many more than the proverbial five or six), man also can discriminate between sensations of burning, tickling, stinging, and limbs "falling asleep." Separate receptors need not necessarily be associated with each of these senses. For example, some of the above sensations result when pressure, temperature, and pain receptors are stimulated simultaneously and in different combinations.

Other animals well might have comparable and also quite different senses, yet the presence of a sensory structure by itself is often insufficient for a determination of the nature of a particular sense. Does an earthworm experience pain, for example? Most animals do react sharply to stimuli that, by analogy with man, might be assumed to be painful. Yet we cannot really be sure, for sense perceptions must be communicated in some way that we can interpret. And in many cases we cannot make such interpretations. It is fairly certain nevertheless that in many instances receptors for so far unidentified senses do exist, particularly among invertebrates. The environments of such animals often produce stimuli quite different from those we would expect in terrestrial or in human surroundings. Invertebrate senses actually have so far been studied far less extensively than those of vertebrates.

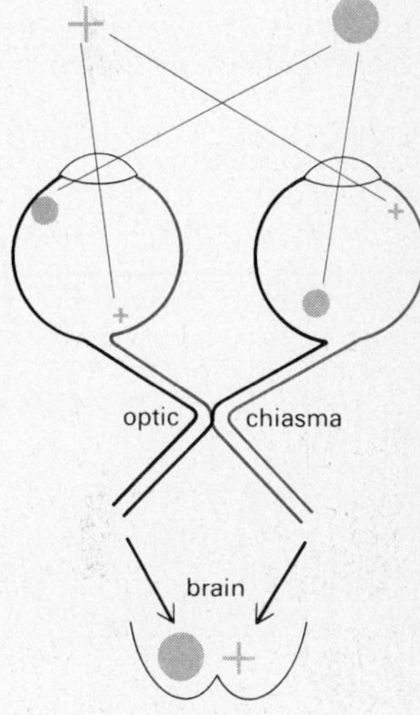

21.28 Eye and brain. *An object in the left field of vision registers on the right halves of both retinas, and impulses are transmitted to the right half of the brain.*

review questions

1 Name the components of a reflex arc and describe the course of a reflex in a vertebrate. Review the structure of a neuron. What are nerves, nerve nets, nerve cords, and ganglia? What is the difference between a ganglion and a brain?

2 Describe the structure of the vertebrate brain. List the main subdivisions and the main components of each, and indicate their general functions.

3 Distinguish between spinal and cranial nerves. List the mammalian cranial nerves, and review the functions of each. What are myelinated and nonmyelinated fibers? Where in the nervous system does each kind occur?

4 Review the structure and functioning of the autonomic nervous system. Distinguish structurally and functionally between the sympathetic and parasympathetic subdivisions of that system. What are sympathetic chain ganglia?

5 What are preganglionic and postganglionic fibers? Describe the detailed course of a reflex in (*a*) the central nervous system, (*b*) the autonomic nervous system. Review the innervation of the heart.

6 What is a nerve impulse? How is an impulse propagated in a nerve fiber? What electrical events take place during impulse transmission? What is an action potential of a nerve fiber?

7 How is an impulse transmitted across a synapse? Distinguish between cholinergic and adrenergic fibers. Where does each kind occur?

8 Describe the activities of neural centers. What are reflex modification, summation, oscillator circuits, and inherited neural programs? Distinguish between learning by habituation, by classical conditioning, and by operant conditioning.

9 What is the basic function of all sensory receptors? Describe the location and general structure of receptors for pain, touch, pressure, heat, and cold stimuli. What is referred pain? Distinguish between neurosensory and epitheliosensory cells.

10 Describe the location and structure of the taste and smell receptors. What are the primary taste sensations? Are tastes and smells inherent in given substances? Discuss.

11 What are mechanoreceptors, and what are their functions? Where in an animal can such receptors be found? Review the structure and function of statoreceptors in general.

12 Describe the organization of the mammalian ear, and show where statoreceptors are located. Distinguish between static and dynamic body balance.

13 What is a phonoreceptor? Describe the structure and function of a lateral-line system. Which animals can hear, and by means of what kinds of receptors? Describe the structure of such receptors. What is a cochlea? An organ of Corti? Show how the human ear operates in hearing.

14 Review the chemistry of vision. What are rods and cones? What is a retina? Which animals have color vision? Distinguish between eyespots, eyecups, and eyes. Describe the structure of the mammalian eye. What components form the focusing mechanism and how is the function of focusing carried out?

15 What is the distribution pattern of rods and cones in the retina of man? What eye structures does light traverse before it reaches the rods and cones? Describe the neural pathways between the eyes and the brain.

collateral readings

Agranoff, B. W.: Memory and Protein Synthesis, *Sci. American,* June, 1967. The relation between memory and proteins is examined by experiments on goldfish.

Amoore, J. E., J. W. Johnston, Jr., and **M. Rubin**: The Stereochemical Theory of Odor, *Sci. American,* Feb., 1964. A classification of odors and of functionally different receptor cells is described.

Baker, P. F.: The Nerve Axon, *Sci. American,* March, 1966. The functioning of these fibers is examined experimentally. Recommended.

Bekesy, G. von: The Ear, *Sci. American,* Aug., 1957. A highly recommended account.

Brazier, M. A. B.: The Analysis of Brain Waves, *Sci. American,* June, 1962. Computers can now be used in the study of electrical brain phenomena.

Dowling, J. R.: Night Blindness, *Sci. American,* Oct., 1966. The role of vitamin A in the mechanism of vision is examined.

Eccles, J.: The Synapse, *Sci. American,* Jan., 1965. An analysis of synaptic functions by electron-microscopic studies of structure.

Fender, D. H.: Control Mechanisms of the Eye, *Sci. American,* July, 1964. Target tracking by the eye is analyzed.

French, J. D.: The Reticular Formation, *Sci. American,* May, 1957. A discussion of the important brain region that functions as "volume" control and governs sleep and wakeful states.

Gazzaniga, M. S.: The Split Brain in Man, *Sci. American,* May, 1967. When two cerebral hemispheres are separated surgically, each becomes an independent center of consciousness.

Gerard, R. W.: What Is Memory?, *Sci. American,* Sept., 1953. Experiments designed to elucidate the mechanisms of memory storage are described.

Gibson, E. J., and **R. D. Walk**: The "Visual Cliff," *Sci. American,* Apr., 1960. A study of depth perception in various animals.

Haagen-Smit, A. J.: Smell and Taste, *Sci. American,* Mar., 1952. A study of the sensitivity and discriminating ability of these chemoreceptors.

Hodgson, E. S.: Taste Receptors, *Sci. American,* May, 1961. The general mechanism of tasting is examined through experiments on receptors in the blowfly.

Hubel, D. H.: The Visual Cortex of the Brain, *Sci. American,* Nov., 1963. Responses of individual interpreter neurons in the optic lobes of cats are examined.

Hydén, H.: Satellite Cells in the Nervous System, *Sci. American,* Dec., 1961. The probable chemical basis of memory is explored, and special attention is given to the neuroglia cells, present together with neurons.

Jouvet, M.: The States of Sleep, *Sci. American,* Feb., 1967. Different biochemical mechanisms appear to be involved in light and deep sleep.

Katz, B.: The Nerve Impulse, *Sci. American,* Nov., 1952. A recommended review on the nature of impulses.

———: How Cells Communicate, *Sci. American,* Sept., 1961. A more recent examination of the nature of nerve impulses.

Kennedy, D.: Inhibition in Visual Systems, *Sci. American,* July, 1963. The nature of neuron inhibition by other neurons is examined in relation to vision.

———: Small Systems of Nerve Cells, *Sci. American,* May, 1967. Small ganglia of invertebrates are used in studies of programs of behavior.

Keynes, R. D.: The Nerve Impulse and the Squid, *Sci. American,* 1958. The physiology of nerve impulses is studied with the aid of the giant axons of squids.

Lissman, H. W.: Electric Location by Fishes, *Sci. American,* March, 1963. Some fishes explore their environment by sensing changes in electric fields they have produced.

Loewenstein, W. R.: Biological Transducers, *Sci. American,* Aug., 1960. The conversion of external stimuli to nerve impulses is examined in the Pacinian corpuscle.

MacNichol, E. F.: Three-pigment Color Vision, *Sci. American,* Dec., 1964. The subject is adequately described by the title.

Melzack, R.: The Perception of Pain, *Sci. American,* Feb., 1961. Factors such as past experiences and cultural backgrounds are shown to affect the sensation of pain.

Miller, W. H., F. Ratcliff, and **H. K. Hartline**: How Cells Receive Stimuli, *Sci. American,* Sept., 1961. The properties of specialized sensory cells are examined, with special reference to the photoreceptors of horseshoe crabs.

Muntz, W. R. A.: Vision in Frogs, *Sci. American,* March, 1964. Data processing in the frog retina is examined.

Peterson, L. R.: Short-term Memory, *Sci. American,* July, 1966. An examination of the separate mechanisms of short- and long-term retention of information.

Rock, J., and **C. S. Harris**: Vision and Touch, *Sci. American,* May, 1967. The dominance of vision over touch is demonstrated by experimental means.

Rosenzweig, M. R.: Auditory Localization, *Sci. American,* Oct., 1961. How the brain interprets sensory information received from the two ears of an animal.

Rushton, W. A. H.: Visual Pigments in Man, *Sci. American,* Nov., 1962. A very interesting discussion. Recommended.

Snider, R. S.: The Cerebellum, *Sci. American,* Aug., 1958. Modern experiments on the functions of this brain part are described.

Sperry, R. W.: The Growth of Nerve Circuits, *Sci. American,* Nov., 1959. An excellent account on how complex neural pathway networks become established in the embryo.

———: The Great Cerebral Commissure, *Sci. American,* Jan., 1964. Fascinating experiments on the corpus callosum are described.

Thomas, E. L.: Movements of the Eye, *Sci. American,* Aug., 1968. The small-scale movements of the eye during object fixation are described.

Wald, G.: Eye and Camera, *Sci. American,* Aug., 1950. A very instructive comparison.

Walter, W. G.: The Electrical Activity of the Brain, *Sci. American,* June, 1954. The patterns and possible meaning of brain waves are examined.

Wooldridge, D. E.: "The Machinery of the Brain," McGraw-Hill, New York, 1963. One of the best and most stimulating recent paperbacks on brain function. Strongly recommended.

chapter 22 behavioral control: the individual

Behavior includes any externally observable activity of an organism—microorganism, plant, or animal. In most cases behavior involves some form of movement, either motion of body parts or outright locomotion. But secretions to the outside, color changes, or slow alterations brought about by growth similarly qualify as behavioral events. Moreover, absence or cessation of an overt activity is itself an expression of behavior.

In all its forms behavior is basically adaptive and has a self-perpetuative function; directly or indirectly it tends to promote survival. Moreover, behavioral acts are just as subject to evolutionary change as their functions; behavior and function evolve together.

forms of behavior

behavior processes

Animal tendencies to behave in self-perpetuating fashion are often called *drives* or *motivations,* terms borrowed from (and most applicable in) the field of human psychology. In a general biological context a drive can be regarded as an expression of internal control operations that are incomplete and still in progress; a drive will be manifested so long as particular stimuli have *not* yet elicited appropriate behavioral responses.

Many motivated activities consist of a sequence of four more or less distinct phases. The first phase is an *elicitation,* a process of activation, triggering, or arousal. In feeding behavior, for example, elicitation includes sighting of food, orienting toward it, and fixing on it visually and posturally. Next follows an *appetitive* phase, in which specific ''appetites'' for certain end results become dominant, and in which various internal and external processes produce a state of readiness for the ensuing events. In the case of feeding this phase includes motion toward food, inspection and testing of food, and reflex initiation of an internal flow of digestive juices. The third part of the sequence is a *consummatory* phase, in which the functional goal is realized—actual food consumption in our example. This activity leads to the terminal *satiation* phase, during which the original arousal stimuli cease to be effective. Thus, after a period of food intake an animal eventually turns away from food and for the time being becomes resistant to further stimulation by it. Feeding behavior has been the original model for naming these phases. But the four-part sequence is also discernible in other behavioral processes, including aggression behavior and mating, for example (Fig. 22.1).

In such sequences the performancé itself can sometimes be just as important as the objective of the performance. Thus, animals often stop eating not so much because they have consumed enough food as because they have become satisfied behaviorally; the feeding drive may be gratified primarily by the *act* of eating, and only secondarily by food as such. For example, men, dogs, and other mammals will often look for food even when well fed, and under certain circumstances men sometimes refuse food despite gnawing hunger. In such cases the actions of an organism appear to be determined by behavioral or psychological states, not by metabolic states. A large body of evidence also indicates that the longer a particular activity has *not* been performed, the more readily it can be evoked; unfulfilled drives (''central excitatory states'') tend to become stronger with time. Such observations suggest that not all of behavior can be explained on the basis of just a few basic motivations, like hunger and sex. Virtually *each* behavior appears to be motivated by a central excitatory state of its own.

behavior patterns

Almost every behavioral process studied closely is now known to include *both* inherited and learned elements. Equivalent to ''inherited'' in this context are also terms such as ''inborn,'' ''innate,'' or ''instinctive,'' all of which signify that given aspects of a behavior are based on the genetic endowment of an organism and are controlled by mechanisms that develop independently of learning. Terms equivalent to ''learned'' include ''acquired,'' ''experiential,'' or ''environmental,'' and they signify that certain aspects of a behavior are based on external influences and are controlled by nongenetic mechanisms.

However, there can be little question that *all* properties and activities of organisms are ultimately under genetic control. At the same time, *no* property or activity can be exhibited without an environment. It is therefore experimentally impossible to filter out environmental influences from genetic effects or genetic influences from environmental effects; genes and environment

22.1 Four components of behavioral sequences, *illustrated here by aggressive behavior in lesser black-backed gulls. A, elicitation phase: two males sight each other at boundary between their territories. B, appetitive phase: the animals approach each other warily and "examine the situation." C, consummation phase: a fight occurs. D, satiation phase: grooming after disengagement.*

A

B

C

D

always form an inseparable continuum. For this reason, behavioral (or other) processes can no longer be categorized—as they usually have been in the past—in sharp alternatives like "instinctive" or "learned."

But although both inherited and learned factors thus play a role in any behavior, the relative contributions of these two sets of determinants are known to vary considerably for different behaviors. Such relative contributions can usually be judged by the degree of modifiability of a behavioral process. A behavior can be largely unlearned and nearly unmodifiable, or partly learned and fairly modifiable, or largely learned and exceedingly modifiable. For present purposes we can arbitrarily refer to these three general categories respectively as *reactive, active,* and *cognitive* forms of behavior.

Reactive behavior includes all largely automatic, stereotyped activities. As a group they probably represent the most primitive behavioral level. Reactive responses by and large are fully "programmed" as soon as an organism has completed its embryonic development, and thereafter they occur in relatively fixed all-or-none fashion. The tropisms of plants and animals are included in this type of behavior. A tropism is an automatic orientational response to an external stimulus. As noted in Chap. 19, for example, plants react to external stimuli such as light by orienting toward or away from the stimulus source. The execution of such responses in plants has a strictly chemical basis, the internal reactions being regulated by hormonal substances and enzymes.

In this respect animal tropisms can be more diverse, for in addition to chemical controls, neural ones usually play an important role as well (Fig. 22.2). Animal tropisms include, for example, the fairly complex balancing, positioning, and orienting processes that are largely under the control of nervous reflexes. Apart from tropisms, the predominantly reactive behaviors of animals also comprise certain routine and recurrent "housekeeping" activities, such as breathing, circulation, pupillary responses, and in general most processes that in vertebrates are controlled primarily by the autonomic nervous system and that in man do not or need not become conscious.

In all organisms reactive behavior evidently maintains some of the most basic vital functions. It is therefore a considerable adaptive advantage that such behavior is comparatively unmodifiable. It would be highly detrimental if, for example, a life-preserving balancing or heat-avoiding response were readily modifiable by external factors. Nevertheless, reactive behaviors actually can be modified, even if only to a minor degree in many cases. Most commonly such modifications occur through habituation—progressive loss of responsiveness to repeated stimulation, as outlined in Chap. 21. In some instances more drastic modifications are possible through classical conditioning. For example, as also pointed out in Chap. 21, the pupillary response in man is amenable to considerable retraining.

In the category of active behavior, genetic inheritance endows an organism with certain behavioral potentials, but the actual realization of these potentials depends to a substantial degree on learning and the directive influence of the environment. Thus whereas an organism behaving reactively is comparable to a robot, a system that passively delivers preprogrammed responses on command, an organism behaving actively first "assesses" and "judges" stimuli and then "chooses" and adjusts its responses. It does so essentially by "comparing" a present situation with the memorized experiences of similar past situations and then behaving accordingly. The organism therefore is not merely automatically reactive, but selectively active (Fig. 22.3).

This form of behavior requires a fairly elaborate nervous system, and in effect it is limited largely to relatively advanced animals, most notably arthropods and vertebrates. The specific behaviors in this category all must become perfected progressively, in part through parental training at immature stages and in part through later experience. Examples are flying and walking, searching for and handling food, grooming and sanitary behavior, communicating, courtship and mating, and most activities associated with offense and defense, family life, and sociality. Where such behavior includes distinct appetitive

22.2 Animal tropism. *Tropistic behavior, or orientational responses to external stimuli, is elicited in the case of these fish by the diver who takes the picture.*

22.3 ***Active behavior*** *based on learning. These circus elephants respond to stimuli selectively and display behavior made possible by earlier training and conditioning.*

and consummatory phases, it has been found that the first is often particularly subject to modification by learning, whereas the second is largely unlearned. For example, food swallowing as such requires little or no training, but the preparatory actions leading up to swallowing generally do. Similarly, the activities preceding copulation in mammals are influenced greatly by experience, but copulation itself appears to be unlearned.

Learning in active behavior often involves conditioned reflexes, particularly those leading to classical conditioning (see Chap. 21). Thus, inasmuch as an animal is normally exposed to a wealth of recurring stimuli in its natural environment, it will gradually come to develop a large variety of conditioned responses. Starting with a basic set of internally controlled activities, any of these activities can, by conditioning in the course of development, come to be used in an increasingly diverse array of environmental circumstances.

The most advanced forms of behavior are represented by cognitive activities. In these, genes provide only a very broad and general background for behavioral potentials, and the actual utilization of such potentials depends very largely on external influences. A cognitive activity in effect is an action pattern elaborated in more or less "deliberate" fashion by the animal itself. The animal here does not merely respond to stimuli actively, but it can search out new means of *how* to respond; it can *invent* its own actions. In the process the animal often also manipulates the environment—an important distinction from merely active behavior, in which such manipulation typically does not occur (Fig. 22.4).

Among the simplest cognitive behaviors, encountered in many arthropods and all vertebrates, are *exploratory* activities through which an animal familiarizes itself with any new condition in its environment. Strange objects are approached and inspected by sight, smell, and touch. Withdrawal usually follows quickly. Inspections are then undertaken repeatedly, but with gradually declining frequency. For any animal studied it has been found that the most complex novelties in the environment always tend to elicit the most exploration; a simple environmental change evidently is not as "interesting" or significant to the animal as an elaborate one. Exploration is also most likely when the stimuli are neither too weak nor too strong. Weak stimulation can fail to arouse curiosity, and strong stimulation can evoke withdrawal or escape rather than approach.

Animals placed in unvaryingly monotonous environments still exhibit exploratory behavior, though in greatly reduced fashion. Also, if mammals, man included, are prevented for extended periods from carrying out exploratory activites, their behavior can become highly abnormal. This is often the case with caged animals and with men suffering prolonged imprisonment. Similarly, if human infants are deprived of opportunities to accumulate experience through visual exploration, the later adults often have difficulty in distinguishing visual patterns such as triangles and circles and they can be handicapped in sight-associated activities in general (Fig. 22.5).

Another type of cognitive behavior is *play,* particularly common in mammals but observed also in most other vertebrates. Play can involve activities more complex and diversified than those of exploration, and in some cases play and exploration can have the same adaptive result: increased familiarization with the environment, including most particularly the social environment. In this respect play among young animals often has an incidental (but nevertheless important) training function for later offensive and defensive behavior, for courtship activity, and for management of social conflicts.

In many animals, for example, play involves activities that are but slightly modified forms of aggression or courtship. Also, mammals raised to adulthood in isolation or with insufficient social play later tend to make poor parents and will often ignore or abandon their offspring. Similarly, rhesus monkeys raised in isolation or by dummy mothers have been shown unable to mate properly. Indeed, when mammals mature without opportunity to play with littermates or to learn from social contacts in general, then not only their later reproductive behavior but *all* aspects of their behavior often tend to be abnormal. In man, for example, social behavior begins to be learned in the period between the sixth week and the sixth month of life. During this time an infant will generally smile at all strangers, and he can readily transfer his affection from mother to other family members, nurse, foster mother, or others. Thereafter, however, fear of strangers increases and emotional attachments become more selective. Consequently, if an infant is protected unduly from exposure to strangers up to his sixth month of life, his normal tendency to play, learn, and practice social responses during this time will remain unexercised, and all later social behavior can be affected adversely.

Both exploration and play often contribute to the development of even more complex cognitive activities, including particularly manipulative, or *instrumental,* behavior. It is characterized by responses that require "insight" and "foresight" and a capacity to analyze and weigh alternative choices. Also, such behavior can include purposeful alterations of environmental conditions and an exercise of skills, creativity, and inventiveness. Behavior of this type is restricted very largely to advanced mammals, particularly to monkeys, apes, and man, the most advanced primates. Behavioral control here (or in man, at any rate) is fully subject to conscious volition, and the result is conspicuously individual-specific; each individual must develop his own level of manipulative competence, and in this respect the members of the species can vary greatly.

Most manipulative behavior, and cognitive behavior as a whole, depends largely on learning through operant conditioning (see Chap. 21). In the human case the reinforcement generally associated with such learning can be exceedingly subtle and indeed need not be immediate. In many instances, for example, we regard the very execution of a particular activity as its own reward, and we often find sufficient incentive for certain behaviors in a mere expectation of potential rewards, even if they accrue to others after our own lifetimes.

In this context it should be pointed out that the amount or kind of learning possible in any animal depends only partly on the relative complexity of its nervous system; the adaptive function that learning has in the life of an animal is just as significant. It is not an accident, for example, that rats turn out to be good test subjects for maze-learning experiments. Rats have a strongly developed exploratory drive, and ability to search through complex terrains is a particularly important adaptation for the survival of these animals. Many other mammals are just as intelligent but are poor maze learners; they have learning abilities specially significant to them. In short,

22.4 ***Cognitive behavior*** *and manipulative activity. Deliberate manipulation of some part of the environment, as exemplified by the actions of this circus bear, is characteristic of most cognitive forms of behavior.*

22.5 ***Exploratory behavior.***

learning ability tends to be specialized for particular survival requirements. Man too is specialized in this respect, and he is not uniformly good in all kinds of learning. He excels in abstract and symbolic learning, capabilities that were of special adaptive importance during his early evolution (see Chap. 30). Yet he is readily outmatched by many fishes, birds, and mammals in, for example, navigational learning, or even by rats in maze learning.

systems of behavior

stimulus and response

Organisms normally respond to *selected* stimuli only; they can filter particular sets of stimuli from the totality of the sensory cues they receive and respond specifically to just these. In many cases the nature of the response depends on the context in which stimuli are perceived, the whole configuration (or "Gestalt") of an environmental situation. As is well known, for example, the same stimuli can elicit diametrically opposite responses in different environmental circumstances. The ability to assess the setting in which stimuli are perceived and to modulate responses accordingly is a function of cognitive behavior and depends on learning and experience.

In many other cases, by contrast, the contexts of stimuli are quite unimportant; selected stimuli often evoke certain responses regardless of the environmental setting. Such stimuli are said to be *symbols,* behavioral *signs,* or *releasers;* they trigger, or "release," certain preprogrammed activities. Behavior in this case is active or even reactive, and the animal needs to learn only how to recognize given sign stimuli. The response then follows in more or less stereotyped fashion.

In herring gulls, for example, young birds peck at the bill of a parent when they wish to receive regurgitated food from the parent. The pecking is directed particularly at a red spot located near the tip of the lower bill of the parent. Experiments with cardboard models show that this pecking behavior does not require an actual parent. Any pencil-shaped object with a red spot near its tip will elicit pecking. Indeed, if the colored area is designed in the shape of several short red stripes, the young gulls will peck more effectively and more vigorously at this substitute "bill" than at that of the natural parent (Fig. 22.6).

Similarly, many birds flee when a flying predator bird comes into their field of vision. Tests with cardboard models show that this standardized escape response can be evoked by any overhead object having the general outline of a long-stemmed cross—suggestive of the short neck, extended wings, and long fuselage typical of most predator birds. Many birds retrieve eggs that have rolled out of the nest. More vigorous retrieval can be induced by dummy eggs that, for example, have larger color speckles or larger sizes than the real eggs.

Among animals other than birds, male sticklebacks are prompted to courtship activity by nearly any model having a pronouncedly swollen, silvery underside, suggestive of a female with eggs. A true fishlike shape is otherwise not required, and male attraction will be the greater the more the model bulges downward. In their home territory these male fish also will attack virtually any round or ovoid model with a red underside, the specific sign of another male in breeding condition. Courtship in certain male butterflies has been shown to be elicited not so much by the presence of females as by the speed with which females flutter their wings. Cardboard models that do not resemble females to any great extent but have winglike parts with particularly high flutter rates can arouse males even more than real females.

These various examples not only reveal the effectiveness of visual signs as such, but they also show clearly that greatly exaggerated stimuli often tend to be more effective than normal ones. In man, too, supernormal stimulation is well known to be preferred in a wide variety of activities, and this phenomenon appears to be a general attribute of sign-induced behavior. Such stimulus preferences presumably can have evolutionary consequences, for individuals having traits that are preferred by other members of the species are more likely to mate and produce numerous offspring.

Many animals also respond in standardized ways to postural signs or symbolic movements exhibited by fellow members of the species. For example, the courtship dance of certain male spiders includes a characteristic waving of the front legs. These movements are trance-inducing signals that suppress attack by the female. The male can then approach and mate. Thereafter female attack is no longer inhibited, however, and the male is usually killed. In other animals, similarly, postural changes involving the head, the tail, or other body parts are "social releasers" evoking standardized responses in fellow members of a group (see also below).

Signs need not necessarily be visual but can also involve auditory, tactile, or any other sensory modes. In sound-producing animals, for example, auditory symbols are well known to be specific releasers in courtship and mating, in offense and defense, and indeed in most social behavior. Numerous releasers are chemical, mediated by the senses of taste and smell. For example, certain clams exhibit an escape response if placed in water in which starfish had been present. But the same water will attract certain polychaete worms that normally live symbiotically with starfish. Pollinating insects undertake nectar searches in stimulus models smelling like certain flowers. Among mammals, aggressive or submissive behavior evoked by chemical signs is particularly well known and familiar. For example, a cat is alerted to flight by dog smells but to attack by rodent smells.

Specially important are *pheromones,* or chemical signals used between members of the same species. For example, bees in a food-rich area secrete pheromones that attract other bees to the location. When wounded, minnows and other fishes release alarm pheromones from the skin that elicit escape responses in other members of a school. Under conditions of stress many types of ant broadcast alarm substances that induce fellow ants to become aggressive. Probably best known are the sex pheromones, by which individuals of either sex attract or evoke reproductive behavior in potential mates. In at least one instance nature herself has performed an evolutionary experiment that reveals the effect of such chemical cues. Several species of orchids are known that not only resemble bees and wasps structurally, but that also secrete chemicals similar to the sex attractants normally released by female bees and wasps. As a result, males of these insects will try to mate with the flowers and in the process will pollinate them.

Apart from functioning as attractants, sex pheromones also can have more subtle effects. For example, a group of caged female mice will become synchronized in their reproductive cycles if the animals are exposed to the scent of a male mouse. Moreover, a pregnant mouse can be induced to abort by exposing her to the odor of a strange male (even if the normal male mate is present). In many animals pheromonal cues also play important roles in the development of parent-young relationships, in recognition of species members, in establishing appropriate spatial distributions among the individuals of a social group, and indeed in influencing most behavioral interactions in the species.

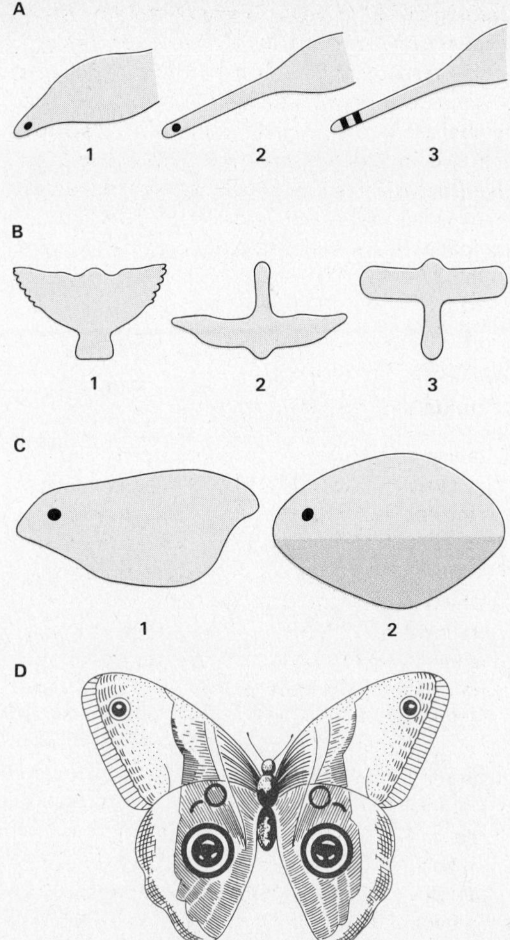

22.6 Releasers. *A, models of bills of herring gulls, effective in eliciting pecking by young birds. Long thin model bills (as in 2) are more effective as symbols than short thick ones, and the models are most effective if the red pigmented areas near the tips have the form of several stripes (as in 3). B, the hawk model (1) will elicit an escape response by birds, but the goose model (2) will not. Model 3 will provoke escape if it is moved in the direction of the top of the page but not if it is moved in the opposite direction. In the first case it suggests a hawk, in the second a goose. C, a male stickleback will court an inanimate model of a fish having a swollen underside (1) suggestive of a female with eggs. Also, a male will attack a model having a red underside (2), suggestive of another male in breeding condition. D, many butterflies have conspicuous pigmented areas on their wings, suggestive of the eyes of an owl. Such eyelike patterns probably serve to protect the insects from predation by owl-fearing birds. (After Tinbergen.)*

Clearly then, signs as a whole represent various forms of *communication.* Moreover, it need hardly be pointed out that signs are particularly significant in human behavior. Man actually responds to more kinds and more complex kinds of signs than any other animal. His entire language is a sign system, and this language includes not only words but also postural and facial expressions, as well as visual, olfactory, and tactile cues. Not every such communication evokes stereotyped responses, to be sure, but many certainly do. For example, the behavioral group response to the sound of the national anthem is quite specific. So to a considerable extent is the

22.7 The "following" response, *illustrated by the offspring of a Canada goose.*

individual response to, for example, the smell of acrid smoke or the sight of well-developed contours in members of the opposite sex. Indeed, the wide occurrence of releasers of this sort is underscored even by common phrases such as "authority symbol," "danger sign," "friendship token," or "sex symbol."

A particularly dramatic demonstration of the importance of releasers is provided by the phenomenon of *imprinting.* Newly hatched chickens, geese, ducks, and other birds develop a strong bond of kinship with their female parent, manifested primarily through a standardized "following" response: the young run behind their mother (Fig. 22.7). It has been found that this response develops during a specific period soon after hatching, the so-called critical period, and that it depends on certain releaser stimuli emanating from the mother bird: her overall size, certain aspects of her shape and coloring, the sounds she produces, and her movement away from the young. If such stimuli become "imprinted" in the young during the critical period, the offspring will henceforth accept the adult as their mother and will acknowledge this acceptance by the "following" response. It has also been found that imprinting normally provides the recognition signs which in later life prompt selection and acceptance of appropriate mates; a mate must have the same stimulus attributes as the parent (which presumably ensures that the mate will be of the right species).

Newly hatched ducklings at first will follow any duck, and a specific attachment to the mother develops only somewhat later. It appears, therefore, that an originally imprinted stimulus pattern can be refined later by experience and can thereby become individual-specific. Note in this connection that imprinting itself probably represents a special kind of learning. It differs from other kinds in that its occurrence is limited to a brief period in life and that it remains permanent thereafter.

Experiments show clearly that imprinting can still occur if the actual mother is dispensed with. All that is required is another stimulus source that will produce the necessary signs during the critical period. Thus, young birds will readily accept foster mothers of the same species, or adults of another species (man included), or even mechanical models or inanimate objects having the requisite stimulus properties. The fixation on such "surrogate" mothers becomes just as strong and permanent as on a natural parent. Indeed, birds raised with surrogates may flee from their real parents; and at maturity such birds sometimes reject potential mates of their own species but will try to mate with the surrogates, even if these are inanimate objects (Fig. 22.8).

Releaser stimuli can also originate inside the animal body. One of the best examples is hunger in mammals, which, as pointed out in Chap. 14, is probably induced when a low sugar concentration in blood stimulates the hunger center in the brain. The irrelevance of stimulus contexts is shown by the finding that an animal will eat whenever its hunger center is stimulated, regardless of the actual nutritional state of the body. More recently a thirst center has been located that is differentially sensitive to salt concentrations in the body. If this concentration exceeds a certain level, an animal will feel thirsty and will drink water. In an experiment on goats, a device was installed in the brain that dripped salt solution into the thirst center whenever the experimenter desired; and as long as this device remained activated, a test animal continued to drink.

Experiments on rats have also revealed the existence of pleasure and displeasure centers in the brain. Test rats were fitted with tiny permanent electrodes that reached to these centers, and such animals were allowed to activate these devices on their own by pressing appropriate control levers. After a rat has stimulated its displeasure center once, it avoided a repeat performance forever. But if such animals stimulated their pleasure centers, they continued this self-stimulation from then on without interruption, not even pausing to eat, until they dropped from exhaustion; and on recovery they promptly resumed the self-stimulation to the exclusion of any other activity.

Under normal conditions, however, responses evoked by sign stimuli are among the most valuable functionally and thus among the most adaptive in the behavioral repertoire of an animal.

time orientation: biological clocks

Much of the behavior of all organisms is regularly recurrent in cyclic fashion, and such behavioral rhythms are often synchronized with some cycle in the physical environment. For example, numerous behaviors in plants and animals have a 24-hour *circadian* rhythm, geared to the solar cycle of day and night and the accompanying cycle of temperature. Most coastal organisms display behavioral periodicities synchronized with *tidal* cycles. Many aquatic and terrestrial animals exhibit *lunar* rhythms. And behavior in nearly all organisms also occurs in annual *seasonal* rhythms. Reproductive activity in particular tends to be seasonally cyclic, both in plants and in animals.

In an attempt to explain such behavioral rhythms, a first obvious hypothesis might be that the rhythms are causally related to the recurrent environmental conditions. If so, it should be readily possible to change a behavioral rhythm by experimentally changing the associated environmental cycle. For example, what would happen to a circadian (or other kind of) rhythm if an organism were maintained artifically under uninterruptedly *constant* conditions of lighting, temperature, humidity, and other relevant environmental variables. Numerous experiments of this sort have actually been carried out on a wide variety of organisms. The results obtained are exceedingly uniform and clear-cut: an original behavioral rhythm always tends to *persist,* despite constant environmental conditions (Fig. 22.9).

It is usually observed in such cases that the successive cycles gradually drift out of phase from an exact 24-hour (or other) periodicity. The rhythm then stabilizes at some shorter or longer cycle interval, yet this new interval nevertheless remains fairly close to the original rhythm. Such results show clearly that rhythmic behavior can occur independently of environmental cycles. Organisms are therefore considered to have built-in *biological clocks,* according to which the timing of recurrent activities is programmed.

That such clocks have an inherited component can be shown experimentally. For example, if adult chickens are maintained in constant, unchanging environments and are allowed to produce fertilized eggs under such conditions, then the offspring hatched from the eggs nevertheless exhibit clear-cut circadian behavior. Biological clocks are also subject to metabolic influences. In one experiment bees were trained to feed at

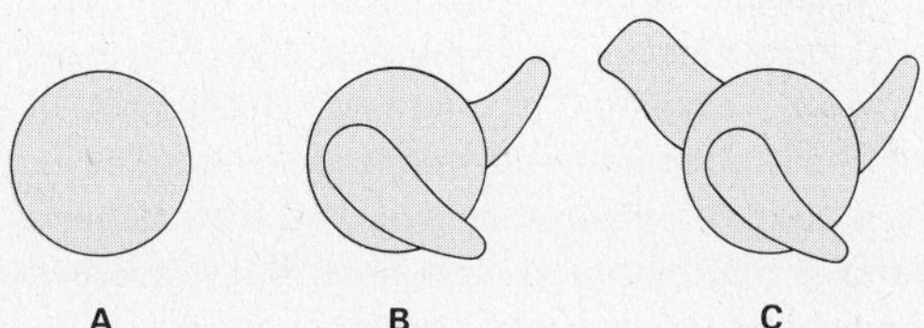

22.8 Imprinting. *Inanimate models such as shown here are effective in eliciting the "following" response in young chickens. A simple model as in A proves to be more effective than a more complex one as in C. Also, blue-colored models are more effective than red ones, and the latter are more effective than yellow ones. Effectiveness is measured by the relative distance a chick will follow a model. (After Hess.)*

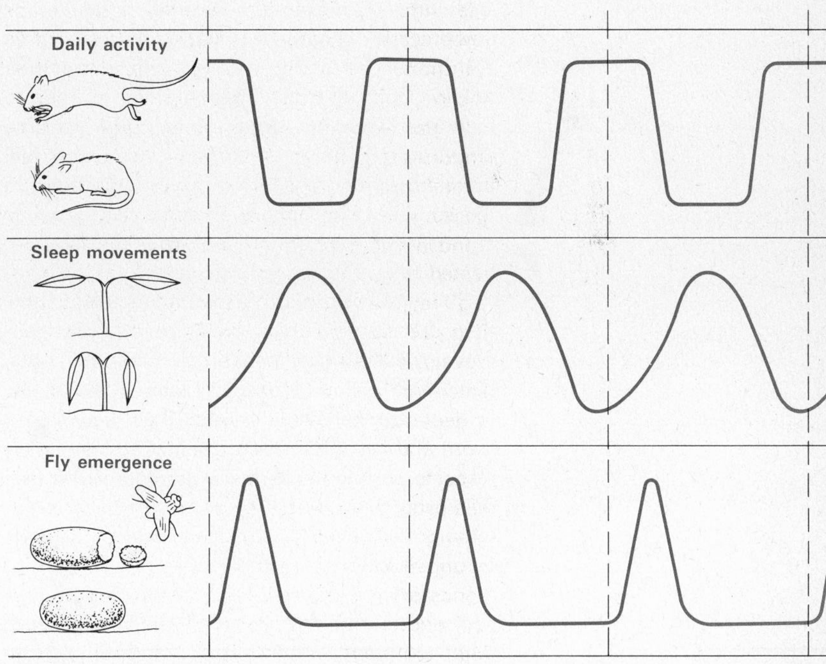

22.9 Circadian rhythms. *In these three examples, the (color) curves indicate the changing intensity of the activities symbolized in column at left. Note the regular repeats during the 3-day-long intervals shown here. The daily activity curve applies specifically to rats but holds also for many other organisms. (After F. A. Brown, Jr.)*

a set time of day and were then chilled to near-freezing for 5 hours. After the insects were brought back to normal temperature, their feeding time proved to be almost 5 hours late. Like other metabolic processes, therefore, the biological clocks apparently were nearly stopped during the extreme cold treatment. However, less drastic temperature changes have remarkably little effect. A 10° temperature difference, which alters the rate of most metabolic processes by a factor of 2 or 3, usually changes the running speed of biological clocks by no more than 15 to 30 minutes every 24 hours. Biological clocks are also quite precise and keep correct time within 1 or 2 minutes per day. For example, caged mice or rats supplied with running wheels start their daily runs at a remarkably exact time each morning.

Much has been learned about the operation of biological clocks by experiments involving a geographic relocation of animals. Organisms are normally adapted to the geographic latitudes and longitudes at which they live, and their behavior follows the rhythm of local time. But it has been found that if organisms are transported to different geographic locations, their activities nevertheless continue in synchrony with the original local time. For example, Atlantic fiddler crabs flown in dark chambers to Pacific waters exhibit cyclic color changes according to the tides at their Atlantic point of origin. Bees trained in Paris to feed at a fixed time of day remain on Paris time after being airfreighted to New York. And fall-breeding sheep transported from the northern to the southern hemisphere continue to reproduce at the time of the northern fall, when the southern hemisphere is in the spring season.

However, relocation experiments also show that after some interval biological clocks invariably do reset to new local times. Thus the crabs, bees, and sheep referred to above eventually synchronize behaviorally with their new longitudes and latitudes. Such gradual adjustment is also the common experience of people who take up residence in new time zones. In general, internally controlled rhythms are said to become *entrained* to local external cycles.

Entrainment proves to be possible only if a new periodicity imposed on an organism does not differ too greatly from that of a natural environmental cycle. In mice, for example, circadian rhythms can be entrained to artificial periodicities as short as 21 hours or as long as 27 hours. But entrainment cannot be readily achieved if an artificial cycle deviates by more than 3 hours from the 24-hour norm. Similarly, the sleeping-waking rhythm in man has repeatedly proved to be resistant to artificial night-day cycles that deviate substantially from 24-hour periods. In general, cycles significantly shorter than 24 hours tend to add together and those longer than 24 hours tend to subdivide, with the result that the behavioral rhythms actually displayed by an organism follow a natural 24-hour cycle as closely as the experimental conditions will allow.

In both circadian and seasonal rhythms, the most common stimuli by which organisms clock the passage of time appear to be light direction, light intensity, and light duration. For example, many animals tell daily time by the progressive change in the position of the sun (see next section). Plants as well as animals are sensitive to the daily and seasonal cycles of light intensity, and many of their rhythmic activities can be reset or modified by experimental alterations of such intensities. Moreover, both plants and animals tell seasonal time most particularly by assessing changes in day lengths, or photoperiods. Thus, as already shown in Chap. 19, appropriate photoperiods are the specific external stimuli that elicit seasonal flowering responses in plants.

In animals, similarly, the onset of a breeding season is generally clocked by the changes in the day lengths during the preceding months. The important photoperiodic stimulus here is the total time during which an animal is exposed to illumination—as though the animal could count the hours of light it receives. In spring breeders, for example, sex organs become active when a certain total amount of illumination has been received in the course of the progressively longer days after the winter solstice. By artificially giving an animal the necessary total amount of light within a shorter or a longer time interval than nature does, the onset of a breeding season can be correspondingly hastened or delayed. After the breeding season most animals enter a refractory period during which light has little effect on sexuality. The termination of this refractory period again appears to be clocked photoperiodically. In temperate-zone animals, for example, renewed sexual sensitivity to light durations can be hastened by exposure to an artificial fall season in which the days become progressively shorter.

In arthropods and vertebrates the clocks that control seasonal reproductive rhythms are well known to have their functional basis in rhythmic neural and endocrine processes (see also Chap. 26). Clearly, however, neural or endocrine components are present neither in microorganisms nor in plants and certain animals; yet such organisms exhibit behavioral rhythms nevertheless. Also, any single organism exhibits numerous behavioral cycles simultaneously, all with their own specific periodicities. An organism must therefore be considered to contain many different biological clocks, with different rhythms, locations, and functional mechanisms.

Even so, the general conclusion is probably warranted that control of cyclic behavior is achieved by interaction of at least two sets of factors. One is internal and is represented by inherited biological clocks that, if left to themselves, keep their own intrinsic time. The other set is external and is represented by cycles in the physical environment. Within definite and relatively narrow limits, the settings of the internal clocks can become adjusted or readjusted until synchrony with the external cycles is established. In this way an organism interacts with its physical environment and can adapt its behavior to the cyclic time changes in its local habitat.

space orientation: directional motion

Just as biological clocks enable organisms to operate effectively in their time environment, so other behavioral mechanisms permit them to relate properly to their space environment.

The most basic orientational behaviors are tropisms, which can maintain even sessile organisms in optimum positions relative to their immediate surroundings. Motile organisms in addition can move to optimum locations in their nearby space through various *kineses,* or movements that intensify in proportion to the strength of particular stimuli. For example, flatworms stay relatively quiescent in darkness but are stimulated to locomotion by light, the more so the stronger the light. As a result, the worms will congregate in the darkest places available to them, as under stones in nature, where locomotor activity will be at a minimum. Similarly, numerous protozoa and other small aquatic organisms intensify their locomotion as light intensity increases. This kinesis accounts for the diurnal migrations of plankton (see Chap. 7). Animals also exhibit kineses in response to stimuli other than light. For example, zoned environmental variations in temperature, humidity, salinity, oxygen content, and many other conditions are well known to elicit locomotor kineses that distribute animals to the optimum habitat zones available (Fig. 22.10).

22.10 Kinesis, *or increase in activity with increased stimulation. In the example illustrated, the stimulus of the toy becomes stronger as the cat's interest increases. Activity then increases correspondingly.*

Many animals move well beyond their immediate home surroundings, and in the process they usually remain fully "aware" of their position and direction in space. A particularly significant navigational aid is *sun compass orientation,* ability to steer by the position of the sun and to compensate course directions according to the apparent motion of the sun across the sky. This process has been studied extensively in honeybees, in which direction finding plays an especially important role: survival of a colony depends on scouting bees that must inform other members of a hive about the exact location of food-yielding fields of flowers.

It has been found that a scouting bee returning to its hive communicates with fellow bees by means of a *waggle dance.* This is a side-to-side wiggle of the abdomen, carried out while the bee moves along the upright surface of the honeycomb. The intensity of the waggle is an indication of the distance to the food source. Actually bees do not communicate distances as such, but elapsed time on the outward flight from the hive. For if a scouting bee has flown against a headwind, its waggling will signal prolonged time in flight, as if it had traveled greater-than-actual distances. Similarly, if a bee is made to *walk* to a food source only a few feet from the hive, its waggling will erroneously imply travel over very great distances.

The angle between the vertical on a honeycomb and the direction of a bee's dancing path indicates the angle between the sun's position and the food source in relation to the hive (Fig. 22.11). The direction of the dancing path therefore differs according to the time of day the dance is performed; it shifts progressively counterclockwise relative to the vertical, in correspondence with the gradual change in the sun's position. If the sky is overcast, polarized and ultraviolet light passing from the sun through the clouds still provides the bee with adequate data on the sun's position. Moreover, bees have also been found to utilize visual clues from landmarks in the environment. During the night waggle dances continue to shift in direction, in line with where the sun would be stationed if it were visible. Thus the orientation mechanism is clearly dependent on the biological clock, and, whether the sun is actually visible or not, a bee "knows what time it is."

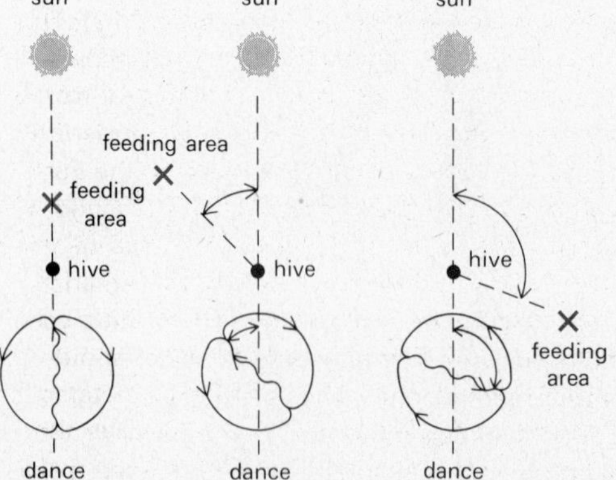

22.11 ***Waggle dances*** *in bees. The angle of the dancing path of a honeybee relative to the vertical on the surface of a honeycomb (wavy lines in lower diagrams) indicates the direction of the feeding area in relation to the position of the sun as seen from the hive. (After von Frisch.)*

Ability to orient by the sun is influenced greatly by learning. If inexperienced bees are trained to search for food only during afternoons but are subsequently allowed to scout only during morning hours, the insects communicate flight directions incorrectly at first. Apparently they have not yet learned to assess the entire daily course of the sun. However, after some days of morning experience the bees do communicate correctly. Similarly, if a bee hive is relocated across the equator, the navigation of the insects becomes disoriented for weeks and possibly for life: the apparent motion of the sun is clockwise north of the equator, counterclockwise south of it. Proper reorientation to such drastically new conditions does not readily occur through entrainment and evidently must await the maturation of a new generation, for which the new environment is the "original" home.

Sun compass orientation is known to occur also in horseshoe crabs, certain ants, beetles, spiders, and in several other arthropod groups. Among vertebrates the process has been demonstrated to date in some fishes, turtles, and birds. In contrast to arthropod navigation, that of vertebrates appears to require actual sun sightings. At night, under overcasts, or even under clear skies with the sun not directly visible, the orientation of these animals becomes confused or less precise.

In certain cases sun compass mechanisms appear to play some role in navigational guidance during seasonal migrations and in homing. For example, certain sea turtles undertake annual migrations of several thousand miles to lay eggs at specific beaches. Correct navigation here appears to depend on the sun, at least in part; as in other vertebrates, location finding becomes confused or less precise if the sun is not visible. Homing pigeons, too, orient by the sun. By entraining these birds to artificial light-dark cycles, it has been found that the flight directions taken in homing are adjusted to solar time and are influenced by the biological clock. However, before homing pigeons can undertake long return flights (up to 500 miles in one day), they must be allowed to become familiar with the landmarks in the vicinity of the home base. They do so through sorties of gradually increasing duration. The birds evidently become more efficient through experience. But their efficiency is reduced if the home territory becomes covered with snow.

Other migrating birds do not appear to navigate specifically by the sun. Indeed such migrants actually travel more by night than by day, and experimental evidence suggests that they probably orient by star sightings. For example, warblers travel south in the fall, north in the spring. If fall birds are placed in a planetarium and are exposed to star patterns characteristic of spring, the animals soon assume a northward heading.

Seasonal migrations serve to bring animals to fixed breeding or feeding grounds. Apart from birds, migrant animals include certain butterflies and some other arthropods, eels, salmon, and other fishes, some turtles, and a large variety of mammals. The record for long-distance travel is held by the arctic tern, a bird that makes an annual round trip of some 22,000 miles between the Arctic and the Antarctic (Fig. 22.12). The methods by which most of these migrant animals navigate remain largely unclear. Although sun and star orientation might serve as navigational aids in certain cases, such mechanisms are insufficient to account for all aspects of migratory behavior. In aquatic types, for example, optical cues can have only limited significance at best. In some cases, as in salmon, navigation appears to be based on *chemotaxis,* or ability to distinguish different kinds of waters by relative oxygen content, amount of silting, and more subtle chemical characteristics that can be smelled or tasted. But for many other animals, aquatic, terrestrial, or aerial, the sensory basis of navigation is still obscure.

The problem is puzzling enough where organisms make the same trip every year, like seals and birds. If nothing else, a remarkable memory for landmarks, prevailing winds, or ocean currents appears to be indicated. The problem becomes even more puzzling, however, when correct navigation takes place without optical cues of any kind and without demonstrable prior experience. For example, migrant birds generally can maintain their course despite zero visibility, as in

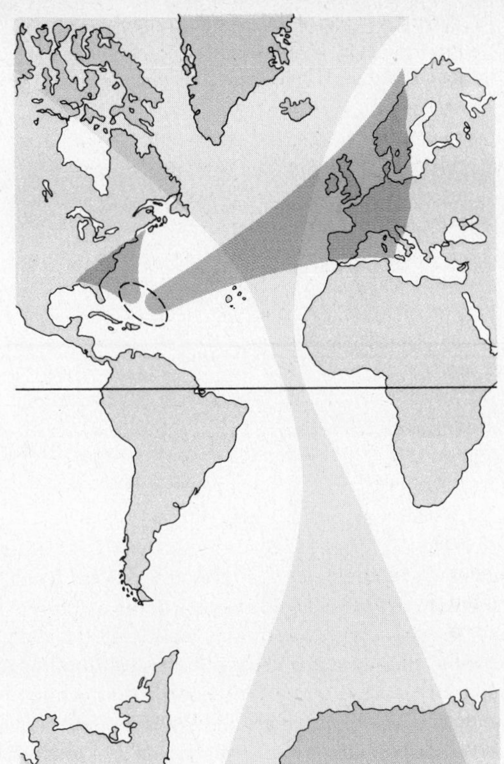

22.12 Migrations. *The migratory paths of Arctic terns are shown in light color, those of Atlantic eels in dark color. American and European eels spawn in the Sargasso Sea (indicated by a dashed line).*

flight through dense fog, and they can correct course after displacement by winds, even over the open sea where the view is the same in all directions. And although young birds generally fly with older ones, experiments show that young birds still navigate correctly when they migrate alone and for the first time. Moreover, optical cues and experience are both often lacking in underwater migrants, as in eels, for example.

The eggs of both American and European eels hatch in the deep waters of the Sargasso Sea, an Atlantic area between and somewhat east of Bermuda and the Caribbean (see Fig. 22.12). The near-microscopic larvae are fishlike, transparent *elvers,* which migrate toward the coasts of North America and Europe. Larvae of the American species hatch farther west than those of the European species, and differences in the direction of deep-ocean currents probably contribute to the initial separation of the two species. American elvers reach continental waters after about a year of travel, and European elvers, after about 3 years. In coastal estuaries the larvae metamorphose to elongated adults, and the males then remain in the estuaries. Females ascend rivers

22.13 ***Magnetic ants.*** *Nests of such Australian ants are shown. The edges of the anthills are oriented in precise compass directions.*

and settle in headwaters and in lakes. After 7 to 15 years the females migrate back to the estuaries and together with the males head out to the Atlantic. Reproductive organs mature during this migration, and on arrival in the Sargasso the eggs are spawned and fertilized. The aduts then die.

How do the larvae find river mouths 1,000 or 2,000 miles away? And how do the adults find a specific area in a vast expanse of ocean? Both larvae and adults make their trip for the first and only time, and optical cues surely play little role in the depths of the ocean. Currents might be significant, but if so this has not been demonstrated. In line with the continental drift hypothesis (see Chap. 6), it has also been suggested that the migration routes might correspond to the courses of ancient river systems, obliterated when North America and Europe split off as separate continents from an originally single land mass. If so, however, it is not at all clear how a fixed "racial memory" could be of any value when the ancient geography has undergone drastic changes during millions of years—even assuming that an acquired trait such as a geographic memory could be inherited, which is not the case.

Neither memories of prior experience nor optical cues would need to be postulated if migrating animals could be shown to orient on the basis of other characteristics that distinguish different points on the earth's surface. For example, might animals be able to find their way essentially as we do, by geomagnetic compass? The magnetic field of the earth would serve adequately as a "map," provided that animals could detect the angle of inclination at which lines of magnetic force passed through their bodies. For at the magnetic equator such lines are parallel to the earth's surface, at the (magnetic) poles they are vertical, and at intermediate latitudes their angles of inclination change progressively from horizontal to vertical.

Special receptors for magnetic stimuli have so far not been demonstrated in any organism. But that organisms are nevertheless sensitive to magnetic forces has been shown in several kinds of experiments. For example, when motile algae such as *Volvox* or protozoa such as *Paramecium* are put into an enclosure with a narrow opening, the organisms emerge and tend to head away from the opening in a straight-line path. But if the region around the opening is subjected to the field of a bar magnet, the paths of the emerging organisms veer significantly to the right or to the left, according to different positions in which the magnetic field is oriented. Similar results can be obtained with flatworm planarians, and ingenious tests with snails have shown that these mollusks can distinguish between different magnetic intensities as well as different directions of magnetic lines of force. Birds that maintain migratory orientation well in wooden enclosures without windows lose their orienting capability in steel-lined enclosures. Also, several species of perching birds have been found to increase their spontaneous activity sharply when subjected to weak magnetic fields. And the "magnetic" termites of Australia build a hive in such a way that its long axis points precisely in the direction of the magnetic north and south. Thus, while sensitivity to magnetic forces appears to be fairly widespread, the possible role of this sensitivity in migratory or other behavior is far from clear (Fig. 22.13).

Some aspects of how long-distance travel is initiated have been clarified for birds, and a similar mechanism presumably operates in other vertebrates. In these animals migrations are associated with the neural and hormonal changes of the annual breeding cycle. Birds typically migrate during the period preceding their breeding season. It has also been demonstrated that day lengths and total light hours received are the specific external stimuli that elicit breeding migrations, just as they are the stimuli for the breeding season itself. For example, migratory behavior can be changed experimentally be resetting the environmental light clock. It is known, moreover, that photoperiodic stimulation leads not only to sexual but also to adaptive metabolic changes in migrating birds: the animals deposit increasing amounts of storage fat in their bodies, and they can then subsist without regular food intake during migrations.

For animals other than vertebrates the controls for the onset of migrations are largely unknown as yet, as are those for the control of return migrations, in which the end result is not breeding but most often feeding. Migratory behavior thus still represents one of the most enigmatic phenomena in all biology.

review questions

1 Describe some of the general characteristics of reactive, active, and cognitive behavior. Give specific examples of each of these behavioral categories.

2 What kinds of learning are common for various categories of behavior? What are the identifying features of exploratory behavior, play, and manipulative behavior?

3 What are the general attributes of releaser stimuli and of sign-induced behavior? Give some examples of visual and chemical stimuli that can act as releasers in particular animals. What are pheromones? Give some examples of their action.

4 What are the specific characteristics of imprinting? How does imprinting differ from other kinds of learning? What stimuli generated by a mother bird can evoke a following response in her young?

5 Describe several different rhythmic behaviors. What kinds of experiments have suggested that organisms have biological clocks? What is meant by entrainment, and to what extent can rhythmic behavior become entrained?

6 Describe some of the properties of biological clocks. How precise are they? Are they affected by temperature? Are they inherited? To what extent can they be reset? How do changing photoperiods affect the behavior of plants and animals?

7 What are tropisms and kineses? Give specific examples of each. What is meant by sun compass orientation? Name different groups of animals in which this process occurs.

8 Show how, at different times of day or night, honeybees communicate distances and directions of feeding areas to other bees. Is this communication capacity inherited or learned?

9 What kinds of stimuli usually clock the onset of breeding seasons? Of seasonal migrations? Describe the migrations of Atlantic eels at various stages of the life cycle. What is chemotaxis?

10 What is the adaptive advantage of seasonal migrations? By what mechanisms do homing pigeons and other birds migrate? To what extent is prior experience important in seasonal migrations?

collateral readings

Blough, D. S.: Experiments in Animal Psychophysics, *Sci. American,* July, 1961. Pigeons can be trained to "tell" what visual stimuli they are exposed to.

Brown, F. A., Jr.: Biological Clocks and the Fiddler Crab, *Sci. American,* Apr., 1954. One of the early studies on rhythmic behavior.

Esch, H.: The Evolution of Bee Language, *Sci. American,* Apr., 1967. Sound communication may have preceded visual communication.

Frantz, R. L.: The Origin of Form Perception, *Sci. American,* May, 1961. The roles of inheritance and learning in the development of form perception.

Harlow, H. F., and **M. K. Harlow**: Social Deprivation in Monkeys, *Sci. American,* Nov., 1962. An examination of the importance of peer groups in the development of emotionality.

Hess, E. H.: Imprinting in Animals, *Sci. American,* March, 1958. An article by a well-known student of the subject.

Hinde, R. A.: "Animal Behavior," McGraw-Hill,

New York, 1966. This text places special emphasis on the psychological aspects of behavior. With valuable references at the end of the book.

Holst, E. von, and **U. von Saint Paul:** Electrically Controlled Behavior, *Sci. American,* March, 1962. The nature of drives is examined by experiments with electrodes placed in the brain of chickens.

Jacobson, M., and **M. Beroza:** Insect Attractants, *Sci. American,* Aug., 1964. Natural and man-made pheromones are discussed.

Johnson, C. G.: The Aerial Migrations of Insects, *Sci. American,* Dec., 1963. The article examines the seasonal migrations of certain insects.

Lorenz, K.: The Evolution of Behavior, *Sci. American,* Dec., 1958. The relative contributions of inheritance and experience to behavioral processes are examined.

Olds, J.: Pleasure Centers in the Brain, *Sci. American,* Oct., 1956. Interesting experiments on electrically self-stimulating rats have revealed the existence of distinct pleasure centers.

Sauer, E. G. F.: Celestial Navigation by Birds, *Sci. American,* Aug., 1958. An interesting article on a specific instance of animal migration.

Thompson, W. R., and **R. Melzack:** Early Environment, *Sci. American,* Jan., 1956. The role of early influences in shaping later behavior is discussed.

Thorpe, W. H.: The Language of Birds, *Sci. American,* Oct., 1956. A discussion of the complex vocal communication systems among birds.

Tinbergen, N.: The Evolution of Behavior in Gulls, *Sci. American,* Dec., 1960. The communication systems of various species of gulls are examined and contrasted.

Van der Kloot, W. G.: "Behavior," Holt, Rinehart and Winston, New York, 1968. A highly recommended paperback.

Von Frisch, K.: "Bees, Their Vision, Chemical Senses, and Language," Cornell, Ithaca, N.Y., 1950.

———: Dialects in the Language of Bees, *Sci. American,* Aug., 1962.

———: "Dance Language and Orientation," Harvard University Press, Cambridge, Mass., 1967.

The discoverer and foremost "translator" of bee language discusses the communication system of these animals.

Wenner, A. M.: Sound Communication in Honeybees, *Sci. American,* Apr., 1964. Bees are now known to communicate by sound in addition to vision-dependent waggle dances.

Wilson, E. O.: Pheromones, *Sci. American,* May, 1963. A good article on animal communication through chemicals.

The following articles from *Scientific American* are adequately described by their titles:

Boycott, B. B.: Learning in the Octopus, March, 1965.

Butler, R. A.: Curiosity in Monkeys, Feb., 1954.

Carr, A.: The Navigation of the Green Turtle, May, 1965.

Emlen, J. T., and **R. L. Fenney:** The Navigation of Penguins, Oct., 1966.

Eysenck, H. J.: The Measurement of Motivation, May, 1963.

Ferster, C. B.: Arithmetic Behavior in Chimpanzees, May, 1964.

Flyger, V., and **M. R. Townsend:** The Migration of Polar Bears, Feb., 1968.

Gilbert, P. W.: The Behavior of Sharks, July, 1962.

Gleitman, H.: Place-Learning, Oct., 1963.

Hasler, A. D., and **J. A. Larson:** The Homing Salmon, Aug., 1955.

Liddell, H. S.: Conditioning and Emotions, Jan., 1954.

chapter 23 behavioral control: the society

Localized groupings of members of the same species are common throughout the living world, but true social populations are not. Individuals of a species group together when extraneous stimuli draw them to the same locale. Thus, plants, animals, and organisms of all kinds tend to aggregate in locations favorable to them, and organisms such as men aggregate temporarily at places of special interest. By contrast, the members of a population form a society only when they interact with each other directly. Social groups therefore occur only among animals.

social groupings

In all social animals the members of a group are interdependent and variously specialized in function, and their survival depends on cooperation in the group. In most cases the member animals are also polymorphic, or specialized structurally. For example, colonial coelenterates, ectoprocts, and tunicates often consist of aggregations of different kinds of polymorphic individuals (see Color Fig. 13). Because their survival requires mutual cooperation in activities such as feeding, locomotion, protection, or reproduction, colonies of this type qualify as simple societies. Polymorphism is also pronounced in the far more complex societies of insects and vertebrates. Insect societies can include structurally different queens, kings, soldiers, drones, and workers, and social vertebrates usually exhibit sexual dimorphism, or structural distinctions between males and females (and their young; see Fig. 6.5).

The adaptive advantages of social living appear to be many. First, an interacting group is often more effective than separate individuals in obtaining food, in finding mates, and in protective and defensive activities. Indeed, a behavior unique to societies is individual self-sacrifice for the sake of the group, as among worker bees, which die after stinging, and among men, who are often prompted to give their lives for others. Second, metabolism and growth in many cases take place more effectively in a social milieu. In a slightly unfavorable environment, for example, goldfish and other aquatic animals survive better in social groups than as separate individuals, apparently because normal body secretions (mainly salts) neutralize toxic substances in the water and thereby "condition" the medium. Also, some secretions of social animals are known to have stimulating (or inhibiting) effects on growth, and the collective body heat generated by a compact group can reduce the level of metabolism that each individual must maintain. Third, social living substantially facilitates learning and imitative behavior, an important factor in individual survival. Above all, by regulating and controlling the interactions among individuals, social life reduces aggression and competition, keeps conflict and combat on largely nonlethal levels, and in general provides standards of behavior that tend to promote survival of both the individual and the whole species.

Advanced societies occur in animals with advanced evolutionary status—insects and vertebrates. Social life has evolved quite independently in these two groups, and the organization of their societies also is quite different. It is interesting nevertheless that certain external forms of their social behavior are superficially rather parallel. Among all animals, only some social insects and some social vertebrates pursue agriculture, domesticate other organisms, practice slavery, engage in war, and commit suicide.

insect societies

In each of four insect groups—termites, ants, bees, and wasps—different species form societies of different degrees of complexity. All typically build *nests,* and all contain structurally and functionally different social *castes;* each member is adapted from the outset to carry out specific social functions.

The best known of these societies is unquestionably that of the honeybees. A population of such bees contains three structurally distinct types: a *queen,* tens or hundreds of male *drones,* and from 20,000 to 80,000 *workers.* The queen and the stingless drones are fertile, and their main functions are reproductive. The smaller-bodied workers are all sterile females. They build the hive, protect the colony from strange bees and enemies, collect food, feed the queen and the drones, and nurse the young (Fig. 23.1).

When a hive becomes overcrowded, the queen together with some drones and several thousand workers secedes from the colony. The emigrants swarm out and settle temporarily in a tree or other

23.1 Social insects: honeybees. *Worker at left, queen in middle, drone at right. See also Fig. 23.3.*

23.2 Honeybees. *A swarm emigrated from a parental hive and searching for a new hive.*

suitable place until a new hive is found (Fig. 23.2). In the old hive the remaining workers then raise a few of the old queen's eggs in large, specially built honeycomb cells. These eggs develop into new queens. The first one to emerge from its cell immediately searches out the other queen cells and stings their occupants to death. If two new queens happen to emerge at the same time, they at once engage in mortal combat until one remains victorious. The young queen, her succession now undisputed, soon mates with one of the drones. In a nuptial flight high into the air she receives millions of sperms that are stored in a receptacle in her abdomen. The sperms from this single mating last through the entire egg-laying career of the queen.

Among the eggs laid individually into honeycomb cells, some escape fertilization even in a young queen. None is fertilized in an older queen once her sperm store is exhausted. Unfertilized eggs develop into drones. Fatherless development of this sort, or *natural parthenogenesis,* is widespread among social insects generally. Fertilized eggs develop either as queens or as workers, depending on the type of food the worker nurses supply to the larvae formed from the eggs. Larvae to be raised as workers are fed a "regular" diet of plant pollen and honey. Queens form when the larvae receive an especially rich *royal jelly,* containing pollen, honey, and comparatively huge amounts of certain vitamins (particularly pantothenic acid). But new queens are not raised while the original queen remains in the hive, healthy and fertile. If the queen produces eggs faster than honeycomb cells can be built she receives less food from her attendants. Egg production then slows down. Conversely, if she is behind in her egg laying she is fed more intensively (Fig. 23.3).

During the 6 weeks or so of its life a worker bee carries out different duties at different ages. Housekeeping tasks are performed by young bees, food-collecting trips are made by older ones. On a food-collecting trip the bee gathers pollen, rich in protein, and nectar, a dilute sugar solution. Pollen is carried home in *pollen baskets* on the hind legs. Nectar is swallowed into the *honey crop,* a specialized part of the alimentary tract, where saliva partially digests the sugar of nectar. On arriving at the hive the bee first passes a security check on the way in, then unloads its pollen in one cell and regurgitates its nectar to another. Other bees pack the pollen tight and start converting nectar to honey. They rapidly beat their wings close to a nectar-filled cell until most of the water has evaporated. Then the honey cell is sealed up with wax. Honey is the main food during the winter, when pollen is unobtainable.

At the approach of winter all drones are expelled from the colony; males would merely use up irreplaceable food but would not contribute to the well-being of the population. The remaining bees cling together in compact masses, with animals in the center working their way out and those near the surface working their way in. A clump of bees thereby withstands freezing even at very low temperatures.

Among other social insects polymorphic distinctions can be considerably more diversified. For example, many species of ants and termites include sterile wingless workers as well as sterile wingless *soldiers.* The latter are strong-jawed, heavily armored individuals that accompany work crews outside and keep order inside the nest. Soldiers in many cases cannot feed themselves and are cared for by workers. Besides a winged fertile queen and one or several winged fertile males (kings), ant and termite societies often maintain structurally distinct lesser "royalty." Such individuals probably develop when larvae are fed more than enough to produce workers but not enough to produce queens (Fig. 23.4).

Agricultural societies occur among both termites and ants. Populations of certain termite species make little garden plots of wood, excrement, and dead termites. There they plant and rear fungi for food. *Leaf-cutting ants,* similarly, prepare pieces of leaves on which fungi are grown. The fungi are systematically pruned and cared for by gardening crews.

Dairy ants keep tiny green aphids (plant lice) as food suppliers. The aphids secrete honeydew, a sugar- and protein-containing mixture, on which the ants depend. A common species of garden ant, for example, places "domesticated" plant lice on the roots of corn. The aphids feed there, and the ants thereafter milk these "ant cows" by gently stroking them. At the approach of winter the aphids are carried into the ant nest and are put back on corn roots the following spring.

Slave-making ants can neither build nests, feed themselves, nor care for their larvae. They form workerless soldier societies capable only of making raids on populations of other ant species. These victims are robbed of their pupae. The captive pupae mature, and the emerging slaves then care for their masters, performing all the functions they would have carried out in their own nest.

Honeypot ants are desert forms that collect nectar from flowers and feed it to some of their fellow workers, which are kept inside the nest. These "living bottles" become greatly distended and serve as bacteria-free storage bins; during the dry season they dispense drops of honey to their thirsty mates.

Army ants in the tropics march cross-country in raiding expeditions. They travel in columns accompanied by larger-bodied "officer" ants. Everything living in the path of such columns is

A

B

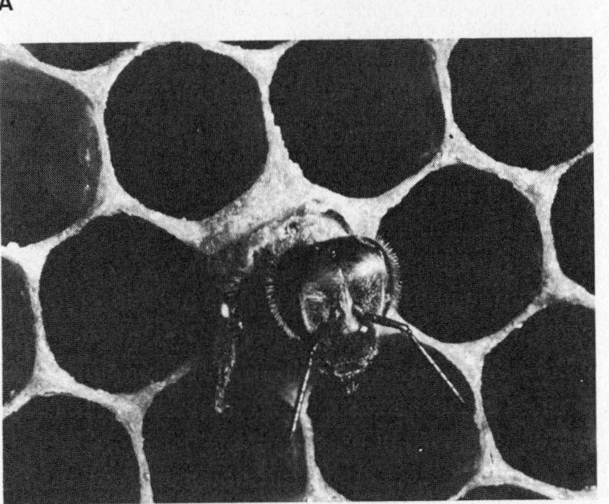

C

D

23.3 Honeybees. *A, queen bee laying eggs, surrounded by attendants. B, nurse bee feeds and cleans the larvae in the brood cells. C, a worker bee just hatching out from its brood cell. D, two enlarged brood cells, capped over with wax, in which queen bees are being raised.*

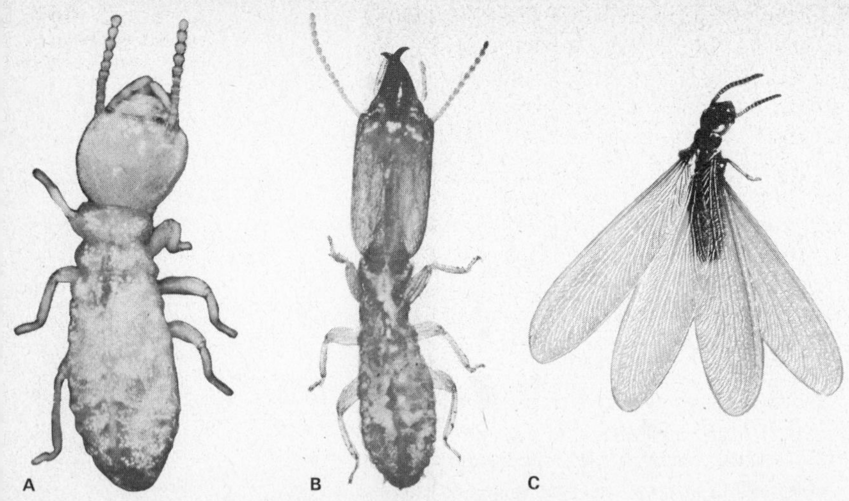

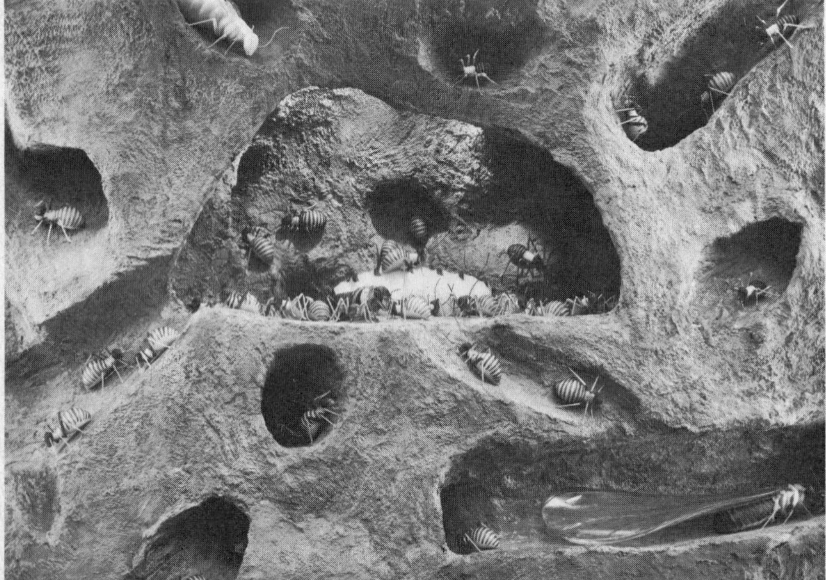

23.4 ***Social insects: termites.*** *A, worker. B, soldier, C, winged king. D, portion of nest. In central chamber note queen, her abdomen swollen with eggs, being cared for by workers. Winged king in lower right corner, larval queen in upper left corner.*

reduced to manageable pieces and carried off, even large animals if these should be unable to move away. It has been shown that the ants establish camps, or bivouacs, from which raids are launched; that chemical trails are laid and used on return trips; and that the timing of major raids coincides with the imminent maturation of large broods of offspring. The stereotyped nature of much of insect behavior is also well shown in these ants. If a column is made to travel in a circle the ants will maintain the circle endlessly, each individual continuing to follow the one before it. Behavior evidently is so automatic that an ant is incapable of thinking itself out of an unproductive situation (Fig. 23.5).

Among bees and insect societies in general, well-ordered group living is a result of the early and permanent subordination of each individual to the group. The essence of the caste system is that an individual is never free to seek its place in the society on its own, but that its place is already predetermined as soon as life begins. Intrasocial competition is thereby forestalled, and the responsibilities of the individual to the group and of the group to the individual remain fully defined at all times.

This social predetermination is nowhere more complete than in reproduction; social conflict is reduced most particularly by the circumstance that reproduction is virtually removed from the field of competition. Reproductive activity revolves around a single female, and the whole social population in effect consists of her own immediate family—which is sterile. All social institutions therefore rest on the genes of this one female, and her genes alone provide continuity from one generation to the next. As a result, internal social conflicts can hardly begin to become an issue.

Vertebrate societies are organized quite differently in this respect.

vertebrate societies

Apart from the sexual dimorphism of males and females, the members of vertebrate populations are structurally more or less alike, at least during the early stages of life. Most important, *all* members of a vertebrate society are potential reproducers. Later specializations and social stratifications are largely functional and are based on differences resulting from various combinations of hereditary *and* acquired traits. The animals therefore come to differ in size, strength, intelligence, emotionality, skill, and in the comparative effectiveness with which they apply these and other attributes of individuality to the problems of living. The general result is that, unlike a social insect, a social vertebrate does have to seek a place in the society on its own, and it must usually do so in direct competition with the other members of the group. The competition revolves primarily around securing personal living space, food, and reproductive opportunity.

In effect, the vertebrate society is founded on a perpetual interaction of two opposing forces.

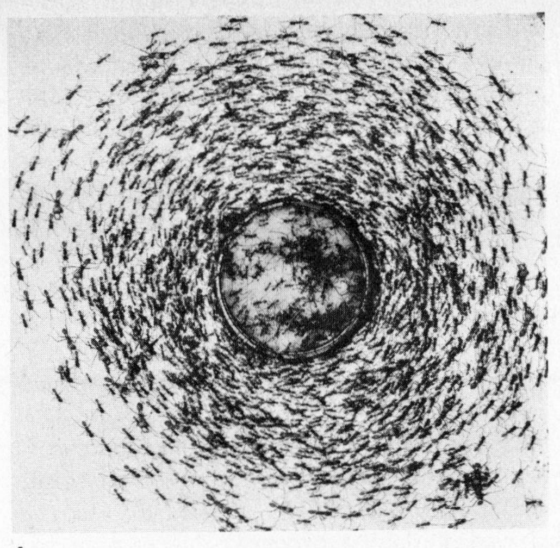

A

B

23.5 Social insects. *A, army ants. If a column of army ants is made to travel in a circle, as in the photo, then the animals will continue to circle endlessly. Evidently this behavior is governed so completely by internal factors that the insects are incapable of modifying their response. B, nest of a wasp colony. See also Fig. 22.13.*

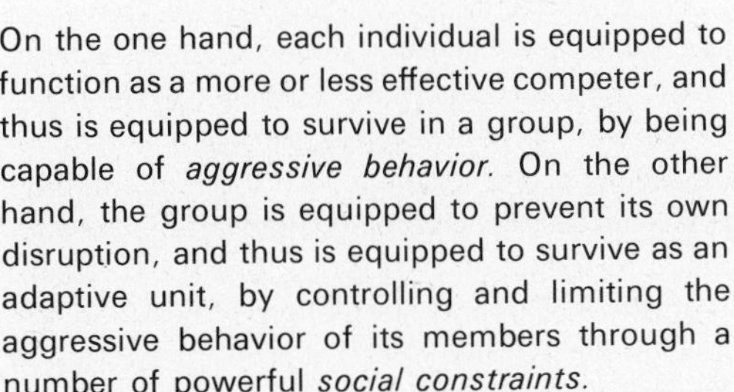

On the one hand, each individual is equipped to function as a more or less effective competer, and thus is equipped to survive in a group, by being capable of *aggressive behavior.* On the other hand, the group is equipped to prevent its own disruption, and thus is equipped to survive as an adaptive unit, by controlling and limiting the aggressive behavior of its members through a number of powerful *social constraints.*

aggression

Aggressive behavior (technically also called *agonistic* behavior) is an activity through which an individual often asserts his membership in the group generally and obtains his share of space, food, and mates specifically. The means of aggression include threat displays and actual fighting.

Aggressive displays follow more or less standardized patterns, and by variously warning, bluffing, or scaring a potential opponent they serve to forestall actual fighting. In many cases such displays are effective even against members of other species. For example, a prominent presentation of weapons, a fixed gaze leveled directly at an opponent, an evident muscular tensing, a slow wary stalk accompanied in some cases by fright-inducing sounds, or a size-increasing fluffing up or puffing up of the body, all are widely recognized among vertebrates as signs of threat. In most instances a series of exchanges of such displays between opponents suffices to elicit flight or submission by one (Fig. 23.6).

Aggressive (and also submissive) displays have

A B

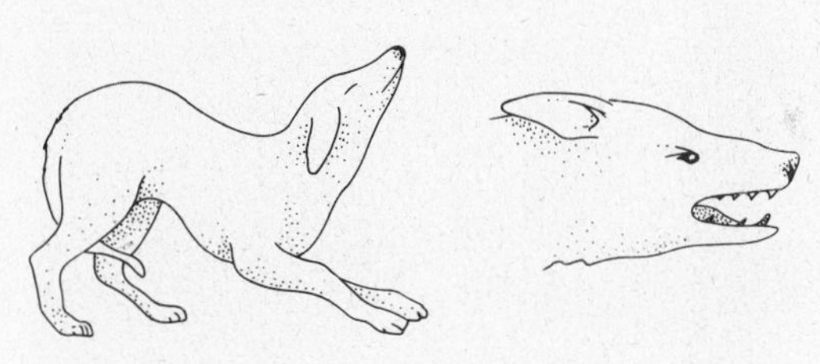

C

D

23.6 Aggressive and submissive displays. *A, sticklebacks assume a threatening stance by pointing the head downward (left), a submissive stance by lying in horizontal position or by pointing the head upward (right). B, top, a male finch in an aggressive posture, with head extended forward and feathers sleeked down tight against the body; bottom, a female finch in a submissive posture, with the body in sitting position, the head retracted, and the feathers fluffed up. C, dogs signal threat and submission by the familiar postures indicated at right and left, respectively. D, in this confrontation, the aggressive protagonist at left bares its teeth, points its ears up, stares at the opponent, raises its tail, and assumes a threat posture. The submissive animal meanwhile crouches down, lays its ears back, closes its mouth, lowers its tail, and carefully looks away from the opponent.*

A

B

23.7 ***Redirection and displacement.*** *A, male baboon in foreground is being threatened by male in background. However, avoiding both aggressive and submissive responses, the threatened male gives a redirected response instead: it focuses attention on uninvolved bystanders and walks over to the grooming couple nearby. B, under threat by male baboon at left, the male at right gives a displacement response: displaying neither aggressive nor submissive behavior, it carries out an activity not pertinent to the confrontation and grooms its mate instead.*

probably evolved as symbolic offshoots of real fights; the actions and movements of displays are often quite similar to those of combat. However, they have become *ritualized,* by increases or decreases in the speeds, intensities, or durations of particular movements, and by behavioral changes that exaggerate or draw attention to specific releaser signs of aggression or submission. Most probably, therefore, such displays represent stylized sham fights adaptively valuable as less dangerous substitutes for real fighting.

When an animal finds itself in a threatening social situation, the necessity of deciding on either fight or flight often creates psychological conflict—in many cases aggression and submission can be equally undesirable. In such circumstances the animal can frequently avoid becoming involved in either aggression or submission by minimizing the attention it creates; it might "freeze" to immobility or feign sleep. Sometimes psychological conflict can also be resolved through *redirection:* directing an aggressive response not at the opponent but at an extraneous third entity—some nearby inanimate object, for example, or an "innocent bystander." Or the animal can carry out a *displacement* response, one not pertinent to the threat situation at all—excessive grooming, for example, or sudden preoccupation with some irrelevant feature of the environment. Responses of this sort are well known in human behavior, and they are also encountered very widely in other mammals and in birds (Fig. 23.7).

Outright combat occurs comparatively rarely, and indeed only when it cannot be avoided by other means—the cost could be death, injury, or at least exhaustion, while the gain could be zero. Also, notwithstanding some known exceptions (man is one), very few animals seek out fights deliberately. In general, fighting tends to occur mainly when the living space, the food, the mates and the young, or the social status of animals is in jeopardy; or more specifically, when the hazards of fighting become less significant than the motivation to compete for space, food, mates, or social status.

Thus it has been shown for most vertebrates studied that the frequency of fighting increases with rising population density. Similarly, many animals require a free personal space immediately around them and will fight if this space is violated. For example, a nonbreeding male chaffinch will permit another male to approach no closer than about 8 in., and a female can approach to no more than about 4 in. A chicken permits a closer approach behind it than in front of it. And the size of a particular personal space tends to increase or decrease according to whether an approaching individual is familiar or not and displays signs of threat or submission (Fig. 23.8). Fighting also increases with progressive food scarcity and at the approach of the breeding season. A good many fights occur when an individual is prevented from completing a goal-directed activity, a situation equivalent to frustration in man.

Whatever the provocation, vertebrates rarely fight to the death (man sometimes being a notable exception). If an exchange of aggressive displays does not establish the dominance of one of the opponents, such a dominance usually becomes apparent fairly quickly once combat has started. The fighting then terminates, and in most cases it terminates in any event as soon as one of the protagonists is wounded. The objective of animal combat is not destruction of an opponent, but merely elimination of the threat that his presence represents—at minimum cost of effort and risk to the threatened animal.

The capacity to behave aggressively or submissively is inherited, but the execution of such behavior is largely learned. Experience teaches not only the techniques of aggressive display and the tactics of combat, but also the acceptable limits of the possible advantages and risks. Similarly significant is learning by imitation and, in predatory types, learning how to obtain food: predation and aggression involve many similar behavior patterns, even though killing is the objective in the first case. Notwithstanding the genetic variations among different individuals, early training to a large extent determines the threshold levels for aggressive responses and the intensities with which an individual will exhibit such responses. As has been shown for mice and as is well known for men, an individual can be *taught* to respond more or less readily and more or less intensely to a given provocation, and thus to be an aggressive or a submissive "type."

In vertebrates, aggressive behavior is under the control of at least two neural-endocrine mechanisms. Both are brought into play by a large variety of stimuli that can be variously visual, auditory, olfactory, tactile, or combinations of these. In one of these mechanisms, nerve impulses are relayed from sense organs to the brain, which in turn stimulates the adrenal medulla. This gland then secretes increased amounts of adrenalin and noradrenalin, hormones that initiate the "alarm reaction" (see Chap. 19). This reaction facilitates the sharply intensified activities that are required under most conditions of emotional or physical stress, including especially those calling for aggressive responses. Adrenalin specifically has been shown to raise emotional tension (manifested by red-faced anger in man), whereas noradrenalin specifically spurs overt action (accompanied by white-faced determination in man).

In the second mechanism, which can operate by itself or in concert with the alarm response, sensory impulses are transmitted to the hypothalamus in the brain. This region in turn transmits chemical signals (neurosecretory transmitter substances, particularly noradrenalin) to the pituitary gland, which secretes increased amounts of gonadotropic hormones as a result (see Fig. 26.8). These now induce the reproductive organs to secrete larger quantities of male and female sex hormones. Acting through effects on the nervous system (and especially the hypothalamus), the male hormones are particularly potent in triggering aggressive behavior. As pointed out in Chap. 19, both sexes produce *both* male and female hormones, though in different relative quantities; and in either sex the male hormone promotes aggressive behavior. That this is so is clearly shown by experimental hormone injections. Female hormones either are without significant effect or, in most vertebrates (man included), they reduce aggressiveness and correspondingly increase submissiveness. In a small group of birds and mammals the female hormones actually promote aggressiveness just as male hormones do. In such animals the females exert dominance over the males at the approach of the breeding season.

In effect, vertebrate aggressiveness waxes and

23.8 ***Personal space.*** *These nesting cormorants illustrate how each individual of a group often requires, and defends, a certain amount of space around it.*

wanes in synchrony with sexuality and the annual breeding cycle. Note, however, that aggressive behavior is not completely dependent on sex hormones; castrated animals do not become totally submissive, and in some cases castration reduces aggressiveness only very slightly.

Note also that actual reproductive capacity tends to be reduced by prolonged periods of heightened aggressiveness, even though sexual behavior can be intensified. The same stimuli that induce aggressiveness through effects on the pituitary also induce this gland to secrete increased amounts of ACTH (adrenocorticotropic hormone). This tropic hormone stimulates the adrenal cortex, and among the hormones then produced there in larger amounts are some that interfere with the proper maintenance of the sex organs. Persistent overstimulation of the adrenal cortex can therefore lead to a gradual structural decline of the sex organs and to lowered reproductive capacity. This effect is often observed in social groups in which the levels of aggressiveness are kept high by excessive population densities or by the repeated introduction of strange individuals. Under such conditions males produce fewer sperms, aggressive female birds such as chickens lay fewer eggs, and aggressive female mammals abort prematurely or cannot produce milk after pregnancy.

Chronic aggressiveness also has other, nonreproductive effects, all ultimately traceable to the endocrine and neural mechanisms just discussed. For example, growth is often inhibited and resistance to infections is lessened. Man in particular is also subject to a distinct ''stress syndrome,'' characterized by an increase in allergic sensitivity, in the frequency of headaches and constipation, in the incidence of ulcers, and in other debilities typically associated with prolonged tension.

It is important to recognize, however, that notwithstanding the undesirable connotations of the idea of ''aggression'' in human affairs, occasional aggressive (or at least self-assertive) individual behavior is probably essential in vertebrate society, human society included. To be sure, a potential to behave aggressively might not even need to exist if every cause of competition and every source of frustration could be removed from all individuals in a social group. But competitive factors are known to play at least some role in all vertebrate groups, for the environmental supply of space and food is inherently limited. Moreover, it has also been pointed out by several investigators that loss of aggressive potentials in a species would probably lead to its destruction: the vertebrate mechanism for aggressive behavior is so intimately connected with other vital functions that abolition of one would amount to abolition of all. As noted, for example, reproduction, breeding cycles, learning through play and imitation, in some cases search for food and migratory behavior, all are based to greater or lesser degree on the same processes that also generate aggressive behavior. In addition, these same neural-endocrine processes regulate numerous internal metabolic reactions, as well as the social constraints against aggression (see below); and in man at least they contribute substantially to derivative motivations such as love and the drive to create, explore, control the environment, or be active in a very general sense. Without this constellation of capacities, aggressiveness necessarily included, a vertebrate would cease to be a functioning animal.

It is clear at the same time, however, that if aggressiveness—or submissiveness—is exaggerated unduly it ceases to be adaptive; like any other biological process, assertiveness or its lack becomes detrimental when carried to excess. In general, then, the *potential* of behaving aggressively can be regarded as an important safeguard for survival, evolved for the self-preservation of the individual under the massive—and not necessarily malicious—impact of the group. But if actual aggressiveness is misapplied and its use is mislearned, its survival function is lost and it becomes a destructive force instead.

social constraints

Every society operates within a framework of rules that serve to reduce individual aggression and that thereby prevent disruption of the group. Like aggression, such constraining rules have a built-in, inherited basis, but their application is largely learned. Two kinds of constraints are characteristic of vertebrate societies in general, *dominance* hierarchies and *territoriality.* Both are based on a structured, organized utilization of the aggressive and submissive tendencies of individuals.

A dominance hierarchy to some extent resembles a caste system in that the members of a group are ranked according to a scale of relative status or superiority. However, whereas in a caste system an individual inherits a fixed rank, in a dominance hierarchy he must seek status on his own. Moreover, this status can become higher or lower in the course of time. The most widespread basis of superiority scales is physical size and strength, or at least display features that suggest size and strength. However, more subtle, psychological attributes of individuals can often be quite as significant. In human society the criteria are exceedingly varied, and, as is well known, factors such as intelligence, economic level, or cultural background can be just as important as size and strength, or even more so.

Social dominance is established more or less automatically if the members of a group differ greatly and obviously. Thus, large vertebrates usually dominate without contest over smaller ones, older individuals dominate over younger ones, and males largely dominate over females. Among individuals of more or less equal apparent status, the actual status is determined by sham or actual contests. Losers then usually indicate their acceptance of subordinate status by various forms of submissive behavior—prominent display of regions of weakness, submissive vocalization and posturing (including genital presentation in some animals), redirected or displacement activity, or outright flight. Submissive behavior does not always guarantee cessation of a contest, to be sure, and in some cases (man included) acceptance of subordinate status actually is often indicated by a resumption of aggressive display. But once the relative status of two individuals has become determined, it tends to have a measure of permanence; in a subsequent encounter the two individuals are not likely to recontest their comparative rank. In this way dominance is effective in reducing social conflict.

Among more than two individuals, hierarchic *peck orders* become established through whole series of pair contests carried out in round-robin fashion. In chickens, for example, the females of a flock become ranked by pecking contests. A given hen can then peck without danger of reprisal all lower-ranking birds, and she in turn can be pecked by any higher-ranking bird. If a new hen is introduced, she is subjected to a pecking contest with each fellow hen. Winning here and losing there, she soon acquires a particular rank. The peck order here has a simple linear pattern, but in other animals triangular, monarchic, or oligarchic relations can develop. Coalitions, factions, and alliances can be formed as well, and all such interrelations can change under changed conditions. As in human society, moreover, an individual can be a member of several different peck orders at the same time, in which case he usually maintains a different rank in each (Fig. 23.9).

The effectiveness of dominance hierarchies in reducing conflict depends greatly on easy rank identification: each individual must be able to recognize on sight the social rank of every other individual he encounters (as in the military organizations of man). Dominance systems actually are most common in comparatively small social units, where every member can become a familiar "acquaintance" of all others. In such units communicative activities usually are important aids in intragroup recognition. For example, mutual grooming serves not only in a sanitary role but also in maintaining social familiarity. Similarly, play, vocalization, sniffing, and various forms of greeting help in enhancing familiarity. Recognition is aided further by the coloration patterns, which tend to be showy and quite individual-specific in their fine details. Also, sexual dimorphism is generally very pronounced. Males tend to be distinctly larger than females, and they usually have conspicuous and flashy display devices. Such males typically contribute little or nothing to the parental duties of building nests and caring for offspring. Because easy recognition and familiarity have great importance in social units of this type, the members tend to exhibit

23.9 Dominance hierarchies. *Peck orders are characteristic in social groups such as flocks of hens.*

ingroup clannishness and considerable antagonism to outsiders.

Individuals of high status (technically often named by the first letters of the Greek alphabet; for example, "alpha-hen," top-ranking; "delta-fish," fourth-ranking) generally are favored in almost all respects. They can claim the best territory, the largest amounts of the choicest food, and the preferential services of members of the opposite sex. Indeed, in the presence of dominant animals low-ranking individuals often exhibit "psychological castration," or inability to mate. However, animals of lower status usually do not surrender their privileges permanently and passively, and the dominant individuals are frequently challenged to reassert their high rank. Dominance thus only reduces conflict but does not eliminate it entirely. If a high-ranking individual succeeds in maintaining his status, jealousy and frustration among subordinates can increase and thus contribute to reinforcing their low social position. If a dominant individual is challenged successfully, his ensuing psychological disorganization can be just as profound. The extreme effect is observed in chickens, where a high-ranking hen soon dies if she is deposed.

Despite such possible detrimental consequences for specific single individuals, the inequalities produced by a rank system are nevertheless adaptive for the group as a whole. If food is scarce, for example, the lowest-ranking members (or "omega-individuals") well might starve while the dominant ones eat all the available food. But at least some individuals will survive under such conditions. If a rank system were absent, however, the whole group could be wiped out, for after the available food were shared equitably a single share might not suffice for survival. In reproduction, similarly, the dominant animals are quite likely to be among the healthiest and therefore the best able to care for their offspring adequately. Hence it will be advantageous for the group if the genes of these animals are propagated preferentially.

Yet there are built-in safeguards that tend to make too high a status disadvantageous in many circumstances. In chickens, for example, alpha-hens are often so aggressive that they dominate and reject even the rooster. More submissive birds then produce most of the offspring. And very dominant male mice will often fight each other so viciously that they make themselves impotent.

Because they are based on aggressive behavior and thus to a major extent on sex-associated endocrine and neural mechanisms, dominance hierarchies become most pronounced—and socially most important—just before and during the breeding season. At other times of the year the social constraints can be more or less relaxed; only food supply represents a possible source of major conflict, for neither mates nor mating territory need be allocated during such periods. In year-round breeders, correspondingly, rank systems remain in full force at all times, as in man.

A quite similar relation with the breeding cycle holds for the second main type of social constraint, territoriality, which has a sex-associated endocrine and neural basis, too. Territoriality is exhibited by social groups in which the available geographic space is subdivided into lots, or domains, each being occupied by specific individuals. The occupants of a domain can be a single individual or a mating pair or a family or even a larger group. In most cases the primary claimant is a male who stakes out a particular area as his personal territory. If the space available to the whole group is extensive enough to make crowding unnecessary, individual domains will generally be just large enough to provide adequate food supplies and nesting materials for the occupants (Fig. 23.10).

The boundaries of a domain are variously identified and protected by scent markers (urine, for example), by intensive patrolling and vocalizing along the borders, and by immediate aggression against intruders. If a male occupant is still without mates, intruding females are usually not attacked, particularly if they behave submissively or display sex recognition signs. On the contrary, males try to attract females by conspicuous displays of their own.

When a domain is occupied by more than one individual of the same species, a male (and during the breeding season often a female) usually establishes dominance over mates and offspring and over other individuals that might be allowed to live in the domain. However, as soon as such a dominant individual leaves his domain and enters another, his behavior becomes wary or even submissive. Being an intruder he prepares to confront the local residents, and even the lowest-ranking of these is normally dominant over any outsider of the same species. Thus even small young animals generally succeed in driving outsiders many times larger out of the territory, and the psychological edge of human property owners against intruders is well known (and also is reflected and reinforced in our many legal safeguards). A given geographic region normally serves as home territory for numerous species simultaneously, but in many cases the occupants of a domain will not tolerate other similar species in the same area. Thus some species of fishes, birds, and mammals display chronic antagonism toward the members of certain other species and will chase such intruders out of their territory. For example, dogs, which are strongly territorial, invariably chase intruding cats.

Adaptively, a territorial system distributes the individuals of a social group in space, and it thereby probably aids in reducing conflict, notwithstanding occasional border disputes. It also reduces competition over the food supply available to the group. Indeed, by making overutilization of the food sources less likely, territoriality facilitates a long-term occupation of an area. Moreover, a territorial organization contributes significantly to population control. As a population grows numerically, the tendency of its original territory to become subdivided into more but smaller individual domains is likely to be counteracted at some stage by increasing aggression and competition. Thereafter, further growth in numbers will tend to spread a population over a progressively larger area. The regions along the periphery will then eventually abut against ecologically unsuitable territory, and at such a stage net population growth is likely to come to a halt.

Territoriality also promotes propagation. Since males are spaced out and more or less bound to their domains, competition over females is lessened. Moreover, mating, nesting, and care of young are all facilitated in the comparatively undisturbed sanctuary of a domain. Further, a territorial system makes all adults effective reproducers; hence it obviates the psychological castration often observed in dominance hierarchies.

Intragroup recognition and familiarity are far less important in territorial than in dominance systems. Indeed, territorial organizations tend to be specially characteristic of animals that form comparatively large social units. Also, such animals usually exhibit relatively strong exploratory drives; their coloration patterns are largely inconspicuous and serve in camouflage and protection more than in recognition; and males and females tend to be more nearly alike in coloration, size, and appearance than is generally the case in

23.10 Territoriality. *A polygamous family of fur seals, consisting of a single male, several females, and their young. Family groups such as this control a particular territory. The animals (especially the males) tend to ward off any fellow members of the species or other potential competitors that might invade their territory accidentally or deliberately.*

23.11 Male cooperation *in nesting gulls. Male (in background) signals to female by means of grass in beak that he is ready to assume nesting duties.*

dominance systems. Moreover, the males typically cooperate with the females in carrying out a variety of parental duties. In some fishes and birds it is actually the male that protects the nest or incubates the eggs (Fig. 23.11).

The fine structure of territorial organizations, like that of dominance systems, varies greatly not only for different species but also for a given species at different times. Moreover, changed conditions can lead to shifts from territoriality to dominance or the reverse. In many cases, for example, territoriality manifests itself only during the breeding season, while at other times a dominance system is in force. In animals that maintain territories the year round dominance often passes from the male to the female during the breeding season. And a normally territorial group can shift to a dominance hierarchy altogether if its living space becomes too small. This is a common occurrence in domesticated animals, for example, and among caged groups in zoos and laboratories. Finally, a social group can be bound together by complex and simultaneous combinations of territoriality and dominance, as is illustrated particularly well in human society.

review questions

1 Describe some of the characteristics of social populations and some of the probable adaptive advantages of social living.

2 Describe the organization of insect societies generally and of honeybee societies specifically. What forms of polymorphism occur in such societies? How do different polymorphic variants develop? What is parthenogenesis?

3 Describe the organization of vertebrate societies, and contrast it with that of insect societies. How does the relation of individual to group differ in the two kinds of societies? Does polymorphism occur among vertebrates?

4 What is the role of individual aggression in social groups? What appears to be the behavioral relation between threat display and combat? Describe the nature of threat displays.

5 What are redirection and displacement responses? Give examples of each, including some from human behavior. What are the functions of such responses?

6 Describe the endocrine and neural mechanisms that regulate aggressive and submissive behavior. To what extent is aggressive behavior inherited and to what extent is it learned?

7 Name and describe as many kinds of behavior as possible that are exhibited under the specific influence of sex-associated neural and endocrine mechanisms.

8 Describe the characteristics and adaptive advantages of dominance hierarchies. What are the usual organizational characteristics of societies in which dominance hierarchies are effective? What is psychological castration? What are the disadvantages of dominance hierarchies?

9 Describe the characteristics and adaptive advantages of territoriality. What are the usual characteristics of societies in which territorial organizations are effective? How does territoriality aid in (*a*) reducing conflict, (*b*) promoting reproduction? What are the limiting conditions that would make a territorial organization ineffective?

10 How do dominance and territorial systems become established? Under what conditions can one kind of system change to the other? Describe some aspects of human society in terms of aggression, dominance, and territoriality.

collateral readings

Ardrey, R.: "The Territorial Imperative," "Atheneum, New York, 1966. A book on territoriality, with emphasis on the "instinctive" basis of both territoriality and aggression. See also the Lorenz entry and the critique by Montagu cited below.

Batra, S. W. T., and **L. R. Batra**: The Fungus Gardens of Insects, *Sci. American,* Nov., 1967. Fungus-rearing social insects are described.

Berlyne, D. E.: Conflict and Arousal, *Sci. American,* Aug., 1966. The role of both phenomena in learning is examined.

Calhoun, J. B.: Population Density and Social Pathology, *Sci. American,* Feb., 1962. An examination of the detrimental social effects of crowding in rats.

Denenberg, V. H.: Early Experience and Emotional Development, *Sci. American,* June, 1963. An analysis of the effects of early socialization in rats on later emotional behavior.

Dilger, W. C.: The Behavior of Lovebirds, *Sci. American,* Jan., 1962. Differences in the nest-building activities of different species shed some light on the evolution of social behavior.

Eibl-Eibesfeldt, I.: The Fighting Behavior of Animals, *Sci. American,* Dec., 1961. The title describes the subject adequately.

Etkin, W. (ed.): "Social Behavior and Organization among Vertebrates," University of Chicago Press, Chicago, 1964. A good, popularly written examination of vertebrate societies. Recommended.

Funkenstein, D. H.: The Physiology of Fear and Anger, *Sci. American,* May, 1955. An examination of the hormonal mechanism of emotional stress.

Gilliard, E. T.: The Evolution of Bowerbirds, *Sci. American,* Aug., 1963. Sexual displays and mating behavior are examined.

Guhl, A. M.: The Social Order of Chickens, *Sci. American,* Feb., 1956. A close look at a specific dominance hierarchy,

Lorenz, K.: "On Aggression," Harcourt, New York, 1966. This book places emphasis on the "instinctive" nature of aggressiveness. It is in line with the book by Ardrey (cited above) but is criticized by Montagu (see below).

Montagu, M. F. A.: "Man and Aggression," Oxford, London, 1969. A counterargument to the books by Lorenz and Ardrey (cited above), with emphasis on the importance of learned and cultural factors in aggressiveness.

Mykytowycz, R.: Territorial Marking by Rabbits, *Sci. American,* May, 1968. A case study of territoriality.

Schneirla, T. C., and **G. Piel:** The Army Ant, *Sci. American,* June, 1948. The senior author of this article is the foremost authority on these social insects.

Shaw, E.: The Schooling of Fishes, *Sci. American,* June, 1962. The society of school-forming fishes is examined.

Tinbergen, N.: The Curious Behavior of the Stickleback, *Sci. American,* Dec., 1952.

———: "Social Behavior in Animals," Wiley, New York, 1953.

———: The Evolution of Behavior in Gulls, *Sci. American,* Dec., 1960.

In these readings a well-known student of animal behavior discusses various expressions of social life.

Washburn, S. L., and **T. DeVore**: The Social Life of Baboons, *Sci. American,* June, 1961. A case study of a complex dominance hierarchy.

Wecker, S. C.: Habitat Selection, *Sci. American,* Oct., 1964. Both heredity and learning are shown to play a role in how mice choose their environment.

Wynne-Edwards, V. C.: Population Control in Animals, *Sci.American,* Aug., 1964. Various social behaviors can limit reproduction and thus contribute to population control.

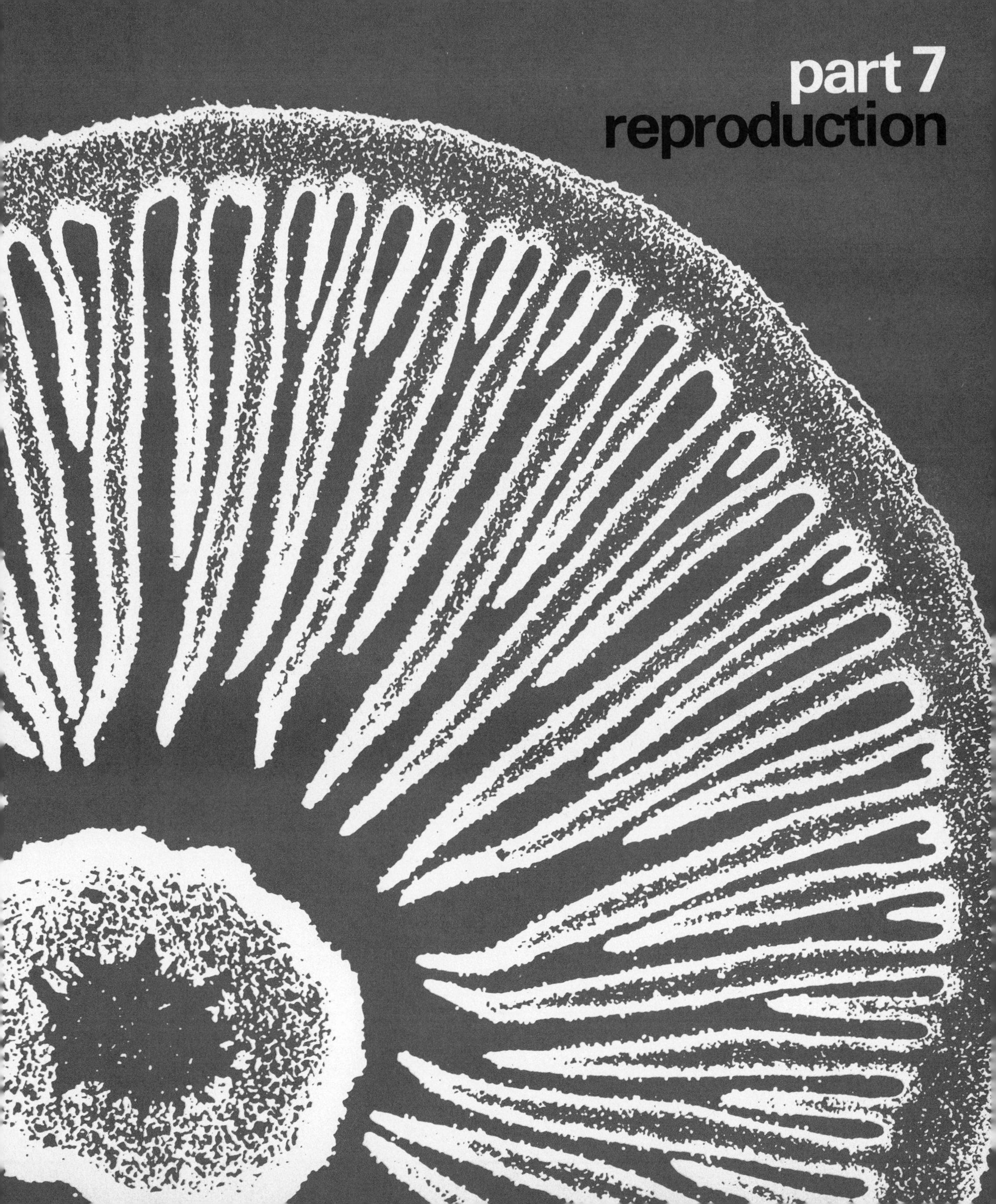

part 7
reproduction

part 7
reproduction

chapter 24
patterns of propagation

chapter 25
reproduction: nonanimal organisms

chapter 26
reproduction: animals

Of all living functions reproduction happens to be among the most noticeable to the casual observer. Metabolism occurs largely on an invisible, molecular scale. Control functions result in steady state—unchanged, even conditions. Adaptation and evolution occur on a scale so vast that man does not perceive them directly or obviously. But reproduction does take place on a directly perceivable, obvious scale: now there is one, then there are two.

To be sure, the deep significance of reproduction lies not in its dramatic nature but in its results. We have assigned "living" properties to the first of the ancient nucleic acids largely because they had reproductive *properties. These properties have been handed down in an unbroken succession from the first genes to all present genes, and they still form the basis of all reproductive events today.*

Just as an organism maintains steady states from its molecules on up, so it also reproduces from its molecules on up; molecular reproduction is the foundation of all reproduction. Accordingly, the first topics in this series of chapters are the reproductive patterns *on the various levels of the living hierarchy. Following this is an examination of the specific reproductive* processes *that occur in all major groups of organisms.*

chapter 24 patterns of propagation

Reproduction can be defined broadly as an extension of living matter in space and time. The self-perpetuative importance of this process is clear, for the formation of new living units makes possible replacement and addition at every level of organization. Among molecules or cells, among whole organisms or species, replacement offsets death from normal wear and tear and from accident and disease. *Healing* and *regeneration* are two aspects of replacement. Apart from such maintenance functions, net addition of extra units results in four-dimensional *growth,* or increase in the amount of living matter.

The creation of new units requires raw materials; reproduction at any level depends on ample nutrition. Duplication of a particular living unit also implies prior or simultaneous duplication of all smaller units in it. Reproduction must therefore occur on the molecular level before it can occur on any other.

reproductive processes: cells

molecular reproduction

The multiplication of molecules in cells can take four different forms, according to the nature of the molecule to be multiplied. All four are already familiar.

If water or another inorganic substance is to be reproduced, additional molecules or ions of such substances must be supplied ready-made by nutrition. Thus, *accumulation* is the simplest form of molecular "reproduction."

If a carbohydrate, a lipid, an amino acid, or any of their numerous derivatives is to be duplicated, it will have to be synthesized from accumulated raw materials with the aid of appropriate enzymes. So long as the enzymes of a cell remain the same, newly formed organic molecules will generally be duplicates of earlier ones. The second form of molecular reproduction therefore is *enzymatic synthesis.* It includes the first form, accumulation, as a component phase.

If a protein molecule is to be duplicated, enzymes must link amino acids together and DNA and RNA must provide the information for the sequence of linking. The third form of molecular reproduction evidently includes the first two forms, but in addition it is a directly *gene-dependent synthesis.*

Finally, if DNA is to be duplicated it must control its own replication. This process depends on the three types of process above: accumulation (of phosphates), enzymatic synthesis (of nitrogen bases and other required components), and DNA-dependent synthesis (of the needed enzymes). But above all DNA duplication is also *self-duplication,* and this is the fourth form of molecular reproduction.

In viruses molecular reproduction is equivalent to reproduction of the whole unit. In all truly living systems molecular reproduction contributes either to normal replacements in cells or to internal additions of molecules. If the rate of such additions exceeds the rate of molecular destruction, the usual result is cell growth. In the opposite case a cell can actually decrease in size and undergo negative growth ("degrowth").

Increase in cell *size* is often followed by increase in cell *number,* or *cell division.* Few biological events are as central to life and as universally characteristic of it as cell division. It is the only means by which unicellular organisms multiply. It creates reproductive cells and transforms them to multicellular adults. It replaces dead cells and thereby offsets normal wear and tear. It heals wounds and regenerates body parts lost or destroyed. And cell division sometimes goes wild and produces tumors, cancers, and other abnormal overgrowths. Indeed, the life histories of organisms well can be described as changing dynamic equilibria between cell division and cell death.

In certain protists a cell divides into *several* offspring cells simultaneously, a process called *multiple fission.* In certain other protists a cell divides by *budding,* or formation of a much smaller offspring cell. In the vast majority of cases, however, cells divide by *binary fission;* one "mother" cell becomes two roughly equally large "daughter" cells. After a period of internal molecular reproduction the daughter cells in turn usually divide, and successive cell generations follow one another in this fashion (Fig. 24.1).

Cell division consists of at least two processes, cytoplasmic cleavage into two parts and gene duplication. All organisms except the Monera have nuclei with chromosomes, and cell division here includes a mathematically precise doubling of the chromosomes and their genes. The two chromosome sets so produced then become separated and become part of two newly formed nuclei. This type of nuclear duplication represents *mitosis* (or *karyokinesis*); and if, as is usually the

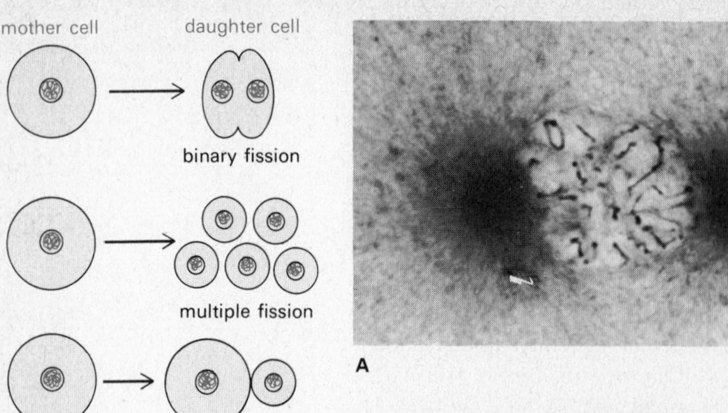

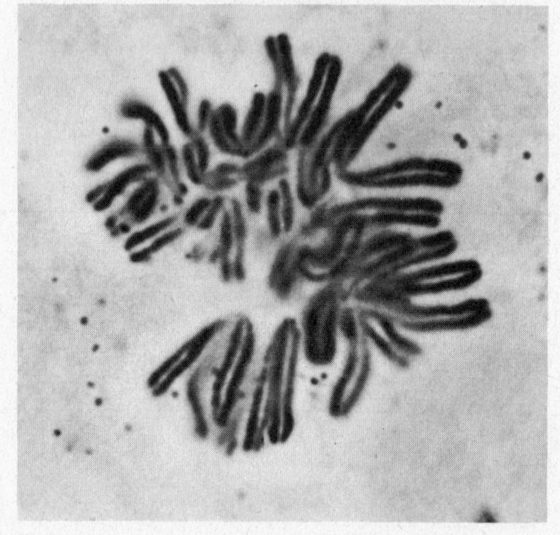

24.1 *(Above)* ***Cell division.*** *The main forms of fission.*

24.2 Animal mitosis: *prophase. A, the nuclear membrane is just dissolving, and chromosomes are already visible. To either side of the nuclear region is a darkly stained centriole area, from which fine aster fibrils are beginning to radiate out. B, close-up view of prophase chromosomes, which have already duplicated. Each member of such a pair is a chromatid, and each pair is still held together at one point, the centromere. See also Color Fig. 23.*

case, mitosis is accompanied by cytoplasmic cleavage (or *cytokinesis*), both processes together represent *mitotic cell division.* Clearly, "mitosis" is not simply another word for cell division but designates a particular kind of *nuclear* division. In Monera, cell division includes gene duplication but not mitosis, since nuclei of the type found in other organisms are not present.

mitosis and division

The microscopically observable events of mitosis are preceded by DNA duplication in the chromosomes. In some as yet unknown way gene reproduction actually might be the stimulus for mitosis and cell division as a whole. A certain amount of time elapses before the visible events of mitosis begin. These consist of four successive, not sharply separated stages: *prophase, metaphase, anaphase,* and *telophase.*

By the time prophase occurs (Fig. 24.2 and Color Fig. 23), the centriole, just outside the nucleus in the cells of Metazoa and most Protista, has already divided. During prophase daughter centrioles then behave as if they repelled each other and migrate toward opposite sides of the cell nucleus. Concurrently portions of the cytoplasm transform to fine gel fibrils (or *microtubules*). Some of these radiate away from each centriole like the spokes of a wheel and form so-called *asters.* Other gel fibrils develop between the two centrioles and produce a *spindle,* with a *spindle pole* marked at each end by the centriole. In Metaphyta centrioles are absent and asters do not form. However, spindles do develop.

The nuclear membrane usually dissolves, the nucleoli disintegrate, and distinct chromosomes become visible. Each chromosome has produced a mathematically exact double shortly before prophase, and this doubled condition now becomes clearly apparent. In each such pair the two chromosomes (here called *chromatids*) lie closely parallel. They are joined to each other at their *centromeres,* single specialized regions at corresponding locations along the two chromatids. Spindle fibrils form between the centromeres and the spindle poles.

The metaphase starts when the paired chromatids begin to migrate. If a line from one spindle pole to the other is considered to mark out a spindle axis, then the chromatid pairs migrate to a plane at right angles to and midway along this axis. Here the chromatid pairs line up in a *metaphase plate* (Fig. 24.3 and see Color Fig. 23). At this stage (or sometimes earlier) the centromeres separate and the two chromatids of each pair thereby become unjoined chromosomes. Such twin chromosomes now begin to move apart; one set migrates toward one spindle pole, and the identical twin set migrates toward the other. This period of chromosome movement represents the *anaphase* of mitosis.

As a set of chromosomes now collects near each spindle pole, spindle fibrils and asters disappear. A new nuclear membrane soon forms around each chromosome set, and the chromosomes manufacture new nucleoli in numbers characteristic of the particular cell type. Two new nuclei form in this manner, the *telophase* of mitosis. If cytoplasmic cleavage accompanies mitosis, this process occurs in conjunction with nuclear anaphase and telophase. Cleavage begins with the appearance of a *cleavage furrow* in animal cells and a *division plate* in plant cells. Both furrow and plate form in the plane of the earlier metaphase plate. The cleavage furrow is a gradually deepening surface groove that cuts through the spindle fibrils and eventually constricts the cell into two daughters. A division plate is a partition of cellulose developed all along the plane of cleavage (see Fig. 24.3 and Color Fig. 23). Two daughter cells arise in this fashion, and mitotic division is completed. In each daughter nucleus the genes now resume control of RNA manufacture and a new growth cycle follows.

The net result of mitotic cell division is the formation of two cells that match each other (and the parent cell) precisely in their DNA contents and that contain approximately equal amounts and types of all other components. This identity of the DNA content is the key to cellular and ultimately to all *heredity;* to the extent that genes are stable, each new cell generation inherits the same genetic codes, hence the same structural and functional potentials, that had been present in the previous cell generation (Fig. 24.4).

In unicellular organisms cell division is equivalent to reproduction of a whole organism. Daughter cells generally separate, but in some forms they remain together and form *colonies.* In multicellular types cell division either contributes to cell *replacement,* as in regeneration and wound healing, or adds to *cell number.* In the last instance the usual result is growth of tissues and organs. A whole organism therefore can grow either by molecular reproduction and increase in cell size, or by cellular reproduction and increase in cell number, or both.

Rates of cell division vary greatly. One rate-limiting factor is nutrition, as noted, and another is cell specialization. Relatively unspecialized cells retain a fairly rapid (but steadily decreasing) rate of division throughout the life of an organism. By contrast, mature liver or muscle cells divide only rarely, and after the embryonic phase mature nerve cells do not divide at all. They can grow in size, but destroyed neurons cannot be replaced. Other highly specialized cells have lost their nuclei (for example, red corpuscles, sieve-tube cells) or their interior substance (for example, sclerenchyma, tracheids), and these, too, do not divide. In general, the more highly specialized a cell is the less frequently it divides, and vice versa.

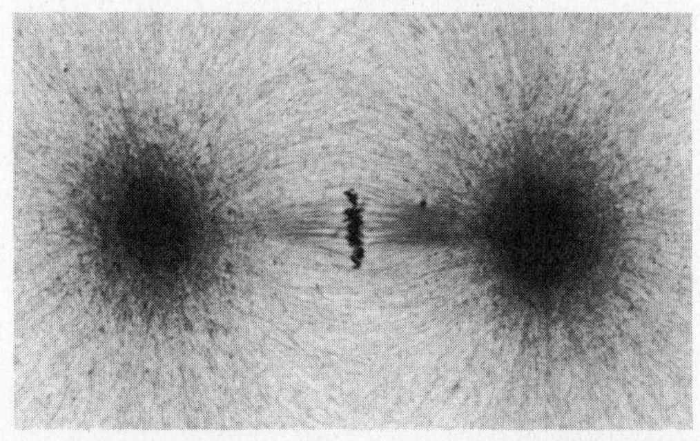

A

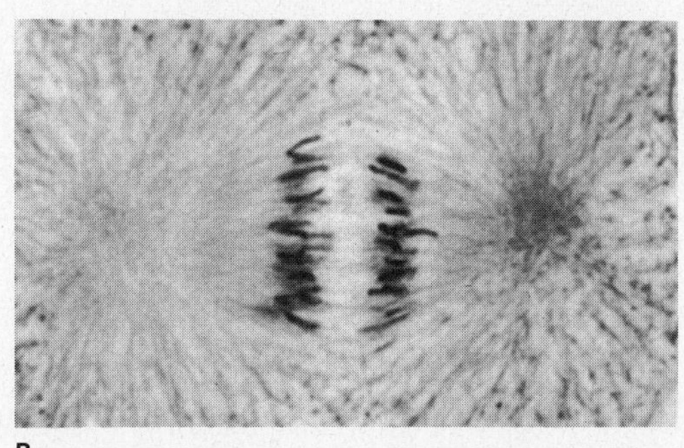

B

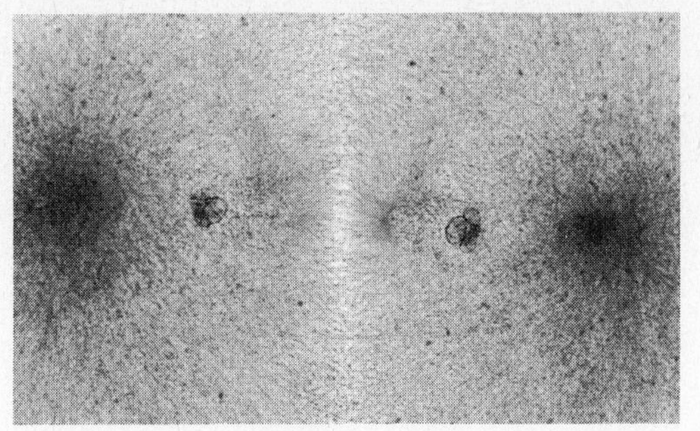

C

24.3 Animal mitosis: *metaphase, anaphase, telophase. A, metaphase. Note asters, spindle, and the metaphase plate, halfway along and at right angles to the spindle axis. Fibrils join the chromosomes in the metaphase plate with the spindle poles. B, anaphase. The two chromosome sets are migrating toward the spindle poles. C, telophase. Asters are subsiding, nuclei are re-forming, chromosome threads have become indistinct, and cytoplasmic cleavage is under way in the same plane as the earlier metaphase plate. See also Color Fig. 23.*

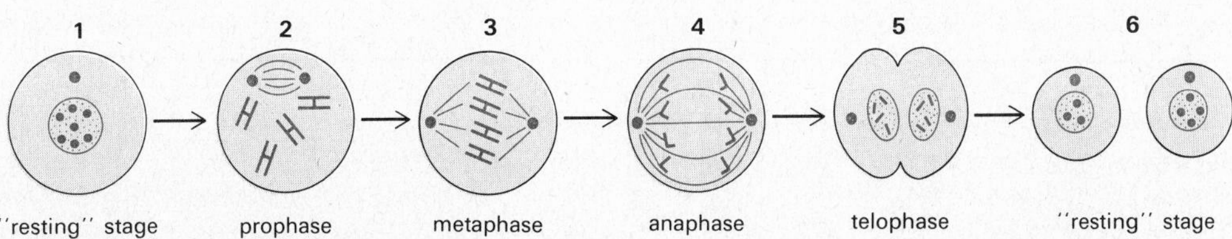

24.4 Mitosis summary. *The assumption here is that cytoplasmic cleavage accompanies mitosis. Note that a ''resting'' cell is resting only from the standpoint of reproductive activity. In all other respects it is exceedingly active.*

Many cells divide when they have grown to double their original volume. However, attainment of such a volume is probably not a specific stimulus, for cells can be made to divide at nearly any prior time. Moreover, they can be prevented from dividing and made to grow into giant cells many times larger than twice the original. Several chemicals are known to inhibit division and several to promote it (for example, various growth hormones). Similarly, physical agents such as X rays can inhibit or promote division, depending on conditions. Experimental use of such agents has gone far toward controlling cell division (in cancer treatment, for example), but in many cases it is still not known how such control actually operates. And it is equally obscure what specific normal (or abnormal) conditions in a cell or outside it so stimulate it that it synthesizes new DNA and then begins to divide.

The highest rates of cell division normally occur in embryonic stages, the lowest in old age. With few exceptions cellular reproductive capacity in the adult remains *potentially* as great as in the embryo. This is shown, for example, by the high rates of cell division in wound healing, in regeneration, in cancers and other tumors, and in *tissue cultures.* Such cultures are prepared by separating groups of cells from an organism and growing them in artificial nutrient solutions. Isolated cells or cell groups then are found to reproduce faster than if they had remained inside an organism (Fig. 24.5).

24.5 ***Tissue culture.*** *A, embryonic mouse tissue produces epithelial masses at higher growth rates than it would have in the intact embryo. B, embryonic mouse tissue from the lung region was grown in tissue culture for 6 days and formed the well-developed lung shown. Note ducts and alveoli.*

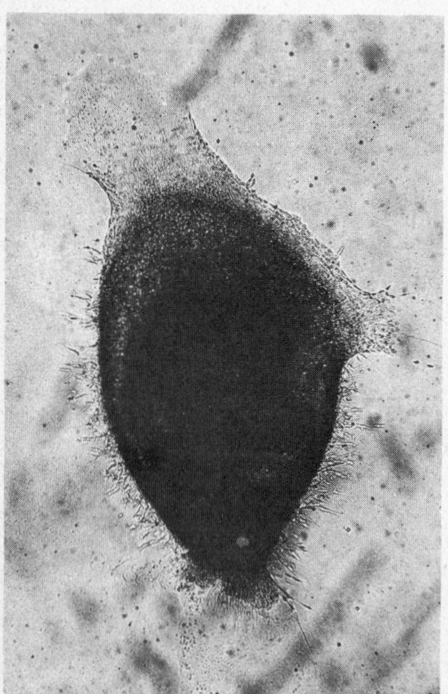

A

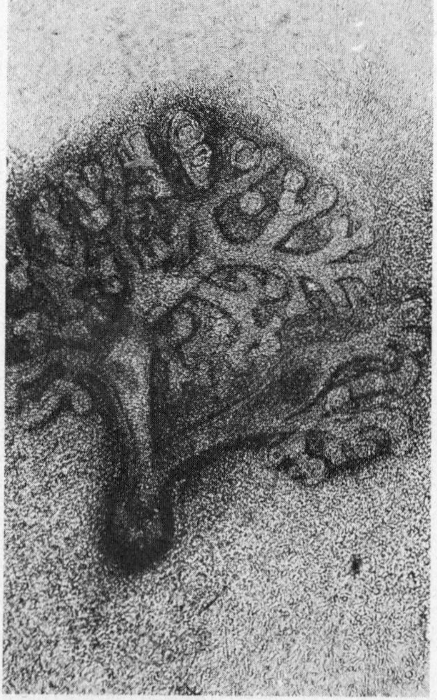

B

Conceivably, therefore, cell reproduction in intact organisms might be slower mainly because the cells are *not* isolated as in a tissue culture. Instead they are part of a larger organization in which their reproductive potential is somehow held in check. Certain cells occasionally escape this check, and normal healing processes or abnormal tumors can then be the result.

Although net growth slows down with increasing age, in most cases it does not cease entirely. All plants and many animals continue to grow somewhat even in old age. The general range of body size is a genetically determined trait of the species, but within this range wide variations are possible. Trees, for example, are well known to be able to grow for hundreds of years. In very large plants and animals, massive bulk arises primarily through continuing increase in cell number, not cell size. Man is one of a group of animals in which net growth does not continue beyond a certain age.

reproductive processes: organisms

After periods of growth by molecular and cellular reproduction, the whole multicellular organism may reproduce. This process generally includes at least two steps. First, a *reproductive unit* separates from the parent organism. Second, a duplicate organism forms from the reproductive unit through *development.*

In many cases the reproductive unit consists of the whole or a substantial portion of the parent organism. For example, in unicellular types the whole adult cell is the reproductive unit and reproduction is accomplished by *cell division.* Multicellular forms often propagate by *budding,* in which one or more offspring grow out from the surface of a parent organism (Fig. 24.6). This process is exemplified by many plants and by animals such as sponges and hydras. In other cases multiplication takes place by *fragmentation,* a spontaneous splitting or breaking of a parent organism into two or more parts. This occurs, for example, in many filamentous algae, in some bryophytes, and in animals such as sea anemones and numerous types of worm. Each separated part of the parent then grows into a whole adult.

Quite similar to fragmentation is *regenerative reproduction,* in which a parent organism splits,

A

B

C

24.6 (Above) ***Vegetative reproduction.*** *A, budding. A leaf of Kalanchoë, with small budded plants developing along the leaf margins. B, fragmentation. A sea anemone fragments lengthwise into two offspring organisms. C, regenerative reproduction. An arm of a starfish regenerates all missing parts and becomes a whole animal.*

not spontaneously, but as a result of injury by external agents. For example, almost any piece of a plant, a few segments of an earthworm, an arm of a starfish, a chunk of tissue from a hydra or a sponge, each is an effective reproductive unit that develops into a whole offspring. The parent organisms that lose such sections of their bodies usually regenerate the missing parts. Regenerative reproduction clearly depends on extensive regeneration capacity, which many organisms do not have. Thus, salamanders can regenerate a whole limb, but a limb cannot regenerate a whole salamander. In most vertebrates the regeneration potential is not even as great as in salamanders but, as in man, is limited to the healing of relatively small wounds.

Cell division, budding, fragmentation, and regenerative reproduction all are different forms of *vegetative reproduction* (Fig. 24.7). The reproductive unit here is always a fairly large part of the parent, and it arises from parental regions that are not specialized for reproduction primarily or exclusively; almost *any* portion of the parent can cease its usual functions and become part of a vegetative reproductive unit. The main adaptive advantage of vegetative reproduction is that the process can be carried out whenever environmental conditions are favorable and food supplies are ample. Special manufacturing processes are not required for the formation of reproductive units, and regenerative reproduction is advantageous also in counteracting environmental hazards. Vegetative multiplication actually is the basic method of propagation in unicellular forms and

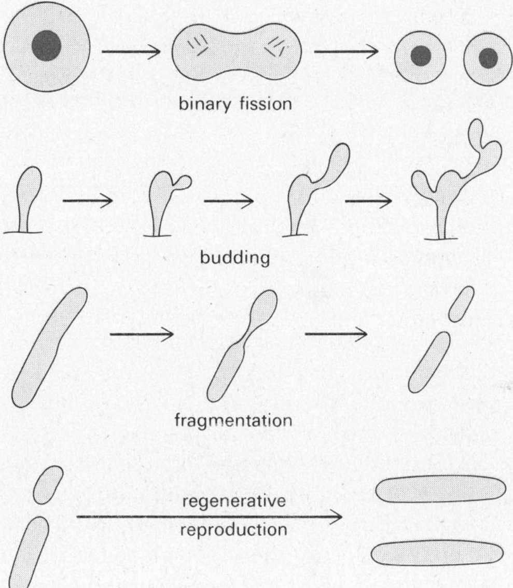

24.7 Vegetative reproduction: *summary of the main variants.*

a major subsidiary method in all but the most complex multicellular ones.

The smallest parental unit that contains the genetic information and the operating equipment representative of the whole organism is a single cell. Accordingly, the minimum unit for the construction of such an organism should be one cell. This is actually the universal case. Regardless of whether or not it can also reproduce vegetatively, every multicellular organism is capable of reproducing through single *reproductive cells.* All such cells are more or less specialized for reproduction, and in most cases they are formed in specialized parental reproductive tissues or organs.

According to their later fate, reproductive cells are of two general types (Fig. 24.8). One includes cells that, like vegetative reproductive units, can develop into adults *directly.* Such cells are *spores.* Their chief advantage is that they represent an excellent device for geographic dispersal. In water, a spore cell equipped with flagella can swim to new territories. On land, spores can be protected against drying out by thick walls and can be distributed widely by wind and animals. As might be expected, therefore, spores are formed mainly by organisms that cannot disperse by locomotion—primarily plants and stationary protists. Sessile animals do not produce spores; they have free-swimming embryos or larvae (and, as in plants and protists, species dispersal can also be achieved by vegetative reproductive units).

Reproductive cells of the second general type *cannot* develop directly. Instead they must first undergo a *sexual process,* in which two of them fuse. Such cells are *sex cells,* or *gametes.* In most cases male gametes are distinct *sperms,* and female gametes are distinct *eggs.* A *mating* process makes possible the pairwise fusion, or *fertilization,* and the fusion product is a *zygote.* Development of gametes into adults cannot normally occur until fertilization has taken place. Where sex occurs, therefore, it is interpolated between the two basic phases of the reproductive sequence, formation of reproductive cells and development of such cells into adults.

In a strict sense, evidently, reproduction should not be labeled as being ''asexual'' or ''sexual,'' as is often done. Sex is *not* a reproductive process but one of gamete *fusion.* The fundamental ''reproductive'' event in all forms of multiplication is formation of reproductive units. The rest is development, and it is this developmental phase that may or may not require sexual triggering.

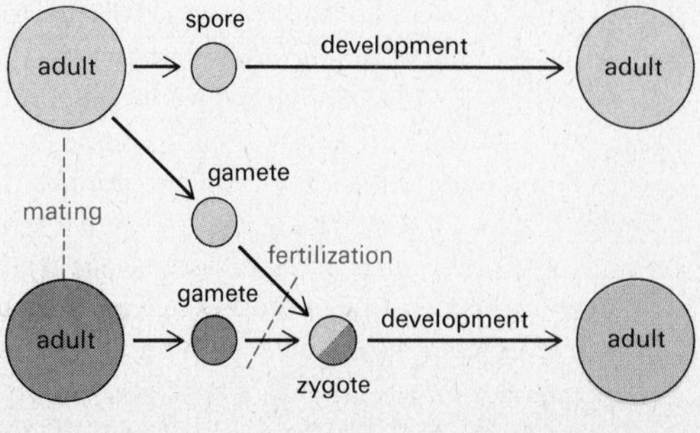

24.8 Reproductive cells. *Many organisms produce reproductive cells capable of developing by themselves (top). Almost all also produce sex cells, or gametes, that after mating by adults must fuse in fertilization and form a zygote before development can occur (bottom).*

Consequently, whereas *development* can be initiated sexually or asexually, reproduction as such, or formation of reproductive units, is always ''asexual.'' In one category of these units sex must *follow,* and we can use the term ''gametic reproduction'' to distinguish this type of organismic multiplication from vegetative and sporulative reproduction.

Gametic reproduction entails serious disadvantages. The process depends on chance, for gametes must meet and very often they simply do not. Meeting requires locomotion, moreover, but neither eggs nor many organisms can move. Above all, gametic reproduction requires a water medium. In air, gametes would dry out quickly unless they had evaporation-resistant shells. But if two cells were so encapsulated they could then not fuse together. As will become apparent, terrestrial organisms actually can circumvent this dilemma only by means of special adaptations.

However, all these various disadvantages are relatively minor compared to the one vital advantage offered by gametes. This advantage is a result of sex.

sexual processes

forms of sexuality

The role of sex is revealed most clearly in many Protista, in which sexual processes and reproduction do not occur together. A good example is *Spirogyra,* a filamentous green alga forming dense growths in freshwater ponds. Throughout spring, summer, and early fall, the cells reproduce vegetatively by mitotic division and add to the length of the filament. Pieces of the alga can break off and form new individuals elsewhere. Later in the fall two cells from two filaments lying side by side may mate through *conjugation;* an interconnecting bridge develops between the two cells. The contents of one cell then move in amoeboid fashion through the bridge to the other cell, and the two cells fuse (Fig. 24.9).

Such cellular fusion, or *syngamy,* is a sexual process. All unmated nonconjugated cells die when autumn temperatures fall, but the fused double cell, or zygote, secretes a heavy wall and lives through the winter. When temperatures begin to rise again the following spring, the cyst wall breaks open and a new *Spirogyra* filament develops from the surviving zygote.

Sex and reproduction occur separately also in,

for example, protozoa. These organisms reproduce vegetatively when food is plentiful, when a population is not too crowded, and when environmental conditions are optimal in general. On the contrary, sexual processes take place under unfavorable conditions, such as overcrowding or lack of food (Fig. 24.10). One kind of sexual response is again syngamy; two whole protozoa come to function as gametes and fuse as a zygote. Another involves mating by conjugation, but the ensuing sexual process here differs from that in *Spirogyra.* In *Paramecium* and other ciliates, for example, two mating partners become interconnected by a cytoplasmic bridge. The nucleus of each partner then gives rise to two *gamete nuclei,* and one of these migrates through the bridge to the other cell. After such a nuclear exchange, the two gamete nuclei now present in each conjugating individual fuse as a zygote nucleus and the two mating partners then separate.

Thus the sexual process is fundamentally quite distinct from reproduction. *Spirogyra* and *Paramecium* do not increase in numbers through sex—if anything quite the contrary: two cells become one in syngamy as in *Spirogyra* conjugation or remain two as in *Paramecium* conjugation. In all other organisms sex and reproduction are equally distinct, even though in most cases the two processes do occur together. Moreover, note that sexual activity tends to take place particularly during periods of environmental stress. Indeed, among most organisms in the temperate zone, sex typically occurs during spring or autumn. The process here is a response to the stress conditions of the preceding season and it anticipates those of the following season.

Just how are sexual processes effective against conditions of stress? Events in *Spirogyra* and *Paramecium* supply the general answer: every cell resulting from the sexual process contains the genes of *both* parental cells. Basically, therefore, sex can be defined as an accumulation, in a single cell, of genes derived from two relatively unrelated cells. One method by which such a gene accumulation is achieved is syngamy, or fusion of two whole cells, as in *Spirogyra* after conjugation and as in most other organisms after variously different mating processes; another method is exchange of duplicate nuclei, as in *Paramecium* after conjugation.

Sex evidently counteracts stress conditions on the principle of "two are better than one." If the self-perpetuating powers of two relatively unrelated parent organisms are joined through union of their genes, then the offspring produced later can acquire a greater survival potential than that of either parent alone (Fig. 24.11). Moreover, a sexual pooling of genes leads to a still poorly

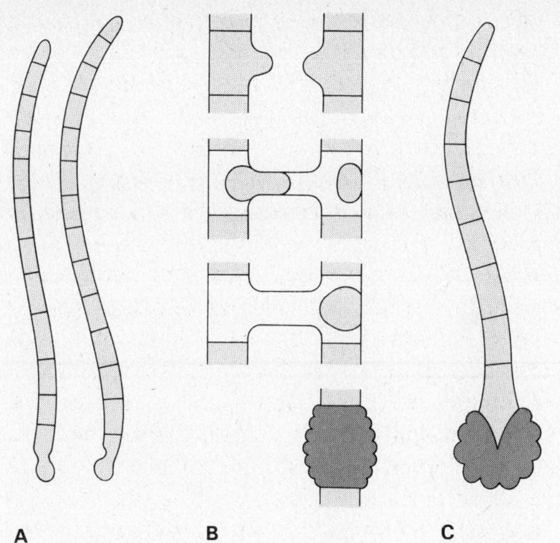

24.9 Sexuality in Spirogyra. *A, two filaments side by side prior to conjugation. B, bridge between opposite cells (top); migration of contents of one cell to the other (center); formation of zygospore cyst (bottom). C, growth of new filament from opened zygospore. See also Fig. 24.13.*

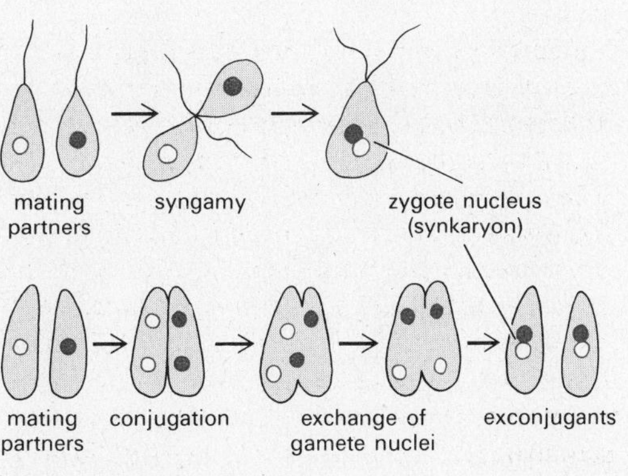

24.10 Sexual patterns, *as in protozoa. Top: syngamy, the fusion of two gamete cells. Bottom: conjugation, or exchange and fusion of gamete nuclei.*

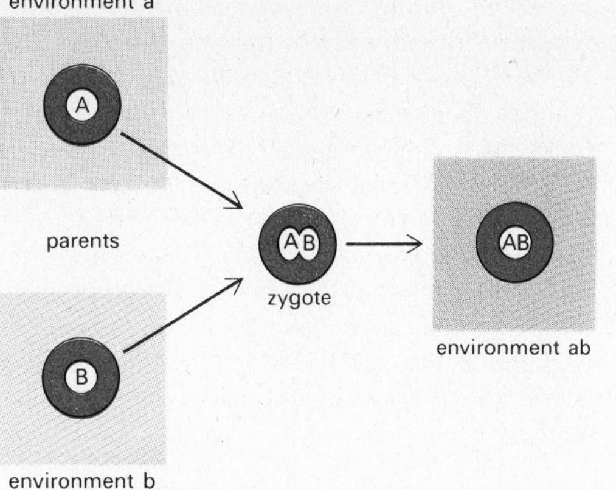

24.11 Sex and stress. *a and b represent two different environments containing two genetically different parents; A and B symbolize their genes. Through sex, the offspring (right) acquires the genes of both parents, hence also the ability to live in either environment a or b.*

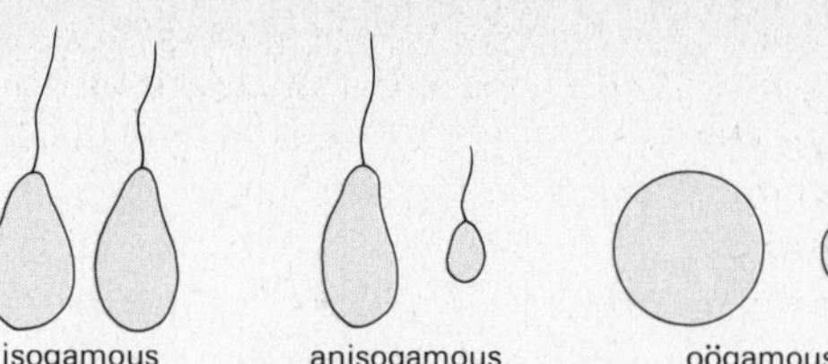

24.12 Gamete types. *In the oögamous pattern, the large gamete is a nonmotile egg, the small gamete, a motile sperm.*

24.13 Mating types. *In the Spirogyra filaments shown, all cells in one filament have the same sexual properties; they are either migrating sexual partners or stationary partners that receive cells from a neighboring filament (and thus form oval zygospores, as shown). All cells of a given filament are of the same mating type and this accounts for their uniform sexual behavior.*

understood "rejuvenation" in the offspring, on a biochemical, metabolic level. For example, if in certain protozoa or fungi sex is experimentally prevented during many successive vegetative generations, the vigor of the line eventually declines. The organisms ultimately die, even under optimal environmental conditions. Genetic malfunctions and imbalances have been found to accumulate in aged vegetative generations, and only a genetic restoration through sex can then save the line from dying out.

Reproduction thus is a "conservative" process, which faithfully passes on parental characteristics unchanged. As long as the external and internal environments remain favorable, succeeding generations survive as well as preceding ones. Sex, by contrast, is a "liberalizing" process which can make possible survival under new or changed conditions. By combining the genes of two parents sex introduces *genetic change* in the later offspring. And to the extent that such change is advantageous for survival in new environments or under new conditions, sex has *adaptive* value. That is the key point. Sex is one of the chief processes of adaptation; it is *not* a process of reproduction.

In *Spirogyra* and numerous other protists, all gametes, though functionally of two different types, are structurally alike (*isogamy*). In another group of protists, the gametes of a species are visibly of two different types; one kind is distinctly smaller than the other, but in other structural respects they are again alike (*anisogamy*). Still other protists, as well as all plants and animals, exhibit *oögamy,* a special form of anisogamy: one gamete type is flagellate and small, the other is nonmotile (or amoeboid) and large. The small types are *sperms,* the large types, *eggs* (Fig. 24.12).

If the two gamete types are produced in different individuals, as is the case in many protists, numerous plants, and most animals, then the sexes are said to be *separate.* If such separately sexed organisms exhibit isogamy or anisogamy, the terms "male" and "female" are not strictly applicable. Thus, filaments of *Spirogyra,* which are isogamous, are neither male nor female. Instead the two sex types, or *mating types,* are customarily identified by distinguishing symbols such as + and − (Fig. 24.13). True male and female sexes are recognized only in cases of oögamy, where distinct sperms and eggs are produced. Such organisms often exhibit a variety of other sex differences, too. For example, sperms and eggs are usually produced in differently constructed sex organs. Among plants, sperms are formed in *antheridia,* eggs in *archegonia.* Among animals, sperms arise in *testes,* eggs in *ovaries.* Male and female sex organs are frequently part of differently structured reproductive systems, and numerous secondary sex characteristics often provide external distinctions as well. Thus where the sexes are separate the degrees of sex distinction can vary considerably. At one extreme are the isogamous protists, where visible differences between sex types are zero. At the other extreme are the advanced plants and animals, in which nearly every part of the body, even every cell, can exhibit characteristics of maleness or femaleness.

In numerous organisms both gamete types are produced in the same individual. Known as *hermaphroditism,* this condition is believed to be more primitive than that of separate sexes; hermaphroditism could have evolved to separate sexuality by suppression of either the male or the female potential in different individuals. For example, all vertebrates have both potentials in the embryonic state, but only one potential later becomes actual in a given individual. Considerable numbers of protists are hermaphroditic, including *Paramecium,* for example, in which each individual produces a gamete nucleus of each sex type. Many, possibly most, Metaphyta are hermaphrodites, and in Metazoa hermaphroditism occurs in some groups of almost every phylum. The condition is sometimes encountered as an abnormality in vertebrates, man included.

In most cases hermaphroditism appears to be a direct adaptation to ways of life that offer only limited opportunities for geographic dispersal, as in sluggish, sessile, and parasitic forms. Since every hermaphrodite can function both as a "male" and a "female," a mating of two individuals often is not even required and *self-fertilization* can take place. But most hermaphrodites carry out mutual *cross-fertilization,* such that two mating partners fertilize each other (Fig. 24.14 and see Fig. 12.22). In such cross-fertilizing species some kind of block normally prevents self-fertilization. Among certain protists, for example, the block operates through so-called "compatibility genes." More often the block results from the anatomy of the body. This is the case in, for example, many flowering plants, and in animals the two reproductive systems of a hermaphrodite often open to the outside in different surface regions. Moreover, as in mollusks, for example, sperms and eggs are frequently manufactured at different times during a breeding season. Some species produce ovaries first and testes next (the same sex organ often switching function and producing both eggs and sperm in succession). Other species form testes first and ovaries later.

The general adaptive advantage of hermaphroditism is that potentially fewer reproductive cells are wasted: sperms from one individual can meet eggs in *any* other individual, for every hermaphrodite produces eggs. In separately sexed types, by contrast, many sperms are wasted through chance misdistribution to the wrong sex. Similarly, if cross-fertilizing hermaphrodites are capable of some locomotion, like land snails or earthworms, then fertilization becomes possible whenever *any* two individuals meet. Sluggish individuals do not meet very frequently, yet every such meeting can result in fertilization.

In any organism, separately sexed or hermaphroditic, it often happens that gametes fail to find compatible partners. Most of such unsuccessful gametes disintegrate very soon, but in exceptional cases single gametes can begin to develop and form normal adults. This phenomenon is *parthenogenesis,* "virginal development" of a gamete *without* fertilization. In many protists a gamete of either type can develop parthenogenetically. In oögamous organisms only eggs are sometimes capable of developing in this way. Thus, *natural* parthenogenesis occurs in, for example, rotifers, bees and other social insects (see Chap. 23), and sporadically also in birds such as turkeys and chickens. In some species *artificial* parthenogenesis can be induced by experimental means. For example, a frog egg can be made to develop before it has become fertilized by pricking its surface with a needle (in conjunction with other treatments). The puncture simulates the entrance of a sperm, and development then begins. It may be noted that a parthenogenetic gamete is functionally indistinguishable from a *spore;* both are single reproductive cells able to develop directly into adults.

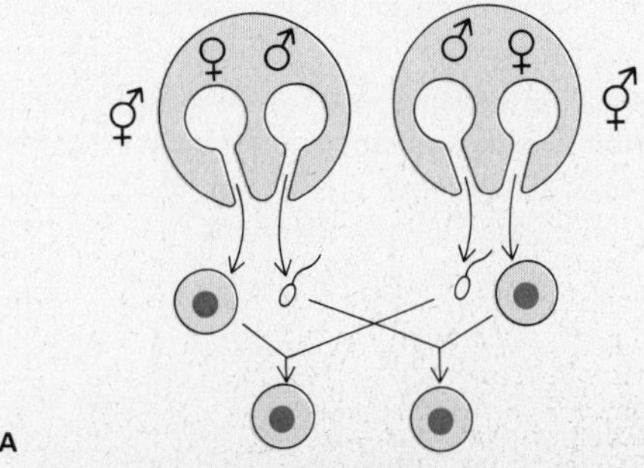

A

B

24.14 Hermaphrodites. *A, the symbols ♀ and ♂ identify female and male reproductive systems, respectively. The symbols ⚥ identify whole hermaphroditic organisms. The figure illustrates the fertilization pattern in cross-fertilizing hermaphrodites. If sperms fertilize eggs from the same organism, the pattern is self-fertilizing. B, copulation of the land snails Helix, which are cross-fertilizing hermaphrodites. See also Fig. 12.22.*

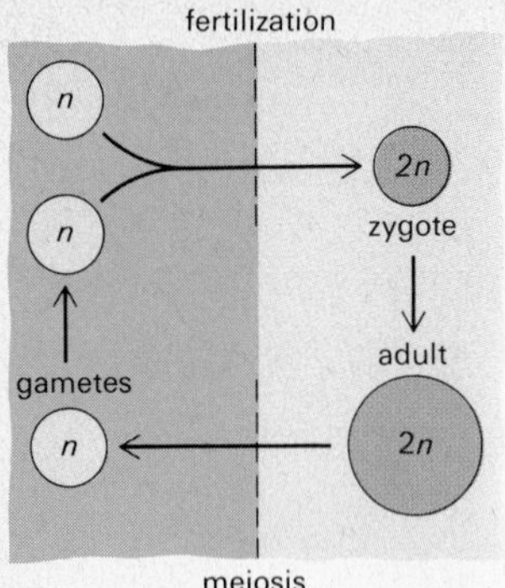

24.15 ***Life cycle*** *and chromosome numbers.*

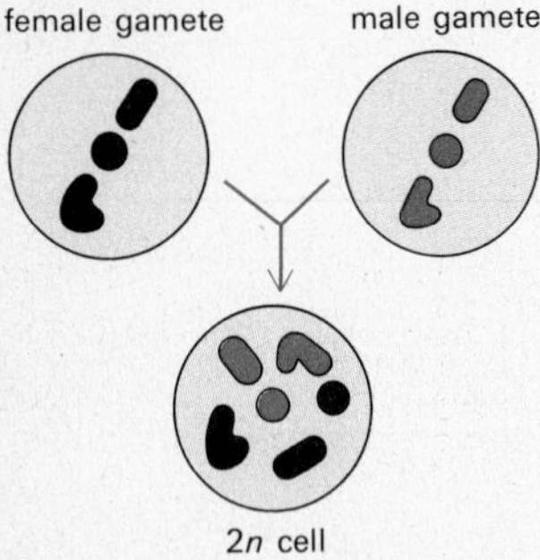

24.16 (Above) ***Genetic effects of fertilization.*** *A diploid cell (bottom) contains two like sets of chromosomes representing maternal-paternal pairs. The maternal set originated in the female gamete, the paternal set, in the male gamete.*

meiosis and life cycles

One consequence of every sexual process is that a zygote formed from two gametes contains twice as many chromosomes as a single gamete. An adult organism developing from such a zygote would consist of cells having a doubled chromosome number. If the next generation is again produced sexually the chromosome number would quadruple, and this process of progressive doubling would continue indefinitely through successive generations.

Such events do not happen, and chromosome numbers do stay constant from one life cycle to the next. This constancy is maintained by a series of special nuclear divisions known as *meiosis.* In many cases meiosis is accompanied by cytoplasmic divisions, and both events are then referred to collectively as *meiotic cell divisions.* It is the function of meiosis to counteract the chromosome-doubling effect of fertilization, by reducing a doubled chromosome number to half. The unreduced doubled chromosome number, before meiosis, is called the *diploid* number, symbolized as $2n$; the reduced number, after meiosis, is the *haploid* number, symbolized as n (Fig. 24.15).

Meiosis occurs in every life cycle that includes a sexual process—in other words, more or less universally. Organisms differ according to when and where meiosis occurs in the life cycle. For purposes of illustration, the life cycle of the unicellular green alga *Chlamydomonas* may be considered. In this organism meiosis takes place right after fertilization, as a first step in the further development of the zygote. Thus, fertilization produces a zygote with a diploid chromosome number, and meiosis then restores the haploid condition immediately. How is this chromosome reduction achieved?

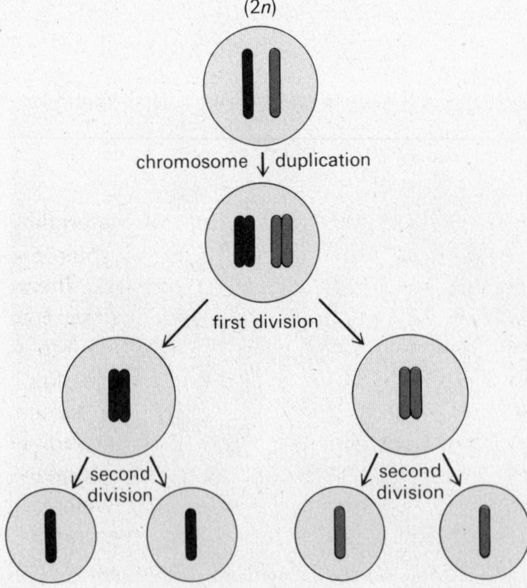

24.17 ***Meiosis.*** *The assumption here is that $2n = 2$. During the meiotic divisions each member of a chromosome pair is referred to as a chromatid, as in mitosis.*

During fertilization, a haploid (n) set of chromosomes from the paternal gamete becomes joined with a similar haploid set from the maternal gamete. Like shoes, therefore, the chromosomes of a diploid cell come in pairs (Fig. 24.16). This $2n$ number of chromosomes is then reduced to half by two meiotic divisions. More specifically, a diploid cell undergoes two successive cleavages that transform the one original cell to four. During or before these cleavages, the chromosomes of the diploid cell duplicate *once.* As a result, $2n$ becomes $4n$. And of these $4n$ chromosomes one n is incorporated in each of the four new cells formed. In short, *one diploid* cell becomes *four haploid* cells (Fig. 24.17).

In *Chlamydomonas,* for example, a zygote contains 16 chromosomes. During meiosis the number doubles to 32, and at the same time the cell cleaves twice in succession. Four cells result that share the 32 chromosomes equally. Hence each mature cell of *Chlamydomonas* contains 8 chromosomes, a complete haploid set.

Meiosis has many features in common with mitosis. As in mitosis, each meiotic division passes through prophase, metaphase, anaphase, and telophase. Moreover, spindles form, and other nonchromosomal events are as in mitotic divisions. The critical difference between mitosis and the *first* meiotic division lies in their metaphases. In mitosis all chromosomes, each of them already duplicated and forming paired chromatids, migrate to the metaphase plate where all the centromeres line up in the same plane. In the first meiotic division the $2n$ chromosomes similarly duplicate during or before prophase. These $2n$ pairs of chromatids then migrate to the metaphase plate, but now only n pairs assemble in one plane. The other n pairs migrate to a plane of their own, closely parallel to the first. Moreover, every pair of chromatids in one plane comes to lie next to the corresponding type of chromatid pair in the other plane. The metaphase plate is therefore made up of *paired chromatid pairs,* or *tetrads* of like chromatids lying side by side. And there are n of these tetrads in the whole plate (Fig. 24.18).

During the following anaphase, two chromatids

of each tetrad migrate to one spindle pole, two to the other. The first meiotic division thus produces two cells, each with *n* pairs of chromatids. In the metaphase of the second meiotic division these *n* pairs line up in the same plane, and *n* single chromosomes eventually migrate to each of the poles during anaphase. At the termination of meiosis as a whole, therefore, four cells are present, each with *n* chromosomes.

In *Chlamydomonas* the four haploid cells resulting from meiosis are four new adult organisms. All available evidence suggests that such a life cycle, in which the adults are haploid, represents a primitive condition. It is reasonable to suppose that early ancestral cells were similarly haploid, each containing only a single complete set of genes. Whenever a sexual process took place a diploid zygote resulted from fertilization, and meiosis then must have been a likely ensuing event: the chromosome-doubling process of fertilization must have been a stimulus to which the chromosome-reducing process of meiosis was the rapidly following response.

A life cycle characterized in this way by haploid adults and meiosis in the zygote stage (or "zygotic" meiosis), is known as a *haplontic* life cycle (Fig. 24.19). It occurs in all Monera (insofar as sex is known among these organisms), in all primitive and many advanced groups of algae, and in many fungi. The list suggests clearly that the haplontic life cycle is basic in the Monera and the Protista. Many of these haplontic groups are capable of producing spores, and such cells are formed at some point in the life cycle between one fertilization and the next. The method of spore formation is mitotic division and, like the adults that produce them, the spores are haploid (*mitospores*).

diploid (2*n*) nucleus

mitosis

meiosis

chromosome duplication

metaphase of mitosis

metaphase of first meiotic division

metaphase of second meiotic division

diploid offspring nuclei

haploid offspring nuclei

24.18 (*Above*) ***Mitosis and meiosis.*** *The assumption is that 2n = 6. The key difference between the two processes is the way the pairs of chromatids line up in the first metaphase.*

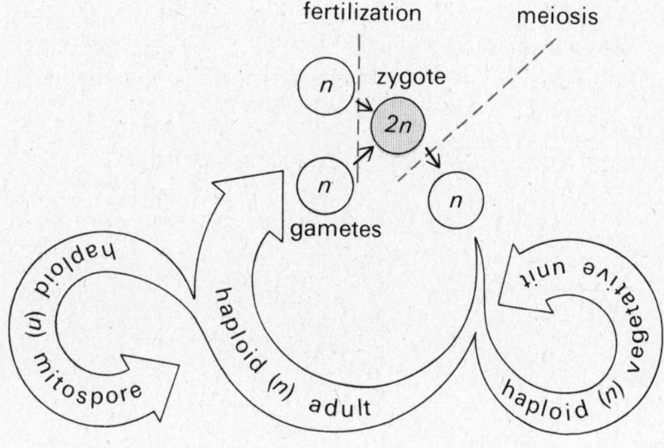

24.19 (*Left*) ***The haplontic life cycle.*** *The zygote is the only diploid stage. Since spores are formed mitotically, they can be called mitospores.*

Haplontic patterns have probably given rise to all other types of life cycle. With regard to the timing of meiosis, the points at which the process possibly *could* occur can be guessed readily. Like sex, meiosis is a cellular process, and it can therefore take place only at a stage when the life cycle passes through a unicellular phase. The zygote represents such a phase. But even a multicellular organism can pass through unicellular stages on two other occasions, at the stage of the *gamete* and at the stage of the *spore.* Meiosis therefore might occur at either of these points, and in many organisms it does.

In man, for example, meiosis takes place during the formation of gametes. In the sex organs of the adult, diploid gamete-producing cells mature as sperms and eggs. As part of this maturation meiosis occurs, and mature gametes thus are haploid, each with 23 chromosomes. These gametes then give rise to a diploid zygote. But now, as the zygote divides and develops into a mature human being, the cells *remain* diploid, each with 46 chromosomes. The whole human adult becomes diploid in this fashion, including the sex organs it eventually forms. Gamete-producing cells therefore are diploid as well, and meiosis occurs again during their maturation.

Such a cycle, characterized by diploid adults and meiosis during gamete formation (or "game-

24.20 ***The diplontic life cycle.*** *Mature gametes represent the only haploid stage.*

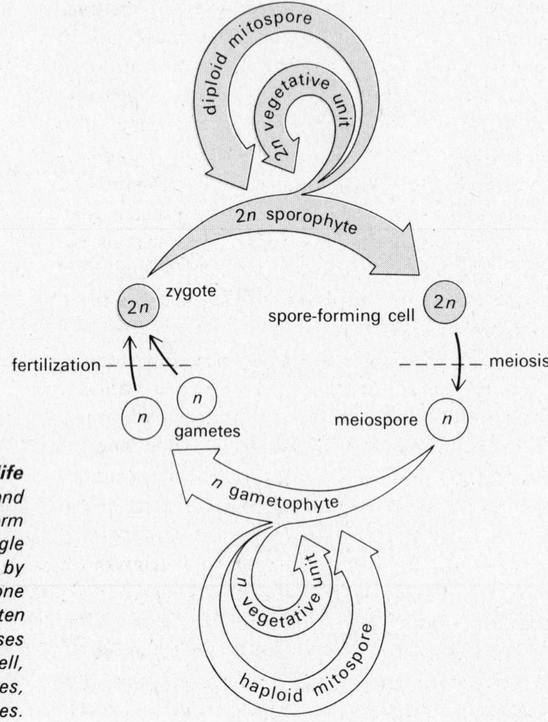

24.21 ***The diplohaplontic life cycle.*** *Diploid sporophyte and haploid gametophyte adults form alternating generations in a single life cycle. Spores produced by the sporophyte have undergone meiosis, hence they are often called meiospores. In many cases mitospores are formed as well, diploid ones by sporophytes, haploid ones by gametophytes.*

togenic'' meiosis), is called a *diplontic* life cycle (Fig. 24.20). The only haploid stage in it is the mature gamete itself; the pattern here is almost the reverse of a haplontic cycle. Diplontic cycles occur not only in man but also in all other animals, in various advanced groups of algae, in some fungi, and in most protozoa. Some of these organisms form spores, and such cells are produced by the diploid adult. The method of spore formation is again mitotic division; hence mature spores (mitospores) are diploid as well.

The evolutionary transition from haplontic to diplontic cycles probably took place through a postponement of meiosis. Thus, diploid adults will from if meiosis is delayed from the zygote stage, the very start of the life cycle, to the gamete-forming stage, the very end of the life cycle. (Because gamete-formation is followed fairly quickly by fertilization, one might be tempted to conclude that, in a diplontic cycle, chromosome reduction by gametogenic meiosis is a ''preparatory'' event for the ensuing chromosome doubling by fertilization. However, responses do not precede or anticipate stimuli. Gametogenic meiosis can be reasonably interpreted only if it is assumed that it represents a long *postponed* chromosome reduction. Then, properly, fertilization at the start of the life cycle becomes the chromosome-doubling stimulus, and gametogenic meiosis at the end of the life cycle, the greatly delayed response.)

Such a postponement is advantageous adaptively, for in a diploid adult each gene in each cell is represented not just once but twice. As a result, genetic redundancy and the stability of the organism are increased. For even if one gene of a pair changes—by mutation, for example—the other gene still preserves the original genetic code. This stabilizing effect of the diploid state evidently has been of sufficient adaptive significance to make diplontic life cycles exceedingly common.

The third possible time of meiosis is the stage of spore production. In this case fertilization produces a diploid zygote, and the developing adult remains diploid. In due course the adult develops a spore-forming structure in which diploid cells give rise to spores. Meiosis occurs during this process, and mature spores are therefore haploid. Since their production includes meiosis, they are called *meiospores.* A haploid meiospore eventually develops into a new *haploid* adult. This adult later manufactures haploid gametes, which participate in fertilization. A new life cycle then begins with the resulting diploid zygote.

Because meiosis here occurs during spore formation, such a life cycle is split up into two generations, each represented by a separate adult. The diploid zygote gives rise to a diploid adult, and since this adult later produces meiospores, it is called the *sporophyte generation.* The haploid meiospore then gives rise to a haploid adult, and since this adult later produces gametes, it is called the *gametophyte generation.*

Cycles of this sort, characterized by meiosis during spore formation (''sporogenic'' meiosis) and by an *alternation of generations*, are known as *diplohaplontic* life cycles (Fig. 24.21). They are exceedingly widespread, occurring in numerous algae, many fungi, all slime molds, and in all plants. Such cycles probably are again derived from the haplontic type by a postponement of meiosis, in this case from the zygote to the spore-producing stage. As might be expected, diplohaplontic cycles combine the adaptive advantages of haplontic and diplontic ones. The diploid sporophytes are genetically relatively stable, but the haploid gametophytes are genetically quite plastic; their traits can change fairly readily by mutation, hence they can evolve and adapt to changing environments comparatively rapidly.

Many diplohaplontic organisms produce not only meiospores but also other spore types during either the sporophyte or the gametophyte generation or both. Spores of this kind are formed by mitotic division. If a sporophyte manufactures such spores, they will be diploid mitospores. These grow into new diploid sporophyte adults. Numerous repeat generations of sporophytes can develop in this way, and the diploid phase of the life cycle ends only when haploid meiospores are formed. If a gametophyte manufactures spores, they will be haploid mitospores and will grow into new gametophyte adults. Here again many repeat generations can succeed one another, and the haploid part of the life cycle will terminate only with gamete formation and subsequent fertilization.

developmental processes

Considered in the most general terms, *any* part of living history is a part of development—development in fact creates living history, and together with structure and function it represents the third fundamental dimension of life. However, in specific association with reproduction and the progression of life cycles, development customarily signifies just those events of living history that relate to the formation of single whole organisms and their parts. Among such events, the most comprehensive is the elaboration of a complex multicellular organism from a single cell—vegetative unit, spore, or zygote. Such a transformation is brought about by groups of processes among which *morphogenesis* and *differentiation* are two of the most essential (Fig. 24.22).

One component of morphogenesis is increase in size, or *growth*. It can occur through an increase in the number of parts, the size of parts, the spacing between parts, or any combination of these. Molecular growth is the basic prerequisite for growth at any other level; organisms grow from their molecules on up. On the cellular level, the most significant growth process is usually increase in cell number by mitotic division. Fully grown organisms differ from undeveloped ones mostly in cell number, not in cell size or spacing.

Growth of any kind generally does not proceed randomly in all directions. How does it happen, for example, that net growth stops just when the nose, the brain, the rootlet, the leaflet, and all other body parts are of the "right" proportional size and shape? Or that the different parts of the fully grown adult *retain* correct proportions and shapes? Or that, when the limb of a salamander is cut off, regenerative growth stops just when the new limb has the size and the shape of the original one? Thus, apart from growth as such, establishment of species-specific body *form* is a second component of morphogenesis.

The main aspects of form are *polarity* and *symmetry*. If they are given, a great deal about the general appearance of an object is already specified. A structure is polarized if one of its

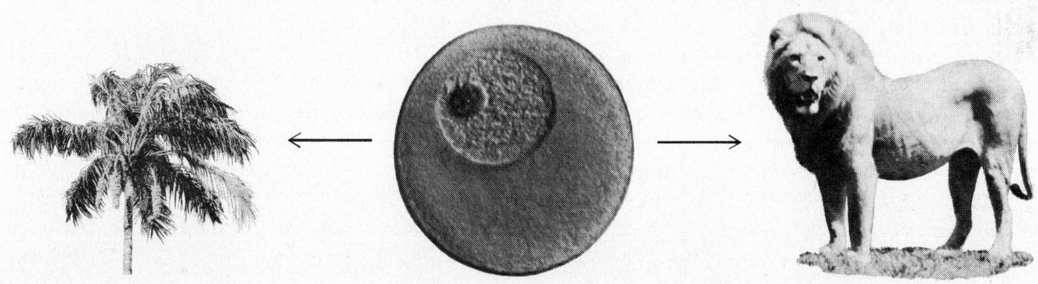

24.22 Development. *The maximum problem of development is to transform an egg, such as shown at center, to a whole plant or animal, such as at left and right.*

three dimensions of space is in some way dominant. For example, the head-tail axis in most animals is longer than the other two. This is the chief axis around which the whole animal is organized, and such organisms are said to be polarized longitudinally. Symmetry indicates the degree of mirror-image regularity. A structure can be symmetrical in three, two, one, or in no dimensions and thus it can be spherical, radial, bilateral, or asymmetrical.

Each organism exhibits a certain polarity and a certain symmetry. These features are the earliest and most permanent expressions of form that appear during the development of any plant or animal. Many traits of an organism can be changed by experimental means, but its original polarity and symmetry can hardly ever be changed. Millions of years later, long after the organism has become a fossil, polarity and symmetry are often still recognizable even if all other signs of form have disappeared. It is a fairly general principle of development that the earlier a particular feature appears, the later it disappears.

24.23 ***Differential growth.*** *The right claw of this crab has been lost and is regenerating. The new claw grows differentially at a far faster rate than the rest of the animal, for in the time the regenerated claw takes to reach the size of the left claw the rest of the body does not increase in size appreciably. (Courtesy Carolina Biological Supply Company.)*

One form-producing process is *differential growth.* Here the amounts and rates of growth are unequal in different body parts, or they differ in different directions (Fig. 24.23). A second such process is *form-regulating movement,* which produces shifts and outright migrations of growing parts relative to one another. Through these processes the form of a body part or a whole organism is first blocked out in the rough, through establishment of polarity and symmetry, and then it becomes progressively more refined in regional detail. Thus the organ system is delineated ahead of its organs; the tissue acquires definitive shape in advance of its cells, and the molecules are last to assume final form. Evidently, form develops as in a sculpture, from the coarse to the fine. Whereas an organism grows from its molecules on up, it forms from gross shape on down.

The net result of growth, differential growth, and form-regulating movements is the emergence of an appropriately shaped and sized anatomy. These processes of morphogenesis thus represent an organizational, architectural component of development.

The second group of processes, differentiation, is an operational, functional component. Development does not produce simply a collection of

24.24 ***Differentiation.*** *Mouse embryo tissue pieces from the region of the future salivary gland were put together in a culture (A). These pieces grew and interacted (B) and eventually differentiated as secretion pockets and ducts characteristic of normal salivary glands (C).*

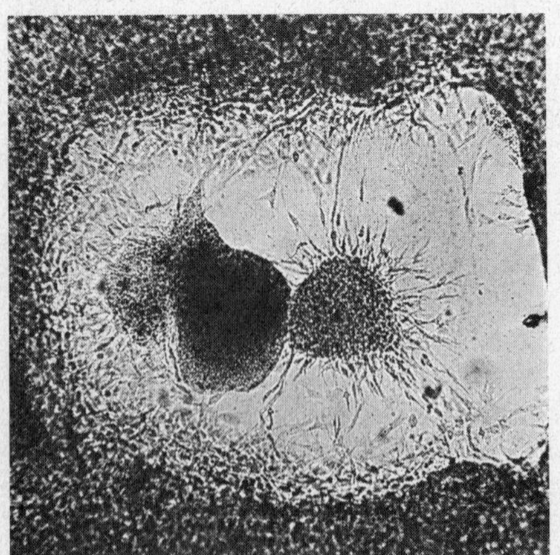

A

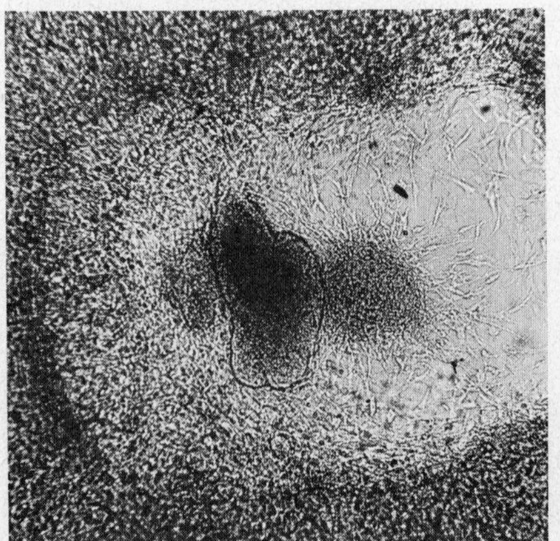

B

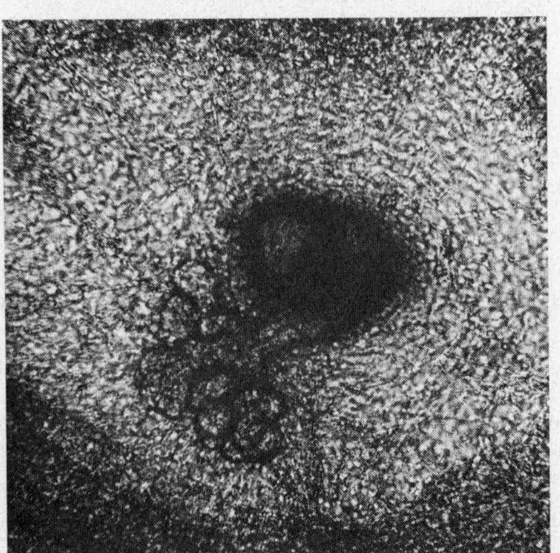

C

many identical cells but a series of widely different cells—for example, some become nerve cells, some liver cells, some skin cells. Yet all arise from the same zygote, and all inherit the same genes from this zygote. Nevertheless, a multitude of different cells is formed (Fig. 24.24).

Moreover, in the course of development body parts often change their operational characteristics; a part frequently carries out functions that are not yet in existence at earlier stages and that no longer exist at later stages. For example, an apical meristem cell today might be a photosynthetic cortex cell tomorrow; a cortex cell today might be a suberized cork cell tomorrow. A mature organism reproduces, but the senile organism no longer can. Thus a developing system need not necessarily grow and it need not necessarily change form, but by the very meaning of development, it must differentiate. Through differentiation, structural units become functionally *specialized* in various ways and at various times.

To be differentiation, operational changes must have a certain degree of permanence. We can make an animal vitamin-deficient, for example, and many of its cells will then behave differently. But if we now add the missing vitamin to the diet, normal cell functions will probably be resumed very promptly. Here cellular capacities have not been changed in any fundamental way. Only their expression has changed temporarily in response to particular conditions. Such easily alterable, reversible changes are *modulations.* On the contrary, differentiation implies a more or less fundamental, relatively lasting alteration of operational potentials. A vitamin-deficient cell that, after addition of the missing vitamin, *maintained* its altered characteristics would have differentiated.

Cell differentiation might come about in three ways. First, the developing differences among cells might be a result of progressive changes in gene action. In a given cell some genes might become active at certain developmental stages, whereas others might become inactive. The operon hypothesis (Chap. 18) suggests how such switching of gene activities might occur. Activity patterns might change differently in different cells, and this might contribute to differentiation. Or, second, gene actions might remain the same, but the operations of the cytoplasm could become altered progressively. For example, one round of cytoplasmic reactions might use up a certain set of starting materials, and in the later absence of these, similar reactions could then no longer take place. A next round of reactions would proceed with different starting materials and would therefore produce different endproducts. The net result could be progressive differentiation. Or, third, both nuclear and cytoplasmic changes might occur in reciprocal fashion. This is probably the likeliest possibility, and much current research is devoted to a study of this very complex problem.

Like growth, differentiation occurs from the molecule on up; the operations of any living level are based on those of subordinated levels. It is this that makes the problem of analysis so enormous. For if differentiation is as complex as the totality of molecular interactions in cells, then it cannot be any less complex than the very process of life itself.

Morphogenesis and differentiation are two of the forces that drive development. A third is metabolism. There could be no development if energy were not available and if molecular synthesis did not occur. To be sure, there could be no metabolism if morphogenesis and differentiation did not develop it. At no point in the life cycle of any organism is metabolism more intensive and development more rapid than during the earliest stages. Both then decline in rate, until the zero point is reached at death; the metabolic clock is wound only once, at the beginning.

This circumstance introduces a number of major problems. For example, respiration in reproductive cells necessitates gas exchange through the cell surfaces. This requirement limits the size of such a cell, however, for diffusion could not be effective in too large a cell mass. But the requirement of smallness in turn limits the amount of food that can be stored in a reproductive cell, which puts a time limit on the amount of development possible. Clearly, the developmental consequences of so "simple" a requirement as oxygen supply are quite far-reaching.

The molecular equipment for energy production is inherited complete by all reproductive units and is functional from the start. This is an absolute necessity for survival. But only relatively few kinds of metabolic syntheses are possible at first, for synthesis must itself develop. Endproducts of a first round of synthesis must become the starting materials for a second, more complex round. In this manner synthetic capacities must be increased and broadened progressively. Synthesis metabolism clearly is as much a result of development as it is a prerequisite; it is one aspect of differentiation.

How do morphogenesis, differentiation, and metabolism mesh together to produce a sensibly functioning whole? A zygote or a spore does not yet have any of the features of the adult. How then does it happen to produce just one stem apex and one root apex, not two stem tips at opposite ends? How does it happen to give rise to just one head and one tail, not two of either, yet also two arms and two legs, not one of each? The developing system evidently behaves as if it "knew" its objectives precisely, and it proceeds without apparent trial and error. For normally there is no underdevelopment, no over-development, and there are no probing excursions along the way. Development is directed straight toward wholeness (Fig. 24.25).

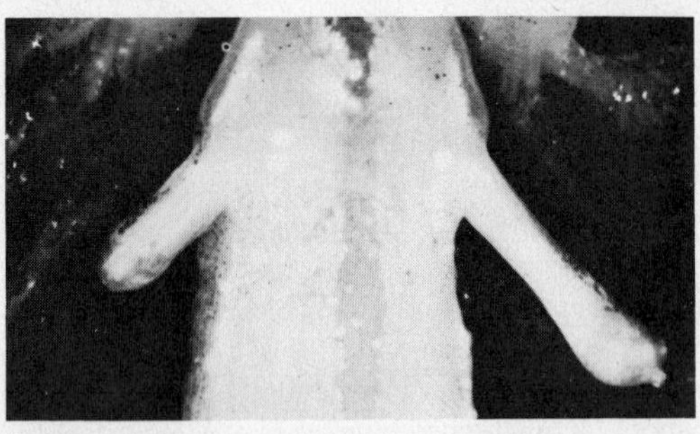

A

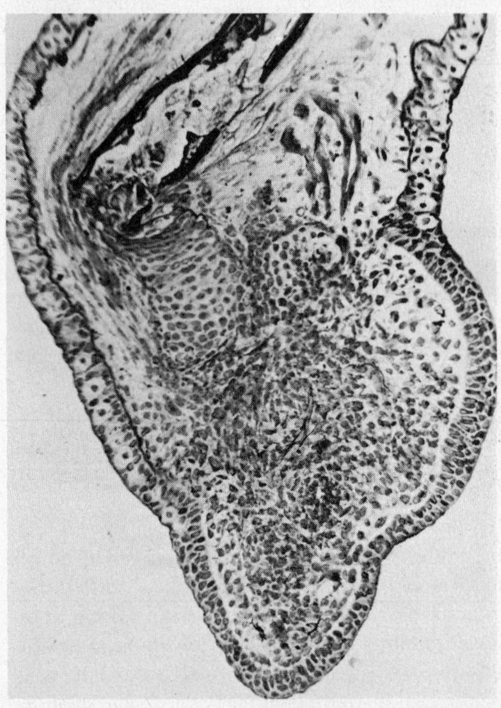

B

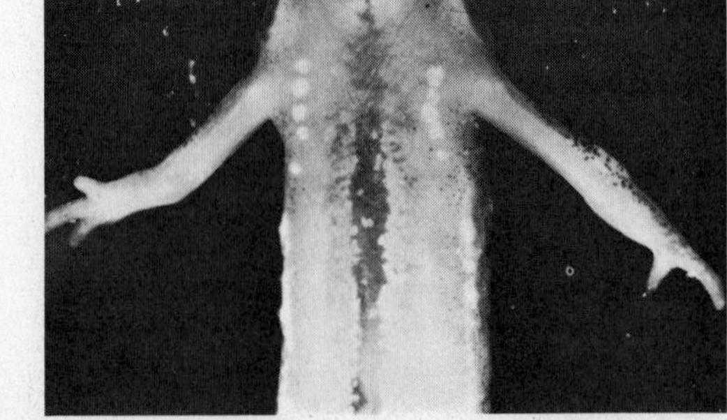

C

24.25 ***Wholeness.*** *If the arms of a salamander are amputated (A), tissues in the stumps gradually reorganize and produce a regenerating cell mass (B). Eventually whole new limbs are re-formed, 31 days later in this case (C). Development evidently tends to produce or restore wholeness in an organism.*

This tendency toward wholeness is manifested at every level of organization and in any developing unit—zygote, spore, or regenerating fragment. It pinpoints the fourth universal component of development, *control.* Ultimately the control of development is undoubtedly genetic, as it is for every living process. But such a generalization is not very informative and actually is little more than a restatement of the problem. *How* do genes control development? More specifically, how does a particular gene, through control over a particular enzyme or other protein, regulate a particular developmental occurrence? Answers to such small problems are just beginning to be obtained. The collective larger issue, the controlled, directed emergence of wholeness in an entire organism, remains a matter of future research.

Another genetic aspect of development is of significance in this context. The course of development varies considerably according to whether the starting point is a zygote or some other unit—spore, vegetative body, or regenerating fragment. As already indicated on earlier occasions, zygotic development usually passes through several distinct phases: fertilization, embryonic period, in animals typically also larval period, and then adulthood. In sharp contrast, all other forms of development are exceedingly direct. In the development of spores or vegetative units of any type there is no sex, hence no fertilization; there is no embryo, hence also no hatching; there is no larva, hence also no metamorphosis. Instead, the reproductive unit becomes an adult in a smoothly continuous single developmental sequence (Fig. 24.26).

This marked difference between sexual and asexual patterns of development is undoubtedly a result of the presence or absence of the sexual process itself. Unlike a spore or a vegetative body, an egg is more than simply a reproductive unit;

it is also the agent for sex and therefore an *adaptive* device. Through fertilization the egg acquires new genes, which often endow the future offspring with new, better-adapted traits. However, before any new traits can actually be displayed they must be *developed* during the transition from egg to adult. Embryonic and larval periods appear to be the outcome. These stages provide the means and the necessary time for translating genetic instructions acquired sexually by the zygote into adaptively improved traits of the adult. Vegetative units do not acquire new genetic instructions through sex, and equivalent developmental processes for executing such instructions are therefore not needed. Correspondingly, embryos and larvae are absent here.

Moreover, to the extent that the genetic instructions received by an egg are different from those received by earlier generations of eggs, embryos and larvae permit introduction of *evolutionary* changes into developmental histories. Indeed, evolutionary change is achieved not by alteration of already developed, fully differentiated adults, but primarily by modifications of eggs, embryos, and larvae. These incompletely developed stages are still plastic and unformed enough to be capable of executing new genetic instructions.

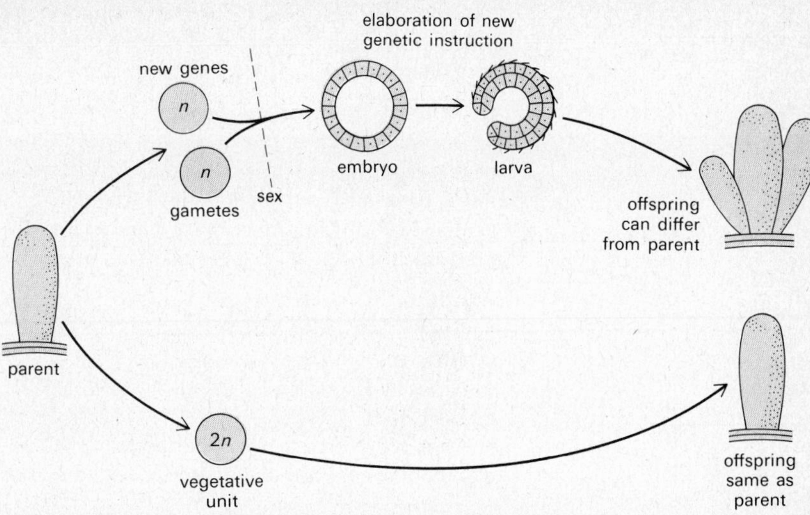

24.26 Sexual and asexual development. *In sexual development* (*top*) *new genetic instructions are introduced in the zygote by the gametes, and later these instructions are elaborated in the embryo and the larva. Hence the mature offspring can differ to greater or lesser extent from the parent. In asexual development* (*bottom*) *new genetic instructions are not introduced, and the offspring therefore resembles the parent fully.*

The following chapters will show how the various reproductive processes, life cycles, and developmental sequences manifest themselves in different groups of specific organisms.

review questions

1 How does reproduction contribute to steady-state maintenance? To self-perpetuation in general? Review the forms of molecular reproduction and the nature of each. How does molecular reproduction contribute to organismic reproduction?

2 Define binary fission, multiple fission. What basic events occur in cell division? What is mitosis? How does cell division contribute to organismic reproduction? Define spindle, aster, centriole, centromere. How does mitotic division differ in plant and animal cells?

3 What molecular events in cells precede the microscopically visible phases of division? Describe the processes of prophase and metaphase. What is the metaphase plate, and where is it located?

4 What are the events of anaphase and telophase? Review the history of the nucleoli during mitotic division. What is the net result of mitotic division?

5 What is a tissue culture? What have experiments with tissue cultures shown about rates of cell division? When and where in an organism are fission rates highest? Lowest?

6 Distinguish between reproduction and development. What is vegetative reproduction? Under what circumstances and in what forms does vegetative reproduction occur? What is sporulation? What is gametic reproduction? How is vegetative reproduction different from sporulation? How is sporulation different from gametic reproduction?

7 What are the most basic events of every sexual process? Under what conditions does sex tend to occur? In what way is sex of adaptive value? Illustrate by the example of *Spirogyra.* Define mating, fertilization, zygote, gamete, spore, isogamy, oögamy, and parthenogenesis.

8 What are the limitations of and the environmental conditions required for (*a*) gametic reproduction and (*b*) sporulation? Contrast in detail.

What is hermaphroditism? What is its adaptive value? Distinguish between self-fertilization and cross-fertilization.

9 What is the basic function of meiosis, and what makes such a process necessary? Where does meiosis occur? Define haploid, diploid. How many *pairs* of chromosomes does a diploid cell contain? Of these, which and how many are maternal and which and how many are paternal?

10 How many chromosome duplications and how many cell duplications occur during meiosis? In what respects are mitosis and meiosis alike? What is the essential difference between the metaphase of mitosis and the metaphase of the first meiotic division? Describe the complete sequence of events during both divisions of meiosis.

11 Describe the nature of a haplontic life cycle. Name organisms in which such a cycle occurs. Do similarly for diplontic and diplohaplontic life cycles.

12 What type of life cycle is probably primitive, and how could it have given rise to the other types? Define mitospore, meiospore, gametophyte, sporophyte, alternation of generations.

13 Define morphogenesis, differential growth, form-regulating movements, polarity. Through what types of growth process does an organism enlarge in size? Explain the meaning of the phrase "organisms grow from their molecules on up."

14 What different symmetries are exhibited by living units? In what ways do polarity and symmetry circumscribe the form of an organism? What is the role of differential growth in the development of form? Define and distinguish between differentiation and modulation. What is the relation between differentiation and specialization?

15 What role does metabolism play in development? How do metabolic rates vary during the developmental history of an organism? Illustrate the tendency of development to produce "wholeness." What are the fundamental differences between asexual and sexual developmental patterns, and what accounts for such differences?

collateral readings

Berrill, N. J.: "Sex and the Nature of Things," Dodd, Mead, New York, 1953. A beautifully and interestingly written paperback on the significance and processes of sex in various organisms.

Chase, H. B.: "Sex: The Universal Fact," Dell, New York, 1965. This paperback reviews sexuality from a structural and functional viewpoint; nontechnical, with special emphasis on man.

Gurdon, J. B.: Transplanted Nuclei and Cell Differentiation, *Sci. American,* Dec., 1968. A description of experiments showing how genes might influence differentiation during embryonic development.

Hadorn, E.: Transdetermination in Cells, *Sci. American,* Nov., 1968. Changes in cellular differentiation are examined.

Hayflick, L.: Human Cells and Aging, *Sci. American,* March, 1968. An article on the decline of vigor in cells grown in tissue culture.

Jensen, W. A.: "The Plant Cell," Wadsworth, Belmont, Calif., 1964. Good discussions of mitosis and meiosis in plants are included in this paperback.

Mazia, D.: Cell Division, *Sci. American,* Aug., 1953. Experiments are described in which the entire mitotic apparatus is isolated from dividing cells.

———: How Cells Divide, *Sci. American,* Sept., 1961. A review of the nature of the mitotic process.

Mittwoch, U.: Sex Differences in Cells, *Sci. American,* July, 1963. Such differences involve the chromosomes and other nuclear structures.

Moscona, A. A.: How Cells Associate, *Sci. American,* Sept., 1961. A case study of tissue culture, illustrating how separated cells reaggregate.

Singer, M.: The Regeneration of Body Parts, *Sci. American,* Oct., 1958. Limb regeneration in salamanders and frogs is contrasted experimentally.

Swanson, C. P.: "The Cell," Prentice-Hall, Englewood Cliffs, N.J., 1960. A general discussion of mitosis and meiosis in various organisms, plant and animal, is included in this excellent paperback.

chapter 25 reproduction: nonanimal organisms

All three basic reproductive methods are encountered in Monera, Protista, and Metaphyta. Vegetative reproduction occurs in all groups, and in aquatic types the spores and gametes are most often flagellate and swimming. In terrestrial forms spores are usually encapsulated. Gametes cannot be, but despite the absence of abundant free water, gametic reproduction is made possible by special evolutionary adaptations.

moneran reproduction

Among bacteria and blue-green algae the main reproductive process is rapid vegetative fission. Such divisions are not mitotic, and it is unknown just how gene sets are distributed equally to daughter cells. But that some such process takes place is not in doubt (Fig. 25.1). Recall that in filamentous blue-greens vegetative reproduction also includes fragmentation at heterocysts and separation of hormogones from parental filaments (see Chap. 8).

Under unfavorable conditions many bacteria secrete cyst walls that protect the cells and keep them in an inactive, dormant state, often for years. Called *endospores,* such cysts are not reproductive units, despite the implications of the name. The same single cell that encysts eventually excysts again, still single (see Fig. 8.11). However, some bacteria and many blue-greens do produce true reproductive spores. In some cases series of spore cells are budded off from the end of a vegetative cell. Spores of this type are *conidia.* In other cases a vegetative cell can come to function as a "fruiting body," or *sporangium,* and its interior then subdivides into numerous spore cells, each with its own nucleus. Such spores are *sporangiospores* (Fig. 25.2).

A sexual process is now known to occur in certain bacteria and blue-green algae as a laboratory phenomenon. Whether or not it also takes place in nature is still undetermined. This sexual process is conjugative; cells join pairwise, exchange portions of their genetic material, and then separate. The classic experiment proving the occurrence of sex was carried out with two different strains of the bacterium *Escherichia coli* (Fig. 25.3). One genetically stable strain could ferment lactose (L+) and was also sensitive to the antibiotic streptomycin (S−). The other genetic type could not ferment lactose (L−) but was resistant to streptomycin (S+). When L+S− and L−S+ strains were cultured together, the vegetative offspring generations contained many bacteria with traits exactly like the parental strains. Occasionally, however, bacteria with stable L+S+ traits were found; such cells could ferment lactose and were streptomycin-resistant at the same time. Other individuals, L−S−, could not use lactose and were streptomycin-sensitive as well. Such traits are mixed combinations of parental characteristics, and their occurrence indicates that mating and sexual exchange of genes must have taken place.

Experiments of this sort have also established that monerans are *haploid* and that some (still unknown) kind of gene-reduction process equivalent to meiosis occurs immediately after conjugation. Insofar as sex occurs in them, therefore,

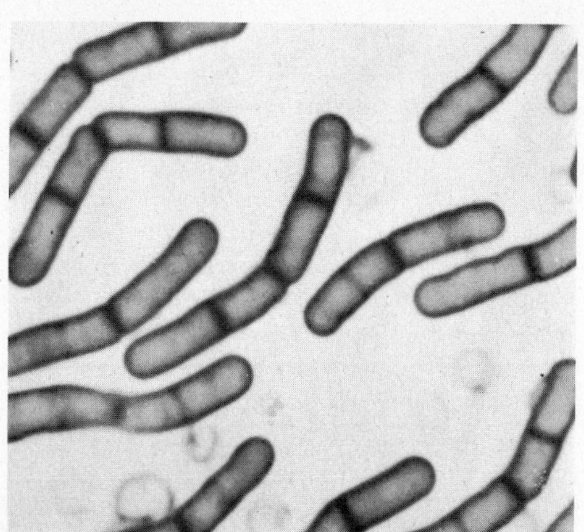

A

B

25.1 Bacterial reproduction. *A, cell division in a species of Bacillus. B, budding in budding bacteria. Note the branch strand with small terminal bud cell.*

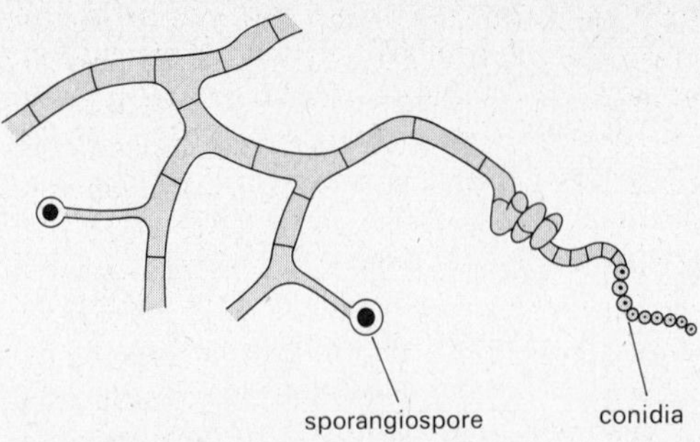

25.2 ***Bacterial spores.*** *Sporangiospores are formed singly at the tips of a branch; conidia are cut off from a branch serially as chains.*

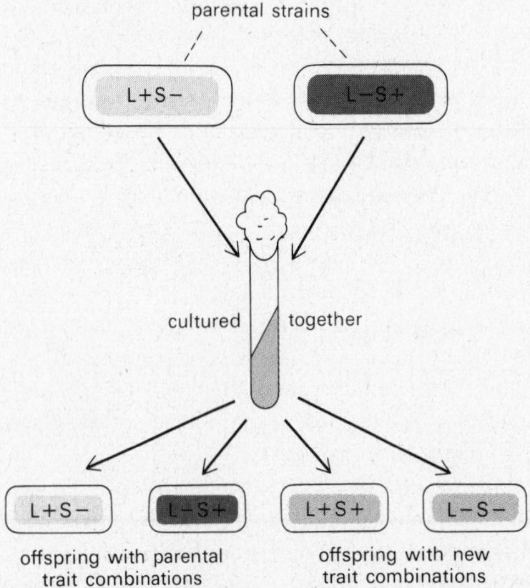

25.3 ***Bacterial sex.*** *L+ symbolizes lactose-utilizing capacity, and S+ symbolizes streptomycin resistance.*

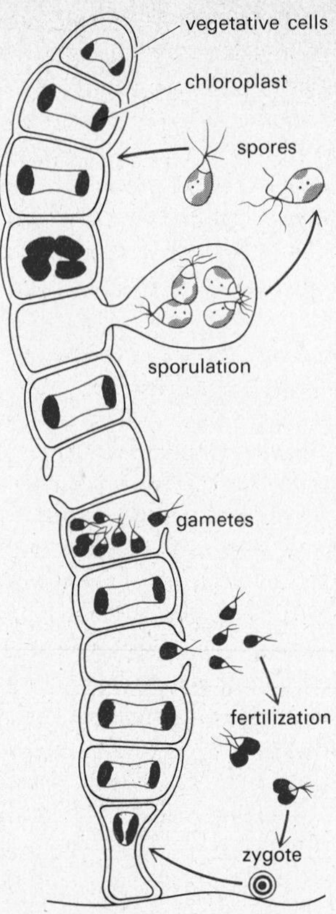

25.4 ***Reproduction and sex in Ulothrix.*** *Haploid vegetative cells give rise to haploid spores that grow into new adult filaments (top). Given cells also produce gametes that fertilize each other and form diploid zygotes (bottom). Germination of the zygotes includes meiosis, and new haploid adults arise thereafter. Thus the life cycle of this green alga is haplontic. Gamete formation is illustrated also in Fig. 9.7.*

moneran life cycles are haplontic.

If sex is rare, how do these organisms adapt to their changing environments? They can do so without sex by their extremely rapid vegetative multiplication. Rapid reproduction facilitates rapid evolution, particularly through mutations. Since Monera are haploid, every mutated gene will immediately produce changes in traits. Therefore even if millions or billions of organisms succumb to one environment, a single survivor with appropriate mutations can within a few hours produce new millions or billions of readapted organisms. Monera evidently rely on safety through numbers, and they generally can do very well without sex.

protistan reproduction

algae

Vegetative multiplication by cell division occurs in all algae that are not coccine. Division increases the number of unicellular types and the sizes of multicellular types. Multicellular algae commonly also propagate by fragmentation and by regenerative reproduction.

Virtually all green algae produce spores, and usually any cell of a mature organism can serve as a spore-forming *sporangium.* The process is well illustrated in the filamentous green alga *Ulothrix.* In a spore-forming cell the living content inside the cell wall divides a number of times. Each small cell so produced then secretes its own wall and matures as a flagellate spore. An opening later develops in the wall of the original cell and the spores escape through it (Fig. 25.4).

All groups of green algae are sexual, and in many cases any vegetative cell can come to function as a gamete-producing *gametangium*. Such a cell in some cases serves as a single gamete directly, as in *Spirogyra* (which has nonflagellate gametes; see Chap. 24) or it subdivides repeatedly and forms numerous smaller gametes, as in *Ulothrix* (where the process resembles spore formation; see Fig. 25.4). These two genera are among the many isogamous algae. *Volvox* and *Oedogonium* are examples of oögamous forms (Fig. 25.5), and *Chlamydomonas* includes species that are isogamous, anisogamous, or oögamous (Fig. 25.6). *Ulothrix* also exemplifies the numerous hermaphroditic types, and *Oedogonium,* those that are separately sexed. In *Spirogyra* some species are hermaphroditic, others, separately sexed.

Haplontic life cycles occur in the flagellate green algae (*Chlamydomonas, Volvox*) and in most of the filamentous sporine types (*Ulothrix, Spirogyra, Oedogonium*). The zygotes here usually encyst and form *zygospores* (as in *Spirogyra*). After zygospore germination the first two divisions are meiotic, and the four flagellate haploid cells that usually result swim about and eventually give rise to four new adults (see Fig. 25.4). *Spirogyra* is unusual in that three of the four cells formed by zygotic meiosis degenerate, and only one produces an adult.

Advanced sporine green algae, the sea lettuce *Ulva* among them, have largely diplohaplontic life cycles. In these groups the sporophyte and gametophyte generations are anatomically identical. Nearly all cells of a sporophyte can undergo meiosis and form (flagellate) spores, and in many cases this process occurs simultaneously in all such cells. Similarly, nearly all cells of gametophyte can produce (flagellate) gametes, and they often do so at the same time (Fig. 25.7). Diplontic life cycles are characteristic of the coccine green algae, exemplified by *Bryopsis* and *Acetabularia.* In these forms flagellate zygotes settle and grow into multinucleate adults. Some of the terminal body parts or branches of such adults then usually give rise to the gametes: the nuclei undergo meiosis, and each resulting haploid nucleus, together with some surrounding cytoplasm, becomes walled off as a cell that eventually develops flagella (Fig. 25.8).

Reproductive processes and patterns as in the green algae are basic also in the other algae phyla, notwithstanding numerous modifications and specializations in various groups. For example, the stoneworts do not form spores, and their gametangia are true organs, each composed of an outer protective tissue and an inner gamete-forming tissue. Such a complexity of the reproductive structures is unique among protists.

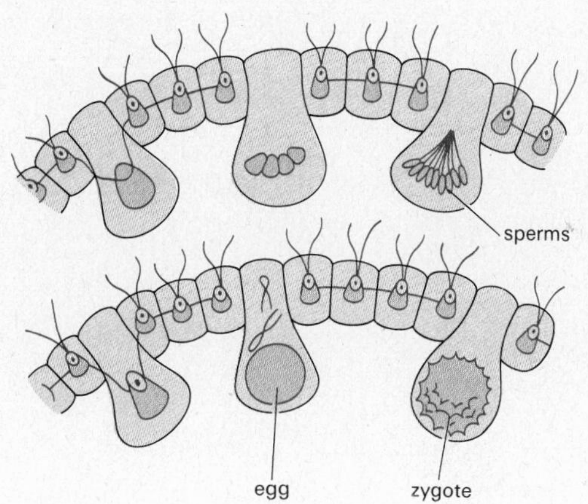

25.5 Oögamy in Volvox. *Eggs and sperms are formed in separate colonies. See also Fig. 9.7 for eggs in Oedogonium.*

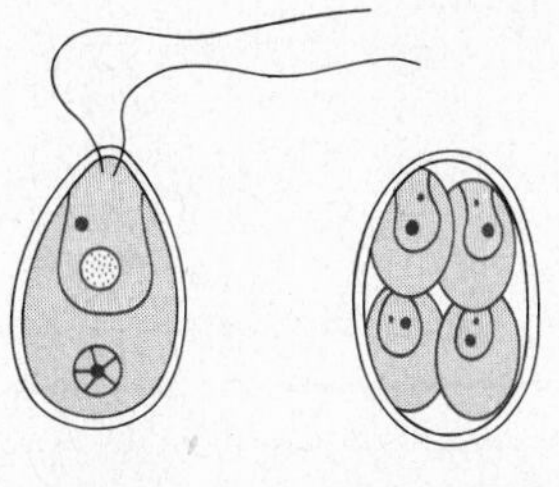

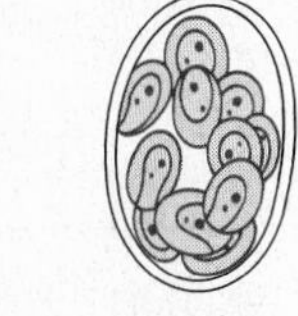

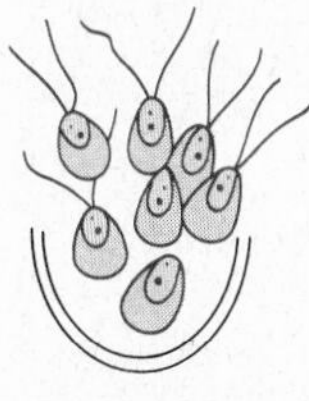

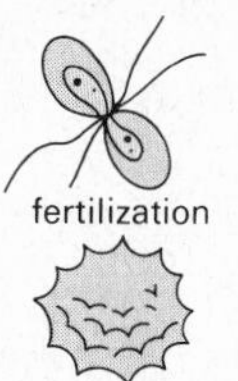

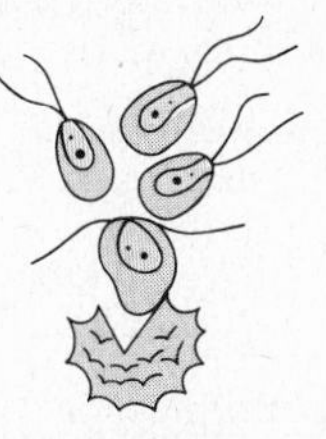

25.6 Haplontic algae. *Sex and the life cycle of Chlamydomonas are illustrated.*

gametophyte (n)
meiospores (n)
sporophyte ($2n$)
fertilization
gamete (n)
zygote ($2n$)

25.7 Diplohaplontic algae. *The life cycle of the sea lettuce Ulva is illustrated. Note that the gametophyte and sporophyte generations look alike, though one is haploid and the other diploid.*

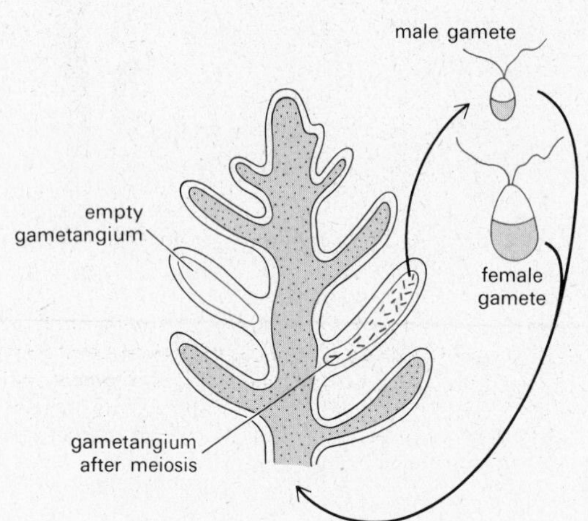

25.8 Diplontic algae. *Detail of a terminal branch of Bryopsis, showing gamete-forming side branches (gametangia) and the appearance of male and female gametes. See Fig. 9.6 for photo of this alga.*

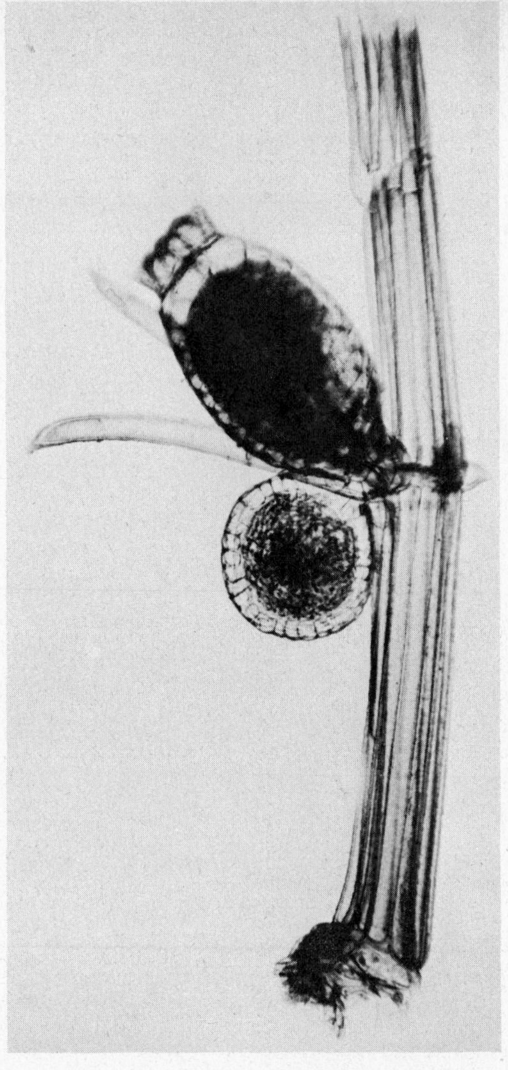

25.9 Sex organs in stoneworts. *Above, an egg-forming oögonium; below, a sperm-forming antheridium.*

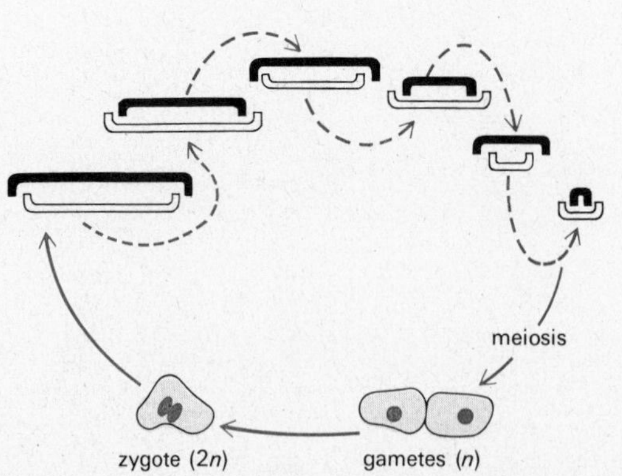

25.10 Diatom life cycle. *Top, left to right, successive vegetative generations. Note that each generation inherits the smaller shell-half from the preceding generation and manufactures an even smaller second shell-half on its own. Bottom, gamete cells escape from their shells, undergo meiosis, and the zygote restores the diploid condition. The life cycle is diplontic.*

Stoneworts are hermaphroditic, oögamous, and haplontic (Fig. 25.9). Among euglenophytes and pyrrophytes sex is virtually unknown, and with some exceptions among pyrrophytes these organisms also do not form spores; fission is the chief reproductive process.

Reproductively the most interesting golden-brown algae are the diatoms. These largely unicellular forms have silica shell halves, one such half fitting over the other like a lid over a box. In cell division one daughter inherits the "lid," the other the "box." The missing half-shell is then newly formed, and it is always a "box" that fits inside the half-shell already present. Some diatoms in a population thus become progressively smaller as cell divisions continue. Normal sizes are restored during the sexual process, in which two cells discard their walls and form gametes by meiosis—diatoms are diplontic. Zygotes grow in size and then secrete new shells (Fig. 25.10).

In the brown algae, one class is diplohaplontic with anatomically similar sporophyte and gametophyte generations. A second class is diplohaplontic, too, but the two generations are structurally dissimilar. And a third class is diplontic, exemplified by the common rockweed *Fucus.* At branch terminals of this alga are gelatinous swellings (*receptacles,* see Fig. 9.12) that contain numerous gamete-forming cavities called *conceptacles.* The lining layers of some conceptacles give rise to distinct sperms, those of others, to distinct eggs. Mature gametes escape through conceptacle openings along the surface of a receptacle. After fertilization in open water a zygote encysts, settles on a rock, and eventually germinates into a new diploid adult (Fig. 25.11).

Among red algae some groups are haplontic, others are diplohaplontic. In a third group the life cycle contains a sporophyte and a gametophyte generation, but the sporophyte here is *haploid,* meiosis occurring in the zygote, not during spore formation. In a fourth and most advanced group, the life cycle contains *three* distinct generations, two diploid (and structurally dissimilar) sporophytes and one haploid gametophyte. Meiosis here takes place when the second sporophyte generation produces spores. The life cycles of these algae are among the most complex encountered in any organisms (Fig. 25.12).

slime molds, protozoa

In slime molds the life cycle is fundamentally diplohaplontic (Fig. 25.13 and Color Fig. 24). An adult plasmodium or pseudoplasmodium represents the diploid sporophyte generation. From it develops a stalked fruiting body, or *sporangium,* in which meiosis occurs during spore formation. The spores give rise to haploid flagellate or amoeboid swarm cells. Successive vegetative generations of such swarmers represent the gametophyte generation, which thus consists not of a multicellular body but of a population of separate single cells. Eventually some of these cells function as gametes, and fertilization reestablishes the diploid condition. Diploid zygotic cells later grow into (or collect together as) plasmodial sporophytes.

Among protozoa (Fig. 25.14), vegetative reproduction takes place through binary fission in most cases. Budding is known to occur in suctorian ciliates, and regenerative reproduction is widespread in ciliates generally. Spores are formed by Foraminifera and particularly by Sporozoa. In the latter a vegetative cell first be-

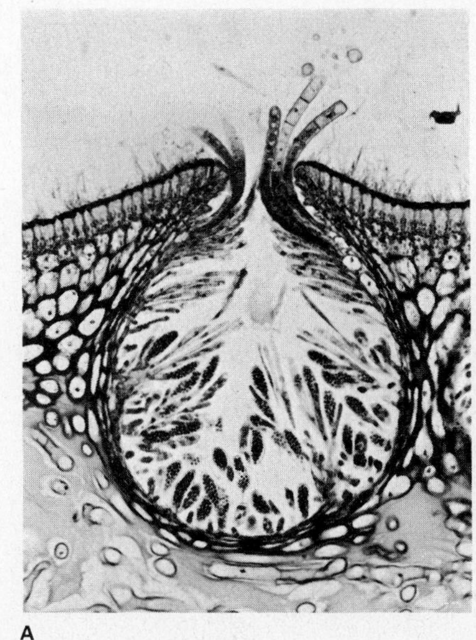

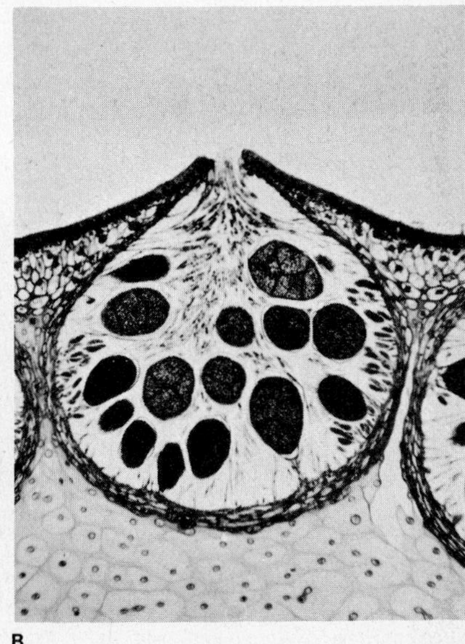

***25.11* Gametes in Fucus.** *A, sperm-forming structure (conceptacle). B, egg-forming conceptacle. The lining layer in A bears branches that produce the sperms. Note the sterile hairs (paraphyses) that project through the conceptacle opening. In B the lining layer bears egg-forming branches. A mature branch of this type contains eight eggs. Conceptacles are located in so-called receptacles, enlarged terminals of branches of this brown alga. Such receptacles are illustrated in Fig. 9.12.*

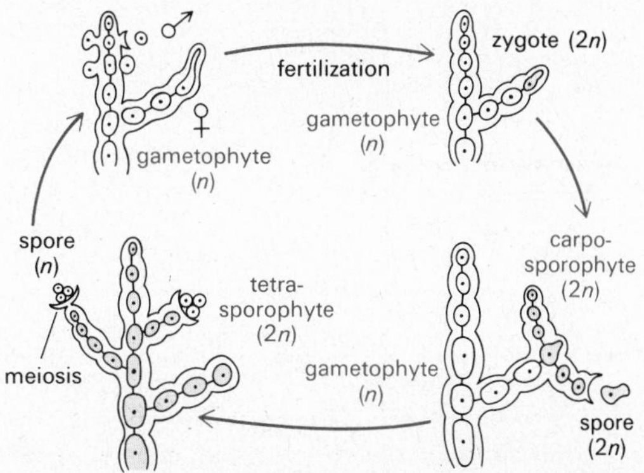

***25.12* Red algae.** *The life cycle of Polysiphonia is illustrated. It consists of three consecutive generations: a haploid gametophyte, which produces sex cells; a diploid carposporophyte, which develops from the zygote, remains attached to the gametophyte, and is anatomically different from the gametophyte; and a diploid tetrasporophyte, a separate organism that looks like a gametophyte but that develops from a diploid spore produced by the carposporophyte. Meiosis occurs in the tetrasporophyte, and the haploid spores then formed develop into a gametophyte again.*

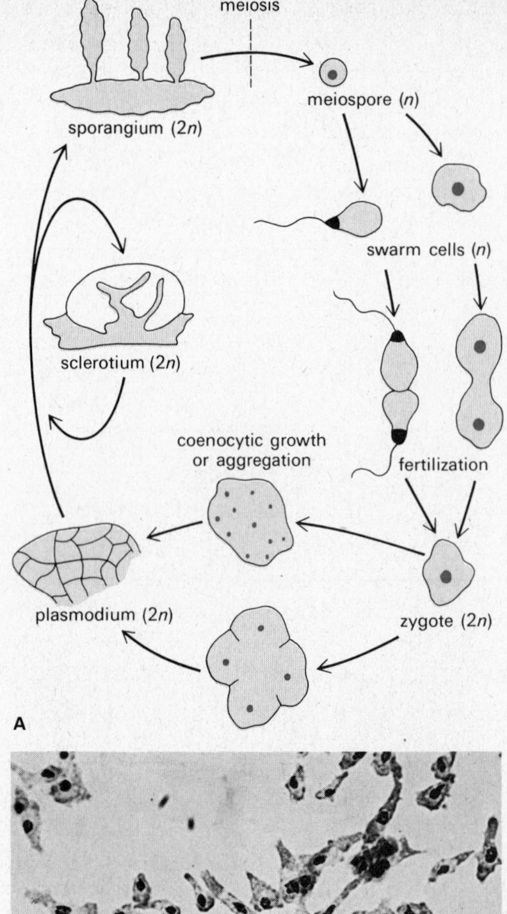

B

25.13 ***Slime mold reproduction.*** *A, the life cycle. A sclerotium is an encapsulated resting stage formed from a plasmodium and germinating again as a plasmodium. Swarm cells derived from the meiospore can alternate between amoeboid and flagellate states. B, amoeboid swarm cells migrating together (after a sexual process) and forming an adult pseudoplasmodium. In this type the cell boundaries are retained, hence the adult is multicellular. Fruiting bodies of slime molds are shown in Color Fig. 24.*

A

B

25.14 ***Protozoan reproduction and sex.*** *A, transverse fission in the ciliate Stentor. The macronucleus (black) condenses to a compact mass and then reelongates as each micronucleus divides mitotically. Concurrently the future anterior offspring inherits the original set of mouth organelles, while the future posterior one develops a new set. After the two offspring separate, the macronuclear portion inherited by each renodulates. B, a mating pair of Paramecium. Note spindles of dividing micronuclei in left individual. See Fig. 24.10 for illustration of nuclear exchange by mating partners. (B, courtesy Carolina Biological Supply Company.)*

comes multinucleate and then undergoes multiple fission (see Chap. 9). The cellular products, each containing one nucleus, represent spores. Foraminiferan life cycles are diplohaplontic; sporozoan life cycles are haplontic. All other protozoa typically are diplontic.

Gametic reproduction occurs universally among all protozoan groups, but some individual types are without sex (for example, *Amoeba*). Fertilization is achieved either by syngamy, as in zooflagellates, or by exchange of gamete nuclei, as in ciliates (see Figs. 24.10 and 25.14). Ciliate protozoa are hermaphroditic, each individual producing a gamete nucleus of each sex type. These gamete nuclei form from the micronuclei, and the macronuclei degenerate during conjugation. Ordinarily conjugation leads to cross-fertilization, or exchange of gamete nuclei between mating partners. Under certain circumstances, however, the two gamete nuclei of a single individual can fuse together and in this manner bring about self-fertilization (here called *autogamy*).

As pointed out in Chap. 9, the ciliate species *Paramecium aurelia* has been shown to consist of at least 16 distinct but structurally indistinguishable sexual varieties, or *syngens.* Each syngen in turn consists of two mating types, and cross-fertilizing conjugation requires one partner from each of these two types. Similar sexual specializations are known to exist in other species of *Paramecium* and indeed in several other types of protozoa.

fungi

Vegetative reproduction in fungi occurs through mitotic nuclear divisions and cytoplasmic growth of the hyphae. Fragmentation of a mycelium can give rise to pieces that settle elsewhere and grow into new mycelia.

In the phycomycete fungi, the spores of aquatic types are flagellate and they are formed more or less as in algae: a cell subdivides internally and releases numerous small spore cells. Terrestrial forms produce encapsulated spores. In the phycomycete breadmold *Rhizopus,* for example, upright branch hyphae with expanded tips grow from many places in the mycelium (Fig. 25.15). The tips are *sporangia,* fruiting bodies in which spores are formed. Each such spore is encapsulated in a wall that turns black as the spore matures. After the spores are dispersed they germinate into new mycelia.

The mycelia, sporangia, and spores of *Rhizopus* are all haploid; the life cycle of the breadmold is haplontic. A sexual process can occur when two mycelia live in close proximity. Each can then develop a short *suspensor* hypha, one growing toward the other. The tip of such a hypha becomes partitioned off as a multinucleate gametelike compartment. When two of these compartments meet they fuse, and a cyst wall is then secreted around the fusion mass (see Fig. 25.15). In the interior the nuclei pair off, one from each compartment joining one from the other. Such nuclear pairs fuse and form diploid zygote nuclei. Unpaired nuclei degenerate. When the cyst later germinates, its contents grow directly into an upright hypha with a terminal sporangium. The zygote nuclei divide in the process, and the first two divisions are meiotic. Numerous haploid nuclei are thereby formed, and some of these participate in spore formation in the sporangium. Mature spores are then released and grow into new vegetative mycelia.

Most Ascomycetes and many Basidiomycetes have life cycles basically equivalent to diplohaplontic ones (Fig. 25.16). The gamete-producing generation of these fungi is repre-

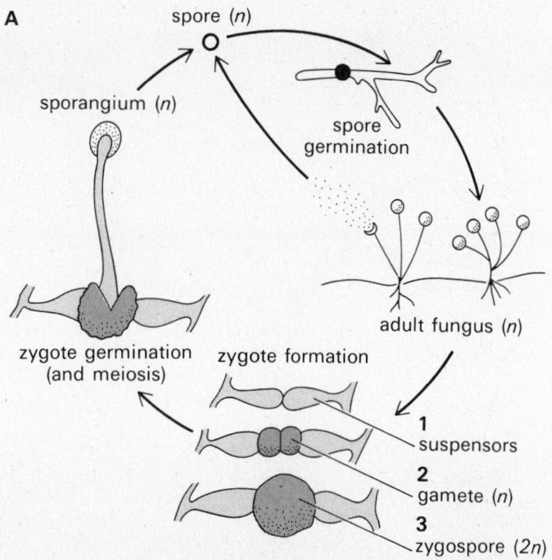

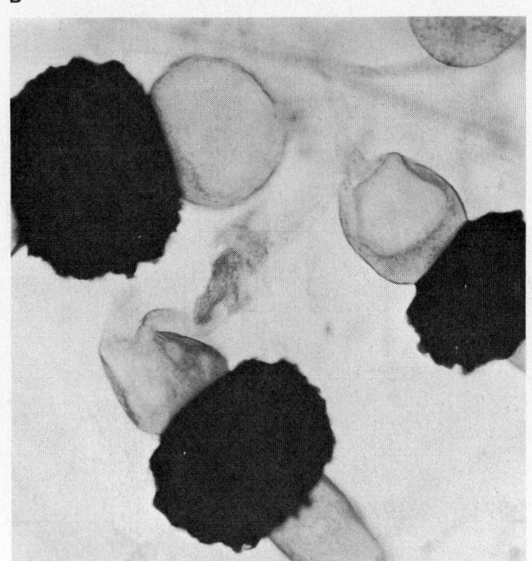

25.15 Bread mold reproduction. *A, the Rhizopus life cycle. B, zygospores.*

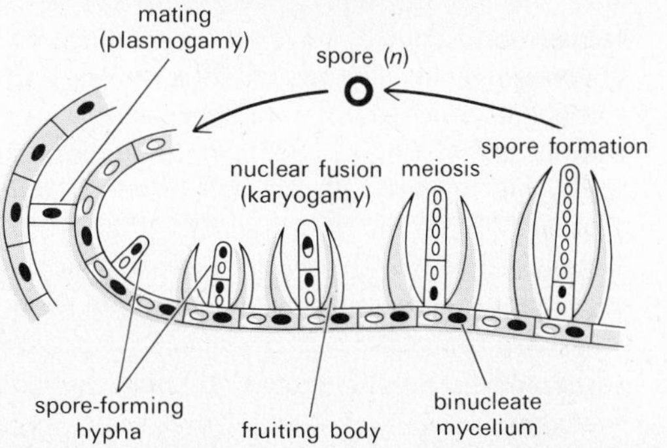

25.16 Ascomycete and Basidiomycete life cycles. *Read the diagram counterclockwise. If two uninucleate, haploid, monokaryotic (gametophytelike) mycelia grow side by side, mating can occur by migration of a nucleus from one mycelium to the other through a cytoplasmic bridge (left). A binucleate, dikaryotic (sporophytelike) mycelium so arises. From it then grow special spore-forming hyphae, which are usually surrounded by packed hyphae that form a fruiting body. In terminal cells of the spore-forming hyphae nuclear fusion occurs, meiosis takes place, and haploid spores are eventually produced. The cell containing such spores is either an ascus or a basidium, depending on the fungal class. Liberated ascospores or basidiospores then germinate and form new uninucleate mycelia.*

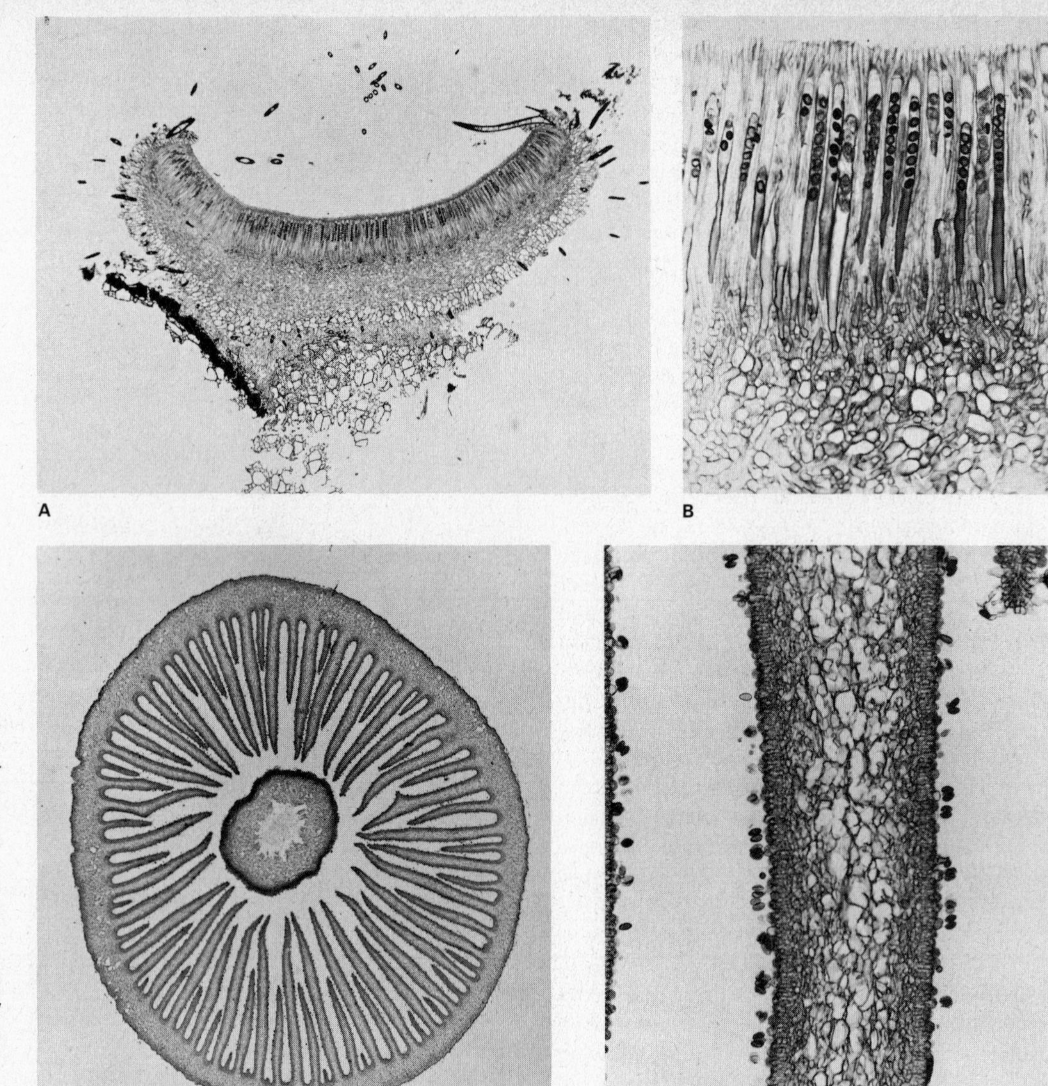

25.17 ***Fungus fruiting bodies.*** *A, section through the cup of a cup fungus, showing the layer of asci lining the cavity of the cup. Whole cups are shown in Color Fig. 9. B, higher magnification of a portion of the ascus layer. Note spores in elongated asci. C, section through the cap of a mushroom, showing the gill arrangement. See also Fig. 9.17. D, section of a gill, showing the mycelial meshwork in the interior and the basidiospores (attached to basidia) projecting from the surface. (A, B, courtesy Carolina Biological Supply Company.)*

sented by mycelia that contain haploid nuclei. Such mycelia are said to be *monokaryotic,* inasmuch as all nuclei are division products of a single original nucleus and are thus similar. If two mycelia of this type live side by side, a cytoplasmic connecting bridge can grow between them, and nuclei from one mycelium can then migrate through the bridge to the other. This is a mating process. The nuclei represent gamete nuclei, and their coming together (but not fusing) in one hypha is called *plasmogamy.* Such a hypha with nuclei from both parental mycelia is roughly equivalent to a diploid stage, and it represents the beginning of the sporophytic generation. It grows into a more or less extensive mycelium in which each of the two kinds of gamete nuclei multiplies numerous times. Mycelia of this type are said to be *dikaryotic,* their nuclei being derived from two parental sources.

Before long a dikaryotic mycelium produces special spore-forming hyphae. Around them usually develop others that collectively form a fruiting body of a particular shape (Fig. 25.17). For example, a mushroom is a stalked fruiting body that grows upright from a mycelium embedded in soil. The gill plates on the underside of the cap of the mushroom contain the ends of the special spore-forming hyphae. Other fungi have cup- or flask-shaped fruiting bodies; still others have spherical ones. In general the fruiting body is the most conspicuous (and also most familiar) part of a fungus.

At the ends of the spore-forming hyphae in fruiting bodies arise cells that become sporangia—saclike *asci* in Ascomycetes, club-shaped *basidia* in Basidiomycetes. A sporangium at first contains two haploid nuclei, derived from the two different kinds of gamete nuclei that originally participated in plasmogamy. These two sporangial nuclei fuse, a process equivalent to fertilization and called *karyogamy* (see Fig. 25.16). The resulting single diploid nucleus then undergoes meiosis, and haploid spore nuclei are thereby formed. Also, some cytoplasm surrounding each such nucleus becomes walled off, and distinct spore cells arise in this fashion—*ascospores* in an ascus, *basidiospores* in a basidium. The spores eventually scatter from a fruiting body, and after they germinate they grow into new gametophytic, monokaryotic mycelia with haploid nuclei.

These fungi are unique in that mating, or plasmogamy, is not followed immediately by fertilization, or karyogamy. In contrast to events in all other organisms, the two processes are separated here by a substantial time interval, and during this interval the original gamete nuclei can divide mitotically many times. As a result the dikaryotic state can be maintained almost indefinitely, and a single mating can be followed by hundreds or thousands of fertilizations that can take place in the course of many ensuing years. For organisms that cannot move to find mates and that must disperse gametes without free external water, their reproductive processes represent highly efficient adaptations to terrestrial life.

Ascomycetes include the unicellular yeasts, in which haploid cells function as gametes. Zygotes in many species then produce populations of diploid sporophytic cells, and these eventually function as spore-producing asci. After meiosis haploid spore cells give rise to new populations of gametic cells (Fig. 25.18). Some yeasts are haplontic, and in these a diploid zygote becomes an ascus directly, without forming a sporophytic cell population.

Among Basidiomycetes either the haploid or the diploid phase of the life cycle is often greatly reduced or prolonged, in many cases as an adaptation to a parasitic way of life. The parasitic *rusts* and *smuts* in particular exhibit very complex life histories. Many of these fungi require several intermediate plant hosts, and they transfer from one such host to the next by means of a succession of specially produced spores. Each type of spore develops into a mycelium that produces the next spore type, adapted to the next host in the series.

plant reproduction

The reproduction of plants is characterized by *diplohaplontic* life cycles with *dissimilar* gametophyte and sporophyte generations; by the presence of *multicellular* sex organs and sporangia; by the development of zygotes into sporophytic *embryos;* and by spores that are always meiospores and not of any other type.

It is most plausible to assume that the multicellular reproductive structures of plants arose from the unicellular ones of ancestral green algae through several evolutionary steps (Fig. 25.19). That algal ancestors had the potential of forming multicellular reproductive parts probably cannot be doubted. Even in modern filamentous and sheetlike chlorophytes, practically the whole body actually is a reproductive structure: any vegetative cell can become a gametangium or sporangium. If in such an organism reproductive capacity were retained only in a restricted region of the body—a

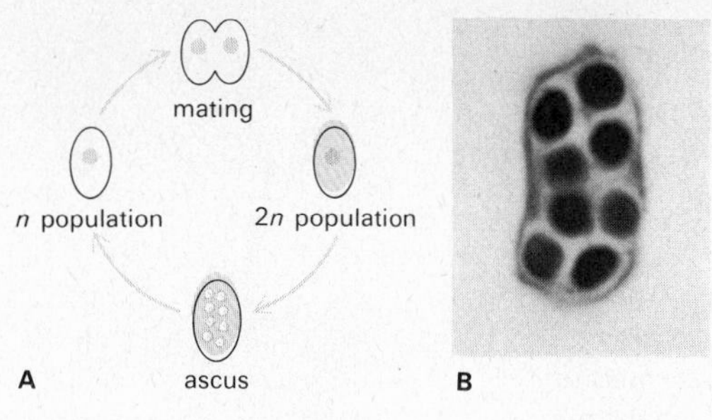

25.18 Yeast reproduction. *After haploid gametophytic cells in a population mate, zygote cells give rise to a diploid sporophytic population of cells. Such cells can later undergo meiosis and become asci; the resulting ascospores give rise to new haploid cell populations. B, a yeast ascus with ascospores.*

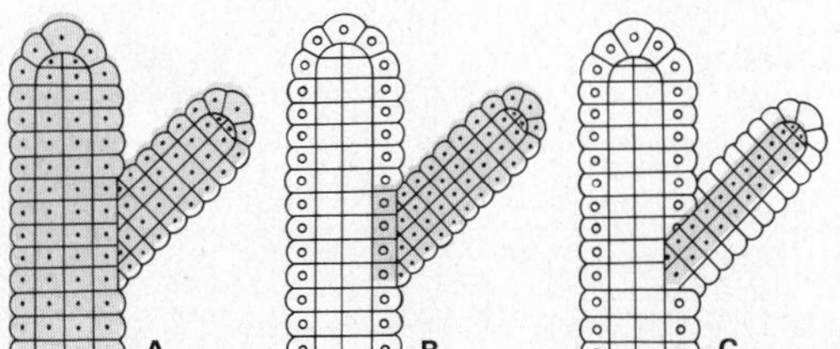

25.19 Sex organs and their probable evolution. *A, all cells of a plant are potentially reproductive. B, reproductive potential restricted to specific groups of cells. C, reproductive potential further restricted to interior cells, outer ones forming sterile sheath.*

25.20 Bryophyte vegetative reproduction. *A, branching growth and posterior decay can lead to the formation of two separate individuals from one parent organism. B, gemma cups of Marchantia.*

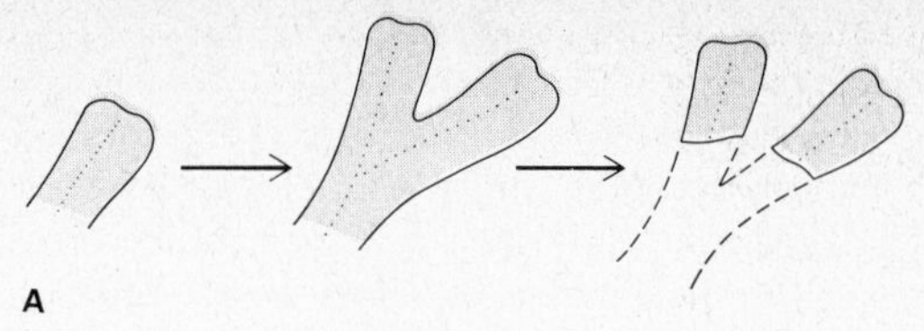

A

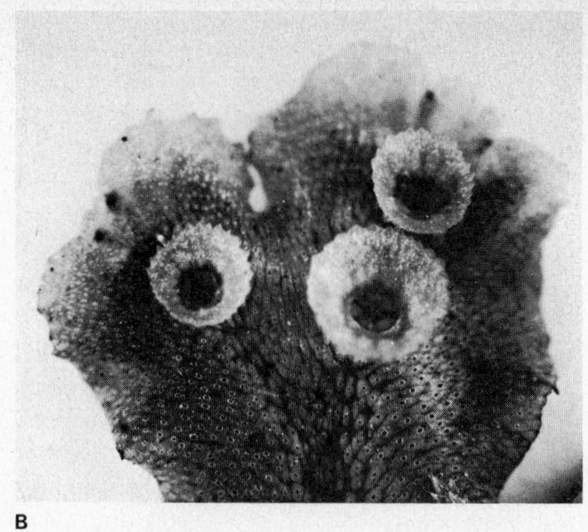

B

25.21 (Below) **Bryophyte sex organs.** *A, structure of antheridia (left) and archegonia (right). B, C, sections through the apical tips of moss shoots, showing the position of an antheridial head (B) and an archegonial head (C). Note the numerous sex organs on each head. D, E, sex-organ-bearing stalks in Marchantia. D, structure containing male sex organs. E, stalk bearing fingerlike processes in which female sex organs are located. (D, E, courtesy Carolina Biological Supply Company.)*

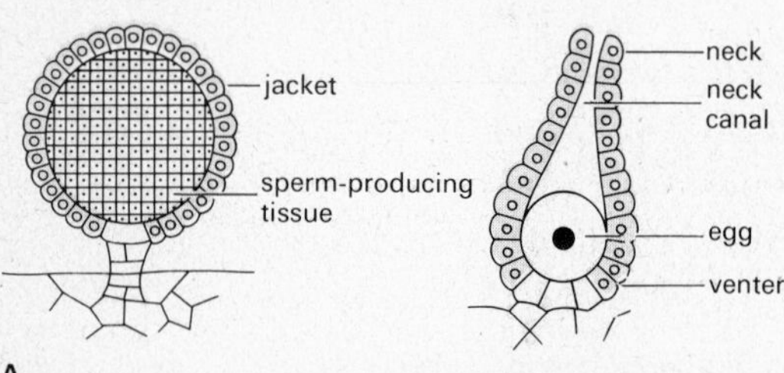

A

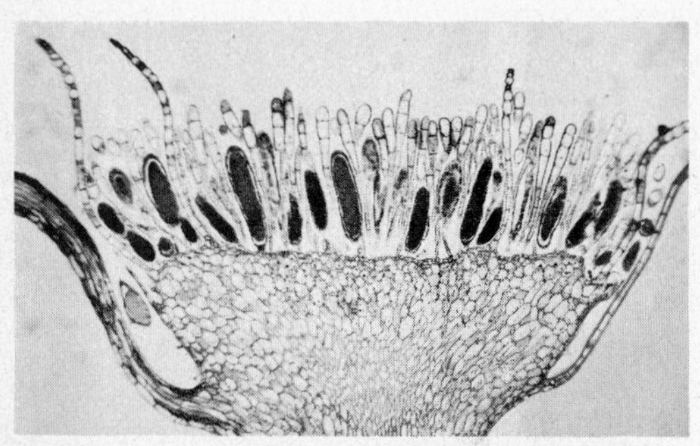

B

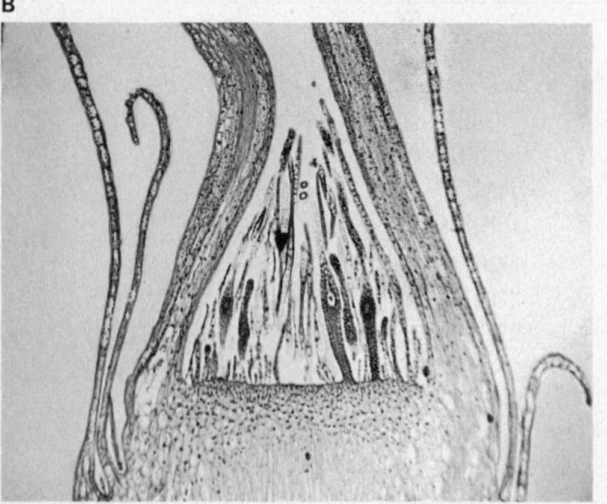

C

D

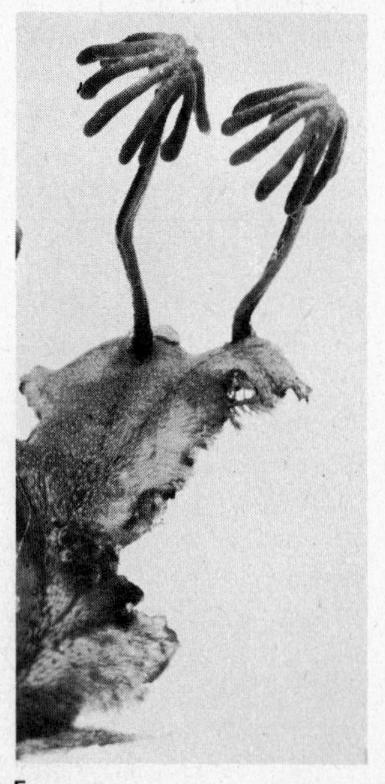

E

terminal branch, for example—but were lost everywhere else, then a specialized reproductive *tissue* would arise. Such a restriction would be advantageous in a terrestrial or semiterrestrial environment. Plants living on land require bodies subdivided into absorptive, conductive, and photosynthetic regions, and effective performance of any one of these specialized functions by a given body part well might preclude a continuing reproductive role at the same time. Thus the evolution of a localized and specialized reproductive tissue would facilitate the adaptation of the rest of the body to terrestrial conditions. Once such a tissue is in existence, furthermore, it can become more efficient if its outermost cell layer were to lose reproductive capacity, too, and were to serve instead as an external sterile sheath. Such a sheath would protect the reproductive cells in the interior, particularly against evaporation. The whole structure in effect now would be an organ composed of two tissues. The sex organs and sporangial organs of plants might have evolved in some such fashion.

In all probability the dissimilar gametophytes and sporophytes of plants likewise have evolved in conjunction with terrestrial ways of life. Since the zygotes of diplohaplontic green algae typically are flagellate and swimming, and since a swimming zygote would be inappropriate on land, a first prerequisite for a diplohaplontic terrestrial plant would be oögamy; eggs and sperms would be formed, and the eggs would be nonmotile and retained in the sex organs. As a result, the sporophytes then developing from fertilized eggs would

A

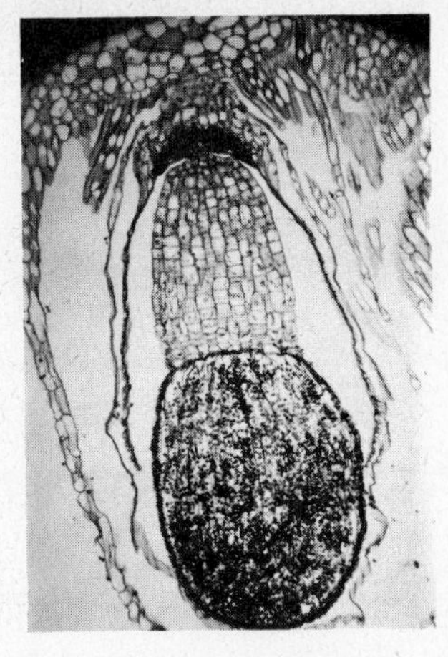
B

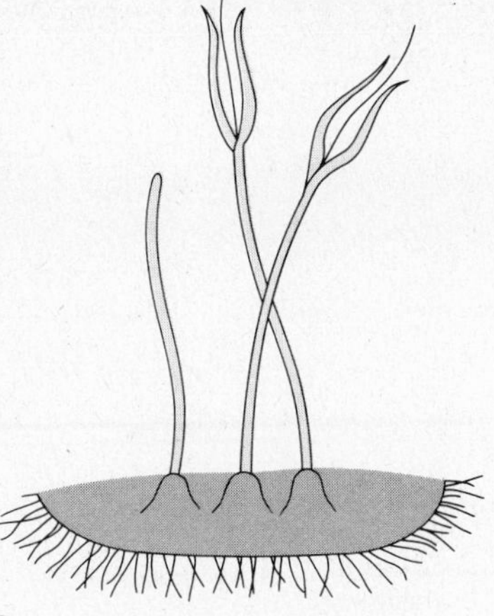
C

25.22 Bryophyte sporophytes. *A, moss gametophytes bearing attached sporophytes on top. B, the sporophyte of the liverwort Marchantia. C, hornwort gametophyte with elongated sporophytes growing from it. Spores are produced inside the whole length of a sporophyte. (A, courtesy Carolina Biological Supply Company.)*

have to remain attached to the gametophytes, on which the sex organs are located. The whole structure and metabolic nature of a sporophyte is therefore likely to change in conjunction with the attached, dependent way of life. For example, the sporophyte no longer absorbs from the physical environment but from the gametophyte, hence it does not require structures for nutrient absorption from soil. Indeed it can become a heterotrophic parasite altogether, as is actually the case in most bryophytic sporophytes. Even in primitive vascular plants the immature sporophytes are temporarily dependent on the gametophytes; and practically the whole reproductive evolution of vascular plants can be characterized as a series of attempts, ultimately successful, of making the sporophytes completely independent of the gametophytes.

bryophytes

The gametophyte generation is dominant in the bryophytes, and, as pointed out in Chap. 10, an unqualified reference to a moss or a liverwort is a reference to the haploid, gamete-producing plant. These gametophytes have well-developed means of vegetative propagation. In the liverwort *Marchantia,* for example, older parts of a thallus often die off, leaving younger branch thalli as separate plants. In addition to such fragmentation by *posterior decay,* many liverworts form *gemma cups* on the surfaces of their thalli. In these cups develop successive sets of buds called *gemmae,* each an upright spindle-shaped cell group attached by a tiny stalk. Gemmae are readily dislodged by rain drops, and if the water carries them to suitable ground they develop into new plants (Fig. 25.20).

The sex organs develop in different regions in different bryophyte groups. Mosses typically form such organs at the tips of their leafy shoots. In liverworts the sex organs arise in some cases directly on the surface of a thallus, in others in receptacles fromed on stalks that grow up from the thallus (Fig. 25.21). Regardless of the location, a male organ, or antheridium, consists of an external protective layer and of sperm-forming cells in the interior. Each such cell matures as a biflagellate sperm. In the female organ, or archegonium, a large egg lies in the expanded part (*venter*) of a flask-shaped protective layer. The narrow neck of this organ provides a sperm path to the egg. Many bryophytes are hermaphroditic, others are separately sexed.

Fertilization requires free water; continuous films of water must be present between nearby sex organs, or fluid droplets must carry sperms to archegonia. After sperms enter an archegonium, one fertilizes the egg. The zygote then grows into a diploid, few-celled embryo that later matures as an adult sporophyte, still attached to the gametophyte. Such a sporophyte consists of a basal *foot* anchored in the archegonium, a *stalk* of different lengths in different bryophyte groups, and a terminal *sporangium* (Fig. 25.22). The cells of developing sporophytes are photosynthetic, but in all except those of hornworts the chlorophyll is lost as sporophytes become mature. Such

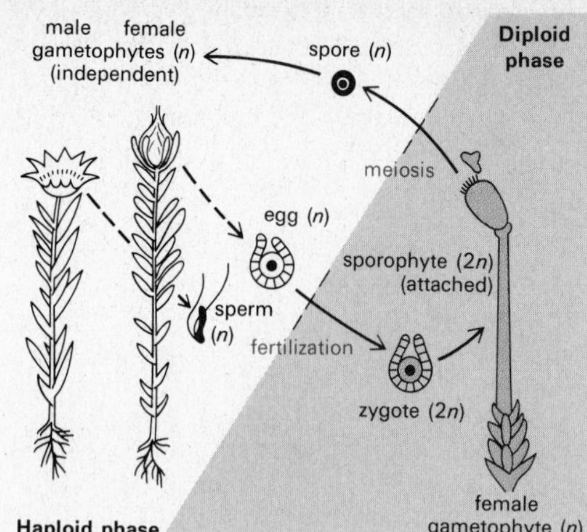

25.23 Bryophyte life cycles. *A moss cycle is summarized.*

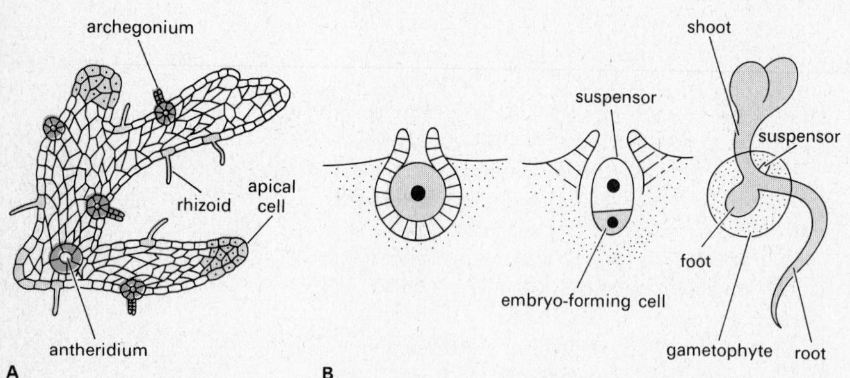

25.24 Development in primitive tracheophytes. *A, diagram of a psilopsid gametophyte. The plantlet is near-microscopic and partly embedded in soil. B, in most of the primitive tracheophytes the zygote formed in an archegonium of a female gametophyte (left) divides into a suspensor-forming and an embryo-forming cell (center). The latter then proliferates and gives rise to a sporophyte (right). See also Fig. 25.25 and Color Fig. 25.*

sporophytes are therefore nutritionally dependent on the green gametophytes to which they remain attached.

In a sporangium, generating cells called *spore mother cells* undergo meiosis and give rise to spores. Each of these secretes a heavy wall around itself. The sporangia of liverworts and hornworts also produce *elaters,* hygroscopic cellular filaments with spirally thickened inner walls. Interspersed among the spores, elaters twist and coil as they dry out. These jerky motions aid in flipping the spores out of a mature sporangium that has become brittle and has broken open. After its spores are shed, a sporophyte dies off. This phase of the bryophyte life cycle is therefore short-lived compared with the gametophyte phase. On suitable ground, spores germinate and develop into new gametophytes (Fig. 25.23).

tracheophytes: the primitive pattern

Regardless of how well adapted to land the gametophyte generation of bryophytes might be in other respects, it is not really well adapted in its reproduction; gametic reproduction requires free external water for the swimming sperms, but ample water is not always available in a terrestrial environment. As noted, bryophytes succeed nevertheless by gearing their sperm release to wet periods.

Primitive tracheophytes actually cannot do much better. However, in their life cycles the emphasis is on the diploid sporophyte, not on the gametophyte. The sporophyte produces encapsulated spores, excellently adapted to terrestrial conditions; and the gametophyte is reduced to microscopic dimensions and to a generally short-lived existence. This deemphasis of the gametophyte reduces the water problem correspondingly.

The pattern is well illustrated in psilopsids, lycopsids, and sphenopsids. Most of these plants have evolved with life cycles in which the sporophyte and gametophyte generations are separate green organisms that live in soil independently. But the gametophytes are exceedingly tiny, often near-microscopic ground-hugging plantlets. Most of them are hermaphroditic, and they usually live only just long enough to produce antheridia and archegonia. These sex organs are structured essentially as in bryophytes (Fig. 25.24).

Fertilization, too, takes place as in bryophytes, during wet periods. A zygote in an archegonium divides, and of the two cells so formed one gives rise to a microscopic holdfast, or *suspensor.* This structure, equivalent to the foot of a bryophytic sporophyte, anchors the embryo to the archegonium and the gametophyte. The second cell formed by the zygote gives rise to the embryo proper. Through repeated divisions it produces an embryonic stem and root (stem only in psilopsids), and these organs soon penetrate through gametophyte tissues and establish independent contact with the ground. Tiny erect branch shoots eventually break through above the soil and on them form the first microphylls. At this stage the sporophyte is a young adult, already far larger than the gametophyte that gave rise to it. Indeed the gametophyte may already have degenerated completely.

Mature sporophytes develop sporangia of different types in the different groups. In psilopsids the sporangia form in bulbous capsules growing on the aerial stems (see Fig. 10.28). Lycopsids and sphenopsids produce cones, or *strobili,* at the upper ends of aerial stems (Color Fig. 25). Each such strobilus bears closely set cone leaves, or *sporophylls,* on which sporangia develop. As in bryophytes, spore mother cells in a sporangium undergo meiosis and give rise to encapsulated spores.

The lycopsid *Selaginella* is of particular interest; it produces *two* types of spore, small *microspores* (formed in *microsporangia*) and larger *megaspores* (formed in *megasporangia,* Fig. 25.25). Microspores develop into *microgametophytes,* which produce sperms only; and megaspores develop into *megagametophytes,* which produce eggs only. Both types of gametophyte are microscopic and nongreen, and they are not independent plants. Instead they are retained inside the sporangia in which they form, and sperms must then swim from microsporangia to eggs in megasporangia. As will become apparent below, production of two spore types (*heterospory*) parallels the pattern encountered in seed plants; *Selaginella* evidently is a result of a reproductive evolution that was followed independently also by seed plants but that did not proceed as far as in seed plants.

A generally bryophytelike reproductive pattern is in evidence also in the most primitive pteropsids, the ferns. The plant familiarly called a "fern" represents the dominant sporophyte. It is large, leafy, green, and it persists the year round. At certain seasons cells on the underside of fern leaves give rise to stalked, lens-shaped sporangia. Several sporangia usually develop in the same area of a leaf. Such a group, called a *sorus,* is often covered by an *indusium,* a single-layered, sometimes pigmented shield of tissue (Color Fig. 26). In many cases sori form in regular double rows, one row on each side of a main leaf vein. Internally a sporangium contains spore mother cells that undergo meiosis and give rise to encapsulated haploid spores.

Sporangia eventually dry out and rupture, and in the process the spores are forcefully catapulted out. Such spores later develop into haploid gametophytes. Each of these is a green plantlet consisting mainly of a heart-shaped plate of tissue, flat on moist, shaded ground and measuring not more than about $\frac{1}{4}$ in. across (see Color Fig. 26). Rhizoids that project from the underside into the soil serve an absorptive function. In size, way of life, and function, this inconspicuous gametophyte greatly resembles a gametophyte of, for example, liverworts.

On the lower side of the gametophyte develop the sex organs. In hermaphroditic ferns the antheridia usually form near the tip of the heart-shaped plant, archegonia near the notch. The locations of these organs are similar also in separately sexed species. As in bryophytes, ground water must be present if the flagellate swimming sperms are to reach eggs (Fig. 25.26). After fertilization the zygote is retained in the archegonium and develops into a small, diploid, sporo-

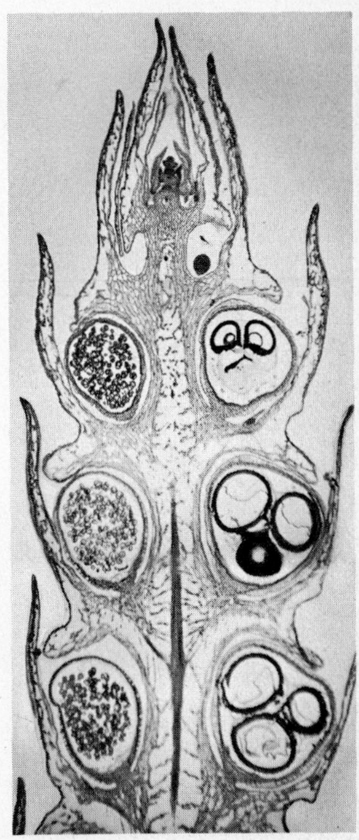

***25.25 Selaginella* reproduction.** *Longitudinal section through a cone showing microsporophylls with microsporangia at left side and megasporophylls with megasporangia on right side.*

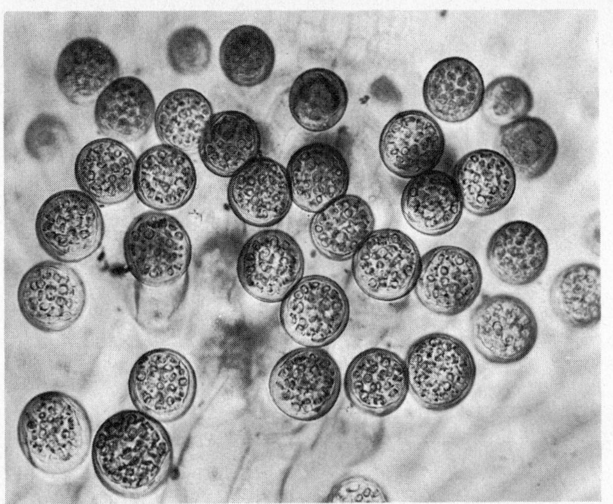

A

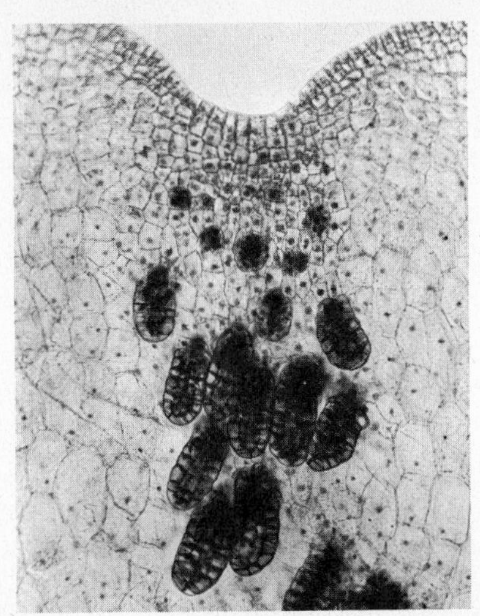

B

25.26 Fern reproduction. *A, some antheridia on a gametophyte. B, some archegonia on a gametophyte. A whole gametophyte is shown in Color Fig. 26. See also Fig. 25.27.*

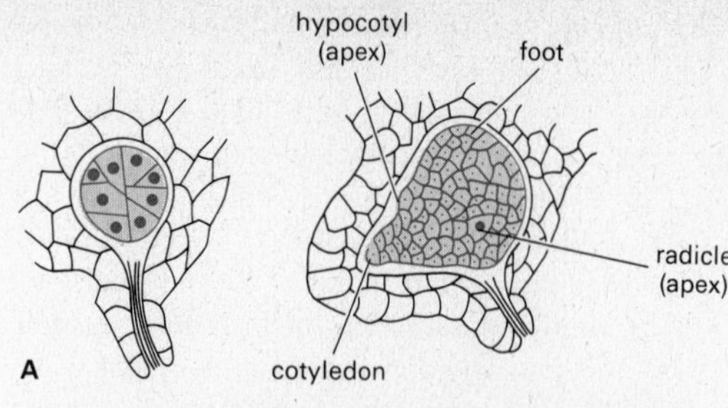

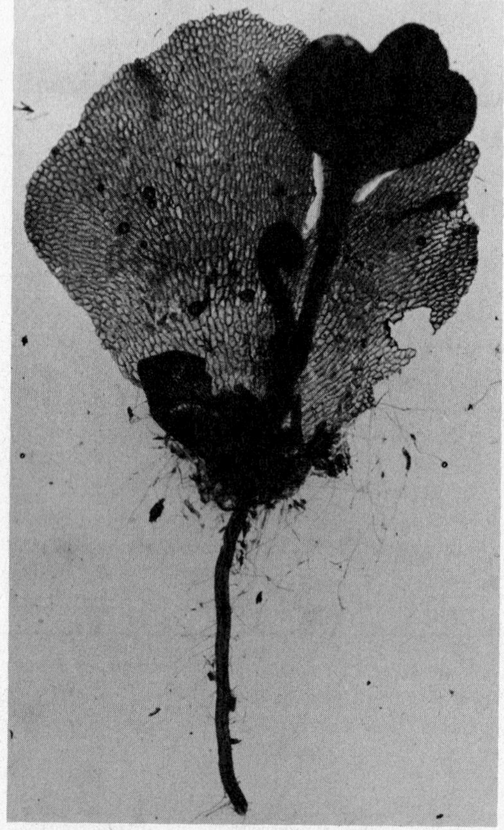

25.27 **Fern reproduction.** *A, two stages in the development of a sporophyte embryo inside an archegonium. B, gametophyte with developing sporophyte still attached. Note sporophyte root and leaf.*

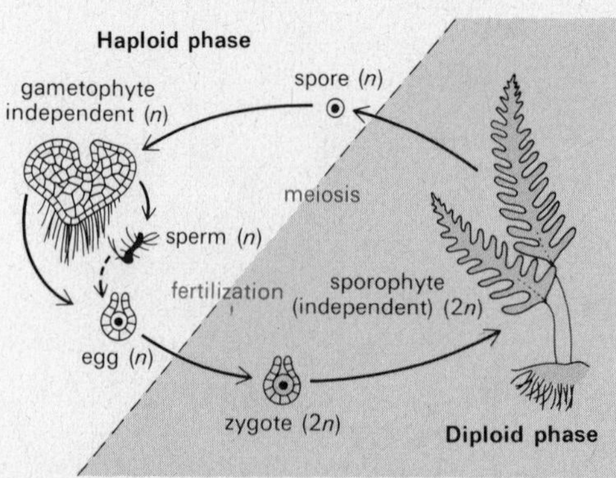

25.28 **Fern life cycle,** *summary.*

phyte embryo. Four organ zones become recognizable in it: a *suspensor,* which anchors the whole embryo to the base of the archegonium; a *radicle,* the embryonic root; a *hypocotyl,* the embryonic stem; and a *cotyledon,* the embryonic leaf (Fig. 25.27). At this stage the embryo is still without chlorophyll and depends on food supplied by the gametophyte. But soon the root and stem penetrate through the archegonial tissues and the leaf greens. Thereafter the gametophyte shrivels and degenerates, leaving the young sporophyte as a separate, independent plant (Fig. 25.28).

Evidently, the primitive vascular plants and the ferns do not differ too greatly in their gametophytes from those of bryophytes. And although these various vascular plants have highly developed sporophytes, well adapted to the general lack of free water on land, their gametophytes still must cope with a fundamental difficulty, the water requirement in fertilization. Only the seed plants have fully circumvented this problem.

tracheophytes: the seed-forming pattern

Apart from *Selaginella* (and also several long extinct fossil lycopsids), all plants discussed so far are *homosporous;* the spores produced by each are indistinguishable, and one cannot tell ahead of time whether a given spore will become a male gametophyte, a female gametophyte, or a hermaphrodite. By contrast, seed plants are *heterosporous* (like *Selaginella*); each produces two kinds of spore (*microspores* in *microsporangia,* forming male *microgametophytes,* and *megaspores* in *megasporangia,* forming female *megagametophytes*). This heterosporous condition, evolved independently in the ancestors of seed plants, has prepared the way for the later evolution of seeds.

The life cycle of a seed plant thus begins with diploid sporophytes that develop microsporangia and megasporangia (Fig. 25.29). Some species form the two types of sporangium in the same plant (*monoecious* condition), others, in different plants (*dioecious* condition). Spore mother cells in the sporangia then undergo meiosis, and the haploid products become microspores and megaspores, respectively.

A microspore gives rise to a male gametophyte that consists of a few cells only and that remains enclosed by the wall of the microspore. Such a walled microgametophyte is a *pollen grain.* In comparable fashion, a megaspore develops into a few-celled female gametophyte that is retained in the megasporangium in which it is produced. Megasporangia are also called *ovules*.

Next, pollen grains are dispersed from the microsporangia and are carried by wind or animals to the ovules. This dispersion, leading eventually to contact between pollen grains and ovules, is called *pollination*.

Thereafter, the male gametophyte inside a pollen grain develops a *pollen tube* that carries sperms or sperm nuclei at the tip. This tube digests a path to the female gametophyte in which an egg has matured by this time. The tip of the pollen tube makes contact with this egg, and a sperm nucleus then enters and brings about *fertilization.* Pollination and fertilization are therefore distinct and separate events; in some cases several months intervene between them. The pollen tube is an evolutionary innovation lacking in *Selaginella* (and all earlier heterosporous plants); and it is this tube that circumvents the requirement of free water in fertilization. The success of seed plants rests in large measure on the evolution of such tubes.

The fertilized egg, the female gametophyte, the surrounding wall of the megaspore, and the surrounding tissues of the ovule, all together now represent a *seed.* The outer layers of the ovule usually harden to a tough *seed coat.* In a seed, the zygote develops as a sporophyte embryo; and through later dispersion from the parent plant and through seed germination, an independent young sporophyte becomes established eventually. In effect, the gametophyte generation remains hidden throughout, and the visible reproductive pattern of a seed plant is sporophyte → seed → sporophyte.

Ripe seeds usually remain *dormant* for variously long periods, even centuries in some cases. Such dormancy is adaptively advantageous, for it lengthens the time available for seed dispersal and thereby improves the chance that germination will occur in a suitable environment. Development of a dormant seed actually appears to be triggered specifically by a favorable environment. The dormant condition is in some respects similar to the state of hibernation encountered in various mammals; the rate of respiration and of metabolism in general is exceptionally low, and reserve foods are used up exceedingly slowly. The mechanisms by which such states are initiated, maintained, and terminated are as yet largely unknown.

gymnosperms

In almost all gymnosperms the reproductive structures form in cones, or *strobili.* In a pine, for example, small microstrobili develop in clusters on the ends of tree branches. In such a cone the underside of each cone leaf (*microsporophyll*) bears two microsporangia (Fig. 25.30). In these, microspore mother cells undergo meiosis and give rise to microspores. Each such spore has a two-layered wall. The outer one will later separate

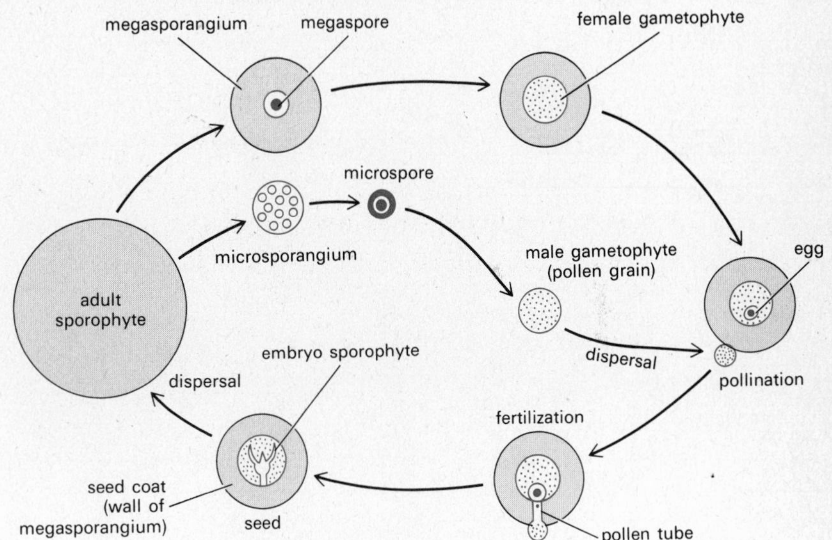

25.29 Seed plant reproduction, basic pattern.

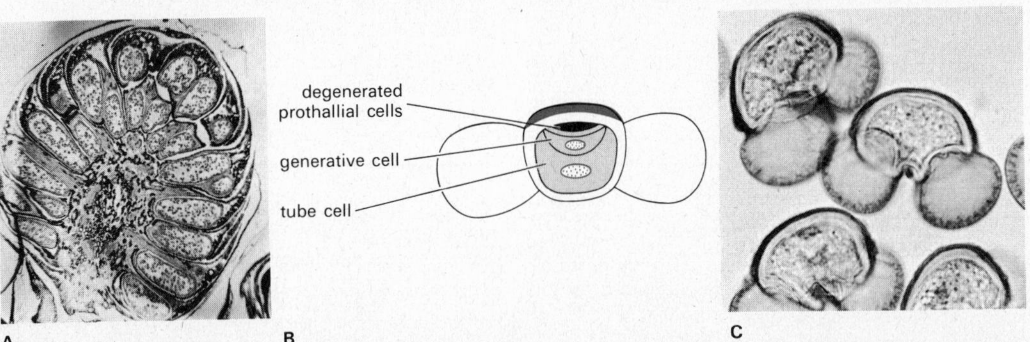

25.30 Pine reproduction: microspores. *A,* longitudinal section through a microspore-producing cone. *B, C,* mature microspores, or pollen grains.

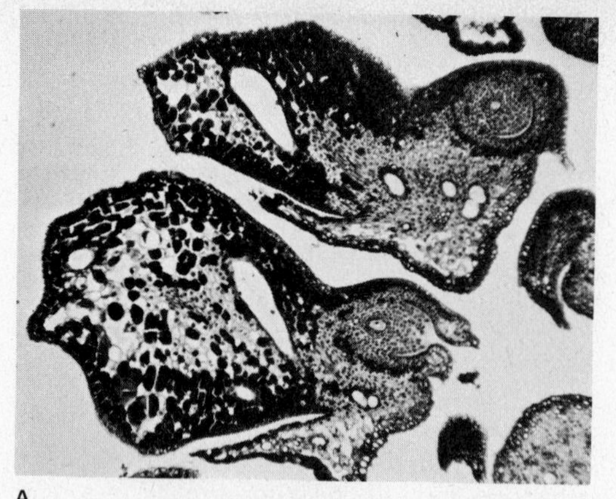

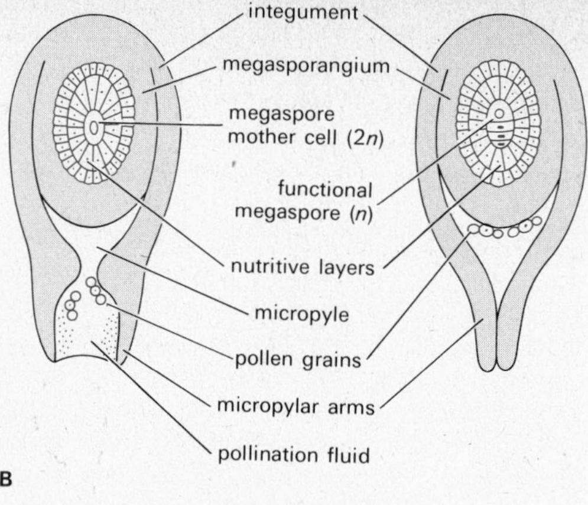

25.31 Pine reproduction: megaspores. *A, section through two ovule-bearing scales of megaspore-producing cone, showing megasporangia. In each megasporangium note the large central megaspore mother cell, the surrounding megasporangial tissues, and the outer integument with micropylar arms (pointing to right). B, the early development of a megasporangium. Left, before meiosis; right, after meiosis.*

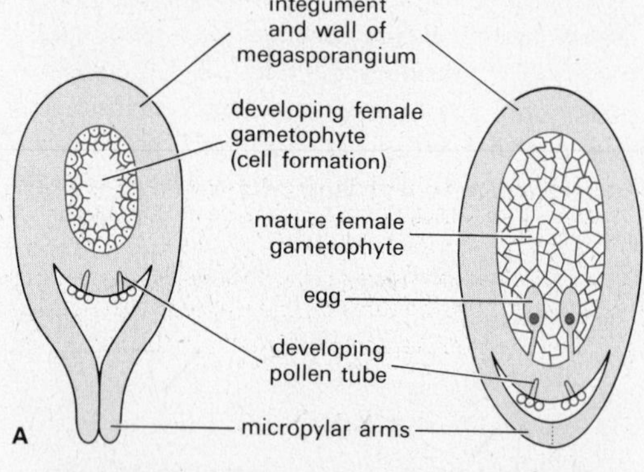

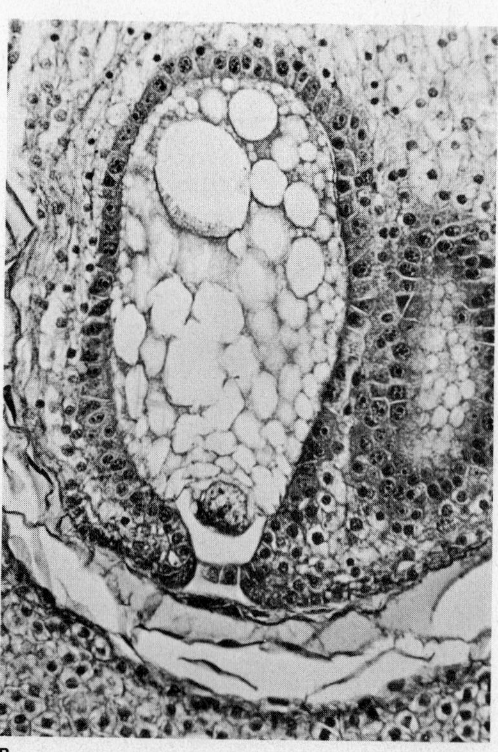

25.32 Pine reproduction: the female gametophyte. *A, cell formation in the developing female gametophyte. B, the mature female gametophyte with egg (near bottom). Megasporangial tissue surrounds the gametophyte.*

partially and form two conspicuous "wings." The inner one encloses the microspore cell, which divides and produces one small and one large cell. The small cell divides once more and forms two *prothallial cells,* which represent the whole vegetative portion of the male gametophyte. They eventually disintegrate and play no further role. The larger cell also divides, producing a smaller *generative cell* and a larger *tube cell.* At such a stage of development a pollen grain is mature and is shed from the microsporangium.

Pines also bear larger *megastrobili,* in which woody cone scales carry paired ovules (Fig. 25.31). An ovule is bounded on the outside by an *integument,* a tissue layer extended on one side as two flaps, the *micropylar arms.* Between these arms is a narrow canal, the *micropyle,* which leads to the main part of the ovule. Deep in this part a single megaspore mother cell undergoes meiosis. Of the four haploid cells so produced three degenerate, and the remaining one is the functional megaspore.

When pollination occurs, some pollen grains usually fall into the space between the micropylar arms. In this region the ovule secretes a *pollination fluid,* which traps pollen grains and permits them to sink deep into the micropyle. In this manner pollen grains come to make contact with the inner tissues of the ovule. After pollination the outer tips of the cone scales fuse to one another, and the whole cone thereby becomes sealed off from the environment.

The following events in a pine ovule occur exceedingly slowly; about a year elapses between pollination and fertilization. During this time the whole cone and its contents increase in size and each megaspore enlarges and elongates. Also, the megaspore nucleus divides repeatedly until some

2,000 haploid nuclei are present. Cell walls are then laid down between these nuclei, and in this way the megaspore is transformed to a multicellular female gametophyte. On the side of the micropyle a few highly reduced sex organs develop, each with an egg (Fig. 25.32).

In the meantime, the pollen grain resting against the ovule develops also (Fig. 25.33). The tube cell of each pollen grain elongates slowly and produces a pollen tube, which secretes enzymes that digest a path through ovule tissue. The generative cell of the male gametophyte divides, and the two resulting cells (*stalk* cell and *body* cell) migrate toward the tip of the pollen tube, where the tube-cell nucleus is already present. The nucleus of the body cell later divides once again, forming two *sperm nuclei.* Fertilization occurs when a pollen tube penetrates into an egg and discharges all four nuclei at the tip into the egg cytoplasm. All except one sperm nucleus degenerates, and that nucleus fuses with the egg nucleus. The resulting diploid zygote represents the beginning of a new sporophyte gneration. (In cycads and ginkgos, division of the body cell results not in two nuclei only but in two whole sperm *cells.* These become multiflagellate and *swim* through the pollen tube to the egg. Undoubtedly this is an evolutionary relic condition reminiscent of the swimming sperms of the ancestors of seed plants.)

Several or all of the eggs present in a female gametophyte can become fertilized independently, but in pines only one zygote usually develops much further. It soon forms 16 cells arranged as four groups of four, one quartet below the other. The four cells of the uppermost quartet are *embryo initials;* each begins to produce an embryo (see Fig. 25.33). One usually develops faster than the others, and eventually only that one develops further; the other three degenerate. The next lower quartet of cells elongates as a suspensor that attaches the embryo to the gametophyte tissues and pushes it deep into these tissues.

Repeated divisions of the embryo initial soon transform it to a distinct embryo with young root, stem, and two or more embryonic leaves (cotyledons). The whole embryo is embedded in the remains of the female gametophyte, which in turn is surrounded by the remains of the ovule and the external integument. The latter has hardened by this time to a seed coat, and the "wings" of the seed have formed (Fig. 25.34).

Pine seeds are ripe several months after fertil-

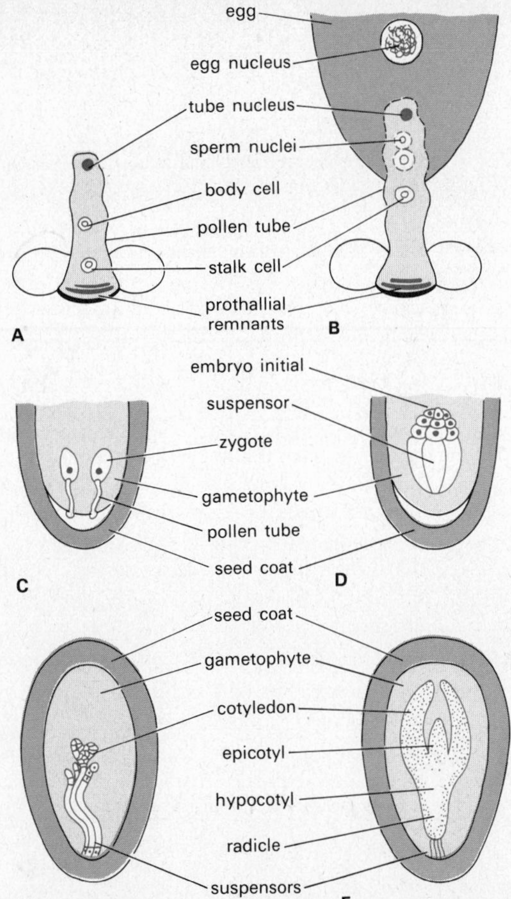

25.33 Pine reproduction: fertilization and development. *A, pollen tube growth. B, fertilization. Sperm nuclei have formed from the body cell; all four nuclei at the tip of the pollen tube are discharged into the egg. C, the zygote has formed from one of the sperm nuclei and the egg nucleus. D, division of the zygote has given rise to tiers of cells, of which the upper will form the embryo, the rest the suspensor. E, the seed coat has hardened, and the embryo initials have proliferated and given rise to an early embryo. F, later embryo, with embryonic leaves (cotyledons), stem apex (epicotyl), and embryonic stem and root (hypocotyl and radicle).*

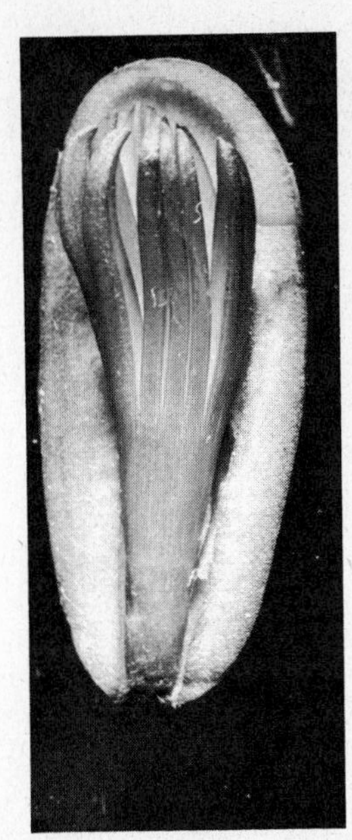

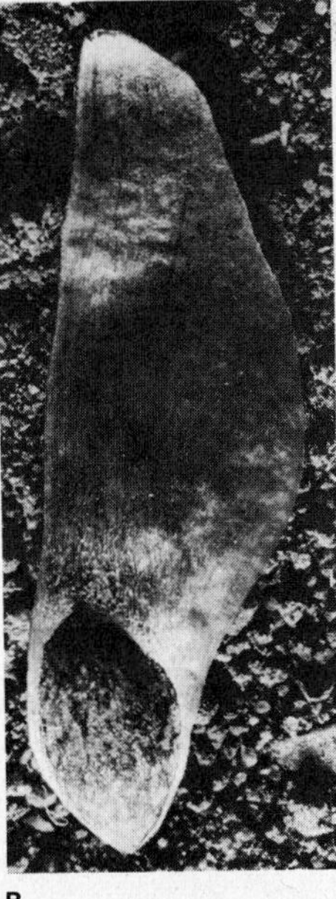

25.34 Pine seeds. *A, dissected seed showing embryo and surrounding female gametophyte. B, the mature winged seed at time of dispersal.*

ization. At that time the cone scales become brittle and spread open, and the seeds can then become dispersed (Color Fig. 27). The name "gymnosperm" indicates that these plants form naked, exposed seeds. Not all gymnosperms require 2 or 3 years for seed formation, like pines, with pollination occurring one year and fertilization not until the next. In spruces, for example, the time interval between pollination and fertilization is only a few weeks. Such time variations notwithstanding, the reproductive processes themselves are basically the same in all gymnosperms.

angiosperms

In this group of plants the equivalents of gymnosperm cones are *flowers* (Color Fig. 28). Whereas cone leaves are attached around a more or less elongated central stem, flower leaves grow out from a highly shortened and flattened stem terminal, the *receptacle.* From this receptacle arise a *calyx,* consisting of a whorl of *sepals;* a *corolla,* consisting of a whorl of *petals;* a circularly arranged set of *stamens;* and a central *pistil* (or *carpel*). Stamens are modified leaves, each composed of a stalk and a terminal *anther* in which the microsporangia develop. Similarly, the pistil is a highly modified, fused set of leaves. It is composed of a terminal *stigma,* a middle *style,* and an expanded basal *ovary* that contains the ovules.

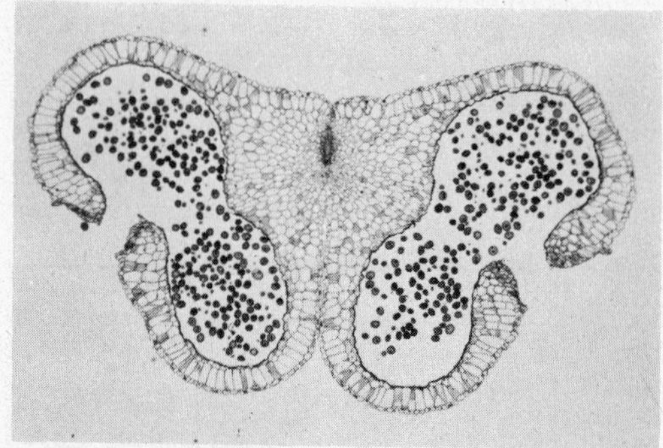

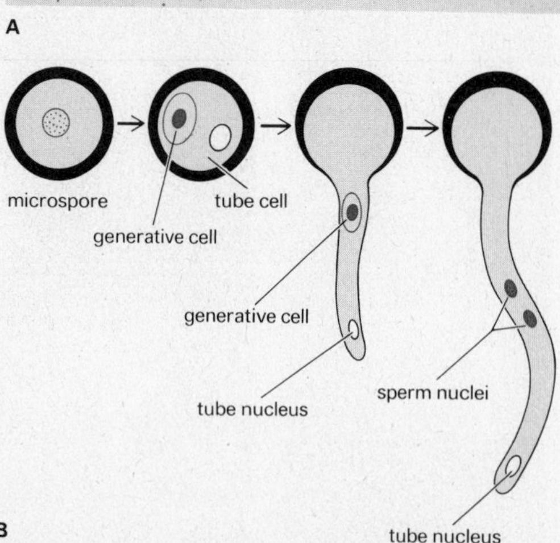

25.35 Pollen grains. *A, cross section through the anther of a lily. Note the two spore sacs, the openings in these sacs, and the microspores (pollen grains). B, development of a microspore.*

Flowers can be with or without calyx or corolla. Where these leaves are present, they may or may not be pigmented (other than green) and they may or may not produce scents. Pigments and scents are familiar adaptations that attract various pollen-dispersing animals (bees, wasps, butterflies, moths, in some cases small birds, as well as men). Plants depending on animals for pollination generally also secrete abundant nectar (sugar water) in their flowers. Many ingenious structural devices have evolved through which only particular animal types can have access to the nectar of a particular flower type. Potential "robbers" either cannot enter the flower or cannot reach the nectar stores. But qualified animals such as bees often find landing platforms, colored guide marks on petals, and other conveniences. As such animals reach for nectar they pick up new pollen on their body surfaces or deposit pollen from other flowers visited earlier.

Some species of angiosperms are regularly *self-pollinating;* pollen grains fall on the stigma of the same flower and develop normally thereafter. Most angiosperms depend on *cross-pollination,* however; pollen grains from one flower must be transferred to the stigma of other flowers of the same species.

In the anthers, formation of microspores occurs as in gymnosperms by meiosis (Fig. 25.35). The microspore nucleus then divides once, producing a *generative nucleus* and a *tube nucleus.* The generative nucleus soon divides once more and forms two *sperm nuclei.* The whole male gametophyte thus consists of a single cell with three nuclei.

A comparably condensed development occurs in the ovary, which contains one or more ovules (Fig. 25.36). As in gymnosperms, a micropyle in each ovule leads past the integument to the inner tissues. A single deep-lying megaspore mother cell there undergoes meiosis, and of the four resulting haploid cells one persists as a functional megaspore. The nucleus of this spore cell divides mitotically three time in succession. Four of the resulting eight haploid nuclei come to lie at one end of the spore cell, four at the other. Three of each group of four soon become partitioned off as independent cells, and the remaining two, called *polar nuclei,* migrate to the center of what is now a seventh large cell. These seven cells represent the entire female gametophyte. Sex organs are not formed at all. Instead, of the three gametophyte cells near the micropyle, one becomes an egg directly.

The pollen of angiosperms is dispersed partly by wind, partly by insects and other animals. Numerous pollen grains can become trapped on the sticky stigma of a pistil (Fig. 25.37). Each grain then produces (usually) one pollen tube, which grows between the cells of the style toward the ovary. Such a tube generally enters an ovule through the micropyle and digests a path through the ovule tissues. The tip of the tube contains the two sperm nuclei, both of which are eventually discharged into the female gametophyte.

The next event is *double fertilization,* unique to the angiosperms (see Fig. 25.37). One of the sperm nuclei enters the egg and fertilizes it. The other sperm nucleus migrates to the two polar nuclei in the large central cell of the female gametophyte, and all three of these nuclei fuse together as a so-called *endosperm nucleus.* Being formed from three haploid nuclei, the endosperm nucleus is *triploid,* with three sets of chromosomes. This nucleus then divides repeatedly, cell walls are usually laid down, and the tissue so formed is the *endosperm.* It soon fills up the space formerly occupied by the female gametophyte. Endosperm cells accumulate food substances from the parent sporophyte.

While the endosperm develops, the zygote divides and gives rise to a sporophyte embryo (Fig. 25.38). In it develop seed leaves, or cotyledons, one or two depending on the subclass of angiosperms (see Chap. 10). The whole embryo is embedded in endosperm, and this tissue gradually contributes more or less of its food to the developing sporophyte. In a mature seed, therefore, endosperm may or may not be present. Where the endosperm is absent, its substance has become incorporated in the cotyledons, and these are likely to be massive, as in peanuts or peas. But if the endosperm is still extensive, the cotyledons are likely to be thin and leafy, as in corn seeds (Fig. 25.39).

The seeds in an ovary soon develop hardened seed coats, and much of the flower then withers. On the contrary, the ovary and in some cases also parts of the receptacle enlarge rapidly and mature as a *fruit.* This structure can become *dry*

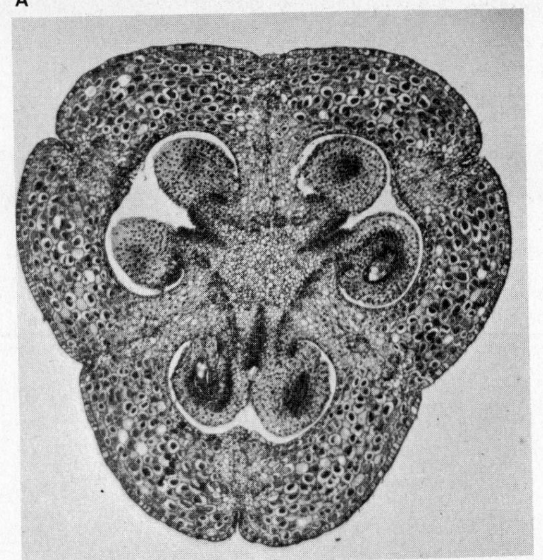

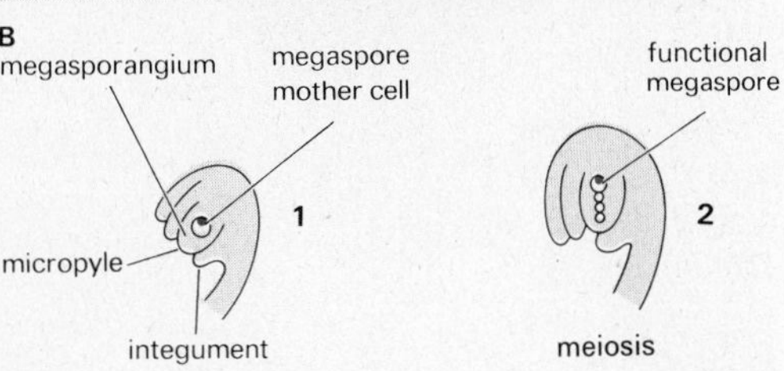

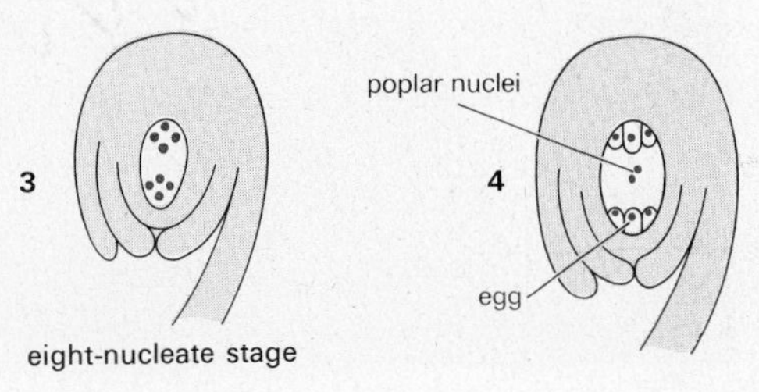

25.36 The female gametophyte. *A, cross section through the ovary of a lily. Note the ovary wall (which will eventually give rise to the "meat" of a fruit) and the three pairs of ovules containing female gametophytes. B, the basic pattern of the development of a female gametophyte in angiosperms. 1, the megasporangium. 2, meiosis and functional megaspore. 3, eight-nucleate stage of gametophyte. 4, egg formation and polar nuclei.*

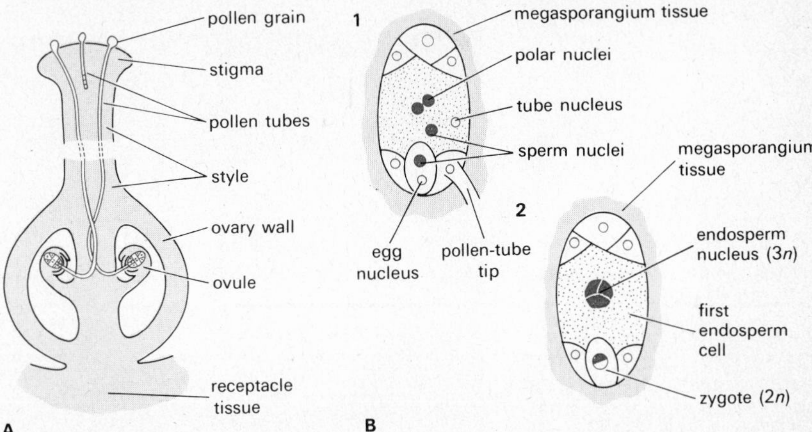

25.37 *(Below)* **Pollen tubes and fertilization.** *A, growth of pollen tubes after pollination. B, fertilization. 1, double fertilization. One sperm nucleus fuses with the egg nucleus, and the other sperm nucleus combines with the two polar nuclei. 2, the triploid endosperm nucleus and the diploid zygote.*

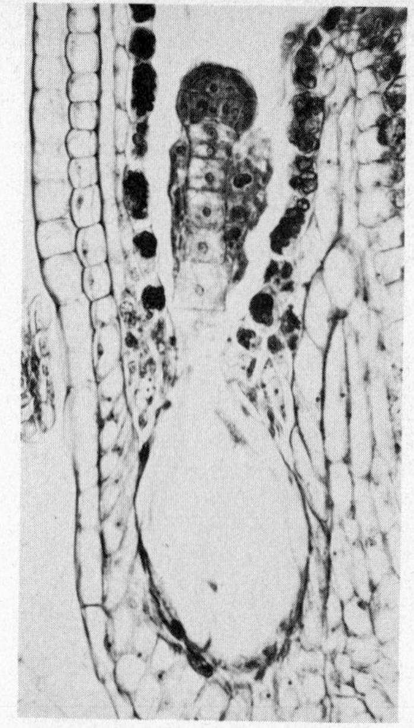

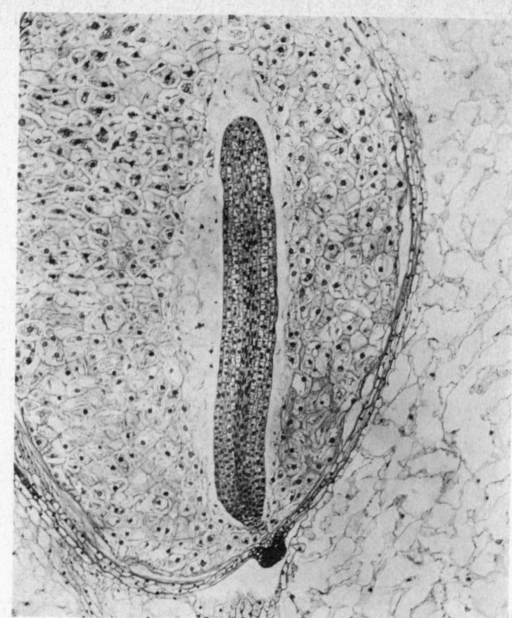

25.38 Early angiosperm development. *A, early embryo attached by suspensor to ovule wall. B, older embryo (of lily) surrounded by endosperm. Note short suspensor.*

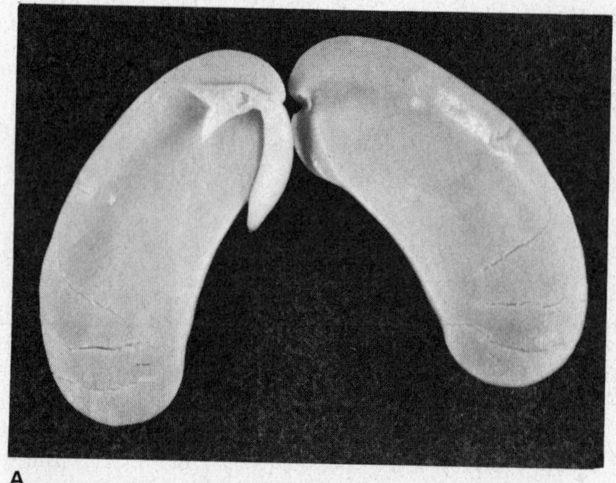

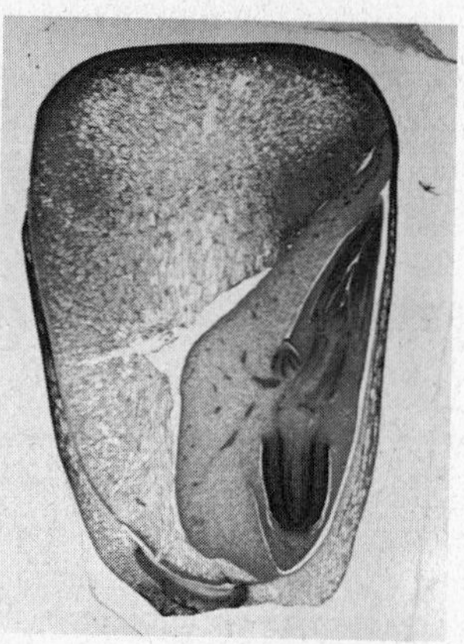

25.39 Seeds. *A, dissected bean seed showing the two large endosperm-filled cotyledons and the small embryo with rootlet and developing leaves. B, section through corn seed (kernel) showing embryo at right and endosperm tissue filling rest of seed. The single seed leaf, or cotyledon, is small in this case.*

25.40 Fruit structure. *Equatorial section through an apple, showing the ovary, composed of five seed chambers (ovules) with seeds, and the expanded ovary wall, which makes up much of the "meat" of this fruit.*

or *fleshy,* and it hides the seeds inside it. The name "angiosperm" indicates that these plants produce "hidden" seeds, embedded in fruits (Fig. 25.40).

Thus the reproduction of angiosperms is characterized by three major features not encountered in gymnosperms: the *flower* itself; double fertilization, resulting in the inclusion of *endosperm* tissue in seeds; and the *fruit,* which contains a number of seeds. Each of these evolutionary innovations is of pronounced adaptive value. The flower often promotes pollination by attracting insects. The endosperm nourishes the embryo. And the fruit promotes seed dispersal and seed germination; for if fleshy fruits are eaten by animals, seeds are usually spit out or egested in new locations. Dry fruits such as nuts may be carried about by squirrels, for example, and are often left in some forgotten hiding place. Fruits with burrs, hooks, or wing blades are distributed widely by animals and wind. And fruits that simply fall to the ground eventually decay and thereby aid seed development indirectly by enriching a patch of soil.

It can be concluded that the solution to the problem of terrestrial reproduction is rather similar in seed plants and terrestrial animals. As the next chapter will show, most terrestrial animals circumvent the requirement of external water by copulation and *internal* fertilization: a male deposits sperms directly into a female containing mature eggs. In seed plants internal fertilization in a sense takes place as well. A sporophyte produces microspores and, through them, sperm nuclei. Another sporophyte produces megaspores and, through them, eggs. The sperm nuclei then reach the eggs by means of pollen tubes, which are the plant equivalents of the copulating organs of animals.

---

review questions

1 Review the reproductive patterns of Monera. What are conidia and sporangiospores? Describe experiments through which bacterial sex has been discovered. What are endospores? How can Monera adapt if sexuality is rare?

2 Describe reproductive processes among green algae. Which groups of these organisms exhibit which type of life cycle? Review the reproduction of charophytes, euglenophytes, and pyrrophytes. In what respects is charophyte reproduction atypical for Protista?

3 Outline the processes of sporulation and gametic reproduction in *Ulothrix*. Show how gametic reproduction occurs in *Spirogyra* and *Oedogonium*. How do these three algal types differ in the degrees of distinction between the sexes?

4 Outline the life cycle of (*a*) *Volvox*, (*b*) diatoms, (*c*) *Fucus*. Describe the life cycle of slime molds. Review the reproductive patterns of protozoa. Which protozoa are syngamous, and which mate with nuclear exchange? Review the reproductive significance of syngens.

5 What reproductive processes occur in Phycomycetes? Through what sequence of processes are ascospores produced? Describe the life cycle of yeasts. Define plasmogamy and karyogamy.

6 What are basidia and how are they formed? What is the reproductive function of a mushroom? In what ways is the reproduction of terrestrial fungi well adapted to the absence of locomotion among the organisms and to the general lack of free environmental water?

7 What features characterize the reproduction of all Metaphyta? Describe the structure of the sex organs in primitive plants. Describe the detailed life cycle of a bryophyte. In what respects is it (*a*) well adapted to terrestrial life, (*b*) poorly adapted?

8 Define homospory, heterospory, microsporangium, megasporophyll, megaspore mother cell. Describe the reproduction and life cycles of primitive tracheophytes. Indicate where gametes and spores are formed. In what respects is the reproduction of *Selaginella* different from that of other lycopsids?

9 Describe the life cycle of a fern. Compare it with that of bryophytes; what is similar and what is different? What are the adaptive advantages of a dominant diploid phase?

10 Review the general reproductive processes among seed plants. What are monoecious and dioecious conditions? Distinguish between pollination and fertilization. In what ways are seeds particularly advantageous in a terrestrial life?

11 Outline the specific life cycle of a pine. Define seed, pollen tube, self-pollination, ovule, microgametophyte.

12 Describe the structure and adaptive significance of a flower and the detailed life cycle of angiosperms. Define ovary, double fertilization, endosperm, fruit. What is the adaptive significance of endosperms and fruits?

collateral readings

Arditti, J.: Orchids, *Sci. American,* Jan., 1966. A case study of adaptations in flower structure.

Biale, J. B.: The Ripening of Fruit, *Sci. American,* May, 1954. The tissue changes and differentiation processes are discussed.

Bonner, J. T.: How Slime Molds Communicate, *Sci. American,* Aug., 1963. An examination of the mechanism by which fruiting bodies are formed.

Clevenger, S.: Flower Pigments, *Sci. American,* June, 1964. An account of the chemical structure and genetic origins of these compounds.

Doyle, W. R.: "Nonvascular Plants: Form and Function," Wadsworth, Belmont, Calif., 1964. The reproduction of protistan groups and of bryophytes is among the topics of this paperback.

Echlin, P.: Pollen, *Sci. American,* Apr., 1968. An electron-microscopic study of these reproductive bodies is described.

Galston, A. W.: "The Life of the Green Plant," 2d ed., Prentice-Hall, Englewood Cliffs, N.J., 1964. A paperback containing accounts on reproductive and developmental processes in vascular plants.

Grant, V.: The Fertilization of Flowers, *Sci. American,* June, 1961. The article discusses the adaptive features of flowers and the related adaptions of pollinating animals.

Haldane, J. B. S.: Some Alternatives to Sex, *New Biol.,* vol. 19, 1955. A noted biologist discusses reproductive processes not followed by sexual events.

Heslop-Harrison, J.: The Sexuality of Flowers, *New Biol.,* vol. 23, 1957. Reproductive structures and functions in flowers are described.

Koller, D.: Germination, *Sci. American,* Apr., 1959. An account of seed dormancy and escape from dormancy by chemical stimuli.

Leopold, A. C.: "Plant Growth and Development," McGraw-HIll, New York, 1964. An advanced book on the physiology of growth processes in plants, including reviews of the roles of flowering and other hormones. Extensive references to original research papers are at the end of each chapter.

Salisbury, F. B., and **R. V. Parke**: "Vascular Plants: Form and Function," Wadsworth, Belmont, Calif., 1964. A paperback with very good coverage of reproduction in tracheophytes.

Wollman, E. L., and **F. Jacob**: Sexuality in Bacteria, *Sci. American,* July, 1956. The conjugative sexual process in bacteria is described.

Vegetative reproduction by fragmentation or budding occurs regularly in some animal groups as a normal process of propagation. Regenerative reproduction after injury is widespread, but in the majority of groups the capacity of regeneration is severely restricted. Sporulation does not occur and indeed is superfluous, since species dispersal can be achieved by locomotion in adult or preadult stages.

Whatever other forms of reproduction may or may not be exhibited in given cases, gametic reproduction occurs in all cases. The sexes typically are separate, but hermaphroditism is common, particularly in sessile and sluggish animals. Reproductive systems contain testes or ovaries, or *gonads* collectively, and generally also ducts that lead to the outside of the body. Gamete formation is accompanied by meiosis; sperms and eggs represent the only haploid phase in the diplontic life cycle. Fertilized eggs develop into embryos that become either adults directly or, more typically, *larvae* first and then adults.

patterns

reproductive cells

Gametes are formed from special groups of diploid generative cells in the gonads. Such cells become sperms or eggs by maturation processes that affect both the cell nucleus and the cytoplasm.

The nuclear phase of gamete maturation is meiosis (Fig. 26.1). In a male, a diploid generative cell in a testis undergoes both meiotic divisions in fairly rapid succession, and all four resulting haploid cells are functional sperms. In a female, a generative cell in the ovary undergoes a first meiotic division and produces two cells. Of these one is small and soon degenerates; called the *first polar body,* it remains attached to the other cell. When this cell passes through the second meiotic division, one of the two resulting cells becomes the egg, and the other again is small and degenerates. It forms the *second polar body,* which like the first remains attached to the egg. Each original generative cell thus gives rise to only one functional egg. In vertebrates and numerous other groups eggs are ready for fertilization as soon as the first meiotic division has occurred. Such eggs remain in a state of meiotic arrest until a sperm enters, which provides the stimulus for the completion of meiosis.

In parallel with the nuclear maturation of gametes cytoplasmic maturation takes place. In sperm-forming cells much of the cytoplasm degenerates. The nucleus enlarges as an oval *sperm head,* and the mature sperm retains only three structures that have a cytoplasmic origin: a long posterior *sperm tail,* which serves as locomotor flagellum; a *middle piece,* which contains energy-supplying mitochondria; and an *acrosome,* an organelle at the forward end of the sperm head that will make contact with an egg (Fig. 26.2). Having lost most of the cytoplasm, mature sperms are among the smallest cells in the body. But mature eggs are among the largest; their cytoplasms accumulate *yolk,* which contains most of the raw materials for the construction of embryos.

As in plants, sperms must fuse with eggs in an aqueous environment. This water requirement has led to the elaboration of two basic animal mating patterns (Fig. 26.3). In *external fertilization,* mating partners are or come close to each other in natural bodies of water and both simultaneously *spawn;* they release sperms and eggs directly into the water, where many fertilizations then take place. This pattern is characteristic of most aquatic animals and also of terrestrial types such as certain insects and amphibia, which migrate to permanent bodies of water for reproduction.

The second pattern is *internal fertilization.* Mating partners here come into physical contact, and by various means the male transfers sperms directly to the reproductive system of the female. The internal tissues of the female here provide moisture for the sperms, and the need for external water is thereby circumvented. Internal fertilization is characteristic of most terrestrial animals, but the process occurs also in numerous aquatic groups (for example, in many fishes).

In most cases internal fertilization is achieved by *copulation,* a process in which sperms leave from the exit of the male reproductive system and enter the female reproductive system directly through its exterior opening. Copulatory organs of various kinds often assist in this transfer. If such organs are lacking, as in birds (see Chap. 13), the mating partners bring their bodies together so that the two reproductive openings touch. In many groups the males shed not loose sperms but compact sperm packets (*spermatophores*). Squids use their tentacles to transfer such packets into females, some amphibia use their mouths, many spiders use their pedipalps, and the females of certain salamanders pick up sperm packets from the ground by means of cloacal lips. Some animals transfer sperms into females by a process akin to hypodermic injection, through any part of the skin.

In all cases of external and also in some of internal fertilization, development of zygotes to adults takes place externally, in natural bodies of water. Such animals, in which eggs are shed to the outside either in an unfertilized or a fertilized state, are said to be *oviparous* (Fig. 26.4). Among vertebrates, for example, many fishes are oviparous and externally fertilizing, whereas all birds are oviparous and internally fertilizing. The developing eggs eventually *hatch,* as larvae or as miniature, immature adults. If development takes place in water, the zygotes often have coats of jelly around them (for example, frog eggs) but are otherwise protected very little. Zygotes developing on land are usually protected against evaporation by cocoons or shells.

Most animals are oviparous as above. Among the rest, one group is *ovoviviparous.* Fertilization here is internal, and the zygotes are retained inside the female reproductive system. Development then occurs there. However, beyond providing a substantial measure of protection the female body does not otherwise contribute to zygote development; as in oviparous types, food is supplied by the yolk stored in each egg. Ultimately the young are *born* rather than hatched, and the females release fully formed animals, not eggs. Among vertebrates some of the fishes, amphibia, and reptiles are ovoviviparous.

A third group of animals comprises *viviparous* types. Here fertilization is again internal, zygotes are retained inside the female, and the young are born as developed animals. However, the female body now provides not merely protection but also food, and it contributes to offspring metabolism in other vital ways. The females in such cases are said to be *pregnant.* Viviparous vertebrates include, for example, some fishes, some snakes, and the majority of the mammals (see Fig. 26.4).

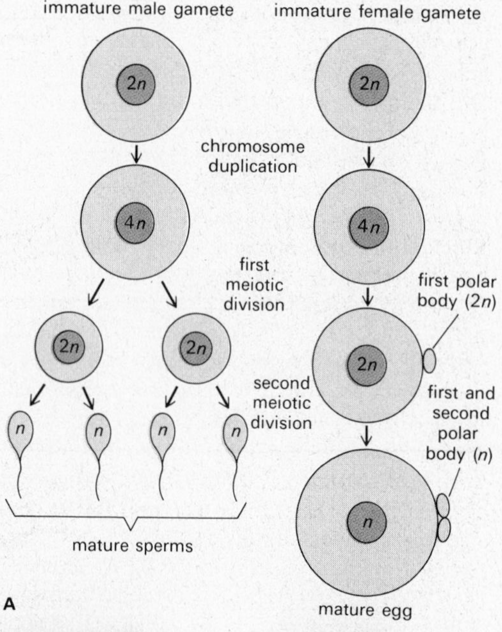

B

C

26.1 ***Meiosis.*** *A, in males all four haploid cells formed become functional sperms. In females one cell formed by the first meiotic division is small and degenerates and becomes the first polar body. Also, one cell formed by the second meiotic division becomes the second polar body. Thus only one cell matures as a functional egg. B, C, polar-body formation. B, section through the edge of an immature whitefish egg, showing the extremely eccentric position of the spindle and the chromosomes during a meiotic division. Chromosomes are in anaphase. Cleavage will occur at right angles to the spindle axis and will therefore produce an extremely large and an extremely small cell. C, cytoplasmic cleavage under way. The small cell formed will degenerate, and its remnant will be a polar body.*

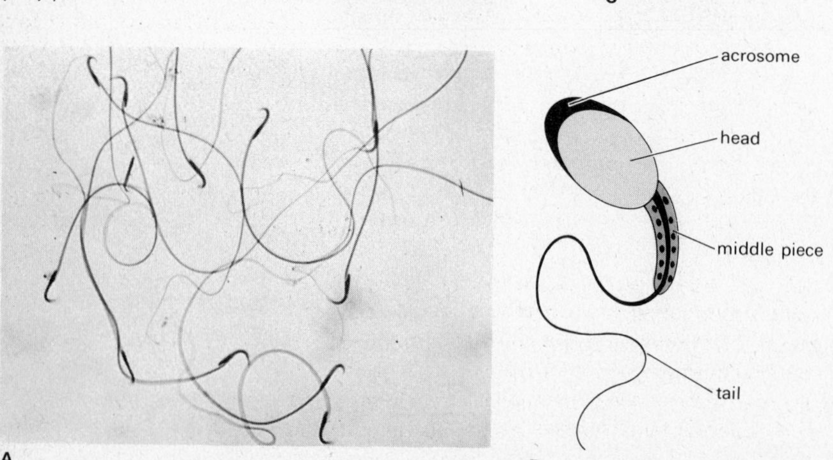

26.2 (*Below*) ***Sperms.*** *A, rat sperms. Note sperm head, with hooklike acrosome faintly visible at forward end; sperm tail; and middle piece darkly stained. B, sperm structure. (A, courtesy Carolina Biological Supply Company.)*

reproductive systems

In vertebrates the gonads arise as a pair of mesodermal pouches that project into the coelom dorsally, near mid-body (Fig. 26.5). Each pouch enlarges and fills with tissue,and the outer layers of the gonad then form a *cortex.* The interior tissue represents a *medulla.* Gamete-producing cells, called *primordial germ cells,* arise not in the developing gonad itself but in anterior regions of

***26.3 Fertilization.** A, external fertilization. Eggs just spawned by the female are about to be fertilized by the male. B, internal fertilization. A copulating pair of land snails, suspended by mucus cord. See also Figs. 12.22 and 13.25. C, female katydid carrying spermatophore. Formed by many different kinds of animals, such sperm packets are transferred by various means into the reproductive systems of females.*

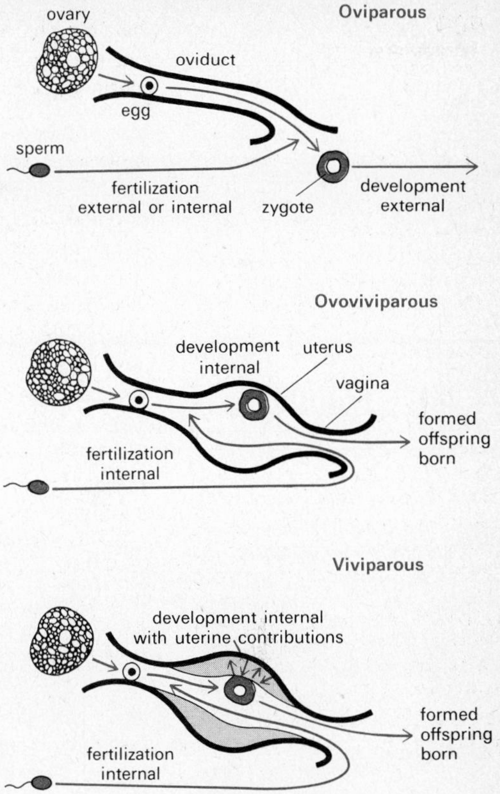

***26.4 Fertilization and development** in relation to the environment and the maternal body.*

the embryo. From such regions the cells migrate to the embryonic gonad and disperse inside it. At this stage the gonad still is sexually undetermined and can develop in either a male or a female direction.

If the gonad becomes a testis, the cortex develops very little more but the medulla proliferates and becomes the bulk of the mature testis. But if the immature gonad develops as an ovary, it is the medulla that undergoes little further growth, whereas the cortex enlarges greatly.

In mammals such as opossums, bats, and whales, testes remain at their original locations permanently. In a second group, which includes elephants and many rodents, the testes leave the trunk when the breeding season begins and migrate to a *scrotum,* a skin sac between the hind legs. After sperms cease to be produced at the end of the breeding season, the testes migrate back to their original positions. In a third group, exemplified by rodents such as mice and rats, the testes descent to a scrotum when the animals reach sexual maturity, and from then on the gonads remain there permanently. And in a fourth group, of which man is a member, the testes are internal only during embryonic stages; the organs migrate

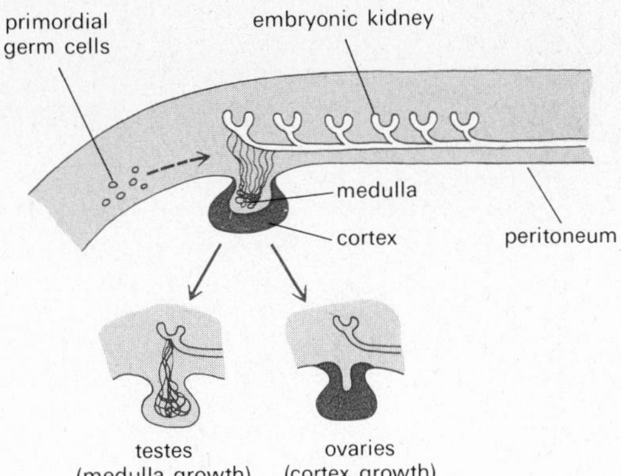

***26.5 Gonad development.** Top, sectional side view of part of vertebrate embryo, indicating place of origin of primordial germ cells in head region in relation to developing gonad, embryonic kidney, and coelom. Bottom, differential growth of the medullary (kidney-derived) tissue results in testes, and differential growth of the cortical (peritoneum-derived) tissue results in ovaries.*

to a scrotum just before birth and then remain in this sac throughout life.

It is known that the temperature in a scrotum is up to 7°C lower than inside the trunk. It is also known that lower temperatures tend to promote and higher temperatures to inhibit sperm production. Temperature, testis location, and continuity of sperm manufacture therefore appear to be interrelated.

The interior of a testis contains interconnected sperm chambers, or *testicular tubules* (Fig. 26.6). Their inside lining is a sperm-producing epithelium formed from the primordial germ cells of the embryo. The cells of this layer divide mitotically, and the new cells so formed accumulate in the testicular tubules and mature as sperms. As noted, meiosis occurs in the process. Ripe sperms then leave the testes through *sperm ducts.*

Various accessory organs are generally associated with such ducts. Thus, sperm ducts often pass through or past *sperm sacs,* chambers that store sperms before discharge. In man, sperms are stored in the *epididymis,* a highly coiled portion of the sperm duct just outside the testis. Nerve impulses can bring about contraction of the walls in these storage regions, and the collected sperms then are expelled. Also connected with the sperm ducts are *prostate glands* and *seminal vesicles,* which secrete *seminal fluids.* Together with sperms these fluids make up *semen.* The seminal fluids appear to contain activating substances that induce the previously quiescent sperms to lash their tails. In animals with copulatory organs, semen may or may not leave the body through such organs. If it does, as in man, the copulatory organ is called a *penis.* The sperm channel in the penis of mammals is the *urethra,* which connects with both the sperm ducts and the excretory channel from the urinary bladder. Simultaneous discharges of semen and urine are prevented by nervous reflexes that bring about closure of one channel when the other is in operation.

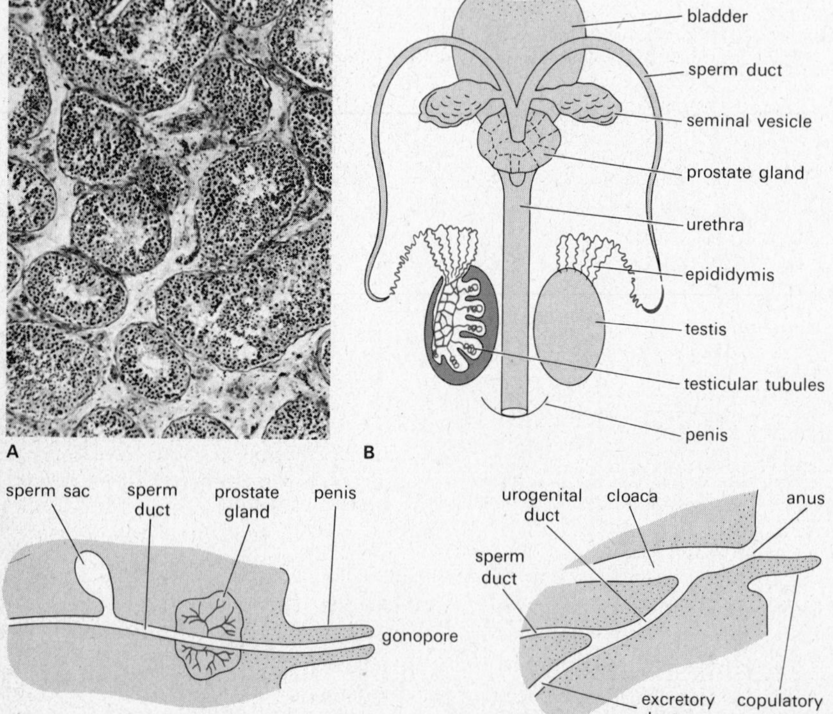

26.6 Male reproductive systems. *A, section through a testis. In the tubular chambers sperms are produced, and mature sperms accumulate in the spaces in the tubules. The tissue between the tubules contains endocrine cells that manufacture androgens, the male sex hormones, under the stimulus of LH from the pituitary. B, the system in man, left testis in section. C, D, some the common component organs and exit modifications according to whether a cloaca or a penis is present.*

In female vertebrates, the primordial germ cells give rise to an egg-producing epithelium on the surface of an ovary (Fig. 26.7). This layer forms successive batches of new cells, but in each batch usually only one undergoes meiosis and matures as a reproductive cell. The surrounding cells are inhibited in some unknown way from also becoming eggs. Instead these cells form a *follicle,* a ball of tissue that soon acquires an enlarging central cavity. The egg is located eccentrically in such a follicle, in a thickened region of the follicular wall. An embryonic ovary of a human female is estimated to contain some 400,000 primordial germ cells; but only about 400 functional eggs are actually formed during adult life.

The reproductive channels that lead away from ovaries are *oviducts.* Along their course in given animals (but not in man) there are *seminal receptacles,* pouches that store sperms after mating and before fertilization, as well as *yolk glands, shell glands,* and other glands that produce nutritive or protective layers around fertilized eggs. Near its exterior termination an oviduct in many cases is enlarged as a *uterus,* in which egg development can occur. In copulating animals the terminal section of the oviduct that receives the male copulatory organ during mating is called a *vagina.* In contrast to the arrangement in human males, the reproductive tract of human females has an independent exit, separate from that of the urinary pore.

reproductive behavior

Like plants, most animals produce gametes only during specific *breeding seasons.* Such seasons are largely annual, most of them occurring in spring or fall. But many animals have two or more breeding seasons per year; for example, there are two in dogs. In some cases breeding seasons last only a single day (or night, as in clamworms and many other marine invertebrates), but in others, as in monkeys, apes, and men, reproduction can occur the year round. Breeding seasons tend to be continuous also where environmental conditions remain uniformly favorable throughout the year, as in domesticated cattle, chickens, and rabbits, and in laboratory mice and rats. Even in such cases, however, fertility is usually greatest during the spring.

As shown in Chap. 22, breeding cycles tend to be synchronized with seasonal rhythms in day lengths and temperatures. Thus breeding seasons in vertebrates are usually initiated after the animals have been exposed to a certain total amount of illumination, counted from the winter solstice in spring breeders and the summer solstice in fall breeders. Such photoperiodic stimuli affect the reproductive system through the eyes and the neural-endocrine mechanism outlined in Fig. 26.8 (see also Chap. 23). The anterior lobe of the pituitary thereby becomes stimulated to secrete increasing amounts of gonadotropic hormones, and all parts of the reproductive system increase in size as a result and become functional. The higher concentrations of sex hormones then produced by the gonads elicit not only reproductive behavior and sexuality, but also enhanced aggressiveness and closer social interrelations based on dominance and territoriality. After a breeding season, the hormone output of the anterior pituitary declines again and the reproductive system becomes quiescent and reduced in size.

The behavioral and social aspects of vertebrate reproduction appear to be just as significant as the internal functional ones. For example, if mature pigeons or mice are prevented from having social contact with other members of the species, they usually fail to come into breeding condition, even at the right season. However, pigeons can be induced to lay eggs if they are at least permitted to see themselves in a mirror, and female mice come into heat when exposed at least to the smell given off by males. In many zoo animals reproduction will not occur even when a male and a female are allowed to live together. Such animals evidently require considerably more elaborate social settings if their neural and endocrine controls of reproductive processes are to function normally.

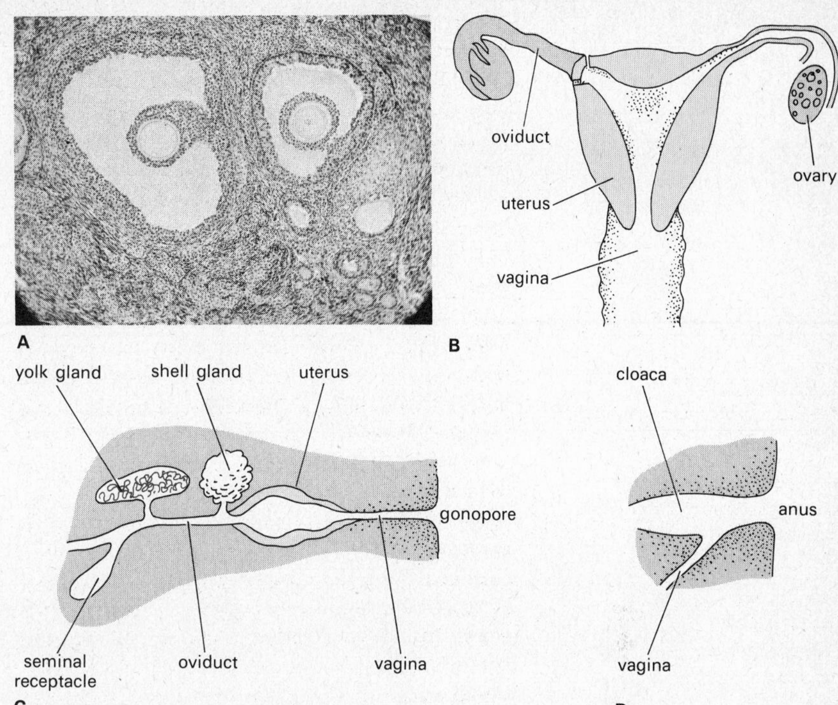

26.7 Female reproductive systems. *A, section through an ovary. Note the two large follicles, the follicular cavities, and the large egg cell in each follicle embedded in a mass of cells along the follicular wall. Endocrine cells secrete estrogens into the follicular cavity. When the eggs are mature they will ovulate and escape by rupture of follicle and ovary walls. B, the system in man. C, D, some of the common component organs and exit modifications according to whether a cloaca is or is not present.*

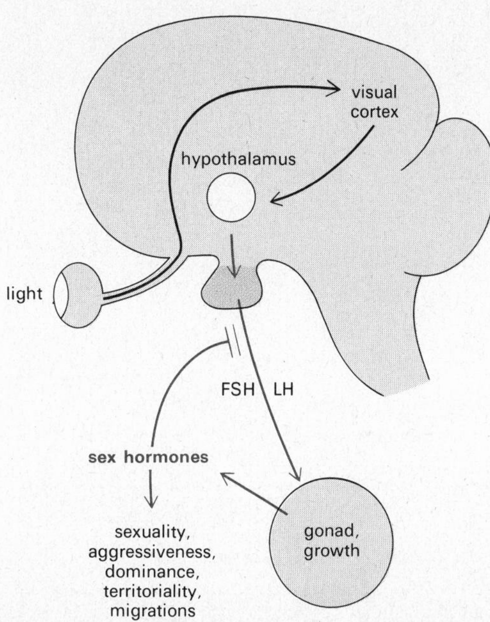

26.8 Neuroendocrine control *of reproductive functions. Light (and many other external) stimuli, as well as internal psychological states, are communicated to the hypothalamus over neural pathways (black arrows). Chemical signals (color arrows) then stimulate the pituitary, which (superimposed on an intrinsic rhythm of activity) secretes gonadotropic hormones (FSH, LH). These induce gonad growth and sex-hormone production. The hormones in turn bring about the onset of breeding seasons and all associated reproductive functions, as well as various sex-associated behaviors. When sex-hormone concentrations exceed certain levels, they inhibit the pituitary (double bar), and the reproductive and associated activities then decline.*

Furthermore, mating in most vertebrates and many invertebrates is functionally dependent on preliminary *courtship.* Consisting of a series of more or less precisely programmed displays and movements, courtship serves to advertise the presence of sexually receptive individuals and to forestall or inhibit aggression by a prospective mate. The last is particularly necessary if the mate is a predator, a high-ranking member of a dominance hierarchy, or the owner of a territory. Thus, courtship by either sex usually includes token or actual submissive behavior, prominent display of sex recognition signs, or other signals indicating nonaggressive intent (Fig. 26.9).

Most important, courtship is often required to bring both mating partners to reproductive readiness simultaneously. In some vertebrates, for example, the internal reproductive mechanism does not become operational unless visual, olfactory, or other stimuli from a mate provide a trigger. Often a whole sequence of successive triggers is needed to initiate a corresponding sequence of internal hormonal processes. For example, courtship by male ring doves elicits production of sex hormones in females, which then are induced by the hormones to build nests. This activity in turn is the specific stimulus for mate acceptance and egg laying. In female canaries, similarly, a progressive sequence of hormonal changes and a succession of steps of nest construction have been found to be reciprocally necessary stimuli. In some instances, as among cats and rabbits, male-female coordination through courtship dovetails so finely that eggs are not released from the ovary until a mating pair is actually copulating.

Like displays of threat and submission, courtship too has probably evolved as a highly ritualized version of combat. In both sexes courtship usually includes behavioral elements that are very similar to those of attack and flight, and that in some instances involve real attack and flight. In sticklebacks and gulls, for example, intermittent bursts of male attack and female flight continue right up to mating. In finches it is the female that attacks the male with increasing vigor until copulation actually takes place. In most cases, however, the ritual elements of courtship appear to differentiate reproductive intent from real hostility. Males use aggressive displays for actual threats but ritualized versions of them to attract females; and whereas females are submissive to discourage real attack, their stylized submission in courtship is used to invite attention from males.

Mating normally terminates when sperms and eggs have been shed. In many vertebrates sexual activity ceases not primarily because the male has released sperms, but because he may be inhibited from further activity by the sight of shed eggs

A

B

26.9 ***Courtship.*** *A, the tail display of male peacocks is one of the familiar courtship behaviors. B, male Siamese fighting fish displaying at female.*

(as in certain fishes) or because he may have become habituated to a particular female. In guinea pigs and cattle, for example, a female is normally inseminated several times in succession during a single mating sequence. The sequence ends when male interest wanes. However, a male that has become inactive with one female will readily and repeatedly copulate with a succession of other females. In the case of bulls this prolonged copulatory capability has become commercially important: prize bulls can be induced to deliver maximal amounts of semen (for use in artificial inseminations) by presenting them with a series of dummy cows.

The mating structure of a social group varies considerably for different species. Most fishes, mammals such as rodents, and numerous other vertebrates mate promiscuously, and in such animals distinct family organizations tend to be absent. Where families are distinguishable, the units are often solitary or they can be parts of larger herds or herdlike groups. In either case a mating unit can be polygamous, like chickens, or monogamous, like parrots or bears. Also, such a unit may stay together either for a single season only or for life. For example, bears and wolves typically mate for life.

Whatever the mating structure, reproductive behavior usually contributes to group sociality well beyond the breeding season. Thus, many vertebrates guard and tend eggs at least until hatching, and many also nourish, care for, and train their young after hatching or birth. Such parental behavior is induced partly by the sex hormones and specifically by *prolactin,* one of the three pituitary gonadotropic hormones (see Chap. 19 and Table 14). In males prolactin promotes protective attitudes toward mates and offspring, intensive food gathering for the family, and expressions of paternalism in general. In females, similarly, the hormone induces maternalism, including broodiness, strong emotional attachment to the offspring, and the drive to bring the young to a state of self-sufficiency (Fig. 26.10). In mammals prolactin also initiates milk secretion in the mammary glands (hence the alternative name *lactogenic* hormone).

Parental behavior does not have an exclusively endocrine basis, however, but is subject also to complex psychological controls. In mammals, for example, development of the emotional bond between mother and offspring, normally firmly established within an hour or two after birth, depends in large part on maternal licking, cleaning, and handling of offspring. If then a just-born offspring is cleaned by an experimenter or is handled by another animal, the mother will refuse to acknowledge this offspring as her own. Similarly, many female mammals will retrieve young that have rolled out of the nest, and since this activity is undertaken even by nonbreeding animals it, too, appears to be independent of hormonal states. Continued milk secretion likewise requires not merely hormonal but also external stimuli, particularly tactile stimulation of the nipples and withdrawal of already accumulated milk by suckling. Moreover, as shown in Chap. 23, adequate social settings and social behavior learned during young stages are essential for normal parental behavior and establishment of proper parent-young relations.

26.10 Parental behavior. *Among less-than-common examples is this black-chinned mouthbrooder female (Tilapis mossambica), which incubates its eggs in the mouth. Even after hatching the fry retreats into the mother's mouth if danger threatens. Experiments show that fry will seek refuge in any dark opening and that surrogate hiding places are accepted as readily as the parental mouth.*

reproductive mechanisms

Males produce sperms continuously during a breeding season and often also to a reduced extent between such seasons. In male vertebrates, pituitary control is exercised chiefly through *LH,* one of the pituitary gonadotropic hormones. (A male function for FSH, a second such hormone, has not been demonstrated, and

26.11 Secondary sex traits. *A, swordtail male at top, female at bottom. B, pintail duck male at left, female at right. Note sexual dimorphism in both examples. See also Fig. 6.5.*

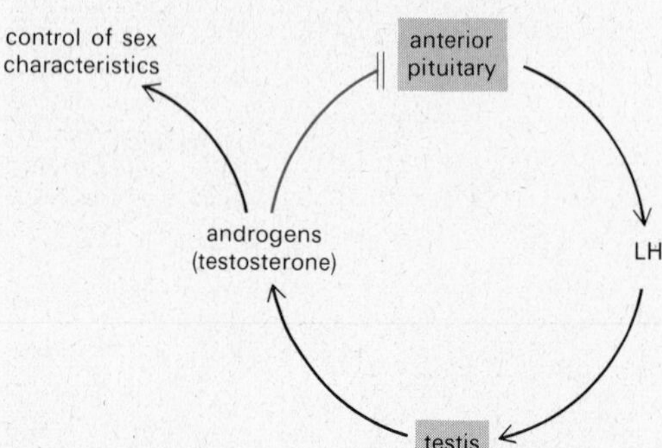

26.12 Androgen secretion control. *LH is one of the gonadotropic hormones of the pituitary. Arrow tipped with transverse double bar (color) signifies inhibition.*

the male function of prolactin has been described above.) Pituitary LH is the specific hormone that stimulates the testes to produce *androgens,* the male sex hormones. These are manufactured in the tissue partitions between the sperm-producing tubules of a testis (see Fig. 26.6). The concentration of *testosterone,* the most potent of the androgens, rises sharply at the start of a breeding season under the influence of LH. Sperms are then actively produced, sex urge increases, and secondary sex traits such as mating colors in skin and plumage become pronounced (Fig. 26.11). If they are present in blood in excessive concentrations, androgens have an inhibitory effect on the pituitary. This gland then produces less LH, and androgen secretions therefore decline as well. Through such feedback control androgen concentrations remain at fairly steady levels during the breeding season (Fig. 26.12). In man, sperm production begins at sexual maturity, or *puberty,* and can then continue for life.

Females produce one or several successive batches of eggs during a breeding season. Periods of egg maturation are called *estrus cycles* in mammals, and female dogs, for example, come into estrus just once per breeding season (*monoestrous* types). Horses and sheep are among *polyestrous* types, which produce several batches of eggs. However, egg manufacture ceases after one batch is fertilized. The hormonal controls of egg production in vertebrates parallel those of sperm production. At the onset of a breeding season the pituitary secretes gonadotropic hormones. Of these, *FSH,* the *f*ollicle-*s*timulating *h*ormone, initiates increased ovarian activity.

More specifically, the follicle cells around an egg are stimulated to produce *estrogens,* the female sex hormones. Corresponding functionally to the male hormones, they promote growth of the follicle, pronounced development of secondary sex traits, and an increase in sex urge (see Fig. 26.11). Certain amounts of estrogen accumulate in the fluid-filled cavity in a follicle, which becomes larger as it develops. At maturity a follicle lies just under the ovary surface, where it produces a conspicuous bulge (see Fig. 26.7).

When estrogen concentrations in blood exceed a certain level, the hormones exert an inhibitory effect on FSH production in the pituitary. At the same time also the estrogens stimulate the pituitary to produce the gonadotropic hormone LH. As a result LH concentrations begin to rise just when FSH concentrations begin to fall. These shifting hormone balances are the specific stimulus for *ovulation;* the ovary surface and the follicle wall both rupture, and the mature egg escapes to the coelom and the oviduct (Fig. 26.13).

An immediate consequence of ovulation is that the ruptured and eggless follicle remaining in the ovary loses its fluid and collapses. Another consequence is that, since FSH production by the pituitary has now ceased, the remnant of the follicle ceases to manufacture estrogen. Instead, under the specific influence of LH, the follicular remains transform to a yellowish body, the *corpus luteum.* (The name "LH" stands for "*l*uteum-producing *h*ormone.") Under the continuing influence of this hormone the corpus luteum begins to secrete a new hormone of its own, *progesterone*.

In oviparous vertebrates progesterone induces the oviducts to secrete jelly coasts or shells around the eggs passing through. When the concentration of progesterone eventually exceeds a certain level, the hormone inhibits LH production in the pituitary. The corpus luteum then ceases to manufacture progesterone, but by this time the eggs have already been shed. A new FSH-initiated egg-growth cycle can then begin if the breeding season has not come to a close.

The pattern of events is somewhat different in the vivparous mammals. Progesterone here stimulates growth of the uterus in preparation for pregnancy: the wall of the uterus thickens greatly and develops numerous glandular pockets and extra blood vessels. An egg is normally fertilized as it passes through the oviduct; and if a fertilized egg reaches the uterus it becomes firmly embedded in the thickened uterine wall (Fig. 26.14). The maternal blood in this wall then supplies the egg with nourishment and oxygen. But if an egg is not fertilized in the oviduct, it soon disintegrates and the uterus will have been made ready for nothing. In that case progesterone again inhibits pituitary LH production eventually, and the corpus luteum then ceases to manufacture progesterone. Without this "pregnancy hormone," however, the ready condition of the uterus cannot be maintained, and the wall soon reverts to its normal thickness.

In Old World monkeys, apes, and men, the preparations for pregnancy in the uterus are so extensive that, if fertilization does not occur and progesterone production then ceases, the inner lining of the uterus actually disintegrates. Tissue fragments separate away and some blood escapes from torn vessels. Over a period of a few days all this debris is expelled to the outside through the vagina, a process called *menstruation* (see Fig. 26.14).

A *menstrual cycle* in such animals lasts about 28 days. Follicle maturation occurs during the first 10 to 14 days under the control of FSH and estrogen, and this *follicular phase* of the cycle terminates with ovulation. During the next 14 to 18 days the uterus grows in preparation for pregnancy under the influence of LH and progesterone. If pregnancy does not begin during this *luteal phase*, menstruation takes place in the course of the first few days of the next menstrual cycle. A new cycle starts when, in the absence of LH and progesterone, the pituitary resumes FSH production and a new follicle matures in the ovary.

Evidently a menstrual cycle is governed by two successive control cycles with built-in feedbacks.

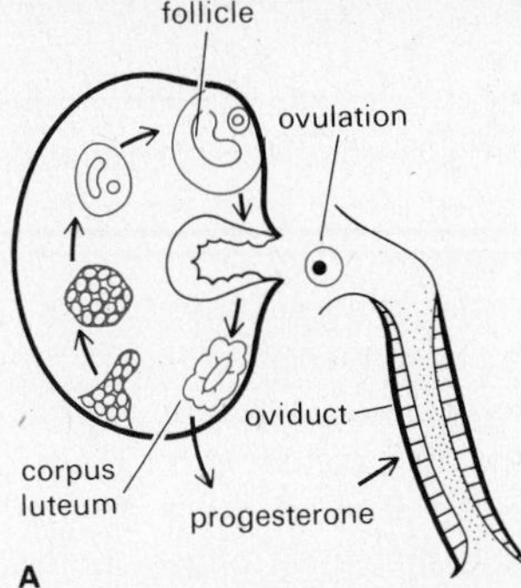

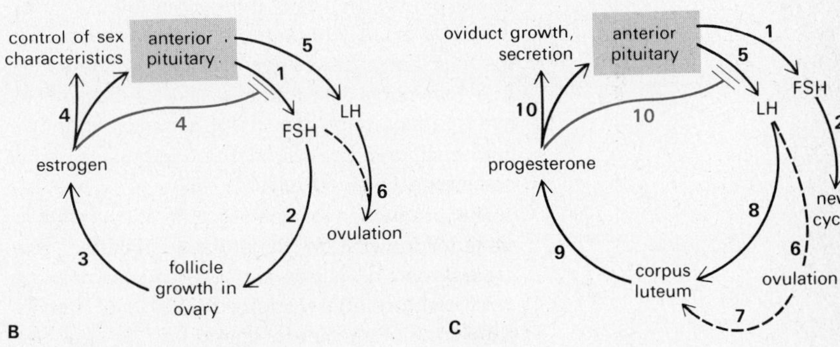

26.13 Egg growth in oviparous vertebrates. *A, progesterone induces the oviduct to secrete jelly coats or shell-forming substances around eggs. B, hormonal changes during the follicular phase, leading to ovulation. Numbers indicate sequence of steps. Black arrows, stimulation; colored double-bar arrows, inhibition; broken lines, decreasing concentrations. C, hormonal changes after ovulation (luteal phase) in oviparous vertebrates. The sequence begins at steps 5 and 6, equivalent to the terminal steps in B, and ends at step 10. Steps 1 and 2 then repeat the first events of B.*

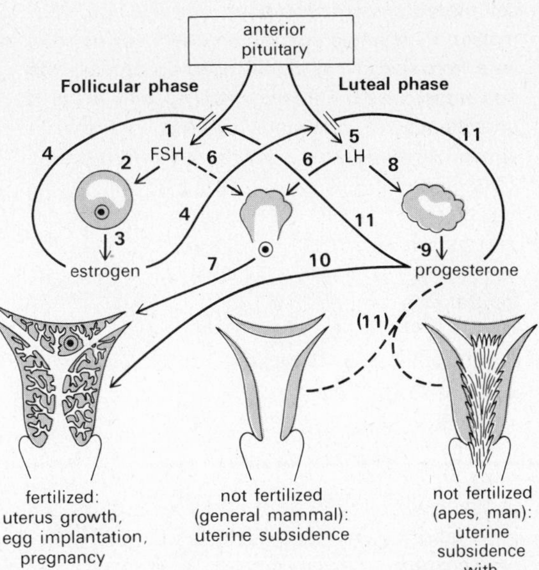

26.14 Egg growth in viviparous vertebrates. *Steps 1 to 9 correspond to the follicular and luteal phases in oviparous vertebrates (see preceding figure). Thereafter events differ according to whether fertilization does or does not take place. If it does, pregnancy ensues (step 10); if it does not, progesterone production declines (via step 11), leading to tissue resorption in the uterus wall in most mammals and to menstruation in monkeys, apes, and man. The cycle then repeats (step 1).*

FSH and estrogen are components of one control cycle, LH and progesterone of the other; and the termination of one is the specific stimulus for initiation of the second. In human females menstrual cycles begin to occur at puberty and continue to the time of *menopause* in middle age, when the sex-hormone control system gradually ceases to operate.

Estrogen is not absent altogether during the luteal phase, nor is progesterone completely absent during the follicular phase of a menstrual cycle. The hormones merely attain definite peak concentrations at particular times. These fluctuations have important consequences. Under the influence of progesterone, for example, which promotes growth of the duct system in the mammary glands, a slight swelling of these glands generally occurs during the luteal phase. Body temperature increases somewhat during the follicular phase, then falls during the luteal phase. Sex drive is likely to be more pronounced during the follicular phase, since estrogen maintains it. And inasmuch as estrogens, like androgens in males, affect many aspects of behavior, monthly hormonal and behavioral fluctuations in some cases tend to be correlated.

The production of sperms and eggs sets the stage for fertilization. Regardless of whether this process occurs in free water after spawning or in an oviduct after copulation, the first step is always the entrance of a sperm into an egg. The union is usually achieved through a fusion of the cell membranes of the sperm and the egg. Normally only a single sperm can enter, for as soon as a first sperm has made head-on contact the egg undergoes metabolic changes that make it unreceptive to additional sperms. In certain aquatic invertebrates, moreover, a *fertilization membrane* has formed during egg maturation, and this membrane lifts away from the egg surface after a sperm has made contact.

During sperm entrance the tail of the sperm usually drops off. At this point the egg is *activated;* its development has been started. Recall here that, in parthenogenesis, eggs become activated by natural or experimental means without sperms. Under more usual circumstances, a sperm nucleus inside an activated egg migrates toward the egg nucleus, and this meeting of the two haploid nuclei completes fertilization. The nuclear membranes dissolve, the now diploid chromosomes line up in a metaphase plate, and the zygote undergoes a first mitotic division. Embryonic development is launched in this manner.

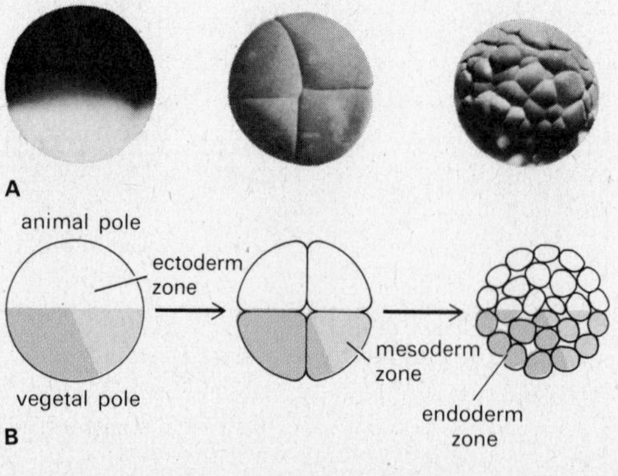

the embryo

As pointed out in Chap. 24, an embryo represents a first developmental phase in which, through morphogenesis and differentiation, all basic structures and functions of an animal become elaborated in at least rough detail. The embryonic period begins with *cleavage,* the subdivision of the fertilized egg.

cleavage and blastula

Mitotic cleavage divisions cut an egg into progressively smaller cells called *blastomeres* (Fig. 26.15). Cleavage typically continues until the blastomeres have attained the size of adult cells. During cleavage different surface regions of an egg differentiate as a series of *organ-forming zones,* areas that will later give rise to the various body parts of the adult. Cleavage *segregates* these zones to different cells and cell groups. On the basis of how soon such zones become established, two categories of eggs can be distinguished: *mosaic* (or *determined*) eggs and *regulative* (or *undetermined*) eggs.

The first type is encountered in most acoelomates, pseudocoelomates, and schizocoelomates. The fate of every egg part here becomes fixed unalterably before or at the time of fertilization. The head-tail, dorsal-ventral, and left-right axes, therefore, are already firmly established in the zygote. After cleavage in such an egg, it is possible to separate the cells from one another experimentally. Each isolated blastomere then develops

A

animal pole
ectoderm zone
mesoderm zone
vegetal pole
endoderm zone

B

26.15 Cleavage and organ-forming zones. *A, egg, four-cell, and later cleavage stage in frogs. B, organ-forming zones. The main egg axis is marked by so-called animal and vegetal poles at opposite areas of the egg. As cleavage progresses, a given zone of the egg becomes segregated in progressively smaller but more numerous blastomeres.*

as a *partial* embryo; it produces the same portion of the embryo it would have produced if the cleaving egg had been left intact. Once it has become determined, the egg thus behaves like a quiltwork, a mosaic, in which the fate of the egg parts cannot be altered after fertilization (Fig. 26.16).

By contrast, the eggs of most enterocoelomates, vertebrates included, are of the regulative variety. In these the fate of various egg portions becomes fixed much later, usually not until three cleavages have produced eight cells. If blastomeres are isolated before that time, each develops as a *whole* embryo, not as a partial one. Formation of two or more whole animals from separated blastomeres is equivalent to the production of identical twins, triplets, quadruplets, or larger sets. Natural *twinning* undoubtedly occurs through similar separations. However, the forces or accidents that actually isolate blastomeres in nature are not understood. If the blastomeres are incompletely separated, Siamese twins result. And if separation occurs after the time of developmental determination, each blastomere forms only a partial embryo, like a part of a mosaic.

Apart from the mosaic or regulative characteristics of an egg, three additional properties influence development greatly: egg *size,* cleavage *rate,* and amount and distribution of *yolk.* Depending on the original size of an egg, cleavage will continue for a longer or a shorter period until the cells are considerably smaller; and starting from a given egg size, a particular rate of cleavage will produce such final cell sizes more or less quickly. Thus, both egg size and cleavage rate govern the number and size of the blastomeres that will be present at the end of cleavage. In their turn, the number and size of the cellular building blocks will influence the later architectural development of the embryo (see below).

With respect to yolk, some eggs, those of mammals included, contain very little. In others the amount of yolk is large, and it is accumulated either in the center of an egg, as in arthropods, or eccentrically in one egg half, as in amphibians (Fig. 26.17). The eggs of birds and squids are among those with so much yolk that the nonyolky part of the cell forms a mere microscopic spot, or *blastodisc,* on top of the yolk mass. Yolk is a mechanically inert material which, when present in large quantities, interferes physically with the subdivision of an egg during cleavage. Thus, yolky eggs generally divide more slowly and form larger blastomeres than nonyolky ones. In extremely yolky eggs, as in birds, the yolk does not even become part of the dividing blastomeres; cleaving yolkless cells come to lie on top of the uncleaved yolk mass.

The general result of cleavage is the formation of an embryonic stage called a *blastula.* In most cases this stage has the form of a solid or hollow ball of cells. Solid blastulas usually are filled with more or less yolky cells or with undivided yolk, and in hollow blastulas the size of the internal

intact two-cell stage

separated two-cell stage

separated two-cell stage

two half-embryos, normal size: mosaic or determined development

two whole embryos, half size: regulative or undetermined development

26.16 Mosaic and regulative development. *If the cells of early cleavage stages of mosaic eggs are isolated experimentally (left), then each cell develops as it would have in any case. The inference is that the fates of cytoplasmic regions in such eggs (dark central parts) are determined very early. But if the cells of early cleaving regulative eggs are isolated (right), then each cell develops as a smaller whole animal. The inference here is that the fate of the cytoplasm is still undetermined. Thus if the two-cell-stage blastomeres are separated, the central cytoplasm, which normally would form central body parts, actually forms left structures in one case, right structures in the other.*

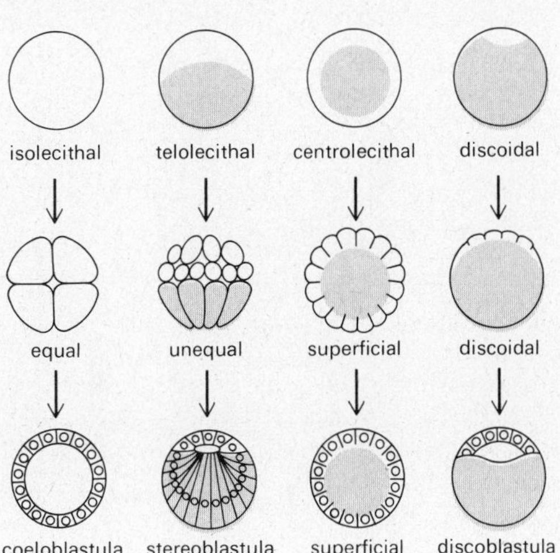

26.17 Eggs, cleavage, and blastulas. *Top row, egg types, named according to yolk content and distribution (indicated by colored areas). Center row, cleavage patterns. Note that yolk influences the nature of a given pattern. Bottom row, blastula types. Any free space in a blastula is a blastocoel.*

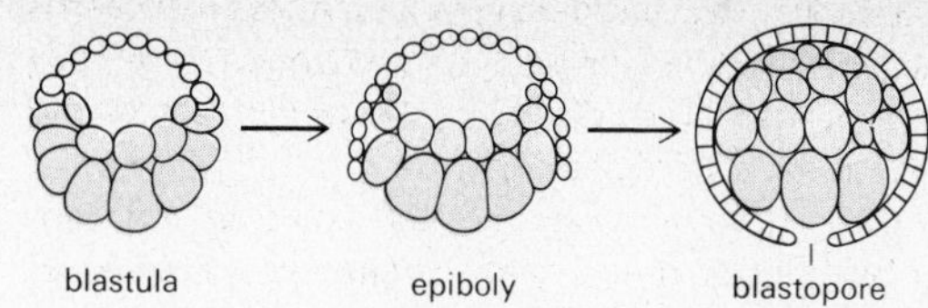

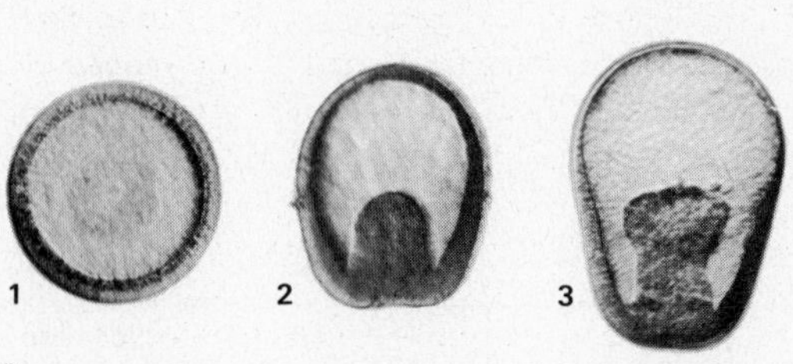

26.18 ***Gastrulation.*** *A, transverse sections. Top, gastrulation by ectodermal overgrowth (epiboly). Bottom, gastrulation by endodermal ingrowth (emboly, or invagination). B, early development and invaginative gastrulation in starfish. 1, blastula; 2, embolic invagination, early gastrula; 3, late gastrula, beginning of mesoderm formation.*

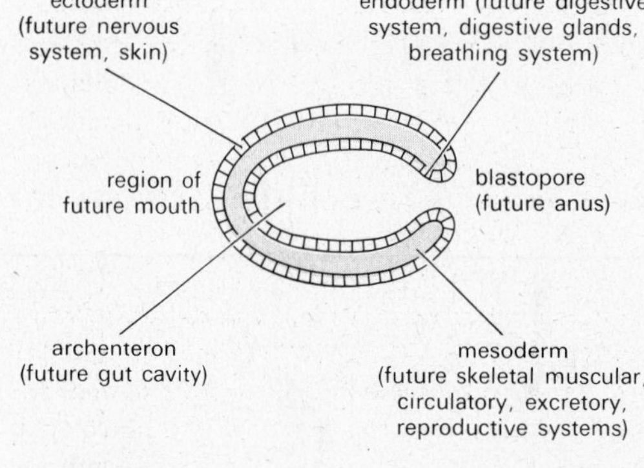

26.19 ***The vertebrate gastrula.*** *In this sectioned side view are shown the adult organ systems formed by each of the primary germ layers.*

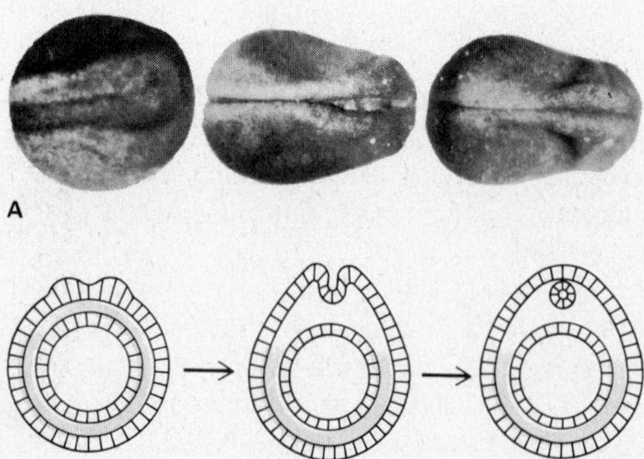

26.20 ***Early development of vertebrate nervous system.*** *A, left to right, dorsal views of progressive stages in neural-tube formation in frogs. The anterior ends of the embryos are toward the right. B, diagrammatic cross sections corresponding to the stages shown in A.*

space, or *blastocoel,* varies according to the size and number of cells that enclose it (see Fig. 26.17).

gastrula and induction

After a blastula has developed, the next major event is the establishment of the three primary germ layers of the embryo—*ectoderm* exteriorly, *endoderm* interiorly, and *mesoderm* between. The processes that transform a blastula to such a developmental stage are collectively called *gastrulation,* and the resulting embryo itself is a *gastrula.*

There are almost as many different methods of gastrulation as there are animal types. In the majority of animals, the organ-forming zones on the original egg surface already mark out the prospective regions that will produce the three germ layers; and gastrulation therefore involves an *interiorization* of the endoderm- and mesoderm-forming zones of the blastula. The prospective endoderm is usually brought to the interior first, generally through one of two processes: *epiboly,* or overgrowth of the ectoderm-forming regions around the endoderm-forming ones; and *emboly,* or ingrowth of the endoderm-forming regions under the ectoderm-forming ones (Fig. 26.18).

Different animals gastrulate by either one of these processes or by a combination of both. If a blastula is composed of but a few, large cells, embolic ingrowth is often difficult or impossible mechanically, and epibolic overgrowth is more likely to occur. By contrast, emboly will be readily possible in a blastula with many small cells and a large blastocoel. The form of emboly usually encountered in such cases is *invagination,* an indenting as when a balloon is pushed in at one side.

The common result of all methods of gastrulation is a basically two-layered gastrula having ectoderm on the outside, endoderm on the inside, a central cavity surrounded by endoderm, and an opening leading from this cavity to the outside. The cavity is the *archenteron,* the future alimentary space. The opening from it, called the *blastopore,* becomes the single alimentary opening of radiate animals and flatworms, the mouth of the *protostomial* groups (acoelomates, pseudocoelomates, and schizocoelomates), and the anus of *deuterostomial* groups (enterocoelomates). A second alimentary opening arises later as a perforation at the opposite side of the embryo.

Development of the third germ layer, the mesoderm, usually begins as soon as endoderm has formed. Mesoderm cells are budded off from ectoderm, endoderm, or both, and they migrate to the space between the ectoderm and the endoderm. According to how mesoderm becomes arranged later, the animal will exhibit an acoelomate, a pseudocoelomate, or a variously coelomate body structure (see Fig. 11.7).

The late gastrula thus represents a key stage in embryonic development. At that time the germ layers are established in proper positions, the future front and hind ends of the animal are marked, and the body cavities are already foreshadowed. In effect, the fundamental architecture of the future animal has become elaborated in rough outline (Fig. 26.19). The ectoderm will give rise to the whole nervous system and the whole integumentary system. Endoderm will form the alimentary system and in vertebrates also the breathing system, as well as all the glands and ducts associated with these. And the mesoderm will develop into most remaining body parts, including (in vertebrates) bones, muscles, and the circulatory, excretory, and reproductive systems. The endocrine system arises from all three germ layers.

After gastrulation all later development consists essentially of a sculpturing of well-defined body parts. In general such transformations occur by outfolding or infolding, outpouching or inpouching, of portions of the three layers of the gastrula. For example, the nervous system of vertebrates forms by an infolding of a tube of ectoderm along the dorsal midline of the embryo (Fig. 26.20). Limbs arise by combined outpouchings from ectoderm and mesoderm. Lungs and digestive glands develop as outpouchings at various regions of the endoderm. All other body parts develop in similar fashion. The ultimate result of these processes of morphogenesis and differentiation is a fully formed embryo, clearly recognizable as a young stage of a particular species.

Experiments have revealed some of the controls that ensure orderly sequences of development. Eye development in vertebrates provides a striking example. An eye begins to form when a pocket grows out from the side of the prospective brain (Fig. 26.21). This pocket has a bulbous tip that soon invaginates as a double-layered cup, the future eyeball. The rim of this cup eventually comes into contact with the outer, skin-forming ectoderm of the body. Just where the eyecup rests against it, skin ectoderm begins to thicken as a ball of cells, and the ball is then nipped off toward the inside. It fits neatly into the eyecup and represents the future lens. The lens cells and the overlying skin ectoderm later become transparent, and in this manner the basic structure of the eye is established.

In experiments on amphibian embryos, the stalked eyecup can be cut off before it has grown very far and can be transplanted to, for example, a region just under the belly ectoderm of another embryo. Under such conditions the patch of belly ectoderm that overlies the transplanted eyecup soon thickens, a ball of cells is nipped off toward the inside, and a lens differentiates. Moreover, lens and overlying skin become transparent. In effect, the transplanted structures have caused the formation of a structurally normal eye in a highly abnormal location (Fig. 26.22).

A common conclusion emerges from this and many similar types of experiment. One embryonic tissue interacts with an adjacent one, and the latter is thereby induced to differentiate, to grow, to develop in a particular way. This developed tissue then interacts with another one and induces it to develop in turn. In such fashion one tissue

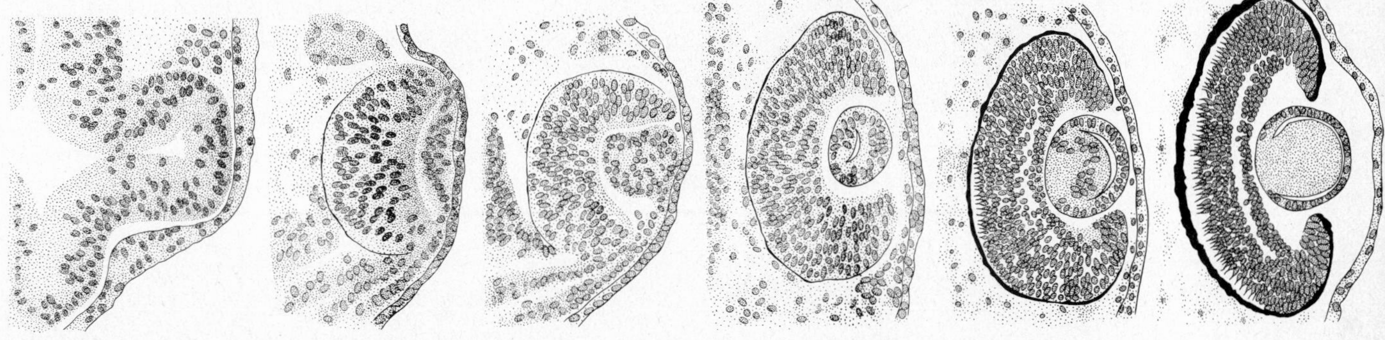

***26.21* Vertebrate (amphibian) eye development.** *This series of diagrams shows the successive outgrowth of a pocket from the brain, contact of this pocket with the outer body ectoderm, formation of an eyecup, gradual formation of a lens from the outer ectoderm, and development of the pigmented and other tissue layers of the eyeball.*

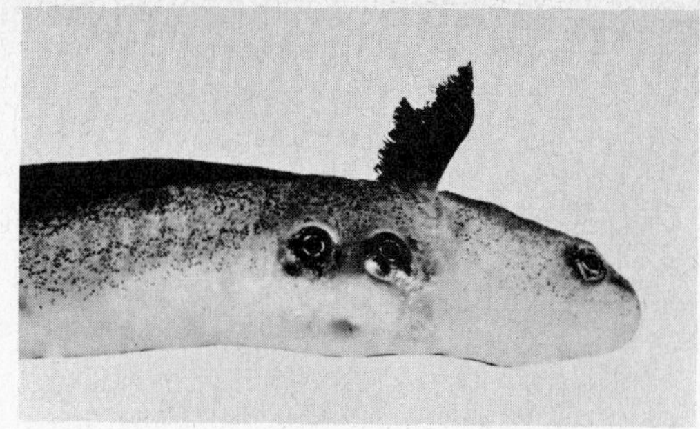

26.22 Eye transplantation. *If an embryonic eyecup is excised from a donor embryo and transplanted to an abnormal location in a host embryo, then a structurally perfect eye can develop at that abnormal location. The photo shows a larva of a salamander (Amblystoma) with two supernumerary eyes grafted to abnormal locations. The photo was taken 43 days after the transplant operation.*

provides the stimulus for development of the next. This phenomenon of *embryonic induction* therefore provides an explanation for the orderly sequence in which body parts are normally elaborated. However, the nature of such inductive processes in terms of reactions in and among cells is still obscure in many respects.

larvae and pregnancy

The embryonic phase of development typically terminates with a process of *hatching,* in which an embryo escapes from its external protective coats and becomes a free-living *larva.* Larvae occur in virtually all animal phyla, but some of the subgroups in a phylum are often without them. In most cases animals with larvae tend to be the comparatively primitive members of a phylum, those without larvae, the more advanced or specialized members.

Larvae serve mainly in one or both of two capacities. In many animals, sessile ones in particular, the larvae are the chief agents for geographic distribution of the species. In some cases such species dispersers are still without fully formed alimentary systems (as in ascidian tadpoles), but locomotor structures are always well developed. Thus tadpoles have strongly muscled tails, and the swimming larvae of many invertebrates have greatly folded and ciliated surfaces, with bands and tufts of extralong cilia in given regions (see Figs. 12.4, 12.29, 13.7). In many other animals the larvae can disperse geographcially far less well than the adults (insect caterpillars, for example). The primary function of larvae here appears to be nutritional; the organisms are transitional feeding stages that accumulate food reserves required for the construction of a more complex adult. In numerous animals a larva is both a dispersal and a feeding device.

Some types of larva exist for only a few hours, others for months or years. The larval period ends with *metamorphosis,* transformation to an adult. In this reorganization three kinds of change usually take place: body parts that have purely larval functions atrophy or disintegrate; body parts that have purely adult functions undergo exceedingly rapid development; and all other body parts are carried over from larva to adult with relatively little restructuring. In a frog tadpole, for example, the tail is of purely larval significance and it

A

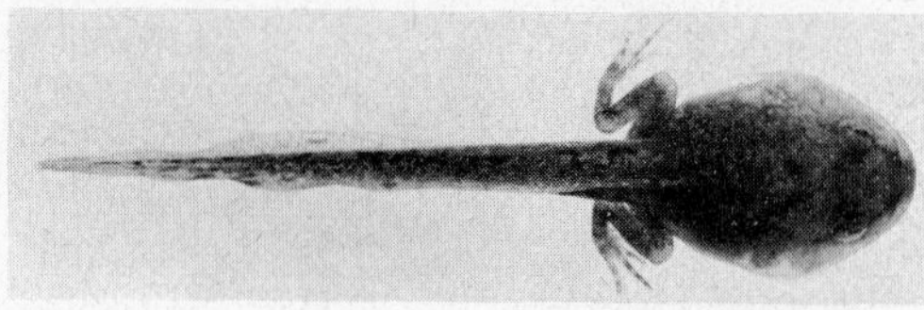

B

C

D

26.23 The nature of metamorphosis. *In these photos of amphibia before and after metamorphosis, some parts of the animal degenerate (e.g., tail), some parts proliferate (e.g., legs), and some parts undergo relatively little change (e.g., skin). A, tadpole, hind legs developing. B, hind legs at advanced stage, forelegs already visible underneath skin. C, forelegs have broken through, tail is degenerating. D, froglet, limbs well developed, tail resorbed almost completely.*

atrophies at the time of metamorphosis. The legs play a purely adult role, and metamorphosis accelerates their growth. And the brain, among body parts that serve both the larva and the adult, undergoes comparatively less metamorphic change (Fig. 26.23).

As might be expected, metamorphic reorganization tends to be relatively slight where a larva resembles the adult greatly. In such cases metamorphosis is usually a more or less gradual process, as among fishes or grasshoppers, for example. By contrast, reorganization is drastic where larva and adult are quite unlike each other. Metamorphosis then tends to be a fairly sudden, sharply defined event, as in insect caterpillars, for example (see Fig. 12.40).

In animals without free-living larvae, the developmental events that elsewhere take place in a larva are either omitted or are part of the late embryonic phase. The embryo then emerges as a miniature adult directly. Good examples among vertebrates are reptiles, birds, and mammals, in which free larval life has been replaced by a long-lasting embryonic phase inside an egg shell or a uterus.

Ancestral reptiles were the first vertebrates without free-swimming aquatic larvae. These animals evolved not only shelled eggs that could be laid on land, but also special adaptations inside the eggs that facilitated egg survival on land. More specifically, a special group of cells came to surround the embryo after gastrulation and formed four so-called *extraembryonic membranes.* All modern reptiles, birds, and mammals have inherited these membranes.

One of them, the *chorion,* lies just inside the shell of a reptile or bird egg and prevents excessive evaporation of water through the shell (Fig. 26.24). A second membrane, the *amnion,* surrounds the developing embryo everywhere except on its ventral side. This membrane holds lymphlike *amniotic fluid,* which bathes the embryo in a "private pond." The fluid represents the substitute of the actual ponds in which the larvae of ancestral land vertebrates developed. Because reptiles, birds, and mammals all have an amnion, these animals are called *amniotes* (and all other vertebrates are *anamniotes*).

Two other extraembryonic membranes pouch out ventrally from the alimentary tract of the embryo. One of these is the *allantois,* which lies against the egg shell just inside the chorion. This membrane is the breathing structure of the embryo; gas exchange occurs between the numerous blood vessels in the allantois and the air outside the shell. Also, the allantois serves as an embryonic urinary bladder in which metabolic wastes are stored up to the time of hatching. The second membrane on the ventral side is the *yolk sac,* which gets smaller gradually as yolk is used up during the growth of the embryo.

Mammals include some primitive types that still lay shelled eggs like reptiles and birds (see Chap. 13), but most mammals become pregnant and the eggs develop in the uterus. The extraembryonic membranes here largely function in new ways. After an egg is fertilized in the oviduct, it reaches the uterus as an embryo just beyond the gastrula stage. Such an embryo then *implants* in the uterus wall, which, as noted earlier, has already become prepared for pregnancy under the influence of progesterone from the corpus luteum (Fig. 26.25 and see Fig. 26.14). The first extraembryonic membrane, the chorion, next develops as an enclosure around the embryo, in direct contact with the tissue of the uterus. In one region the chorion produces numerous branching, fingerlike outgrowths that erode paths through the uterus wall. In this manner the tissues of chorion and uterus become attached to each other firmly. These interfingering and interlacing tissues represent the *placenta.* When fully formed, the placenta functions both as a mechanical and a metabolic connection between the embryo and the maternal body (Fig. 26.26).

The developing allantois still serves as in reptiles and birds as an embryonic lung, except that now gas exchange occurs in the placenta, between the blood vessels of the allantois and the

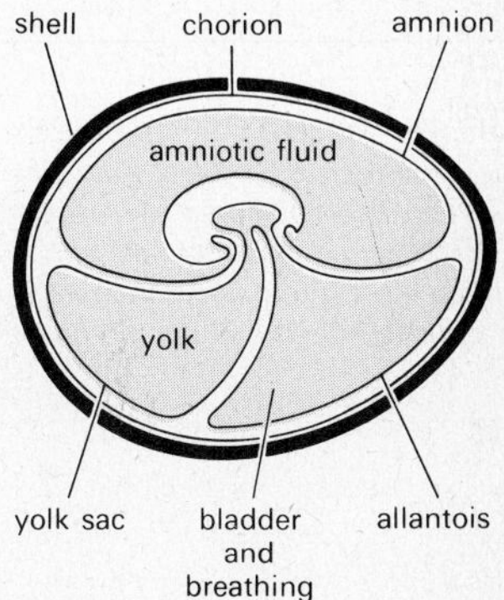

26.24 Extraembryonic membranes *in reptile and bird eggs. Yolk sac and allantois are large and functional.*

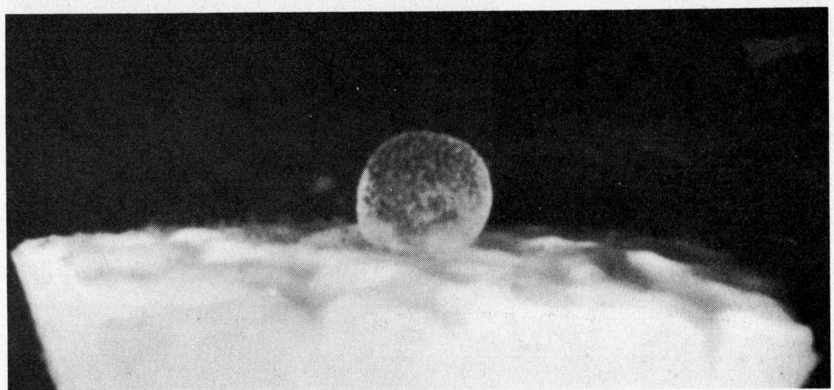

26.25 Placentation. *Early monkey embryo just arrived in the uterus and beginning to implant in the uterus wall.*

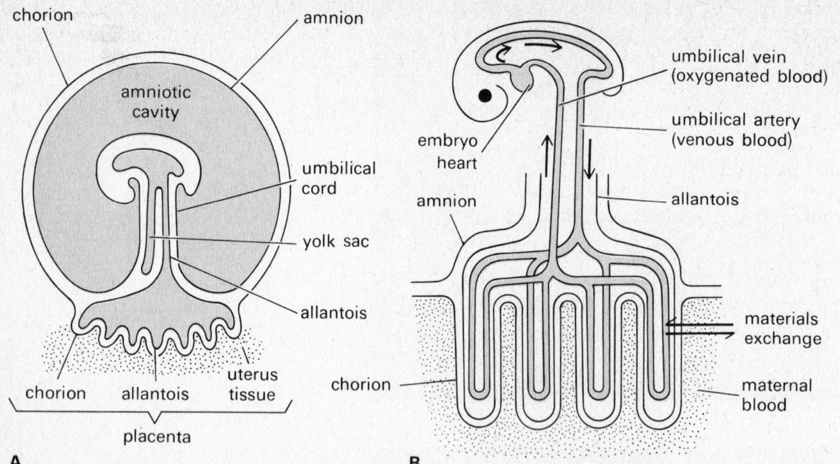

26.26 Placenta and embryo. *A, the yolk sac is rudimentary and collapsed, and the allantois is no longer a bladder. However, it still functions as a breathing organ, via blood vessels it carries from placenta to embryo. The amnion and chorion are ectodermal, the yolk sac and allantois are endodermal, and the white areas correspond to mesodermal regions. B, the embryonic blood circulation in the placenta. Embryonic and maternal bloods do not mix, being separated by the chorionic and allantoic membranes.*

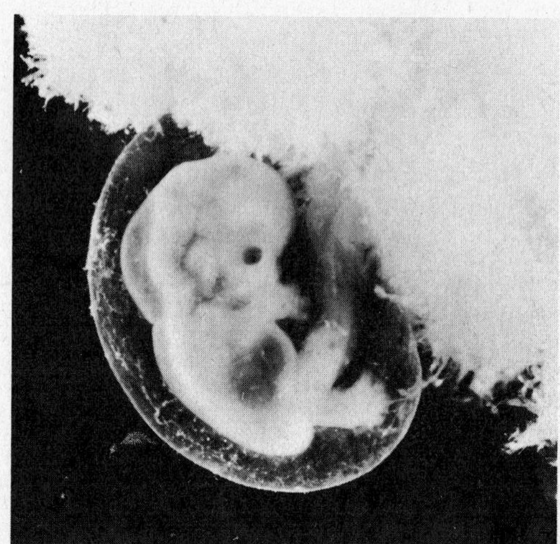

26.27 Extraembryonic membranes in man. *Embryo about 8 weeks after fertilization, obtained after surgical removal of portions of the reproductive system of a female patient. The chorion is pushed to the side, revealing the amniotic sac. Note umbilical cord.*

maternal blood of the uterus. The embryonic and maternal bloods do not mix in the placenta; the chorion always separates the two circulations. Maternal blood also carries off embryonic wastes and provides nutrients. If a raw material is in low supply in the maternal circulation, it is usually in still lower supply in the embryonic circulation. Needed metabolites therefore tend to diffuse to embryonic blood even if this produces a pronounced deficiency in the prospective mother. In this sense the embryo is parasitic on maternal metabolism. Conversely, waste substances pass preferentially to maternal blood, which is then usually rebalanced fairly quickly by increased maternal kidney activity. The maternal circulation also supplies defensive antibodies to the embryo. An offspring thereby acquires much of his mother's immunity for the first few months of life. Such a period usually just suffices to allow the young to manufacture his own antibodies in response to exposure to infectious agents.

Because the maternal circulation removes wastes from the embryo and supplies food and other necessary materials to it, the allantois no longer functions as a urinary bladder and the yolk sac no longer contains yolk. Both these membranes are collapsed, empty sacs. They later become enveloped by connective tissue and skin, the whole representing the *umbilical cord.* The blood vessels in the allantoic membrane make the umbilical cord a lifeline between placenta and embryo; it leaves a permanent mark in the offspring in the form of the navel. The amnion still forms as in reptiles and birds, and its fluid again serves as a "private pond." It is this enlarging amnion, more than the embryo itself, that produces the bulging abdomen of the pregnant female (Fig. 26.27).

The presence of placenta and embryo inhibits further egg production (and menstruation) during the period of pregnancy. The pituitary continues to produce LH and the corpus luteum at first continues to secrete progesterone. Thus the thickened wall of the uterus can be maintained and the developing embryo can remain implanted in it. Moreover, the placenta itself soon specializes as an endocrine organ. It manufactures slowly increasing amounts of estrogen and progesterone, and the progesterone output eventually becomes far greater than that of the corpus luteum. This body degenerates at some stage during pregnancy (roughly the twelfth week in man). From that time on the placenta provides the main hormonal control of pregnancy, and through its progesterone output it maintains its own existence (Fig. 26.28).

This period when the *luteal phase* of pregnancy changes over to the *placental phase* is generally rather critical. For if the corpus luteum should degenerate a little too soon and the placenta should reach full development a little late, then the amount of progesterone available during this gap is likely to be inadequate. In the absence of

color figure 23

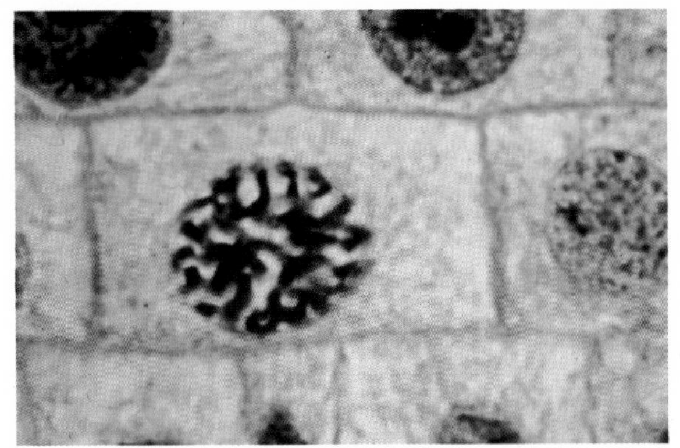

A

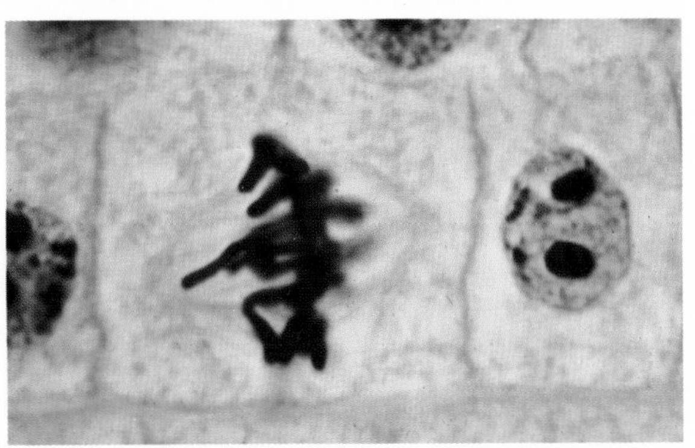

B

C

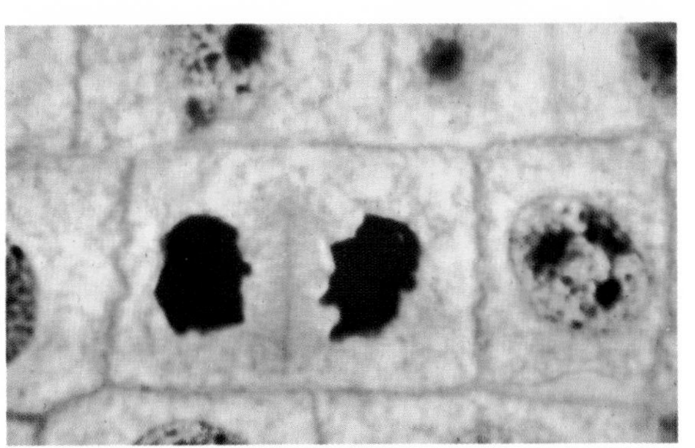

D

23. Mitosis, *as in plant cells. A, prophase. Distinct chromosomes are clearly visible, and the nuclear membrane has just dissolved. A spindle is not yet sharply marked. B, metaphase. Note spindle and metaphase plate, at right angles to spindle axis. C, anaphase. D, telophase. Two daughter nuclei are in process of being formed. Note faint indications of division plate, midway between daughter nuclei and at right angles to former spindle axis. (Courtesy Carolina Biological Supply Company.)*

color figure 24

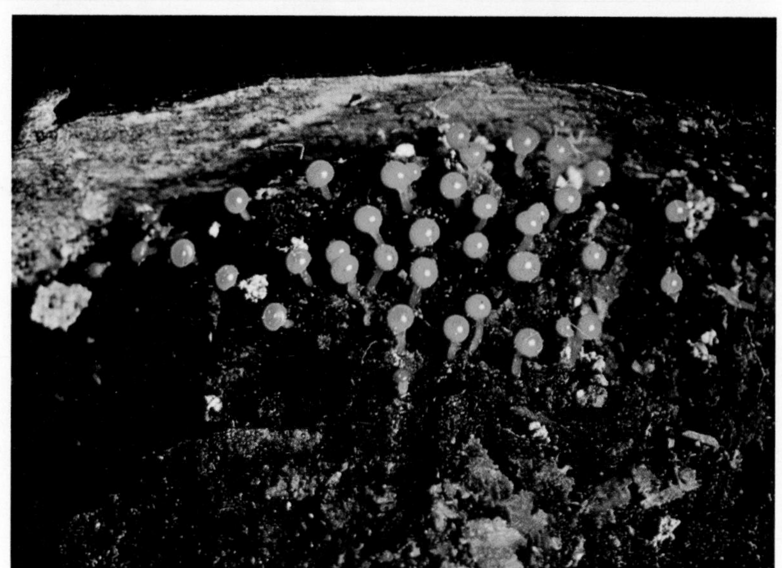

*24. **Fruiting bodies** of two kinds of slime mold. (Courtesy Carolina Biological Supply Company.)*

25. Equisetum, *strobili on upright shoots. (Courtesy Carolina Biological Supply Company.)*

color figure 26

A

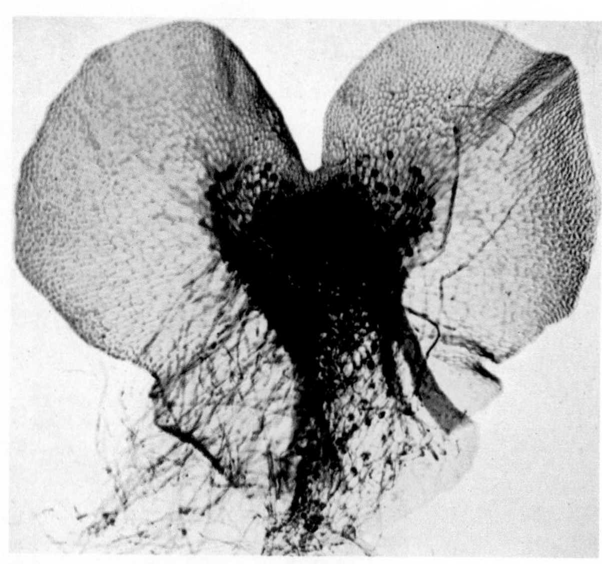

C

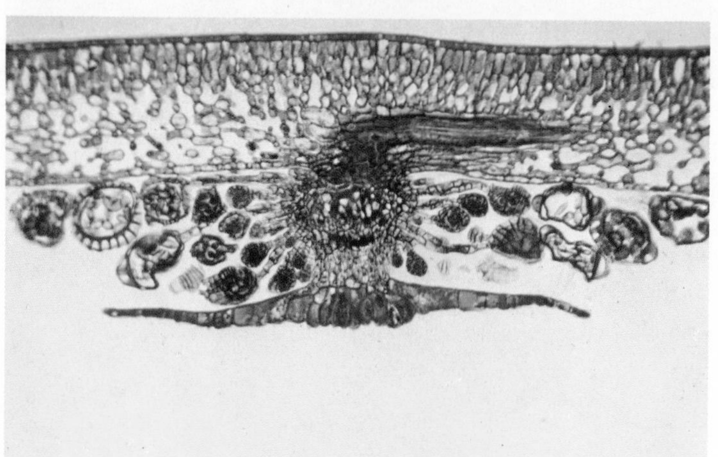

B

26. Fern reproduction. *A, underside of fern leaf with sori. Indusia are absent in this type. B, section through a fern sorus, showing arrangement of stalked sporangia and covering indusium. C, fern gametophyte. Note heart-shaped body, rhizoids, and region of sex organs (dark area near notch of heart). (B, C, courtesy Carolina Biological Supply Company.)*

27. Pine seed germination, *two stages.*

color figure 28

28. Flower anatomy. *In this cutaway specimen the pistil is in the center, with stigma at top, ovary at bottom, and a style connecting these two parts. Halfway along the style are the stamens, with yellow anthers. The reproductive structures are surrounded by yellow petals, and these in turn are enveloped by green sepals.*

enough hormone, however, placental tissues could not be maintained. The uterine lining would then disintegrate just as during menstruation, and the embryo, no longer anchored securely, would be aborted. In man miscarriages occur frequently near the end of the third month of pregnancy. Such mishaps can be prevented by hormone injections.

At the time of the hormonal phase change in man, it is already amply clear that the embryo will be a member of the human species. Basic forms and functions have already become elaborated earlier. Thus, 3 weeks after fertilization the human embryo is about the size of a coarse grain of sand, some three-quarters of it consisting of head structures. After 4 weeks the eyes are partly developed and the heart is already beating (Fig. 26.29). Limb buds appear in the fifth week, the ears are developed at that time, and the embryo now responds to mechanical stimuli by muscular contractions. Human form is first vaguely recognizable 8 weeks after fertilization, when the embryo is about 1 in. long. Once the species of a developing mammal can be identified, one speaks of a *fetus* rather than an embryo.

In a 12-week-old human fetus the fingers have formed, the semicircular canals in the ears are functional, and the fetus now moves of its own accord. Eyelids are still fused, but the eyes can move underneath. Five months after fertilization, the fetus is about 8 in. long and weighs about 1 lb, and the facial features show signs of individuality. In the following weeks the breathing machinery develops rapidly. The fetus is now in a perpetual drowsy state, neither sleeping nor waking. Overt body movements are sporadic and uneven, but eyelids open and close and lips purse rhythmically. In the eighth and ninth months periods of true wakefulness occur increasingly. Arms and legs are moved frequently and the hands open and close. Body fat is being laid down and the fetus acquires a sturdier stature. Growth in size has proceeded apace, and by the end of the ninth month the microscopic fertilized egg has become a whole human being.

In parallel with the development of the fetus the amnion gradually enlarges and the uterus stretches. Also, the mammary glands enlarge markedly under the stimulus of the sex hormones from the placenta and lactogenic hormone from the pituitary. Numerous ducts form in the interior of the glands, and in later stages the milk-secreting cells mature. For the first day or so after birth their product is not milk but *colostrum,* a lymphlike fluid that has some laxative action in the offspring.

Birth begins when the chorion and amnion rupture and the amniotic fluid escapes to the outside. Labor contractions of the uterine muscles occur with increasing frequency and strength, pressing against the offspring and pushing it out

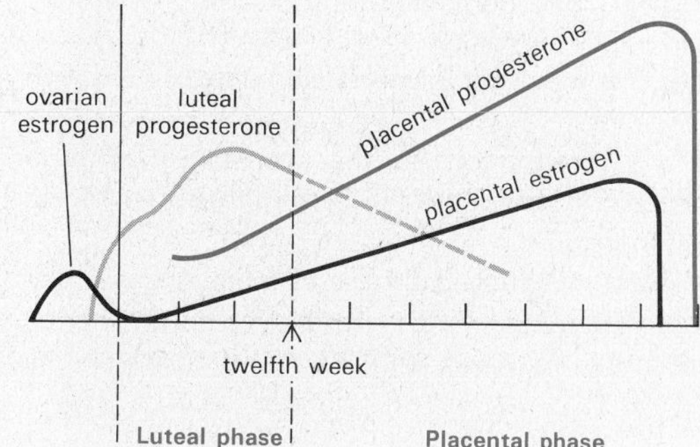

26.28 Hormones in pregnancy. *Curves indicate the amounts and sources of sex hormones during pregnancy in human females.*

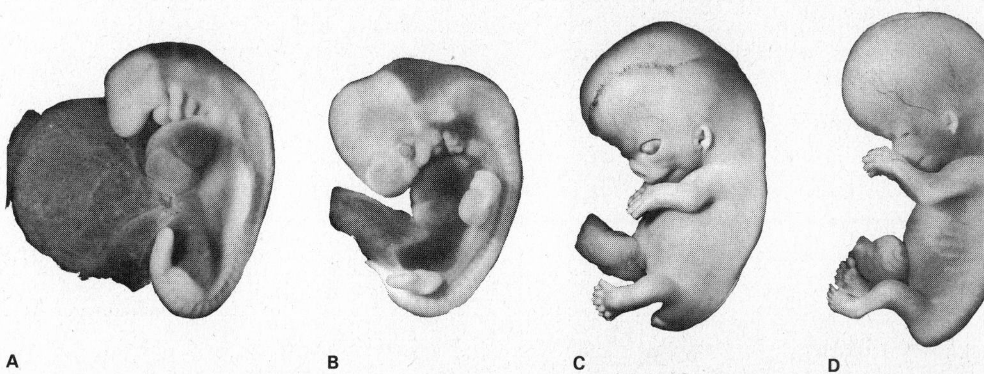

26.29 The human embryo. *A to D, four successive stages: 25 days, 33 days, 6 weeks, and 8 weeks after fertilization, respectively. The series indicates that chordate features arise first (e.g., dorsal skeletal supports, gill pouches, as in A); that vertebrate features develop next (e.g., anteroposterior segments, paired limb buds, tail, as in B); that tetrapod and mammalian traits appear later (e.g., four legs, umbilical cord, as in C); and that distinctly human traits appear last (e.g., arm-leg differences, flat face, individualized facial expression, as in D).*

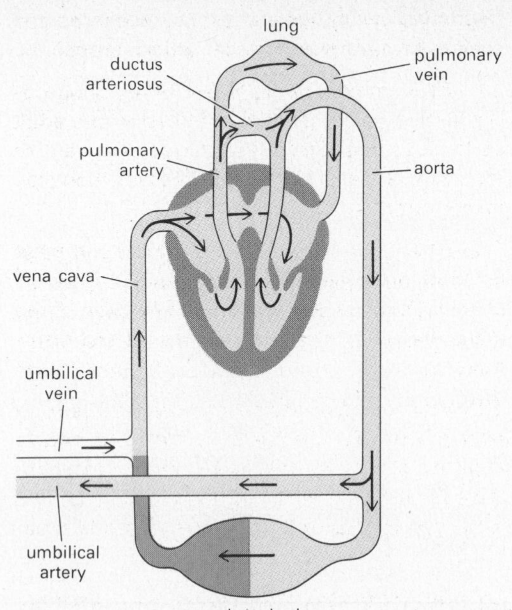

***26.30* Embryonic circulation in mammals.** *Oxygenated blood, white (only in umbilical vein, from placenta); venous blood, dark gray (from embryo body to vena cava); mixed blood, light gray (in vena cava, heart, lung, and aorta). The embryo lung is nonfunctional, and blood can pass directly from the pulmonary artery via the ductus arteriosus to the aorta. Note also the open passage between the two atria. The ductus arteriosus is a portion of the sixth aortic arch of the vertebrate gill circulation (see Fig. 13.18). Determine the effect if the umbilical vessels, the ductus, and the atrial passage all disappear and the lungs become functional, as at birth. Compare with adult circulation, Fig. 20.7.*

through the vagina. Concurrently the placenta loosens from the wall of the uterus and the connection between mother and offspring is thereby severed. An important result is that CO_2 produced by the offspring must accumulate in its own circulation. However, within seconds or minutes the concentration of the gas becomes high enough to stimulate the breathing center of the offspring.

In conjunction with this switchover from placental to lung breathing a structural change occurs in the heart (Fig. 26.30). Before birth the dividing wall between the right and left atria is incomplete, and a movable flap of tissue provides a passage between these chambers. Once lung breathing is initiated the blood-pressure pattern in the heart changes and the tissue flap is pressed over the opening between the atria. The flap eventually grows in place, and the left and right sides of the heart then are separated permanently. Another structural change involves an embryonic blood vessel (*ductus arteriosus,* see Fig. 26.30), which before birth leads from the pulmonary artery to the aorta and thus shunts blood around the nonfunctional lung. At birth a specially developed muscle in this vessel constricts and never relaxes thereafter. Blood is thereby forced to pass through the lungs. The muscle degenerates to scar tissue and the blood vessel as a whole degenerates soon after birth.

The loosened placenta, still connected to the umbilical cord, is expelled to the outside as the *afterbirth* within an hour or so after the offspring is expelled. Mammalian mothers (modern human ones excepted) bite off the umbilical cord and eat the cord and the placenta. Even herbivorous mothers do so, though they are vegetarians at all other times. Normal egg-producing cycles generally are not resumed as long as milk production and nursing continue. (In this context it is perhaps appropriate to point out that, contrary to a surprisingly wide belief among urban people, cows do not give milk at just any time; they must have been pregnant first.)

After the offspring is weaned, FSH is formed again by the pituitary and a new follicle then begins to mature in the ovary.

review questions

1 What are the first and second polar bodies? Are they found in males as well as females? Explain. What is the general structure of a mature sperm and a mature egg?

2 In which animals is fertilization (*a*) external, (*b*) internal? Define oviparity, ovoviviparity, viviparity. In which vertebrates does each occur?

3 Describe the general structure of the reproductive system in male and female animals. How does the structure of the reproductive system generally vary for externally and internally fertilizing animals? What are primordial germ cells? Show how an immature vertebrate gonad develops as either a testis or an ovary.

4 Review the structure of the reproductive system of human males. Where, specifically, are sperms produced? Describe the hormonal controls of sperm production. What is semen? Describe the relation of testis location and breeding season in different mammals.

5 Review the structure of the reproductive system of human females. Specifically where, and from what tissues, are eggs produced? What is a follicle, and what is its structure?

6 How are vertebrate breeding seasons initiated, maintained, and terminated? Show in what ways reproductive behavior is under hormonal control, and describe such reproductive behavior. What are the behavioral characteristics of animal courtships?

7 Describe the hormonal controls and the process of follicle growth in man up to the time of ovulation. What events take place during ovulation? After ovulation, what happens to (*a*) the egg and (*b*) the follicle?

8 Which animal groups have menstrual cycles? Describe the hormonal controls and the events in the uterus up to the time of menstruation. What happens during menstruation in the ovary and the uterus?

9 How and where does fertilization occur in vertebrates? What is an activated egg? Define blastomere, mosaic egg, organ-forming zone. What events occur during cleavage, and how is cleavage affected by the yolk content of an egg? How and from what types of egg can identical twins develop?

10 What is a blastula? In what general ways does gastrulation occur? Show how the three primary germ layers develop in vertebrates, and name the adult body parts that arise from each layer. Review the processes of mesoderm and coelom formation in different animal groups.

11 By what general processes of morphogenesis do the primary germ layers develop into adult structures? Illustrate this in the development of the vertebrate eye. What role does induction play in such transformations?

12 What are the functions of larvae, and what kinds of processes take place during metamorphosis? Describe the location and function of the extraembryonic membranes in reptiles and mammals.

13 What happens to a mammalian fertilized egg after it arrives in the uterus? When and how is a placenta formed and what are its functions? Describe the hormonal controls during (*a*) the luteal phase and (*b*) the placental phase of pregnancy.

14 Review the structure of the human placenta, with attention to embryonic and maternal blood circulation through it. Describe the whole pathway of the embryonic circulation. What is a fetus? What are puberty and menopause?

15 What events take place in the reproductive system of a pregnant mammal during birth of offspring? What changes take place in the blood circulation of the offspring at birth? How is milk production initiated and maintained?

collateral readings

Barth, L. J.: "Development," Addison-Wesley, Reading, Mass., 1964. This paperback deals with selected developmental topics, with special emphasis on cellular and early embryonic development.

Berrill, N. J.: "Growth, Development, and Patterns," Freeman, San Francisco, 1961. Numerous special aspects of embryonic and later development in both plants and animals are discussed in this highly recommended book.

Bullough, W. S.: "Vertebrate Reproductive Cycles," Wiley, New York, 1961. An account on breeding behavior and the hormonal controls of vertebrate reproduction.

Csapo, A.: Progesterone, *Sci. American,* Apr., 1958. A good review of the function of this hormone.

Dahlberg, G.: An Explanation of Twins, *Sci. American,* Jan., 1951. Obviously pertinent in the context of this chapter.

Ebert, J. D.: The First Heartbeats, *Sci. American,* March, 1959. An analysis of early chemical differentiation in heart development.

———: "Interacting Systems in Development," Holt, New York, 1965. A strongly recommended analytical paperback on some of the mechanisms at work in developing units.

Edwards, R. G.: Mammalian Eggs in the Laboratory, *Sci. American,* Aug., 1966. Eggs raised in culture media and fertilized there produce embryos outside the body that can be studied directly.

Farris, E. J.: Male Fertility, *Sci. American,* May, 1950. The fertilizing capacity of the male depends on normally structured sperms and certain proportions of them in semen.

Fischberg, M., and **A. W. Blackler**: How Cells Specialize, *Sci. American,* Sept., 1961. Progressive differentiation from the egg stage onward is discussed.

Konigsberg, I. R.: The Embryological Origin of Muscle, *Sci. American,* Aug., 1964. The differentiation of muscle is described.

Lehrman, D. S.: The Reproductive Behavior of Ring Doves, *Sci. American,* Nov., 1964. External stimuli, the behavior of the mating partner, and hormones form a sequence of triggers that initiate successive steps of reproductive activity.

Levine, S.: Sex Differences in the Brain, *Sci. American,* Apr., 1966. Masculine behavior in both males and females appears to be a consequence of the effect of testosterone on the brain of just-born offspring.

Monroy, A.: Fertilization of the Egg, *Sci. American,* July, 1950. The fine details of the process are examined.

Nelsen, O. E.: "Comparative Embryology of the Vertebrates," McGraw-Hill, New York, 1953. Vertebrate reproductive processes are reviewed in detail in this large text.

Pincus, G.: Fertilization in Mammals, *Sci. American,* March, 1951. Fertilization and early development can be studied in isolated mammalian eggs.

Puck, T. T.: Single Human Cells in Vitro, *Sci. American,* Aug., 1957. The article shows how from single starting cells human cells can be cultured like bacteria in artificial media.

Reynolds, S. R. M.: The Umbilical Cord, *Sci. American,* July, 1952. A recommended article in the context of this chapter.

Tinbergen, N.: The Courtship of Animals, *Sci. American,* Nov., 1954. A noted student of animal behavior discusses the requirements for mating.

Tyler, A.: Fertilization and Antibodies, *Sci. American,* June, 1954. Experiments showing that fertilization in sea urchins is chemically equivalent to an antigen-antibody reaction.

Waddington, C. H.: How Do Cells Differentiate? *Sci. American,* Sept., 1953. A review of the embryonic and genetic aspects of differentiation during egg development.

———: "Principles of Development and Differentiation," Macmillan, New York, 1966. A recommended paperback on animal morphogenesis, differentiation, and the relation of gene action to development.

part 8
adaptation

part 8
adaptation

chapter 27
heredity

chapter 28
evolution

chapter 29
change with time

chapter 30
the history and races of man

On the molecular as on the organismic level, in structure as in function, every organism is adapted *to its environment. Thus among thousands of different shapes that a fish* might *possess, its actual shape is well suited for rapid locomotion in water. A bird is cast in a form eminently suited for aerial life, yet its ancestry traces to fish. Organisms evidently can change their particular adaptations in response to new environments, and this property makes them potentially immortal as a group.*

Based on steady-state control and reproduction, adaptation is achieved through sex, heredity, *and* evolution. *The adaptive role of sex has already been discussed, and this series of chapters therefore concentrates on the roles of heredity and evolution.*

chapter 27 heredity

Life began after the first nucleic acids had originated. The creation of the first living units took billions of years, for it had to occur by physical and chemical chance; there was no blueprint to follow. But after nucleic acids were in existence creation of new life could become a very rapid process. Today it takes only 20 min to create a new bacterium, only 22 months to create a new elephant. This great acceleration is made possible by genes, the modern descendants of the first nucleic acids. Organisms now produce offspring according to instructions provided by genes, and through the inheritance of genes by successive generations construction of new life becomes a nonrandom, controlled process. What an organism inherits in large measure also determines its survival potential; heredity therefore has adaptive significance.

But organisms do *not* inherit strong muscles, green leaves, red blood, or any other trait. Organisms inherit the genes and all the other contents of reproductive cells. Visible traits then *develop* in an offspring, under the control of the inherited genes. The result of such heredity is an adult exhibiting *likeness* to its parents in certain major respects and *variation* from parents in many minor respects. If the variations are not lethal or do not cause infertility, the organism will survive and pass on its genes to following generations.

Modern studies of heredity were begun in the last half of the nineteenth century by the Austrian monk Gregor Mendel. He discovered two basic rules that laid the foundation for all later advances in genetics, the biological subscience dealing with inheritance. Accordingly, this discussion will include an examination of the rules of *Mendelian inheritance,* and an account of some of the main aspects of *non-Mendelian inheritance* brought to light since the time of Mendel.

mendelian inheritance

the chromosome theory

Most traits of organisms occur in two or more variant forms: some traits are exhibited in more or less sharp alternatives, like the different eye colors in man, while others form graded series between extremes, like body height in man. By studying the offspring from matings between such variant organisms, the patterns of trait inheritance can often be determined. For example, in the fruit fly *Drosophila,* one of the most widely used organisms in genetic research, the trait of body pigmentation is expressed in at least two alternative forms. In one the general coloration of the animal is gray and the abdomen bears thin transverse bands of black melanin pigment. A gray body represents the *wild type,* or predominant form of coloration in nature. By contrast, some flies are pigmented black uniformly all over the skin, a coloration pattern referred to as the *ebony* trait (Fig. 27.1).

If two gray-bodied wild-type flies are mated, all offspring produced are also gray-bodied. Indeed, all later generations again develop only wild-type colorations. Similarly, a mating of two ebony flies yields ebony offspring in all later generations. Gray and ebony body colors here are said to be *true-breeding* traits (Fig. 27.2).

In Mendel's time it was generally supposed that if alternative forms of a trait are cross-bred, a *blending* of the traits would result. Thus if gray and black were mixed together, like paints, a dark-gray color should be produced. And if blending really occurred dark-gray should be true-breeding as well; for mixed traits, like mixed paints, should be incapable of "unblending." In reality, however, the results of cross-breeding are strikingly different. When a wild type and an ebony fly are mated (parental generation, P), all offspring (first filial generation, F_1) are gray-bodied, exactly like the wild-type parent (Fig. 27.3). And when two such gray-bodied F_1 flies are then mated in turn, some of the offspring obtained are gray-bodied, others are ebony; color mixtures do not occur. Numerically, some 75 percent of the second generation (F_2) are gray-bodied, like their parents and one of their grandparents; and the remaining 25 percent are ebony, unlike their parents but like the other grandparent.

Evidently, the color traits of the offspring do not breed true; from gray-bodied flies in the F_1 can arise ebony flies in the F_2. Large numbers of tests of this kind have clearly established that, quite generally for any trait, blending inheritance does not occur and traits remain distinct and intact. If they become joined together in one generation, they can again become separated, or *segregated,* in a following generation. Mendel was the first to reach such a conclusion from studies on plants. Moreover, he not only negated the old idea of blending but postulated a new interpretation.

He realized that traits trace back to the gametes

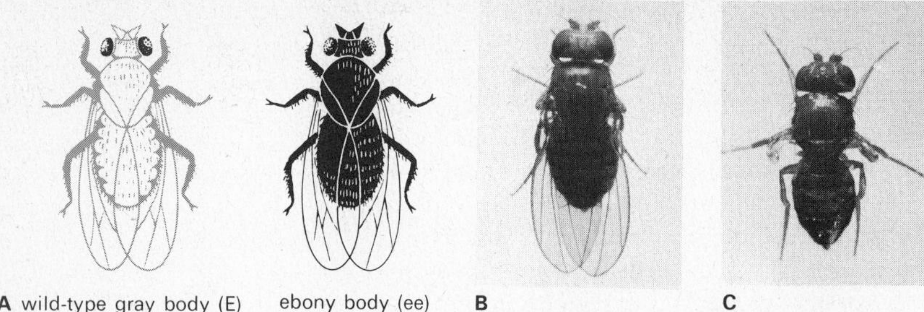

27.1 ***Traits of fruit flies.*** *A, female gray-bodied wild type on left, ebony-bodied fly on right. B, photo of wild-type fly. C, vestigial-winged fly, produced by a mutation of a single gene affecting wing structure. The animal is unable to fly.*

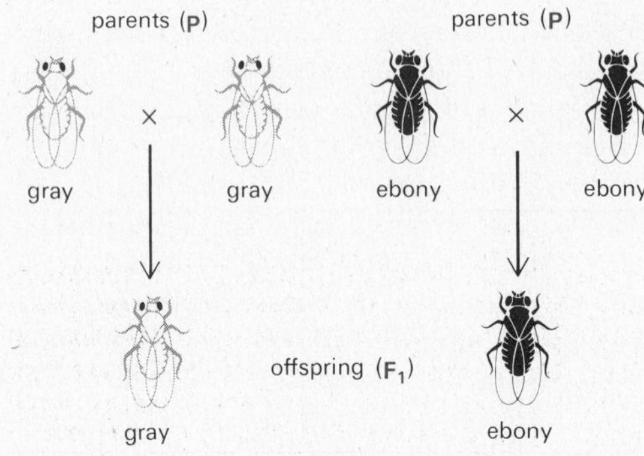

27.2 ***True-breeding in Drosophila.*** *If two gray-bodied (wild-type) flies are mated, all offspring will be wild-type (left); and if two ebony flies are mated, all offspring will be ebony (right).*

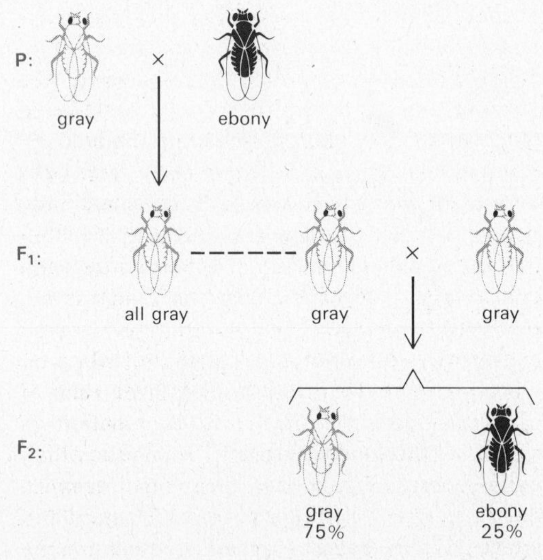

27.3 *If a gray-bodied fly is mated with an ebony fly (P generation), all offspring will be gray-bodied (F_1 generation). And if two of the F_1 flies are then mated in turn, the offspring will be gray-bodied and ebony in the ratio shown.*

that produce an organism, and he suspected that some "factors" in the gametes controlled the later development of traits. For any given trait, he argued, an organism must inherit at least one factor from the sperm and one from the egg. The offspring must then contain at least two factors for each trait. When that offspring in turn becomes adult and produces gametes, each gamete must similarly contribute one factor to the next generation. Hence before gametes are mature, two factors must be reduced to one. Mendel therefore postulated the existence of a factor-reducing process.

With this he in effect predicted meiosis. Near the end of the nineteenth century meiosis was actually discovered, and it was later recognized that chromosome reduction during meiosis corresponded precisely to Mendel's postulated factor reduction. Chromosomes therefore came to be regarded as the carriers of the factors, and the *chromosome theory of heredity* emerged. This theory has since received complete confirmation, and Mendel's factors eventually became the genes of today.

segregation

On the basis of the chromosome theory the fruit-fly data above can be interpreted as follows. A true-breeding wild-type fly contains a pair of gray-color-producing genes on some pair of chromosomes in each cell. These genes can be symbolized by the letters *EE*. Thus the gene content, or *genotype,* is *EE,* and the visible appearance, or *phenotype,* is gray. When such an animal produces gametes, meiosis occurs. Mature gametes therefore contain only one of the two chromosomes, hence only one of the two genes (Fig. 27.4).

It is entirely a matter of chance which of the two adult chromosomes will become incorporated in a particular gamete. Since both adult chromosomes here carry the same color gene, all gametes will be genetically alike in this respect. That is why *EE* animals are true-breeding, and why a mating of $EE \times EE$ will produce only gray-bodied offspring. In similar fashion, the genotype of a true-breeding ebony fly can be symbolized as *ee.* A mating of two such flies will yield only black-bodied offspring (see Fig. 27.4).

If now a wild type and an ebony fly are mated, all offspring will be gray-bodied (Fig. 27.5). In such offspring the *E* and *e* genes are present together, yet the effect of the *e* gene evidently is overridden or masked completely. The single gene *E* by itself exerts the same effect as two *E* genes. By contrast, the single gene *e* by itself is without visible effect; a double dose, *ee,* is required if a visible result is to be produced.

Genes that exert a maximum effect in a single dose, like *E*, are said to produce *dominant* traits. Such genes mask more or less completely the effect of corresponding genes such as *e*, which are said to produce *recessive* traits.

Genes that affect the same trait in different ways and that occur at equivalent (*homologous*) locations in a chromosome pair are called *allelic* genes, or *alleles*. Genes such as *E* and *e* are alleles, and pairs such as *EE*, *ee*, and *Ee* are different allelic pairs. If both alleles of a pair are the same, as in *EE* or *ee*, the combination is said to be *homozygous*. The combination *EE* is *homozygous dominant*, the combination *ee*, *homozygous recessive*. A *heterozygous* combination is one such as *Ee*, in which one allele produces a dominant and the other a recessive trait.

Thus the F_1 resulting from a mating of a wild type and an ebony fly as above is heterozygous, and this F_1 reveals that the wild-type trait is dominant over the ebony trait. That the heterozygous F_1 condition is not a true-breeding blend is now shown if two F_1 flies are mated (Fig. 27.6). After meiosis, each fly will produce two types of gamete. Of the genes *Ee*, either the *E* gene or the *e* gene could by chance become incorporated in any one gamete. Approximately 50 percent of the gametes will therefore carry the *E* gene, and the other 50 percent, the *e* gene.

In almost all organisms it is wholly a matter of chance which of the two genetically different sperm types fertilizes which of the two genetically different egg types. If many fertilizations occur simultaneously, as is usually the case, then all possibilities will be realized with appropriate frequency. The result is that three-quarters of the offspring are gray-bodied and resemble their parents in this respect. One-quarter is ebony and these offspring resemble one of their grandparents. Evidently, the result can be explained fully on the basis of nonblending, freely segregating genes and the operation of chance. Offspring in ratios of $\frac{3}{4}:\frac{1}{4}$ (or 3 : 1) are usually characteristic for matings of heterozygous organisms as above.

However, not all genes produce sharply dominant and sharply recessive forms of a trait. Many allelic genes give rise to traits that are neither dominant nor recessive. In such cases *each* allele in a heterozygous combination such as *Aa* can exert a definite effect, and the result usually is a visible trait intermediate between those produced by *AA* and *aa* combinations. For example,

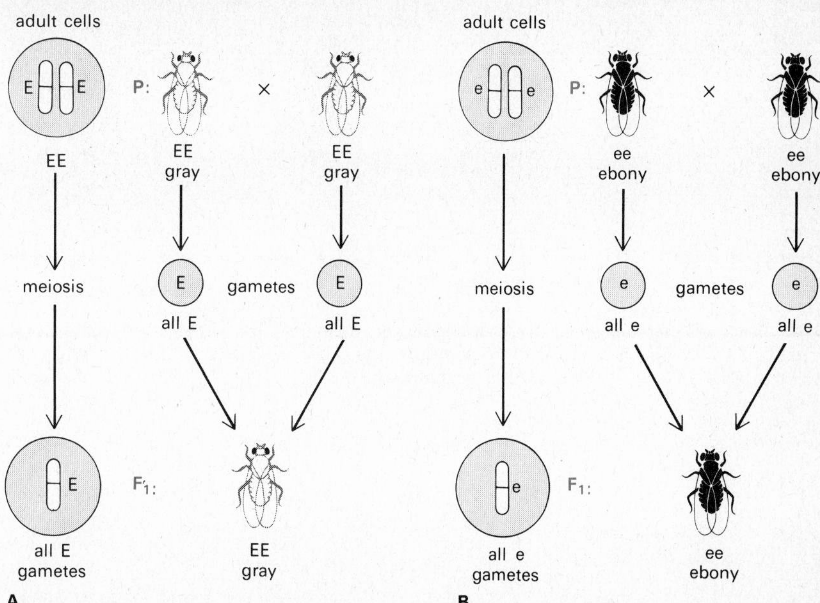

***27.4* Genetic effects of meiosis.** *A and B left: because of meiotic chromosome reduction, allelic gene pairs in adult cells become reduced to single genes in the gametes. A and B, right: gray-bodied wild-type flies and ebony flies, respectively, breed true because in each case all offspring receive the same kinds of gray-body-controlling or ebony-controlling genes from each of the two parents.*

27.5 (Below) **Genetic dominance.** *A mating between a gray-bodied and an ebony fly yields all gray-bodied offspring, indicating that the gray-body trait is dominant and masks the recessive ebony trait.*

snapdragon plants occur in true-breeding red-flowered (*AA*) and true-breeding white-flowered (*aa*) forms. If two such plants are cross-bred, all F_1 offspring (*Aa*) are *pink*-flowered; neither gene in the *Aa* combination is fully dominant, and neither is fully recessive. But even here the intermediate result is again not produced by color blending, for the pink-flowered condition is not true-breeding. A mating of two pink-flowered plants segregates red *and* pink *and* white F_2 offspring, in a characteristic phenotype ratio of $\frac{1}{4}:\frac{1}{2}:\frac{1}{4}$ (or 1 : 2 : 1). The inheritance pattern of the genotypes here is precisely the same as where genes have sharply dominant and recessive effects, and only the phenotype ratios are different (Fig. 27.7). Evidently, when genes are inherited in a particular pattern, the expressions of visible traits can differ according to the particular effects that the genes have on one another and on cell metabolism generally.

In modern terminology, Mendel's first law, the *law of segregation*, can now be stated as follows:

Genes do not blend but behave as independent

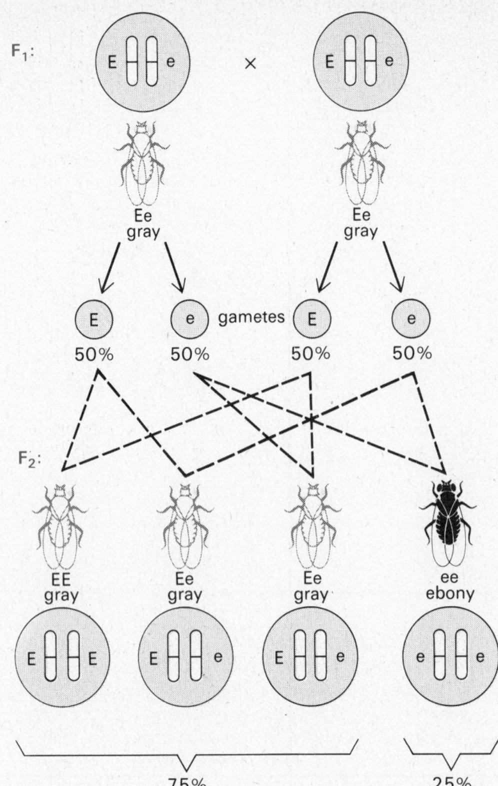

27.6 Dominance and segregation. *If two heterozygous gray-bodied (F_1) flies are mated, the offspring (F_2) will be 25 percent gray-bodied and homozygous like one of their gray parents (P in Fig. 27.5), 50 percent gray-bodied and heterozygous like their parents, and 25 percent ebony and homozygous like the other grandparent (P in Fig. 27.5).*

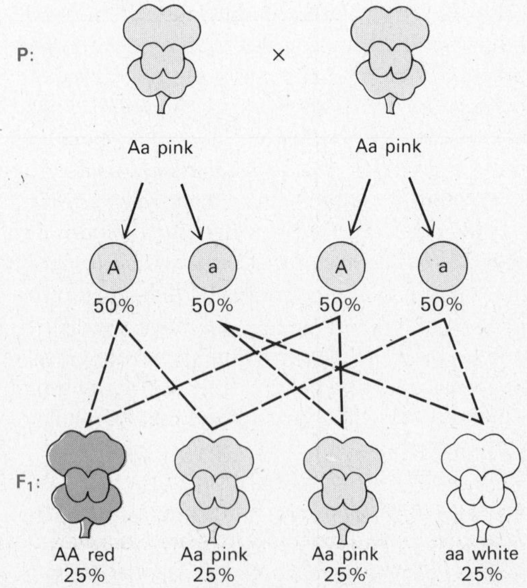

27.7 Partial dominance. *Allelic genes (A and a) can each have their own definite effect on phenotype, and neither thus produces completely dominant or recessive traits. This is the case in snapdragons, where gene A produces red flowers, gene a produces white flowers, and the gene combination Aa yields pink flowers. If two such pink-flowered adults are mated, the F_1 will have phenotypes and genotypes in the ratios shown. In this F_1 only 50 percent of the offspring are like the parents, the other 50 percent resembling two of their grandparents (verify this).*

units. They pass intact from one generation to the next, where they may or may not produce visible traits depending on their dominance characteristics. And genes segregate at random, thereby producing predictable ratios of visible traits among the offspring.

Implied in this law are chromosome reduction by meiosis and the operation of chance in the transmission of genes.

independent assortment

Organisms do not inherit genes one at a time, but all of them are inherited together. What then will offspring be like with respect to two or more simultaneous traits inherited from particular parents? Mendel discovered a fundamental rule here. Phrased in modern terms, this *law of independent assortment* states:

The inheritance of a gene pair located on a given chromosome pair is unaffected by the simultaneous inheritance of other gene pairs located on other chromosome pairs.

In other words, two or more traits produced by genes located on two or more different chromosome pairs "assort independently;" each trait is expressed independently, as if no other traits were present.

The meaning of the law emerges from an examination of the simultaneous inheritance of, for example, two traits of fruit flies, *body color* and *wing shape.* As already noted, body color can be either wild-type gray or recessive ebony. Wing shape can be either normal or *vestigial.* In the latter condition the wings are reduced in size to such an extent that the animal cannot fly (see Fig. 27.1). Such stunted wings can be shown to develop whenever a recessive gene *vg* is homozygous, *vgvg.* Normal wings represent the dominant wild type, produced by either *VgVg* or *Vgvg* gene combinations. The body-color and wing-shape genes are located on different chromosome pairs of *Drosophila,* and the wing genes, like the color genes, obey the law of segregation.

What will now be the results of a mating between two *EeVgvg* flies, individuals that are heterozygous for both traits simultaneously? After meiosis, each gamete will contain only *one* color gene and only *one* wing gene. But which of each pair—the dominant or the recessive gene? This is a matter of chance. Thus a gamete might contain the genes *E* and *Vg,* or *E* and *vg,* or *e* and *Vg,* or *e* and *vg.* If many gametes are produced, all four combinations will occur with roughly equal frequency (Fig. 27.8).

Fertilization, too, is governed by chance. Consequently *any* one of the 4 sperm types might fertilize *any* one of the 4 egg types. Hence there are 16 different combinations that can occur in fertilization. If large numbers of fertilizations take place simultaneously, all 16 combinations will occur with roughly equal frequency. These 16 combinations can be determined from a grid in which the gametes of one parent are put along a horizontal edge and the gametes of the other parent along a vertical edge (Fig. 27.9).

Among the 16 offspring types so formed, some individuals contain *both* dominant genes at least once, some contain one *or* the other of the dominant genes at least once, and some contain none of the dominant genes. A count reveals gray-normal, gray-vestigial, ebony-normal, and ebony-vestigial to be present in a ratio of 9:3:3:1.

This result proves the law of independent assortment. For if body color is considered *alone,* there are 9 plus 3, or 12 animals out of every 16 that are gray, and 3 plus 1, or 4 that are ebony. But 12:4 is a 3:1 ratio. Similarly, if wing shape is considered *alone,* again 12 out of every 16 animals have normal wings and 4 have vestigial wings; here, too, the ratio is 3:1. Evidently, although the color and wing traits are inherited simultaneously and yield a 9:3:3:1 offspring ratio overall, each trait considered *separately* nevertheless gives a 3:1 ratio of offspring. Each trait therefore is inherited as if the other trait were not present; or, in Mendel's phrase, the traits assort independently.

Mendel's second law applies specifically to gene pairs located on different chromosome pairs. The law will therefore hold for as many different gene pairs as there are chromosome pairs in each cell of an organism. Suppose we considered the inheritance of *three* different gene pairs, each located on a different chromosome pair, in a mating of two triple heterozygotes *AaBbCc* × *AaBbCc.*

As shown above, a double heterozygote *AaBb* produces *four* different gamete types. Applying the same principles, it can be verified readily that a triple heterozygote produces *eight* different gamete types: *ABC, ABc, AbC, Abc, aBC, aBc, abC,* and *abc.* To determine all possible genotypes of the offspring, we can use a grid 8 squares by 8 squares and place the 8 gamete types of each parent along the edges, as above. The result

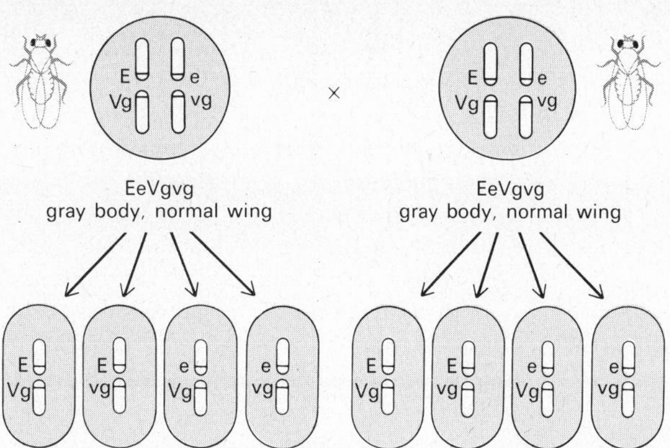

27.8 Double heterozygotes. *If two flies heterozygous for both body color and wing shape are mated (top), each fly will produce gametes as shown.*

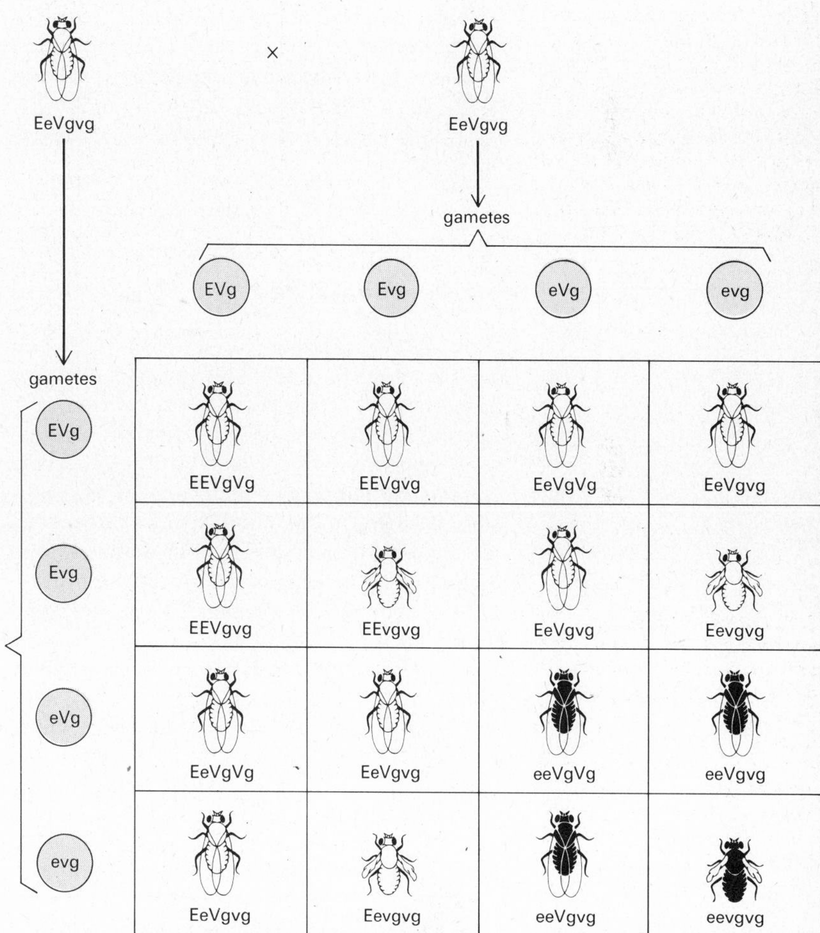

27.9 The Punnett square. *Gametes produced by flies as in Fig. 27.8 and at top of this figure can combine in the 16 combinations shown inside the square. The offspring then have a 9:3:3:1 phenotype ratio.*

will be 64 offspring types, of which 27 will express all the three traits in dominant form. The complete phenotype ratio can be easily verified as 27:9:9:9:3:3:3:1.

Two quadruple heterozygotes, *AaBbCcDd,* would manufacture 16 gamete types each, and we would need a grid 16 by 16 to represent the 256 different genotype combinations. The possibilities evidently become rapidly astronomical once more than a few traits are considered simultaneously.

Organisms heterozygous for a large number of gene pairs are called *hybrids,* and one, two, or three heterozygous gene pairs can be referred to as monohybrids, dihybrids, or trihybrids, respectively. In man there are 23 pairs of chromosomes per cell. Mendel's second law will therefore apply to any 23 traits controlled by genes located on different chromosome pairs. What then would be the geneotypes resulting from a mating of, for example, two 23-fold hybrids: *AaBb . . . Ww* × *AaBb . . . Ww?* We know that:

a monohybrid yields $2^1 = 2$ gamete types

a dihybrid yields $2^2 = 4$ gamete types

a trihybrid yields $2^3 = 8$ gamete types

a quadruple hybrid yields $2^4 = 16$ gamete types

Carrying this progression further, a 23-fold hybrid can be shown to produce 2^{23} or over 8 million genetically different gamete types. Hence in considering just 23 gene pairs on different chromosome pairs, a grid of 8 million by 8 million would be required to represent the over 64 trillion possible genotypes. This number is far larger than the totality of human beings ever produced, and a good many millions or billions of these genotypes therefore have probably never yet arisen during the entire history of man.

Accordingly, chances are great that every newborn human being differs from every other one, past or present, in at least some genes controlling just 23 traits. And the genetic differences for *all* traits must be enormous indeed. Here is one major reason for the universal generalization that no two organisms produced by separate fertilizations are precisely identical.

A chromosome contains not just one gene but anywhere from a few hundred to a few thousand. What is the inheritance pattern of two or more gene pairs located on the *same* chromosome pair? This question leads beyond Mendel's two laws.

linkage

Genes located on the same chromosome are said to be *linked;* as the chromosome is inherited, so are all its genes inherited. Such genes clearly do not assort independently but are transmitted together in a block. The traits controlled by linked genes are similarly expressed in a block. In fruit flies, for example, the same chromosome pair that carries the wing-shape genes also carries one of many known pairs of eye-color genes: a dominant allele *Pr* produces red, wild-type eyes, and a recessive allele *pr* in homozygous condition produces distinctly purple eyes. If now a normal-winged, red-eyed heterozygous fly *VgvgPrpr* produces gametes, only two types should be expected, *VgPr* and *vgpr,* 50 percent of each (Fig. 27.10). In actuality, however, four gamete types are produced, in proportions as in Fig. 27.10.

If these four types occurred in approximately equal numbers, each about 25 percent of the total, then the result could be regarded simply as a case without linkage, governed by Mendel's second law. But the actual results include significantly *more* than 25 percent of each of the expected gamete types and significantly *less* than 25 percent of each of the unexpected types.

To explain odd results of this sort, T. H. Morgan, a renowned American biologist of the early twentieth century, proposed a new hypothesis. He postulated that, during meiosis, paired chromosomes in some cases might twist around each other and might break where they were twisted. The broken pieces might then fuse again in the "wrong" order (Fig. 27.11). Such occurrences could account for the large percentage of expected and the small percentage of unexpected gamete types. The hypothesis was tested by microscopic examination of cells undergoing meiosis, and it could indeed be verified that chromosomal *crossing over* actually takes place. Crossing over is now believed to involve a breaking of DNA chains and subsequent synthesis of new connections between the broken ends of these chains.

The implications of crossing have proved to be far-reaching. It has been reasoned that the frequency of crossovers should be an index of the *distance* between two genes. If two genes on a chromosome are located near each other, the chances should be relatively small that a twist would occur between these close points. But if two genes are relatively far apart, twists between them should be rather frequent. In general, the frequency of crossovers should be directly proportional to the distance between two genes (Fig. 27.12). Inasmuch as the crossover percentage of two genes can be determined by breeding experiments, it should therefore be possible to construct *gene maps* showing the actual location of particular genes on a chromosome. Indeed, since Morgan's time the exact positions of a few hundred genes have been mapped in the fruit fly. Smaller numbers of genes have similarly been located in corn plants, in mice, and in various other organisms.

A second implication of crossing over is that genes on a chromosome must be lined up single file. Only if this is the case can linkage and crossing over occur as it actually does occur. This generalization has become known as the *law of the linear order of genes.* It represents the third major rule that governs Mendelian inheritance.

Third, crossing over makes meiosis a *source of genetic variations.* For example, when a diploid cell in a testis undergoes meiosis and produces four haploid sperms, these four do not contain merely the same whole chromosomes as the original cell. Rather, because of crossing over, the chromosomes in each sperm will be quiltworks composed of various joined pieces of the original chromosomes; and the four sperms are almost certain to be genetically different not only from one another but also from the original diploid cell. Moreover, any two genetically identical diploid cells are almost certain to give rise to two genetically different quartets of sperms. Genetic variations thus are produced by both phases of sex: through fertilization, which doubles chromosome numbers, and through meiosis, which reduces numbers and also shuffles the genes of the chromosomes.

The three rules of heredity here outlined describe and predict the consequences of *sexual recombination*—the various results possible when different sets of genes become joined through fertilization and are pooled in the zygote. In other words, sexual recombination of genes leads to Mendelian inheritance. However, a great many hereditary events have been found that do not obey the three basic rules.

non-mendelian inheritance

Non-Mendelian inheritance occurs on occasion when genetic material is introduced into bacteria by nonsexual means. In bacterial *transformation,* DNA extracted from one strain can be put in a medium that contains another strain of bacteria. These organisms then absorb some of the foreign DNA and thereby acquire some of the genetic traits of the original DNA donors. Similar in prin-

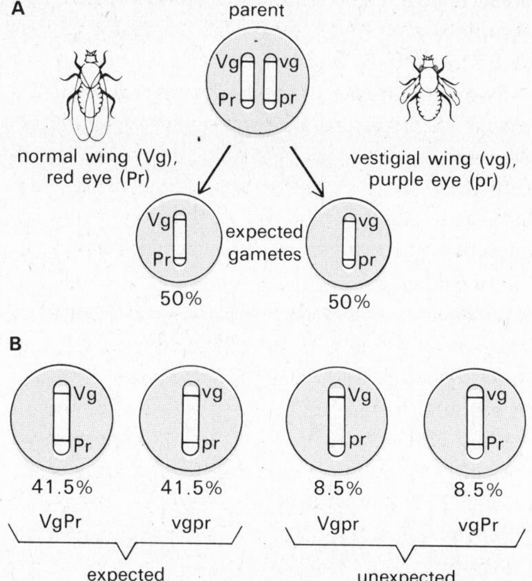

27.10 ***Linkage.*** *A, left and right, the phenotypes of wing shape and eye color in Drosophila, two traits controlled by linked genes. Center, the expected gametes of a heterozygous fly VgvgPrpr. B, the proportions of the actual gamete types obtained. Expected types appear in smaller numbers than predicted, and considerable numbers of wholly unexpected types appear as well.*

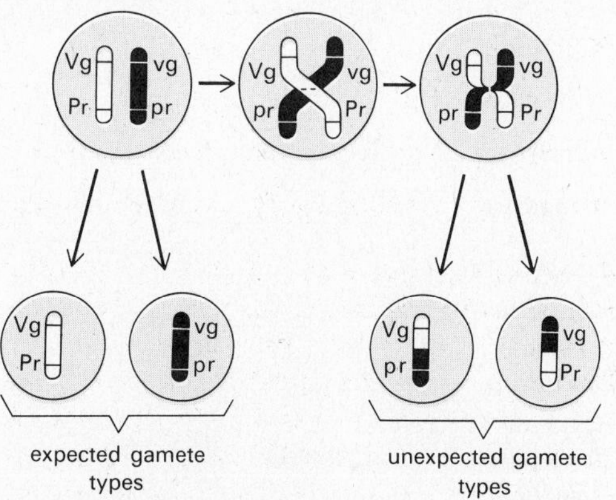

27.11 ***Crossing over.*** *If during meiosis chromosomes twist, break, and re-fuse at the break points in the wrong order, then unexpected gamete types will appear.*

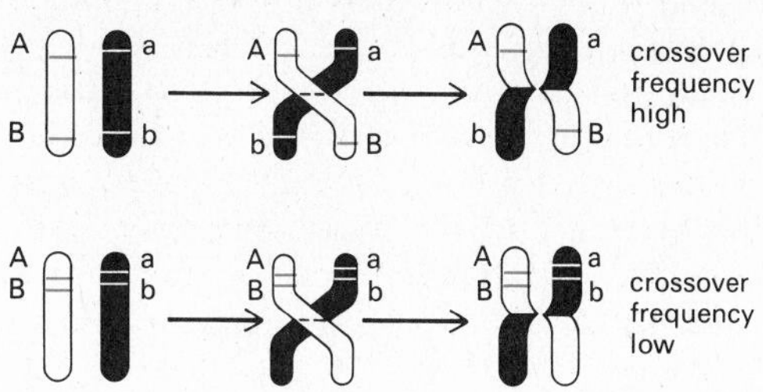

27.12 ***Crossing over and gene distances.*** *If two genes are far apart, crossing over between them is likely to occur fairly frequently (top). But if genes are close together, crossing over between them is less likely (bottom). In general, the farther apart given genes are on a chromosome, the more frequent crossing over will be.*

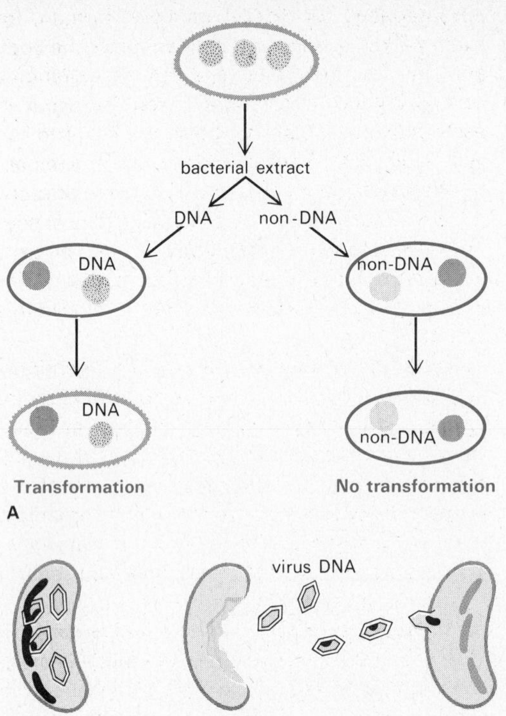

27.13 Transformation and transduction. *A, the cell substance of a rough-coated bacterial type is extracted, and separate DNA and non-DNA fractions are prepared. If a smooth-coated bacterial type is allowed to absorb the DNA fraction, it will change to a rough-coated type (but it will remain smooth-coated if it absorbs only the non-DNA fraction). Such gene transfers and the resulting transformations are instances of non-Mendelian inheritance. B, left: newly forming bacteriophage viruses incorporate in their own structure some of the DNA of the host bacterium (dark color). Center and right: when such viruses infect a new bacterial host, this host acquires additional bacterial genes. Such gene transfers by virus transductions again result in non-Mendelian inheritance.*

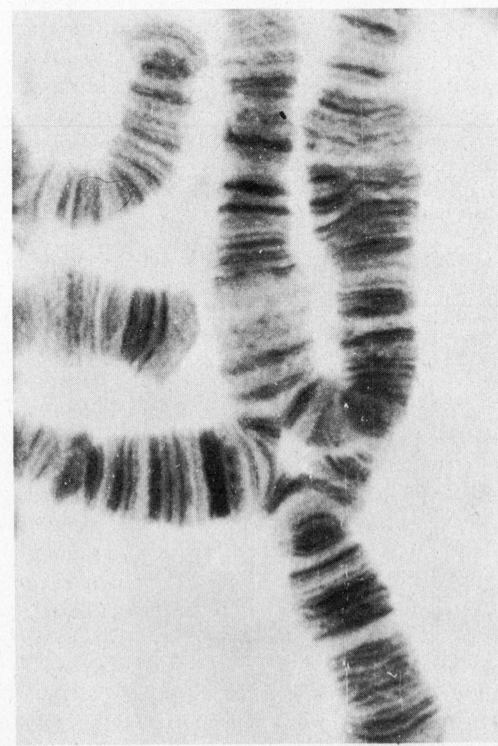

27.14 Chromosome mutations. *The U-shaped portion in the upper part of this photo is a normal (stained) salivary-gland chromosome of a midge. The branches leading away from the bottom of the U are parts of other chromosomes that have become translocated and attached here. These translocations have been induced by irradiation with X rays.*

ciple is bacterial *transduction,* in which viruses, not human experimenters, accomplish a transfer of DNA from one bacterial type to another. When a virus reproduces in an infected bacterium, pieces of bacterial DNA occasionally become incorporated in the offspring viruses. If one of these offspring then infects a new bacterial host, additional bacterial genes are introduced into that host (Fig. 27.13).

As instances of non-Mendelian inheritance, bacterial transformation and transduction have strictly limited significance. Far more important, universally significant in all organisms, are *mutations.*

mutation

Any stable, inheritable change in the genetic material of a cell is a mutation. The most common type is a *point mutation,* a stable change of one gene. In such cases it is not necessary that all the DNA of a whole gene become altered; a change in not more than a single pair of nucleotides in a double DNA chain can amount to a mutation. Such a change can alter the genetic code for a single amino acid in a protein, and one different amino acid often suffices to affect the function of the protein; if the protein is an enzyme, for example, a particular metabolic reaction could become altered or even blocked, and the consequences in a cell could be very significant.

The smallest portion of a gene that can produce a mutational effect is called a *muton;* the smallest muton would be a single pair of nucleotides in DNA. A ''gene,'' consisting of numerous mutons in linear series, can therefore be defined as a *unit of mutation:* a section of a chromosome that, after becoming altered in at least one of its mutons, changes just one trait of a cell.

Traits are affected not only by point mutations but also by various kinds of so-called *chromosome mutations.* These include, for example, *inversions*—a piece breaks off a chromosome and reattaches itself in inverted position; *translocations*—a piece breaks off a chromosome and attaches itself to another chromosome; *duplications*—a section of a chromosome doubles; and *deletions*—parts of chromosomes break off and become lost. All such chromosome mutations alter the nucleotide sequences of DNA and thus the genetic messages transmitted to RNA (Fig. 27.14).

Mutational changes can be induced by high-energy radiation such as X rays, and the frequency of mutation has been found to be directly proportional to the amount of radiation a cell receives. Some of the naturally occurring mutations are probably produced by cosmic rays and other space radiation and by radioactive elements in the earth. But this unavoidable natural radiation is not sufficiently intense to account for the mutation frequency characteristic of genes generally, about one per million replications of a given gene. Most of these mutations probably represent errors in gene reproduction. Others are undoubtedly caused by man-made radiation, which adds to and increases the natural "background" radiation. Mutations can also be produced experimentally by physical agents other than radiations, and by various chemical agents.

Mutations occur at random. Any gene can mutate, at any time and in unpredictable ways. It can mutate several times in rapid succession, then not at all for considerable periods. It can mutate in one direction, then back to its original state or in new directions. Every gene existing today undoubtedly is a *mutant* that has undergone many mutations during its past history.

The effect of a mutation on a trait is equally unpredictable. Some are "large" mutations that affect a major trait in a radical, drastic manner. Others are "small," with but little effect on a trait. Some mutations have dominant effects and produce immediate alterations of traits. Others have recessive effects, and in diploid cells they remain masked by normal dominant alleles.

In view of the structural and functional complexity of a cell it might be expected that nearly any permanent change in cell properties would be disruptive and harmful. Indeed, most mutations are disadvantageous, and if they have dominant effects they tend to impair cellular functions. Most mutations with dominant effects actually tend to be eliminated as soon as they arise, through death of the affected cell. In some cases, however, a dominant effect of a mutation (particularly a "small" dominant effect) can become integrated successfully with cellular functions. Such a cell then survives with an altered trait. Yet most of the mutations in surviving diploid cells have recessive effects, which are masked by the effects of the normal dominant alleles.

A small percentage of mutants produces advantageous traits or new traits that are neither advantageous nor disadvantageous. In man, for example, many trillions of cells compose the body and, in view of the average rate of mutations, several million mutations are likely to occur in each individual. Many of these are lethal to the cells in which they occur, and many others remain masked by normal dominants. But some produce nonlethal dominant traits. Such new traits arising in individual cells are then transmitted to all cells formed from the original ones by division. For example, "beauty spots" probably develop in this manner.

Gene changes that occur in body cells generally are *somatic mutations.* They affect the heredity of the cell progeny—a patch of tissue at most. In multicellular organisms such mutations usually have little direct bearing on the heredity of the whole individual. An entire multicellular organism is likely to be affected only by *germ mutations,* stable genetic changes in immature and mature reproductive cells. Such mutations will be transmitted to all cells that ultimately compose the offspring. To the extent that germ mutations are recessive and masked by normal dominants, the traits of the offspring will not be altered. But if the offspring is haploid, or is diploid but homozygous recessive for a mutation, or if a mutation is dominant, then a particular trait can be expressed in altered form. Provided such a new trait is not lethal or does not cause sterility, it will persist as a non-Mendelian variation. Mutations can therefore affect the adaptation of an individual as much as sexual recombination of genes.

sex determination

Groups of genes in a cell often cooperate in controlling a single composite trait. One of the best illustrations is the trait of sexuality, which in numerous organisms is controlled not by individual genes acting separately but by whole chromosomes acting as functionally integrated units.

Each organism is believed to have genes for the production of both male and female traits. Such genes need not necessarily be specialized "sex genes" but could be of a type that, among other effects, also happen to influence sexual development. Organisms thus are considered to have a genetic potential for *both* maleness and femaleness, and two categories can be distinguished according to how this genetic potential is translated to actual sexual traits.

27.15 Nongenetic sex determination. *Left, M and F in zygote and adults indicate that male- and female-determining genetic factors are equally balanced. The actual maleness, femaleness, or hermaphroditic condition of the adult depends on external nongenetic influences acting at some point during development. Right, such influences act at different developmental stages in different types of organism (progressively lower down along the vertical development line of the zygote). Thus, separate sexuality can become manifest in the embryo or, by contrast, not until the adult produces gametes. Up to such an externally influenced determination stage the organism retains a bisexual (hermaphroditic) potential.*

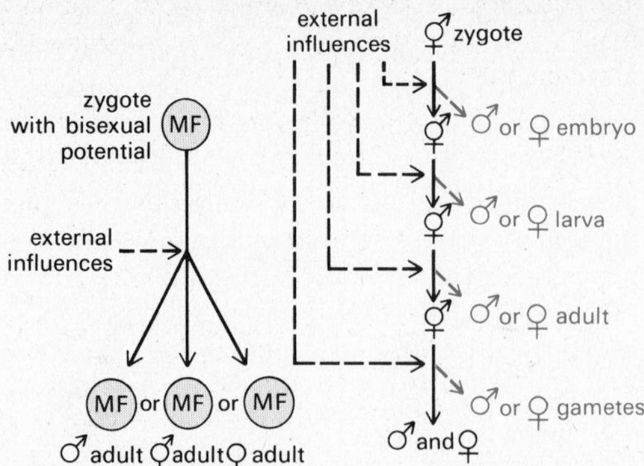

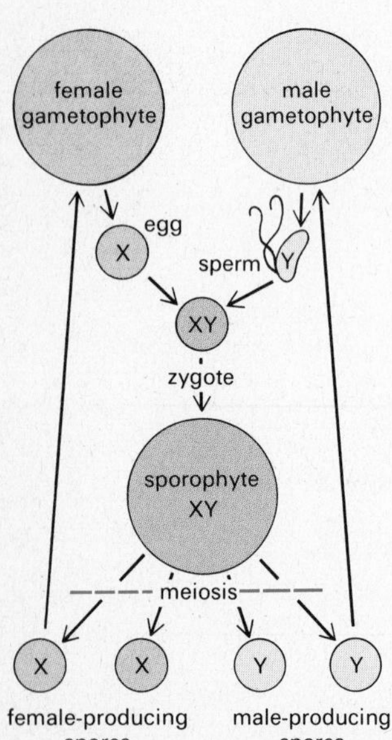

27.16 Sex determination in *Sphaerocarpos*. *The X chromosome in this bryophyte determines femaleness, the Y chromosome, maleness. Gametophytes are haploid and carry only a single sex chromosome per cell; sporophytes are diploid and carry both X and Y. Sporophytes thus have potential genetic bisexuality, though the plants are asexual anatomically.*

In one category, comprising probably the majority of all types of organism, the masculinizing genes are exactly equal in effect, or "strength," to the feminizing genes. In the absence of other influences an organism will then develop as a hermaphrodite. If other sex-determining factors do exert an influence, they are *nongenetic* and *environmental;* different conditions in the external or internal environment affect an organism in such a way that it develops either as a male or as a female. In most cases the precise identity of these environmental conditions has not yet been discovered. The genetic nature of a species determines whether nongenetic influences will or will not play a role (Fig. 27.15).

Also, the genetic nature of the species determines *when* during the life cycle the sex of such organisms becomes fixed by nongenetic means. In hydras, for example, sex determination does not occur until an adult is ready to produce gametes. Up to that time the animal is potentially bisexual. In other animals sex is determined during the larval phase. After metamorphosis, therefore, such animals are already males or females.

In at least one case, the echiuroid worm *Bonellia,* the sex-determining factor is known to be environmental CO_2. The relatively low concentrations of CO_2 in sea water cause free-swimming larvae of this worm to develop as females. But if a sexually still undetermined larva happens to make contact with an adult female or with a larva already determined as a female, then the added respiratory CO_2 produced by that animal causes the undetermined larva to develop as a male; it becomes a small, sperm-producing, structurally simplified parasitic animal, permanently attached inside the excretory organ of the female (see Fig. 12.5).

In still other animal groups, nongenetic sex determination occurs even earlier during the life cycle—for example, after cleavage or in the fertilized egg itself. In general, the portion of the life cycle before the stage of determination is always potentially bisexual, and if the determination occurs no later than the time of gamete production in the adult, the organism will produce either sperms or eggs. But if by then a determination has not taken place, the organism will be a hermaphrodite.

An altogether different form of sex determination occurs in a second category of organisms, including some protists, some plants, and some animals (particularly insects and vertebrates). In these the masculinizing genes are *not* equal in their effects to the feminizing genes, and the primary determination of sex has a purely genetic basis. Every individual becomes either a male or a female; hermaphroditism does not occur except as an abnormality. Also, sex always becomes fixed at the time of fertilization, and every cell later formed is genetically male or female.

Organisms of this type contain special *sex chromosomes,* different in size and shape from all other chromosomes, the *autosomes.* Sex chromosomes are of two kinds, *X* and *Y*. In some of these organisms, chromosomal differences control sex distinctions in the haploid phase of the life cycle. For example, in the liverwort *Sphaerocarpos* each cell of a female gametophyte and each egg contains one *X* chromosome. Similarly, cells of male gametophytes and sperms contain *Y* chromosomes (Fig. 27.16). Fertilization then produces diploid *XY* zygotes, and each cell of the resulting sporophyte inherits the *XY* chromosomes (and is therefore sexually undetermined).

When a spore-producing cell of the sporophyte later undergoes meiosis, the two sex chromosomes become segregated in different spore cells. The result is that, of the four mature spores formed, two contain an *X* chromosome each and two a *Y* chromosome each. Thus although all spores look alike, they are genetically of two different sex types. Spores with *X* chromosomes subsequently mature as female gametophytes, and spores with *Y* chromosomes, as male gametophytes. An entirely similar sex-determining mechanism exists in a number of other bryophytes and also in several protists.

The pattern is somewhat different where both the haploid and the diploid phases of the life cycle exhibit chromosomal sex distinction. Each diploid cell of such organisms contains a pair of sex chromosomes, either *XX* or *XY,* and all such cells are genetically either male or female. For example, *XY* cells are genetically female and *XX* cells genetically male in strawberry sporophytes, butterflies, most moths, some fishes, and birds. In such organisms maleness appears to be controlled by the genes of the *X* chromosomes, and femaleness, by the genes of the autosomes (and in part perhaps also by those of the *Y* chromosomes). By contrast, *XY* cells are male and *XX* cells female in the sporophytes of, for example, holly and *Elodea,* and in flies and mammals. Femaleness here is controlled by the genes of the *X* chromosomes; maleness is known to be determined by the autosomes in fruit flies, but to a large extent by the *Y* chromosomes in mammals (Fig. 27.17).

In man, for example, each adult cell contains 22 pairs of autosomes plus either an *XY* or an *XX* pair. Female cells, $44A + XX$, thus have two female-determining chromosomes, whereas male cells, $44A + XY$, contain one female-determining and one male-determining chromosome. This difference of one whole chromosome lies at the root of the sexual differences between males and females. More specifically, in a female cell the feminizing effect of the two *X* chromosomes outweighs any masculinizing influence the autosomes might have; and in a male cell, the masculinizing effect of the *Y* chromosome (and probably also the autosomes) outweighs the feminizing influence of the single *X* chromosome.

These relations suggest that the sexual nature of an individual might depend on a particular numerical ratio or balance between different chromosomes. That this is actually the case has been shown by experiments in fruit flies. In these animals, in which maleness is controlled by the autosomes, it is possible to vary the normal number of *X* chromosomes and autosomes that occur in sperms and eggs. One can then obtain offspring with, for example, normal paired sets of autosomes but three *X* chromosomes instead of two. Such individuals grow into so-called *superfemales;* all sexual traits are accentuated in the direction of femaleness. Other chromosome balances give rise to *supermales* and *intersexes,* the latter with sexual traits intermediate between those of normal males and females (Fig. 27.18). Paradoxically, supersexes and also intersexes are generally sterile; for as a result of the abnormal chromosome numbers meiosis occurs abnormally, and the sperms and eggs then produced are defective.

In the light of such balances, the normal mechanism of sex determination at the time of fertil-

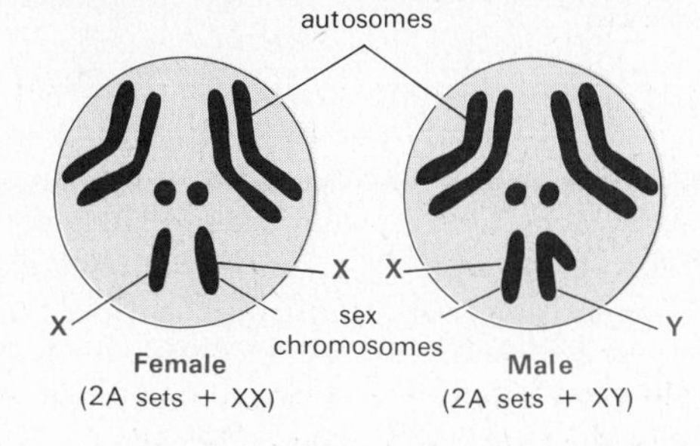

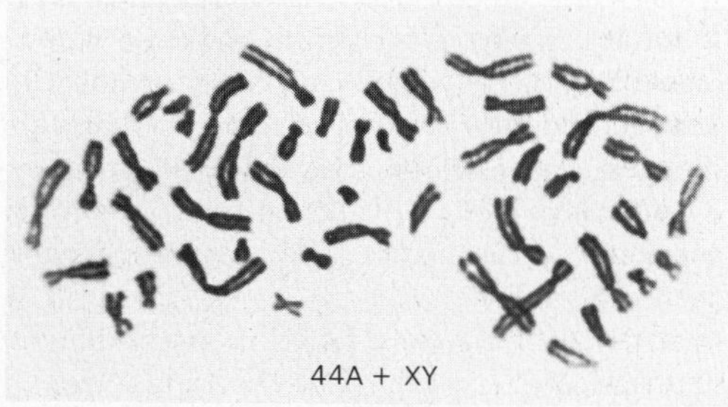

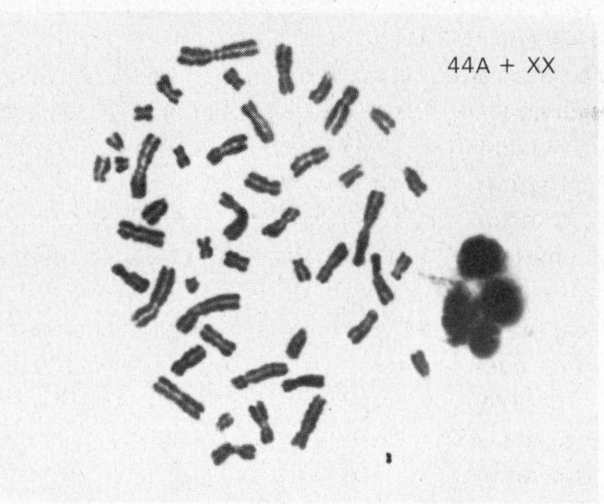
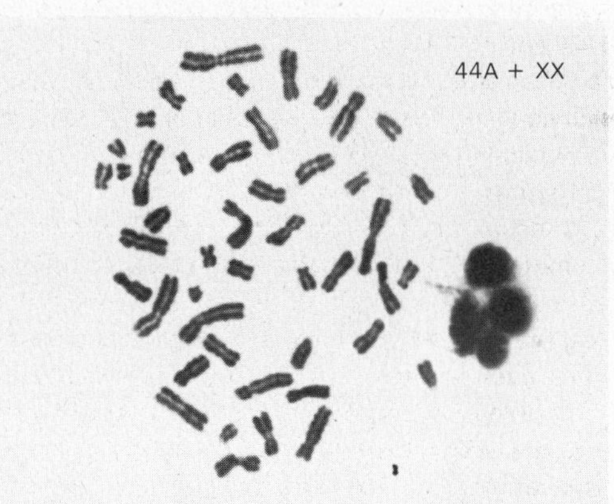

27.17 Sex chromosomes and autosomes. *A, chromosome types and numbers in the fruit fly, where 2n = 8. Note male and female differences. B, C, isolated chromosomes from cells of a human male and female, respectively. In both cases 46 pairs of chromosomes are present; each of the original 46 chromosomes has duplicated as a preliminary to cell division. (B, C, courtesy Carolina Biological Supply Company.)*

27.18 Chromosome balances. *The sexual character of a fruit fly is determined by the specific balances of autosomes and X chromosomes, as shown.*

ization becomes clear. For example, human females produce eggs of which each contains 22*A* + *X* after meiosis (Fig. 27.19). Males produce two kinds of sperm, 22*A* + *X* and 22*A* + *Y*, in roughly equal numbers. Fertilization now occurs at random, and a sperm of either type can unite with an egg. Therefore, in about 50 percent of the cases the result will be 44*A* + *XX*, or female-producing zygotes; and in the remaining 50 percent the zygotes will be 44*A* + *XY*, or prospectively male. In man therefore it is the paternal parent who at the moment of fertilization determines the sex of the offspring. When only a single offspring is produced, a 50:50 chance exists of its being a son or a daughter. When many offspring are produced the number of males will generally equal the number of females.

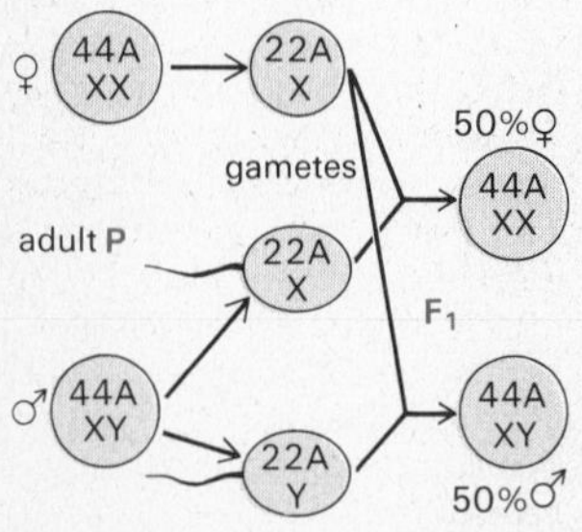

27.19 Sex determination in man. *Males produce two genetically different sperm types, roughly 50 percent of each. Offspring will then be male and female in a 1:1 ratio.*

Note that, in females, the recessive effect of a gene located on one *X* chromosome can be masked by an allele with a dominant effect located on the other *X* chromosome. In males, by contrast, genes on the *X* chromosome can exert even recessive effects, since another *X* chromosome with masking dominants is not present.

Genes located on *X* chromosomes are said to be *sex-linked*, and they are inherited in a characteristic pattern. For example, red-green color blindness in man is a trait produced by a sex-linked recessive gene *c*. Suppose that a color-blind male, X_cY, marries a normal female, *XX*. In this symbolization an *X* chromosome without subscript is tacitly assumed to contain the dominant gene *C*, which prevents the expression of color blindness. All offspring of such a mating have normal vision, but the daughters carry the recessive gene *c* (Fig. 27.20).

If now one of these daughters marries a normal male, all female offspring will be normal but half the sons will be color-blind. Thus the trait has been transmitted from color-blind grandfather to normal mother to color-blind son. Such a zigzag pattern of inheritance is typical for all recessive sex-linked traits; males exhibit the traits, females merely transmit them. The second *X* chromosome in females prevents expression of recessive sex-linked traits. Among other characteristically male, sex-linked abnormalities is *hemophilia*, a bleeder's disease resulting from absence of blood platelets.

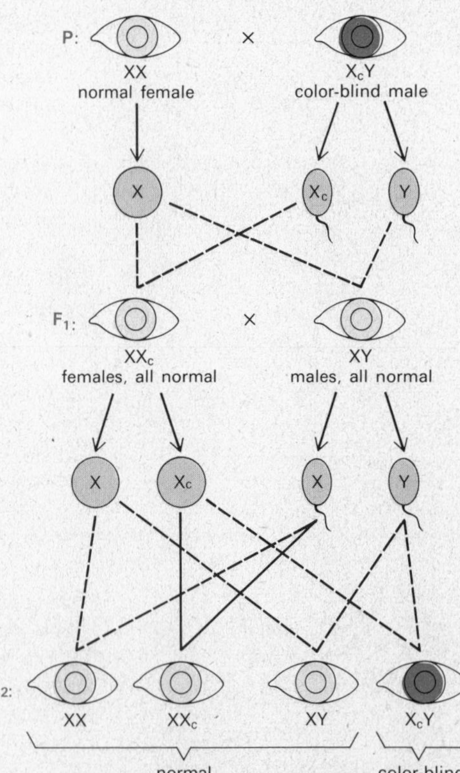

27.20 Sex linkage. *The inheritance of the sex-linked recessive gene for color blindness is illustrated. Note that a color-blind male (P) transmits the gene X_c to all his daughters, who have normal vision, however. Such females then transmit the gene to half their sons, who are color-blind. The abnormality thus is expressed in males and only transmitted by females.*

genetic systems

The example of genetic sex determination shows clearly that genes of one or more chromosomes can act in concert and control one highly composite trait. Many other illustrations of such gene interactions are known. For example, if genes were simply independently functioning units, then it should not matter if the position of genes relative to one another were rearranged. Yet experiment shows that gene rearrangements actually do produce altered traits in a cell, as in chromosome mutations in which genes are neither added nor lost but only repositioned. Such findings indicate clearly that genes normally interact with their neighbors. The same conclusion is suggested by paired allelic genes with dominant and recessive effects; for if any trait is to be dominant over another, the genes and gene products that control these traits must certainly interact. Interactions have also been described among the operator, regulator, and structural genes discussed in the context of the operon hypothesis (Chap. 18). It appears, indeed, that *all* genes in a cell, collectively called the *genome*, are closely interdependent and interacting.

This generalization is reinforced further by recent studies indicating that genes actually are not the smallest hereditary units. As already pointed out earlier, for example, a mutational change can be produced by alteration of a single muton, a unit far smaller than a whole gene. It has also been found that adjoining mutons act cooperatively and form larger functional blocks called *cistrons.* A gene might contain a single cistron only, or it can consist of two or more. Whatever the number, if the cooperating mutons in a cistron happen to become disjoined by a break in the chromosome, then the hereditary function of that cistron is abolished. But whole cistrons in a gene can become disjoined without loss of function. Such data show clearly that, in addition to interaction among whole genes, considerable interaction also occurs among the smaller functional units within genes.

Moreover, genes operate in an environment that includes not only other genes and their subunits but also the cell cytoplasm. It is there that the basic function of genes is exercised, through control of protein synthesis. A second, molecular definition of "gene" can be formulated on this basis: a gene is a chromosomal DNA unit that controls the synthesis of a single type of polypeptide. Such amino acid chains form proteins and thus enzymes or structural components, and these can be regarded as the *primary* traits of a cell.

Various *secondary,* sometimes visible traits then are produced as a result. For example, an enzyme that catalyzes a particular metabolic reaction contributes to the formation of a reaction product, which represents a secondary trait. In certain cases such a reaction product is a visible, final trait—a pigment, for example. In other instances a final trait is a composite of numerous separate reaction products, formed not only in one cell but often in many. For example, disease resistance is a functional property of a whole organism, a composite trait produced by millions of cells. Each of these contributes some particular function to the total trait, and specific genes in each of these cells control each of these functions. Similarly, body size, general vigor, intelligence, fertility, and many others—all, like sexuality, are interaction products of several dozens or hundreds or thousands of different genes.

In all probability, most of such highly composite traits are controlled by the collective action of possibly all genes of an organism, each contributing a tiny effect to the total trait. Such traits can then be expressed in a correspondingly great variety of ways. As is well known, for example, traits like body size or intelligence range from one extreme to another, through enormously varied series of intergradations. But if all genes contribute to the control of numerous composite traits, then any one gene clearly must contribute to the control of more than one trait. We are led to the generalization that one trait can be controlled by many genes, and one gene can contribute to the control of many traits.

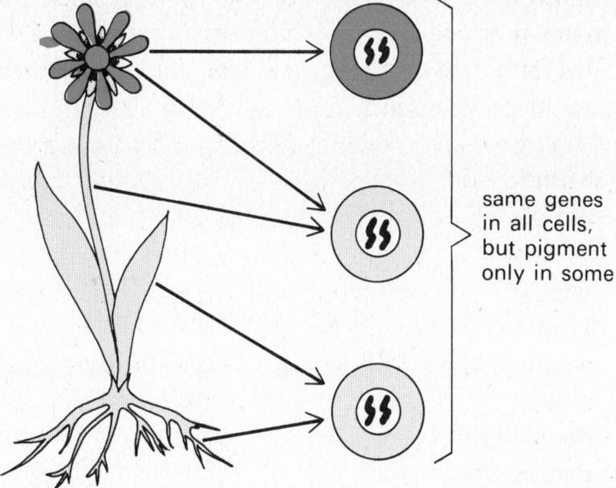

27.21 ***Gene expression.*** *Although all cells of an organism have the same kinds of genes, gene action is influenced differently by different cells. The result is a differential expression of traits. Thus all cells of a plant can have pigment-producing genes, but an actual pigmentation (other than green) might develop only in the cells of flower petals.*

That critical interactions occur between genes and their cellular surroundings is perhaps best shown by the observation that the same kinds of genes often produce different traits in different cells of an organism. For example, *all* cells of a flowering plant contain flower-color genes, but only cells in the petals produce the colors; *all* cells of man contain eye-color genes, but only iris cells actually develop the color. Evidently, the cytoplasms of different cells react differently to the genes they contain, and the various cell differentiations and specializations are the result (Fig. 27.21).

So-called "inherited diseases" likewise must be interpreted in the light of gene-cytoplasm interactions. Certain mental diseases, diabetes, alcoholism, cancer, and many other abnormalities are known to "run in families." What is inherited here is not the disease itself; a child of diabetic ancestry is not automatically diabetic. However, *susceptibility* to disease might be inherited. The genes are present, but before the disease can develop particular cellular environments must make gene expression possible. Similarly, a person who performs physical exercise regularly will develop strong muscles and so will acquire traits differing from those of a person who does not exercise. In both cases, however, the genes controlling muscular development might be the same.

Clearly, then, the actual visible traits of an organism are always an interaction product of genetic heredity *and* environment. Genes supply a reasonable promise, as it were, and the total environment of the genes then permits or does not permit a translation of promise to reality. Furthermore, whereas the pre-Mendelians thought that traits were inherited, and whereas the Mendelian era advanced to the idea that individual factors, or genes, were inherited, the present post-Mendelian era recognizes that actually neither traits nor genes nor even subunits of genes are inherited. Instead, the hereditary units turn out to be whole chromosome sets, coordinated complexes of genes, subtly interacting *genetic systems*. Moreover, as long as a cell is alive such genetic systems never lose their functional integration with the nongenetic parts of cells; and it is biologically almost meaningless to consider genes separately from their immediate or even more distant environment. Ultimately, therefore, the smallest real unit of inheritance is one whole cell.

In the individual organism the interplay between sex, heredity, and environment results in various degrees of individual adaptation. In the long reproductive succession of organisms, this same interplay results in *evolution*.

review questions

1 What was meant by ''blending inheritance''? Describe breeding tests showing that blending inheritance does not occur. What hypothesis did Mendel substitute for the blending concept?

2 State the chromosome theory of heredity. What is the evidence that genes actually are contained in chromosomes? Define genome, true-breeding, phenotype, genotype, allele, dominant and recessive traits, homozygous, heterozygous.

3 Review the breeding tests on inheritance of gray and ebony body colors in fruit flies, and explain them on the basis of genes and chromosomes.

4 What are the quantitative results of the mating *Aa* × *Aa* if (*a*) *A* is dominant over *a*, (*b*) neither gene is dominant over the other?

5 In your own words, state the law of segregation. If *A* is dominant over *a*, what phenotype ratios of offspring are obtained from the following matings: (*a*) *Aa* × *aa*, (*b*) *AA* × *aa*, (*c*) *Aa* × *Aa*, (*d*) *Aa* × *AA*?

6 In your own words, state the law of independent assortment. By what kinds of breeding experiments and by what reasoning did Mendel come to discover this law? Interpret the law on the basis of genes, meiosis, and gametes.

7 How many genetically different gamete types will be produced by an organism heterozygous for 10 gene pairs? If two such organisms were mated, how many genetically different offspring types could result?

8 Define linkage. Why does inheritance of linked genes not obey Mendel's second law? What were Morgan's observations that led him to the hypothesis of crossing over? Describe this hypothesis.

9 How do crossover data permit the construction of gene maps? State the law of the linear order of genes. Show how crossing over can be a source of genetic variations.

10 What is the genetic significance of bacterial transformation and transduction? Distinguish between chromosome mutations and point mutations and between somatic mutations and germ mutations. What is the relation between mutation frequency and radiation intensity?

11 What are the characteristics of mutations from the standpoint of (*a*) predictability, (*b*) functional relation to normal alleles, (*c*) effects on traits, and (*d*) relative advantage to the organism?

12 Review the patterns of sex determination based on (*a*) nongenetic, (*b*) genetic mechanisms. How is sex determined in (*a*) *Sphaerocarpos*, (*b*) man?

13 What is the significance of a given numerical balance between autosomes and sex chromosomes? What are supersexes and intersexes? What are mutons and cistrons?

14 What are sex-linked genes? Describe the inheritance pattern of the sex-linked recessive hemophilia gene *h*, assuming that a hemophilic male mates with a normal female.

15 Cite examples of interactions among genes and between genes and their environment. What contributions are made to the expression of traits by (*a*) genes, (*b*) the environment? What does the phrase "inherited disease" mean?

collateral readings

Bearn, A. G., and **J. L. German:** Chromosomes and Disease, *Sci. American,* Nov., 1961. Visually demonstrable abnormalities in human chromosomes are associated with genetic diseases.

Benzer, S.: The Fine Structure of the Gene, *Sci. American,* Jan., 1962. A review of experiments that have led to the concept of mutons and cistrons.

Bonner, D. M.: "Heredity," Prentice-Hall, Englewood Cliffs, N.J., 1961. A paperback covering general aspects of both Mendelian and non-Mendelian genetics.

Cook, S. A.: "Reproduction, Heredity, and Sexuality," Wadsworth, Belmont, Calif., 1964. This paperback represents an introduction to general genetic principles and deals particularly with inheritance in protists and plants.

Deering, R. A.: Ultraviolet Radiation and Nucleic Acid, *Sci. American,* Dec., 1962. A discussion of mutations induced by this form of energy.

Edgar, R. S., and **R. H. Epstein:** The Genetics of a Bacterial Virus, *Sci. American,* Feb., 1965. An interesting article showing how genetic information becomes translated to actual structural characteristics in viruses.

Hollaender, A., and **G. E. Stapleton:** Ionizing Radiation and the Cell, *Sci. American,* Sept., 1959. The primary and secondary genetic effects of radiation are discussed.

Hotchkiss, R. D., and **E. Weiss:** Transformed Bacteria, *Sci. American,* Nov., 1956. The mechanism and significance of bacterial transformation are described.

Kellenberger, E.: The Genetic Control of the Shape of a Virus, *Sci. American,* Dec., 1966. The topic is similar to that in the Edgar-Epstein article cited above.

Knight, C. A., and **D. Fraser:** The Mutation of Viruses, *Sci. American,* July, 1955. An examination of genetic change and the possibility of inducing such change predictably by chemical means.

Kormondy, E. J.: "Introduction to Genetics," McGraw-Hill, New York, 1964. A programmed paperback designed for self-instruction in general genetic principles; recommended as a study aid.

Ledley, R. S., and **F. H. Ruddle:** Chromosome Analysis by Computer, *Sci. American,* Apr., 1966. A computer technique analyzes human cells for genetic abnormalities and their associated chromosome defects.

Mendel, G.: "Experiments in Plant Hybridization," Harvard, Cambridge, Mass., 1941. A translation of the 1865 original, on which modern genetics is based.

Mittwoch, U.: Sex Differences in Cells, *Sci. American,* July, 1963. Differences in sex chromosomes and other cellular traits of males and females are examined.

Müller, H.: Radiation and Human Mutation, *Sci. American,* Nov., 1955. The discoverer of the genetic effects of radiation discusses the influence of mutations on human evolution.

Sager, R.: Genes Outside the Chromosomes, *Sci. American,* Jan., 1965. A sequel to the article by Sonneborn cited below. Recommended.

Sonneborn, T. M.: Partner of the Gene, *Sci. American,* Nov., 1950. A recommended article, showing that genetic control is exercised not only by genes but also by cytoplasmic factors.

Stahl, F. W.: "The Mechanics of Inheritance," Prentice-Hall, Englewood Cliffs, N.J., 1964. An excellent nonintroductory paperback on "molecular" genetics; virus and bacterial research is reviewed in detail, and references to original papers are given.

Wood, W. B., and **R. S. Edgar**: Building a Bacterial Virus, *Sci. American,* July, 1967. Test-tube experiments with different genetically determined components of viruses are described.

Zinder, N. D.: Transduction in Bacteria, *Sci. American,* Nov., 1958. An examination of the mechanism and the significance of this genetic process.

chapter 28 evolution

No biologist today seriously questions the principle that species arise from preexisting species. Evolution on a small scale can be brought about by experimental means, and the forces that drive and guide evolutionary processes are understood quite thoroughly.

That evolution really occurs did not become definitely established till the nineteenth century. The first section below outlines this historical *background* of evolutionary thought. Following sections then deal with the *forces* of evolution as understood today, and with the *nature* of evolution determined by the underlying forces.

background

The earliest written discussion of organic creation is contained in the Old Testament: God made the world and its living inhabitants in six days, man coming last. Later ideas included those of *spontaneous generation* and of *immutability of species,* which largely held sway until the eighteenth and nineteenth centuries. Each species was considered to have been created spontaneously, completely developed, from dust, dirt, and other nonliving sources. And once created, a species was held to be fixed and immutable, unable to change its characteristics.

In the sixth to fourth centuries B.C., Anaximander, Empedocles, and Aristotle independently considered the possibility that living forms might represent a *succession* rather than unrelated, randomly created types. However, the succession was thought of in an essentially philosophical way, as a progression from "less nearly perfect" to "more nearly perfect" forms. The historical nature of succession and the continuity of life were not yet recognized.

Francesco Redi, an Italian physician of the seventeenth century, was the first to obtain evidence against the idea of spontaneous generation by showing experimentally that organisms could not arise from nonliving sources. Contrary to notions held at the time and earlier, Redi demonstrated that maggots would not form spontaneously in meat if flies were prevented from laying their eggs on the meat. But old beliefs die slowly, and it was not until the nineteenth century, chiefly through the work of Louis Pasteur on bacteria, that the notion of spontaneous generation finally ceased to be influential.

By this time the idea of continuity and historical succession, or *evolution,* had occurred to a number of thinkers. An important evolutionary hypothesis was that of the French biologist Lamarck, published in 1809. To explain how evolution occurred, Lamarck proposed the two ideas of *use and disuse of parts* and of *inheritance of acquired characteristics.* He had observed that if a body part of an organism was used extensively such a part would enlarge and become more efficient; but that if a structure was not fully employed it would degenerate and atrophy. Therefore, by differential use and disuse of various body parts during its lifetime, an organism would change to some extent and would acquire certain traits. Lamarck then thought that such acquired traits were inheritable and could be transmitted to offspring.

According to this Lamarckian scheme evolution would come about somewhat as follows. Suppose a given short-necked ancestral animal feeds on tree leaves. As it clears off the lower levels of a tree it stretches its neck to reach farther up. During a lifetime of stretching the neck becomes a little longer, and a slightly longer neck is then inherited by the offspring. These in turn feed on tree leaves and keep on stretching their necks; and so on, for many generations. In time a very long-necked animal is formed, something like a modern giraffe.

This theory was exceedingly successful and did much to spread the idea of evolution. But Lamarck's views ultimately proved to be untenable. That use and disuse do lead to acquired traits is quite correct. For example, it is common knowledge that much exercise builds powerful muscles. However, Lamarck was mistaken in assuming that such acquired (nongenetic) variations were inheritable. Acquired traits are *not* inheritable, since they are effects produced by environment and development, not by genes. Only *genetic* traits are inheritable, and then only if such traits are controlled by genes that are present in the reproductive cells. What happens to cells other than gametes through use and disuse, or in any other way for that matter, does not affect the genes of the gametes. Accordingly, although Lamarck observed some of the effects of use and disuse correctly in some cases, such effects cannot play a role in evolution.

One famous attempt at experimental refutation of Lamarckism was carried out by Weismann, an eminent biologist of the nineteenth century. The tails of mice were cut off for very many successive generations. According to Lamarck such enforced disuse of tails should eventually have led to tailless mice. Yet mice in the last generation of the experiment still grew tails as long as their ancestors.

The year in which Lamarck published his theory—1809—was also the year in which Charles Darwin was born. During his early life Darwin undertook a 5-year-long circumglobal voyage as naturalist on the naval expeditionary ship *H.M.S. Beagle.* He made innumerable observations and collected a large number of different plants and animals in many parts of the world. He then spent nearly 20 years sifting and studying the collected data. In the course of his work he found evidence for certain generalizations. Another naturalist, Alfred Russell Wallace, had been led independently to substantially the same generalizations, which he communicated to Darwin. In 1858 Darwin and Wallace together announced a new theory of evolution, which was to supplant that of Lamarck. Darwin also elaborated the new theory in book form. This famous work, entitled *On the Origin of Species by Means of Natural Selection, or the Preservation of Favored Races in the Struggle for Life,* was published in 1859.

In essence, the Darwin-Wallace *theory of natural selection* is based on three observations and on two conclusions drawn from these observations.

Observation. Without environmental pressures, every species tends to multiply in geometric progression.

In other words, a population that doubles its number in a first year has a sufficient reproductive potential to quadruple its number in a second year, to increase eightfold in a third year, etc.

Observation. But under field conditions, although fluctuations occur frequently, the size of a population remains remarkably constant over long periods of time.

This point has already been noted in the discussion of food pyramids (Chap. 6).

Conclusion. Evidently, not all gametes will become zygotes; not all zygotes will become adults; and not all adults will survive and reproduce. Consequently there must be a ''struggle for existence.''

Observation. Not all members of a species are alike; considerable individual variation is exhibited.

Conclusion. In the struggle for existence, therefore, individuals that exhibit favorable variations will enjoy a competitive advantage over others. They will survive in proportionately greater numbers and will produce offspring in proportionately greater numbers.

Darwin and Wallace thus identified the *environment* as the principal cause of natural selection; the environment would gradually weed out organisms with unfavorable variations but preserve those with favorable variations. Over a long succession of generations, and under the continued selective influence of the environment, a group of organisms would eventually have accumulated so many new, favorable variations that a new species would in effect have arisen from the ancestral stock.

Nonbiologists are often under the impression that this Darwin-Wallace hypothesis is *the* modern explanation of evolution. This is not the case. Indeed, Darwinism was challenged even during Darwin's lifetime. What, it was asked, is the source of the all-important individual variations? How do individual variations arise? Here Darwin actually could do no better than fall back on the Lamarckian idea of inheritance of acquired characteristics. Ironically, the correct answer regarding variations began to be formulated just 6 years after Darwin published his *Origin,* when Mendel announced his rules of inheritance. But Mendel's work remained unappreciated for more than 30 years, and progress in understanding evolutionary mechanisms was retarded correspondingly.

Another objection to Darwinism concerned natural selection itself. If this process simply preserves or weeds out what already exists, it was asked, how can it ever create anything new? As will soon become apparent, natural selection actually does create novelty. The earlier criticism arose in part because the meaning of Darwin's theory was—and still is—widely misinterpreted. Social philosophers of the time and other ''press agents'' and disseminators of scientific information, not biologists, thought that the essence of natural selection was described by the phrase ''struggle for existence.'' They then coined alternative slogans like ''survival of the fittest'' and ''elimination of the unfit.'' Natural selection thus came to be viewed almost exclusively as a negative, destructive force. This had two unfortunate results. First, a major implication of Darwin's theory—the creative role of natural selection—was generally overlooked; and second, the wrong emphasis was often accepted in popular thinking as the last word on evolution.

Such thinking proceeded in high gear even in Darwin's day. Many people thought that evolution implied "man descended from the apes," and man's sense of superiority was duly outraged. Also, because evolutionary views denied the special creation of man, they were widely held to be antireligious. Actually, the idea of evolution is not any more or less antireligious than the idea of spontaneous generation. Neither really strengthens, weakens, or otherwise affects belief in God; to the religious person only the way God operates, not God as such, is in question.

Moreover, under the banner of phrases like "survival of the fittest," evolution was interpreted to prove an essential cruelty of nature; and human behavior, personal and national, often came to be guided by the ethic of "jungle law," "might is right," "every man for himself." Only in that way, it was thought, could the "fittest" prevail. Even today, unfortunately, evolution is still commonly—and erroneously—thought to be a matter of "survival of the fittest."

By now, a full century after Darwin and Wallace, it has become clear that natural selection is preeminently a peaceful process that has little to do with "struggle," "weeding out," or "the fittest." Also, natural selection is recognized to represent only a part of the evolutionary mechanism since, like Lamarck, Darwin was unsuccessful in identifying the genetic causes of evolutionary change. In short, Darwin (and Wallace) supplied an incomplete explanation; but as far as it went theirs was the first to point in the right direction.

The current modern theory of evolution is not the work of any one man, though it is the spiritual offspring of Mendel and of Darwin. It evolved slowly during the first half of the current century, and many biologists of various specializations contributed to its formulation.

forces of evolution

the evolutionary process

As now understood, the mechanism of evolution can be described as *natural selection acting on the genetic variations that appear among the members of a population.*

Recall from Chap. 6 that a population is a geographically localized group of individuals of the same species, in which the members interbreed preferentially with one another and also occasionally with members of neighboring sister populations. The result of this close sexual communication in a population is a *free flow of genes.* Hereditary material present in some portion of a population can in time spread to the whole population, through the gene-pooling and gene-combining effects of sex. Moreover, interbreeding also can interconnect the *gene pools* of sister populations, and the total genetic content of a whole species can thus to some extent become shuffled and reshuffled among the member organisms (Fig. 28.1).

Chapter 27 has shown that genetic variations in a gene pool can arise by *sexual recombination,* by *mutation,* or both. Where reproduction is uniparental, as in vegetative reproduction and sporulation, mutation is the only source of genetic variation; and in biparental reproduction, where organisms are produced by gametes from two parents, both mutation and sexual pooling of genes in zygotes are sources of genetic variations.

Thus, in each generation some individuals appear that have new, variant traits as a result of either recombinational or mutational processes. If such variant organisms survive and have offspring of their own, then their new genetic characteristics will persist in the gene pool of the population. And in the course of successive generations the genetic novelty can spread to many or all members of the population.

Whether or not such spreading actually takes place depends on natural selection. The real meaning of this term is *differential reproduction;* some members of a population leave more offspring than others. Those that have more offspring will contribute a proportionately greater percentage of genes to the gene pool of the next generation than those that have fewer offspring. Therefore, if differential reproduction continues in the same manner over many generations, the abundant reproducers will contribute a progressively larger number of individuals to the whole population. And as a result *their* genes will become preponderant in the gene pool of the population (Fig. 28.2).

Which individuals leave more offspring than others? Usually (but not necessarily) those that are best adapted to the environment. Being well adapted, such individuals on the whole are healthier and better fed, can find mates more

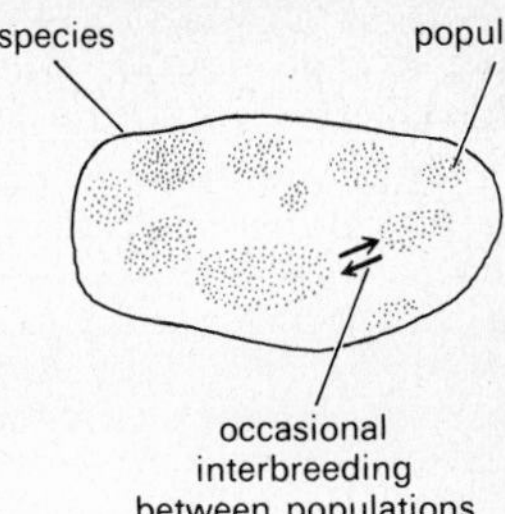

28.1 The gene pool. *In a species genes flow in and between populations. The total gene content of the species thus represents a gene pool to which all members of the species have access. Genes normally cannot flow between the gene pools of two different species.*

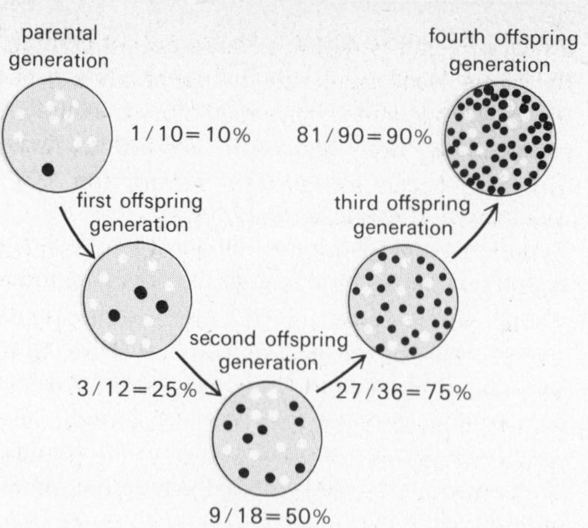

28.2 Differential reproduction, *or natural selection. Assume that a variation arises in one individual of a parental generation (black dot) and that the variant organism is able to leave three offspring. Each nonvariant organism (white dots) on the other hand only manages to leave one offspring. The complexion of the population will then change as shown during subsequent generations; the variant type will represent a progressively larger fraction of the numerical total. Such spreading of variations, brought about by differential reproduction, constitutes natural selection.*

readily, and can care for their offspring appropriately. To be sure, on occasion comparatively poorly adapted individuals have the most offspring. Yet what counts here is not how well or poorly an organism copes with its environment, but only how many offspring it manages to leave. The more there are, the greater the role that the parental genes will play in the total gene pool of the population. By and large the well-adapted organism contributes most to the gene pool.

It can happen, therefore, that a new trait that originates in one organism spreads by differential reproduction and in time becomes a standard feature of the whole population. This is the unit of evolutionary change. Many such unit changes must accumulate in a population before the organisms are altered enough in structure or function to be recognizable as a new species. In any event, evolution operates through this basic two-step process:

1 appearance of genetic variations by sexual recombination and mutation

2 spreading of these variations through a population by differential reproduction in successive generations

To the extent that genetic variations originate at random, evolutionary innovations similarly appear at random. But inasmuch as the best reproducers are generally the best adapted, evolution as a whole is directed by adaptation and is oriented toward continued or improved adaptation. It is therefore not a wholly random process.

In this modern view of evolution, evidently, natural selection is fundamentally a *creative* force, one that spreads genetic novelty. And while it eliminates the reproductively ''unfit,'' it does not necessarily eliminate the behaviorally or socially ''unfit.'' The mightiest and grandest organism in the population could be exceedingly ''fit'' in a behavioral sense, but if it happened to be sterile it would be inconsequential in a reproductive and therefore an evolutionary sense. Conversely, a sickly weakling might be behaviorally or socially ''unfit,'' yet have numerous offspring. Natural selection thus operates basically through reproduction, not through struggle for survival. Such struggles certainly occur, often in a very physical sense, and indirectly they also can affect the reproductive success of organisms. To that extent such factors can have evolutionary consequences. But the important issue is neither ''struggle'' nor ''elimination'' nor even individual ''survival;'' all that finally matters is comparative reproductive success.

the genetic basis

From the preceding discussion, evolution can be described as a *progressive change of gene frequencies;* in the course of successive generations the proportion of some genes in a population increases and the proportion of others decreases. Clearly, the *rates* with which gene frequencies change will be a measure of the *speed* of evolution. What determines such rates?

Suppose we consider a large population made up of individuals of three genetic categories, *AA, Aa,* and *aa,* in the following numerical proportions:

AA	*Aa*	*aa*
36%	48%	16%

Assuming further that the choice of sexual mates is entirely random, that all individuals produce roughly equal numbers of gametes, and that the genes *A* and *a* do not mutate, we can then ask how the frequency of the genes *A* and *a* will change from one generation to the next.

Since *AA* individuals make up 36 percent of the population, they will contribute approximately 36 percent of all the gametes formed in the population. These gametes will all contain one *A* gene. Similarly, *aa* individuals will produce 16 percent of all gametes in the population, and each will contain one *a* gene. The gametes of *Aa* individuals will be of two types, *A* and *a,* in equal numbers. Since their total amounts to 48 percent, 24 percent will be *A* and 24 percent will be *a*. The overall gamete output of the population will therefore be:

parents		*gametes*	*parents*		*gametes*
36% *AA*	⟶	36% *A*	16% *aa*	⟶	16% *a*
48% *Aa*	⟶	24% *A*	48% *Aa*	⟶	24% *a*
		60% *A*			40% *a*

Fertilization now occurs in four possible ways: two *A* gametes join; two *a* gametes join; an *A* sperm joins an *a* egg; and an *a* sperm joins an *A* egg. Each of these possibilities will occur with a frequency dictated by the relative abundance of the *A* and *a* gametes. Since there are 60 percent *A* gametes, *A* will join *A* in 60 percent of 60 percent of the cases—60×60, or 36 percent of the time. Similarly, *A* sperms will join *a* eggs in 60×40, or 24 percent of the cases. The total result:

		eggs		*offspring*
$A + A$	⟶	60×60	⟶	36% *AA*
$A + a$	⟶	60×40	⟶	24% *Aa*
$a + A$	⟶	40×60	⟶	24% *Aa*
$a + a$	⟶	40×40	⟶	16% *aa*

The new generation in our example population thus will consist of 36 percent *AA*, 48 percent *Aa*, and 16 percent *aa* individuals—precisely the same proportions that were present originally. Evidently, gene frequencies have not changed.

By experiment and calculation it can be shown that such a result is obtained regardless of the numbers and the types of gene pairs considered simultaneously. The important conclusion is that, *if mating is random, if mutations do not occur, and if the population is large, then gene frequencies in a population remain constant from generation to generation.* This generalization is known as the *Hardy-Weinberg law.* It has somewhat the same central significance to the theory of evolution as Mendel's laws have to the theory of heredity.

The Hardy-Weinberg law indicates that, when a population is in genetic equilibrium and gene frequencies do not change, the rate of evolution is zero. Genes then continue to be reshuffled by sexual recombination and, as a result, genetic variations continue to originate from this source. But the overall gene frequencies do not change. Of themselves, therefore, the variations are not being propagated differentially, and evolution consequently does not occur. What does make evolution occur are deviations from the "ifs" specified in the Hardy-Weinberg law.

First, mating is decidedly *not* random in most natural situations. For example, it happens often that all genetic types in a population do not reach reproductive age in proportionate measure. Suppose that, in the sample population of *AA, Aa* and *aa* individuals above, the *AA* genes cause death in one-third of the embryos of the population. Under such conditions 36 percent of all zygotes will be *AA,* but only two-thirds of their number will reach reproductive age. The *Aa* and *aa* individuals will then form a proportionately larger fraction of the reproducing population and will contribute proportionately more to the total gamete output. The ultimate result over successive generations will be a progressive decrease in the frequency of the *A* gene and a progressive increase of the *a* gene. Hence the *effective* mating population correspondingly will become more and more nonrandom.

In an effective mating population, moreover, mating pairs are usually formed on the basis of nonrandom criteria such as health, strength, mentality, external appearance, sexual attraction, or simply availability and geographic proximity of particular males and females. Mating thus becomes even more nonrandom, and the overall result is an uneven, nonrandom shuffling of genes—in effect, a form of natural selection. As some genes then spread more than others, gene frequencies become altered, and a Hardy-Weinberg equilibrium is not maintained. This represents evolutionary change. Through nonrandom mating a certain *intensity* of natural selection, or *selection pressure,* operates for or against most genes, and in time even a very slight selection pressure substantially affects the genetic makeup of a population.

Second, mutations do occur in populations, and Hardy-Weinberg equilibria change for this reason also. Depending on whether a mutation has a beneficial or harmful effect on a trait, selection will operate for or against the mutated gene. In either case gene frequencies will change, for the mutated gene will either increase or decrease in abundance. Note, however, that the effect of selection on mutations will vary according to whether the trait changes produced are dominant or recessive. A newly originated mutation with dominant effect will influence traits immediately, and selection for or against the mutation will take place at once. But if in a diploid organism a mutation has a recessive effect, it does not influence traits immediately. Natural selection then will not influence the mutation immediately either. This is the case with most mutations, since, as noted earlier, most mutations in diploid organisms produce recessive effects.

A recessive mutant gene can nevertheless spread through a population if it happens to be closely linked to another gene that produces a dominant, adaptively desirable trait. Both genes are then inherited and propagated together. The recessive mutant here simply remains in the gene pool without effect, until two individuals carrying the same mutation happen to mate. Then one-fourth of their offspring will be homozygous recessive; if the mutant gene is *a'*, then a mating of *Aa'* × *Aa'* will yield 25 percent *a'a'* offspring. These will exhibit altered visible traits, and natural selection will now affect the frequency of the mutation directly (Fig. 28.3).

The evolutionary role of mutations varies according to how greatly a given mutation influences a given trait. A "large" mutation that affects a vital trait in major ways is likely to be exceedingly harmful and will usually be lethal. But a "small" mutation that has only a minor effect on a trait can persist far more readily. Evolutionary alterations actually occur almost exclusively through an accumulation of *many, small* changes in traits, not through single, large changes.

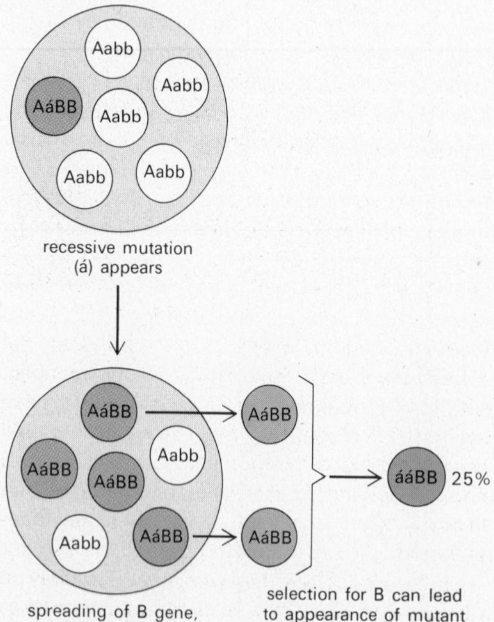

***28.3* Gene spreading.** *If a recessive mutation a' appears in an organism and if that organism also carries a gene B that is strongly selected for, then both B and a' can spread through a population together. The appearance of mutant phenotypes a'a' then becomes rather likely.*

The third condition affecting Hardy-Weinberg equilibria is population size. If a population is large, regional imbalances of gene frequencies that might arise by chance are quickly smoothed out by the many random matings among the many individuals. The underlying principle here applies to statistical systems generally. In a coin-flipping experiment, for example, heads and tails will each come up 50 percent of the time, but only if the number of throws is large. If only three or four throws are made, it is quite possible that *all* will come up heads by chance alone. Similarly, gene combinations attain Hardy-Weinberg equilibria only if a population is large. In small groups (less than about 100 individuals), chance alone can lead to *genetic drift,* a random establishment of genetic types that are numerically not in accordance with Hardy-Weinberg equilibria. For example, if *AA, Aa,* and *aa* individuals are expected in certain proportions, chance alone could result in the formation of many more *AA* and many fewer *aa* individuals if the population is small.

Such a genetic drift effect resembles that of natural selection; if several genotypes are possible, a particular one would likewise come to predominate if there were a selection pressure for it. But because genetic drift is governed by chance, natural selection plays little role. Genes are being propagated not for their adaptive value as in natural selection, but because they happen to be spread by chance. The result is that, in small populations, nonadaptive and often bizarre traits can become established. These can actually be harmful to the population and can promote its becoming even smaller. Or, genetic drift might by chance happen to adapt a small population rather well to a given environment, and such a population might later evolve through natural selection and eventually give rise to a new species. Genetic drift is believed to be a significant factor in the evolution of organisms on islands and in small, reproductively isolated groups in general.

Evolution as it actually occurs must be—and indeed can be—interpreted on the basis of the mechanism here described.

effects of evolution

speciation

The key process to be explained is how evolutionary changes in a population eventually culminate in the establishment of new species. As pointed out in Chap. 6, a species can be defined as a reproductive unit in which the member organisms interbreed with one another but not usually with members of other species. In other words, a reproductive barrier isolates one species from another. A more or less free gene flow is therefore maintained within a species but not normally between species. Thus the problem of speciation is to show how reproductive barriers arise.

Primary barriers usually appear through *geographic* changes, as when water comes to intrude on land or vice versa, or when a forest belt grows through a prairie or vice versa, or when mountains or new climatic conditions become interposed across a region. Sister populations of the same species on each side of such barriers then become isolated geographically, and reproductive contact is lost. Most commonly, populations become isolated geographically simply by distance. As a species in time occupies a progressively larger territory, two populations at opposite ends of this territory will eventually be too far apart to permit direct interbreeding (Fig. 28.4).

Regardless of how isolation is actually brought about, an interruption of gene flow between sister populations will be followed by independent natural selection in each. In the course of many generations numerous genetic differences will appear, and these are likely to include *biological* barriers to interbreeding. For example, anatomic changes in reproductive organs might make mating mechanically impossible; or gametes might become incompatible through altered protein specificities; or the times of the annual breeding seasons might shift; or psychological changes might make mates from neighboring populations no longer acceptable. In effect, two sister populations of the same species will in time become two separate, new species.

At first newly formed sister species tend to be rather similar structurally and functionally, and in some cases interbreeding might still take place if the species were not isolated geographically. Thus it sometimes happens that, when members of two similar species are brought together under artificial conditions, they can interbreed readily. Evidently, the circumstance that two different species *do not* interbreed in nature does not always mean that they cannot interbreed (Fig. 28.5). But after two sister species have been separated for long periods, interbreeding will eventually become impossible even if contact is provided artificially; the differences sooner or later become pronounced enough to preclude interbreeding.

Speciation by this means is the chief way in which new species evolve. Such a process takes on an average about 1 million years. Consciously

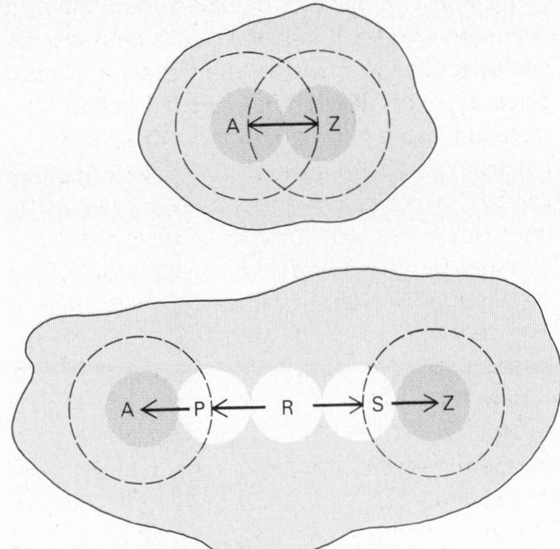

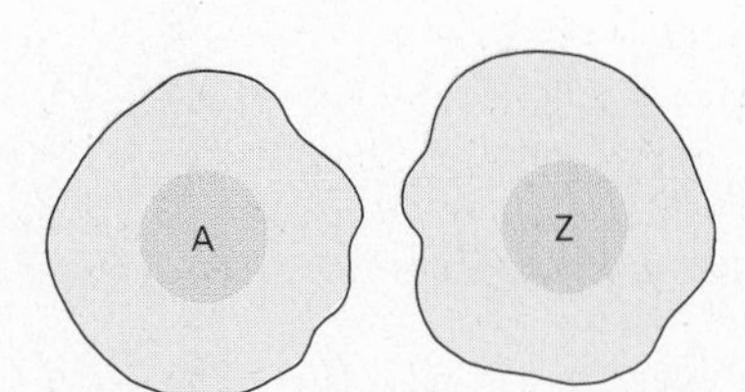

28.4 ***Speciation.*** *Top: two populations (A, Z) in a parent species have overlapping reproductive ranges (dashed circles); hence gene flow can be direct. Center: after population growth and territorial expansion the reproductive ranges of A and Z no longer overlap, and gene flow between them must now be indirect, via intervening populations (P, R, S). Bottom: if gene flow between A and Z ceases altogether, the two populations will have become reproductively isolated and will be independent offspring species.*

28.5 ***Interbreeding.*** *Platyfish female at top, swordtail male at bottom. These animals belong to different species, and in nature they do not interbreed, but they can and do interbreed in the laboratory.*

A

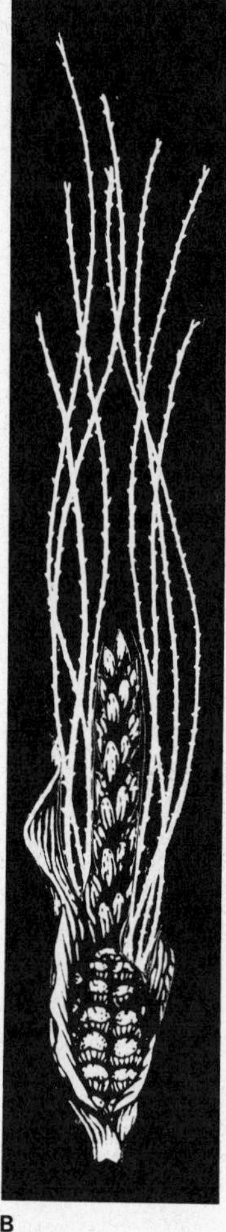

B

***28.6* Artificial selection.** *A, red jungle fowl, an example of a wild organism from which man has bred domesticated varieties. B, reconstruction of the most primitive known archeological corn plant (from the remains of Tehuacan, Mexico), a form clearly different from but in the ancestry of modern domesticated corn.*

or unconsciously making use of this principle of reproductive isolation, man has been and is now contributing to the evolution of many other organisms. The most ancient evolution-directing effort of man is his successful *domestication* of various plants and animals. Darwin was the first to recognize the theoretical significance of domestication, and indeed it was this that led him to his concept of natural selection. He reasoned that if man, by *artificial* selection and isolation, can transform wild varieties of plants and animals to domesticated forms, then perhaps *natural* selection and isolation, acting for far longer periods, can produce even greater evolutionary transformations in nature. The domesticating process actually does involve all the elements of natural evolution: deliberate isolation of a wild population by man, followed by carefully controlled, differential reproduction of those member organisms that have traits considered desirable by man. The result is the creation of new strains, subspecies, and even species (Fig 28.6).

During the last few decades, furthermore, rather rapid, man-caused evolution has taken place among certain viruses, bacteria, insects, various parasites, and other pests. These live now in an environment in which antibiotics and numerous pest-killing drugs have become distinct hazards. And the organisms have evolved and are still evolving increasing resistance to such drugs.

Clearly then, these examples offer direct proof that evolution actually occurs and is observable, and that it can be made to occur under conditions based on the postulated modern mechanism of evolution. Incidentally, speciation also accounts for the establishment of genera, families, and other higher taxonomic groups: the differences between newly created species or groups of species can be sufficiently extensive that we classify such organisms as members of different higher taxonomic categories.

Some biologists have argued that the distinctions between high-ranking taxonomic categories are far too great to be explainable by gradual accumulation of many small, minor variations in different species. A hypothesis of "large" mutations has been postulated instead. According to it, a major mutation that affects many vital traits simultaneously is assumed to transform an organism suddenly, in one jump, to a completely new type. Such a type would represent not only a new species but also a new high-ranking taxonomic group. In most cases an organism of this sort would not survive, for it would probably be entirely unsuited to the local environment. But it is assumed that in extremely rare cases such "hopeful monsters" might have arisen by freak chance in environments in which they could survive. Only relatively few successes of this sort would be needed to account for the existing classes, phyla, or superphyla of organisms.

Few biologists accept this hypothesis of jump evolution. In studies of natural and experimental mutations over many years it has always been found that sudden genetic changes with major effects are immediately lethal. This is the case not only because the external environment is unsuitable but also, and perhaps mainly, because the internal metabolic upheaval caused by a major mutation is far too drastic to permit continued survival. But even supposing that a hopeful monster could survive, it would by definition be so different from other individuals that it would be structurally, functionally, and behaviorally incompatible as a mate.

Furthermore, although the differences between phyla and other major categories are great, they are not so great that such categories could not have arisen through gradual evolution of different representative species. Indeed, the evidence from fossils and embryos shows reasonably well in what pattern this evolution might have occurred (see Fig. 11.9). Also, as the next section will show, important aspects of the evolutionary process cannot be explained by jump evolution but can be explained rather well on the basis of gradual evolution.

diversification

Even at the species level evolution is an exceedingly slow process. As noted, a very large number of small variations must accumulate before a significant alteration of organisms can occur Moreover, since genetic variations arise at random, organisms must *await* the appearance of adaptively useful changes. But there is no guarantee that useful variations will appear in successive generations or that they will appear at all. Thus even though evolution might occur, it could occur too slowly to permit successful adaptation to changed environments.

As a rule, the actual *rates* of past evolution have been proportional to the instability of the environment. Terrestrial organisms by and large have evolved faster than marine types, land being a less stable environment than the sea. Also, evolution has generally been fairly rapid in times of major geologic change, as during ice ages or periods of mountain formation (see Chap. 29). By contrast, the rate of evolution has been practically zero for several hundred million years in a few marine groups—horseshoe crabs, brachiopod lamp shells, and some of the radiolarian protozoa, for example. The environments in which such "living fossils" exist evidently have remained stable enough to make the ancient way of life still possible (Fig. 28.7).

Apart from variations in rates, evolution has tended to occur through successive *adaptive radiations.* Just as a parent species can give rise simultaneously to two or more descendant species, so a similar pattern of bushlike *branching* descent characterizes evolution on all levels; a newly evolved type becomes a potential ancestor for many different simultaneous lines of descendants. For example, the ancestral mammalian type has given rise simultaneously to several lines of modern grazing plains animals (horses, cattle, goats), to burrowing animals (moles), to flying animals (bats), to several lines of aquatic animals (whales, seals, sea cows), to animals living in trees (monkeys), to carnivorous predators (dogs, cats), and to many others. Each such line of descent has become specialized for a different way of life, and the sum of all these branch lines leading away from the common ancestral type represents an adaptive radiation (see Fig. 13.31).

Further, in the course of its history a branch line can give rise to one or more adaptive radiations of smaller scope. In the line of tree-living mammals, for example, simultaneous sublines and subsublines have evolved that have resulted in contemporary animals as varied as monkeys, lemurs, tarsiers, apes, and men. The important implication here, as also pointed out in Chap. 2, is that evolution is not a "ladder" or a "scale." Man for example did not descend from apes, but both have had a common ancestor and are contemporary members of the same adaptive radiation (see Fig. 2.10). All such radiations generally exhibit *divergence,* or development of more or less dissimilar traits in groups descended from a common ancestor.

Not all the branches on a bush lead right to the top, but some terminate abruptly at various intermediate points. In evolution, similarly, *extinction* has been a general feature. In many cases

A

B

28.7 Speeds of evolution. *A, model of the fossil psilopsid Rhynia, one of the most ancient tracheophytes that lived some 350 million years ago. Plants like this gave rise to modern psilopsids, and, as shown in Fig. 10.28, these modern descendants are not too different from the ancestors even now. But during the same interval another line of descent gave rise to pteropsid plants such as the peach tree shown in B, which is very different from the ancestral type. The rate of evolution evidently was minimal in the psilopsid line but high in the pteropsid line.*

A

B

C

D

28.8 ***Recent extinctions.*** *A, dodo. B, Irish elk. C, sabertooth cat. D, woolly mammoths. The dodo survived till just a few hundred years ago. Mammoths and sabertooths became extinct some 20,000 years ago, and Irish elks, some thousands of years before that.*

placentals
dolphins
†
†
marsupials
ichthyosaurs
ancestral mammals
ancestral reptiles

28.9 ***Replacement.*** *Left, immediate replacement: very soon after placental mammals evolved they replaced the earlier marsupials virtually everywhere except in Australia. Right, delayed replacement: dolphins replaced the ichthyosaurs many millions of years after the latter had become extinct.*

of extinction the specific causes may never be known. However, in line with the nature of the evolutionary mechanism, the general cause of all extinctions is an inability of organisms to adapt rapidly enough to environmental changes. In the past, extinctions have been the more common the lower the taxonomic category. Extinction of species and even of genera has been a nearly universal occurrence, but relatively few orders and still fewer classes have become extinct. And practically all phyla that ever originated continue to be in existence today. The phylum evidently includes so broad and far-flung an assemblage of different adaptive types that at least some of them have always survived, regardless of how environments have changed. By contrast, species are usually adapted rather narrowly to limited, circumscribed environments, and the chances for extinction are therefore greater (Fig. 28.8).

In conjunction with extinction, *replacement* has been another common occurrence in evolution. Replacement occurs when, after one group of organisms has become extinct, another group evolves that adopts the vacated environment and way of life. For example, pouched marsupial mammals were very abundant in the Americas a few million years ago, but with the exception of forms like the opossum they were replaced in the Western Hemisphere by the competing placental mammals. In this case replacement was more or less immediate, but on occasion millions of years can elapse before a new group evolves into a previously occupied environmental niche. Such *delayed* replacement took place, for example, in the case of the ichthyosaurs. These fishlike marine reptiles became extinct some 100 million years ago. Their particular mode of living then remained unused for about 40 million years, when a newly evolved mammalian group, the whales and dolphins, replaced the ichthyosaurs. Similarly delayed replacement occurred between the flying reptilian pterosaurs and the later mammalian bats (Fig. 28.9).

Replacing organisms usually exhibit some degree of evolutionary *convergence,* or *parallelism;* they resemble each other in one or more ways even though they need not be related particularly closely. For example, the development of finlike appendages in both ichyosaurs and dolphins or of wings in both pterosaurs and bats illustrates evolutionary convergence in replacing types. Since both an original and a replacing group are adapted to the same type of environment and way of life, their evolution has been oriented in the same direction; and the appearance of similar, or convergent, traits is therefore not surprising. But convergence occurs also in nonreplacing types. For example, the eyes of squids and of fish are remarkably alike. Squids and fish are not related directly, and neither replaces the other. However, both types of animal are large, fast swimmers, and good eyes of a particular construction are a distinct advantage in the ways of life of both. Selection evidently has promoted variations that have led to eyes of similar structure, and the observed convergence is the result (Fig. 28.10).

Although the eyes of squids and fish are strikingly alike, they are by no means identical. Convergence leads to *similarity,* not identity. Moreover, neither squids nor fish have a theoretically "best" eye structure for fast swimmers. Similarly, none of the various animal groups that fly has a theoretically "best" wing design. An organ or organism actually need not be theoretically "best" or "most efficient." The structure only needs to be practically workable and just efficient enough for a necessary function. In a way of life based on flying, wings of *some* sort are clearly essential. But most requirements for living can have *multiple* solutions, and so long as a certain solution works at all, it does not matter how the solution is arrived at. The various animal wings do represent multiple solutions of the same problem, each evolved from a different starting point and each functioning in a different way.

This consideration focuses attention on one of the most important characteristics of evolution, that of *random opportunism.* Evolution has produced not what is theoretically desirable or best, but what is practically possible. There has been no predetermined plan, no striving for set "goals," but only the exploitation of actually available opportunities offered by selection among random hereditary changes. For example, although it might have been adaptively exceedingly useful for terrestrial plants to grow legs or for terrestrial animals to grow wheels, neither development occurred because it could not occur; the ancestors simply did not have the necessary structural and functional potential. However, they did have the potential to evolve adequate and workable alternative solutions. Among plants, already existing spores could become encapsulated and distributed by wind; and among animals, already existing fins could be reshaped as walking legs.

Evidently, evolution can only remodel and build on what already exists, in small, successive steps. Since, given a long enough time span, every feature of every organism undergoes random variations in many different directions, opportunities for diverse evolutionary changes have been and still are very numerous. Every organism in effect represents a patchwork of good opportunities seized by natural selection at the right time. In man, for example, the bones of the middle ear have arisen opportunistically from pieces of earlier vertebrate jawbones. The musculature of the lower face has evolved from the gill muscles of ancestral fish. The larynx has developed from the gill skeleton of ancient fish (Fig. 28.11).

Such instances of evolutionary opportunism are legion. Organisms clearly are not the result of any planned, goal-directed, or predetermined course of creation. Instead they are the result of a cumulative, opportunistic process of piece-by-piece building, based on existing organisms and gov-

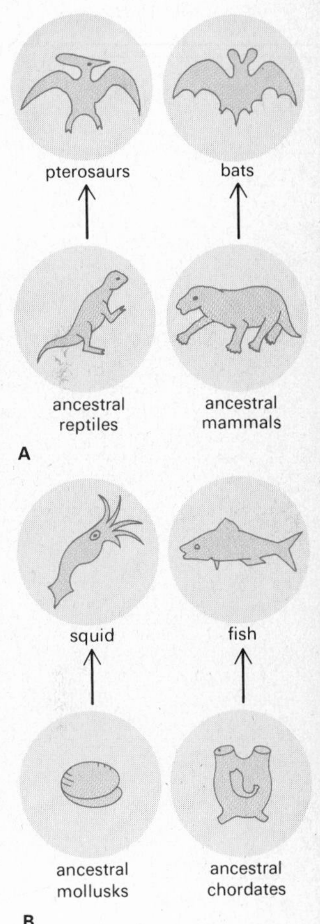

28.10 Convergence. *Relatively unrelated ancestors give rise to descendants whose ways of life and even superficial appearance are similar in many respects. In A the convergence is replacing: bats now occupy the same kinds of niches that pterosaurs did many millions of years ago. In B the convergence is nonreplacing: squids and fishes coexist today, each group occupying its own niche.*

28.11 ***Evolutionary opportunism.*** *Parts of the lower jaw and the upper bone of the next bony gill arch of ancestral fishes have been the evolutionary sources of the middle-ear bones of man (black). Similarly, parts of the other gill supports of fishes have evolved into the cartilages of the mammalian larynx (dark color), and the gill musculature of fishes has contributed to the muscles of the lower part of the face of mammals (hatched areas).*

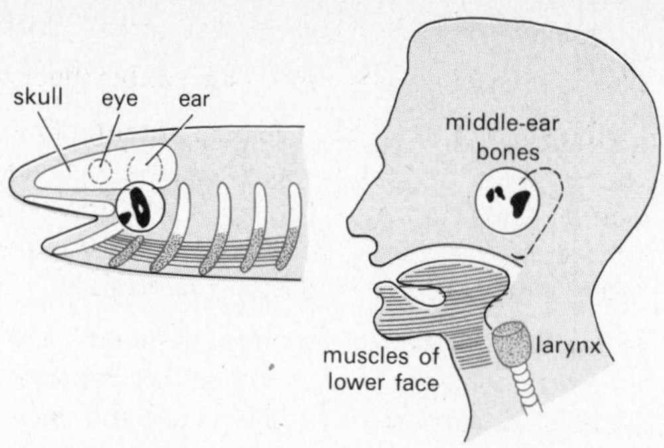

erned entirely by natural selection acting on random variations.

Through past evolution the living mass on earth has increased fairly steadily in individual numbers and types and has seeped into practically all possible environments. Indeed it has created new environments in the process. For example, the evolution of trees has created new possibilities of life in the treetops, exploited later by very many new animals, including our own ancestors. The evolution of warm-blooded birds and mammals has created a new environment in the blood of these animals, exploited later by many new parasites. The evolution of man has created numerous new environments in human installations, and these have been exploited by a large variety of new plants and animals.

We recognize here yet another general characteristic of evolution: a progressive, creative *expansiveness* with respect to both living mass and ways of life. The expansion is still under way, faster in some cases than in others, and the end cannot be predicted as yet.

review questions

1 Describe the essential points of the evolutionary theories of (*a*) Lamarck, (*b*) Darwin and Wallace. How could the evolution of giraffes from short-necked ancestors be explained in terms of these two theories? What are the weaknesses of each theory?

2 What different kinds of inheritable variation can arise in organisms? Do such variations appear randomly, or are they oriented toward usefulness? How do noninheritable variations arise, and what role do they play in evolution?

3 Define the modern meaning of natural selection. Show how natural selection basically has little to do with "survival of the fittest" or "struggle" or "weeding out," and how it is a creative force. How does it happen that natural selection is oriented toward improved adaptation?

4 State the Hardy-Weinberg law. If a population contains 49 percent *AA,* 42 percent *Aa,* and 9 percent *aa* individuals, show by calculation how the law applies. If a Hardy-Weinberg equilibrium exists in a population, what are the rate and amount of evolution?

5 What three conditions disturb Hardy-Weinberg equilibria? For each condition show in what way such equilibria are disturbed and how evolution is therefore affected. How do recessive genes spread through a population? What is genetic drift and where is it encountered?

6 Define species in genetic terms. Describe the process of speciation. What are some common geographic isolating conditions, and what is their effect on gene pools? How do reproductive barriers arise between populations?

7 Review some actual evidence for past and present evolution. Describe the hypothesis of jump evolution. What are its weaknesses, and what is the commonly accepted alternative hypothesis?

8 How have rates of evolution varied in the past? What is an adaptive radiation? Illustrate in the case of mammals. What are the general causes of extinction? What has been the pattern of extinction on different taxonomic levels?

9 What is evolutionary replacement? Distinguish between immediate and delayed replacement, and give examples. Distinguish between evolutionary divergence and convergence, and give examples. In what important way is evolution randomly opportunistic?

10 List five structural and functional features of man and show for each (*a*) how it has evolved opportunistically, and (*b*) that it cannot be labeled as being "theoretically best." Show how evolution has created new environments and therefore new opportunities for evolution.

collateral readings

Crow, J. F.: Ionizing Radiation and Evolution, *Sci. American,* Sept., 1959. A discussion of the effects of radiation-induced mutations on evolution.

Darwin, C.: "The Origin of Species and The Descent of Man," Modern Library, New York, 1948. A reprint of two of Darwin's classic books.

——— and **A. R. Wallace**: On the Tendency of Species to Form Varieties; and of the Perpetuation of Varieties and Species by Natural Means of Selection, in "Great Experiments in Biology," Prentice-Hall, Englewood Cliffs, N.J., 1955. A reprint of the original 1858 statement of the theory of natural selection.

Dobzhansky, T.: The Genetic Basis of Evolution, *Sci. American,* Jan., 1950. Genetic experiments on evolution are described, including the production of bacterial strains resistant to bacteriocides.

———: "Genetics and the Origin of Species," 3d ed., Columbia, New York, 1951. A well-known and recommended analysis of evolutionary theory.

Dodson, E. O.: "Evolution: Process and Product," Reinhold, New York, 1960. A good text on general principles and specific evolutionary processes and phenomena.

Ehrlich, P. R., and **R. W. Holm**: "Process of Evolution," McGraw-Hill, New York, 1963. A nonintroductory, recommended book on genetics, populations, and evolutionary principles.

Eiseley, L. C.: Charles Darwin, *Sci. American,* Feb., 1956. A biographical article.

Kettlewell, H. B. D.: Darwin's Missing Evidence, *Sci. American,* March, 1959. A study of evolution in progress; the case of body colors of certain species of moths is analyzed.

Lack, D.: Darwin's Finches, *Sci. American,* Apr., 1953. An examination of the famous Galapagos birds on which Darwin based much of his theory.

Lamarck, J. B. P. A. de: Evolution through Environmentally Produced Modifications, in "A Source Book in Animal Biology," McGraw-Hill, New York, 1951. A translation of the original 1809 statement of Lamarck's hypothesis.

Mayr, E.: "Animal Species and Evolution," Harvard, Cambridge, Mass., 1963. An important (nonintroductory) book on speciation and evolutionary theory.

Pasteur, L.: Examination of the Doctrine of Spontaneous Generation, in "Great Experiments in Biology," Prentice-Hall, Englewood Cliffs, N.J., 1955. A translation of the famous 1862 original.

Redi, F.: Experiments on the Generation of Insects, in "Great Experiments in Biology," Prentice-Hall, Englewood Cliffs, N.J., 1955. A translation of the 1688 refutation of the doctrine of spontaneous generation.

Ross, H. H.: "A Synthesis of Evolutionary Theory," Prentice-Hall, Englewood Cliffs, N.J., 1962. A stimulating book on all kinds of evolving systems, from galaxies and stars to living populations on earth.

Simpson, G. G.: "The Meaning of Evolution," Yale, New Haven, Conn., 1949, or Mentor Books M66, New York, 1951. A most highly recommended analysis of modern evolutionary theory by one of the principal students of the subject; hard cover and paperback.

Volpe, E. P.: "Understanding Evolution," W. Brown, Dubuque, Iowa, 1967. A recommended paperback reviewing general evolutionary theory and principles.

Wallace, B.: "Chromosomes, Giant Molecules, and Evolution," Norton, New York, 1966. This paperback deals with the genetic aspects of the evolutionary mechanism.

chapter 29 change with time

One of the main lines of investigation that reveals the time course of past evolution is *paleontology,* the study of fossils. Representing the remains of formerly living individuals, fossils provide the most direct evidence of the kinds of organism in existence at various earlier times.

Unfortunately a reasonably extensive fossil record does not go back more than 500 million years, whereas life probably began as long as 3 billion years ago. Events during the earliest periods of living history must therefore be inferred indirectly, as in Chap. 8, through experiments and deductions based on existing organisms.

the fossil record

Any long-preserved remains of organisms are fossils. They can be skeletons or shells, footprints later petrified, impressions left by body parts on solidifying rocks, or the remnants of organisms trapped in amber, gravel pits, swamps, and other places. Whenever a buried organism or any part of it becomes preserved in some way before it decays it will be a fossil. Fossils embedded in successive earth layers provide a time picture of evolution. Deep-lying fossils are normally not accessible, but on occasion a canyon-cutting river or an earthquake fracture exposes a cross section through rock strata. Moreover, erosion gradually wears away top layers and exposes deeper rock (Fig. 29.1).

The age of a rock layer can be determined by "clocks" in the earth's crust: radioactive substances. For example, a given quantity of radium is known to "decay" to lead in a certain span of time. When radium and lead are found together in one mass in a rock the whole mass presumably had been radium originally, when the rock was formed. From the relative quantities of radium and lead present today, one can then calculate the time required for that much lead to form. A similar principle is used in potassium-argon dating and radiocarbon dating. In the first process one measures how much of a naturally occurring unstable form of potassium has decayed to argon. Radiocarbon dating involves measurement of how much of an unstable form of carbon is still present in a rock or fossil sample. The potassium-argon method can be used for dating fossils many millions of years old, but the carbon method is accurate only for fossils formed within the last 50,000 years. Fossils themselves often help in fixing the age of a rock layer. If such a layer contains a fossil known to be of a definite age (*index fossil*), then the whole layer, including all other fossils in it, is likely to be of the same general age.

Based on data obtained from radioactive and fossil clocks, geologists have constructed a *geologic time table* that indicates the age of successive earth layers and provides a calendar of the earth's past history. This calendar consists of five successive main divisions, or *eras.* The last three are subdivided in turn into a number of successive *periods* (Table 16). The beginning and terminal dates of the eras and periods have not been chosen arbitrarily but have been made to coincide with major geologic events known to have occurred at those times. For example, the transition from the Paleozoic to the Mesozoic dates the *Appalachian revolution,* during which the mountain range of that name was built up. Similarly, the transition between the Mesozoic and the Cenozoic was marked by the *Laramide revolution,* which produced the Himalayas, the Rockies, the Andes, and the Alps.

The first geologic era, the immensely long Azoic, spans the period from the origin of the earth to the origin of life. Living history begins with the next era, the Precambrian. The fossil record from this era is exceedingly fragmentary, and it shows mainly that simple cellular life already existed about 2 billion years ago. From the end of the Precambrian on, a continuous and fairly abundant fossil record is available.

It is a very curious circumstance that rocks older than about 500 million years are so barren of fossils, whereas younger ones are comparatively rich in them. Did the Precambrian environment somehow preclude the formation of fossils? Or were Precambrian organisms still too insubstantial to leave fossilizable remains? We simply cannot be sure. But we *are* reasonably sure that Precambrian evolution must have led to the origin of three of the four present main groups of organisms, the Monera, the Protista, and the Metazoa. Virtually all phyla in these three groups were in existence by the end of the Precambrian, but not a single species of these ancient organisms has survived to the present.

Thus the long Precambrian spanned not only three-quarters of evolutionary time but also three-quarters of evolutionary substance. Nearly all the organisms in existence at the end of the Precambrian were aquatic. With the probable

***29.1* Rock layers** *of different ages are often exposed to view. Generally speaking, the deeper a layer in the earth's crust, the older it is.*

*Table 16. The geologic time table**

era	*period*	*duration*		*beginning date*
Cenozoic ("new life")	Quaternary	75	1	1
	Tertiary		74	75
Mesozoic ("middle life")	Cretaceous	130	60	135
	Jurassic		30	165
	Triassic		40	205
Paleozoic ("ancient life")	Permian	300	25	230
	Carboniferous		50	280
	Devonian		45	325
	Silurian		35	360
	Ordovician		65	425
	Cambrian		80	505
Precambrian		1,500		3,000
Azoic ("without life")		3,000		5,000

*All numbers refer to millions of years; older ages are toward bottom of table, younger ages toward top.

exception of some of the bacteria and some of the protists, the land apparently had not been invaded as yet. After the Precambrian, evolution brought about an extensive diversification in the existing phyla and a repeated replacement of ancient forms by new ones. In each of the three main categories this process also included an evolution of types that could live on land. Among these new forms were the Metaphyta, which arose as land-adapted descendants of the green algae. And very soon after the appearance of this last of the four large groups now in existence, some of the animals began to follow the plants to the land.

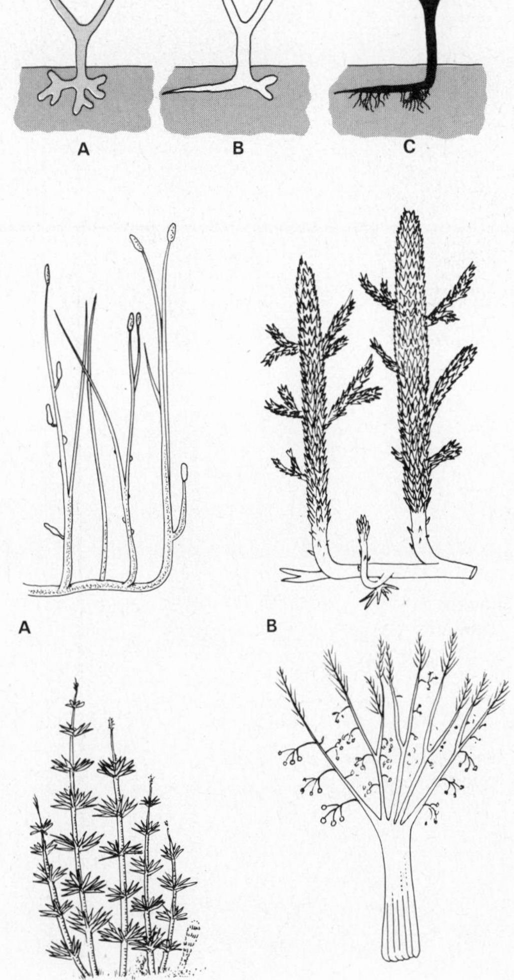

29.2 The Lignier hypothesis. *Branching algae as in A may have evolved via stages as in B into primitive, rhizome-possessing tracheophytes as in C.*

29.3 Fossil tracheophytes. *A, Rhynia, a psilopsid resembling present psilopsids. See also Fig. 28.7. B, Asteroxylon, a psilopsid with lycopsidlike traits. C, Hyenia, suggesting a sphenopsid direction of evolution. D, Pseudoporochnus, a psilopsid with pteropsidlike characteristics.*

plant evolution

The Cambrian and Ordovician periods lasted for almost half of the entire 300-million-year-long Paleozoic era. During this time the seas and later also the fresh waters abounded with many diverse moneran, protistan, and animal types. The first truly terrestrial organisms appear in the fossil record of the Silurian. These were tracheophytes, specifically psilopsids.

the paleozoic

In 1903 the French botanist Lignier proposed the hypothesis that the ancestors of terrestrial tracheophytes were green algae with a branching, rather *Fucus*-like structure. Such an ancestral stock was postulated to have become terrestrial by development of an epidermis with cuticles and stomata; by gradual straightening of some of the branches, leading to the formation of a main stem with smaller lateral branches; by growth of some of the lowest branches into the ground as roots; by development of vascular tissue in the interior; and by restriction of reproductive capacity to the terminals of stems. Lignier considered that the evolution of algae to tracheophytes might have occurred along sea or freshwater shores, where intermittent terrestrial conditions would have promoted the development of adaptations to land life (Fig. 29.2).

Later evidence has supported this hypothesis amply, and it is now widely accepted. Numerous psilopsid fossils have been discovered that were structured more or less exactly as postulated by Lignier's hypothesis. A case in point is *Rhynia,* a Silurian fossil psilopsid with rhizoids, forked upright branches about 1 ft in height, and terminal sporangia. Leaves were absent (Fig. 29.3).

Other fossil tracheophytes give some indication of what the ancestors of the other evolutionary lines of vascular plants appear to have been like. For example, the psilopsid *Asteroxylon* exhibited rootlike branches, numerous microphylls, and other traits suggesting evolutionary trends in a lycopsid direction. The sphenopsid direction is suggested by fossil plants such as *Hyenia,* which had its microphylls arranged in nodal whorls. Several fossil psilopsids, among them *Pseudosporochnus,* point to the pteropsid direction of evolution. In these 9-ft-high treelike plants the

29.4 (*Above*) ***Fossil lycopsids.*** *A, reconstruction of Lepidodendron. B, reconstruction of Sigillaria.*

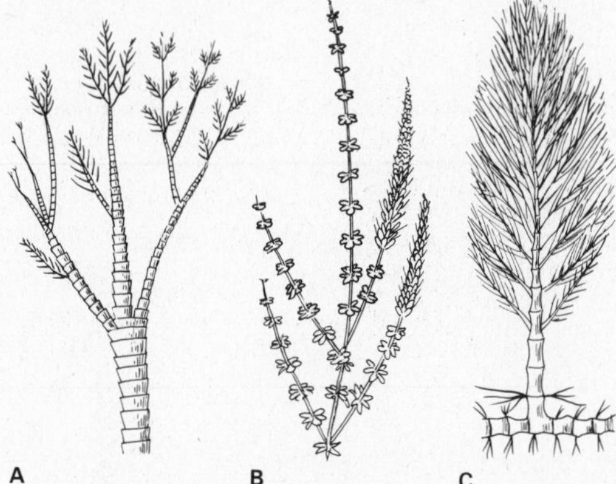

29.5 Fossil sphenopsids. *A, Calamophyton. B, Sphenophyllum. C, Calamites. (After Krausel and Wayland, Zeiller, and Hirmer.)*

leaves were flattened and quite large, with a webbing that could have foreshadowed the macrophylls characteristic of ferns (see Fig. 29.3).

By Devonian times clearly defined lycopsids, sphenopsids, and pteropsids were already in existence and flourishing. The lycopsids were represented by *lepidodendrids,* the giant club mosses (Fig. 29.4). All were huge trees up to 120 ft in height, with active secondary growth, leaves some 20 in. long, and cones up to 1 ft long. The ''scale tree'' *Lepidodendron* became particularly abundant, as did *Sigillaria,* the ''seal tree.'' The 60-ft-high stem of this tree bore leaves in a terminal tuft that gave the plant the general appearance of a giant paintbrush. Most of the lepidodendrids were heterosporous (like *Selaginella* today), and some of them came exceedingly close to forming seeds. Heterospory was exhibited also by many Devonian sphenopsids, some of which were giant trees often up to 100 ft high (Fig. 29.5).

By contrast, the pteropsids of the Devonian were still relatively small and had not yet attained the stature they were to achieve later. Among ferns then living, some gave rise to a line that led to the seed plants. Late Devonian rocks include two groups of fossil gymnosperms, the *seed ferns* and the *fossil conifers.* The former (which were not really ''ferns'' despite their name) probably evolved first and were ancestral to the latter (Fig. 29.6).

During the Carboniferous, bryophytes appear for the first time in the fossil record. It is possible that the evolution of this phylum was promoted by the generally wet, tropical and subtropical conditions then prevailing over much of the earth. The Carboniferous is also the period when most of the tracheophytes that had arisen earlier attained their greatest abundance. Lycopsids and sphenopsids produced vast forests, and ferns, too, attained the stature of trees. Fossil conifers became abundant, with giant representative such as *Cordaites,* an up to 100-ft-high tree that had parallel-veined, often 3-ft-long leaves. Seed ferns in particular flourished, and the Carboniferous is often called the ''age of seed ferns'' (Fig. 29.7). These plants produced a third gymnosperm group, the *fossil cycads,* and thus they appear to have been the ancestors of all other gymnosperms, extinct as well as living. Moreover, they probably also gave rise later to the flowering plants (see Fig. 29.6).

During the later part of the Carboniferous many regions became so wet that they were transformed to vast tracts of swamps and marshes. In these much of the woody flora of the time died. Later geologic changes converted the bodies of the plants to coal, hence the name of the whole period, ''coal-bearing.'' The rich coal beds of Pennsylvania and West Virginia came into being at that time, and the coal itself represents the remains of forests of lycopsids, sphenopsids, tree ferns, seed ferns, and fossil conifers (Color Fig. 29).

However, many of these plants survived to the Permian. They were joined then by the newly evolved ginkgoes. The long Paleozoic eventually terminated with the geologic upheavals of the Appalachian revolution, which in turn precipitated a so-called *Permo-Triassic crisis* among living organisms. This unstable time of transition was marked by widespread extinction of archaic forms and later replacement with rapidly evolving new types. Also, the total amount of life decreased temporarily, both in the sea and on land. Many groups of land plants became extinct—virtually all of the psilopsids, lepidodendrids, and early sphenopsids, as well as many of the ancient ferns, seed ferns, and fossil conifers. Only remnant groups of psilopsids, lycopsids, and sphenopsids managed to survive, and their descendants still linger on as relics today. But the surviving groups of ferns and gymnosperms soon began to flourish anew and became the ancestors of the expanding flora of the new Mesozoic era (see Fig. 29.6).

the mesozoic and cenozoic

The Mesozoic as a whole is often called the "age of gymnosperms" in plant evolution. Fossil cycads came to form extensive forests during the Jurassic. Trees like *Bennettites* were some 10 ft high, with terminal leaves almost as long as the tree trunk (Fig. 29.8). These plants died out during the Cretaceous (and their ample remains can still be found in, for example, the Fossil Cycad National Monument in the Black Hills of South Dakota). The group was replaced on a reduced scale by the true cycads, probably evolved independently from seed ferns. Descendants of these cycads are still living in various warm-climate areas today.

The ginkgoes reached their peak during the Jurassic and early Cretaceous. Concurrently, new groups of coniferous gymnosperms related to the earlier *Cordaites* came into ascendancy. These dominated the whole later part of the Mesozoic and included many of the presently living conifers, among them cypresses, yews, redwoods, and pines.

But the forests formed by these large trees had to share space with the flowering plants, which produced a first extensive radiation at that time. Fragmentary fossils of angiosperms date back to the Jurassic, and the first ample finds occur in Cretaceous layers. As will become apparent be-

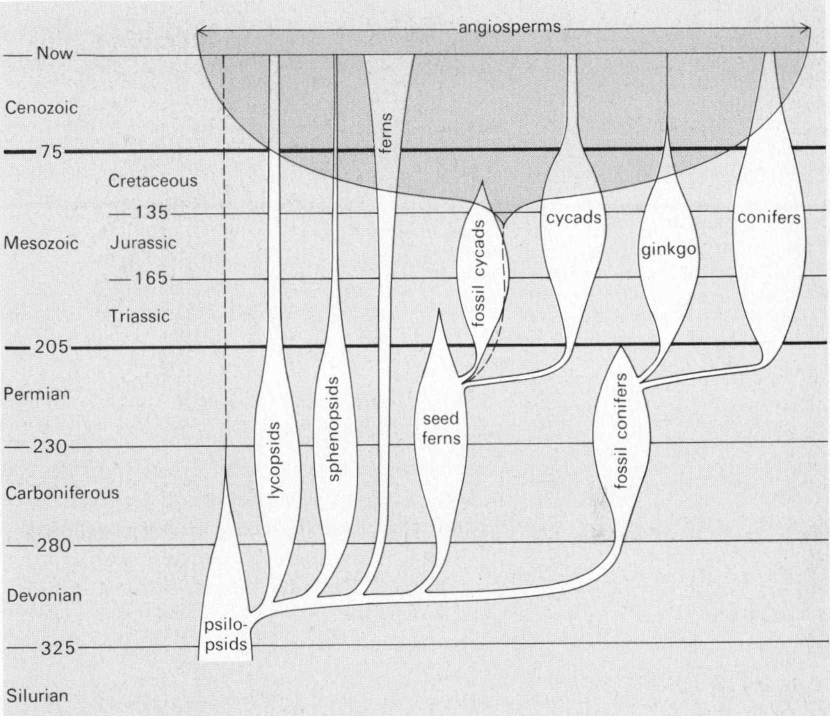

29.6 The fossil record of plants. *Numbers at left indicate past time in millions of years. The varying width of the graph for each plant group approximates the changing abundance of the group in the course of time.*

29.7 Fossil pteropsids, *Devonian. A, a fossil fern. B, a gymnospermous seed fern. C, Cordaites, a gymnospermous fossil conifer.*

29.8 ***Fossil cycads.*** *Model of a terminal flowerlike cone of Bennettites, seen in top view. The radial array of feathery structures is a whorl of microsporophylls, each containing many microsporangia. The dark tips underneath are hairy bracts without reproductive significance.*

low, the late Mesozoic expansion of angiosperms coincided with a similarly extensive radiation of insects. Most of the Mesozoic angiosperms were woody. They included many of the tree-forming types still living today, such as elms, oaks, maples, magnolias, and palms. Forests of these were already flourishing in the closing phases of the Mesozoic, when they began to rival the forests of conifers.

If the Mesozoic was the age of gymnosperms, the Cenozoic was unquestionably the "age of angiosperms" in plant evolution (see Fig. 29.6). The increasing dominance of the angiosperms and the corresponding decline of the gymnosperms was in large measure a consequence of the Laramide revolution, which terminated the Mesozoic.

Before the Cenozoic, much of the earth, polar regions included, was tropical and subtropical and permitted uninterrupted year-round growth. Fossil trees from the Mesozoic and Early Cenozoic actually are without annual rings, a sure indication that climates were uniformly warm. But after the Laramide revolution had produced the high mountain ranges of today, cooler climates developed gradually at higher latitudes. For example, the east-west barrier of the Himalayas in Asia and of the Alps in Europe prevented warm south winds from reaching the northern portions of Eurasia. These regions then became colder. In effect, the Laramide revolution eventually led to the establishment of distinct tropical, temperate, and polar zones on earth.

Consequently, seed plants already living in the tropics could remain tropical, but species in other regions could not. Such plants would have had to become extinct unless they could migrate to the tropics or could readapt right where they lived to the yearly succession of winter and summer. Many groups actually did migrate to warmer regions, but among those that did not many came to have reduced significance or died out altogether. The decline of gymnosperms traces to this time. Today only some 700 species are left, and those living in regions with cold seasons protect themselves against the low temperatures through processes of winter-hardening. Similarly, many woody angiosperms in temperate and northern regions now survive winter conditions by shedding their leaves. Even so, the luxuriant forests of coniferous and flowering plants once characteristic of northern regions thinned out and became less extensive. Fossil trees from the later Cenozoic do show annual rings, like trees today, indicating clearly that uninterrupted year-round growth was no longer possible.

Furthermore, some of the angiosperms of temperate and northern regions evolved a new way of coping with the cool seasons, by becoming nonwoody herbaceous biennials and annuals. Winter then could not harm them, for during the winter they simply died and ceased to exist as mature plants. For the rest of the year their primary growth gave them only a minimum body, just barely large enough to permit them to reproduce.

Thus the long-range consequences of the Laramide revolution were, first, a decreased abundance of the woody seed plants in all regions except the tropics, and second, the gradual emergence of modern small-bodied flowering herbs in northern and arctic zones. Today these areas are characterized particularly by large populations of herbaceous angiosperms, whereas the tropics are inhabited by large populations of woody angiosperms.

As will become apparent shortly, the reduction of forest during the middle and late Cenozoic also was to prove highly significant for animal evolution, human evolution in particular.

animal evolution

early history

Since most animal phyla already appear to have been in existence 500 million years ago, when abundant fossil formation first began, the various basic animal types must have evolved earlier during the Precambrian. This early evolution consequently cannot be documented by fossils but must be inferred from the nature of the animals now living.

One of the notable attempts at inferring the course of animal evolution from existing forms was made by Ernst Haeckel, a German biologist of the late nineteenth century. Most of his views are now largely discredited, but they were once so influential that many of them still persist today under various guises. For this reason it may be of some value to review them briefly.

Haeckel recognized, as did others before him, that animal development typically passes through certain common embryonic stages—zygote, blastula, gastrula, mesoderm formation. Haeckel thought that this succession of embryonic stages mirrored a succession of past evolutionary stages (Fig. 29.9). Thus the zygote would represent the unicellular protistan stage of evolution. The blastula would correspond to an evolutionary stage when animals were, according to Haeckel, hollow one-layered spheres. Haeckel coined the term *blastea* for such hypothetical adult animals, and he thought that his ancestral blasteas may have been quite similar to currently living green algae such as *Volvox.* The gastrula stage would correspond to a hypothetical ancestral adult type that Haeckel called a *gastrea.* He believed that gastreas were still represented by the living coelenterates, which in some respects do resemble early gastrulas—the body consists chiefly of two layers and the single alimentary opening is reminiscent of the blastopore of a gastrula.

On such grounds Haeckel considered the gastrea to have been the common ancestor of all Eumetazoa. He assumed the two-layered gastrealike condition to represent a *diploblastic* stage in animal evolution, attained by radiates such as the coelenterates. Further evolution then added mesoderm to the gastrealike radiates and so produced a three-layered *triploblastic* condition, as in flatworms and all other Bilateria. By extension the hypothesis also implied that, for example, a caterpillar larva represented an annelid stage in insect evolution, that a frog tadpole represented a fish stage in frog evolution, and that a human embryo, which exhibits rudimentary gill structures at certain periods, represented a fish stage in man's evolution.

Haeckel condensed his views into a *''law of recapitulation,''* the essence of which is described by two phrases: ''ontogeny recapitulates phylogeny'' and ''phylogeny causes ontogeny.'' The first statement means that the embryonic development of an egg (ontogeny) repeats the evolutionary development of the phyla (phylogeny); and the second, that *because* animals have evolved one phylum after another, their embryos still pass through this same succession of evolutionary stages.

Therefore, if one wishes to determine the course of animal evolution, he need only study the course of embryonic development. For, according to Haeckel, evolution occurs by the addition of extra embryonic stages to the end of a given sequence of development. If to a protozoon is added cleavage, the protozoon becomes a zygote and the new adult is a blastea. If to a blastea is added gastrulation, the blastea becomes a blastula and the new adult is a gastrea. Similarly, if to a fish are added lungs and four legs, the

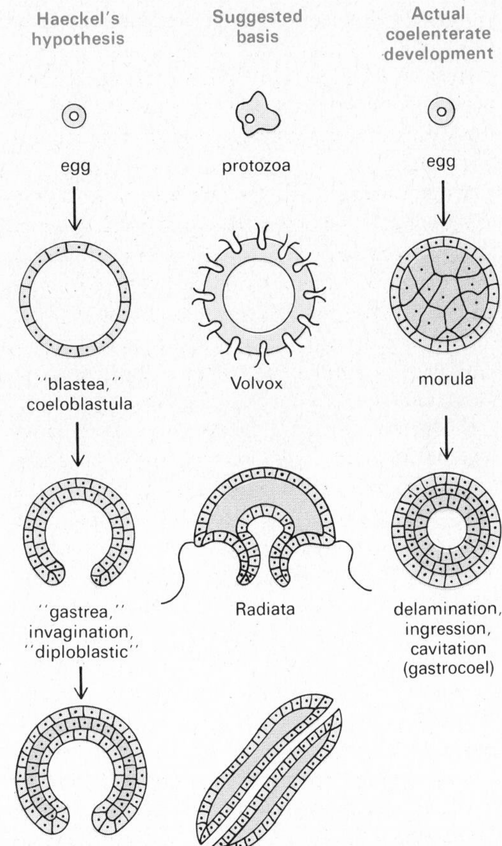

29.9 Haeckel's ''gastrea'' hypothesis. *Based primarily on coelenterate development, the hypothesis is at variance with the actual developmental patterns typical of most coelenterates (as at right). Thus, most coelenterates have solid, not hollow, blastulas; most do not gastrulate by invagination but by a variety of other processes, as indicated. Moreover, again contrary to Haeckel's hypothesis, the presence of mesoderm in coelenerates makes not only the Bilateria but also the Radiata (hence all Eumetazoa) ''triploblastic,'' or formed from three primary germ layers.*

fish represents a tadpole and the new adult is a frog. And if to such an amphibian are added a four-chambered heart, a diaphragm, a larger brain, an upright posture, and a few other features, then the frog is a human embryo and the new adult is a man.

We can attribute to the lingering influence of Haeckel, not to Darwin, this erroneous idea of an evolutionary "ladder" or "scale," proceeding from "simple ameba" to "complex man," with more and more rungs added on top of the ladder as time proceeds. All such notions are invalid because Haeckel's basic thesis is invalid. Indeed, Haeckel's arguments were shown to be unsound even in his own day, but his generalizations were so neat and they seemed to explain so much so simply that the fundamental difficulties were ignored by many.

For example, it was already well known in Haeckel's time that, apart from exceptional forms, the radiate animals do not really have two-layered bodies but distinctly three-layered ones, with a mesoderm often highly developed (as in sea anemones, for example). Two-layered animals in effect do not exist, and a distinction between diploblastic and triploblastic types cannot be justified. Thus the conceptual foundation on which the recapitulatory law was based was never valid.

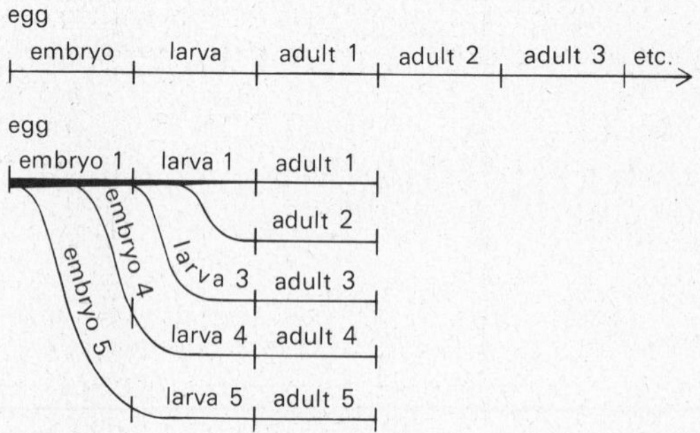

29.10 Developmental divergence. *Top, the pattern of evolution according to Haeckel, by addition of extra stages to a preexisting ancestral path of development. Bottom, the actual pattern of evolution, by divergence of new developmental paths (2, 3, 4, 5) from various points of a preexisting ancestral path (1). Thus if divergence occurs comparatively late, as in adult 2, its embryonic and most of its larval development can be very similar to that of adult 1. But if divergence takes place early, as in adult 5, then almost the whole developmental pattern will be quite dissimilar from that of adult 1. Adults 1 and 5 then might represent different phyla, whereas adults 1 and 2 might belong to the same class or order.*

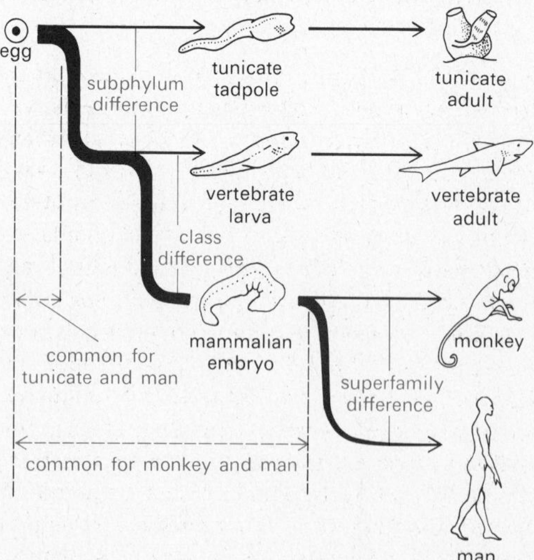

29.11 Developmental divergence in chordate evolution. *Tailed, tadpolelike early stages are characteristic of all chordates, and the earlier the developmental paths diverge from the ancestral one, the more different will be the adults and the taxonomic results. Thus the developmental paths of tunicates and men diverge early, and the adult differences are at the level of subphyla. But monkeys and men develop similarly for far longer periods, and the adult differences here are only at the level of superfamilies. To be sure, chordate eggs are not all the same but are merely similar. Also, "common" developmental stages of two animals are merely similar, not identical.*

Moreover, new types are not known to evolve by addition of extra stages to ancestral adults. Instead, new evolution occurs for the most part through *developmental divergence;* a new path of embryonic or larval development branches away from some point along a preexisting ancestral path of development (Fig. 29.10). The best example is evolution by larval *neoteny,* a common process by which numerous new groups are believed to have arisen from the *larvae* of ancestral groups. An ancestral larva here does not metamorphose into the customary adult, but instead develops sex organs precociously and becomes established in this larval form as a new type of adult animal.

As pointed out in Chap. 13, for example, tunicates have tadpole larvae that develop into sessile adults. It is now considered most probable that vertebrates represent neotenous tunicate tadpoles. The tadpoles of certain tunicate ancestors are believed to have retained their tails, with notochord and dorsal hollow nerve cord intact, and to have become reproductively mature in such a larval condition. These permanent larvae then came to represent a new chordate subphylum, the vertebrates (Fig. 29.11).

Numerous other instances of evolution by neoteny are known, and as will appear in the next chapter man, too, is a neotenous product. In all these cases the new developmental path branches away sooner or later along the course of the old path. The sooner two such paths do diverge, the more dissimilar will be the two types of resulting adult. For example, the embryos of man and of apes resemble each other till relatively late in development, and the developmental paths diverge only then. The embryos of man and of tunicates are similar for considerably shorter periods; their developmental paths correspondingly diverge much sooner (see Fig. 29.11).

Such developmental correlations were clearly recognized before Haeckel and even before Darwin. They do have evolutionary meaning, but not in the Haeckelian sense. It is quite natural that related animals descended from a common ancestor should resemble each other in some of

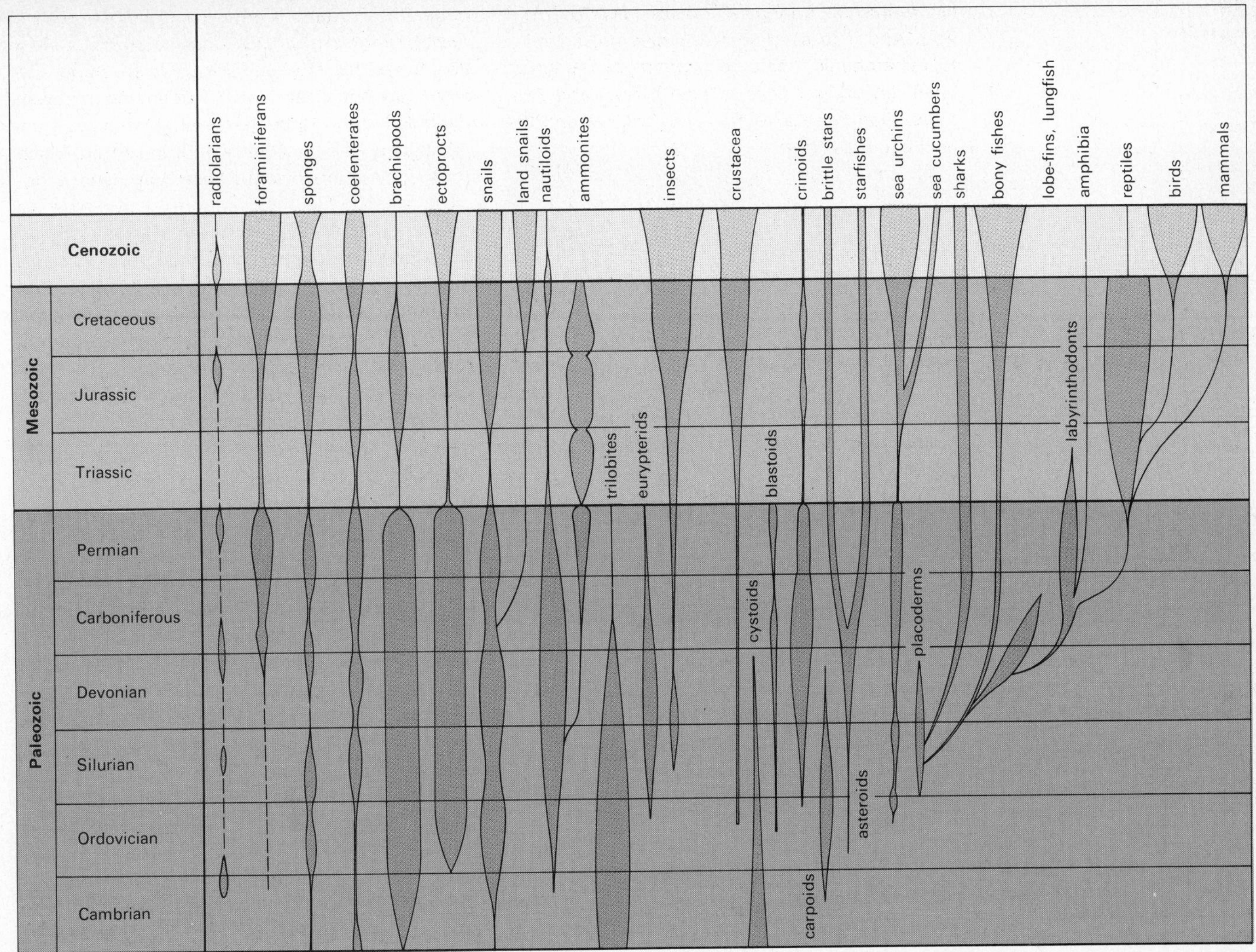

their developmental features. Thus, human embryos resemble those of fish and frogs in certain respects not because an egg of man becomes a fish embryo first, a frog embryo next, and a human embryo last. The similarities arise, rather, from the common ancestry of all these three animal types, including their common developmental histories up to certain stages. Beyond these stages each type has modified its developmental processes in its own way.

Moreover, it can be shown that the formation of a particular structure in one type of organism often depends on the existence of an anatomical precursor that had evolved in an ancestral type of organism. Some of the evolutionary opportunisms discussed in Chap. 28 illustrate this generalization. As noted, for example, the human larynx has evolved opportunistically as a derivative of skeletal gill supports of ancestral fishes. An important point here is that, from an architectural standpoint, a larynx cannot be put together unless gill-derived skeletal components are available in the human embryo as structural raw materials. In other words, human embryos today still form rudimentary, nonfunctioning gills, not because they "recapitulate" fish evolution as Haeckel supposed, but because gill rudiments must serve as necessary intermediate steps in the building process that leads to larynx construction. Similarly, gill rudiments are still required in human development as intermediate structural steps in the elaboration of the face musculature.

29.12 The fossil record of animals. *The varying width of each graph approximates the changing abundance of a given group in the course of time. Such widths are directly comparable only for different times within a group, not between groups. For example, the absolute Cenozoic abundance of insects would equal or exceed that of all other groups combined. The graphs clearly show the major decline that took place at the end of each era, particularly during the Permo-Triassic transition and on a smaller scale during the Mesozoic-Cenozoic transition.*

A

B

29.13 ***Paleozoic fossils, restorations.*** *A, Cambrian seas. Various algae, trilobites (in center foreground), eurypterids (in center background), sponges, jellyfishes, brachiopods, and different types of worms are the most prominent organisms shown. B, Ordovician seas. The large animal in foreground is a straight-shelled nautiloid.*

In like fashion also, most other supposed instances of "recapitulation" turn out to involve precursor stages still necessary today for the development of other structures.

It should be pointed out, furthermore, that a branching pattern of developmental divergence is fully in line with the known bushlike pattern of evolution, whereas ladderlike end addition is not. It is quite obvious also that mammalian development, for example, does not really represent a successive transformation of an actual protozoan to an actual coelenterate, flatworm, tunicate, fish, etc. Indeed it is hardly conceivable that the billion or more years of animal evolution could be crowded into the few weeks or months of animal development. The common stages in animal development thus give evidence of general similarities only, not of specific identities.

For these various reasons the Haeckelian idea of recapitulation is not tenable; the embryonic stages of animals do not repeat the adult stages of earlier animals. Moreover, phylum evolution also cannot be the "cause" of the progressive stages in animal development. If anything, just the reverse probably holds; as pointed out above, developmental stages provide the sources from which new groups can evolve. What is acceptable today—as it was even before Haeckel—is the generalization that the embryonic development of different animals tends to be similar if the animals are related historically, and that the embryonic similarity generally lasts the longer the closer the relationship. Indeed, as has become apparent in Chap. 11, developmental resemblances are important aids in both classifying animals and elucidating phylogenies—the "family trees" of animal groups before fossils were left. Figure 11.9 can serve as a summary of current views on this subject.

the paleozoic

All animal phyla in existence 500 million years ago still survive today, but most subgroups in these phyla have since become replaced; all the ancient species and genera have become extinct long ago. The present brachiopod genus *Lingula* goes back 400 million years and represents the most ancient of the known "living fossils" among animals.

During the very long Cambrian and Ordovician periods, life in the sea was already abundant. A large variety of protists probably existed already long before the Cambrian, and fossil algae, foraminiferans, and radiolarians are known from earliest Cambrian times onward (Fig. 29.12). The fossil history of animals begins with Cambrian sponges and jellyfishes and Ordovician corals and sea anemones. A variety of tube-forming worms is known from these and even earlier periods, and stalked brachiopods already existed in the Cambrian. The Ordovician marks the beginning of a rich record of entoprocts and ectoprocts (Fig. 29.13 and Color Fig. 30).

Echinoderms were amply represented by six archaic groups. Three of these (*cystoids, carpoids, blastoids*) have since become extinct, but the stalked sessile *crinoids* and the ancient *asteroids* and *echinoids* gave rise to the present-day echinoderms (Fig. 29.14 and see Fig. 29.12). Mollusks included archaic clams and snails, as well as *nautiloids,* a group closely related to squids and octopuses and still represented today by the chambered nautilus. Early nautiloids had both coiled and uncoiled shells, and the uncoiled forms probably were the largest animals of the time; their shells were up to 5 or 6 yd long (see Fig. 29.13).

The most ancient arthropod types were the *trilobites,* which are believed to have been ancestral to all other arthropod groups (Fig. 29.15). Their body was marked into three lobes by two longitudinal furrows, hence the name "trilobites." These animals were already exceedingly abundant when the Cambrian began, and they are among the most plentiful of all fossil forms. A somewhat later group of arthropods comprised the *eurypterids,* large animals that well may have been ancestral to all chelicerate arthropods (horseshoe crabs, sea spiders, and arachnids). The surviving horseshoe crab genus *Limulus* has existed unchanged for the last 200 million years.

Vertebrate history begins in the late Ordovician (Fig. 29.16). The marine tunicate ancestors probably were already present at or near the start of the Paleozoic, and the vertebrates evolved from them as freshwater forms. The first fossil vertebrates are *ostracoderms,* bone-plated members of the class of jawless fishes. Most of them became extinct near the end of the Devonian, and their only surviving descendants are the lampreys and hagfishes. All traces of external bone have been lost in these animals (Fig. 29.17).

The Silurian was the period during which the first tracheophytes evolved, and these land plants were soon followed by land animals: late Silurian land scorpions, probably evolved from earlier sea scorpions, are the earliest known terrestrial animals. Other groups of arthropods invaded the land during the latter part of the Silurian and the beginning of the Devonian. The first spiders, mites, centipedes, and insects appeared during these times. In the sea the nautiloids gave rise to a new molluscan group, the shelled *ammonites,* which were to flourish for long ages (see Fig. 29.17). Among echinoderms the ancient asteroids branched into two descendant groups, the brittle stars and the starfishes. And among vertebrates a major adaptive radiation occurred during the Silurian and Devonian (see Fig. 29.16).

During the early Silurian some of the jawless ostracoderms gave rise to a new vertebrate class, the *placoderms.* Bone-plated like their ancestors, these fishes were generally small, but some reached lengths of 12 yd or more. Most placoderms used their jaws in a carnivorous mode of

***29.14* Paleozoic echinoderms.** *A, a cystoid. B, a blastoid. C, a crinoid. See Fig. 29.12 for history of first two.*

***29.15* Paleozoic arthropods.** *A, trilobites. B, a eurypterid.*

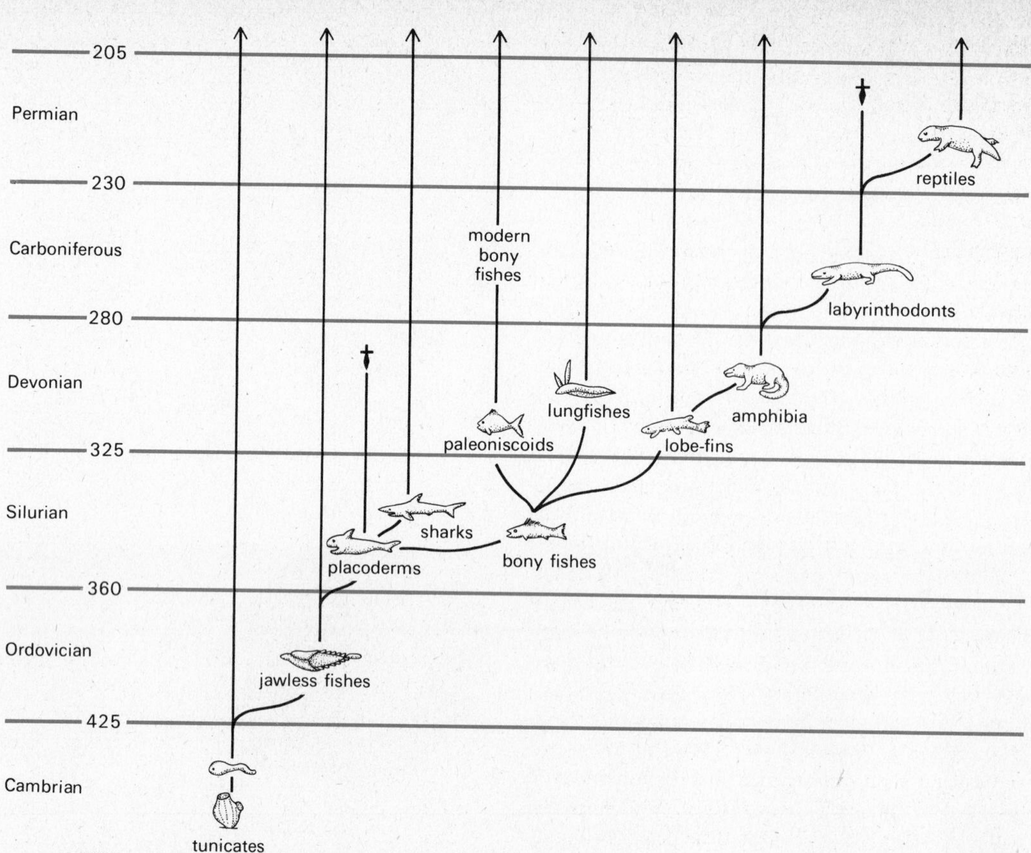

29.16 Paleozoic vertebrates. *The name of each group is shown roughly at the time level at which this group first appears in the fossil record. Daggers indicate extinction of a group.*

29.17 Paleozoic fossils. *A, ostracoderm, an ancient jawless fish. Note bony armor. A placoderm is illustrated in Fig. 2.4. B, an ammonite, a cephalopod mollusk related to the chambered nautilus (see Fig. 12.14).*

29. Carboniferous swamp forest, *reconstruction. The trees at left are* Sigillaria. *Cones of lepidodendrids can be seen in upper left corner. Small plants in center foreground are* Sphenophyllum. *The tree at right is* Calamites.

color figure 30

30. Ordovician seascape, *reconstruction. The large animal in foreground is a straight-shelled nautiloid. Coral and other coelenterates, and more nautiloids, are shown in background.*

31. ***Ichthyosaurs,*** *reconstruction.*

color figure 32

32. Mammal-like reptiles, *reconstruction. Of the two Triassic therapsids shown, the larger one in mid-foreground is a herbivore* (Kannemeyeria), *which is under attack by a group of carnivorous types* (Cynognathus).

A

B

33. Cenozoic animals, *reconstruction. A, an 8-ft high titanothere* (Brontotherium) *from the Oligocene. Tortoises* (Stylemys) *are in foreground. B, the Miocene mammals shown are long-necked camels* (Oxydactylus) *in background, 3-toed horses* (Parahippus) *in middle ground, and 2-horned rhinos* (Menoceros) *in foreground.*

color figure 34

34. Pleistocene animals, *reconstruction. A huge ground sloth* (Megatherium) *and two armadillo-like glyptodonts* (Glyptodon) *are shown.*

life (see Fig. 2.4). In time the placoderms replaced the ancestral ostracoderms as the dominant animals, and late in the Silurian they produced two descendant lines of fishes that in turn came to replace the placoderms themselves; by the end of the Paleozoic the placoderms had disappeared completely, the only vertebrate class (and one of the few animal classes in general) that has become extinct.

The two new groups of fishes evolved from placoderms were the *cartilage fishes* and the *bony fishes,* each representing a separate class. Both groups arose in fresh water, but the cartilage fishes rapidly adopted the marine habit that sharks and rays still display today. The bony fishes at first remained in fresh water, where they soon radiated into three main subgroups: the *paleoniscoid fishes,* the *lungfishes,* and the *lobe-finned fishes.* During the Devonian, often called the "age of fishes," the paleoniscoids spread to the ocean and became the ancestors of practically all present bony fishes, both freshwater and marine. The lungfishes declined in later Paleozoic times, and only three genera survive today. The lobe-fins similarly now are almost extinct (Fig. 29.18 and see Figs. 13.21. and 29.16).

But the Devonian representatives of the lobe-fins included the ancestors of the *amphibia,* the first land vertebrates. Lobe-fins probably lived in fresh waters that dried out periodically, and their air sacs and fleshy fins probably enabled them to crawl overland to other bodies of water or to embed themselves in mud and breathe air through the mouth. It appears likely, therefore, that terrestrial vertebrates arose not because certain fish preferred the land, but because they had to become terrestrial if they were to survive as fish.

Thus when the Devonian came to a close sharks were dominant in the ocean and bony fishes in fresh water. On land, terrestrial arthropods had become abundant and the first amphibia had made their appearance. Many of these land animals could shelter in the lycopsid and sphenopsid forests then already in existence.

During the Carboniferous and Permian periods the first crablike and crayfishlike animals and the first land snails appeared, and insects produced extensive adaptive radiations. Some of these ancient insect types had wingspreads of close to a yard. Among vertebrates the early amphibia gave rise to more or less clumsy, often bizarre forms, the *labyrinthodonts* (see Fig. 29.18). These became the ancestors of two groups, the modern amphibia and the *reptiles.* This new class was represented at first by the stem reptiles, or *cotylosaurs,* the first vertebrates that laid eggs on land. Cotylosaurs produced a major reptilian radiation during the Permian, which brought about the decline of the labyrinthodonts and also set the stage for an "age of reptiles" during the Mesozoic era (Fig. 29.19).

The Paleozoic era terminated with the Appalachian revolution, as noted, and, as among plants, this geologically unstable time precipitated a Permo-Triassic crisis in the animal world.

A

B

29.18 Devonian and Permian vertebrates. *A, restoration of fossil lobe-finned fishes. See Fig. 13.2 for photo of modern lungfish. B, reconstruction of Diplovertebron, a labyrinthodont amphibian.*

A

B

29.19 Reptile evolution. *A, reconstruction of Seymouria, a transitional amphibian type probably related to the stock from which reptiles appear to have evolved. B, reconstruction of Labidosaurus, one of the cotylosaurian stem reptiles.*

Archaic forms became extinct and were replaced by rapidly evolving new groups, and the total amount of animal life—particularly in the sea—decreased temporarily (see Fig. 29.12). Brachiopods and ectoprocts became almost extinct. All mollusks passed through a major decline; nautiloids became extinct with one exception, and ammonites were reduced to a small group. Trilobites and eurypterids disappeared altogether. Only a few crinoid types and a single echinoid type survived into the Triassic. Placoderms died out, and extensive replacements occurred among the cartilage and bony fishes. Land animals were less affected on the whole, though their numbers did decline temporarily. Labyrinthodonts lingered on to the Triassic, but soon they, too, became extinct. The reptiles on the contrary survived the crisis well, and when the new Mesozoic era opened, they were already dominant.

the mesozoic

The era as a whole was characterized by a re-expansion of nearly all groups that survived the Permo-Triassic crisis and by extensive replacements within groups (see Fig. 29.12). Sponges and coelenterates underwent major adaptive radiations during the Jurassic, with the result that these animals exist today in greater numbers than ever before. Ectoprocts and brachiopods similarly increased in abundance, but the latter became virtually extinct again at the end of the Mesozoic. Clams and snails diversified greatly and became the predominant mollusks from then on. The ammonites also reexpanded during the late Mesozoic, yet not a single one survived beyond the end of the era. The crinoids managed to linger on as relics, and the more abundant brittle stars and starfishes held their own. But the single echinoid group that survived from the Paleozoic underwent an explosive expansion during the late Mesozoic. In the course of it the modern sea urchins and sea cucumbers evolved. Crustacea gained slowly and steadily in numbers and types. Insects diversified explosively in parallel with the rise of flowering plants, and the present importance of insects traces to this Mesozoic expansion. An extensive radiation occurred also among the bony fishes, which became the dominant animals of the aquatic world from the Cretaceous on.

The most spectacular Mesozoic event was the expansion of the reptiles. These not only evolved into numerous terrestrial types but also invaded the water and the air. As a group they reigned supreme on earth for 130 million years, longer than any other animal group before or since. When their dominance was eventually broken, they were replaced by two new groups that they themselves had given rise to, the birds and the mammals.

At the beginning of the Mesozoic five major reptilian groups were in existence, all evolved from the Permian stem reptiles (Fig. 29.20). One group, the *thecodonts,* reradiated extensively during the Triassic and gave rise to the following types: the ancestral *birds;* the ancestors of the modern *crocodiles, lizards,* and *snakes;* the flying *pterosaurs;* and two other groups collectively called *dinosaurs.* A second group was ancestral to the modern *turtles.* A third and fourth produced two kinds of marine reptile, the porpoiselike *ichthyosaurs* and the long-necked *plesiosaurs.* The fifth group comprised the *therapsids,* which included the ancestors of the mammals.

These various reptilian types did not all flourish at the same time. The Triassic was dominated largely by early therapsids and thecodonts. The former were four-footed walkers, but thecodonts were rather birdlike, with large hind limbs for walking, an enormous supporting tail, and diminutive forelimbs. During the Jurassic, ichthyosaurs became abundant in the ocean, and one of the thecodont lines evolved into birds. This transition is documented beautifully by the famous fossil animal *Archeopteryx* (Fig. 29.21). The reptile had teeth and a lizardlike tail, but it was also equipped with feathers and wings and presumably flew.

Like mammals, birds remained inconspicuous during the whole remaining Mesozoic. They were overshadowed particularly by their thecodont kin, the flying pterosaurs. These animals had their heyday during the Cretaceous, when reptiles as a whole attained their greatest abundance and variety. The unique, long-necked plesiosaurs were then common in the ocean, and the dinosaurs gained undisputed dominance on land. Not all dinosaurs were large, but some were enormous. The group included, for example, *Brontosaurus,* the largest land animal of all time, and *Tyrannosaurus,* probably the fiercest land carnivore of all time (Fig. 29.22 and Color Figs. 31 and 32).

Mammals arose from therapsids during the late Triassic (Fig. 29.23 and see Color Fig. 32). Some of the factors that probably promoted this mammalian evolution can be deduced. The ancestors of mammals among therapsid reptiles generally were small, in the size range of mice, and this smallness must have entailed perpetual danger in a world dominated by far larger animals. Survival must have depended on ability to escape danger, mainly by running. But the running capacity of early reptiles was probably as limited as that of their modern descendants. Reptilian lungs hold only moderate amounts of air, and breathing movements are fairly shallow. Also, the oxygen-holding capacity of blood is comparable to that of fish and amphibian blood, which suffices for high levels of metabolic activity in water. On land, however, such capacities cannot support sustained body activity; most living reptiles actually are active only in brief bursts and are otherwise relatively slow and sluggish.

Living mammals give clear evidence that the

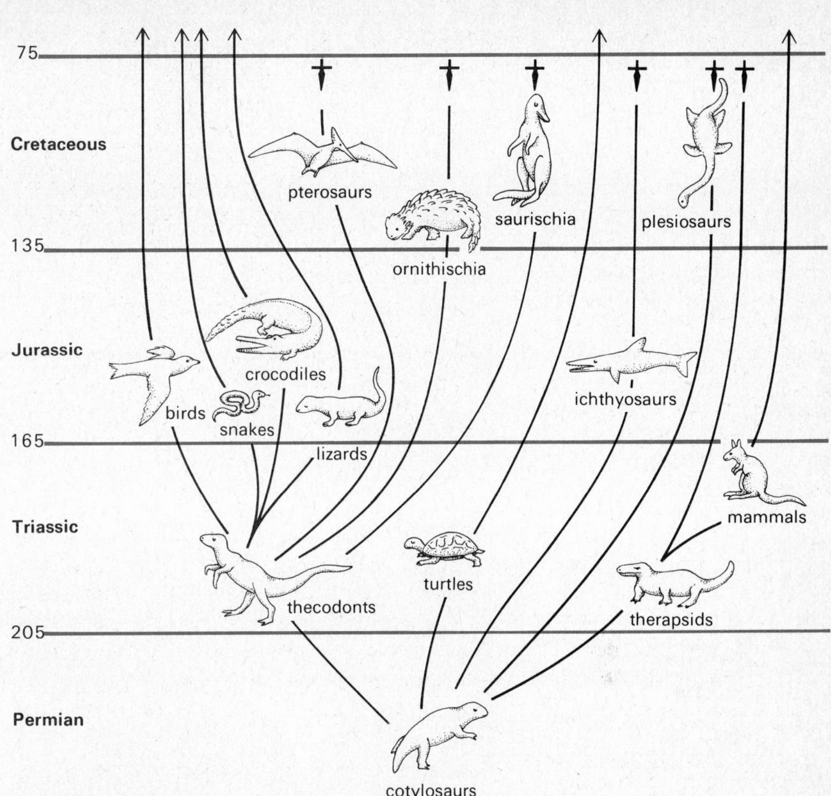

***29.20* Mesozoic reptiles.** *Placement of groups corresponds roughly with the time of their greatest abundance. Numbers at left indicate past time in millions of years.*

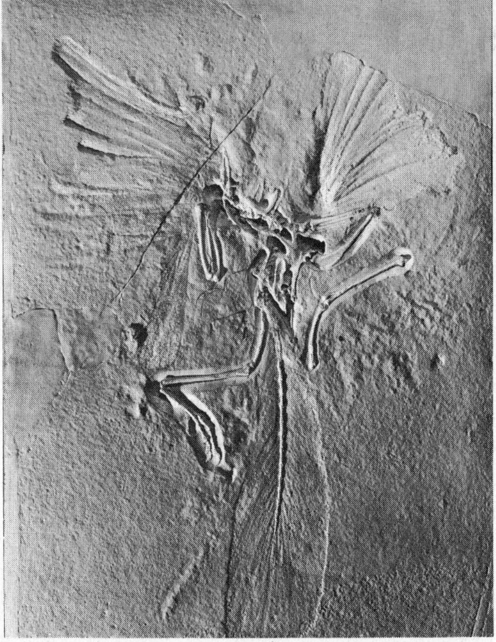

***29.21* Bird evolution.** *Plaster cast of Archeopteryx. Note feathered tail, wings. The head is bent back, and the tooth-bearing mouth is not easily visible here.*

29.22 (*Above*) ***Dinosaurs.*** *Left, Triceratops, a Cretaceous horned herbivore. Right, Tyrannosaurus, a giant Cretaceous carnivore. See also Color Figs. 31 and 32.*

29.23 Mammalian evolution. *A Triassic therapsid, a mammal-like reptile. See also Color Fig. 32.*

evolution of the group from reptiles involved a pronounced elevation of metabolic levels. A newly developed diaphragm increased breathing efficiency; red blood corpuscles became nonnucleated and maximally specialized for oxygen transport; new chemical variants of hemoglobin permitted blood to carry almost three times as much oxygen as before; and along with a change from reptilian scales to mammalian hair, a temperature-control mechanism came into being that permitted maintenance of a constant, uniformly high body temperature. The whole *rate* of metabolism intensified, and mammals thus became perhaps the most active animals of all time. (In part for similar reasons of escaping danger, in part because of the energy requirements of flight, birds became nearly as active. However, they did not evolve a diaphragm, the oxygen capacity of their blood is only twice that of reptiles, and their red blood cells remain nucleated. Yet body temperature is maintained at an even higher level than in mammals.)

It can be inferred that, as early mammals adapted to a life of running, they must have sought safety in the forests. They became primarily nocturnal and furtive, with a distinct preference for hiding in darkness. Their sense of sight was of limited value in such an existence and, like almost all mammals today, they were colorblind. The sense of smell became dominant instead, and the basic orientation to the environment came to depend on odor cues from the forest floor. Furthermore, in an active life of running and hiding it is unsafe merely to lay eggs and leave them in reptilian fashion. The first mammals probably did just that, and the primitive egg-laying mammals today still do likewise. Later mammals evolved means to carry the fertilized eggs with them, inside the females; they became viviparous. The pouched marsupial mammals and the placental mammals are their modern descendants.

After mammals had originated late in the Triassic, they remained inconspicuous for the rest of the Mesozoic, a period of about 80 million years. But, as the Cretaceous came to a close, most of the reptilian multitude became extinct, probably because of cooler climates following the Laramide revolution. The lower temperatures appear to have caused an extinction of much tropical vegetation, and with their food sources thus reduced the reptiles would have died out as well. Whatever the precise causes may have been, extinction of the Mesozoic reptiles cleared the way for a great Cenozoic expansion of mammals and birds.

the cenozoic

The progressively cooler climates after the Laramide revolution culminated in the ice ages of the Pleistocene epoch, a subdivision of the Quaternary period of the Cenozoic (Table 17). Four ice ages occurred during the last 600,000 years. In each, ice sheets spread from both poles to the temperate zones and then receded. Warm interglacial periods intervened between the successive glaciations. The last recession began less than 20,000 years ago, at the beginning of the Recent epoch, and it is still in progress; polar regions are still covered with ice. Cenozoic climates played a major role in plant evolution, as noted earlier, and animal evolution was greatly affected as well. Pleistocene ice in particular influenced human history, modern man in a sense being one of the products of the ice ages.

The adaptive radiations of mammals and birds were the main evolutionary events of the Cenozoic, the "age of mammals." Terrestrial mammals replaced the dinosaurs; aquatic mammals eventually took the place of the former ichthyosaurs and plesiosaurs; and bats, but more especially birds, gained the air left free by the pterosaurs. A total of some two dozen independent mammalian lines came into existence, each ranked as an order (see Fig. 13.31). The fossil record is fairly extensive for nearly all these groups, and it is extremely good for a few, horses and elephants in particular (Fig. 29.24 and Color Figs. 33 and 34).

Each mammalian line exploited either a new way of life available at the time or one left free after the extinction of the Mesozoic reptiles. One mammalian line is of particular interest, for it eventually led to man. The members of this line still made their home in the forests, like many earlier mammalian groups, but they adapted to an *arboreal* life in the treetops. Fossils show that such arboreal mammals of the early Paleocene were the ancestors of two orders, the *Insectivora* and the *Primates.* Some of the shrews now living still have the joint traits of primitive insect eaters and primitive primates, but the later members of the two groups became very different; insectivores now also include moles and hedgehogs, and primates include men.

Nevertheless, there can be little doubt that the distant mammalian ancestors of men were shrewlike, 2 to 3 in. long, with a long snout and a bushy tail (Fig. 29.25). They lived in trees and, like modern shrews, they were probably furtive, quick, color-blind and given to hiding in dark places, as well as ferocious and voracious; they

*Table 17. The epochs and periods of the Cenozoic era**

period	*epoch*	*duration*	*beginning date*
Quaternary	Recent	20,000 years	20,000 B.C.
	Pleistocene	1	1
Tertiary	Pliocene	11	12
	Miocene	16	28
	Oligocene	11	39
	Eocene	19	58
	Paleocene	17	75

*Unless otherwise stated, numbers refer to millions of years.

29.24 Horse evolution, *Cenozoic. This reconstructed sequence begins at left, with the fossil horse Eohippus, and proceeds via Mesohippus, Hypohippus, and Neohipparion to Equus, the modern horse at right. The drawings are to scale and show how the average sizes and shapes of horses have changed. Progressive reduction in the number of toes took place, as well as changes in dentition. Note, however, that the animals shown represent a highly selected series, and it should not be inferred that horse evolution followed a straight-line pattern. Here, as elsewhere, a bush pattern is evident. See also Color Figs. 33 and 34.*

ate anything eatable of appropriate size, insects particularly, and they ate nearly continuously, consuming their own weight every 3 hr or so: a highly active but small body requires comparatively very large amounts of fuel. These early primates then gave rise to several sublines, of which five still survive: *lemuroids, tarsoids, ceboids, cercopithecoids,* and *hominoids* (Fig. 29.26).

29.25 Early mammals. *An arboreal squirrel shrew, order Insectivora, is shown.*

Lemuroids include the *lemurs* and *aye-ayes,* now found largely on the island of Madagascar (Fig. 29.27). These animals still have long snouts and tails, but instead of claws and paws they have strong flat nails, a general characteristic of all modern primates. Long nails are probably more useful than claws in anchoring the body on a tree branch.

In a tree, moreover, smelling is less important than seeing, and in lemuroids an important visual adaptation has evolved: each of the eyes can be directed forward independently, which permits better perception of branch configurations than if the eyes were fixed on the side of the head (as in shrews).

Tarsoids are represented today by the *tarsiers* of Southern Asia and Indonesia. In these animals the ancestral "smell brain" has become a "sight brain;" the olfactory lobes have become small, but the optic lobes have increased in size. Reduction of the olfactory lobes has also led to shortening of the snout, hence to the appearance of a fairly well-defined face. Indeed the eyes have moved into the face, and, although they can move independently, both can be focused on the same point. As a result tarsiers are endowed with stereoscopic vision and efficient depth perception, traits that all other primates also share. Such traits are of considerable adaptive value if balance is to be maintained in a tree. Tarsiers also have independently movable fingers and toes, with a branch-gripping pad at the end of each. Moreover, whereas most mammals produce litters of several to many offspring, tarsiers have a single

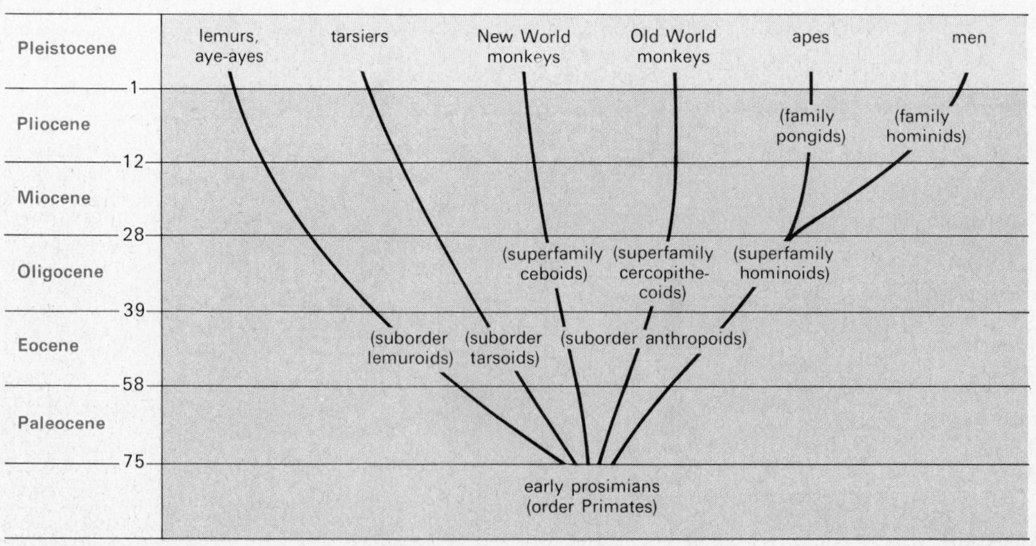

29.26 The primate radiation. *Numbers at left indicate past time in millions of years.*

offspring at a time, a safer reproductive pattern in the branches of a tree.

Ceboids comprise the *New World monkeys,* confined today to South and Central America. These animals have long strong tails used as fifth limbs. Cercopithecoids are the *Old World monkeys,* found in Africa and Asia. They are identified by tails that are not used as limbs (Fig. 29.28). The two groups represent separate, though remarkably similar, evolutionary developments; monkeys evolved twice independently. In both groups adaptations to arboreal life have developed a good deal farther than in the earlier primates.

If tarsoids have a "sight brain," monkeys can be said to have a "space brain." The eyes are synchronized like those of man, and each also contains a fovea centralis, a retinal area of most acute vision. Moreover, monkeys are endowed with color vision, the only mammals other than the hominoids so characterized. Color is actually there to be seen: flowers, foliage, sky, and sun provide an arboreal environment of light and space, far different from the dark forest floor that forced the ancestral mammals literally to keep their noses to the ground. Indeed, the smelling capacity of monkeys is as poor as their sight is excellent. Correspondingly, the cerebrum is greatly enlarged and contains extensive vision-memory areas; monkeys store visual memories of shape and color as we do.

Monkeys also adopt a predominantly *sitting* position at rest, a posture that in a tree is probably safer than lying and that also relieves the forelimbs of locomotor functions. As a direct consequence, monkeys have a new freedom to use hands for touch exploration. Evolution of ability to *feel* out the environment and one's own body has led to a new self-awareness and to curiosity. Ability to touch offspring and fellow inhabitants of the tree has contributed to new patterns of communication and social life, reinforced greatly by good vision, by voice, and by varied facial expressions. Touch-control areas of the brain and centers controlling hand movements are extensive, and the brain as a whole has thus enlarged in parallel with the new patterns of living. The mind has quickened as a result, and the level of intelligence has increased well above the earlier pri-

A B

29.27 Primitive mammals. *A, a lemur from Madagascar. B, a tarsier from Indonesia. Both these groups are arboreal.*

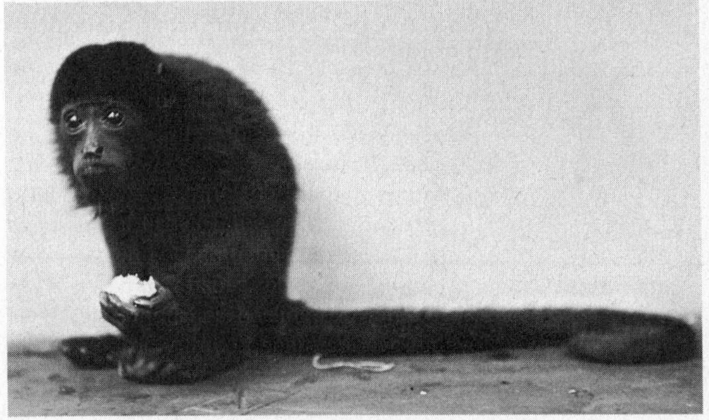

A

B

29.28 Monkeys. *A, howler monkey, a ceboid (New World) type. Note prehensile tail. B, rhesus monkey, a cercopithecoid (Old World) type.*

mate average. A ground mammal such as a dog still sniffs its environment, but monkeys and the later primates explore it by sight and by touch. Evolution of intelligence has been associated specifically with improved coordination between eye and hand. Fundamentally, we note, primate intelligence is an adaptation to the arboreal way of life.

Tree life also provides a basically secure existence. Actually only two kinds of situation represent significant dangers, the hazard of falling off a branch and the hazard of snakes. The first is minimized by opposable thumbs, independently movable fingers on all limbs, and precocious gripping ability in general (displayed also in newborn human babies). The second is countered by the strength of the body, which is larger than in earlier primates. Perhaps partly because of this emancipation from perpetual fear, the life span is lengthened considerably; monkeys live up to four decades, whereas shrews have a life expectancy of a single year. Furthermore, absence of danger and continuously warm climates make feasible a breeding season spanning the whole year, and in Old World monkeys this year-round breeding potential is accompanied by menstrual cycles.

The fifth primate line, the hominoids, evolved important locomotor modifications over and above those attained by the monkeys. Early hominoids developed universal limb sockets and a fully upright posture, and by hand-over-hand locomotion between two levels of branches they became tree *walkers* more than tree sitters; even a monkey cannot match the acrobatic tree swinging of hominoids. Moreover, only hominoids can swivel their hips, and only they have long, strong collar bones and chests that are broader than they are deep. Hominoid locomotion has also become facilitated by a shortening of the tail and its interiorization under the skin between the hindlimbs. In this position the tail skeleton helps in counteracting the internal sag produced by gravity acting on an upright body.

During the early Miocene, some 30 million years ago, the hominoid line branched into two main sublines. One of these led to the *pongids,* the family of apes, the other to the *hominids,* the family of man (see Fig. 29.26). Apes are represented today by four genera, gibbons, orangutans, chimpanzees, and gorillas. Gibbons are survivors of an early branch of ape evolution, characterized by comparatively small, light bodies and retention of a fully arboreal way of life. Indeed the gibbon is undoubtedly the most perfectly adapted arboreal primate (Fig. 29.29).

But the other three types of ape, representing later and heavier pongid lines, have abandoned life in the trees to greater or lesser extent. It appears that these later apes ceased to be completely arboreal after their bodies had become so large and heavy that trees could no longer support them aloft. The feet of these apes give ample evidence of the weight they have to support; foot bones are highly foreshortened and stubby, as if crushed by heavy loads. Correspondingly, the agile grace of the arboreal gibbon is not preserved in the ground apes. These do not actually walk, but they *scamper* along in a crouching shuffle gait.

So far as is known the hominid line left the trees right after it split away from the common hominoid stock, just when the adaptations to tree life had finally become perfected. Was this descent, too, prompted by great body weight, as in the case of the large apes? Probably not, or else the human foot would resemble that of the ground apes and man would scamper rather than walk. In actuality the human gait is unique among ground forms, and as a gibbon swings in a tree so a man literally swings on the ground. It is likely, therefore, that the hominid line left the trees when its evolution had progressed to a gibbonlike level and when the body was still comparatively small and light. The walking grace perfected in the trees could then persist on the ground. Early hominids thus appear to have been

A

B

***29.29* Apes.** *A, a gibbon from Malaya. B, a mountain gorilla from Africa.*

small, perhaps only 3 to 4 ft tall, and in contrast to the later apes their size probably increased only *after* they had come out of the trees (Fig. 29.30).

But if not body weight, what other conditions could have forced hominids to the ground? The chief cause appears to have been the progressively cooler climate, which led to a thinning out of forests in many regions. Our prehuman ancestors thus may have been forced to travel on the ground if they wished to move from one stand of trees to another. Such forced excursions often must have been fraught with considerable danger, however, for saber-toothed carnivores and other large mammals dominated the ground at those times (see Fig. 28.8). Ability to dash quickly across open spaces would then have had great selective value, and such conditions probably promoted the evolution of *running* feet. Also, strong muscles would be required to move the hindlimbs in new ways. Indeed, a unique trait of the hominid line is the presence of such muscles in the form of curving calves, thighs, and buttocks. In conjunction with this muscular change the hips have become broad and the waist narrow, and in these respects, too, man differs from apes.

These and other features that now distinguish men and apes came to be superimposed on the traits of the earlier arboreal primates. Clearly then, the modern human type could not have evolved if the ancestral type had not first been specialized for life in trees.

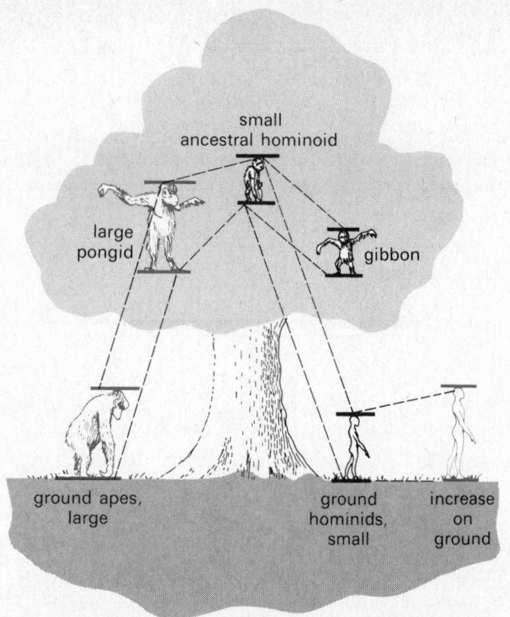

29.30 Hominoid size evolution. *One group of apes probably developed to a large size in the trees, and modern descendants such as gorillas therefore were already heavy when they adopted life on the ground. Another group, exemplified by the gibbons, remained light and arboreal. Early hominids likewise probably remained light and small. They presumably left the trees as small types and their evolutionary size increase then occurred on the ground.*

review questions

1 What is a fossil? How can the age of a fossil be determined? Review the names and dates of the geologic eras and periods. What were the Appalachian and Laramide revolutions?

2 List the major groups of organisms not yet in existence 500 million years ago. Review Lignier's hypothesis regarding the origin of tracheophytes.

3 Describe the key events of plant evolution during the Silurian and the Devonian periods. Cite fossil evidence in support of the view that psilopsids were ancestral to all other vascular plants. What were the characteristics of lepidodendrids?

4 Name and describe fossil sphenopsids. Which pteropsid groups were in existence by the end of the Devonian? Describe the key events of plant evolution during the Carboniferous and Permian periods.

5 What were the seed ferns? Which other plant groups are they believed to have given rise to? Describe the causes and events of the Permo-Triassic crisis. At what date did it take place? When did bryophytes first leave fossils?

6 Review the key events of plant evolution during (*a*) the Mesozoic era, and (*b*) the Cenozoic era. Name the time and the events of the Laramide revolution. What were the consequences of the Laramide revolution on plants? When did the last ice ages occur?

7 Review the recapitulatory hypotheses of Haeckel, and show why they are not tenable. Does comparative animal embryology give any clues about the probable course of early animal evolution? Discuss. What are neoteny and developmental divergence?

8 Describe the key events of animal evolution during the (*a*) Cambrian-Ordovician, (*b*) Silurian-Devonian, (*c*) Carboniferous-Permian. Review the course of vertebrate evolution during the entire Paleozoic.

9 Review the evolutionary happenings during the Mesozoic among groups other than reptiles. Make a similar review for reptile evolution. Which reptilian groups exist today, and what ancient groups did they derive from?

10 What group was ancestral to mammals? What factors probably promoted the evolution of mammals from reptiles? What factors appear to have promoted the evolution of birds from reptiles, and in what ways has the direction of bird evolution been different from that of mammals?

11 Describe the main features of the Cenozoic mammalian radiation, with special attention to the origin of primates. Describe the major features and the time pattern of the primate radiation, and name living animals representing each of the main lines. When and from where did the line leading to man branch off?

12 Describe the various adaptations of each of the primate groups to arboreal life. Which structural, functional, and behavioral traits of man trace back specifically to the arboreal way of life of his ancestors? How do hominoids differ from other primates? How does the hominid line differ from the pongid line?

collateral readings

Abelson, P. H.: Paleobiochemistry, *Sci. American,* July, 1956. A study of amino acids in 300-year-old fossils.

Andrews, H. N.: "Ancient Plants and the World They Lived In," Comstock, Ithaca, N.Y., 1947. A book on plant fossils and evolution.

Berrill, N. J.: "The Origin of Vertebrates," Oxford, Fair Lawn, N.J., 1955. A documentation of the probable evolution of ancestral vertebrates from ascidian stocks.

Bitterman, M. E.: The Evolution of Intelligence, *Sci. American,* Jan., 1965. Experiments on various groups of vertebrates reveal qualitative and quantitative differences in brain power.

Brues, C. T.: Insects in Amber, *Sci. American,* Nov., 1951. Up to 90-million-year-old fossil insects are compared with modern ones.

Colbert, E. H.: The Ancestors of Mammals, *Sci. American,* March, 1949. Therapsids and other Triassic reptiles are examined.

———: "Evolution of the Vertebrates," Wiley, New York, 1955. A good text on fossil vertebrates.

Deevey, E. S.: Living Records of the Ice Age, *Sci. American,* May, 1949. An examination of Pleistocene history in the living world.

———: Radiocarbon Dating, *Sci. American,* Feb., 1952. This technique of age determination in fossils is described.

Ericson, D. B., and **G. Wolin**: Micropaleontology, *Sci. American,* July, 1962. The new field of fossil study by microscope is described.

Glaessner, M. F.: Precambrian Animals, *Sci. American,* March, 1961. Recent fossil finds predating the 500-million-year mark are discussed.

Hurley, P. M.: Radioactivity and Time, *Sci. American,* Aug., 1949. An examination of the various atomic "clocks" that can be used to date given earth layers.

Millot, J.: The Coelacanth, *Sci. American,* Dec., 1955. An account of a recently discovered living lobe-finned fish, formerly believed to have been extinct for 300 million years.

Moore, R. C., C. G. Lalicker, and **A. G. Fisher:** "Invertebrate Fossils," McGraw-Hill, New York, 1952. A good source book for further information on extinct invertebrates.

Napier, J.: The Antiquity of Human Walking, *Sci. American,* Apr., 1967. A million-year-old fossil toe sheds light on the origin of our gait.

Newell, N. D.: Crises in the History of Life, *Sci. American,* Feb., 1963. An examination of the several geologic periods during which organisms died out on a large scale.

Seilacher, A.: Fossil Behavior, *Sci. American,* Aug., 1967. The behavior of extinct animals is analyzed from fossil tracks, burrows, and other fossilized artifacts.

Simmons, E. L.: The Early Relatives of Man, *Sci. American,* July, 1964. An examination of primate fossil history during the last 60 million years.

———: The Earliest Apes, *Sci. American,* Dec., 1967. A 28-million-year-old fossil ape is described, and its evolutionary significance is assessed.

Simpson, G. G.: "Life of the Past," Yale, New Haven, Conn., 1953. A very good review of paleontological events; see also the reference by the same author at the end of Chap. 28.

Stebbins, G. L.: "Variation and Evolution in Plants," Columbia, New York, 1950. For further background on this subject.

Zuckerkandl, E.: The Evolution of Hemoglobin, *Sci. American,* May, 1965. Evolutionary clues are obtained from chemical comparisons of hemoglobin in man and other vertebrates.

The fossil evidence of the hominid group is tantalizingly scant; we can trace the recent evolution of almost any mammal far better than our own. Moreover, the exact path of descent of our own species remains undiscovered as yet, and other known hominids are related to us somewhat as uncles or cousins. With the exception of the line leading to ourselves, all other lines of the hominid radiation have become extinct at various periods during the last 30 million years.

Apart from their biological distinctions, fossil hominids are defined as prehuman or truly human on the basis of cultural achievements. Any hominid that *made* tools in addition to using them can be called a "man." If a hominid only used stones or sticks found ready-made in his environment he is considered prehuman; if he deliberately fashioned natural objects into patterned tools, no matter how crude, he is considered human. By this criterion quite a few hominid types were men.

prehistoric man

Some clues about the common ancestor of both pongids and hominids are provided by *Proconsul,* a 25-million-year-old fossil ape of East Africa. *Proconsul* clearly belongs to the pongid line, but certain features of the head and the teeth suggest that the base of the hominid radiation well could have been represented by an animal similar to this ape. Also more nearly allied to the pongid rather than the hominid line is *Oreopithecus,* an Alpine fossil primate dating back some 10 million years, to the early Pliocene. Such an age also characterizes *Ramapithecus* of India and Africa, but this primate appears to have been rather distinctly hominid. New finds dating back to the early and middle Pliocene continue to be reported now and then; yet it is often difficult to determine if or how such finds add specifically to our knowledge of hominid evolution (Fig. 30.1).

For the moment, the earliest fossils now acknowledged by all investigators to be hominid date back to the late Plicocene, about two or more million years ago. Still earlier ones well might be discovered at any time. The Pliocene hominids are generally assigned to several different species of the genus *Australopithecus* (Fig. 30.2). One such species is *A. africanus* (previously called *Homo africanus* and originally named *Homo habilis*), which dates back roughly 2 million years. About $1\frac{3}{4}$ million years old is *A. paleojavanus* (originally named *Zinjanthropus*), a type that, like *A. africanus,* was discovered in East Africa. *A. paleojavanus* used wooden clubs and stone hammers as tools and thus was a true man. As his large molars indicate, his diet probably was mainly coarse vegetation. The skull reveals that the head was held erect and that jaw muscles were attached as they are in modern man, suggesting that *A. paleojavanus* probably had some form of speech. A forehead was almost absent; the volume of the brain could not have been larger than 600 cm^3, comparable to the brain of a modern gorilla. Other species of *Australopithecus* might not have been as far advanced, and at least some of them apparently did not make tools.

Representatives of *Australopithecus* also lived in Pleistocene times, and the genus appears to have persisted till about half a million years ago. Some so far unidentified species of *Australopithecus* is generally believed to have evolved into the genus *Homo,* to which we belong. The time of this transition is not known, nor is the place—many investigators believe it to have been eastern Africa. The earliest known species of *Homo* is *H. erectus* (originally called *Pithecanthropus*), which lived from about 600,000 to about 250,000 years ago (Fig. 30.3). Thus the first representatives of this species were probably contemporaries of late representatives of *Australopithecus.*

H. erectus came to have a wide distribution, with subspecies known from southeastern Asia ("Java man"), China ("Peking man"), Europe ("Heidelberg man"), as well as various regions of Africa. All these groups were true men who made tools of stone and bone and used fire for cooking. The brain volume averaged 900 to 1,000 cm^3, nearly double that of *Australopithecus.* The skull had a flat, sloping forehead and thick eyebrow ridges, and the massive protruding jaw was virtually chinless. *H. erectus* probably practiced cannibalism—some of his fossil remains include skullcaps separated cleanly from the rest of the skeleton; sheer accident does not appear to have caused such neat separations.

Some 500,000 to 250,000 years ago *H. erectus* appears to have given rise to our own species, *Homo sapiens.* The place of this event is again unknown, and if it indeed occurred in just one place *H. sapiens* must have rapidly spread from there to most parts of the world; early

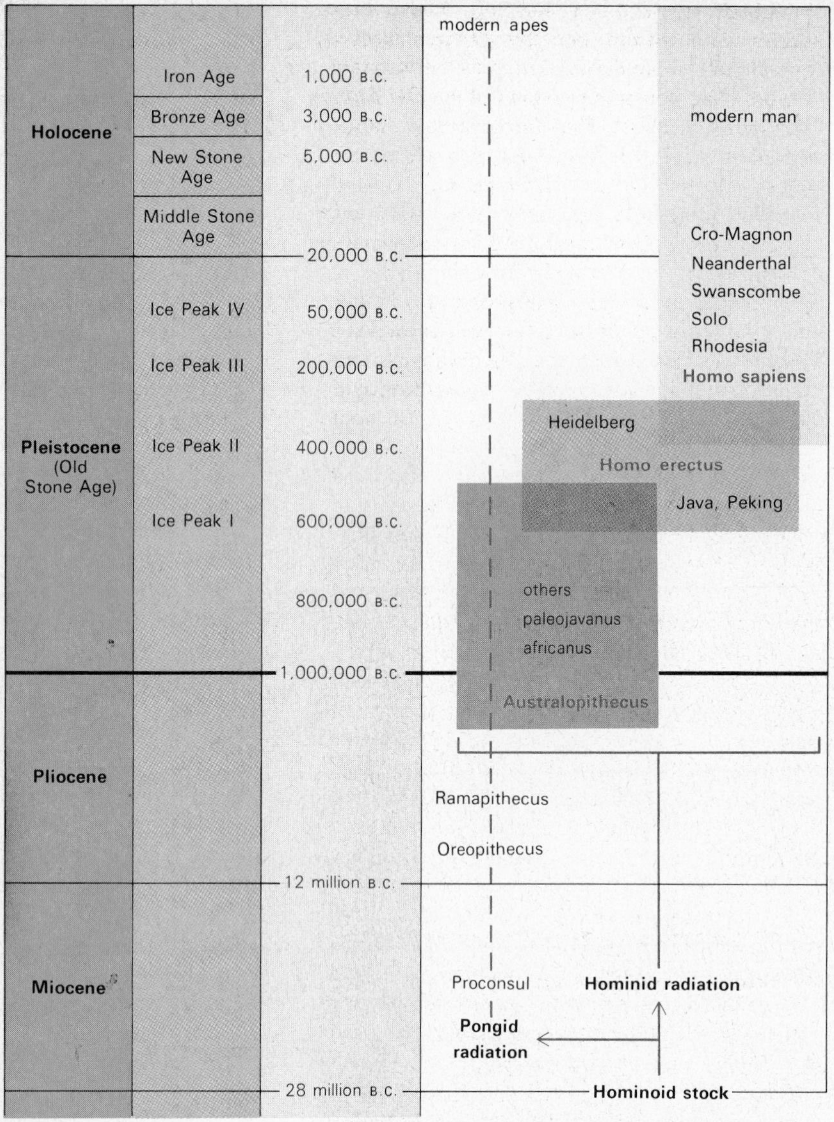

Epoch	Period	Date		
			modern apes	
Holocene	Iron Age	1,000 B.C.		
	Bronze Age	3,000 B.C.		modern man
	New Stone Age	5,000 B.C.		
	Middle Stone Age			Cro-Magnon
Pleistocene (Old Stone Age)		20,000 B.C.		Neanderthal
	Ice Peak IV	50,000 B.C.		Swanscombe
				Solo
				Rhodesia
	Ice Peak III	200,000 B.C.		Homo sapiens
				Heidelberg
	Ice Peak II	400,000 B.C.		Homo erectus
	Ice Peak I	600,000 B.C.		Java, Peking
				others
		800,000 B.C.		paleojavanus
				africanus
Pliocene		1,000,000 B.C.		Australopithecus
			Ramapithecus	
			Oreopithecus	
Miocene		12 million B.C.		
			Proconsul	Hominid radiation
			Pongid radiation	
		28 million B.C.	Hominoid stock	

30.1 The hominid radiation. *Each main hominid group (in color boxes) is shown roughly at a time level at which it is known to have existed. Within each such group several more subgroups than indicated are known. In most cases the exact period at which the subgroups have lived is not certain.*

A

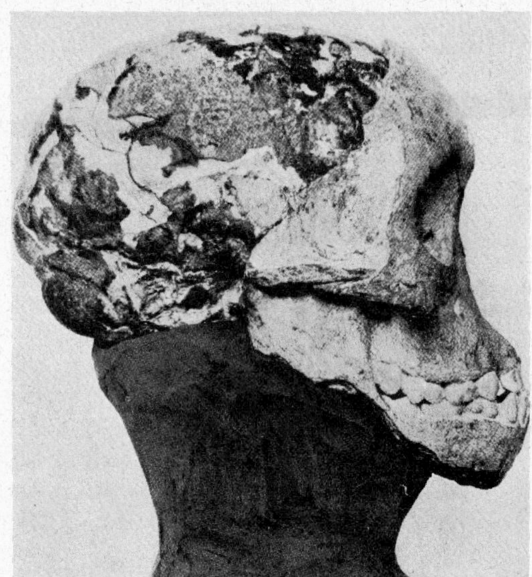

B

30.2 Australopithecus. *A, drawing of A. paleojavanus (Zinjanthropus), the East Africa man. Note the exceptionally low forehead and small braincase. B, skull of a later species of Australopithecus.*

subspecies of *H. sapiens* are known from, for example, Africa (''Rhodesia man''), Java (''Solo man''), England (''Swanscombe man''), and the Eurasian land mass (''Neanderthal man''). Some investigators consider it possible that various populations of *H. erectus* in different parts of the world might have evolved locally into populations of *H. sapiens.* In that case our species would have arisen in more than one place. It is interesting, for example, that certain similarities do exist between Java man and Solo man and between other *erectus* and *sapiens* groups that lived in the same region.

The best known of all prehistoric men is the Neanderthal subspecies, *Homo sapiens neanderthalis* (Fig. 30.4). Neanderthalers probably arose 150,000 years ago or even earlier, they flourished during the period of the last ice age, and they became extinct only about 25,000 years ago, when the ice sheets began to retreat. The brain of these men had a volume of 1,450 cm^3, which compares with a volume of only 1,350 cm^3 for modern man. The Neanderthal brain was also proportioned differently; the skull jutted out in back, where we are relatively rounded, and the forehead was low and receding. Heavy brow ridges were present, and the jaw was massive and almost without chin. Culturally the Neanderthalers were nomadic cavemen of the *Old Stone Age* (see Fig. 30.1). They fashioned a variety of weapons, tools, hunting axes and clubs, and household equipment. Their territory covered most of Europe and west and central Asia, with fringe populations along the Mediterranean coasts.

Late groups of Neanderthalers were contemporaries of early representatives of our own subspecies, *Homo sapiens sapiens.* One such early representative was *Cro-Magnon man,* who lived in Europe from about 50,000 to 20,000 years

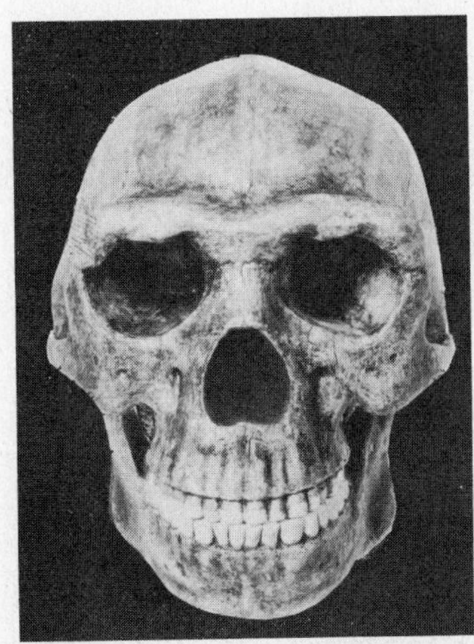

A

B

C

30.3 Homo erectus. *A, skull, and B, C, reconstructions of Peking man (formerly Pithecanthropus).*

A

B

30.4 ***Homo sapiens neanderthalis.*** *A, B, reconstructions of Neanderthal man.*

A

B

30.5 ***Cro-Magnon man.*** *Two reconstructions are shown.*

ago. Cro-Magnon man appears to have interbred with the Neanderthalers, and he is also believed to have caused the extinction of the European Neanderthal populations. Cro-Magnon was 6 ft tall on the average, with a brain volume of about 1,700 cm^3 (Fig. 30.5). In addition to stone implements he used bone needles for sewing animal skins into crude garments. The dog became his companion, and he was a cave-dwelling hunter who also painted remarkable murals on cave walls.

Cro-Magnon man was a contemporary of other populations of *H. sapiens sapiens* in different parts of the world. Through evolution, migration, and interbreeding these groups gradually developed into the present populations found around the globe. By the time the Pleistocene came to a close, some 20,000 or 25,000 years ago, the ice had started to retreat, and eventually even nontropical man no longer needed to shelter in caves. For the next 10,000 years or more man was culturally in the *Middle Stone Age,* characterized chiefly by great improvements in stone tools. Man was still a nomadic hunter, however. The *New Stone Age* began about 7,000 to 10,000 years ago, about the time Abraham settled in Canaan. A great cultural revolution took place then. Man learned to fashion pottery, he developed agriculture, and he was able to domesticate animals. From that period on modern civilization developed very rapidly. By 3,000 B.C. man had entered the *Bronze Age* (see Fig. 30.1). Some 2,000 years later the *Iron Age* began. And not very long after that man discovered steam, electricity, and now the atom and outer space.

H. sapiens sapiens has been the only human group in existence since the late Pleistocene, and its evolution has continued ever since. That it is still continuing now is shown perhaps most obviously by the changing racial structure of mankind. Before this topic is examined, however, it is important to consider the nature of man as a whole and the environmental pressures that changed the first men to the unique biological and social beings we are today.

modern man

the human animal

Man has evolved through operation of the same forces that produced all other creatures. Also, by nearly any standard the human creature is by far the most remarkable product of evolution. Man is sometimes described as "just" another animal. Often, on the contrary, he is considered to be so radically distinct that the appellation "animal" assumes the character of an insult. Neither view is justified.

Man certainly *is* an animal, but an animal with unique attributes. Structurally man is fully erect, with a double-curved spine, a prominent chin, and walking feet with arches. He is a fairly generalized type in most respects, being not particularly specialized for either speed, strength, agility, or rigidly fixed environments. However, he has a brain proportionately far larger and functionally far more elaborate than any other animal. And most of the uniquely human traits have their basis in man's brain.

Man acquired his brain by an exceedingly rapid, explosive process of evolution. Judging from Miocene fossils and living apes, the first hominids 30 million years ago might have had a brain volume of about 300 to 400 cm^3, comparable to that of a newborn human baby today. From then to the beginning of the Pleistocene brain volume increased to an average of 600 to 800 cm^3, as at the *Australopithecus* stage. Thus, in a span of about 29 million years, brain size doubled (and body volume increased by roughly the same factor). But during the first half of the Pleistocene, in only $\frac{1}{2}$ million years, brain size more than doubled again, from the 600 to 800 cm^3 range to the 1,400 to 1,700 cm^3 range of *Homo sapiens,* while the size of the whole body remained relatively unchanged (Fig. 30.6).

Evidently, the human brain has become considerably larger than might be expected on the basis of general increase in body size alone. Moreover, the increase is not due simply to a proportional enlargement of all brain parts; certain parts have grown far more than others. The greatest growth has occurred in the temporal lobes, which contain speech-control centers, and especially in the frontal lobes, which control abstract thought. As a result, a basic *qualitative* difference between man and an ape or any other primate is that man has the capacity to think in a new time dimension, the *future.* An ape or other mammal has a mind that can grapple well with the present and the past; the central and back portions of the cerebrum are well developed. But such an animal at best has only a rudimentary conception of future time. It does not have elaborate frontal lobes, which contain the control centers for this dimension of existence.

Man does, and he alone therefore, far more so than even a genius chimpanzee, is able to plan, to reason out the consequences of future actions not yet performed, to choose by deliberation, and to have aims and purposes. Also, only man can think in symbolic terms to any appreciable extent,

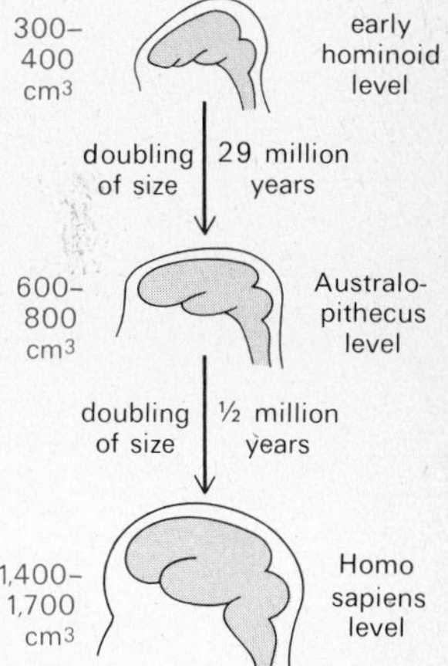

30.6 The hominid brain. *During the last 29 million years the brain has not only doubled in overall size twice in succession, but has also changed in the relative proportion of parts. The frontal and temporal lobes have increased more than proportionately, which is indicated also by the changes in the contours of the skull.*

30.7 ***Neoteny in man.*** *Two equivalent developmental stages of pig and man are shown, drawn to the same scale. The openings behind the eyes at left mark the ears; note also the rudimentary gill arches, tissues of which contribute to the development of the lower parts of the face. In the time the pig embryo has grown to a stage at which its head is about one-quarter of its total length (right), the human embryo has grown only to a stage at which its head is still roughly one-half its total length. The slopes of the black dashed lines indicate this comparatively slower human growth, and the vertical color arrows mark the time difference of attaining equivalent body proportions. The result is that at birth man is in a neotenous state compared with mammals generally. See also next figure.*

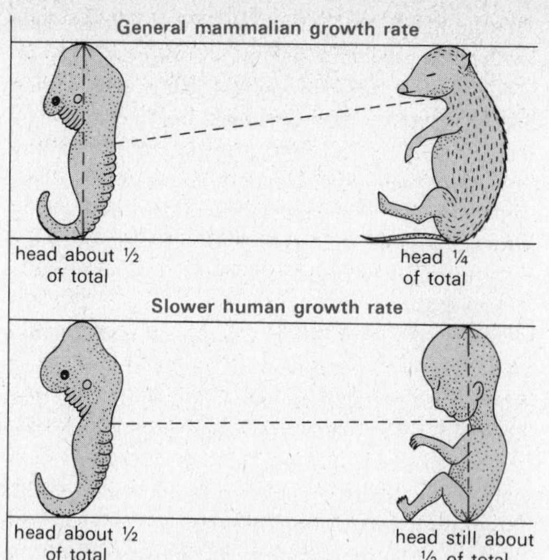

and only he can generalize, weep, laugh, and envision beauty. Directly or indirectly all such unique attributes of human mentality are based on ability to deal with the nonconcrete, the nonspecific, and on ability to project abstractly to the future. Man rightly has been called both a "time binder" and the only philosophical animal.

There can be little doubt that the key event that led to this remarkable enlargement of the human brain, and that in fact gave man nearly all his other most characteristically human traits, was a genetic change that slowed down the processes of embryonic development. In all animal embryos the head region begins to develop sooner and faster than more posterior body parts; the tail region begins last and catches up later. Thus, when a mammalian embryo is about the size of a sand grain, roughly three-quarters of it comprise head structures. But at birth the head usually takes up no more than a sixth or an eighth of the total length. If now the rate of embryonic development were to slow down, the stage of birth would be reached when the head is still relatively large and the rest of the embryo still comparatively undeveloped. In other words, a slowing down of developmental processes leads to *neoteny,* or retention of early developmental features (see Chap. 29), including comparatively larger heads with larger brains. Such a developmental slowdown accompanied by neoteny unquestionably took place during the first part of the Pleistocene, when *Australopithecus* evolved to *Homo* and when *H. erectus* became *H. sapiens.* In this manner the uniquely large brain of modern man came into being (Fig. 30.7).

Furthermore, the deceleration of development also resulted in a host of other neotenous traits in man—traits that in other mammals have a chance to attain a more mature condition through faster prenatal development. For example, late during the development of a four-footed mammal an earlier right-angle bend between head and neck straightens out, and when such a mammal is born its head therefore points forward. Men (and hominoids in general) reach the stage of birth before the head tilts up, hence the human head retains a right angle with the axis of the neck. The result is that in our normal upright position we do not look to the sky (and when we assume an unstrained four-footed posture we look down, not forward). Another neotenous trait is our lack of furry skin—our birth occurs before the stage at which other mammals develop extensive body hair. In similarly neotenous fashion, man has a smaller jaw with fewer teeth than apes; a smooth round skull without the prominent eyebrow ridges and skull crests characteristic of apes; thinner, more delicate skull plates and skeletal components in general; and several other, less conspicuous anatomical distinctions (Fig. 30.8).

But above all, the deceleration of early development resulted in a substantial lengthening of the whole human life cycle. Not only the prenatal but also the postnatal stages became stretched out in time, including the periods of infancy, adolescence, maturity, and senility. As a result man became virtually the longest-lived of all animals, and he acquired yet another and most significant characteristic, a proportionately very long *youth.* No other animal passes through such an extended preadult stage; and at an age when a man is just entering adulthood, an ape is already senile and a dog or a horse has been dead for several years. The long postnatal growth period gives man *time* to make use of his already large brain—time to develop unequalled functional potentials, time to *learn,* to play, to explore, to be young.

By the same token man's prolonged infancy makes him more helpless for far longer than any other animal. Man thus is critically dependent on fellow individuals when he is young, and he needs to be fed, groomed, protected, trained, and *taught* if he is to survive; he has been well described not only as the "naked ape" but also as the "infantilized ape." Clearly, man's basic *social* nature is another consequence of his neotenous condition. We note that all the fundamental and peculiarly human aspects of our "nature" arose in one stroke, as it were, as interlocked results of the initial developmental slowdown—"fetal" body, longevity, and large brain; long infancy and dependency; long youth and learning capacity; long maturity to rear and teach infants and to apply learning; and continuous sociality. In these traits lies our basic difference from apes, the essence of our humanity.

Our very existence is proof that this evolutionary development actually took place, but it is another matter to identify the adaptive pressures that made it take place at all.

the human society

Is it possible to pinpoint the environmental forces or conditions that promoted the evolution of a long-lived, large-brained, future-contemplating type of primate? To some extent yes; the causes appear to have been the twin problems of food and family.

Like apes and most other primates, early hominids at first probably lived in small polygamous bands of perhaps 10 to 30 members. In such a band each male exerted dominance over as many females as he could and aggressively warded off any likely competitors. But unlike other primates, which are herbivorous, hominids eventually became omnivorous and meat-eating. This change in dietary habits appears to have been the start of a long chain of other evolutionary events that brought about the biological and social transformation of early hominids to men. Meat had to be hunted on the hoof and, as today, food procuring probably was always a major function of the male. However, since nearly every desirable food animal was either far stronger or far faster than a hominid, a single individual stood very little chance of hunting successfully on his own. Operating in groups therefore must have become a necessity. But group hunting in turn must have depended on a mentality of a very specific kind, one that did not yet exist at the time.

First, the group hunter must be able to produce and comprehend a comparatively complex system of communication; concerted action by a team necessitates frequent and diversified signaling among the participants, over long as well as shorter distances and both in and out of sight of other team members. For maximum effectiveness, such a communications system should be highly symbolic, with signal elements as simple and distinct, yet as informative as possible. Even at minimum complexity, such a system would have had to be far more complex than any other type of communication then in existence. It is therefore probable that natural selection operated in favor of enlarged temporal lobes, which made possible speech and language, hence efficient communication and teamwork. The genetic potential for language speech appears to have evolved in hominids that preceded *H. sapiens* and could already have been in existence in at least some species of *Australopithecus*. It is associated with a prominent chin, which provides jaw room for a larger, looser tongue.

Further, the group hunter must be able to formulate some sort of hunting plan before going into action, to coordinate the activities of all team members, to relate a planned program with specific actual terrains and the varied habits of prey, and to provide for safety, alternative possibilities, and unforeseen contingencies. It is therefore likely that natural selection favored the development of enlarged frontal lobes, which made possible abstract reasoning, foresighted, future-directed conceptualization, and thus again efficient teamwork, food, and survival.

Considerable foresight would also have been

30.8 ***Neoteny in man.*** *In these skulls of a gorilla (left) and a man (right), note that man has a proportionately far larger braincase, a more prominent forehead, much thinner cheek bones, and a less massive lower jaw. See also body proportions of an ape in Fig. 29.29, and compare with those of man.*

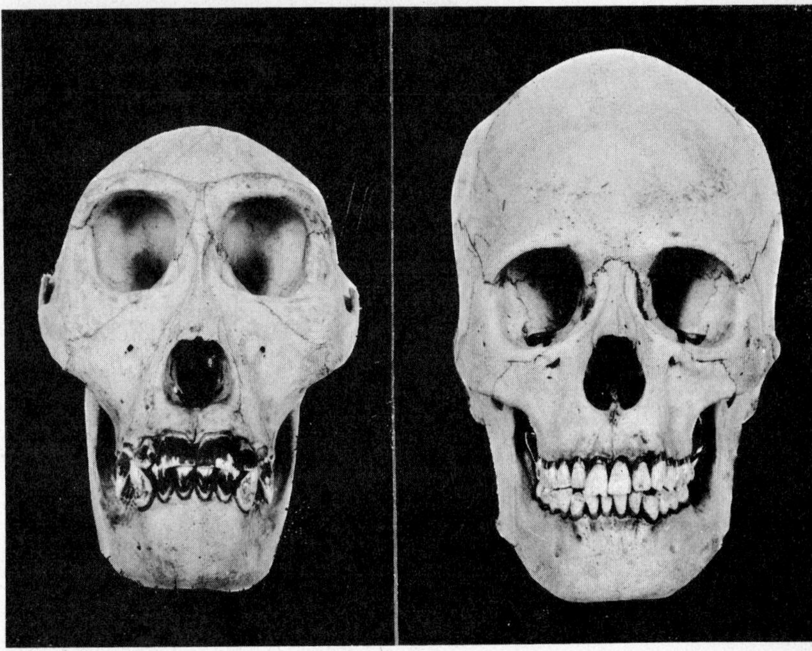

required to resolve two major emotional conflicts that group hunting would have entailed. First, it must have become mandatory that every participant subordinate his individuality to the common purpose of the group, if not to actual direction by a leader. Yet subordination would have required a hitherto nonexistent mode of social behavior. The customary mode took the form of dominant self-assertion by each male and aggressiveness toward any other male who ventured too near. Hence the new motivation for obtaining meat by cooperating with others must have conflicted badly with the ancient motivation to be automatically hostile to others. Simple reason could have reduced this conflict, however, for it would have shown that temporary suppression of hostility might be more desirable than certain future hunger.

Second, a male on a hunt is absent from his domain for often prolonged periods, and his females are left unguarded and subject to the attentions of other males. Thus the male habit of residing in a domain and jealously asserting dominance over females must have conflicted strongly with the desirability of going out in search of meat. Here again reason would have helped to resolve the conflict; for in a choice between "a full house and a full stomach," as one biologist put it, the foresighted option would ultimately be a full stomach and survival —particularly since effective propagation can occur even without a harem.

It could have been pressures of this kind that led to the most significant social development of the hunting age, the modern *monogamous family.* Inasmuch as males and females are born in roughly equal numbers, a society based on polygamy nearly always suffers shortages of females and unrelieved male rivalry. As long as such a social system persisted among hominids, reason alone probably could not have fostered the male cooperation and teamwork necessary in a hunting economy. In a monogamous pattern, by contrast, a single female suffices adequately for reproduction and no adult need be without mate. Hence sexual competition can decrease substantially, a main cause of male aggressiveness can be minimized, and male teamwork can be enhanced correspondingly. Moreover, a male can be absent from his domain without sexual anxiety; the neighboring males already have their females, and even if such neighbors are not out hunting they will be occupied in their own domains and will be less likely to intrude on others. In effect, the monogamous family probably was the only feasible social institution compatible with *both* hunting and reproduction.

It appears, then, that the hunting stage in human history was made possible by a major biological change, which produced an enlarged brain, and a major social change, which introduced the monogamous family. The main behavioral result of the new brain was speech and reasoning, and of the new family, increased male cooperation and reduced aggressiveness. The chance for an exercise of reason was probably enhanced by several structural and functional body changes that made aggressiveness less necessary as well as less possible: reduction of sexual dimorphism, males and females becoming more nearly equal in size and strength than among apes; disappearance of externally visible signs of estrus in females and year-round mating readiness; reduction in the size of the canine teeth (by neoteny), adaptive in lessening aggressiveness; and lowered neural and endocrine responsiveness—man on the whole has far slower reflexes and is emotionally far less "touchy" than almost any other animal.

In the monogamous family the less aggressive male then came to be not merely a biological parent but also a social one; he became a *father.* Moreover, the growing young ceased to be potential rivals, and the pressure for rapid development and early expulsion of offspring was thereby lessened. On the contrary, the father came to contribute actively to the care of the young, not only by supplying food but also by being a *teacher;* the offspring could be taught hunting skills and social conduct, and in this way the long period of dependence on adults could be turned from potential liability to vital asset. Indeed this new relation between father-teacher and young came to be the basis of human *culture.* Teaching and learning led to traditions, to accumulation of knowledge, and to transmission of such knowledge over successive generations. The vehicle for this cultural transmission was speech, and in effect we deal here with a new kind of evolution. Man is unique in that he evolves not only biologically, through inherited characteristics passed on by genes, but also socially, through an inherited culture passed on by words. And by means of words and deeds prompted by words, man can modify and manipulate the chance operations of nature and can control his environment to a certain extent.

In the later development of human society the next major stage after the hunting phase began at the start of the New Stone Age, when man learned to domesticate food plants and animals. The economy then shifted from hunting to agriculture, and human society became soil-bound and settled. Two of man's most significant cultural concepts developed at that time, property and wealth. And for the protection of human and material wealth man invented legal codes, religious and moral doctrines that prescribed acceptable rules of conduct, as well as professional defenders and organized war. Wealth and war then gave impetus to the emergence of nation-states and defended centers, and the latter soon became cities and hubs of trade. In their turn, cities and trade fostered the recent technological revolution, which is now in process of changing the agrarian base of human society to an industrial one.

Today, just as in our distant hunting past, procreation and raising offspring remain the basic functions of the family and thus ultimately of society as a whole. As in the past also, effective execution of these familial functions still depends on overcoming socially disruptive emotions with reason, on curbing individual aggressiveness, and on furthering cooperation within the group. The specific role of the mother has remained more or less unchanged, but that of the father-teacher has not. Since in an industrial society offspring no longer need to learn how to hunt or how to work the fields, the family head has become more or less obsolete as a teacher of survival techniques; bread-winning methods are now learned largely outside the family. Consequently, although a father still contributes to the social and behavioral training of the very young, his importance for adolescent youth has declined. The family in the industrial society therefore often tends to be less cohesive, and in many cases it is no longer the all-encompassing social center it has been in the agrarian and the hunting society.

On the level of the large-scale community the governing social forces still are chiefly those of the agrarian age—property and its accumulation and protection. Dominance hierarchies and territoriality are paramount concerns of nation-states, and these assert their ranks and domains as aggressively as individuals—as if some of the aggressiveness of each individual had become transferred to a communal pool. As a result, collective communal aggressiveness has come to have a delegated, impersonal character. The "enemy" is no longer a hated group of actual individuals on the other side of a territorial boundary, but a symbolic, statistical conceptualization that need generate neither hate before it is crushed nor feelings of guilt thereafter.

Evidently, our facility with symbols has been both gain and loss. Symbols have brought us from the hunting family to the agrarian nation-state, and in the process we have acquired wealth and war. One might be prompted to conclude, as has occasionally been done, that war will continue as long as wealth does, and that therefore one can be abolished by abolishing the other. Such a denial of symbols would probably be fruitless, however, and it actually has been fruitless whenever it has been tried in the past. For better or worse, man *is* a symbol-using and symbol-requiring creature. Instead of trying to abolish symbols, therefore, we need to be more realistic and perhaps try to update the agrarian symbols of our past to a more modern level and make them consistent with the industrial future.

Indeed, the meaning of communal wealth is already changing slowly. Although our outlook is still agrarian to the extent that many of us tend to equate wealth with land, money, or static "possessions" in general, we are beginning to show signs of industrial conditioning when we value economic symbols such as rates of growth, productivity, or full employment. Moreover, the wealthy community today is no longer necessarily the one that is territorially large or rich in money and property, but the one in which the inhabitants can lead psychologically satisfying lives by being productive and useful. In other words, "having" is becoming less important than "doing." And here, as in other behavioral situations, we are beginning to find that action itself can be more gratifying than the result of the action.

One evolutionary attribute of the human species, as of any other, is the polymorphic diversity of the populations that live in different geographic regions. It is known that such a diversity has characterized mankind ever since it originated, and that its nature has changed continually in the course of the long ebb and flow of human populations. The popular name for this diversity is "race," an aspect of human evolution that is examined next.

races of man

the concept of race

A race is a subunit of a species—subspecies or subsubspecies—that differs from other such subunits in the *frequency of one or more genes.* Thus the Neanderthalers, Swanscombe men, Solo men, and other subspecies of *H. sapiens* mentioned previously were early racial subunits, and the subunits of the species today (all members of the subspecies *H. sapiens sapiens*) are the variously different human groups found around the globe. *These are races if, and only if, they differ from one another in the percentage frequencies with which genes occur in them.*

It follows from this definition that racial distinctions are exhibited by *populations,* not by individuals. Single individuals cannot differ in the "frequency" of a particular gene; they can differ only in having or not having a gene, and thus they can exhibit *individual variations.* Frequency differences occur between *groups* of individuals; a particular gene might be present in a certain percentage of individuals of one population, in a different percentage of individuals of another. In biological (if not in social) usage, therefore, race is a population attribute, not an individual one. Moreover, race is also a *statistical* concept—races differ relatively, not absolutely; the differences are of degree, not of kind: distinctions result not from different types of gene sets but from frequency variations in the *same* types. Thus *all* races of a species share the basic species traits, including, for example, full cross-fertility of all members. Organisms having different types of gene sets are by definition not members of the same species.

The definition above implies, furthermore, that a race is not a permanent subunit of a species. Any change that affects gene frequencies also affects racial differences. Such changes can occur through nonrandom mating, through mutation, through genetic drift—in short, all those processes that bring about evolution as discussed in Chap. 28. Races in effect represent *temporary* collections of genes, transient stages in the evolutionary history of a species. Thus there have been races of man ever since mankind originated, and the ones today are different from earlier ones—and undoubtedly from later ones as well. Races usually evolve when a species covers a large territory and when the populations in different parts of this territory have relatively little reproductive contact. As shown in Chap. 28, evolution is then likely to take different directions in the various localities. Some or many of the resulting population differences can be adaptive and might improve the survival chances of the populations in their local environments. Most often the ultimate result of racial evolution is speciation, a splitting of the original large parent species into two or more new offspring species. Under certain conditions, however, the speciation process can become slowed down or blocked completely. In man, for example, extensive migration and interbreeding have so far prevented formation of separate species, and in many areas have even reduced or obliterated racial differences.

Basically, therefore, races are temporary geographic variants of a species. Among variants that cover large areas, species traits usually tend to change gradually from one end of the territory to another, in line with gradual variations in flora and fauna, climate, and environmental conditions in general. In such cases large adjacent racial groups are said to form *clines,* or gradual transitions from one to the other: the frequency of a particular gene changes in small steps from one racial median value to another. Most of the large, continental populations of man intergrade clinally in this way. In other instances the transitions are more abrupt; a relatively small population sometimes forms a fairly distinct genetic "island" surrounded by populations of large racial groups. The isolating factors are usually environmental and ecological and in man also cultural and social. Among examples in man are the Basques and Lapps of Europe, the Ainus of Japan, the Aborigines of Australia, the Bushmen and Pygmies of Africa, and many others.

This present statistical and genetic meaning of race is far different from what was believed in the days before modern genetics—and what is commonly believed even today by most laymen. The early hypothesis was a "typological" one. Mankind was assumed to have started out as a structurally homogeneous collection of individuals, which in the course of time became split into a number of pure racial "types"—australoids ("Browns"), negroids ("Blacks"), mongoloids (''Yellows''), caucasoids (''Whites''), amerinds (''Reds''), and several or many more depending on the classifier. It was also thought that, because of extensive interbreeding and migration, the purity of these types could not have lasted long. Thus a major objective of race studies was to determine what kind of ''racial mixture'' each individual represented and how close he was to one of the original pure types or how far from it. Another objective was to deduce from the racial mixes how many pure types there really were, in what sequence they might have evolved, and how crossbreeding and migration could have produced the race distributions actually observed today.

In practice this hypothesis of ''racial types'' often proved to be clearly untenable, yet in most cases it was psychologically, socially, politically, and even scientifically more expedient not to change the basic typological premise. As a result, in order to make fact fit preconception, it was frequently necessary to invent all sorts of human migrations for which there was—and is—no evidence. For example, to account for the occurrence of black-skinned people in both Africa and Melanesia, it was necessary to postulate that an ancestral group of Blacks migrated from one place to the other or from some intermediate point to both places. To account for the beaked ''Jewish nose'' (or ''Roman nose'' or ''Spanish nose'') common both among Melanesian Blacks and among all peoples around the Mediterranean, it had to be assumed that some wandering Mediterraneans left this trait somewhere in Southeast Asia or Oceania. From there the nose was supposed to have found its way also to certain Indian tribes in America, where this facial adornment was later immortalized on a United States 5-cent coin. Curiously, migrations were not invoked in other instances, although the distances involved often would have been shorter. For example, hardly anyone thought it likely that the yellowish skins and slit eyes common both in African Bushmen and Asian Mongols indicated a common origin of these two groups.

Another consequence of typological thinking was that individuals in one type category could differ more than individuals of different such categories. In the case of skin colors, for example, some ''Whites'' are far darker than many ''Blacks,'' some are far redder than many ''Reds,'' some are far yellower than many ''Yellows.'' Skins actually run through the *whole* human color spectrum in *each* of the postulated type categories, and a similar conclusion holds for any other racial trait—an excellent illustration that racial traits actually differ only in relative degree, not in absolute kind. Moreover, attempts to classify races were just as inadequate when the distinguishing criteria were several traits simultaneously. Thus, no combination of differences in skin color, hair form, head conformation, body shape, eye, nose, and lip structure, etc., could provide a satisfactory description of the actual range of human variation. Regardless of how few or how many type categories were established arbitrarily, some individuals always fitted into more than one such category and some fitted into none.

The difficulty here was an inescapable and inherently insoluble boundary problem. In a sense it corresponded to the task of classifying, for example, the pebbles on a beach according to size. If we were given this task we might begin by setting up a number of arbitrary size categories. The actual size of many pebbles would then fall between our categories and we would be forced to make the categories finer and more numerous. But there would still be gaps between any two adjoining categories—and no matter how many categories we established such gaps would not disappear. In the end we would probably give up trying to classify each single pebble. We would recognize that pebble sizes varied continuously between two extremes and that any absolute categorization would therefore be inadequate and artificial. Hence instead of imposing preconceived categories on the stones, we would let the stones communicate their real size distributions to us; we would consider them not as individuals but as populations, and we would measure them statistically: from one or more samples we would try to establish a frequency curve—so many percent of this size, so many of that, and so on. The resulting curve might have one or more peaks and it would be without fixed, arbitrary categories of our making.

Just so with races; as emphasized earlier, racial differences are statistical population differences in gene frequencies, *not* absolute differences between individuals. But, one might be prompted to ask here, is there not a very evident racial difference between, for example, this particular white-skinned individual and that particular black-skinned one? No! There is an *individual* difference, obviously, but not a ''racial'' one! The genetic difference between the two well might be less great than between the White and another White or than between the Black and another Black; or the difference might be greater. The important point is that the White and the Black are each members of *populations*—often, indeed, the same population; and unless we compared the genetic characteristics of such populations in statistical terms, we would be back to imposing arbitrary type categories on nature, as on pebbles. By calling the color difference between one "Black" and one "White" a "racial" distinction we might—as has actually happened many times—be assigning to different "races" two individuals that could have one grandparent in common and thus would be members of the same family group! However, if it could be shown that the five or so genes believed to control skin color actually differed in frequency in the populations to which our individuals belonged, then we would be describing a real racial distinction—of these *populations, not* of the individuals.

Note also that, although gene-frequency variations do measure racial *differences,* they do not give us a count of the number of races. Because large racial groups usually intergrade clinally, it is generally impossible to draw sharp boundary lines between them. And even if we counted the number of "racial centers," where the gene frequencies for a given trait attained peak values, we would have counted not the number of races but only the number of racial distinctions with respect to *one* trait. For the gene-frequency curve for one trait rarely matches that of another; and there are thousands of such traits, each with its own distinctive frequency distribution. Any "race count" therefore becomes completely arbitrary. In the past, typological classifiers have named as few "races" as two or as many as 200. They might as well have identified 2,000 or 200,000; no fixed number corresponds to reality, because preconceived type categories are themselves unreal.

Thus it is impossible to say how many human races there "really" are. Some investigators in fact have adopted the position that there are *no* races at all, mankind simply representing a single genetic continuum in which traits intergrade more or less smoothly around the globe. Such an extreme view is probably unjustified for, as noted, the frequency distributions of some genes do show abrupt transitions. Moreover, inasmuch as racial differences certainly exist, it would be difficult logically to deny that races exist. Yet what these are or how many there are remains unanswerable.

A major part of the difficulty appears to lie with the term "race" itself, which almost invariably implies fixed, outdated typologies. For this reason modern investigators generally avoid using the term. Thus they speak of geographic populations instead of artificial "races;" of population differences instead of "racial traits;" and they measure gene frequencies. These concepts do describe human variations as they occur in reality. Furthermore, when considered in the light of populations and gene frequencies, human variations also acquire a significant biological meaning related to evolution and adaptation, as outlined in the next section. The old race typologies lacked such a meaning; they could not explain what they intended to, and basically they were labeling schemes that in the end turned out to be pointless.

the meaning of race

What "good" are racial differences? Is a population with a high percentage of whorled fingerprints somehow better or worse off than one with a high percentage of looped prints? Numerous attempts have been made to uncover possible adaptive values of such traits, but in many instances the results have been inconclusive; an adaptive significance in a relatively minor trait is often difficult to demonstrate, if indeed there is any.

For example, it has been suggested that dark skin pigmentation might be a protective adaptation against the ultraviolet radiation of the sun, and perhaps also against the low night temperatures in humid, swampy, tropical regions. By contrast, light pigmentation might facilitate the formation of vitamin D in the skin under the influence of ultraviolet light, particularly in misty, cloudy regions at high latitudes, where the amount of sunlight is reduced. Similarly, it has been hypothesized that frizzy hair might maintain an insulating layer of dead air over the head and thus protect the brain against excessive heat, whereas long thick hair covering the nape of the neck might serve as a cold protection. Or that noses tend to be short and broad-based where the air is humid and warm but long and narrow in cool, dry regions. Or that squat, short-limbed bodies with small hands and feet and appreciable fat padding might be well adapted to cold climates, whereas tall, lean, long-limbed bodies might fare better in hot ones. Such explanations that relate a trait to particular climatic or environmental conditions have also been sought for many other external features of man.

It is possible, and perhaps even probable, that some of these hypotheses actually might be valid or at least come close to being valid. But it is another matter to prove their validity—or prove that they really relate to *racial* distinctions. One difficulty is that in nearly all such cases the genetics of the trait in question is virtually unknown, as is the frequency distribution of the genes involved. Moreover, in most instances it is not even known to what extent a trait actually is determined by genes and to what extent its expression depends on environmental—or cultural—variables. There is little question, for example, that the varied nutritional customs of man have an important bearing on the size, shape, and fat distribution of the developing body. In a similar vein, it was believed for many years that a characteristic flattening of the back of the head was a racial trait of a so-called "Dinaric race" in southeastern Europe. But this head shape was later found to be simply a result of a particular way of infant cradling. In short, there has been far too little study as yet on the actual nature of numerous human traits; hence we cannot really be sure if such traits are genetic and thus "racial" at all. Their possible adaptive significance therefore remains unproved, too—and indeed untested experimentally.

Furthermore, it is quite possible that certain traits might not be adaptive in any case. Mongolian peoples exhibit a high frequency of dry earwax, and black-skinned ones, a high frequency of sticky earwax. Or, as noted, some populations have many whorls in their fingerprints, others have a preponderance of loops. If such trait differences were shown to be truly racial, are they necessarily adaptive? No one has yet proposed a plausible hypothesis. Indeed, certain traits well could be adaptively neutral. Yet even such neutral traits could be important. As pointed out in Chap. 27, many genes are known to control more than one trait (so-called *pleiotropic* effects of genes). One such trait might be vital or adaptive in some way whereas another is not, and both could be controlled by the same gene and thus would be expressed simultaneously. Hence the importance of, for example, dry earwax—or slit eyes or even frizzy hair or white skin—might lie not in that trait itself but in another, perhaps internal trait that happened to be controlled through the same genes. Actual pleiotropic correlations of this sort have not yet been made, but they might explain the occurrence of adaptively neutral traits.

The best and so far the only really significant clues about possible adaptive values of racial differences have come from studies of *blood groups.* The genes that control human blood groups have been identified, and the frequency distributions of these genes in nearly all peoples have become known through medical determinations of the compatibilities of various blood types. Blood group differences turned out to be proved racial differences, and in some cases their adaptive significance has begun to be clarified as well.

Blood group genes control the manufacture of the blood proteins discussed in Chap. 20. The genes occur in different combinations in different individuals, and people thus can be grouped into several categories according to their blood types. The blood corpuscles of an individual act as foreign proteins, or antibodies, when they are introduced into the blood of a person of different type. An antibody-antigen reaction then occurs; the blood proteins of the recipient can make the foreign corpuscles clump together. Such clumps block up capillary vessels and can cause death. Blood compatibility must therefore be established before a transfusion is made. Blood-type differences evidently represent yet another expression of protein specificity.

The most widely studied blood group is the ABO system, which is controlled by three allelic genes. The blood types produced by them are the familiar A, B, AB, and O categories (Fig. 30.9). Well-studied blood groups also include the Rh system and several others—the MN, Kell,

30.9 ABO genes and phenotypes. *The blood group is indicated by the blood cell antigens, or proteins manufactured under the control of the genes shown. A person of group A contains antigen A in the cells but no anti-A antibody in the serum. Anti-B antibody is present, however; hence such serum will cause clumping of blood cells of groups B or AB (both having the B antigen). Cells of group A will themselves be clumped by serum of O or B donors, both of which contain the anti-A antigen. Group AB blood contains antigens A and B in the cells but neither anti-A nor anti-B antibodies in the serum; hence such serum will not cause clumping of cells of any blood type. Conversely, group O blood contains both serum antibodies but neither cellular antigens; hence such cells will not clump when mixed with serum of any blood type.*

genes	*blood cell antigens*	*serum antibodies*	*serum agglutinates cells of group*	*cells agglutinated by serum of group*
I^AI^B	AB	—	none (universal donor)	O, A, B
I^AI^A or I^Ai	A	anti-B	B, AB	O, B
I^BI^B or I^Bi	B	anti-A	A, AB	O, A
ii	O	anti-A,B	A, B, AB	none (universal recipient)

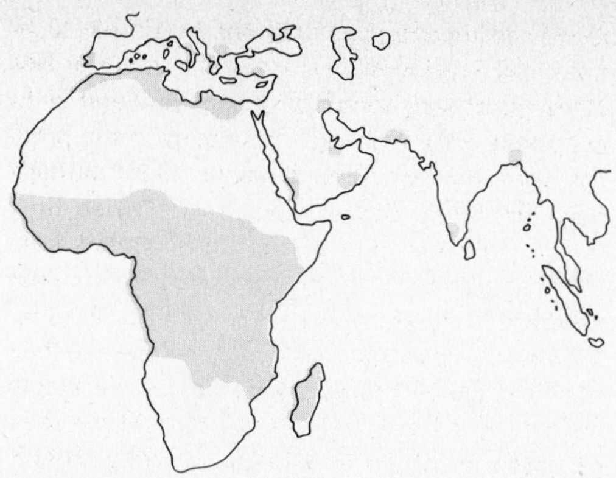

30.10 The distribution of the sickle-cell gene (*color*).

Lutheran, Duffy, Diego, and Kidd systems, for example. The blood of every person belongs to a particular type in each of these systems, and human populations around the globe differ in the frequencies with which these types are represented. For example, the highest frequency of the gene for type A, up to 80 percent, occurs among the Blackfoot Indians of North America. The B group is most frequent in central and south-central Asia. One of the Rh-positive genes is extremely common in native African populations but rarely exceeds frequencies of 5 or 6 percent in others. Over 50 percent of the Basques are Rh-negative, while this condition is virtually unknown in native Australasian groups. Every other blood group similarly has its own distinctive frequency distribution.

Why are these distributions nonrandom? Is it possible that blood groups are somehow adaptive and are being maintained at various frequencies by natural selection? The suspicion that selective forces might be at work has been strengthened greatly by the continued existence of the Rh-negative condition. If a mother is Rh-negative (*rr*) and a father Rh-positive (*RR* or *Rr*), the fetus can be Rh-positive (*Rr*), hence different from the Rh type of the mother. Under such conditions the mother's body manufactures anti-Rh antigens that can pass to the fetal circulation and there destroy the red corpuscles of the offspring. The result can be severe infant anemia at birth and death.

In view of this apparent adaptive disadvantage, why are the genes for Rh negativity not being eliminated rapidly by strong natural selection against them? Could they perhaps contribute to certain adaptive advantages that match or even outweigh their known disadvantage? Some positive selection pressure might then maintain the observed gene frequencies, and although the genes do cause many deaths they might conceivably prevent many more. If so, could not similar protective effects be produced also by the ABO and the other blood groups?

An affirmative answer is strongly suggested by a landmark study on another gene-controlled trait of the blood, the so-called *sickle-cell trait*. The gene for that trait occurs in two allelic forms, *Si* and *si*. Homozygous dominants, *SiSi*, usually die in infancy from sickle-cell anemia; the blood corpuscles are deformed in sickle shapes, and they contain only reduced amounts of hemoglobin that correspondingly reduce the oxygen-carrying capacity. Heterozygotes, *Sisi*, are carriers of the sickle gene; they are essentially normal, with far fewer blood corpuscles affected and only mild or occasional symptoms of anemia. Homozygous recessives, *sisi*, are completely normal. Here evidently is another gene that can be lethal, and therefore should rapidly eliminate itself through the death of the homozygous dominants.

Yet the gene persists. Moreover, when its distribution is examined, an important relation becomes evident. The gene is most frequent in central and western Africa, in many regions along the Mediterranean coasts, and spottily also in Asian areas bordering the Indian Ocean (Fig. 30.10). In all these places the gene is especially common among populations that inhabit humid, swampy lowlands—where malaria is most abundant and where deaths from malaria occur in the greatest numbers. In view of this matching distribution of sickle-cell anemia and malaria, could there be some interconnection between the two diseases? Indeed, extensive investigations actually have revealed that most malarial deaths take place among normal individuals without the sickle trait (*sisi* homozygotes), whereas malaria is far less lethal in the heterozygotes (*Sisi*)—as if the sickle trait afforded protection. Further studies have shown that the malarial parasite (*Plasmodium*, see Chap. 9) cannot readily parasitize sickled blood corpuscles. And experimental injections of malarial organisms into volunteers of both the *Sisi* and *sisi* types have proved conclusively that the sickle trait actually does protect against malaria. Homozygotes thus die either from abnormal blood or from malaria, but the heterozygotes, who can be slightly afflicted by both diseases, can nevertheless survive them. It is this protective effect of the sickle gene that preserves it at high frequencies in certain populations.

The sickle trait has provided the first clear-cut demonstration of *balanced polymorphism*—self-adjusting frequency balances of different genes in a population. Thus, whereas by themselves genes such as *Si* and *si* can have lethal consequences, together they become far less detrimental. Certain other genes have been discovered that function in very similar fashion. For example, thalassemia major, or "Cooley's anemia," is an invariably fatal disease common in the Mediterranean region. It is produced when a gene *Th* is homozygous dominant. Heterozygotes, *Thth,* are subject to a much milder anemia, thalassemia minor. Such individuals not only survive but seem to be protected against malaria just as the carriers of the sickle traits are. Balanced polymorphism appears to be indicated again.

Adaptive advantages of this sort have not yet been clearly proved for the ABO and other blood types. But a number of relations have come to light which suggest that balanced polymorphisms might maintain the observed frequencies of the blood group genes too. For example, some studies have indicated that type A individuals might have the highest incidence of pernicious anemia and of cancer of the stomach and of the female reproductive system. Ulcers seem to be associated most frequently with type O, and in such individuals syphilis also appears to be easier to treat than in other groups. Moreover, type O babies might be least affected by bronchopneumonia and by smallpox. In general, the most common selective advantage associated with given blood groups seems to be protection against various diseases, including many of the well-recognized infant killers of the past. If substantiated, such a finding actually would not be too surprising, for blood groups have their basis in blood proteins, and these are well known as the agents that confer immunity (see Chap. 20).

A tentative but nevertheless highly significant conclusion appears to emerge from these various data: a major selective force—and possibly *the* major selective force—in human racial evolution might have been disease and genetic protection against disease. Compared to the hazard of disease other environmental stresses actually might have been relatively insignificant. After all, even primitive man is known to have lived in virtually all climates and regions; and having had the human potential, he must have adapted quite readily to most local conditions by simple technological expedients like use of fire, more or less clothing, or shelters of various kinds—and without necessarily evolving a new body in the process. An early blond Scandinavian might perhaps have been less comfortable in the Congo than an early Pygmy, and a prehistoric nomad from the Nile Valley well might have found it colder during a Canadian winter than an early Eskimo. They would have adjusted, however, and like their modern globe-trotting counterparts they would have survived quite readily, most probably without impairment of reproduction capacity. That is what counts in evolution, racial evolution included. Thus it is conceivable that climates and geographic locations of early human populations might have had relatively little direct bearing on whether they evolved black, yellow, or white skins, long or short limbs, lean or chubby physiques, or other external traits.

However, man has been exposed to one environmental hazard that until quite recently he could not cope with by simple technological means: disease. This contingency has entailed not only frequent lethality but quite often also lethality before reproductive age. Genes that protected against the different diseases of various regions thus must have had a strong selective advantage. And as internal traits such as blood chemistries then underwent evolutionary change, perhaps some of the external traits became altered in parallel—in part through pleiotropic effects, for example. In any case, the best historical assessment now possible appears to be that human races might have evolved as populations that, apart from other distinctions, were characterized by particular collections of disease-resisting traits. Some investigators have pointed out, for example, that resistance to malaria as through sickle genes might have been an important adaptive factor that could have contributed specifically to the evolution of African Blacks.

If such a disease hypothesis should prove to be valid, it would follow that racial evolution should slow or even stop as a result of modern medical techniques; for these technological protections would substitute for the earlier evolutionary ones. An obliteration of racial distinctions is hastened also by the great mobility of modern man, which tends to increase the frequency of interbreeding. However, this trend is often counterbalanced by reproductive barriers that have social and cultural foundations. The racial future of man thus is as unpredictable as the future of mankind as a whole. It is certain only that man today is just as subject to evolutionary forces as he was in the past, with the important difference that modern man creates many of these forces himself—and is usually unaware where they might lead. Unlike all other organisms, therefore, man will decide his fate largely on his own, under the impetus of his own reasoned or unreasoned purposes.

review questions

1 Describe some of the characteristics of *Australopithecus* and *Homo erectus.* When and where did these hominids live? Were they men? Roughly when did *Homo sapiens* arise? What traits distinguish Neanderthalers from modern men?

2 Review the biological characteristics that *Homo sapiens* shares with all other (*a*) hominids, (*b*) hominoids, (*c*) primates, (*d*) mammals. Review some of the traits that distinguish man uniquely from all other animals.

3 List as many neotenous traits of modern man as you can. What basic biological changes appear to have produced such a constellation of neotenous features? What quantitative changes have occurred in the human brain during the last 30 million years?

4 Describe some of the selective pressures that might have promoted the evolution of a large brain in man. What particular significance might future-directed thinking and language ability have had in human evolution? Would such capacities not be equally useful in other animals, and if so why did they not evolve in other groups?

5 Describe some of the selective pressures that might have promoted the development of monogamy in man. What were some of the social and familial consequences of monogamy? What biological traits tend to make male rivalry less intense in man than in other primates?

6 Show how the social role of the human male differs from that of other male primates, and how male functions have changed during human social and cultural evolution. Contrast the social organization of man and apes.

7 Define ''race'' and ''racial difference.'' Why can an individual not be assigned to a race? What is a cline? Why is it not possible to specify a precise number of human ''races''? What has so far prevented mankind from evolving into several species?

8 Contrast the outdated typological and the modern genetic definitions of race. What makes typological race concepts no longer tenable? Show how differences in human skin colors were interpreted along typological lines and how they are now interpreted in terms of population genetics.

9 Describe adaptive values that have been ascribed to some external human traits and show how such traits actually might be neither racial nor adaptive. What is pleiotropy, and what is its possible significance in the development of human traits? Give examples of how cultural factors can influence human biological traits and how biological factors can influence cultural traits.

10 Describe the biology of the sickle-cell trait and how it has been discovered that it protects against malaria. What is balanced polymorphism? What is the possible significance of the nonrandom frequency distribution of blood group genes? What kind of hypothesis about racial evolution is tentatively suggested by studies on blood group distributions?

collateral readings

Allison, A. C.: Sickle Cells and Evolution, *Sci. American,* Aug., 1956. Very pertinent in the context of this chapter.

Andrew, R. J.: The Origin of Facial Expressions, *Sci. American,* Oct., 1965. The evolution of nonverbal communication in man is examined.

Berrill, N. J.: ''Man's Emerging Mind,'' Dodd, Mead, New York, 1955, or Premier Books,

Fawcett World Library, New York, 1957. An extremely fascinating and stimulating account on human evolution. Highly recommended.

Braidwood, R. J.: The Agricultural Revolution, *Sci. American,* Sept., 1960. The transition from the hunting to the agricultural age in human history is described.

Broom, R.: The Ape-men, *Sci. American,* Nov., 1949. A description of *Australopithecus* by the discoverer of the first fossils of this hominid.

Clark, J. D.: Early Man in Africa, *Sci. American,* July, 1958. A personal account of searches for human fossils.

Dobzhansky, T.: The Present Evolution of Man, *Sci. American,* Sept., 1960. A discussion of how human evolution is influenced by man's control over his environment.

Glass, H. B.: The Genetics of Dunkers, *Sci. American,* Apr., 1953. Evidence for genetic drift is found in this religious sect, and the evolutionary significance of this evidence is assessed.

Hockett, C. F.: The Origin of Speech, *Sci. American,* Sept., 1960. The article traces the development of human speech from more primitive systems of animal communication.

Howells, W. W.: The Distribution of Man, *Sci. American,* Sept., 1960. An examination of some of the strain differences among geographic variants of man.

———: Homo Erectus, *Sci. American,* Nov., 1966. A good description of this human species and a discussion of its ancestral role for *Homo sapiens.* Recommended.

Krogman, W. M.: The Scars of Human Evolution, *Sci. American,* Dec., 1951. A discussion of the adaptations that parallel the upright posture evolved in man.

Leakey, L. S. B.: Finding the World's Earliest Man, *Nat. Geographic,* Sept., 1960.

———: Exploring 1,750,000 Years into Man's Past, *Nat. Geographic,* Sept., 1961.

Two articles by the discoverer of *Australopithecus paleojavanus.*

Malefijt, A. de Waal: Homo Monstrosus, *Sci. American,* Oct., 1968. Early beliefs and superstitions about giant human races in remote places are laid to rest.

Mulvaney, D. J.: The Prehistory of the Australian Aborigine, *Sci. American,* March., 1966. Man appears to have reached Australia very soon after the end of the last ice age.

Napier, J.: The Evolution of the Hand, *Sci. American,* Dec., 1962. The ancestry of the modern human hand appears to trace back more than 1 million years, as shown by fossil finds described in this article.

Sahlins, M. D.: The Origin of Society, *Sci. American,* Sept., 1960. A subordination of sexual drives appears to have been basic in the development of human society; on this point see also Berrill's book above.

Tanner, J. M.: Earlier Maturation in Man, *Sci. American,* Jan., 1968. A discussion of changes in human growth patterns during the last 100 years, indicating that trait alterations can be substantial without being "racial."

Washburn, S. L.: Tools and Human Evolution, *Sci. American,* Sept., 1960. The article shows how inferences about human evolution can be made from fossil tools.

Weckler, J. E.: Neanderthal Man, *Sci. American,* Dec., 1957. A hypothesis about the relation of modern man and Neanderthalers is discussed in this article.

Wiener, A. S.: Parentage and Blood Groups, *Sci. American,* July, 1954. The nature of blood groups and the genetics of their inheritance are discussed.

section A

common prefixes, suffixes, and anatomical terms in biological usage*

The meaning of many terms not listed in Section B, below, can be ascertained from Section A. For example, certain fishes are known as the *Actinopterygii.* The parts of this term are the prefix *actino-* and the suffix *-pterygii;* the list below indicates the meanings of these word parts as "ray" and "fin," respectively. Hence the whole term denotes "ray-finned." A large number of technical designations can be translated into English equivalents by separating the words into parts and consulting this first section of the glossary.

a- [Gr. not]: negates succeeding part of word; for example, *acoel,* without coelom.

ab- [L. away, off]: opposite of *ad;* for example, *aboral,* away from mouth.

acro- (ăk'rō) [Gr. *akros,* outermost]: for example, *acrosome,* body at tip of animal sperm.

actino- (ăk'tĭ·nō) [Gr. *aktis,* ray]: for example, *actinopodial,* ray-footed.

ad- [L. toward, to]: opposite of *ab-;* for example, *adrenal,* at (near) the kidney.

afferent (ăf'ĕr·ĕnt) [L. *ad* + *ferre,* to carry]: to lead or carry toward given position, opposite of efferent; for example, afferent nerve, afferent blood vessel.

amphi- (ăm'fĭ) [Gr. on both sides]: for example, *amphioxus,* pointed at both ends.

an- [Gr. not]: like *a-,* used before vowel or "h"; for example, *anhydride,* compound without hydrogen.

ana- [Gr. up, throughout, again, back]: for example, *analogy,* likeness, resemblance; *analysis,* thorough separation; *anatomy,* cutting apart.

andro- (ăn'drō) [Gr. *aner,* man, male]: for example, *androgen,* male-producing hormone.

anterior, antero- (ăntē'ĭ·ēr, ăn'tĕr·ō) [L. *ante,* before, in front of]: at, near, or toward front end.

antho- (ăn'thō) [Gr. *anthos,* flower]: for example, *Anthozoa,* flowerlike (coelenterate) animals; *anther,* part of flower.

anthropo- (ăn'thrō·pō) [Gr. *anthrōpos,* man, human]: for example, *anthropocentric,* man-centered.

apical (ăp'ĭ·kăl) [L. *apex,* tip]: belonging to an apex, being at or near the tip; as in apical meristem, the embryonic plant tissue at the tip of root or stem.

arch-, archeo- (ärch, är'kē·ō) [Gr. *archos,* chief]: first, main, earliest; for example, *archenteron,* first embryonic gut.

arthro- (är'thrō) [Gr. *arthron,* joint]: for example, *arthropod,* jointed-legged; *arthritis,* joint inflammation.

asc-, asco- (ās'kō-) [Gr. *askos,* sac]: for example, *aschelminth,* sac worm; *ascomycete,* sac-forming fungus.

aster-, -aster (ăs'tēr) [Gr. star]: for example, *asteroid,* star-shaped.

auto- (ô'tō) [Gr. same, self]: for example, *autogamy,* self-fertilization; *autotroph,* self-feeding organism.

axo- (ăk'sō) [fr. Gr. *axine,* axis]: pertaining to an axis; for example, *axoneme,* axial filament.

bi- (bī) [L. *bis,* twice, double, two]: for example, *bilateral; bicuspid,* having two points.

bio- (bī'ō) [Gr. *bios,* life]: pertaining to life; for example, *biology; amphibia,* living in water and on land.

-blast, blast-, blasto- (blăst, blăst'ō) [Gr. *blastos,* embryo]: pertaining to embryo; for example, *blastopore,* embryonic opening.

* NOTE: The system of indicating pronunciation is used by permission of the publishers of Webster's New Collegiate Dictionary. Copyright 1949, 1951, 1953, 1956, 1958 by G. C. Merriam Co.

brachio- (brā′kĭ·ō) [L. *brachium,* arm]: for example, *brachiopod,* arm-footed animal.

-branch, branchio- (brăng′kĭ·ō) [Gr. *branchia,* gills]: for example, *branchial* sac, breathing sac.

cardio- (kär′dĭ·ō) [Gr. *kardia,* heart]: for example, *pericardial,* around the heart.

caudal (kô′dăl) [L. *caudo,* tail]: at, near, or toward the tail.

cephalo- (sĕf′ȧ·lō) [Gr. *kephalē,* head]: for example, *cephalopod,* head-footed animal.

cerci, cerco- (sûr′sĭ, sûr·kō) [Gr. *kērkos,* tail]: pertaining to tail: for example, *anal cerci,* tail-like appendages, near anus.

cervical (sûr′vĭ·kăl) [L. *cervix,* neck]: at, near, or toward the neck region.

chaeto- (kē′tō) [Gr. *chaitē,* bristle, hair]: for example, *chaetognath,* bristle-jawed animal.

chloro- (klō′rō) [Gr. *chloros,* green]: for example, *chlorophyte,* green alga.

choano- (kō′ă·nō) [Gr. *choanē,* funnel]: for example, *choanocyte,* funnel-bearing cell.

chondro- (kŏn′drō) [Gr. *chondros,* cartilage]: for example, *Chondrichthyes,* cartilage fishes.

-chord, chorda- (kôrd, kôr′dă) [L. *chorda,* cord, string]: for example, *notochord,* cord along back.

-chrome, chromo-, chroma- (krōm, krō′mō) [Gr. *chroma,* color]: for example, *cytochrome,* cell pigment; *chromosome,* stainable body (in cell nucleus).

-clad, clado- (klăd, klă′dō) [Gr. *klādos,* branch, sprout]: for example, *triclad,* three-branched.

cocco-, cocci- (kŏkō, kŏk′sĭ- [Gr. *kokkos,* grain]: for example, *coccine,* grainlike; *coccus,* grain-like (spherical) bacterium.

-coel, coela-, coelo- (sēl) [Gr. *koilos,* hollow, cavity]: for example, *pseudocoel,* false coelomic cavity; *coelenterate,* having "gut cavity."

coeno- (sē′nō-) [Gr. *koinos,* common]: refers to aggregated or colonial groupings; for example, *coenocyte,* multinuclear cell.

cten-, cteno- (tĕn) [Gr. *kteis,* comb]: for example, *Ctenophora,* comb-bearing animals.

cyano- (sī·ȧ′nō-) [Gr. *kyanos,* dark-blue]: for example, *cyanophyte,* blue-green alga.

-cyst (sĭst) [Gr. *kystis,* bladder, pouch, sac]: for example, *sporocyst,* spore-containing cyst.

-cyte, cyto- (sīt) [Gr. *kytos,* vessel, container]: pertaining to cell; for example, *cytoplasm,* cell substance; *fibrocyte,* fiber-forming cell.

de- (dē) [L. away, from, off]: like Gr. *apo-;* for example, *dehydration,* removal of water.

-dent, denti- (dĕnt) [L. *dens,* tooth]: like Gr. *-dont;* for example, *denticle,* little tooth.

dermis, -derm (dûr′mĭs) [Gr. *derma,* skin]: for example, *ectoderm,* outer skin tissue; *epidermis,* exterior layer.

di- (dī) [Gr. twice, double, two]: like L. *bi-,* for example, *disect,* to cut in two (distinct from *dis-,* see below).

dia- (dī′ȧ) [Gr. through, across, thorough]: for example, *diaphragm,* across the midriff.

dino- (dī′nō-) [Gr. *dinos,* whirling]: for example, *dinoflagellate;* dinosaur, "whirling lizard."

diplo- (dĭ′plō) [Gr. *diploos,* twofold]: for example, *diploid,* with two chromosome sets.

dis- [L. apart, away]: for example, *dissect,* cut apart (distinct from *di-,* see above).

distal (dĭs′tăl): situated away from or far from point of reference (usually the main part of body); opposite of *proximal.*

-dont (dŏnt) [Gr. *odontos,* tooth]: for example, *thecodont,* having encased (socketed) teeth.

dorsal (dôr′săl) [L. *dorsum,* back]: at, near, or toward the back; opposite of *ventral.*

echino- (ē·kī′nō) [Gr. *echinos,* spiny, bristly]: for example, *echinoderm,* spiny-skinned.

eco- (ēkŏ) [Gr. *oikos,* house, home]: for example, *ecology,* study of relationships between organisms and their home territory.

ecto- (ĕk′tō) [Gr. *ektos,* outside]: for example, *ectoproct,* outside-anus (that is, exterior to tentacle ring).

-ectomy (ĕk'tômĭ) [Gr. *ek,* out of, + *tomein,* to cut]: excision; for example, *thyroidectomy,* excision of thyroid gland.

efferent (ĕf'ĕr·ĕnt) [L. *ex,* out, away + *ferre,* to carry]: to lead or carry away from given position; opposite of *afferent;* for example, efferent nerve, efferent blood vessel.

endo- (ĕn'dō) [Gr. *endon,* within]: for example, *endoderm,* inner tissue layer.

entero-, -enteron (ĕn'tĕrō) [Gr. *enteron,* intestine]: for example, *enterocoel,* coelom formed from intestine; *archenteron,* first intestine.

ento- (ĕn'tō) [Gr. var. of *endo-,* within]: for example, *entoproct,* inside-anus (that is, inside tentacle ring).

epi- (ĕp'ĭ) [Gr. to, on, over, against]: for example, *epidermis,* outer skin.

erythro- (ē·rĭth'rō) [Gr. *erythros,* red]: for example, *erythrocyte,* red (blood) cell.

eu- (ū) [Gr. good, well, proper]: for example, *Eumetazoa,* metazoa proper.

ex-, exo-, extero- (ĕks, ĕk'sō, ĕks'tĕr·ō) [L. out, from, exterior]: for example, *exopterygote,* exterior-winged.

-fer, -fera (fĕr, fĕ'rȧ) [L. *ferre,* to carry]: like Gr. *-phore;* for example, *foraminifer,* hole-carrier; *rotifer,* wheel-carrier; *Porifera,* pore-carrying animals (sponges).

flori- (flō'rĭ-) [L. *flos,* flower]: pertaining to flowers; for example, *florigen,* flower-producing (hormone).

-form, -formes (fôrm, fôr'mēz) [L. *-formis,* having the form of]: for example, *perciform,* perchlike.

frontal [L. *front, frons,* forehead]: in a horizontal plane separating dorsal from ventral half.

gamo-, -gamy (gă'mō) [Gr. *gamein,* to marry]: pertaining to gametes or fertilization; for example, *autogamy,* self-fertilization.

gastro- (găs'trō) [Gr. *gaster,* stomach]: for example, *gastrozooid,* feeding individual.

-gen, -genic, geno- [Gr. *genēs,* born, created]: for example, *hydrogen,* water-producing; *genotype,* genetic constitution.

geo- (jē·ō-) [Gr. *gē,* earth]: for example, *geotropic,* growing toward center of earth.

-gest, gest- (jĕst) [L. *gestare,* to carry]: for example, *ingest,* to carry in (food).

gluco-, glyco- (glōō'kō-, glī'kō-) [Gr. *gleukos,* sweet]: pertaining to sugars; for example, *glucogenic,* sugar-producing; *glycolysis,* breakdown of sugar.

gnatho-, -gnath (nā'thō) [Gr. *gnathos,* jaw]: for example, *agnath,* jawless.

gon-, gono-, -gonium (gŏn'ō) [Gr. *gonos,* seed, generation]: pertaining to reproduction; for example, *gonopore,* reproductive opening.

gymno- (jĭm'nō) [Gr. *gymnos,* naked]: for example, *gymnosperm,* naked-seed former.

gyn-, -gyne, gyno- (jīn'nō) [Gr. *gynē,* woman, female]: opposite of *andro-;* for example, *gynogenic,* female-producing.

haem-: see *hem-*

haplo- (hăp'lō) [Gr. *haploos,* single]: for example, *haploid,* with one chromosome set.

-helminth (hĕl'mĭnth) [Gr. *helminthos,* worm]: for example, *platyhelminth,* flatworm.

hem-, hemo-, hemato- (hēm, hē'mō, hĕm'ȧ tō) [Gr. *haima,* blood]: var. of *haem-;* for example, *hemoglobin,* red blood pigment.

hemi- (hĕm'ĭ) [Gr. half]: like *semi-;* for example, *hemichordate,* similar to chordate.

hepato- (hē·păt'ō-) [Gr. *hēpar,* liver]: pertaining to the liver; for example, *hepatopancreas,* liverlike digestive gland.

hetero- (hĕt'ĕr·ō) [Gr. *heteros,* other, different]: opposite of *homo-;* for example, *heterotrophic,* feeding on other living things.

hex-, hexa- (hĕks, hĕk'sȧ) [Gr. six]: for example, *hexapod,* six-legged; *hexose,* six-carbon sugar.

holo- (hŏl'ō) [Gr. *holos,* whole, entire]: for example, *holotrophic,* eating whole (bulk) food.

homo-, homeo-, homoio- (hō'mē,·ō, hō·moi'ō) [Gr. similar]: for example, *homeostatic,* remaining similar in state; *homoiothermic,* possessing constant temperature.

hydro- (hī'drō) [Gr. *hydōr,* water]: for example, *hydrolysis,* dissolution by water.

hyper- (hī'pēr) [Gr. above, over]: opposite of *hypo-;* for example, *hypertrophy,* overgrowth.

hypo- (hī'pō) [Gr. under, less]: opposite of *hyper-;* for example, *hypotonic,* less concentrated (than reference system).

ichthyo- (ĭk'thĭ·ō) [Gr. *ichthyos,* fish]: for example, *Osteichthyes,* bony fishes; *ichthyosaur,* fishlike reptile.

inter- (ĭn'tēr) [L. between, among]: for example, *intercellular,* between cells.

intra- (ĭn'trȧ) [L. within]: for example, *intracellular,* in cells.

iso- (īsō) [Gr. *isos,* equal]: like *homo-;* for example, *isolecithal,* having evenly distributed yolk.

leuko- (lū'kō) [Gr. leukos, white]: for example, *leukocyte,* white (blood) cell.

lip-, lipo- (lĭp-, lĭ'pō-) [Gr. *lipos,* fat]: pertaining to fats and fatty substances; for example, *lipase,* fat-digesting enzyme.

-logy (lō'jĭ) [Gr. *logos,* discourse, study]: for example, *biology,* study of living things.

lumbar (lŭm'bēr) [L. *lumbus,* loin]: at, near, or toward loin region.

-lysis, -lytic, -lyte [Gr. *lysis,* a loosening]: pertaining to dissolving; for example, *electrolytic,* dissolution by electricity.

macro- (mă'krō) [Gr. *makros,* long]: opposite of *micro-;* for example, *macromere,* large embryo cell.

mastigo- (măs'tĭ·gō) [Gr. *mastix,* whip]: for example, *Mastigophora,* flagellum-bearing (protozoa).

mega- (mĕg'ȧ-) [Gr. *megas,* large]: opposite of *micro-;* for example, *megaspore,* large spore; used like *macro-.*

meri-, mero-, -mere, -mer (mĕr'ĭ, mē'rō, mẹ̄r, mĕr) [Gr. *meros,* part]: for example, *blastomere,* embryo part (cell); *polymer,* chemical of many (similar) parts; *meristem,* dividing region.

meso- (mĕs'ō) [Gr. *mesos,* middle]: for example, *mesophyll,* middle of leaf.

meta- (mĕt'ȧ) [Gr. after, behind]: for example, *Metazoa,* later (advanced) animals.

micro- (mī'krō) [Gr. *mikros,* small]: for example, micromere, small embryo cell.

mono- (mŏn'ō) [Gr. *monos,* single]: for example, *monosaccharide,* single sugar (unit).

-morph, morpho- (mŏrf, mŏr'fō) [Gr. *morphē,* form]: for example, *morphology,* study of form (structure); *metamorphosis,* process of acquiring later (adult) structure.

myc-, myco- (mīk-, mī'kō) [Gr. *mykēs,* mushroom]: pertaining to fungi; for example, *mycelium,* fungus filaments; *Mycophyta,* the phylum of fungi.

myo- (mī'ō) [Gr. *mys,* muscle]: for example, *myofibril,* contractile fibril.

myx-, myxo-, (mĭks-, mĭk·sō-) [Gr. *myxa,* slime]: for example, *myxophyte,* slime mold.

-neme, nemato- (nē'mē, nĕm'ȧ·tō) [Gr. *nema,* thread]: for example, *nematode,* threadlike worm; *protonema,* first filament (in moss).

nephro- (nĕf'rō-) [Gr. *nephros,* kidney]: for example, *nephric tubule,* excretory tubule.

neuro- (nū'rō) [Gr. *neuron,* nerve]: for example, *neurofibril,* impulse-conducting fibril.

noto- (nō'tō) [Gr. *nōton,* the back]: for example, *notochord,* cord along back.

octo- [Gr. *okto,* eight]: for example, *octopus,* eight-"legged" animal.

-oid, -oida, -oidea (oid, oid'ȧ, oi'dē·ȧ) [Gr. *eidos,* form]: having the form of; like L. *-form;* for example, *echinoid,* like *Echinus* (sea urchin).

oligo- (ŏl'ĭ·gō) [Gr. *oligos,* few, small]: for example, *oligochaete,* having few bristles.

omni- (ŏm-nĭ-) [L. *omnis,* all]: for example, *omnivore,* animal eating all kinds of foods.

onto- (ŏn′tŏ) [Gr. *on,* being]: for example, *paleontology,* study of ancient (fossil) beings.

oö- (ō′ō) [Gr. *ōion,* egg]: for example, *oöcyte,* egg cell; *oögonium,* egg-forming structure.

oral (ō′răl) [L. *or-, os,* mouth]: at, near, or toward mouth.

osteo- (ŏs′tē·ō) [Gr. *osteon,* bone]: for example, *osteoblast,* bone-forming cell; *periosteum,* tissue layer covering a bone.

ostraco- (ŏs′trȧ·kō) [Gr. *ostrakon,* shell]: pertaining to a skeletal cover or shield; for example, *ostracoderm,* armor-skinned.

oto-, otic (ō′tō, ŏ′tĭk) [Gr. *ous,* ear]: for example, *otolith,* ear stone.

ovi- ovo- (ō′vĭ, ō′vō) [L. *ovum,* egg]: for example, *oviduct; ovary,* egg-producing organ.

paleo- (pā′lē·ō-) [Gr. *palaios,* old]: for example, *paleontology,* study of ancient (fossil) life.

para- (păr′ȧ) [Gr., beside]: for example, *parapodium,* side foot; *Parazoa,* animals on side branch of evolution (sponges).

pectin- (pĕk′tĭn) [L. *pecten,* comb]: for example, *pectine,* comblike organ.

pectoral (pĕk′tō·răl) [L. *pectorale,* breastplate]: at, near, or toward chest or shoulder region.

-ped, -pedia, pedi- (pĕd, pĕd′ĭ·ȧ, pĕd′ĭ) [L. *pes,* foot]: like Gr. *-pod;* for example, *bipedal,* two-footed; *pedipalp,* leglike appendage.

pelvic (pĕl′vĭk) [L. *pelvis,* basin]: at, near, or toward hip region.

pent-, penta- (pĕnt, pĕn′tȧ) [Gr. *pente,* five]: for example, *pentose, five-carbon sugar.*

peri- (pĕr′ĭ) [Gr. around]: for example, *peristalsis,* wavelike compression around tubular organ (like gut).

phago-, -phage (făg′ō, fāj) [Gr. eating]: for example, *phagocyte,* cell eater; *bacteriophage,* bacterium eater (virus).

phello- (fĕl′ō-) [Gr. *phellos,* cork]: pertaining to cork region of bark; for example, *phellogen,* cork-producing tissue (cambium).

phono-, -phone (fōn′ō, fōn) [Gr. *phonē,* sound]: for example, *phonoreceptor,* sound-sensitive sense organ.

phoro-, -phore (fŏr′ō, fōr) [Gr. *phoros,* bearing, carrying]: like L. *-fer;* for example, *trochophore,* ''wheel''-bearing (larva).

photo-, photic (fō′tō, fō′tĭk) [Gr. *photos,* light]: for example, *photosynthesis,* synthesis with aid of light.

-phragm (frăm) [Gr. barrier]: for example, *diaphragm.*

phyco- (fī′kō-) [Gr. *phykos,* seaweed]: refers to aquatic protists; for example, *phycomycete,* primitive (often aquatic) fungus; *phycoerythrin,* red pigment in blue-green and red algae.

phyllo-, -phyll (fĭl′ō, fĭl) [Gr. *phyllon,* leaf]: for example, *chlorophyll,* green pigment in leaf.

phyto-, -phyte (fī′tō, fīt) [Gr. *phyton,* plant]: for example, *Metaphyta,* later (advanced) plants.

-pithecus (-pĭ·thē′cŭs) [Gr. *pithēkos,* ape]: for example, *Australopithecus,* southern ape.

placo- (plă′kō) [Gr. *plax,* tablet, plate]: for example, *placoderm,* plate-skinned.

-plasm, plasmo-, -plast (plăz′m, plăz′mō, plăst) [Gr. *plasma,* form, mold]: for example, *protoplasm,* first-molded (living matter); *chloroplast,* green-formed (body).

-pleur, pleuro- (pl$\overline{oo}$r, pl$\overline{oo}$r′ō) [Gr. *pleuron,* side, rib]: for example, *pleura,* membrane lining rib cage.

-ploid [Gr. *-ploos,* -fold]: number of chromosome sets per cell; for example, *haploid, diploid.*

poly- (pŏl′ĭ) [Gr. *polys,* many]: for example, *polymorphic,* many-shaped; *polychaete,* many-bristled.

post-, postero-, posterior (pōst, pŏs′tēr·ō) [L. behind, after]: opposite of *pre-, antero-;* at, near, or toward hind end or part.

pre- (prē) [L. before, in front of]: opposite of *post-;* for example, *preoral,* in front of mouth.

pro- (prō) [Gr. before, in front of]: like L. *pre-;* for example, *prostomial,* in front of mouth.

-proct, procto- (prŏkt, prŏk′tō) [Gr. *proctos,* anus]: for example, *ectoproct,* having anus outside of ring of tentacles.

proto- (prō′tō) [Gr. *prōtos,* first]: for example, *Protozoa,* first animals.

proximal (prŏk′sĭ·măl) [L. *proximus,* near]: situated near to point of reference (usually the main part of body); opposite of distal.

pseudo- (sū′dō) [Gr. *pseudēs,* false]: for example, *pseudocoel,* false coelom; *pseudopodium,* false foot.

ptero-, -ptera, -ptery (tĕr′ō, tĕr′ȧ, tĕr′ĭ) [Gr. *pteron,* wing, fin]: for example, *exopterygote,* exterior-winged.

renal (rē′năl) [L. *renes,* kidneys]: pertaining to kidney.

rhabdo- (răb′dō) [Gr. *rhabdos,* rod]: for example, *rhabdocoel,* flatworm possessing straight (rodlike) intestine.

rhizo- (rī′zō) [Gr. *rhiza,* root]: for example, *rhizopod,* having rootlike feet; *rhizoid,* rootlike hair.

-rhynch, rhyncho- (rĭngk, rĭng′kō) [Gr. *rhynchos,* snout]: for example, *kinorhynch,* having movable snout.

sagittal (săj′ĭ·tăl) [L. *sagitta,* arrow]: at, near, or toward plane bisecting left and right halves; in median plane.

sarco-, -sarc (sär′kō, särk) [Gr. *sarx,* flesh]: for example, *coenosarc,* common flesh (living portions).

saur-, -saur (sôr) [Gr. *sauros,* lizard]: for example, *pterosaur,* flying reptile.

schizo- (skĭz′ō) [Gr. *schizein,* to split, part]: for example, *schizocoel,* coelom formed by splitting of tissue layer; *schizophyte,* fission "plant" (bacterium).

sclero- (sklę̄r′ō) [Gr. *sklēros,* hard]: for example, *scleroprotein,* hard (horny) protein; *sclereid,* hard-walled cell.

scypho- (sī′fō) [Gr. *skyphos,* cup]: for example, *Scyphozoa,* cup-shaped animals (jellyfish).

semi- (sĕ′mī-) [L. half]: for example, *semiherbaceous,* intermediate between herbaceous and woody.

sipho-, siphono- (sī′fō-) [Gr. *siphōn,* a pipe]: for example, *siphonaceous,* tubular.

-soma, -some, somato- (sō′mȧ, sōm, sō′mȧ·tō) [Gr. *sōma,* body]: for example, *chromosome,* stainable body.

-sperm, spermo-, sperma-, spermato- (spûrm, spûr′mō, spûr′mȧ, spûr′mȧ·tō) [Gr. *sperma,* seed]: for example, *endosperm,* interior (region of) seed.

spora-, sporo- (spō′rȧ, spō′rō) [Gr. *sporā,* seed]: for example, *Sporozoa,* spore-forming (protozoa); *sporophyte,* spore-forming plant.

stato- (stăt′ō) [Gr. *statos,* standing stationary, positioned]: for example, *statolith,* position (-indicating) stone.

stereo- (stĕr′ē·ō) [Gr. *stereos,* solid]: for example, *stereoblastula,* solid blastula.

-stome, -stoma, -stomato-, (stōm, stōm′ȧ, stŏm′â·tō) [Gr. *stoma,* mouth]: *peristomial,* around the mouth.

sub-, sus- (sŭb-, sŭs-) [L. under, below]: for example, *subepidermal,* underneath the epidermis; *suspensor,* suspending structure.

sym-, syn-, (sĭm, sĭn) [Gr. *syn,* together, with]: like L. *con-;* for example, *syngamy,* coming together of gametes; *synapse,* looping together (of neurons); *synthesis,* construction, putting together; *symbiosis,* living together.

taxo-, taxi-, -taxis (tăksō, tăksĭ, tăks′ĭs) [Gr. *taxis,* arrangement]: for example, *taxonomy,* "arrangement" laws; *taxidermy,* skin arrangement.

tel-, tele-, teleo- (tĕl, tĕl′ē, tĕl′ē·ŏ) [Gr. *telos,* end]: for example, *telophase,* end phase; *teleost,* (fish with) bony end (adult) state; *teleology,* knowledge of end conditions.

tetra- (tĕr′rȧ) [Gr. four]: for example, *tetrapod,* four-footed.

thallo- (thăl′ō-) [Gr. *thallos,* young shoot]: for example, *prothallium,* precursor of definitive plant (fern gametophyte); *thallophyte,* old term for plantlike protists (those without leaf, stem, or root).

theco-, -theca (thē′kō, thē′kȧ) [Gr. *thēkē,* case,

capsule]: for example, *thecodont,* having socketed teeth.

thigmo- (thĭg′mō) [Gr. *thigma,* touch]: for example, *thigmotropy,* movement due to touch.

thoracic (thō·răs′ĭk) [L. *thorax,* chest]: at, near, or toward chest region, or region between head and abdomen.

-tome, -tomy (tōm, tō′mĭ) [Gr. *tomē,* section, a cutting apart]: for example, *anatomy,* study of structure based on dissection.

trans- [L. across]: for example, *transpiration,* water evaporation from exposed plant parts.

transverse (trăns′vûrs) [L. *transversare,* to cross]: at, near, or toward plane separating anterior and posterior; cross-sectional.

tri- (trī) [L. *tria,* three]: for example, *triclad,* three-branched (digestive tract).

-trich, tricho- (trĭk, trĭk′ō) [Gr. *trichos,* hair]: for example, *trichocyst,* hair-containing sac.

-troch, trocho- (trŏk, trŏk′ō) [Gr. *trochos,* wheel]: for example, *trochophore,* (larva) bearing wheel (of cilia).

-troph, tropho- (trŏf, trŏ′fō) [Gr. *trophos,* feeder]: for example, *autotrophic,* self-nourishing.

uro-, ura (ū′rō, ūrȧ) [Gr. *oura,* tail]: for example, *uropod;* tail foot; *urochordate,* tailed chordate.

ventral (vĕn′trăl) [L. *venter,* belly]: opposite to *dorsal;* at, near, or toward the belly or underside.

xantho- (zăn′thō-) [Gr. *xanthos,* yellow]: for example, *xanthophyll,* yellow pigment (of leaf).

xero- (zē′rō-) [Gr. *xēros,* dry]: for example, *xerophyte,* dry-climate plant.

zoo-, -zoa, -zoon (zō′ō, zōȧ, zō′ŏn) [Gr. *zōion,* animal]: for example *protozoon,* first animal; *zooid,* individual animal (in colony).

zygo- (zī′gō) [Gr. *zygon,* yoke, pair]: for example, *zygote,* fertilized egg.

---

section B
general listing of technical terms

Where derivations of particular word parts are not given in this section, such parts and their derivations can in many cases be found in Section A, above.

abdomen (ab′dŏ·mĕn) [L.]: region of animal body posterior to thorax or chest.

abscission (ăb·sĭzh′ŭn) [L. *abscindere,* to cut off]: separation of a body part from a plant, particularly after a special layer of cells weakens and dies.

Acanthocephala (ȧ·kăn′thō·sĕf′ă·lȧ) [Gr. *akantho,* thorn]: spiny-headed worms, a phylum of pseudocoelomate parasites.

acid (ăs′ĭd) [L. *acidus,* sour]: a substance that releases hydrogen ions in water; having a pH of less than 7.

acoel, acoelomate (ā·sēl′): (1) without coelom; (2) an animal without coelom; flatworms, nemertine worms.

acromegaly (ăk′rō·mĕg′ȧ·lĭ): skeletal overgrowths, particularly in the extremities, produced by excessive growth-hormone secretion from the pituitary.

acrosome (ăk′rō·sōm): structure at tip of head (nucleus) of animal sperm, which makes contact with egg during fertilization.

actinostele (ăk·tĭn′ō·stēl) [Gr. *stēlē,* upright post]: a type of stele in roots, in which the cross-sectional arrangement of vascular tissues has the form of a star with various numbers of points.

adenine (ăd'ē·nēn): a purine component of nucleotides and nucleic acids.

adenosine (di-, tri-) phosphate (*ADP, ATP*) (ȧ·dĕn'ō·sēn): adenine-ribose-phosphates functioning in energy transfers in cells.

adenylic acid: equivalent to adenosine monophosphate, or AMP.

adipose (ăd'ĭ·pōs) [L. *adipis,* fat]: fat, fatty; fat-storing tissue.

ADP: abbreviation of adenosine diphosphate.

adrenal, adrenalin (ăd·rē'năl, ăd·rĕn'ăll·ĭn) [L. *renalis,* kidney]: (1) endocrine gland; (2) the hormone produced by the adrenal medulla.

adrenergic (ăd'rĕn·ûr'jĭk): applied to nerve fibers that release an adrenalinlike substance from their axon terminals when impulses are transmitted across synapses.

adventitious (ăd'vĕn·tĭsh'ŭs): appearing not in usual place; as an adventitious root, which can sprout from anywhere on a stem.

aerobe, aerobic (ā'ēr·ōb, -ō'bĭk) [Gr. *aeros,* air]: (1) oxygen-requiring organism; (2) pertaining to oxygen-dependent form of respiration.

Agnatha (ăg'nȧ·thȧ); jawless fishes, a class of vertebrates including lampreys and hagfishes.

aldehyde (ăl'dē·hīd) [L. abbr. for *alcohol-dehydrogenatum,* dehydrogenated alcohol]: organic compound with —CHO grouping.

alga (ăl'gȧ), pl. *algae* (-jē): any member of a largely photosynthetic superphylum of protists.

alkaline (ăl'kȧ·lĭn): pertaining to substances that release hydroxyl ions in water; having a pH greater than 7.

allantois (ă·lăn'tō·ĭs) [Gr. *allantoeides,* sausage-shaped]: one of the extraembryonic membranes in reptiles, birds, and mammals; functions as embryonic urinary bladder or as carrier of blood vessels to and from placenta.

allele (ă·lēl') [Gr. *allēlōn,* of one another]: one of a group of alternative genes that can occupy a given locus on a chromosome; a dominant and its associated recessive are allelic genes.

alveolus (ăl·vē'ōl·ŭs), pl. *alveoli* (-lī) [L; dim. of *alveus,* a hollow]: a small cavity or pit; for example, a microscopic air sac of lungs.

ambulacrum, ambulacral (ăm'bū·lā'krŭm, -ăl) [L. walk, avenue]: (1) tube-feet-lined ciliated groove leading over arm to mouth in certain echinoderms; conducts food to mouth; (2) adjective.

amino, amino acid (ă·mē'nō): (1) $—NH_2$ group; (2) acid-containing amino group, constituent of protein.

ammocoete (ăm'ō·sēt) [Gr. *ammons,* sand]: lamprey larva.

amnion, amniote, amniotic (ăm'nĭ ŏn) [Gr. dim. of *amnos,* lamb]: (1) one of the extraembryonic membranes in reptiles, birds, and mammals that forms a sac around the embryo; (2) any reptile, bird, or mammal, that is, any animal with an amnion during the embryonic state; (3) pertaining to the amnion, as in *amniotic fluid.*

Amphineura (ăm'fĭ·nū'rȧ): a class of mollusks, including the chitons.

ampulla (ăm·pŭl'ă) [L. vessel]: enlarged saclike portion of a duct, as in ampullas of semicircular canals in mammalian ear, or in ampullas of echinoderm tube feet.

amylase (ăm'ĭ·lās) [L. *amylum,* starch]: an enzyme that promotes the decomposition of polysaccharides into smaller carbohydrate units.

amyloplast (ăm'ĭ·lō·plăst'): a starch-storing, nonpigmented plastid; a type of leucoplast.

amylose (ăm'ĭ·lōs): a polysaccharide composed of glucose units, a usual component of starch.

anaerobe, anaerobic (ăn·ā'ēr·ob, -ō'bĭk): (1) an oxygen-independent organism; (2) pertaining to an oxygen-independent form of respiration.

anamniote (ăn·ăm'nĭ·ōt); any vertebrate other than a reptile, bird, or mammal, that is, one in which an amnion does not form during the embryonic phase.

anaphase (ăn'ȧ·fāz): a stage in mitotic division

characterized by the migration of chromosome sets toward the spindle poles.

anatomy (ȧ·năt′ō·mĭ): the gross structure of an organism, or the science that deals with gross structure; a branch of the science of morphology.

androgen (ăn′drō·jĕn): one of a group of male sex hormones.

angiosperm (ăn′jĭ·ō·spûrm′) [Gr. *angeion,* a vessel]: a member of a class of tracheophytic plants, characterized by flowers and fruits; a flowering plant.

anisogamy (ăn·ī′sŏg′ȧm·ī): sexual fusion in which the gametes of opposite sex types are unequal in size.

Annelida (ăn′ĕ·lĭd·ȧ) [L. *anellus,* a ring]: the phylum of segmented worms.

anther (an′thẽr): the microsporangia in a stamen of flowering plants.

antheridium (ăn′thẽr·ĭd′ĭ·ŭm) [Gr. *antheros,* flowery]: the sperm-producing organ of plants.

anthocyanin (ăn′thō·sī′ȧ·nĭn): a water-soluble pigment in plants that produces red, purple, and blue colors.

antibody (ăn′tĭ·bŏd′ĭ): a protein that combines and renders harmless an antigen, that is, a foreign protein introduced into an organism by infectious processes.

antigen (ăn′tĭ·jĕn): a foreign substance, usually protein in nature, which elicits the formation of specific antibodies in an organism.

Arachnida (ȧ·răk′nĭd·d·ȧ) [Gr. *arachnē,* spider]: a class of chelicerate arthropods, including spiders, scorpions, mites, and ticks.

archegonium (ȧr′kē·gō′nĭ·ŭm) [Gr. *archegonos,* first of a race]: the egg-producing organ of plants.

archenteron (ȧr·kĕn′tẽr·ŏn): the central cavity of a gastrula, lined by endoderm and representing the future digestive cavity of the adult.

Arthropoda (är·thrō′pŏd·ȧ): the phylum of jointed-legged invertebrates.

Aschelminthes (ăs·kĕl·mĭn′thēs): sac (bladder-like) worms; a pseudocoelomate phylum including rotifers, roundworms, and other groups.

asconoid (ă′skŏn·oid): saclike; refers specifically to a type of sponge architecture.

ascus (ăs′kŭs): the tubular spore sac of a class of fungi.

atactostele (ă·tăkt′ō·stēl) [Gr. *tassein,* to arrange]: type of stele in which vascular bundles are scattered throughout stem, as in monocots.

atom (ăt′ŭm) [Gr. *atomos,* indivisible]: the smallest whole unit of a chemical element; composed of protons, neutrons, and other particles, which form an atomic nucleus, and of electrons, which orbit around the nucleus.

ATP: abbreviation of adenosine triphosphate.

atrium, atrial (ā′trĭ·ŭm, -ăl) [L. yard, court, hall]: entrance or exit cavity; for example, entrance chamber to heart, exit chamber from chordate gill region.

auricle (ô′rĭ·k′l) [L. dim. of *auris,* ear]: ear-shaped structure or lobelike appendage; for example, atrium in mammalian heart, lateral flap near eyes in planarian worms.

autosome (ô′tō·sōm): a chromosome other than a sex chromosome.

autotroph, autotrophism (ô′tō·trŏf′, -ĭz′m): (1) an organism that manufactures organic nutrients from inorganic raw materials; (2) a form of nutrition in which only inorganic substances are required as raw materials.

auxin (ôk′sĭn) [Gr. *auxein,* to increase]: a plant hormone promoting cell elongation, hence growth.

axil, axillary (ăk′sĭl) [L. *axilla,* armpit]: (1) the angle between a branch or leaf and the stem from which it arises; (2) adjective.

axon (ăk′sŏn): an outgrowth of a nerve cell that conducts impulses away from the cell body; a type of nerve fiber.

bacillus (bȧ·sĭl′ŭs) [L. dim. of *baculum,* rod]: any rod-shaped bacterium.

bacteriophage (băk·tẹr′ĭ·ō·fāj) [*bacterium* + Gr.

phagein, to eat]: one of a group of viruses that infect, parasitize, and eventually kill bacteria.

bacterium (băk·tẹ̄r'ĭ·ŭm) [Gr. dim. of *baktron,* a staff]: a small, typically unicellular organism characterized by the absence of a formed nucleus; genetic material is dispersed in clumps through the cytoplasm.

basidium (bȧ·sĭd'ĭ·ŭm) [Gr. dim. of *basis,* base]: a spore-bearing structure of a class of fungi.

benthos, benthonic (bĕn'thŏs) [Gr. depth of the sea]: (1) collective term for organisms living along the bottoms of oceans and lakes; (2) adjective.

beriberi (bĕr'ĭ·bĕr'ĭ) [Singhalese *beri,* weakness]: disease produced by deficiency of vitamin B_1 (thiamine).

bicuspid (bī·kŭs'pĭd) [L. *cuspis,* point]: ending in two points or flaps, as in bicuspid heart valve; syn. *mitral.*

biennial (bī·ĕn'ĭ·ăl) [L. *annus,* year]: occurring once in two years; as in biennial plant, which flowers and forms seeds the second year.

bioluminescence (bī'ō·lū'mĭ·nĕs'ĕns) [L. *lumen,* light]: emission of light by living organisms.

biome (bī'ōm): habitat zone; for example, desert, grassland, tundra.

biota, biotic (bī·ō'tä, -ŏt'ĭk): (1) the community of organisms of a given region; (2) adjective.

bipinnaria (bī'pĭn·ăr'ĭ·ȧ) [L. *pinna,* feather, fin]: larva of asteroid echinoderms, with ciliated bands suggesting two wings.

blastopore (blăs'tō·pōr): opening connecting archenteron of gastrula with outside; represents future mouth in some animals, future anus in others.

blastula (blăs'tū·lȧ): stage in early animal development, when embryo is a hollow or solid sphere of cells.

brachiopod, Brachiopoda (brā'kĭ·ō·pŏd, brā·kĭ·ŏp'ō·dȧ): (1) a sessile, enterocoelomate, marine animal with a pair of shells (valves) and a lophophore; (2) phylum name.

bronchus, bronchiole (brŏng'kŭs, brŏng'kĭ·ōl) [Gr. *bronchos,* windpipe]: (1) a main branch of the trachea in air-breathing vertebrates; (2) a smaller branch of a bronchus.

bryophyte, Bryophyta (brī'ō·fīt) [Gr. *byron,* moss]: (1) a moss, liverwort, or hornwort; any metaphyte that is not tracheophytic; (2) phylum name.

buffer (bŭf'ēr): a substance that prevents appreciable changes of pH in solutions to which small amounts of acids or bases are added.

bulb (bŭlb): an underground stem with thickened leaves adapted for food storage.

caecum (sē'kŭm) [L. *caecus,* blind]: cavity open at one end; for example, the blind pouch at the beginning of the large intestine, connecting at one side with the small intestine.

callus (kăl'ŭs) [L., hardened skin]: a tissue consisting of parenchymalike cells and formed as a tumorous overgrowth or over a wound or in tissue culture.

calorie (kăl'ō·rĭ) [L. *calor,* heat]: unit of heat, defined as the amount of heat required to raise the temperature of 1 g of water by 1 °C; a *large,* or *dietary, calorie* (kilocalorie) is a thousand of the units above.

calyx (kā'lĭks) [Gr. *kalyx*]: the outermost whorl of leaves (sepals) in a flower.

cambium (kăm'bĭ·ŭm) [L. exchange]: embryonic tissue in roots and stems of tracheophytes that gives rise to secondary xylem and phloem.

carapace (kăr'ȧ·pās) [Sp. *carapacho*]: a hard case or shield covering the back of certain animals.

carbohydrate, carbohydrase (kär'bō·hī'drāt): (1) an organic compound consisting of a chain of carbon atoms to which hydrogen and oxygen, present in a 2:1 ratio, are attached; (2) an enzyme promoting the synthesis or decomposition of a carbohydrate.

carnivore, Carnivora (kärnĭv'ō·rȧ) [L. *carnivorus,* flesh-eating]: (1) any holotrophic animal subsisting on other animals or parts of animals; (2) an order of mammals; includes cats, dogs, seals, walruses.

carotene, carotenoids (kăr'ō·tēn, kȧ·rŏt'ē·noid) [L. *carota,* carrot]: (1) a pigment producing cream-yellow to carrot-orange colors; precursor of vitamin A; (2) a class of pigments of which carotene is one.

catalysis, catalyst (kȧ·tăl'ĭ·sĭs) [Gr. *katalysis,* dissolution]: (1) acceleration of a chemical reaction by a substance that does not become part of the endproduct; (2) a substance accelerating a reaction as above.

ceboid (sē'boid): a New World monkey; uses its tail as a fifth limb.

Cenozoic (sē'nō·zō'ĭk) [Gr. *kainos,* recent]: geologic era after the Mesozoic, dating approximately from 75 million years ago to present.

centriole (sĕn'trĭ·ōl): cytoplasmic organelle forming spindle pole during mitosis and meiosis.

centrolecithal (sĕn'trō·lĕs'ĭ·thăl): pertaining to eggs with yolk accumulated in center, of cell, as in arthropods.

centromere (sĕn'trō·mēr): region on chromosome at which spindle fibril is attached during mitosis and meiosis.

Cephalochordata, Cephalopoda, cephalothorax (sĕf'ȧ·lō-): (1) a subphylum of chordates; the lancelets or amphioxus; (2) a class of mollusks; squids, octopuses, nautiluses; (3) the fused head and thorax in certain arthropods.

cercaria (sûr·kā'rĭ·ȧ): a larval stage in the life cycle of flukes; produced by a redia and infects fish, where it encysts.

cercopithecoid (sûr'kō·pĭ·thē'koid): Old World monkey; its tail is not used as limb.

cerebellum (sĕr'ē·bĕl'ŭm) [L. dim. of *cerebrum*]: a part of the vertebrate brain; controls muscular coordination.

cerebrum (sĕr'ē·brŭm) [L. brain]: a part of the vertebrate brain; controls many voluntary functions and is seat of higher mental capacities.

Chaetognatha (kē'tŏg·năth·ȧ): a phylum of wormlike enterocoelomates; animals with curved bristles on each side of mouth.

Charophyta (kä·rŏf'ĭ·tȧ): the phylum of stoneworts.

chelate (kē'lāt) [Gr. *chēlē,* claw]: claw-possessing, esp. a limb or appendage.

chelicera (kē·lĭ'sēr·ȧ): a pincerlike appendage in a subphylum of arthropods (chelicerates).

chemolithotroph (kĕm'ō·lĭth'ō·trōf) [Gr. *lithos,* stone]: an organism that manufactures food with the aid of energy obtained from chemicals and with inorganic raw materials.

chemoorganotroph (kĕm'ō·ôr·găn'ō·trōf): an organism that manufactures food with the aid of energy obtained from chemicals and with organic raw materials.

chemosynthesis (kĕm'ō·sĭn'thē·sĭs): a form of autotrophic nutrition in certain bacteria, in which energy for the manufacture of carbohydrates is obtained from inorganic raw materials.

chemotaxis (kĕm'ō·tăk·sĭs): a movement oriented by chemical stimuli.

chitin (kī'tĭn): a horny organic substance forming the exoskeleton or epidermal cuticle of many invertebrates (arthropods particularly,) and the cell walls of most fungi.

chloragogue (klō'ră·gŏg) [Gr. *agōgos,* leader]: excretory cell in annelids and some other invertebrates; leads wastes from body fluids to epidermis.

chlorocruorin (klō'rō·kroo͞'ôr·ĭn) [L. *cruor,* blood, gore]: green blood pigment in plasma of certain annelids.

chloroplast, chlorophyll, chlorophyte (klō'rō-): (1) chlorophyll-containing plastid; (2) green light-trapping pigment essential as electron donor in photosynthesis; (3) a green alga, member of the phylum Chlorophyta.

cholinergic (kō'lĭn·ûrjik): refers to a type of nerve fiber that releases acetyl choline from the axon terminal when impulses are transmitted across synapses.

Chondrichthyes (kŏn·drĭk'thĭ·ēz): fishes with cartilage skeleton, a class of vertebrates comprising sharks, skates, rays, and related types.

Chordata (kôr·kā'tȧ): animal phylum in which all members have notochord, dorsal nerve cord, and pharyngeal gill slits at some stage of life cycle.

chorion (kō′rĭ·ŏn) [Gr.]: one of the extraembryonic membranes in reptiles, birds, and mammals; forms outer cover around embryo and all other membranes and in mammals contributes to structure of placenta.

choroid (kō′roid)— pigmented mid-layer in wall of vertebrate eyeball, between retina and sclera; also blood vessel–carrying membranes in vertebrate brain.

chromatid (krō′mȧ·tĭd): a newly formed chromosome in mitosis and meiosis.

chromatophore (krō′mȧ·tō·fōr′): pigment-containing body; refers specifically to chlorophyll-bearing granules in bacteria and to pigment cells in animals.

chromoplast (krō′mō·plăst): a pigmented plastid without chlorophyll but usually containing carotenoids.

chromosome (krō′mō·sōm): gene-containing filament in cell nucleus, becoming conspicuous during mitosis and meiosis.

Chrysophyta (krĭs′ō·fī t ȧ): [Gr. *chrysos,* gold]: phylum of golden-brown algae.

chymotrypsin (kī′mŏ·trĭp′sĭn): enzyme promoting protein digestion; acts in small intestine, produced in pancreas as inactive chymotrypsinogen.

Ciliophora (sĭl′ĭ·ŏf′ôrȧ) [L. *cilium,* eyelid]: a protozoan subphylum in which member organisms have cilia on body surface.

cilium (sĭl′ĭ·ŭm): microscopic bristlelike variant of a flagellum; functions in cellular locomotion and in creation of currents in water.

circinate (sûr′sĭ·nāt) [Gr. *kirkinos,* circle]: rolled up along an axis, as in young fern leaves.

cirrus (sĭr′ŭs) [L. tuft, fringe]: a movable tuft or fingerlike projection from a cell or a body surface.

cloaca (klō ā′kȧ) [L. sewer]: exit chamber from alimentary system; also serves as exit for excretory and/or reproductive system.

Cnidaria (nī·dā′rĭ·ȧ) [Gr. *knidē,* nettle]: coelenterates; the phylum of cnidoblast-possessing animals.

cnidoblast (nī′dō·blăst): stinging cell characteristic of coelenterates; contains nematocyst.

cnidocil (nī′dō·sĭl): spike of hair trigger on cnidoblast serving in nematocyst discharge.

coccine (kŏk′sēn) [Gr. *kokkos,* grain]: pertaining to sessile protistan state of existence in which reproduction does not take place during vegetative condition.

coccus (kŏk′ŭs), pl. ***cocci*** (kŏk′sī): any spherical bacterium.

cochlea (kŏk′lē·ȧ) [Gr. *kochlias,* snail]: part of the inner ear of mammals, coiled like a snail shell.

coelenterate (sē·lĕn′tĕr·āt): an invertebrate animal having a single alimentary opening and tentacles with sting cells; for example, jellyfish, corals, sea anemones, hydroids.

coelom (sē′lŏm): body cavity lined entirely by mesoderm, especially by peritoneum.

coenocyte (sē′nō·sīt): a multinucleate cell, particularly among algae.

coenzyme (kō·ĕn′zīm): one of a group of organic substances required in conjunction with many enzymes; usually carries and transfers parts of molecules.

collenchyma (kŏ·lĕng′kĭ·mȧ) [Gr. *kolla,* glue]: a type of plant cell with somewhat thickened walls, especially at the angles; frequently present as support in maturing plant tissues.

colloid (kŏl′oid): a substance divided into fine particles, where each particle is larger than one of a true solution but smaller than one in a coarse suspension.

colon (kō′lŏn): the large intestine of mammals; portion of alimentary tract between caecum and rectum.

colostrum (kō·lŏs′trŭm): the first, lymphlike secretion of the mammary glands of pregnant mammals.

columella (kŏl′ū·mĕl′ȧ) [L. little column]: an axial shaft; for example, in a sporangium.

commensal, commensalism (kŏ·mĕn′săl, ĭz′m) [L. *cum,* with, + *mensa,* table]: (1) an organism that lives symbiotically with a host, where the host neither benefits nor suffers from the association; (2) noun.

compound (kŏm′pound) [L. *componere,* to put together]: a combination of atoms or ions in definite ratios, held together by chemical bonds.

conceptacle (kŏn · sĕp′tȧ · k′l) [L. *conceptaculum,* container]: a cavity containing gamete-forming structures, as in *Fucus.*

conidium, conidiophore (kō · nĭd′ĭ · ŭm, -ō · fōr′) [Gr. *konis,* dust]: (1) one of a linear series of spores formed on a conidiophore; (2) a spore-producing branch or body part in bacteria and fungi.

conjugation (kŏn · joo · gā′shŭn) [L. *conjugare,* to unite]: a mating process characterized by temporary fusion of the mating partners.

convergence (kŏn · vûr′jĕns) [L. *convergere,* to turn together]: the evolution of similar characteristics in organisms of widely different ancestry.

Copepoda (kō′pē · pŏd · ȧ) [Gr. *kope,* oar]: a subclass of crustaceans.

corm (kôrm) [Gr. *kormos,* tree trunk]: an axially shortened and enlarged underground stem.

corolla (kō · rōl′ȧ) [L. little crown]: the whorl of petals in a flower.

corona (kō · rō′nȧ) [L. garland, crown]: any wreath or circlet of cilia, tentacles, or cells.

corpus allatum (kôr′pŭs ă · lā′tŭm) pl. ***corpora allata*** [L. added body]: endocrine gland in insect head behind brain; secretes hormone inducing larval molt.

corpus callosum (kôr′pŭs kă · lō′sŭm) pl. ***corpora callosa*** [L. hard body]: broad tract of transverse nerve fibers that unites cerebral hemispheres in mammals.

corpuscle (kôr′pŭs′l) [L. dim. of *corpus,* body]: a small, rounded structure, cell, or body.

corpus luteum (kôr′pŭs lū′tē · ŭm) pl. ***corpora lutea*** [L. yellow body]: progesterone-secreting bodies in vertebrate ovaries, formed from remnants of follicles after ovulation.

cortex (kôr′tĕks) pl. ***cortices*** [L. bark]: the outer layers of an organ or body part; for example, adrenal cortex, cerebral cortex, stem cortex.

cotyledon (kŏt′ĭ · lē′dŭn) [Gr. *kotylēlōn,* a cup shape]: the first leaf of a seed plant, developed by embryo in seed.

cotylosaur (kŏt′ĭ · lō sôr′) [Gr. *kotylē,* something hollow]: a member of a group of Permian fossil reptiles, evolved from labyrinthodont amphibian stock and ancestral to all other reptiles.

cretinism (krē′tĭn · ĭz′m) [fr. L. *christianus,* a Christian]: an abnormal condition in man resulting from underactivity of the thyroid in the young.

crinoid (krī′noid) [Gr. *krinoeides,* lilylike]: a member of a class of echinoderms; a sea lily or feather star.

Crustacea (krŭs · tā′shē ȧ) [L. *crusta,* shell, rind]: a class of mandibulate arthropods; crustaceans.

Cryptophyceae (krĭp′tō · fī′sē · ē) [Gr. *kryptos,* hidden]: a class of algae, vaguely related to dinoflagellates.

crystalloid (krĭs′tăl · oid) [Gr. *krystallos,* ice]: a system of particles in a medium, able to form crystals under appropriate conditions; a true solution.

Ctenophora (tē · nŏf′ō · rȧ): a phylum of radiate animals characterized by comb plates; the comb jellies.

CTP: abbreviation of cytidine triphosphate.

cutaneous (kū · tā′nē · ŭs) [L. *cutis,* skin]: pertaining to the skin; for example, cutaneous sense organ.

Cyanophyta (sī · ă · nŏf′ · ĭtȧ): the phylum of blue-green algae.

cyclosis (sī · klō′sĭs) [Gr. *kyklos,* circle]: circular streaming and eddying of cytoplasm.

cytidine (di-, tri-) phosphates (sī′tĭ · dēn): cytosine-ribose-phosphates (CDP, CTP).

cytidylic acid: equivalent to cytosine monophosphate, of CMP.

cytochrome (sī′tō · krōm): one of a group of iron-containing hydrogen or electron carriers in cell metabolism.

cytolysis (sī · tŏl′ĭ · sĭs): dissolution or disintegration of a cell.

cyton (sī'tŏn): the nucleus-containing main portion (cell body) of a neuron.

cytoplasm (sī'tō·plăz'm): the substance of a cell between cell membrane and nucleus.

cytosine (sī'tō·sēn): a nitrogen base in nucleotides and nucleic acids.

deamination (dē·ămĭ·nā'shŭn): removal of an amino group, especially from an amino acid.

decapod (dĕk'ä·pŏd) [Gr. *deka,* ten]: 10-footed animal, specifically decapod crustacean (for example, lobster), decapod mollusk (for example, squid).

decarboxylation (dē·kär·bŏk'sĭ·lā'shŭn): removal of a carboxyl group (—COOH).

deciduous (dē·sĭd'ū·ŭs) [L. *decidere,* to fall off]: to fall off at maturity, as in trees that shed foliage in autumn.

dedifferentiation (dē'dĭf·ẽr·ĕn'shĭ·ā'shŭn): a regressive change toward a more primitive, embryonic, or earlier state; for example, a process changing a highly specialized cell to a less specialized cell.

degrowth (dē'grōth): negative growth; becoming smaller.

dehydrogenase (dē·hī'drō·jĕn·ās): an enzyme promoting dehydrogenation.

denaturation (dē·nā'tūr·ā'shŭn): physical disruption of the three-dimensional structure of a protein molecule.

dendrite (dĕn'drīt) [Gr. *dendron,* tree]: filamentous outgrowth of a nerve cell; conducts nerve impulses from free end toward the cell body.

denitrify, denitrification (dē·nī'trĭ·fī): (1) to convert nitrates to ammonia and molecular nitrogen, as by denitrifying bacteria; (2) noun.

denticle (dĕn'tĭ·k'l) [L. *denticulus,* small tooth]: small toothlike scale, as on shark skin.

deoxyribose (dē·ŏk'sĭ·rī'bōs): a 5-carbon sugar having one oxygen atom less than parent–sugar ribose; component of deoxyribose nucleic acid (DNA).

Deuterostomia (dū'tẽr·ō·stō'mē·ȧ) [Gr. *deuteros,* second]: animals in which blastopore becomes anus; mouth forms as second embryonic opening opposite blastopore.

diabetes (dī'ȧ·bē'tēz) [Gr. *diabainein,* to pass through]: abnormal condition marked by insufficiency of insulin, sugar excretion in urine, high blood-glucose levels.

diastole (dī·ăs'tō·lē) [Gr. *diastolē,* moved apart]: phase of relaxation of atria or ventricles, during which they fill with blood; preceded and succeeded by contraction, or systole.

diastrophism (dī·ăs'trō·fĭz'm) [Gr. *diastrophē,* distortion]: geologic deformation of the earth's crust, leading to rise of land masses.

dichotomy (dī·kŏt'ō mĭ) [Gr. *dicha,* in two + *temnein,* to cut]: a repeatedly bifurcating pattern of branching.

dicotyledon (dī·kŏt'ĭ·lē'dŭn) [Gr. *kotylēdōn,* a cup shape]: a plant having two seed leaves or cotyledons; often abbreviated as dicot.

dictyostele (dĭk'tĭ·ō·stē'lē): a type of stele in which the vascular tissue is arranged in circularly placed bundles.

diencephalon (dī'ĕn·sĕf'a·lŏn) [Gr. *enkephalos,* brain]: hind portion of the vertebrate forebrain.

differentiation (dĭf'ẽr·ĕn'shĭ·ā'shŭn): a progressive change toward a permanently more mature, advanced, or specialized state.

diffusion (dĭ·fū'zhŭn)[L. *diffundere,* to pour out]: migration of particles from a more concentrated to a less concentrated region, leading to equalization of concentrations.

dimorphism (dī·môr'fĭz'm): difference of form between two members of a species, as between males and females; a special instance of polymorphism.

Dinophyceae (dĭ'nō·fī'sē·ē): a class of Pyrrophyta.

dioecious (dī·ē'shŭs) [Gr. *oikos,* house]: megaspores and microspores are produced in different individuals of a heterosporous plant species.

dipleurula (dī·ploor'ŭ·lȧ): hypothetical ancestral form of most enterocoelomate animals, resembling developmental stage of hemichordates and echinoderms.

diplohaplontic (dĭp′lō · hăp · lŏn′tĭk): designating a life cycle with alternation of diploid and haploid generations.

diploid (dĭp′loid): a chromosome number twice that characteristic of a gamete in a particular species.

diplontic (dĭp · lŏn′tĭk): designating a life cycle with gametogenic meiosis and diploid adults.

disaccharide (dī · săk′ă rĭd) [Gr. *sakcharon,* sugar]: a sugar composed of two monosaccharides; usually refers to 12-carbon sugars.

dissociation (dĭ · sō′sĭ · ā′shŭn) [L. *dissociare,* to dissociate]: the breakup of a covalent compound in water; results in formation of free ions.

diurnal (dī · ûr′năl) [L. *diurnalis,* daily]: for example, as in daily up and down migration of plankton in response to absence or presence of sunlight.

divergence (dī · vûr′jĕns) [L. *divergere,* to incline apart]: evolutionary development of dissimilar characteristics in two or more lines descended from the same ancestral stock.

DNA: abbreviation of deoxyribose nucleic acid.

dominance: a functional attribute of genes; the dominant effect of a gene masks the recessive effect of its allelic partner.

ductus arteriosus (dŭk′tŭs är · tē′rĭ · ō′sŭs): an artery in the embryo and fetus of mammals that conducts blood from the pulmonary artery to the aorta; shrivels at birth, when lungs become functional.

duodenum (dū′ō · dē′nŭm) [L. *duodeni,* twelve each]: most anterior portion of the small intestine of vertebrates.

Echinodermata (ē · kī′nō · dûr′mȧ · tȧ): the phylum of spiny-skinned animals; includes starfishes, sea urchins.

Echiuroida (ē · kī′ŭr · oi′dȧ): a phylum of wormlike, schizocoelomate animals, characterized by spines at hind end.

ectoderm (ĕk′tō-): outer tissue layer of an animal embryo.

Ectoprocta (ĕk′tō · prŏk · tȧ): a phylum of sessile coelomate animals in which the anus opens outside the lophophore.

egestion (ē · jĕs′chŭn) [L. *egerere,* to discharge]: elimination of unusable and undigested material from the alimentary system.

elasmobranch (ē · lăs′mō · brăngk) [Gr. *elasmos,* plate]: a member of a subclass of cartilage fishes (sharks and rays); also used as adjective.

elater (ĕl′ȧ · tēr) [Gr. *elatēr,* driver]: a hygroscopic filament in the sporangium of, for example, certain bryophyte groups; functions in spore dispersal.

electrolyte (ē · lĕk′trō · līt) [Gr. *ēlektron,* amber]: a substance that dissociates as ions in aqueous solution; permits conduction of electric current through the solution.

electron (ē · lĕk′trŏn): a subatomic particle that carries a unit of negative electric charge; orbits around atomic nucleus.

element (ĕl′ē · mĕnt): one of 103 distinct types of matter, which, singly or in combination, compose all materials of the universe; an atom is the smallest representative unit of an element.

emboly (ĕm′bō · lĭ): invaginative gastrulation.

embryo (ĕm′brĭ · ō) [Gr. *en* in, + *bryein,* to swell]: an early developmental stage of an organism following fertilization.

emulsion (ē · mŭl′shŭn) [L. *emulgere,* to milk out]: a colloidal system in which both the dispersed and the continuous phase are liquid.

endemic (ĕn · dĕm′ĭk) [Gr. belonging to a district]: pertaining to or occurring in a limited locality; opposite of cosmopolitan.

endergonic (ĕn′dēr · gŏ · nĭk): energy-requiring, as in a chemical reaction.

endocrine (ĕn′ · dō · krīn) [Gr. *krinein,* to separate]: applied to type of gland that releases secretion not through a duct but directly into blood or lymph; equivalent to hormone-producing.

endoderm, endodermis (ĕn′dō · dûrm): (1) innermost tissue layer of an embryo; (2) single layer of tissue in a root or stem separating cortex from stele.

endoplasm, endoplasmic (ĕn′dō · plăz′m): (1) the

portion of cellular cytoplasm immediately surrounding the nucleus; contrasts with ectoplasm or cortex, the portion of cytoplasm immediately under the cell surface; (2) adjective.

endosperm (ĕn′dō·spûrm): triploid, often nutritive tissue in seed, formed by union of one sperm nucleus with two polar nuclei of female gametophyte.

endospore (ĕn′dō·spōr): a dormant cell commonly formed in bacteria.

energy (ĕn′ēr·jĭ) [Gr. *energos,* active]: capacity to do work; the time rate of doing work is called power.

enterocoel, enterocoelomate (ĕn′tēr·ō·sēl′): (1) a coelom formed by outpouching of a mesodermal sac from endoderm; (2) an animal having an enterocoel.

enterokinase (ĕn′tēr·ō·kē′nās) [Gr. *kinētos,* moving]: an enzyme in intestinal juice that converts trypsinogen to trypsin.

enthalpy (ĕn′thăl·pĭ) [Gr. *enthalpein,* to warm in]: a measure of the amount of energy in a reacting system.

Entoprocta (ĕn′tō·prŏk′tȧ): a phylum of sessile pseudocoelomate animals in which the anus opens inside a ring of ciliated tentacles.

entrainment (ĕn·trān′mĕnt): synchronization of a rhythmic behavior and rhythmic environmental stimuli.

entropy (ĕn′trō·pĭ) [Gr. *entropia,* transformation]: a measure of the distribution of energy in a reacting system.

enzyme (ĕn′zīm)[Gr. *en,* in + *zymē,* leaven]: a protein capable of accelerating a particular chemical reaction; a type of catalyst.

epiboly (ē·pĭb′ō·lĭ) [Gr. *epibolē,* throwing over]: gastrulation by overgrowth of animal upper region over vegetal lower region of blastula.

epidermis (ĕp′ĭ·dûr′mĭs): the outermost surface tissue of an organism.

epididymis (ĕp′ĭ·dĭd′ĭ mĭs) [Gr. *didymos,* testicle]: the coiled portion of the sperm duct adjacent to the mammalian testis.

epiglottis (ĕp′ĭ·glŏt′ĭs) [Gr. *glōssa,* tongue]: a flap of tissue above the mammalian glottis; covers the glottis in swallowing and thereby closes the air passage to the lungs.

epinasty (ĕp′ĭ·năs′tĭ) [Gr. *nastos,* pressed together]: faster growth on the upper or inner surface of a leaf or other flattened plant part, leading to outfolding.

epiphyte (ĕ′pĭ·fīt): a plant that lives as a commensal on another plant.

epitheca (ĕp′ĭ·thē′kȧ): the larger half of a diatom shell.

epithelium (ĕp′ĭ·thē′lĭ·ŭm) [Gr. *thēlē,* nipple]: animal tissue type in which cells are packed tightly together, leaving little intercellular space.

esophagus (ē·sŏf′ȧ·gŭs) [Gr. *oisō,* I shall carry]: part of alimentary tract that connects pharynx and stomach.

estrogen (ĕs′trō·jĕn) [Gr. *oistros,* frenzy]: one of a group of female sex hormones of vertebrates.

estrus (ĕs′trŭs) [L. *oestrus,* gadfly]: egg production and fertilizability in mammals; for example, estrus cycle, monestrous, polystrous.

etiolation (ē′tĭ·ō·lā′shŭn) [F. *étioler,* to blanch]: pathological condition in plants produced by prolonged absence of light; characterized by whitened leaves, excessively long, weak stems.

eurypterid (ū·rĭp′tēr·ĭd) [Gr. *eurys,* wide]: extinct Paleozoic chelicerate arthropod.

eustachian (ū·stā′shŭn): applied to canal connecting middle-ear cavity and pharynx of mammals.

exergonic (ĕk′sēr·gŏ·nĭk): energy-yielding, as in a chemical reaction.

exocrine (ĕk′sō·krīn): applied to type of gland that releases secretion through a duct.

exteroceptor (ĕk′stēr·ō·sĕp′tēr): a sense organ receptive to stimuli from external environment.

FAD: abbreviation of flavin adenine dinucleotide.

feces (fē′sēz) [L. *faeces,* dregs]: waste matter discharged from the alimentary system.

fermentation (fûr′mĕn·tā′shŭn): synonym for anaerobic respiration; fuel combustion in the absence of oxygen.

fetus (fē'tŭs) [L. offspring]: prenatal stage of mammalian development following the embryonic stage; in man, roughly from third month of pregnancy to birth.

fiber (fī'bĕr) [L. *fibra,* thread]: a strand or filament produced by cells but located outside cells; also a type of sclerenchyma cell.

fibril (fī'brĭl) [L. dim. of *fibra*]: a strand of filament produced by cells and located inside cells.

fibrin, fibrinogen (fī'brĭn, fī·brĭn'ō·jĕn): (1) coagulated blood protein forming the bulk of a blood clot in vertebrates; (2) a blood protein which on coagulation forms a clot.

flagellate, flagellum (flăj'ĕ·lāt, -ŭm) [L. whip]: (1) equipped with one or more flagella; an organism or cell with flagella; (2) a microscopic, whiplike filament serving as locomotor structure in flagellate cells.

flavin: multiple-ring compound forming component of riboflavin and hydrogen carriers such as FAD and FMN.

floridean (flō·rĭd'ē·ăn): pertaining to red algae.

florigen (flō'rĭ·jĕn): flowering hormone believed to be produced as a result of appropriate photoperiodic treatment of plants.

flourescence (flo͞o'ō·rĕs'ĕns) [L. *fluere,* to flow]: emission of radiation (light) by a substance that has absorbed radiation from another source.

FMA: abbreviation of flavin mononucleotide.

follicle (fŏl'ĭ·k'l) [L. *folliculus,* small ball]: ball of cells; as in egg-containing balls in ovaries of many animals, or cellular balls at base of hair of feather.

food (fūd): an organic nutrient.

Foraminifera (fō·râmĭ·nĭf'ĕr·ȧ) [L. *foramen,* hole]: sarcodine protozoa characterized by calcareous shells with holes through which pseudopods are extruded.

fovea centralis (fō'vē·ȧ sĕn·trā'lĭs) [L. central pit]: small area in optic center of mammalian retina; only cone cells are present here and stimulation leads to most acute vision.

fucoxanthin (fū'kō·zăn'thĭn): a brownish pigment found in diatoms, brown algae, and dinoflagellates.

gamete (găm'ēt): reproductive cell that must fuse with another before it can develop; sex cell.

gametophyte (găm·ē'tō·fīt): a gamete-producing plant; phase of life cycle in diplohaplontic organisms that alternates with a sporophyte phase.

ganglion (găng'glĭ·ŭn) [Gr. a swelling]: a localized collection of cell bodies of neurons, typically less complex than a brain.

ganoid (găn'oid) [Gr. *ganos,* brightness]: pertaining to shiny, enamel-covered type of fish scale.

gastrin (găs'trĭn): a hormone produced by the stomach wall of mammals when food makes contact with the wall; stimulates other parts of the wall to secrete gastric juice.

Gastropoda (găs·trŏp'ō·dȧ) a class of mollusks; comprises snails and slugs.

Gastrotricha (găs'trŏt'rĭ·kȧ): a class of minute, aquatic, pseudocoelomate animals, members of the phylum Aschelminthes.

gastrozooid (găs'trō·zōóid): a feeding individual in a polymorphic colony.

gastrula, gastrulation (găs'troo·lȧ, -lā'shŭn): (1) a two-layered and later three-layered stage in the embryonic development of animals; (2) the process of gastrula formation.

gel (jĕl) [L. *gelare,* to freeze]: quasi-solid state of a colloidal system, where the solid particles form the continuous phase and the liquid is the dispersed phase.

gemma (jĕm'ȧ) [L. a bud]: vegetative bud in cup-shaped growth on bryophyte body, capable of developing into whole plant.

gemmule (jĕm'ūl): vegetative, multicellular bud of (largely freshwater) sponges.

gene (jēn) a segment of a chromosome, definable in operational terms as a unit of biochemical action; repository of genetic information.

genome (jēn'ōm): the totality of genes in a haploid set of chromosomes, hence the sum of all different genes in a cell.

genotype (jĕn'ō·tīp): the particular set of genes in an organism and its cells; the genetic constitution.

genus (jē'nŭs) [L. race]: a rank category in taxonomic classification between species and family; a group of closely related species.

geotropism (jē·ŏt'rō·pĭz'm) [Gr. *tropē,* a turning]: behavior governed and oriented by gravity; for example, growth of roots toward center of earth.

gestation (jĕs·tā'shŭn): process or period of carrying offspring in uterus.

globulin (glŏb'ū·lĭn): one of a class of proteins in blood plasma of vertebrates; can function as antibody.

glochidia (glō·kĭd'ĭä) [Gr. *glochis,* arrow point]: pincer-equipped bivalve larvae of freshwater clams, parasitic on fish.

glomerulus (glō·mĕr'ū·lŭs) [L. dim. of *glomus,* ball]: small meshwork of blood capillaries or channels, as in a vertebrate nephron.

glottis (glŏt'ĭs) [Gr. *glōssa,* tongue]: slitlike opening in mammalian larynx formed by vocal cords.

glucogenic (glōō'kō·jĕn'ĭk): glucose-producing, esp. amino acids which, after deamination, metabolize like carbohydrates.

glucose (gloo'kōs): a 6-carbon sugar; main form in which carbohydrates are transported from cell to cell.

glycerin (glĭs'ẽr·ĭn): an organic compound with a 3-carbon skeleton; can unite with fatty acids and form a fat; syn. *glycerol.*

glycogen (glī'kō·jĕn): a polysaccharide composed of glucose units; a main storage form of carbohydrates.

glycolysis (glī·kŏl'ĭ·sĭs): respiratory breakdown of carbohydrates to pyruvic acid.

goiter (goi'tẽr) [L. *guttur,* throat]: an enlargement of the thyroid gland.

Golgi body (gôl'jē): a cytoplasmic organelle playing a role in the manufacture of cell secretions.

gonad (gōn'ăd) [Gr. *gonē,* generator]: animal reproductive organ; collective term for testes and ovaries.

gonozooid (gōn'ō·zō'oid): a reproductive individual in a polymorphic colony.

gradation (grā·dā'shŭn) [L. *gradus,* step]: leveling of land by geologic effects of erosion.

granum (grăn'ŭm) [L. grain]: a functional unit of a chloroplast; smallest particle capable of carrying out photosynthesis.

guanine (gŭ'â·nēn): purine component of nucleotides and nucleic acids.

guanosine (di-, tri-) phosphates (gū·â'nō·sēn): guanine-ribose-phosphates (GDP, GTP).

guanylic acid: equivalent to guanosine monophosphate, or GMP.

guttation (gŭ·tā'shŭn) [L. *gutta,* drop]: extrusion of water droplets from leaf pores by root pressure.

gymnosperms (jĭm'nō·spûrm): a plant belonging to a class of seed plants in which the seeds are not enclosed in an ovary; includes the conifers.

haploid (hăp'loid): a chromosome number characteristic of a mature gamete of a given species.

haplontic (hăp·lŏn'tĭk): designating a life cycle with zygotic meiosis and haploid adults.

helix (hē'liks) [L. a spiral]: spiral shape; for example, polypeptide chain, snail shell.

heme (hēm): an iron-containing red blood pigment.

Hemichordata (hĕm'ĭ·kŏr dă'tȧ): a phylum of enterocoelomate animals.

hemoglobin (hē'mō·glō'bĭn) [L. *globus,* globe]: oxygen-carrying constituent of blood; consists of red pigment heme and protein globin.

hemophilia (hē'mō fĭl'ĭȧ) [Gr. *philos,* loving]: hereditary disease in man characterized by excessive bleeding from even minor wounds; clotting mechanism is impaired by failure of blood platelets to rupture.

herbivore (hûr'bĭ·vōr) [L. *herba,* herb + *vorare,* to devour]: a plant-eating animal.

hermaphrodite (hûr·măf'rō·dīt) [fr. Gr. *Hermes* + *Aphrodite*]: an organism that contains both male and female reproductive structures.

heterocyst (hĕt′ēr·ō·sĭst′) colorless cell in filamentous blue-green algae that permits easy fragmentation of a filament.

heterosporous (hĕt′ēr·ŏs′pō·rŭs): producing two different types of spores, microspores and megaspores; microspores give rise to male gametophytes, megaspores to female gametophytes.

heterotroph, heterotrophism (hĕt′ēr·ō·trŏf): (1) an organism dependent on both inorganic and organic raw materials from the environment; (2) form of nutrition characteristic of heterotrophs.

heterozygote (hĕt′ēr·ō·zī′gōt): an organism in which a pair of alleles for a given trait consists of different (for example, dominant and recessive) kinds of genes.

holothuroid (hŏl·ō·thū′·roid) [L. *holothuria,* water polyp]: a member of a class of echinoderms; a sea cucumber.

holotroph, holotrophism (hō′lō·trŏf): (1) a bulk-feeding organism; nutrition usually includes alimentation; (2) form of nutrition characteristic of holotrophs.

hominid (hŏm′ĭ·nĭd) [L. *homo,* man]: a living or extinct man or manlike type; the family of man or pertaining to this family.

hominoid (hŏm′ĭ·noid): superfamily including hominids, the family of man, and pongids, the family of apes.

homology (hō·mŏl′ō·jĭ) [Gr. *homologia,* agreement]: similarity in embryonic development and adult structure, indicative of common evolutionary ancestry.

homosporous (hō·mŏs′pō·rŭs): producing spores of the same size or form; each gives rise either to a male or to a female gametophyte.

homozygote (hō′mō·zī′gōt): an organism in which a pair of alleles for a given trait consists of the same (for example, either dominant or recessive, but not both) kinds of genes.

hormogone (hôr′mō·gōn): a section of a filament of blue-green algae, located between two consecutive heterocysts.

hormone (hôr′mōn) [Gr. *hormaein,* to excite]: a secretion produced in an organism and affecting another part of that organism.

humoral (hū′mēr·ăl) [L. *humor,* moisture, liquid]: pertaining to body fluids, esp. biologically active chemical agents carried in body fluids; for example, hormones or similar substances.

humus (hū′mŭs) [L. soil]: the organic portion of soil.

hybrid (hī′brĭd) [L. *hibrida,* offspring of tame sow and wild boar]: an organism heterozygous for one or more (usually many) gene pairs.

hydathode (hī′dȧ·thōd) [Gr. *hydatis,* water vesicle]: channel or gland in leaf for water excretion.

hydranth (hī′drănth): flowerlike terminal part of coelenterate polyp, containing mouth and tentacles; a feeding polyp.

hydrolysis (hī·drŏl′ĭ·sĭs): dissolution through the agency of water; esp. decomposition of a chemical by addition of water.

hydrophyte (hī′drō·fīt): a water plant, or one living in water-rich areas.

hydroponics (hī′drō·pŏn′ĭks) [Gr. *ponos,* labor]: plant culture without soil by immersing the roots in a nutrient-rich water medium.

hyperparasitism (hī′pēr-): infection of a parasite by one or more other parasites.

hypertonic (hī′pēr·tŏn′ĭk): exerting greater osmotic pull than the medium on the other side of a semipermeable membrane; hence having a greater concentration of particles and acquiring water during osmosis.

hypha (hī′fȧ) [Gr. *hyphē,* a web]: a filamentous structural unit of a fungus; a meshwork of hyphae forms a mycelium.

hyponasty (hī′pō·năs′tĭ) [Gr. *nastos,* pressed together]: faster growth on the lower or outer surface of a leaf or other flattened plant part, leading to infolding.

hypothalamus: forebrain region containing various centers of the autonomic nervous system.

hypotheca (hī′pō·thē′kȧ): the smaller half of a diatom shell.

hypothesis (hī·pŏth'ē·sĭs) [Gr. *tithenai,* to put]: a guessed solution of a scientific problem; must be tested by experimentation.

hypotonic (hī'pō·tŏn'ĭk): exerting lesser osmotic pull that the medium on the other side of a semipermeable membrane; hence having a lesser concentration of particles and losing water during osmosis.

ichthyosaur (ĭk'thĭ·ō·sôr): extinct marine Mesozoic reptile, with fish-shaped body and porpoiselike snout.

imago, imaginal (ĭ·mā'gō, ĭ·măj'ĭ·nȧl) [L. image]: (1) an adult insect; (2) adjective.

induction (ĭn·dŭk'shŭn) [L. *inducere,* to induce]: process in animal embryo in which one tissue or body part causes the differentiation of another.

indusium (ĭn·dū'zĭ ŭm) [L. undergarment]: tissue covering sori in ferns.

ingestion (ĭn·jĕs'chŭn) [L. *ingerere,* to put in]: intake of food from the environment into the alimentary system.

insulin (ĭn'sū·lĭn) [L. *insula,* island]: hormone produced in the pancreas; promotes conversion of blood glucose to tissue glycogen.

integument (ĭn·tĕg'ū·mĕnt) [L. *integere,* to cover]: covering; external coat; skin.

intermedin (ĭn·tēr·mē'dĭn): hormone produced by the mid-portion of the pituitary gland.

internode (ĭ'tēr·nōd'): section of a plant stem between two successive nodes.

interoceptor (ĭn'tēr·ō·sĕp'tēr): a sense organ receptive to stimuli generated in the interior of an organism.

invagination (ĭn·vaj'ĭ·nā'shŭn) [L. *in,* + vagina, sheath]: local infolding of a layer of tissue, leading to formation of pouch or sac; as in invagination during a type of embolic gastrulation.

invertase (ĭn·vûr'tās) [L. *invertere,* to invert]: enzyme promoting a splitting of sucrose into glucose and fructose.

ion, ionization (ī'ŏn, -ĭ·zā'shŭn) [Gr. *ienai,* to go]: (1) electrically charged atom or group of atoms; (2) addition or removal of electrons from atoms.

isogamy (ī·sŏg'ȧ·mĭ): sexual fusion in which the gametes of opposite sex types are structurally alike.

isolecithal (ī'sō·lĕs'ĭ·thăl): pertaining to animal eggs with yolk evenly distributed throughout egg cytoplasm.

isomer (ī'sō·mēr): one of a group of compounds identical in atomic composition but differing in structural arrangement.

isotonic (ī'sō·tŏn'ĭk): exerting same osmotic pull as medium or other side of a semipermeable membrane, hence having the same concentration of particles; net gain or loss of water during osmosis is zero.

isotope (ī'sō·tōp) [Gr. *topos,* place]: one of several possible forms of a chemical element differing from other forms in atomic weight but not in chemical properties.

karyogamy (kăr'ĭ·ŏg'·ȧ·mĭ) [Gr. *karyon,* nut]: fusion of nuclei during fertilization.

keratin (kĕr'ȧ·tĭn) [Gr. *keratos,* horn]: a protective protein formed by the epidermis of vertebrate skin.

ketogenic, ketone (kē'tō·jĕn'ĭk, -tōn): (1) keto-acid-producing, esp. amino acids which after deamination metabolize like fatty acids; (2) organic compound with a —CO— group.

kilocalorie: see *calorie.*

kinesis (kĭ·nē'sĭs): locomotor movement that changes in intensity in direct proportion with the intensity of a stimulus.

kinetosome (kĭ·nĕt'ō·sōm) [Gr. *kinētos,* moving]: granule at base of flagellum, presumably motion-controlling.

Kinorhyncha (kĭn'ō·rĭng'kȧ): a class of pseudocoelomate animals in the phylum Aschelminthes.

labium, labial (lā'bĭ·ŭm, -ăl) [L. lip]: (1) any liplike structure, esp. underlip in insect head; (2) adjective.

labrum (lā'brŭm) [L. lip]: a liplike structure; esp. upper lip in arthropod head.

labyrinthodont (lăb'ĭ rĭn'thō·dŏnt) [Gr. *labyrinthos,* labyrinth]: extinct, late-Paleozoic fossil amphibian.

lacteal (lăk'tē·ȧl) [L. *lactis,* milk]: lymph vessel in a villus of intestinal wall of mammals.

lactogenic (lăk'tō jĕn'ĭk): milk-producing; as in lactogenic hormone, secreted by vertebrate pituitary.

lamella (lȧ·mĕl'ȧ) [L. small plate]: layer cementing adjacent plant cells in a tissue; usually called middle lamella.

lamina (lăm'ĭ·nȧ) [L. thin plate]: the blade of a leaf.

larva (lär'vă) pl. ***larvae*** (-vē) [L. mask]: period in developmental history of animals between hatching and metamorphosis.

larynx (lăr'ĭngks) [Gr.]: voice box; sound-producing organ in mammals.

lenticel (lĕn'tĭ·sĕl) [F. *lenticelle,* little lentil]: porous region on surface of woody stem, aiding gas exchange.

leukocyte (lū'kō·sīt): a type of white blood cell in vertebrates characterized by a beaded, elongated nucleus; formed in bone marrow.

leukoplast (lū'kō·plăst): an unpigmented plastid; see also *amyloplast.*

lichen (lī'kĕn) [Gr. *leichēn*]: mutualistic association of algal and fungal types.

lignin (lĭg'nĭn) [L. *lignum,* wood]: a complex substance present in substantial quantities in wood.

lipase (lī'pās): enzyme promoting conversion of fat to fatty acids and glycerin or reverse.

lipid (lĭp'ĭd): fat, fatty, pertaining to fat; syn. *lipoid.*

lithosphere (lĭth'ō·sfēr) [Gr. *lithos,* stone]: collective term for the solid, rocky components of the earth's surface layers.

littoral (lĭt'ō·răl) [L. *litus,* seashore]: the sea floor from the shore to the edge of the continental shelf.

lophophore (lō'fō·fōr) [Gr. *lophos,* crest]: tentacle-bearing food-trapping arm in anterior region of certain coelomates (lophophorate animals).

luciferse, luciferin (lū·sĭf'ẽr·ās, -ĭn) [L. *lux,* light]: (1) enzyme contributing to production of light in organisms; (2) a group of various substances essential in the production of bioluminescence.

lutein (lū'tē·ĭn) [L. *luteus,* yellow]: a yellow xanthophyll pigment.

lycopsid (lī·kŏp'sĭd) [Gr. *lykos,* wolf]: a member of a subphylum of tracheophytes; the club mosses.

lymph (lĭmf) [L. *lympha,* goddess of moisture]: the body fluid outside the blood circulation.

lymphocyte (lĭm'fō·sīt): a type of white blood cell of vertebrates characterized by a rounded or kidney-shaped nucleus; formed in lymphatic tissues.

macromolecule (măk'rō-): a molecule of very high molecular weight; refers specifically to proteins, nucleic acids, polysaccharides, and complexes of these.

macronucleus (măk'rō·nū'klē·ŭs): a large type of nucleus found in ciliate protozoa; controls all but sexual functions.

madreporite (măd'rē·pō·rīt) [It. *madre,* mother, + *poro,* passage]: a sievelike opening on the surface of echinoderms; connects the water-vascular system with the outside.

maltose (môl'tōs): a 12-carbon sugar formed by the union of two glucose units.

mandible (măn'dĭ·b'l) [L. *mandibula,* jaw]: in arthropods, one of a pair of mouth appendages, basically biting jaws; in vertebrates, the main support of the lower jaw.

marsupial (mär·sū'pĭ·ăl) [Gr. *marsypion,* little bag]: a pouched mammal, member of the mammalian subclass Metatheria.

mastax (măs'tăks) [L. *masticare,* to chew]: horny, toothed chewing apparatus in pharynx of rotifers.

Mastigophora (măs′tĭ gŏ′fôrȧ): the subphylum of flagellate protozoa; zooflagellates.

maxilla (măk · sĭl′ȧ) [L.]: in arthropods, one of the head appendages; in vertebrates, one of the upper jawbones.

maxilliped (măk · sĭl′ĭ · pĕd): one of three pairs of segmental appendages in lobsters, located posterior to the maxillae.

medulla (mē · dŭl′ȧ) [L.]: the inner layers of an organ or body part; for example, adrenal medulla; the *medulla oblongata* is a region of the vertebrate hindbrain that connects with the spinal cord.

medusa (mē · dū′sȧ): free-swimming stage in the life cycle of coelenterates; a jellyfish.

megagametophyte (mĕg′ȧ · gȧ · mē′tō · fīt): the gametophyte produced by a megaspore; the female gametophyte.

megaphyll (mĕg′ȧ · fĭl): a leaf with numerous vascular bundles in a vein; it leaves a leaf gap in the stele of the stem.

megasporangium (mĕg′ȧ · spō · răn′jĭ · ŭm): a sporangium that produces megaspores; an ovule.

megaspore (mĕg′ȧ · spōr′): a meiospore formed in a megasporangium and developing into a megagametophyte.

megastrobilus (mĕg′ȧ · strŏ′bĭ · lŭs) [Gr. *strobilos,* a pine cone]: a megasporangium-bearing cone.

meiosis (mī · ō′sĭs) [Gr. *meioun,* to make smaller]: nuclear division in which the chromosome number is reduced by half; compensates for the chromosome-doubling effect of fertilization.

meiospore (mī′ō · spōr): a spore produced by meiosis.

melanin (mĕl′ȧ · nĭn) [Gr. *melas,* black]: black pigment in organisms.

menopause (mĕn′ō · pôz) [Gr. *menos,* month + *pauein,* to cause to cease]: the time at the end of the reproductive period of (human) females when menstrual cycles cease to occur.

menstruation (mĕn′stroo · ā′shŭn) [L. *mensis,* month]: discharge of uterine tissue and blood from the vagina in man and apes at the end of a menstrual cycle in which fertilization has not occurred.

meristem (mĕr′ĭ · stĕm): embryonic tissue in plants, capable of giving rise to additional tissues.

mesencephalon (mĕs′ĕn · sĕf′ȧ · lŏn) [Gr. *enkephalos,* brain]: the vertebrate midbrain.

mesenchyme (mĕs′ĕng · kĭm) [Gr. *enchyma,* infusion]: mesodermal connective tissue cells; often jelly-secreting.

mesogloea (mĕs′ō · glē′ȧ) [Gr. *gloisos,* glutinous substance]: the often jelly-containing layer between ectoderm and endoderm of coelenterates and comb jellies.

mesophyll (mĕs′ō · fĭl): tissue in interior of leaves, composed of chlorophyll-containing cells arranged either as compact layers (palisade mesophyll) or as loose aggregations (spongy mesophyll).

mesophyte (mĕs′ō · fīt): a plant adapted to live in regions with intermediate amounts of water supply.

metabolism (mĕ · tăb′ō · lĭz′m) [Gr. *metabolē,* change]: a group of life-sustaining processes including mainly nutrition, respiration, and synthesis of more living substance.

metabolite (mĕ · tăb′ō · līt): any chemical participating in metabolism; a nutrient.

metamorphosis (mĕt′ȧ môr′fō · sĭs) [Gr. *metamorphoun,* to transform]: transformation of a larva to an adult.

metaphase (mĕt′ä · fāz): a stage during mitotic division in which the chromosomes line up in a plane at right angles to the spindle axis.

Metaphyta (mē · tăf′ĭ · tȧ): a major category of living organisms comprising the phyla Bryophyta and Tracheophyta; plants.

Metazoa (mĕt′ȧ · zō′ȧ): a major category of living organisms comprising all animals.

metencephalon (mĕt′ĕn · sĕf′ȧ · lŏn) [Gr. *enkephalos,* brain]: anterior portion of vertebrate hindbrain.

microgametophyte (mī′krō-): the gametophyte produced by a microspore; the male gametophyte.

micron (mī′krŏn) pl. ***microns, micra:*** one-thousandth part of a millimeter, a unit of microscopic length.

micronucleus (mī'krō·nū'klē·ŭs): a small type of nucleus found in ciliate protozoa; controls reproductive functions and macronucleus.

microphyll (mī'krō·fĭl): a leaf with a vein consisting of a single vascular bundle; it does not leave a leaf gap in the stele of the stem.

micropyle (mī'krō·pīl) [Gr. *pilē,* gate]: an opening in the integument of an ovule; permits entry of a pollen grain or pollen tube.

microsporangium (mī'krō·spō·răn'jĭ·ŭm): a sporangium that produces microspores.

microspore (mī'krō·spōr): a meiospore formed in a microsporangium and developing into a microgametophyte; in seed plants, equivalent to pollen grain.

microstrobilus (mī'krō·strŏ'bĭ·lŭs): a microsporangium-bearing cone.

mictic (mĭk'tĭk) [Gr. *mixis,* act of mixing]: pertaining to fall and winter eggs of rotifers, which if fertilized produce males and if not fertilized produce females.

mimicry (mĭm'ĭk·rĭ) [Gr. *mimos,* mime]: the superficial resemblance of certain animals, particularly insects, to other more powerful or more protected ones, or to leaves and other plant parts.

mineral (mĭn'ēr·ăl) [L. *minera,* ore]: an inorganic material.

miracidium (mī'ră sĭd'ĭ·ŭm): larval stage in the life cycle of flukes; develops from an egg and gives rise to a sporocyst larva.

mitochondrion (mī'tō·kŏn'drĭ·ŏn) [Gr. *mitos,* thread, + *chondros,* grain]: a cytoplasmic organelle serving as site of respiration.

mitosis (mī·tō'sĭs): nuclear division characterized by complex chromosome movements and exact chromosome duplication.

mitospore (mī'tō·spōr): spore produced by mitosis.

mitral (mī'trăl) [fr. *miter*]: applied to valve between left atrium and ventricle of mammalian heart; syn. *bicuspid.*

mole (mōl) [L. *moles,* mass]: the gram-molecular weight of a substance; its weight in grams equal to its molecular weight.

molecule (mŏl'ē·kūl) [L. *moles,* mass]: a compound in which the atoms are held together by covalent bonds.

Mollusca, mollusk (mŏ·lŭs'kȧ, mŏl'ŭsk) [L. *molluscus,* soft]: (1) a phylum of nonsegmented schizocoelomate animals; (2) a member of the phylum Mollusca.

Monera (mōn·ē'rȧ) [Gr. *monos,* alone]: a major category of living organism comprising bacteria and blue-green algae.

monestrous (mōn·ĕs'trŭs) [Gr. *oistros,* frenzy]: having a single estrus (egg-producing) cycle during a given breeding season.

monocotyledon (mŏn'ō·kŏt'ĭ·lē'dŭn): a plant having a single seed leaf or cotyledon; often abbreviated as monocot.

monoecious (mō·nē'shŭs) [Gr. *oikos,* house]: megaspores and microspores are produced in same individual of a heterosporous plant species.

monophyletic (mŏn'ō·fī·lĕt'ĭk) [Gr. *phylon,* tribe]: developed from a single ancestral type; contrasts with polyphletic.

monosaccharide (mŏn'ō·săk'ȧ·rīd) [Gr. *sakcharon,* sugar]: a simple sugar, such as 5- and 6-carbon sugars.

morphogenesis (môr'fō·jĕn'ē·sĭs): development of size, form, and other architectural features of organisms.

morphology (môr·fŏl'ō·jĭ): the study or science of structure, at any level of organization; for example, cytology, study of cell structure; histology, study of tissue structure; anatomy, study of gross structure.

morula (mŏr'ū·lȧ) [L. little mulberry]: solid ball of cells resulting from cleavage of egg; a solid blastula.

mucosa (mū·kō'sȧ)[L. *mucosus,* mucus]: a mucus-secreting membrane; for example, the inner lining of the intestine.

mutation (mū·tā'shŭn) [L. *mutare,* to change]: a stable change of a gene or gene part (muton);

the changed condition is inherited by offspring cells.

mycelium (mī·sē′lĭ·ŭm): the vegetative portion of a fungus, consisting of a meshwork of hyphae.

Mycophyta (mī′kō·fī′tȧ): the phylum of fungi.

myelencephalon (mī′ĕ·lĕn·sĕf′ȧlŏn) [Gr. *myelos,* marrow]: the most posterior part of the vertebrate hindbrain, confluent with the spinal cord; the medulla oblongata.

myelin (mī′ĕ·lĭn): a fatty material surrounding the axons of nerve cells in the central nervous system of vertebrates.

myofibril (mīō·fī′brĭl): a contractile filament inside a cell.

myosin (mī′ō·sĭn): a muscle protein.

myxedema (mĭk′sē·dē′mȧ) [Gr. *oidēma,* a swelling]: a disease resulting from thyroid deficiency in the adult characterized by local swellings in and under the skin.

myxomycete (mĭk′sō·mī·sēt′): a slime mold, member of a class of Myxophyta.

Myxophyta (mīks·ŏf′ĭ·tȧ): the phylum of slime molds.

NAD: abbreviation of nicotinamide-adenine-dinucleotide.

NADP: abbreviation of nicotinamide-adenine-dinucleotide-phosphate.

nastic (năs′tĭk): pertaining to a change in position, as in nastic growth movement; see *epinasty, hyponasty.*

nauplius (nô′plĭ·ŭs) [L. shellfish]: first in a series of larval phases in crustacea.

nekton (nĕk′tŏn) [Gr. *nēktos,* swimming]: collective term for the actively swimming animals in the ocean.

Nematoda (nĕm′ä tō′dȧ): the class of roundworms in the phylum Aschelminthes.

Nematomorpha (nĕm′ä tō·môr′fä): the class of hairworms in the phylum Aschelminthes.

Nemertina (nĕm·ēr tīn′ä): ribbon or proboscis worms, an acoelomate phylum (also called Rhynchocoela).

neoteny (nē·ŏt′ē·nĭ) [Gr. *neo,* new + *teinein,* extend]: retention of larval or youthful traits as permanent adult features.

nephric, nephron (nĕf′rĭk, -rŏn): (1) pertaining to a nephron or excretory system generally; (2) a functional unit of the vertebrate kidney.

neuron (nū′rŏn) [Gr. nerve]: nerve cell.

neutron (nū′trŏn): a subatomic particle with a unit of mass; it is uncharged and occurs in an atomic nucleus.

nicotinamide: a derivative of nicotinic acid (niacin, one of the B vitamins), a component of the hydrogen carriers NAD and NADP.

nitrify, nitrification (nī′trĭ·fī, -fĭ·kā′shŭn): (1) to convert ammonia and nitrite to nitrate; (2) noun.

node (nōd) [L. *nodus,* knot]: place where branches and leaves are joined to a stem.

notochord (nō′tō·kôrd): longitudinal elastic rod serving as internal skeleton in the embryos of all chordates and in the adults of some.

nucleic acid (nū·klē′ĭk): one of a class of molecules composed of joined nucleotides; DNA or RNA.

nucleolus (nū·klē′ō·lŭs): an RNA-containing body in the nucleus of a cell; a derivative of chromosomes.

nucleoprotein (nū′klē·ō-): a molecular complex composed of nucleic acid and protein.

nucleotide (nū′klē·ō·tīd): a molecule consisting of a phosphate, a 5-carbon sugar (ribose or deoxyribose), and a nitrogen base (adenine, guanine, uracil, thymine, or cytosine).

nucleus (nū′klē·ŭs) [L. a kernel]: an organelle in all cell types except those of the Monera; consists of external nuclear membrane, interior nuclear sap, and chromosomes and nucleoli suspended in the sap; also the central body of an atom.

nutation (nū·tā′shŭn) [L. *nutare,* to nod]: a slow, nodding growth movement in plants, more or less rhythmic and produced by internal stimuli.

nutrient (nū′trĭ·ĕnt) [L. *nutrire,* to nourish]: a

substance usable in metabolism; a metabolite; includes inorganic materials and foods.

ocellus (ō·sĕl′ŭs) [L. dim. of *oculus,* eye]: eye or eyespot, of various degrees of structural and functional complexity; in arthropods, a simple eye, as distinct from a compound eye.

oidiospore (ō·ĭd′ĭ·ō·spōr) [Gr. *eidos,* form]: a spore formed by partitioning of a body part or filament.

olfaction, olfactory (ŏl·făk′shŭn, -tō·rĭ) [L. *olfacere,* to smell]: (1) the process of smelling; (2) pertaining to smell.

ommatidium (ŏm′*á* tĭd′ĭ·ŭm) [Gr. *omma,* eye]: single visual unit in compound eye of arthropods.

omnivore (ŏm′nĭ·vōr) [L. *omnis,* all]: an animal living on plant foods, animal foods, or both.

Oncopoda (ŏn·kŏ′pō·d*á*) [Gr. *onkos,* bulk]: a small phylum comprising schizocoelomate animals related to arthropods.

Onychophora (ōnĭ·kŏ′fŏr·*á*) [Gr. *onych,* claw]: a subphylum of Oncopoda, comprising *Peripatus* and related types.

oögamy (ō·ŏg′*á*·mĭ): sexual fusion in which the gametes of opposite sex type are unequal, the female gamete being a nonmotile egg; the male gamete, a motile sperm.

oögonium (ō′·ō·gō′nĭ·ŭm): the female gametangium of oögamous fungi and other Protista; contains one or more eggs.

operculum (ō·pûr′kū·lŭm) [L. a lid]: a lidlike structure.

ophiuroid (ŏf′ĭ·ū·roid) [Gr. *ophis,* snake]: a member of a class of echinoderms; a brittle star.

organ (ôr′găn) [Gr. *organon,* tool, instrument]: a group of different tissues joined structurally and cooperating functionally to perform a composite task.

organelle (ôr·găn·el′): a structure or body in a cell.

organic (ôr·găn′ĭk): pertaining to compounds of carbon of nonmineral origin.

organism (ôr′găn·ĭz′m): an individual living creature, either unicellular or multicellular.

ornithine (ôr′nĭ·thēn) [Gr. *ornithos,* bird]: an amino acid which, in the liver of vertebrates, contributes to the conversion of ammonia and carbon dioxide to urea.

osmosis (ŏs·mō′sĭs) [Gr. *ōsmos,* impulse]: the process in which water migrates through a semipermeable membrane, from the side containing a lesser to the side containing a greater concentration of particles; migration continues until concentrations are equal on both sides.

ossicle (ŏs′ĭ·k′l) [L. dim. of *ossis,* bone]: a small bone or hard bonelike supporting structure.

Osteichthyes (ŏs·tē·ĭk′thĭ·ēz): the vertebrate class of bony fishes.

ostium (ŏs′tĭ·ŭm) [L. door]: orifice or small opening; for example, one of several pairs of lateral pores in arthropod heart, pore for entry of water in certain sponges.

ovary (ō′v*á*·rĭ): the egg-producing organ of animals; the ovule- (megasporangium-) containing organ of flowering plants.

oviparity, oviparous (ō′vĭ·păr′ĭ·tĭ, ō·vĭp′*á*rŭs) [L. *parere,* to bring forth]: (1) animal reproductive pattern in which eggs are released by the female and offspring development occurs outside the maternal body; (2) adjective.

ovoviviparity, ovoviviparous (ō′vō·vĭv′ĭ·păr′ĭ·tĭ, ō′vō·vĭ vĭp′*á*·rŭs): (1) animal reproductive pattern in which eggs develop inside the maternal body, but without nutritive or other metabolic aid by the female parent; offspring are born as miniature adults; (2) adjective.

ovulation (ō′vū·lā′shŭn): expulsion of an animal egg from ovary and deposition of egg in oviduct.

ovule (ō′vūl): the integument-covered megasporangium of a seed plant.

oxidation (ŏk′sĭ·dā′shŭn): one half of an oxidation-reduction (redox) process; the process is exergonic and the endproducts are more stable than the starting materials; often takes the form of removal of hydrogen (or electrons) from a compound.

paleoniscoid (pā'lē·ō·nĭs'koid): extinct Devonian bony fish, ancestral to modern bony fishes, lungfishes, and lobe-fin fishes.

paleontology (pā'lē·ŏn·tŏl'ō·jĭ): study of past geologic times by means of fossils.

Paleozoic (pā'lē·ō·zō'ĭk): geologic era between the Precambrian and the Mesozoic, dating approximately from 500 to 200 million years ago.

palp (pălp) [L. *palpus,* feeler]: a feelerlike appendage.

Pantopoda (păn·tŏ'pōdȧ) [Gr. *pantos,* all]: a subphylum of Oncopoda.

papilla (pȧ·pĭl'ȧ) [L. nipple]: any small nipplelike projection.

paramylum (pȧ·răm'ĭ·lŭm) [L. *par,* equal, + Gr. *amylon,* fine meal]: starchlike food-storage compound in Euglenophyta.

paraphysis (pȧ·răf'ĭ·sĭs) [Gr. *physis,* nature]: one of the sterile filaments in the reproductive organs of many organisms (for example, *Fucus*).

parapodia (păr'ȧ·pō'dĭ·ȧ): fleshy segmental appendages in polychaete worms; serve in breathing, locomotion, and creation of water currents.

parasite (păr'ȧ·sīt) [Gr. *sitos,* food]: an organism living symbiotically on or in a host organism, more or less detrimental to the host.

parasympathetic (păr'ä·sĭm'pȧ·thĕt'ĭk): applied to a subdivision of the autonomic nervous system of vertebrates; centers are located in brain and most anterior part of spinal cord.

parathyroid (păr'ȧ·thī'roid): an endocrine gland of vertebrates, usually paired, located near or in the thyroid.

parenchyma (pä·rĕng'kĭ·mȧ) [Gr. *para* + *en,* in + *chein,* to pour]: a thin-walled cell type of plants, relatively little specialized but often with chlorophyll; can function in food storage and is a component of many other tissue types.

parthenogenesis (pär'thē·nō·jĕn'ē·sĭs) [Gr. *parthenos,* virgin]: development of an egg without fertilization; occurs naturally in some animals (for example, rotifers) and can be induced artifically in others (for example, frogs).

pathogenic (păth'ō jĕn'ĭk) [Gr. *pathos,* suffering]: disease-producing.

pectin (pĕk'tĭn) [Gr. *pektos,* curdled]: one of a group of compounds frequently present in cell walls of plants.

pectine (pĕk'tīn) [L. *pecten,* comb]: one of a pair of comblike segmental appendages on scorpion abdomen, tactile in function.

pedicellaria (pĕd'ĭ·sĕl ā'rĭ·ȧ) [L. *pedicellus,* little stalk]: a pincerlike structure on the surface of echinoderms; protects skin gills.

pedipalp (pĕd'ĭ·pălp): one of a pair of head appendages in chelicerate arthropods.

pelagic (pē·lăj'ĭk) [Gr. *pelagos,* ocean]: oceanic habitat zone comprising the open water of an ocean basin.

Pelecypoda (pĕ'lē·sĭp'ō·dȧ): a class of the phylum Mollusca, comprising clams, mussels, oysters.

pellicle (pĕl'ĭ·k'l) [L. dim. of *pellis,* skin]: a thin, membranous surface coat, as on many protozoa.

pepsin (pĕp'sĭn) [Gr. *peptein,* to digest]: a protein-digesting enzyme in gastric juice of vertebrates.

peptidase (pĕp'tĭ·dās): an enzyme promoting the liberation of individual amino acids from a whole or partially digested protein.

peptide (pĕp'tīd): the type of bond formed when two amino acid units are joined.

perennial (pĕr·ĕn'ĭ·ȧl) [L. *perennis,* throughout a year]: a plant that lives continuously from year to year.

pericycle (pĕr'ĭ·sī'k'l) [Gr. *perikyklos,* spherical]: a tissue layer composed of parenchymatous or sclerenchymatous cells surrounding the vascular tissues of the stele; often reduced or absent in stems.

periderm (per'i·dûrm): collective term for cork cambium and its products (cork and phelloderm).

peristalsis (pĕr'ĭ·stăl'sĭs) [Gr. *peristaltikos,* compressing]: successive contraction and relaxation of tubular organs such as the alimentary tract, resulting in a wavelike propagation of a transverse constriction.

peritoneum (pē·rĭ'tō·nē'ŭm) [Gr. *peritonos,* stretched over]: a mesodermal membrane lining the coelom.

permeability (pûr'mē·ȧ·bĭl'ĭ·tĭ) [L. *permeare,* to pass through]: penetrability, as in membranes that let substances pass through.

petal (pĕt''l) [Gr. *petalos,* outspread]: one of the leaves of a corolla in a flower.

petiole (pĕt'ĭ·ōl) [L. *petiolus,* little foot]: leafstalk; the slender stem by which a leaf blade is attached to a branch or a stem.

pH: a symbol denoting the relative concentration of hydrogen ions in a solution; pH values normally run from 0 to 14, and the lower the value, the more acid is a solution.

Phaeophyta (fē'ō·fī't·ȧ): the phylum of brown algae.

pharynx (făr'ĭngks) [Gr.]: the part of the alimentary tract between mouth cavity and esophagus.

phellem (fĕl'ĕm) [Gr. *phellos,* cork]: cork, the exterior product of cork cambium.

phelloderm (fĕl'ō·dûrm): the interior, parenchymatous tissue formed by the cork cambium; becomes part of cortex.

phellogen (fĕl'ō·jĕn): cork cambium.

phenotype (fē'nō·tīp) [Gr. *phainein,* to show]: the physical appearance of an organism resulting from its genetic constitution (genotype).

phloem (flō'ĕm) [Gr. *phloos,* bark]: one of the vascular tissues in tracheophytic plants; consists of sieve tubes and companion cells and transports organic nutrients both up and down.

Phoronida (fō·rŏn'ĭ·dȧ): a phylum of wormlike lophophore-possessing animals.

phosphagen (fŏs'fă·jĕn): collective term for compounds such as creatine-phosphate, which store and may be sources of high-energy phosphates.

phosphorylation (fŏs'fō·rĭ·lā'shŭn): the addition of a phosphate group ($—O—H_2PO_3$) to a compound.

photolithotroph (fō'tō·lĭth'ō·trōf) [Gr. *lithos,* stone]: an organism that manufactures food with the aid of light energy and with inorganic raw materials.

photolysis (fō·tŏl'ĭ·sĭs): a phase of photosynthesis in which water is decomposed and the hydrogen is joined to NADP under the indirect influence of solar energy.

photoorganotroph (fō'tō·ôr·găn'ō·trōf): an organism that manufactures food with the aid of light energy and with organic raw materials.

photoperiod, photoperiodism (fō'tō·pḛr'ĭ·ŭd, -ĭz'm): (1) day length, (2) the responses of plants to different day lengths.

photosynthesis (fō'tō·sĭn'thē·sĭs) [Gr. *tithenai,* to place]: process in which light energy and chlorophyll are used to manufacture carbohydrates out of carbon dioxide and water.

phototropism (fō·tŏt'rō·pĭz'm) [Gr. *tropē,* a turning]: behavior oriented by light; for example, growth of plant stems toward light source.

phrenic (frĕn'ĭk) [Gr. *phrenos,* diaphragm]: pertaining to the diaphragm; for example, phrenic nerve, which innervates the diaphragm.

phycocyanin, phycoerythrin (fī'kō·sī'ă·nĭn, fī'kō·ē·rĭth'rĭn): blue and red pigments found in blue-green and red algae.

Phycomycetes (fī'kō·mī·sē'tēz): the class of tubular fungi.

phyllotaxy (fĭl'ō·tăk'sĭ): the geometric arrangement of leaves on a stem.

phylogeny (fī·lŏj'ē·nĭ) [Gr. *phylon,* race, tribe]: the study of evolutionary descent and interrelations of groups of organisms.

phylum (fī'lŭm), pl. ***phyla:*** a category of taxonomic classification, ranked above class.

physiology (fĭz'ĭ·ŏl'ō·jĭ) [Gr. *physis,* nature]: study of living processes, activities, and functions in general; contrasts with morphology, the study of structure.

phytoplankton (fī'tō·plăngk'tŏn) [Gr. *planktos,* wandering]: collective term for the plants and plantlike organisms in plankton; contrasts with zooplankton.

pineal (pĭn'ē·ăl) [L. *pinea,* pine cone]: a structure in the brain of vertebrates; functions as a median dorsal eye in lampreys and tuataras.

pinocytosis (pĭ′nō · sī · tō′sĭs) [Gr. *pinein,* to drink]: intake of fluid droplets through cell surface.

pistil (pĭs′til) [L. *pistulus,* a pestle]: the megaspore-producing organ of a flower; consists of stigma, style, and ovary.

pituitary (pĭ · tū′ĭ · tĕrĭ) [L. *pituita,* phlegm]: a composite vertebrate endocrine gland ventral to the brain; composed of anterior, intermediate, and posterior lobes, each a functionally separate gland.

placenta (plȧ · sĕn′tȧ) [L. cake]: a mammalian tissue complex formed from the inner lining of the uterus and the chorion of the embryo; serves as mechanical, metabolic, and endocrine connection between adult female and embryo during pregnancy.

placoderm (plăk′ō · dûrm) [Gr. *plakos,* flat plate]: a member of an extinct class of Devonian fishes.

planarian (plȧ · nâr′ĭ · ăn) [L. *planarius,* level]: any member of the class of free-living flatworms.

plankton (plăngk′tŏn) [Gr. *planktos,* wandering]: collective term for the largely microscopic, passively floating or drifting flora and fauna of a body of water.

planula (plăn′ü · lȧ) [L. dim. of *planus,* flat]: basic larval form characteristic of coelenterates.

plasmodesma (plăz′mō · dĕz′mȧ), pl. ***plasmodesmata*** [Gr. *desmos,* chain]: fine cytoplasmic strand interconnecting adjacent cells in many plant tissues.

plasmodium (plăz · mō′dĭ · ŭm): multinucleate amoeboid mass representing aggregated diploid phase in certain slime molds.

plasmogamy (plăz · mŏ′gă · mĭ): mating union of cytoplasms, a component of fertilization.

plastid (plăs′tĭd): a cytoplasmic organelle with or without pigments; chlorophyll-containing plastids are chloroplasts, sites of photosynthesis.

plastron (plăs′trŏn) [It. *piastrone,* breastplate]: a ventral shell part, as in turtles.

Platyhelminthes (plăt′ĭ · hĕl · mĭn′thēz) [Gr. *platys,* flat]: flatworms, a phylum of acoelomate animals; comprises planarians, flukes, and tapeworms.

plesiosaur (plē′sĭ · ō · sôr) [Gr. *plesios,* near]: a long-necked, marine, extinct Mesozoic reptile.

plexus (plĕk′sŭs) [L. braid]: a network, esp. nerves or blood vessels.

pluteus (ploot′ē · ŭs) [Gr. *plein,* to sail, float, flow]: the larva of echinoids and ophiuroids; also called echinopluteus and ophiopluteus, respectively.

Pogonophora (pō · gŏ′nō · fōr′ȧ) [Gr. *pōgōn,* beard]: beard worms, a phylum enterocoelomate deep-sea animals.

poikilothermic (poi′kĭ · lō · thûr′mĭk) [Gr. *poikilos,* multicolored]: pertaining to animals without internal temperature controls; "cold-blooded."

pollen (pŏl′ĕn) [L. fine dust]: microspore of seed plants.

pollination (pŏl′ĭ · nā′shŭn): transfer of pollen to the micropyle or a receptive surface associated with an ovule (for example, a stigma).

polyclad (pŏl′ĭ · klăd): a member of an order of free-living flatworms, characterized by a digestive cavity with many branch pouches.

polyestrous (pŏl′ĭ · ĕs′trŭs): having several estrus (egg-producing) cycles during a given breeding season.

polymer (pŏl′ĭ · mĕr): a large molecule composed of many like molecular subunits.

polymorphism (pŏl′ĭ · môr′fĭz′m): differences of form among the members of a species; individual variations affecting form and structure.

polyp (pŏl′ĭp) [L. *polypus,* many-footed]: the usually sessile stage in the life cycle of coelenterates.

polyphyletic (pŏl′ĭ · fī · lĕt′ĭk) [Gr. *phylon,* tribe]: derived from more than one ancestral type; contrasts with monophyletic.

polyploid (pŏl′ĭ ploid): having many complete chromosome sets per cell.

polysaccharide (pŏl′ĭ · săk′ȧ · rīd): a carbohydrate composed of many joined monosaccharide units; for example, glycogen, starch, cellulose, all formed out of glucose units.

Porifera (pō · rĭf′ĕr · ȧ): the phylum of sponges.

Priapulida (prī'ă · pū' · lĭ · dȧ): a class in the phylum Aschelminthes.

primordium (prī · môr'dĭ · ŭm) [L. beginning]: the earliest developmental stage in the formation of an organ or body part.

proboscis (prō · bŏs'ĭs) [L.]: any tubular process or prolongation of the head or snout.

progesterone (prō · jĕs'tĕr · ōn): hormone secreted by the vertebrate corpus luteum and the mammalian placenta; functions as pregnancy hormone in mammals.

proglottid (prō · glŏ'ĭd): a segment of a tapeworm.

prophase (prō'fāz'): a stage during mitotic division in which the chromosomes become distinct and a spindle forms.

proprioceptor (prō · 'prĭ · ō · sĕp' · tĕr) [L. *proprius,* one's own]: sensory receptor of stimuli originating in internal organs; a stretch receptor.

protein (prō'tē · ĭn) [Gr. *prōteios,* primary]: one of a class of organic compounds composed of many joined amino acids.

proteinase (prō'tē · ĭn · ās): an enzyme promoting the conversion of protein to amino acids or the reverse; also called *protease.*

prothrombin (prō · thrŏm'bĭn) [Gr. *thrombos,* clot]: a clotting factor in vertebrate blood plasma; converted to thrombin by thrombokinase.

Protista (prō · tĭs'tȧ) [Gr. *prōtistos,* first]: a major category of living organisms, including algae (except blue-greens), slime molds, protozoa, and fungi.

proton (prō'tōn): a subatomic particle with a unit of positive electric charge and a mass of 1; a component of an atomic nucleus.

protonema (prō'tō · nē'mȧ): the first-formed, often filamentous portion of a moss gametophyte.

protoplasm (prō'tō · plăz'm): synonym for living matter, living material, or living substance.

protostele (prō'tō · stēl') [Gr. *stēlē,* upright post]: a general type of stele in which the vascular tissues form a solid central aggregation in the stem or root, phloem being outside the xylem; the main variants are haplosteles and actinosteles.

Protostomia (prō'tō · stō'mē · ȧ): animals in which blastopore becomes mouth; anus forms as second embryonic opening opposite blastopore.

protozoon (prō'tō · zō'ŏn): a member of either of four subphyla (Mastigophora, Sarcodina, Ciliophora, Sporozoa) of a protistan phylum.

pseudocoel, pseudocoelomate (sū'dō · sēl, -ō · māt): (1) an internal body cavity lined by ectoderm and endoderm; (2) an animal having a pseudocoel.

pseudoplasmodium (sū'dō · plăz · mō'dĭ · ŭm): multicellular amoeboid mass representing diploid phase in certain slime molds.

pseudopodium (sū'dō · pō'dĭ · ŭm): a cytoplasmic protrusion from an amoeboid cell; functions in locomotion and feeding.

Psilopsida (sī · lŏp'sĭ · dȧ) [Gr. *psilos,* bare]: a subphylum of tracheophytes; includes the earliest representatives of the vascular plants.

Pteropsida (tē · rŏp'sĭ · dȧ) [Gr. *pteridos,* fern]: a subphylum of tracheophytes; includes large-leafed vascular plants (ferns and all seed plants).

pterosaur (tĕr'ō · sôr): extinct Mesozoic flying reptile.

pulmonary (pŭl'mō · nĕr'ĭ) [L. *pulmonis,* lung]: pertaining to the lungs.

pupa (pū'pȧ)[L. doll]: a developmental stage, usually encapsulated or in cocoon, between larva and adult in holometabolous insects.

purine (pū'rēn): a nitrogen base such as adenine or guanine; a component of nucleotides and nucleic acids.

pylorus (pī · lō'rŭs) [Gr. *pylōros,* gatekeeper]: the opening from stomach to intestine.

pyrenoid (pī'rē · noid) [Gr. *pyrēn,* fruit stone]: a starch-containing granular body on or near a chloroplast in many Protista.

pyrimidine (pĭ · rĭ'mĭ · dēn): a nitrogen base such as cytosine, thymine, or uracil; a component of nucleotides and nucleic acids.

Pyrrophyta (pĭ · rŏf'ĭ · tȧ) [Gr. *pyrros,* fiery]: a phylum of algae; includes dinoflagellates and possibly also Cryptophyceae.

Radiata (rā·dĭ·ă′tȧ) [L. *radius,* ray]: a taxonomic grade within the Eumetazoa, comprising coelenterates and ctenophores.

Radiolaria (rā′dĭ·ō·lār′ĭ·ȧ): sarcodine protozoa characterized by silicon-containing shells.

radula (răd′ū·lȧ) [L. *radere,* to scrape]: a horny rasping organ in the mouth of many mollusks.

receptacle (rē·sĕp′tȧ·k′l) [L. *receptaculum,* receiver]: (1) conceptacle-containing thallus tip in *Fucus;* (2) modified branch of thallus bearing sex organs in *Marchantia;* (3) expanded terminal of stalk bearing the components of a flower.

recessive (rē·sĕs′ĭv) [L. *recedere,* to recede]: a functional attribute of genes; the recessive effect of a gene is masked if the allelic gene has a dominant effect.

rectum (rĕk′tŭm) [L. *rectus,* straight]: a terminal nonabsorptive portion of the alimentary tract in many animals; opens via the anus.

redia (rē′dĭ·ȧ): a larval stage in the life cycle of flukes; produced by a sporocyst larva and gives rise to many cercarias.

reduction (rē·dŭk′shŭn) [L. *reducere,* to lead back]: one half of an oxidation-reduction (redox) process; the phase that yields the net energy gain; often takes the form of addition of hydrogen (or electrons) to a compound.

reflex (rē′flĕks) [L. *reflectere,* to bend back]: the unit action of the nervous system; consists of stimulation of a receptor, interpretation and emission of nerve impulses by a neural center, and execution of a response by an effector.

renal (rē′năl) [L. *renes,* kidneys]: pertaining to the kidney.

rennin (rĕn′ĭn) [Middle Engl. *rennen,* to run]: an enzyme in mammalian gastric juice, promotes coagulation of milk.

respiration (rĕs′pĭ·rā′shŭn) [L. *respirare,* to breathe]: liberation of metabolically useful energy from fuel molecules in cells; can occur anaerobically or aerobically.

reticulum (rē·tĭk′ū·lŭm) [L. little net]: a network or mesh of fibrils, fibers, filaments, or membranes, as in *endoplasmic reticulum.*

retina (rĕt′ĭ·nȧ)[L. *rete,* a net]: the innermost tissue layer of the eyeball; contains the photoreceptor cells.

rhabdocoel (răb′dō·sēl) [Gr. *rhabdos,* rod]: member of a group of free-living flatworms having a straight, unbranched digestive cavity.

rhizoid (rī′zoid) [Gr. *rhiza,* root]: a rootlike absorptive filament.

rhizome (rī′zōm) [Gr. *rhizōma,* mass of roots]: an underground stem.

Rhodophyta (rō′dŏf′ĭ·tȧ) [Gr. *rhodon,* red]: the phylum of red algae.

ribosome (rī′bō·sōm): an RNA-containing cytoplasmic organelle; the site of protein synthesis.

ribotide (rī′bō·tīd): a nucleotide in which the sugar component is ribose.

rickettsia (rĭk·ĕt′sĭ·ä) [after H. T. Ricketts, American pathologist]: a type of microorganism intermediate in nature between a virus and a bacterium, parasitic in cells of insects and ticks.

RNA: abbreviation of ribonucleic acid.

Rotifera (rō·tĭf′ĕrȧ) [L. *rota,* wheel]: a class of microscopic animals in the phylum Aschelminthes.

rudimentary (roo′dĭ·mĕn′tȧ·rĭ) [L. *rudis,* unformed]: pertaining to an incompletely developed body part.

saccule (săk′ūl) [L. *sacculus,* little sac]: portion of the inner ear of vertebrates containing the receptors for the sense of static balance.

saprotroph (săp′rō·trōf) [Gr. *sapros,* rotten]: an organism subsisting on dead or decaying matter.

Sarcodina (sär′kō·dī′nȧ): a subphylum of protozoa; amoeboid protozoa.

Scaphopoda (skä·fŏp′ō·dȧ) [Gr. *skaphē,* boat]: tooth shells, a class of the phylum Mollusca.

schizocoel, schizocoelomate (skĭz′ō·sēl): (1) coelom formed by splitting of embryonic mesoderm; (2) an animal having a schizocoel.

Schizophyta (skī·zŏf′ĭ·tȧ): the phylum of bacteria.

sclera (sklē'rȧ): the outermost coat of the eyeball, continuous with the cornea.

sclereid (sklḗ'êr·ĭd): a type of sclerenchyma cell.

sclerenchyma (sklê·rĕng'kĭ·mȧ) [Gr. *en,* in, + *chein,* to pour]: plant cells with greatly thickened and lignified walls and without living substance when mature; two variants are fibers and sclereids.

scolex (skō'lĕks) [L. worm, grub]: the head of a tapeworm.

scrotum (skrō'tŭm) [L.]: external skin pouch containing the testes in most mammals.

sebaceous (sê·bā'shŭs) [L. *sebum,* tallow, grease]: pertaining to sebum, an oil secreted from skin glands near the hair bases of mammals.

seminal (sĕm'ĭ·nȧl) [L. *semen,* seed]: pertaining to semen or sperm-carrying fluid.

septum, septate (sĕp'tŭm, -tāt) [L. enclosure]: (1) a complete or incomplete partition; (2) adjective.

sere (sḗr) [fr. L. *series,* series]: stage in an ecological succession of communities, from the virginal condition to a stable climax community.

serum (sḗ'rŭm) [L.]: the fluid remaining after removal of fibrinogen from vertebrate blood plasma.

sinus (sī'nŭs) [L. a curve]: a cavity, recess, space or depression.

siphon (sī'fōn): tubular structure for drawing in or ejecting fluids.

siphonaceous (sī'fŏn·ā'shŭs): tubular; applied specifically to coccine, elongate Protista.

siphonoglyph (sī·fŏn'ô·glĭf) [Gr. *glyphein,* to carve]: flagellated groove in pharynx of sea anemones; creates water current to gastrovascular cavity.

Sipunculida (sī'pŭng·kū'lĭ·dȧ): a phylum of wormlike schizocoelomate animals.

sol (sŏl): quasi-liquid state of a colloidal system, where water forms the continuous phase and solid particles the dispersed phase.

somatic (sô·măt'ĭk): pertaining to the animal body generally.

somite (sō'mīt): one of the longitudinal series of segments in segmented animals; especially an incompletely developed embryonic segment or a part thereof.

sorus (sō'rŭs) [Gr. *soros,* heap]: a cluster of sporangia on a fern leaf.

species (spē'shĭz), pl. ***species*** (spē'shēz) [L. kind, sort]: a category of taxonomic classification, below genus rank, defined by breeding potential or gene flow; interbreeding and gene flow occur among the members of a species but not between members of different species.

specificity (spĕs'ĭ·fĭs'ĭ·tĭ): uniqueness, esp. of proteins and genes in a given organism and of enzymes in given reactions.

spectrum (spĕk'trŭm) [L. image]: a series of radiations arranged in the order of wavelengths; for example, solar spectrum, visible spectrum.

spermatangium (spûr'mȧ·tăn'jĭ·ŭm): sperm-producing structure; male gametangium.

spermatogenous (spûr'mȧ·tŏj'ê·nŭs): sperm-producing.

Sphenopsida (sfê·nŏp'sĭ·dȧ) [Gr. *sphēn,* a wedge]: a subphylum of tracheophytes; includes the horsetails.

spicule (spĭk'ūl) [L. *spiculum,* little dart]: a slender, often needle-shaped secretion of sponge cells; serves as skeletal support.

spiracle (spī'rȧ·k'l) [L. *spirare,* to breathe]: reduced evolutionary remnant of first gill slit in fishes; also surface opening of breathing system in terrestrial arthropods.

spirillum (spī·rĭl'ŭm) [L. *spirilla,* little coil]: any bacterium having a wavy, coiled, or spiral shape.

sporangiospore (spô·răn'jĭ·ô·spōr'): a spore produced in a sporangium (as distinct from conidia and oidiospores).

sporangium (spô·răn'jĭ·ŭm): a spore-producing structure.

spore (spōr): a reproductive cell capable of developing into an adult directly.

sporine (spō'rēn): pertaining to a sessile state of protistan existence in which cell division can occur during the vegetative condition.

sporocyst (spō'rō·sĭst): a larval stage in the life cycle of flukes; produced by a miracidium larva and gives rise to many redias.

sporogenous (spō·rŏj'ē·nŭs): spore-producing.

sporophyll (spō'rō·fĭl): a sporangium-bearing leaf.

sporophyte (spōr'ō·fīt): a spore-producing organism; phase of diplohaplontic life cycle that alternates with a gametophyte phase.

Sporozoa (spō'rō·zō'ȧ): a subphylum of parasitic protozoa.

stamen (stā'mĕn) [L. a thread]: the microspore-producing organ of a flower; consists of stalk and anther.

stele (stēl) [Gr. *stēlē,* upright post]: collective term for those portions of stem and root that contain vascular tissues and, where present pericycle and pith.

sternum (stûr'nŭm) [Gr. *sternon,* chest]: vertebrate breastbone, articulating with ventral ends of ribs on each side.

sterol, steroid (stĕr'ōl, stĕr'oid): one of a class of organic compounds containing a molecular skeleton of four fused carbon rings; includes cholesterol, sex hormones, adrenocortical hormones, and vitamin D.

stigma (stĭg'mȧ) [Gr. the mark of a pointed instrument]: the uppermost part of a pistil, serving as receptive surface for pollen grains.

stimulus (stĭm'ū·lŭs) [L. goad, incentive]: any internal or external environmental change that activates a receptor structure.

stipule (stĭp'ūl) [L. *stipula,* stalk]: one of a pair of appendages at the base of the petiole in many plants.

stoma (stō'mȧ) pl. ***stomata*** [Gr. a mouth]: a microscopic opening in the epidermis of a leaf, formed by a pair of guard cells.

streptococcus (strĕp'tō·kŏk'ŭs) [Gr. *streptos,* curved]: member of a type of colony of bacterial cocci in which the cells divide in one plane only, forming chains.

strobilus (strŏb'ĭ·lŭs): a cone or conelike aggregation of (usually modified) leaves.

stroma (strō'mȧ) [Gr. couch, bed]: the connective tissue network supporting the epithelial portions of animal organ.

style, stylet (stīl, stī'lĕt) [Gr. *stylos,* pillar]: a stalklike or elongated body part, often pointed at one end.

suberin (sū'bẽr·ĭn) [L. *suber,* cork tree]: a waterproofing material secreted by cork and endodermis cells.

substrate (sŭb'strāt) [L. *substratus,* strewn under]: a substance that is acted on by an enzyme.

suspensor (sŭs·pĕn'sẽr) [L. *suspensus,* suspended]: an elongated strand connecting a plant embryo to the surrounding tissue layers.

symbiont, symbiosis (sĭm'bī·ŏnt, sĭm'bī·ō'sĭs): (1) an organism living in symbiotic association with another; (2) the intimate living together of two organisms of different species, for mutual or one-sided benefit; the main variants are mutualism, commensalism, and parasitism.

sympathetic (sĭm'pȧ·thĕt'ĭk): applied to a subdivision of the autonomic nervous system; centers are located in the mid-portion of the spinal cord.

synapse (sĭ·năps'): the microscopic space between the axon terminal of one neuron and the dendrite terminal of an adjacent one.

syncytium (sĭn·sĭ'shĭ·ŭm): a multinucleate animal tissue without internal cell boundaries.

syngen (sĭn'jĕn): a mating group (or variety) within a protozoan species; mating can occur in a syngen but not usually between syngens; a functional (as distinct from taxonomic) "species."

synthesis (sĭn'thē·sĭs) [Gr. *tithenai,* to place]: the joining of two or more molecules resulting in a single larger molecule.

systole (sĭs'tō·lē) [Gr. *stellein,* to place]: the contraction of atria or ventricles of a heart.

taiga (tī'gȧ) [Russ.]: terrestrial habitat zone characterized by large tracts of coniferous forests, long, cold winters, and short summers; found particularly in Canada, northern Europe, and Siberia.

tardigrade (tär'dĭ·grād) [L. *tardigradus,* a slow stepper]: a member of a subphylum of Oncopoda; water bears.

taxon (tăks'ŏn) pl. ***taxa:*** the actual organisms in a taxonomic rank.

taxonomy (tăks·ŏn'ō·mĭ) [Gr. *nomos,* law]: classification of organisms, based as far as possible on natural relationships.

tectorial membrane (tĕk·tō'rĭ·*a*l) [L. cover, covering]: component of the organ of Corti in cochlea of mammalian ear.

telencephalon (tĕl'ĕn·sĕf'*ȧ*·lŏn) [Gr. *enkephalos,* brain]: the vertebrate forebrain.

telolecithal (tĕl'ō·lĕs'ĭ·th*ă*l): pertaining to eggs with large amounts of yolk accumulated in the vegetal (lower) half; for example, as in frog eggs.

telophase (tĕl'ō·fāz): a stage in mitotic division during which two nuclei form; usually accompanied by partitioning of cytoplasm.

telson (tĕl's*ŭ*n) [Gr. boundary, limit]: terminal body part of an arthropod (not counted as a segment).

template (tĕm'plĭt): a pattern or mold guiding the formation of a duplicate.

temporal lobe (tĕm'pō·r*ȧ*l) [L. *tempora,* the temples]: a part of the vertebrate cerebrum; contains centers for speech and hearing.

testis, pl. ***testes*** (tĕs'tĭs, -tēs) [L.]: sperm-producing organ in animals.

tetrad (tĕt'răd): a pair of chromosome pairs during the first metaphase of meiosis.

tetrapyrrol (tĕt'r*ȧ*·pĭ'rŏl): a molecule consisting of four joined rings of carbon and nitrogen; heme and chlorophyll pigments are of this type.

thalamus (thăl'*ȧ*·mŭs) [Gr. *thalamos,* chamber]: a lateral region of the diencephalic portion of the vertebrate forebrain.

thallus (thăl'*ŭ*s) [Gr. *thallos,* young shoot]: a plant or plantlike body without differentiation into root, stem, and leaf.

theory (thē'ō·rĭ) [Gr. *theōrein,* to look at]: a scientific statement based on experiments that verify a hypothesis; the usual last step in scientific procedure.

therapsid (thē·răp'sĭd) [Gr. *thērion,* beast]: extinct Mesozoic mammal-like reptile.

thigmotropism (thĭg·mŏt'rō·pĭz'm) [Gr. *thigma,* touch]: growth of organisms toward or away from contact stimuli.

thorax (thō'răks) [L.]: part of animal body between neck or head and abdomen; chest.

thrombin (thrŏm'bĭn) [Gr. *thrombos,* clot]: a clotting factor in vertebrate blood; formed from prothrombin and in turn converts fibrinogen to fibrin.

thrombokinase (thrŏm'bō·kĭn'ās): enzyme released from vertebrate blood platelets during clotting; transforms prothrombin to thrombin; also called thromboplastin.

thymidine (di-, tri-) phosphates (thī'mĭ·dēn): thymine-deoxyribose-phosphate (TDP, TTP).

thymidylic acid (thī·mĭ·dĭ'lĭk): equivalent to thymine monophosphate (TMP).

thymine (thī'mēn): a pyrimidine component of nucleotides and nucleic acids.

thymus (thī'm*ŭ*s) [Gr.]: a lymphatic gland in most young and many adult vertebrates; disappears in man at puberty; located in lower part of throat and upper part of thorax.

thyroxin (thī·rŏk'sĭn): the hormone secreted by the thyroid gland.

tissue (tĭsh'ū) [L. *texere,* to weave]: a group of cells of similar structure performing similar functions.

trachea, tracheal (trā'kē·*ȧ*) [Gr. *trachys,* rough]: (1) air-conducting tube, as in windpipe of mammals and breathing system of terrestrial arthropods; (2) adjective.

tracheid (trā'kē·ĭd): plant cell type specialized for water conduction; component of xylem.

tracheophyte, Tracheophyta (trā'kē·ō·fīt): (1) a vascular plant (one with xylem and phloem); (2) phylum name.

transduction (trăns·dŭk'sh*ŭ*n): transfer of genetic material from one bacterium to another through the agency of a virus.

translocation (trăns·lō·kā'shŭn): transport of organic substances in phloem.

transpiration (trăn'spĭ·rā'shŭn) [L. *spirare,* to breathe]: evaporation of water from leaves or other exposed plant surfaces.

triclad (trī'klăd): a member of a group of free-living flatworms, characterized by a digestive cavity with three branch pouches; a planarian.

tricuspid (trī·kŭs'pĭd) [L. *cuspis,* a point]: ending in three points or flaps, as in tricuspid valve of mammalian heart.

trilobite (trī'lō·bīt): an extinct marine Paleozoic arthropod, marked by two dorsal longitudinal furrows into three parts or lobes.

triploid (trĭp'loid) [Gr. *triploos,* triple]: having three complete chromosome sets per cell.

trochophore (trŏk'ō fōr): a free-swimming ciliated marine larva, characteristic of schizocoelomate animals.

tropic, tropism (trŏp'ĭk) [Gr. *tropē,* a turning]: (1) pertaining to behavior or action brought about by specific stimuli; for example, phototropic (light-oriented) motion, gonadotropic (stimulating the gonads); (2) noun.

trypsin (trĭp'sĭn) [Gr. *tryein,* to wear down]: enzyme promoting protein digestion; acts in small intestine, produced in pancreas as inactive trypsinogen.

tuber (tū'bẽr) [L. knob]: a short, fleshy, underground stem; for example, potato.

tundra (to͞on'drȧ) [Russ.]: terrestrial habitat zone between taiga and polar region, characterized by absence of trees, short growing season, and frozen ground during much of the year.

Turbellaria (tûr'bĕ·lâr'ĭ·ȧ) [L. *turba,* disturbance]: the class of free-living flatworms; planarians.

turgor (tûr'gŏr) [L. *turgere,* to swell]: the distension of a cell by its fluid content.

typhlosole (tĭf'lō·sōl) [Gr. *typhlos,* blind]: dorsal fold of intestinal wall projecting into gut cavity in oligochaete annelids (earthworms).

umbilicus (ŭm·bĭl'ĭ·kŭs) [L.]: the navel of mammals; during pregnancy, an umbilical cord connects the placenta with the offspring, and the point of connection with the offspring later becomes the navel.

ungulate (ŭng'gū·lāt) [L. *ungula,* hoof]: hoofed, as in certain orders of mammals.

uracil (ū'rȧ·sĭl): a pyrimidine component of nucleotides and nucleic acids.

urea (ū·rē'ȧ)[Gr. *ouron,* urine]: compound formed in the mammalian liver out of ammonia and carbon dioxide and excreted by the kidneys.

ureter (ū·rē'tẽr) [Gr.]: duct carrying urine from a mammalian kidney to the urinary bladder.

urethra (ū·rē'thrȧ) [Gr.]: duct carrying urine from the urinary bladder to the outside of the body; in the males of most mammals the urethra also leads sperms to the outside during copulation.

uridine (di-, tri-) phosphates (ū'rĭ·dēn-): uracil-ribose-phosphates (UDP, UTP).

uridylic acid (ū·rĭ·dĭ'lĭk): equivalent to uridine monophosphate (UMP).

Urochordata (ū'rō·kôr·dā'tȧ): a subphylum of chordates; comprises the tunicates.

uropod (ū'rō·pŏd): an abdominal appendage in lobsters and other crustaceans.

uterus (ū'tẽr·ŭs) [L. womb]: enlarged region of a female reproductive duct in which animal embryo undergoes all or part of its development.

utricle (ū'trĭ·k'l) [L. *utriculus,* little bag]: portion of the vertebrate inner ear containing the receptors for dynamic body balance; the semicircular canals lead from and to the utricle.

vacuole (văk'ū ōl) [L. *vacuus,* empty]: a small, usually spherical space in a cell, bounded by a membrane and containing fluid, solid matter, or both.

vagina (vȧ·jī'nȧ) [L. sheath]: the terminal, penis-receiving portion of a female reproductive system.

vagus (vā'gŭs) [L. wandering]: the 10th cranial nerve in vertebrates.

valence (vā′lĕns) [L. *valere,* to have power]: a measure of the bonding capacity of an atom; bonds can be electrovalent, formed through electron transfer, or covalent, formed through electron sharing.

vasomotion (văs′ō · mō′shŭn) [L. *vasum,* vessel]: collective term for the constriction (vasoconstriction) and dilation (vasodilation) of blood vessels.

veliger (vēl′ĭ · jĕr) [L. *velum,* veil]: posttrochophoral larval stage in many mollusks.

venous (vē′nŭs) [L. *vena,* vein]: pertaining to veins; also applied to oxygen-poor, carbon dioxide–rich blood.

ventricle (vĕn′trĭ · k′l) [L. *ventriculus,* the stomach]: a heart chamber that receives blood from an atrium and pumps out blood from the heart.

vernalization (vûr′năl · ĭ · zā′shŭn) [L. *vernalis,* spring]: induction of flowering by cold (or heat) treatment of seeds or later developmental stages.

vestigial (vĕs · tĭj′ĭ · ȧl) [L. *vestigium,* footprint]: degenerate or incompletely developed, but more fully developed at an earlier stage or during the evolutionary past.

villus (vĭl′ŭs) pl. ***villi*** [L. a tuft of hair]: a microscopic fingerlike projection from the intestinal lining (mucosa) into the cavity of the mammalian gut.

virus (vī′rŭs) [L. slimy liquid, poison]: a submicroscopic noncellular particle, composed of a nucleic acid core and a protein shell; parasitic inside host cell.

viscera (vĭs′ĕr · ȧ), sing. ***viscus*** [L.]: collective term for the internal organs of an animal.

vitamin (vī tȧ · mĭn) [L. *vita,* life]: one of a class of growth factors contributing to the formation of coenzymes.

vitreous (vĭt′rē · ŭs) [L. *vitrum,* glass]: glassy; as in vitreous humor, the clear transparent jelly filling the posterior part of the vertebrate eyeball.

viviparity, viviparous (vĭv′ĭ · păr′ĭ · tĭ, vī · vĭp′ȧ · rŭs) [L. *vivus,* living + *parere,* to bring forth]: (1) animal reproductive pattern in which eggs develop inside female body with nutritional and other metabolic aid of maternal parent; offspring are born as miniature adults; (2) adjective.

xanthophyll (zăn′thō · fĭl): one of a group of yellow pigments, members of the carotenoid group.

xerophyte (zē′rō · fīt): a plant adapted to live under dry or desert conditions.

Xiphosurida (zĭf′ō · sū′r · ĭ · dȧ) [Gr. *xiphos,* sword]: a class of chelicerate arthropods; the horseshoe crabs (*Limulus*).

xylem (zī′lĕm) [Gr. *xylon,* wood]: plant tissue that conducts water from roots upward; consists of tracheids, vessels, and other cell types; in bulk represents wood.

zoaea (zō · ē′ä) pl. ***zoaeae:*** a larval form of crustaceans.

zooid (zō′oid): an individual animal in a colony; often physically joined with fellow zooids and can be a polymorphic variant.

zooplankton (zō′ō · plăngk′tŏn): collective term for the nonphotosynthetic organisms in plankton; contrasts with phytoplankton.

zoospore (zō′ō · spōr): a motile, flagellate spore.

zygospore (zī′gō · spōr): an encysted zygote, as in *Spirogyra.*

zygote (zī′gōt) [Gr. *zygōtos,* paired together]: the cell resulting from sexual fusion of two gametes; a fertilized egg.

Page numbers with an asterisk refer to illustrations or tables.

index

A bands, 347*
A vitamins, 365, 366*
Aardvarks, 281*
Abalone, 232*
Abdomen, arthropod, 240, 246, 252
Abdominal breathing, 400
Abducens nerve, 410*
Abiotics, ecosystem, 101
ABO blood groups, 587
  racial significance of, 589
Abortion, 515
Abscission, 376, 377*
Absolute zero, 40
Absorption:
  cellular, 73
  of glucose, 291
  intestinal, 300, 302
  as nutritional process, 290
  in plants, 175, 292
  in root, 292
  and secretion, 291
Abyssal plain, 115
Acanthocephala, 219
Acetabularia, 155, 156*, 479
Acetaldehyde, 316
Acetic acid, 52, 53*
Acetyl choline, 350, 413
Acetyl CoA, 314, 316, 318, 334
Acid, 30
  as oxidation level, 310
Acoela, 217
Acoelomata, 209, 216
Acorn worms, 260
Acquired characteristics, 537
Acrasieae, 166
Acromegaly, 383*, 384
Acrosome, 499
ACTH, 383*, 450
Actin, 347, 348
Actinomycetales, 146
Actinopodea, 168
Actinopterygii, 274*, 275
Actinostele, 183
Actinotroch larva, 226
Actinula larva, 214
Action potential, nerve, 412
Activation:
  amino acid, 343
  in β-oxidation, 318
  of egg, 508
  energy, 40, 41
  and free-energy change, 41
Active behavior, 429, 430
Active site, enzyme, 43
Active transfer, parasitic, 108
Active transport, 63, 290
Actomyosin, 347
Adam's apple, 297, 399
Adaptation, 17, 520
  DNA in, 346
  by evolution, 539, 540, 588
  genetic control of, 346
  by heredity, 520, 521
  sensory, 416
  by sex, 464
Adaptive enzymes, 361
Adaptive radiation, 545
Addison's disease, 383*
Adenine, 57, 58*, 335*
Adenosine, 58
Adenosine phosphates, 58
  (*See also* ADP; ATP)
Adenylic acid, 58
Adipose tissue, 83
ADP, 58
  in glycolysis, 315
  in muscle, 348, 349
  in respiration, 310
Adrenal gland, 385
Adrenalin, 333, 337, 386, 413
Adrenergic nerve fibers, 413
Adrenocortical hormones, 383*, 385
Adrenocorticotropic hormones, 383*, 386
Adventitious root, 179
Aerial root, 180
Aerobe, 313
Aerobic respiration, 142, 312
Aerosol, 61
Afferent nerve fiber, 407
Afterbirth, 516
Agar jelly, 161
Aggression, 447–450
Aging, colloidal, 62
Agnatha, 269, 272
Agonistic behavior, 447
Agricultural insects, 445
Air:
  in breathing, 399, 400
  environmental, 121, 124
  in leaf, 185
  in photosynthesis, 323
  in plant nutrition, 293
Air sac:
  as lung, 271, 400
  as swim bladder, 275
Alanine, 53, 319
Alarm reaction, 386, 449
Albumin, 392
Alcohol:
  in fermentation, 313
  as oxidation level, 310
Aldehyde, as oxidation level, 310
Aldose sugars, 51
Algae, 154, 160, Color Figure 8
  life cycles in, 478
  in ocean, 113
  origin of, 143, 153
  pigments in, 154
  reproduction of, 478
Algin, 160
Alimentary system, 89, 208, 295
  enzymes in, 298*
  excretion in, 300
  mammalian, 299*
  in taxonomy, 208
Alimentation, 203, 208, 289, 295
Alkali, 35
All-or-none action, 87
Allantoic acid, 335*
Allantoin, 335*
Allantois, 513, 514
Alleles, 523
Allergy, 57
Alligators, 278
Alloeocoela, 217
Alpha carbon, 53
Alpha helix, 55
Alternate leaf pattern, 186
Alternate pathway effects, 363
Alternation of generation, 176, 470
  in algae, 479
  in bryophytes, 487
  in ferns, 489
  in plants, 486
  in seed plants, 490
  in tracheophytes, 488
Altitude, as ecological factor, 119, 120*
Alveolus, 400
Ambulacral groove, 262, 263*, 264
Ametabola, 249
Amictic eggs, 220*
Amino acid, 53, 55*
  activation, 343
  in animal nutrition, 295
  conversion to carbohydrate, 33
  conversion to lipid, 334
  deamination, 319, 334
  degradation, 335
  essential, 295, 335
  genetic code for, 342, 343*
  in liver, 334
  metabolism, 334, 335
  in protein, 53
  in protein synthesis, 343
  respiration, 319
  and RNA, 343
  synthesis, 334, 335
  transamination, 319
Amino group, 53, 295, 319, 334, 335
Amino peptidase, 298
Ammocoete, 271*, 272
Ammonia:
  in amino acid, 319, 334, 335*
  in deamination, 319, 334
  in decay, 126, 127
  on early earth, 137
  excretion, 334
  formation, 319, 334
  metabolism, 333
  in nitrogen cycle, 126, 127
  in origin of life, 137
  in urea, 335*
Ammonites, 561, 562*
Amnion, 513, 514*
Amniotes, 513
Amniotic fluid, 513
Amoeba, 21*, 168, 169*, 482, Color Figure 11
Amoeboid movement, 74
Amoeboid protozoa, 167–169
Amoeboid state, 152, 166, 168
AMP, 58
Amphibia, 269, 275, 511, 563, Color Figure 14
Amphiblastula, 211*
Amphineura, 229, 230
Amphioxus, 266, 268
Amphiuma, 276*

Amplification, pollutant, 128
Amplifier in steady state, 358*
Ampulla:
  in semicircular canal, 419
  in tube foot, 262
Amylase, 298
Amylose, 51, 52*, 330*, 331
Anabolism, 307, 331*
Anaerobe, 313
Anaerobic respiration, 142, 313
Anal cerci, 252
Analogy, biological, 27*
Anamniotes, 513
Anaphase:
  meiotic, 468
  mitotic, 460, Color Figure 23
Androgens, 386
Anemia, 366*, 588, 589
  Cooley's, 589
  sickle-cell, 588, 589
Angiosperm, 178, 194, 196
  adaptations, 178–182
  embryo, 182, 495, 496*
  evolution, 556
  flower, 494, Color Figure 28
  fruit, 197, 495, 496
  growth, 182–189
  life cycle, 494
  ovule, 494
  pollination, 495
  reproduction, 494
  seeds, 495
  types, 196
  wood, 197*
Angler fish, 114*
Anhydride, 308, 309*, 310
Animal, 26*, 203
  adaptations, 203
  alimentation, 203, 208, 295
  behavior, 204, 427
  breathing, 400
  cells, 74, 81
  circulation, 301
  classification, 26*, 207
  connective tissues, 81
  deep-sea, 113, 114
  dependence on plant, 295
  development, 508
  digestion, 296
  endocrines, 204, 381
  epithelia, 84
  evolution, 143, 210*, 556
  excretion, 206, 401
  fats, 317, 318
  fertilization, 499, 501*
  food intake, 296
  fossils, 559*, 560, Color Figures 30–34
  growth, 206
  hormones, 381
  ingestion, 295
  interrelations, 210*
  levels of organization, 207
  locomotion, 203
  mating, 503–505
  migrations, 439
  muscles, 86, 87, 203
  nervous system, 294
  nutrition, 295
  organs, 87
Animal:
  reproduction, 499
  senses, 415–423
  skeletons, 84, 85*, 205
  skin, 86
  structure, 204*
  symmetry, 204
  systems, 88, 89, 203–205
  tissues, 81
  types, 26*, 210*
  ways of life, 203
Animalia, kingdom, 25*
Anisogamy, 466
Annelida, 26*, 228, 236, 421*
Annual plants, 181, 378, 380
Annual rings, 191
Anopheles, 170
Anoplura, 250
ANS, 411
Ant, 95*, 251*, 255
  magnetic, 440*
  society, 443
Anteater, 280*
Antenna, 240
Antennal gland, 246
Anterior lobe of pituitary, 382, 383*
Anther, 494, Color Figure 28
Antheridia, 466, 486*, 487, 489
Anthoceropsida, 176
Anthoceros, 178
Anthocyanin, 324
Anthozoa, 213, 216, Color Figure 17
Anthropoids, 568
Antibody, 392, 587
Antigen, 392, 587
Anus, 300
Anvil in ear, 420
Aorta, 396
Aortic arch, 266*, 268, 271*
Apemen, 575–579
Apes, 570, 575, 576*
Apex, plant, 182
Aphids, 445
Aphotic zone, 111, 113
Apical dominance, 375
Apical growth, 157, 182
Apical meristem, 182
  auxin in, 375
Appalachian revolution, 551, 555, 563
Appendages:
  annelid, 237
  arthropod, 240
  chelicerate, 242
  crustacean, 246
  insect, 246, 252
  mandibulate, 245, 246
  vertebrate, 266, 269
Appendicularians, 266, 268
Appendix, 300, 301*
Appetitive phase, behavioral, 427
Applied science, 5
Apterygota, 249
Aquatic life, 111, 115
Aqueous humor, 421
Arachnida, 242, 244
Arboreal primates, 567–571
Arcella, 168, 169*
Archegonia, 466, 486*, 487, 489, 491, 492
Archenteron, 510
Archeopteryx, 565
Archiannelida, 236, 237
Arctic tern, 439
Arginine, 55*, 335*, 348
Arm:
  echinoderm, 262
  micropylar, 492, 495
Armored fish, 17*, 561, 562*
Army ants, 445
Arrowworms, 260
Arteries, 394*, 395
Arthropoda, 26*, 228, 240, 242, 245
  evolution of, 561
  eye in, 240, 241*
  hormones in, 247, 253
Artificial parthenogenesis, 467
Artificial selection, 544
Ascaris, 221*, 223
Aschelminthes, 219–223
Ascidia, 267*
Ascidians, 266, 267
Ascomycetes, 162, 164*, 483–485, Color Figure 9
Asconoid sponges, 211, 212*
Ascophyllum, 161*
Ascorbic acid, 367
Ascospores, 485
Ascus, 163, 484*, 485
Asexual development, 464, 475*
Aspartic acid, 55*, 319
Assortment, law of, 524
Astasia, 157
Aster, mitotic, 460
Asterias, 263*
Asteroids, 261, 559*, 560, Color Figure 22
Asteroxylon, 553
Atactostele, 184*, 185, 196
Atmosphere, 125
  in breathing, 399, 400
  carbon dioxide in, 126
  cycles in, 125
  early, 141, 142
  inert gases in, 125
  modern, 125
  nitrogen in, 126
  oxygen in, 125
  in photosynthesis, 323
  in plant nutrition, 293
Atom, 19, 31, 32, 137
Atomic nucleus, 31
Atomic number, 32*
Atomic weight, 32*
ATP, 58, 310
  and acetyl CoA, 316
  and actomyosin, 347, 348
  in amino acid activation, 343
  in amino acid respiration, 319
  in β-oxidation, 318
  in bioelectricity, 350
  in bioluminescence, 350
  and calories, 317, 318
  in carbon dioxide fixation, 328, 329*
  in citric acid cycle, 314, 315
  in cyclic electron transfer, 325, 326
  in DNA synthesis, 345

ATP:
as energy carrier, 58, 310
in fat respiration, 318
formation, 310, 313*
in glycolysis, 316
as heat source, 349
in hexose shunt, 317
in hydrogen transfer, 311, 313
in movement, 347, 348
in noncyclic electron transfer, 326, 327
in origin of life, 137
as phosphate donor, 291
in phosphorylation, 291
in photolysis, 326
in photophosphorylation, 326
in photosynthesis, 326, 327
physical roles of, 347, 348
in protein respiration, 319
in protein synthesis, 342, 343*
in respiration, 310
in synthesis, 331
in urea synthesis, 335
in vision, 421
ATPase, 349
Atrial siphon, 267
Atriopore, 268
Atrium, 267, 268
of heart, 295
Auditory nerve, 410*
Augmentation, nervous, 414
Aurelia, 215*, 216
Auricle, 395
Auriculoventricular node and valve, 396
Australopithecus, 575, 576
Autogamy, 482
Autonomic ganglia, 412
Autonomic nervous system, 411
Autosomes, 530
Autotrophism, 15, 289
in ecosystem, 101
forms of, 289, 290*
origin of, 141
Auxin, 335*, 337, 371
in abscission, 376
in bud development, 375
in callus, 376
in cambium, 376
cell elongation by, 371
concentrations, 373
in cuttings, 376
effects, 371, 372, 375
geotropic effect of, 373
inhibition by, 373
and light, 371
in meristems, 375, 376
phototropic effect of, 372
in root development, 376
in weed control, 377
AV node and valve, 396
Aves, 269, 278
Axial gland and sinus, 264
Axil leaf, 186
Axon, 407
Axoneme, 168
Axopodium, 168
Aye-aye, 568
Azoic, 551, 552*
B vitamins, 366, 367
Bacillariophyceae, 158, 480, Color Figure 5
Bacillus, 146*, 477*
Bacillus, 144
Bacteria, 144, 145
bioluminescent, 350*
budding in, 477
chemosynthetic, 141
chlorophyll in, 145, 289
classification of, 146
colonies of, 144, 145*
conidia in, 478
in decay, 126, 127
disease-producing, 106
endospores in, 146*, 477
heterotrophic, 289
intestinal, 105, 301
in nitrogen cycle, 104*, 105, 126
nutrition in, 289
origin of, 143
parasitic, 106, 145
photosynthetic, 289
reproduction in, 477
saprotrophic, 145
sex in, 477, 478
in soil, 126, 127, 145
sporangia of, 478*
sulfur, 289
transduction in, 528
transformation in, 527, 528*
Bacteriochlorophyll, 145, 289
Bacteriophage, 106
Balance senses, 418, 419
Balanced polymorphism, 589
Balanus, 248*
Bark, 189, 190
Barnacles, 247, 248*
Barriers:
geographic, 97, 543
reproductive, 543
Basal granules, 72
Base, chemical, 35
Basement membrane, 84, 86*
Basic science, 5
Basidiomycetes, 162, 165, 483–485, Color Figure 10
Basidiospores, 485
Basidium, 165, 484*, 485
Basilar membrane, 420
Basket stars, 261
Bats, 281*, 547*
Bean seed, 496*
Beard worms, 260
Beat of heart, 396
Bedbug, 250*
Bee, 254*, 255
behavior, 438
society, 443, 444
Beetles, 250*, 255
Behavior, 204, 427
active, 429
aggressive, 447
animal, 204
biological clocks in, 435
and brain function, 414, 415
breeding, 502–505
cognitive, 430, 431
courtship, 504
dominance in, 450, 451
Behavior:
drives in, 427
environment and, 427
exploratory, 430
forms of, 427
heredity in, 427
hormones in, 379, 449, 503*
of insects, 443
light and, 436
manipulative, 431
migratory, 438
parental, 505
patterns in, 427
photoperiodism and, 377, 378
plant, 371, 372, 377, 378
play, 430
programmatic, 415, 429
reactive, 428
redirected, 448
reproductive, 502–505
rhythmic, 435–437
seasonal, 435, 438, 502, 503
social, 443
stimuli in, 432
structure of, 427
and temperature, 380
territorial, 450, 452
and tropisms, 372, 429
vertebrate, 446
Bennettites, 556*
Benthonic zone, 111
Benthos, 111
Benzene, 50
Beriberi, 367
Beta carbon, 53
Beta helix, 55
Beta oxidation, 318
Bicarbonate ion, 401
Bicuspid valve, 396
Biennial plants, 181, 378, 380
Bilaterality, 204, 207
Bilateria, 207, 209, 211, 216
Bile, 298*, 300, 336*, 368
Bile pigments, 336*
Bile salts, 300, 336
Binary fission, 459
Binucleate cell, 67
Bioelectricity, 350
Biological barriers, 97, 543
Biological clocks, 435–437
Biological evolution, 138, 140
Biology, 13
Bioluminescence, 350
Biomass, 101
Biomes, 116
Biophysical metabolism, 347
Biosphere, 99, 111, 121
Biotin, 366
Biparental heredity, 522–527
Bipinnaria larva, 264
Bird, 278, 279
egg, 513
evolution, 564, 565
migrations, 439
peck orders, 451
territoriality, 452, 453
Bird's-nest fungi, 165, Color Figure 10
Birth, 515, 516
control, 130

Bisexual potentials, 530
Biting-chewing mouth parts, 250, 251*
Bitter taste, 417
Bivalves, 226, 228
Bladder, urinary, 402
Blade, leaf, 185, 186
Blastea hypothesis, 557
Blastocoel, 509*, 510
Blastodinium, 160
Blastodisc, 509
Blastoids, 560, 561
Blastomeres, 508
Blastopore, 510
Blastula, 509
Bleeder's disease, 394
Blending inheritance, 521
Blights, 162
Blind spot, 422
Blood, 205, 391
  antibodies, 392, 587
  antigens, 392
  arterial, 395, 396
  carbon dioxide, 398
  cells, 68*, 392
  circulation, 395
  clotting, 393
  components, 392*
  corpuscles, 392, 394
  in defense, 392, 393
  distribution, 398
  flukes, 108, 218*
  genetics of, 587
  glucose, 296, 333
  groups, 587, 588
  hemoglobin, 394
  in immunization, 392
  ions, 391, 392
  leeches, 239
  in marrow, 393
  minerals, 391, 392
  nutrient transport, 391, 392
  osmotic pressure, 391
  oxygen, 394, 401
  pH, 391, 392
  phagocytes, 392
  pigments, 394
  in placenta, 514
  plasma, 391
  platelets, 393
  pressure, 398
  production, 393
  proteins, 392
  as racial trait, 587, 588
  respiratory pigments, 394
  serum, 393
  sinuses, 230
  transfusion, 392
  in transport, 391
  types, 392
  and vasomotion, 398
  venous, 395, 396
  vessels, 394*, 395
  in wound healing, 393, 394*
Blood-brain barrier, 413
Blue-green algae, 143, 147, 477, 478, Color Figure 6
Bobcat, 117*
Bodo, 168*
Body cavity, 209
Body cell, 493
Body fluids, 391
Bond:
  carbohydrate, 50, 51*
  carbon, 34
  chemical, 32–34
  covalent, 34
  electrovalent, 33
  energy, 38, 310
  high-energy, 58, 310
  hydrogen, 56
  ionic, 33
  molecular, 34
  in organic compounds, 50
  in proteins, 56
  in reactions, 36, 37
Bone, 84, 85*
  growth, 367
  vertebrate, 274, 275
Bonellia, 229*, 530
Bony fishes, 269, 274, 562*, 563
Book gills, 240, 242
Book lungs, 240, 243
Bordered pits, 79
Botrydiopsis, 158*
Brachiopoda, 226, 227*
Bracket fungi, 162, 165
Brain, 407
  blood barrier in, 413
  centers, 414, 415
  channel selection in, 414
  development, 510*
  evolution, 575, 579*, 580, 581
  in food intake, 296
  functions, 414, 415
  in heart control, 396, 397
  hunger centers in, 296
  in learning, 415
  and memory, 415
  as modulator, 414, 415
  nerves of, 410*
  rhythms in, 414
  in sense perception, 423
  structure, 407, 409*, 410
  types, 409*
Branch:
  bud of, 186
  gap, 184*, 186
  lateral, 186
  root, 186, 187
  stem, 186
  taxonomic, 207
Bread mold, 162, 163*, 483
Breathing, 400
  at birth, 516
  blood pigments in, 304, 401
  carbon dioxide in, 401
  center, 400
  control, 400
  oxygen in, 401
  oxygen debt in, 313
  placental, 513, 514
  process, 400
  vertebrate, 399
Breathing system, 89, 206, 398*, 399
  excretion in, 401
  tracheal, 252
Breeding cycles, 449
  annelid, 237
  and behavior, 440, 449, 452, 502
Breeding cycles:
  and environment, 503
  hormones in, 449, 503, 506
  seasonal, 502–505
Bristles, 237
Brittle stars, 261, Color Figure 22
Bronchus, 400
Brontosaurus, 565
Bronze Age, 579
Brook lamprey, 272
Brown algae, 160, 161*, 480, 481
Brown-line algae, 154
Brownian motion, 61
Bryophyta, 176, 486*–488
Bryopsida, 176
Bryopsis, 156, 479, 480*
Bryozoa, 227
Bud:
  of branch, 184*, 186
  of leaf, 184*, 185
  in plants, 375
  scale, 186
  terminal, 186, 187*
Budding:
  animal, 464
  bacterial, 477*
  cellular, 459
  by gemmae, 486*, 487
  sponge, 212
  as vegetative reproduction, 464
Buffers, 36
Bugs, 250*, 255
Bulb, 179
Bundle of His, 396
Bush pattern, evolutionary, 29, 545
Buttercup structure, 183*, 184*
Butterflies, 251*, 255

C vitamins, 367
Cactus, 117*, 180
Caecum, 300, 301*
Caiman, 278
Calamites, 554*, Color Figure 29
Calamophyton, 554*
Calcarea, 211
Calcareous skeletons, 205
Calcareous sponges, 211
Calcium:
  blood, 393, 394*
  hormone control, 385
  skeletal, 205
  vitamin control, 366*, 367
Callus, 376
Calorie, 40, 317–320
Calvin cycle, 328, 329*
Calyx, 494, Color Figure 28
Cambium, 188, 189, 376
Cambrian, 552*, 560
Camouflage, 103, Color Figure 4
Capillary, 394*, 395
Carapace, 245, 277
Carbohydrase, 44
Carbohydrate, 50
  acetyl CoA from, 314
  balance, 332, 333
  bonds, 50, 51*
  conversion to amino acid, 334
  conversion to fatty acid, 334
  digestion, 297, 298*, 300

Carbohydrate:
energy, 317
as fat precursor, 333
functions, 51, 52
hormone control of, 333*, 383*
liver storage, 302, 333
metabolism, 332
phosphorylation, 291
in photosynthesis, 289, 328, 329
in respiration, 308, 315
storage, 331, 333
synthesis, 329, 332
utilization, 332, 333
Carbon, 34, 308
in citric acid cycle, 314
electrons, 34
environmental, 121, 126
global cycle of, 126
in living matter, 49, 50
in origin of life, 137
oxidation, 308, 309
oxidation states, 308, 311*
in photosynthesis, 323, 328
reduction, 308
in respiration, 308, 314, 317, 319
valences, 34
Carbon dioxide, 34, 49
atmospheric, 121, 126
at birth, 516
in blood, 398, 401
in breathing, 400, 401
in citric acid cycle, 314
in decay, 126
effect on heart, 398
fixation of, 323, 328
in flowering, 378, 379
global cycle of, 126
greenhouse effect of, 126, 128
in nutrition, 289
in photosynthesis, 323, 328
in pollution, 128
in respiration, 308, 309*, 314
in sex determination, 530
in urea synthesis, 335*
in vasomotion, 398
Carbon monoxide, 401
Carboniferous, 552*, 554, 563, Color Figure 29
Carboxyl group, 52
Carboxypeptidase, 298
Cardiac muscle, 86, Color Figure 1
Carnivores, 101, 204, 281*
Carotene, 53, 54*, 155, 175, 365
Carotenoids, 53, 54*, 175, 323
Carpel, 494, Color Figure 28
Carpoids, 560
Carposporophyte, 481*
Cartilage, 84, 269, 273
Cartilaginous fishes, 269, 273, 562*, 563
Casein, 299
Castration, psychological, 452
Catabolism, 307, 331*
Catalysis, 42, 43
Categories, taxonomic, 23
Caterpillars, 253, 254*
Cattails, 116*
Causalism, 12
Ceboids, 568, 569
Cedars, 196
Cell, 19, 67
absorption by, 73, 290
animal, 74
in blood, 392
body in neuron, 407
cilia, 75
compounds, 49
constancy, 219, 220
controls in, 360, 362, 364
cuticle, 74
cytoplasm, 67
differentiation, 471, 473
DNA control of, 360, 361*
elongation by auxin, 371
evolution, 139, 142*
functions, 76*
as gamete, 464
genetic control of, 345, 346
gland, 351
glucose uptake by, 291
growth, 459
membrane, 67
metabolism control, 361–364
minerals, 49
multiplication, 459, 460
nucleus, 66
nutrition, 290, 291
organelles, 67
as organization level, 19, 21*
origin, 137–139
plant, 73, 77
replacement, 461
reproduction, 459, 460
reproductive, 464
secretions, 351
shells of, 74
skeletons of, 74
spore, 464
surfaces, 73
theory, 67
wall, 67, 73
Cell division, 459, 460, Color Figure 23
chromosomes in, 460
DNA in, 461
as growth, 462
in heredity, 522, 527
meiotic, 468
mitotic, 460
nucleus in, 460
plant hormones in, 371
as reproduction, 459, 460
in tissue culture, 462
Cell structure, 68, 69*, 76
animal, 74
moneran, 144*
plant, 73
protistan, 152*
Cellulose, 51, 52*, 147, 154, 175, 265
Cement organ, 220
Cenozoic, 552*, 556, 567
climates, 556, 567
Centers, neural, 414, 415
Centipede, 245, 246*, 248
Central excitatory state, 427
Central nervous system, 411
Centriole, 72
Centrolecithal eggs, 509*
Centromere, 460
Cephalin, 53
Cephalochordates, 266, 268
Cephalopoda, 229, 234
Cephalothorax, 240, 242
Ceratium, 159*, 160
Cercaria larva, 109
Cercopithecoids, 568, 569
Cerebellum, 409*, 410
Cerebrum, 409*, 410
Cestodes, 217
Chaetae, 237
Chaetognatha, 260
Chaetopterus, 238*
Chain tunicates, 266, 268
Chalk, 170
Chalk sponges, 211
Chamaeleon, 277*
Chamaeosiphonales, 147
Chambered nautilus, 235
Channel selection in brain, 414
Chara, 157*
Charophyta, 157, 480
Chelate legs, 242
Chelicera, 240, 242
Chelicerata, 240, 242
Chemical:
bonds in, 32, 38
energy in, 38, 39, 310
in living matter, 19
reactions of, 36, 37
Chemical control, 360, 364
Chemical evolution, 137
Chemical senses, 416
Chemolithotrophs, 289
Chemoorganotrophs, 289
Chemoreceptors, 416, 417
Chemosynthesis, 141, 289
Chemotaxis, 439
Chemotropism, 372
Chert, 168
Chest, 400
Chilaria, 242
Chilomonas, 159
Chilopoda, 245, 248
Chimpanzees, 570
Chinese liver fluke, 108, 109, 218*
Chitin, 74, 236, 240, 260
Chiton, 229, 231
Chlamydomonas, 155, 468, 479
Chloragogue cells, 239
Chlorella, 155, 156*
Chlorocruorin, 394
Chlorophyll, 15, 53, 72, 324*
algal, 147, 154
bacterial, 145
in chloroplast, 324*
ionization of, 325
in leaf, 185
in origin of life, 141
in photosynthesis, 323, 325
in plants, 175
variants, 154
Chlorophyta, 155, 156, 479, Color Figure 7
Chloroplast, 72, 323, 324*
Choanocytes, 211, 212*
Choline, 366
Cholinergic fibers, 413
Chondrichthyes, 269, 273
Chondroblasts, 85*

Chondroclasts, 85*
Chondrus crispus, 161
Chordata, 27, 28*, 260, 265
  development in, 508
  evolution of, 266, 268, 270, 558, 561
  subphyla of, 266–269
Chords, nematode, 221
Chorion, 513, 514
Choroid:
  in eye, 421
  plexus, 409*
Chromatids, 460, 468
Chromatophore, 144, 145
Chromoplast, 71
Chromosome, 67, 68*
  in cell division, 459, 460
  in cell evolution, 143, 151
  in DNA reproduction, 345
  functions, 339
  in genetic code, 339, 341
  in heredity, 521
  homologous, 523
  independent assortment of, 524
  interactions of, 532, 533
  in meiosis, 468
  in Mendelian inheritance, 522
  in mitosis, 459, 460, Color Figure 23
  movements, 347, 460
  mutations, 528, 529
  ploidy, 468
  in protists, 151
  puffs, 341, 342*
  sex balances of, 530, 531
  in sex determination, 529
  theory of inheritance, 521, 522
Chroococcales, 147
Chrysamoeba, 158*
Chrysophyceae, 158
Chrysophyta, 158, 480
Chymotrypsin, 298
Cilia, 75, 170*
Ciliary body, 421
Ciliate protozoa, 167, 170, 171
Ciliophora, 167, 170, 171
Ciona, 267*
Circadian rhythms, 435
Circinate vernation, 194*, 195
Circulatory system, 89, 205, 395
  blood in, 391, 395
  in breathing, 395, 400
  closed, 235, 270, 395
  in fetus, 516
  in intestine, 302
  lymph, 302, 395
  nervous control of, 396, 397
  in nutrition, 302
  open, 230, 240, 268
  in placenta, 513, 514
  in vertebrate evolution, 266*, 271
  vessels of, 394*, 395
Cirri, 170*, 171
Cistron, 533
Citric acid cycle, 314, 315*
Citrulline, 335*
Cladophora, 156*
Clam, 229, 233
Clamworms, 236, Color Figure 20
Class, taxonomic, 23
Classification, 23, 25–27
Clay, 124
Cleavage, 508, 509*
  in cell division, 460
  cytoplasmic, 460
  egg, 508
  furrow, 460
  initiation, 508
  twinning by, 509
Climate:
  and atmosphere, 125
  in fresh water, 115
  and hydrosphere, 122
  and ice ages, 122
  and lithosphere, 123
  and mountains, 123
  in ocean, 111
  plant adaptations to, 180, 181
Climax community, 100
Clines, 584
Clitellum, 239
Cloaca, 273, 402
Clocks, biological, 435–437
Clonorchis, 218*
Closed circulation, 235, 270, 395
Closed system, 121
Clotting, blood, 393, 394*
Club fungi, 162, 165
Club mosses, 192, Color Figure 12
Clupeiform fishes, 275
CMP, 58
Cnidaria, 213
  (*See also* Coelenterates)
Cnidoblasts, 213
Cnidocil, 213*
CNS, 411
CoA, 59
Coagulation protein, 56
Coal formation, 554
Cocarboxylase, 316
Coccine state, 152, 155, 162
Coccolithophorids, 158*
Coccus, 144, 145*
Cochlea, 420
Cocoon:
  earthworm, 239
  pupal, 254*
Code, genetic, 339–346
Codosiga, 168*
Coelacanth, 274*, 275
Coelenterates, 26*, 213, Color Figures 15–17
  coral-forming, 216
  eye in, 421
  polymorphism in, 213
Coeloblastula, 509*
Coelom, 208*, 209
  enterocoelomate, 226, 259
  lophophorate, 225, 226
  schizocoelomate, 228
  segmented, 237
Coelom sacs, 228, 240
Coelomata, 209, 225, 259
Coenocyte, 67
Coenzyme, 58
  as controller, 365, 366*
  in hydrogen transfer, 312, 313*
  as nucleotide derivative, 58, 59*
  in respiration, 312, 313*
  and vitamins, 365, 366*
Coenzyme A, 59
Coenzyme Q, 313*
Cofactor, 43*
Cognitive behavior, 430, 431
Coldbloodedness, 350
Coleoptera, 250*, 255
Collar, 235, 260
  cells, 211
  flagellates, 167, 168*, 211
Collenchyma, 78*, 79
Colloid, 61, 62
Colon, 300
Colonies, 19, 144, 461
Color blindness, 532
Color vision, 421, 422
Colostrum, 515
Columnar epithelium, 84, 86*
Comb jellies, 213
Combustion, respiratory, 307
Commensalism, 104, 105
Communication, symbolic, 432, 433
Community, 20, 99
  balances, 101
  climax, 100
  in ecosystem, 99
  food pyramids in, 101
  in fresh water, 115
  history of, 100
  marine, 111
  nutrition in, 101
  populations in, 99
  protection in, 103
  reproduction in, 102
  structure, 100
  succession, 100
  terrestrial, 115
Compact bone, 85*
Companion cell, 70, 80*
Compatibility, sexual, 467
Competition, 21
  chemical, 363
  interspecific, 98
  intraspecific, 96
Compound, 19, 32, 33*
  inorganic, 49
  ionic, 33
  in living matter, 49, 50
  molecular, 34*
  organic, 49
  properties of, 35
Compound eye, 240, 241*
Compound leaf, 186
Concentration:
  in diffusion, 62
  in osmosis, 64
  in reactions, 40, 41
Conceptacles, 481
Conditioned reflexes, 415
Conditioning, 415, 430, 431
Conduction, nutrient, 175, 292, 295
Cone:
  in eye, 421, 422
  in gymnosperms, 491
  in lycopsids, 489, Color Figure 25
  in plants, 491
  in sphenopsids, 489, Color Figure 25
Conflict, behavioral, 448, 451, 452
Conidia, 477, 478*
Coniferous plants, 195, 491–494

Conjugation, 464, 479, 482
Connective tissues, 81, 84
Conservation:
of energy, 37
environmental, 121, 127, 131
of plant water, 180
Consumer in ecosystem, 101
Consummation, behavioral, 427
Contact movements, 374, 375
Continental drift, 98
Continental shelf, 115
Continental slope, 115
Continuous phase, colloidal, 61
Contour plowing, 125*
Contractile vacuole, 170*, 171
Contraction, muscular, 347, 348
Control, experimental, 6
Control system, 357, 359
animal, 204
in behavior, 371, 381, 427, 432
brain as, 414, 415
in cell, 360, 362, 364
in development, 474
DNA in, 360, 361
enzymatic, 362
feedback in, 358
in flowering, 379, 380
in food intake, 296
genetic, 339–346
growth factors in, 362
hormonal, 371, 381
information in, 357
metabolic, 360
minerals in, 362, 364
molecular, 359, 361, 362
neural, 414
in protein synthesis, 360, 361
of reactions, 361, 362
in steady state, 16, 357, 414
supracellular, 359, 360
vitamins in, 364, 366*
Convergence, evolutionary, 547
Cooley's anemia, 589
Cooperation, 21
intraspecific, 96
social, 453
Copepods, 247, 248*
Copulation, 467*, 499, 501*
Coralline algae, 160, Color Figure 8
Corals, 113, 213, 215*, Color Figure 17
Cordaites, 554, 555*
Cork, 189
cambium, 188, 189
Corm, 179, 193
Corn seed, 496*
Corn stem, 184*
Cornea, 421
Corolla, 494, Color Figure 28
Corpus allatum, 253, 255
Corpus callosum, 409*, 410
Corpus luteum, 506, 507
Corpuscles, blood, 394
Cortex:
adrenal, 385
in bark formation, 190
gonadal, 500, 501*
in plants, 77
renal, 402
Corti, organ of, 420
Cortisone, 54*, 386
Cosmopolitan species, 97
Cotyledon, 197, 490, 493, 495
Cotylosaurs, 563, 565
Courtship behavior, 504
Covalence, 34
Crab, 248*
Cranial nerves, 410*, 411
Creatine, 348
Cretaceous, 552*
Cretinism, 384
Crinoids, 261, 560, 561*, Color Figure 22
Crisis, ecological, 127
Cristae, mitochondrial, 71
Crocodiles, 278
Cro-Magnon man, 577, 578
Crop, 239
Crop rotation, 124
Cross-fertilization, 467
Cross-pollination, 494
Crossing over, 526, 527*
Crown galls, 376
Crustacea, 245, 248
Crustose lichens, 163, Color Figure 3
Cryptoflagellates, 159
Cryptomonas, 159
Cryptophyceae, 159
Ctenidia, 230
Ctenoid scales, 275
Ctenophora, 213
CTP, 342
Cuboidal epithelium, 84, 86*
Cucumaria, 264*
Cup fungi, 162, 484*, Color Figure 9
Currents:
oceanic, 122
river, 115
Cutaneous receptors, 423
Cuticle, 73*, 74
Cuttings, plant, 376
Cyanide, 137
Cyanophycean starch, 147
Cyanophyta, 147, 477, 478, Color Figure 6
Cycads, 195, 554
Cycles:
atmospheric, 124
behavioral, 435, 437
in ecosystem, 101
environmental, 121, 436
hydrospheric, 121
lithospheric, 122
in ocean life, 122
Cyclic electron transfer, 325, 326*
Cycloid scales, 275
Cyclops, 248*
Cyclosis, 73
Cypresses, 196
Cyst, protistan, 151
Cysteine, 55*, 56
Cystoids, 560, 561
Cytidilic acid, 58
Cytidine, 58
Cytochrome, 53, 54*
in hydrogen transport, 312, 313*
in photosynthesis, 325, 326*
in respiration, 312, 313*
Cytokinesis, 460
Cytoplasm, 67
in cell division, 460
in cell evolution, 143
Cytosine, 57, 58*

2,4-D, 371
D vitamins, 367
Dairy ants, 445
Damselfly, 250*
Daphnia, 247, 248*
Dark reaction, photosynthetic, 323
Darwin, Charles, 538
Day length:
and animal, 436
and plant, 378
Deamination, 319, 334
Decay, 126, 127, 290
bacterial, 145
environmental, 127
evolution of, 140
intestinal, 301
posterior, 486*, 487
radioactive, 550
results of, 126, 127
by saprotrophs, 289, 290
Deciduous forests, 117, 118*
Deciduous plants, 181
Decomposers in ecosystem, 101
Decomposition:
chemical, 37
of methane, 309*
respiratory, 308
Deep-sea fishes, 114
Degrowth, 459
Dehydrogenase, 311
Dehydrogenation, 308
Deletion, chromosomal, 528
Demospongiae, 211
Denaturation, protein, 56
Dendrite, 407
Denitrification, 127
Denticles, 273*
Deoxyribose, 51*, 57
Deoxyribose nucleic acid (*see* DNA)
Deoxyribotides, 57
Depolarization, nerve, 412
Derepression, chemical, 362
Dermal bone, 84, 85*
Dermal skeleton, starfish, 262, 263*
Dermis, 88
Desert, 116, 117*
Desmids, 116*
Determined eggs, 508
Detorsion, 232*, 233
Deuterostomia, 208, 259, 510
Development, 17, 462, 471
animal, 508
asexual, 474, 475
of blastula, 508, 509
in classification, 207–211
control of, 474
differentiation in, 471–473
divergence in, 558
evolutionary divergence in, 545
of eye, 511
fertilization in, 508
of fetus, 514, 515
of form, 471
of gastrula, 510

Development:
genes in, 473
growth in, 471, 472
induction in, 511, 512
larval, 512
metabolism in, 473
modulation in, 473
morphogenesis in, 471, 472
neoteny in, 558, 580, 581
nutrition in, 473
operons in, 473
paths of, 474, 475
plant, 375
plant behavior by, 375
sexual, 475
stages of, 474, 508, 512
Devonian, 552*, 554, 563
Diabetes, 291, 333, 383*
Diaphragm, 400
Diastrophism, 122
Diatomaceous earth, 159
Diatoms, 112, 158, 480, Color Figure 5
Dichlorophenoxyacetic acid, 371
Dicots, 196, 198
Dicotyledonae, 196
Dictyostele, 184*, 185, 196
Didinium, 171*
Diencephalon, 409*, 410
Dietary calorie, 40
Differential growth, 472
Differential reproduction, 539, 541
Differentiation, 471, 473
Difflugia, 168, 169*
Diffusion, 62, 290, 291*
Digestion, 296, 298*, 300
Digestive enzymes, 298
Digestive glands, 297
Digestive juices, 298
Digestive systems, 89, 208
Dikaryophase, 483*, 484
Dimorphism, 95
Dinoclonium, 159*
Dinoflagellates, 159
Dinophyceae, 159
Dinosaurs, 564, 566*
Dioecious plants, 490
Dipeptide, 54*, 55
Diphosphoglyceric acid, 316*
Dipleurula, 261
Diplococcus, 144, 145*
Diplohaplontic life cycle, 471, 479, 485
Diploid mitospores, 470, 471
Diploidy, 468
Diplontic life cycle, 470, 479, 499
Diplopoda, 245, 248
Diptera, 251*, 255
Disaccharase, 298
Disaccharide, 51
Discoblastula, 509*
Discoidal eggs, 509*
Disease, 17, 359, 363
"inherited," 533
in racial evolution, 587–590
Dispersed phase, colloidal, 61
Displacement behavior, 448
Display, aggressive, 447
Dissociation:
ionic, 35

Dissociation:
and pH, 36
Distribution:
blood, 398
blood group, 587, 588
gene frequency, 584
species, 97
Disulfide bond, 56
Diurnal migration, 112
Divergence:
developmental, 558
evolutionary, 545
Division:
cell, 459
of labor, 21
meiotic, 460
mitotic, 460
plate, 461
DNA, 59, 60
in adaptation, 345
in cell, 67
in cell control, 345
in chloroplast, 323
in chromosomes, 339
in code transcription, 339–346
in control system, 345, 360
duplication of, 345
in evolution, 345
functions of, 345, 346*
as genes, 339–346
in genetic code, 339–346
in heredity, 528, 533
in metabolism, 345
in mitosis, 461
mutability, 345, 346
nitrogen bases in, 339–346
in operons, 361
in origin of life, 139
polymerase, 345
in protein synthesis, 339–344
in reproduction, 345
stability of, 345
in steady state, 360, 361
structure, 59, 60
synthesis, 345
in transduction, 528
in transformation, 527, 528*
Watson-Crick model of, 60, 339
Dodo, 546*
Doliolum, 268
Dolphins, 547
Domestication, 544
in ants, 445
Dominance:
apical, 375
genetic, 523, 532
hierarchy, behavioral, 450, 451
incomplete, 523
Dormancy:
bacterial, 145
of plant, 186
of seed, 491
of stem, 186, 187*
Dorsal antenna, rotifer, 221
Double bond, 34
Double fertilization, 495
Drift:
continental, 98
genetic, 542
Drives, behavioral, 427

Drones, 443, 444
Drosophila, 521, 522*
Duck-billed platypus, 280
Ductus arteriosus, 516
Dugesia, 217*
Duodenum, 299*, 300
Duplication, mutational, 528
Dwarfism, 384
Dynamic equilibrium, 419

E vitamins, 367
Ear, 420
balance senses in, 419
drum, 420
hearing in, 420
of insect, 420*
stones, 419
Earth:
atmosphere, 125
crust formation, 137, 138
as environment, 111, 121, 122
habitats on, 111, 115
hydrosphere, 121
lithosphere, 121, 122
Earthworm, 236, 238, 239
Eating, 295, 296
Echidna, 280*
Echinoderms, 260, 261, 560, 561, Color Figure 22
Echinoids, 262, 560, 561, Color Figure 22
Echiuroids, 228, 229*
Ecological crisis, 127
Ecological management, 131
Ecological niche, 96
Ecological succession, 100
Ecology, 93
Ecosystem, 93, 99
community in, 100
food utilization in, 101
freshwater, 115
growth of, 102
on land, 115
links in, 101–103
marine, 111
nutritional structure of, 101
physical factors in, 100, 101
species structure of, 100
steady state in, 100
succession in, 100
Ectoderm, 207, 510
Ectoparasites, 106, Color Figure 2
Ectoprocta, 226, 227*
Edible fungi, 163, Color Figure 9
Edible snails, 233, Color Figure 18
Eel migrations, 439
Effectors, 357, 359, 360*
Efferent nerve fiber, 407
Egestion, 301
Egg, 464, 466
activation, 508
as adaptive device, 475
amniote, 276*, 513
animal, 499, 502, 506
cleavage, 508, 509*
cocoon, 239
determined, 508
ducts, 502, 503*
fertilization, 508

Egg:
growth, 506, 507
implantation, 513
maturation, 499, 500*
membranes, 508, 513, 514
mosaic, 508
in oogamy, 466
in ovary, 502, 506, 507*
plant, 486, 488, 490, 492*
regulative, 508
in sex, 475
shell, 276*, 513
undetermined, 508
vertebrate, 271
yolk, 499, 509
Egg-laying mammals, 279, 280*
Elastic fibers, 83
Elastic tissue, 83
Elaters, 488
Electric eels, 350
Electric organs, 350
Electric potential in nerve, 412
Electricity:
atomic, 31
biological, 350
colloidal, 61
Electrolyte, 35
Electron, 31, 32*
acceptor, 33
cyclic transfer of, 325, 326*
donor, 33
energies, 309
noncyclic transfer of, 326, 327
orbits, 31, 32*
in photoexcitation, 325
in photoionization, 325
in photosynthesis, 325, 326*
in respiration, 309
sharing, 34
shells, 31, 32*
shifts, 34, 308
transfer, 33, 325, 326*
valence, 33, 34
Electrovalence, 33
Elementary particle, 31
Elements:
chemical, 31
in living matter, 49, 50*
Elephantiasis, 222*, 223
Elephants, 281*
Elicitation, behavioral, 427
Elver, 439
Emboly, 510
Embryo:
animal, 206, 508
as adaptive device, 475
in classification, 207–211
cleavage in, 508, 509*
development, 508–516
differentiation in, 471, 473
hatching, 512
human, 514*, 515*
induction in, 511, 512
morphogenesis in, 471, 472
organ-forming zones of, 508
polarity in, 471
symmetry in, 471
twinning in, 509
plant, 182, 485
in flowering plant, 494
Embryo:
plant: initials, 493
in Metaphyta, 176, 486
in seed plant, 182, 490–493
in tracheophytes, 182, 488*, 490
Embryophyta, 25*
Emotion centers, 409, 410
Emu, 278*
Emulsion, 61
Encapsulation, protistan, 151
Encystment, protistan, 151
Endemic species, 97
Endergonic reaction, 39
Endocrine, 381–387
control, 204, 381
glands, 352, 381
in nerve fibers, 413
systems, 381
vertebrate, 89, 204, 382, 383*
(*See also* Hormones)
Endoderm, 207, 510
Endodermis, 77*, 79
Endoparasites, 106
Endoplasmic reticulum, 69, 70*
Endopterygota, 249, 251*
Endoskeleton, 205
echinoderm, 262, 264
molluscan, 235
vertebrate, 84, 205
Endosperm, 495, 496*
Endospore, 145, 477
Endothelium, 394*
Endothermic reaction, 39
Endproduct inhibition, 361
Energetics:
of reactions, 37
of respiration, 307
Energy, 15, 37, 307
activation, 40, 41*
in ATP, 58, 310
of bonds, 38, 310
and calories, 317–319
carriers, 58
in chemicals, 38, 39
conservation, law of, 37
in control functions, 358
distributions, 39
and ecology, 101, 121
electric, 350
of electrons, 31, 309
and enthalpy, 38
and entropy, 39
environmental, 121
in glycolysis, 316
heat, 349, 350
light, 323, 350
mechanical, 347
muscular, 348
nutrient, 307
in origin of life, 138
in oxidation, 308, 309
in photosynthesis, 323–327
in reactions, 38, 39
in redox reactions, 308
in respiration, 58, 308, 310, 320
solar, 121, 323
thermal, 349
transfer, 308, 310
Entamoeba, 168, 169*
Enterocoel, 210, 226
Enterocoelomates, 210, 226, 259, 260*
Enterokinase, 298
Enteron, 259
Enthalpy, 38
Entoprocta, 219
Entrainment, 436
Entropy, 39
Environment, 111, 121
in behavior, 427, 503
in ecological crisis, 127
evolutionary role of, 538, 539
freshwater, 115, 121
marine, 111, 121
terrestrial, 115, 122
Environmental decay, 127
Enzymes, 42, 362
active sites in, 43
adaptive, 361
and cofactors, 43
competition of, 363
in control system, 362
digestive, 297, 298
as growth factors, 362
hydrolysis by, 297
induced fit of, 43
inhibition, 360, 361
as modulator, 362
in molecular reproduction, 459
in operons, 361
and pH, 43
as protein, 42
specificity of, 43
and substrate, 43
and temperature, 43
as template, 42
Eocene, 567*
Ephemeroptera, 250*
Epiboly, 510
Epichrysis, 158*
Epicotyl, 493*
Epidermis:
animal, 87
plant, 77, 177, 189
Epididymis, 502
Epiglottis, 297, 300*, 399
Epinasty, 373
Epinephrine, 333, 386
Epineural canal, 262*
Epiphyte, 105
Epitheliosensory receptor, 415, 416*
Epithelium, 84, 86
Epochs, geologic, 567*
Equilibrium:
chemical, 41
senses, 418, 419
Equisetum, 193, 489, Color Figures 12, 25
Eras, geologic, 551, 552*
Ergot, fungus, 163
Erosion, 123, 124, 125*
Errors:
in control, 359
in DNA duplication, 345
Erythrocyte, 394
Escherichia coli, 146, 477
Esophagus, 297
Essential amino acids, 295, 334
Essential fatty acids, 295
Estradiol, 54*

Estrogens, 386, 506
Estrus cycles, 506, 507
Etiolation, 378
Eubacteriales, 146
Euglena, 157
Euglenophyta, 157, 480
Eukaryota, 143
Eumetazoa, 207, 213
Euplotes, 171
Eurypterids, 561
Eustachian tubes, 399, 420
Eutheria, 279
Evergreen plants, 181, 195
Evidence, scientific, 7
Evolution, 17, 537
  as adaptive function, 539, 540
  adaptive radiation in, 545
  animal, 210*, 556, 559*, 560
  artificial selection in, 544
  biological, 140
  bush pattern of, 29, 545
  cellular, 137, 142, 143
  characteristics of, 545–548
  chemical, 137
  in classification, 23, 25, 29
  convergent, 547
  Darwinian, 538
  differential reproduction in, 539, 540
  divergent, 546
  DNA in, 137, 138, 345
  by domestication, 544
  early theories of, 537
  environment in, 538, 539
  expansiveness of, 548
  extinction in, 545, 546
  and fossils, 551
  genetic basis of, 540, 541
  genetic drift in, 542
  and geology, 551
  isolating mechanisms in, 543
  jump hypothesis of, 544
  Lamarckian, 537
  of life, 137
  of major categories, 544
  man-controlled, 544
  mechanisms of, 539
  modern theory of, 539, 540
  mutations in, 539, 541, 542, 544
  natural selection in, 539, 540
  nature of, 539, 543, 545
  by neoteny, 558, 580, 581
  nutritional, 141, 142
  opportunism in, 547
  and paleontology, 551
  parallel, 547
  plant, 553, 555*
  population in, 539, 540
  in Precambrian, 551
  in progress, 544
  racial, 584, 587, 589
  random mating in, 540, 541
  and recapitulation, 557
  replacement in, 546, 547
  of species, 538, 543
  speeds in, 545
  in taxonomy, 23, 25
  time table of, 551, 552*
Exchange reaction, 37
Excitation, central, 427
Excretion, 401
  in alimentary system, 300
  as animal trait, 206
  in breathing system, 401
  cellular, 73
  by chloragogues, 239
  filtration in, 402, 403
  by flame bulbs, 217*, 218
  in freshwater types, 115
  by kidney, 402, 403*
  in land animals, 270, 402
  in large intestine, 300
  by Malpighian tubules, 242
  in mesonephros, 270
  by metanephridia, 226
  in metanephros, 402, 403
  minerals in, 403
  of nitrogenous wastes, 335
  osmosis in, 403
  process of, 402
  in pronephros, 270
  reabsorption in, 403
  and secretion, 402
  selectivity in, 403*
  thresholds of, 403
  urine formation in, 402
Excretory system, 89, 401, 402
Excurrent siphon, 234, 267
Exergonic reaction, 38
Exhalation, 400
Exocrine glands, 352
Exopterygota, 249, 250*
Exoskeleton, 205, 240
Exothermic reaction, 38
Experiment, 6
Exploratory behavior, 430
Extension, muscular, 348
External fertilization, 499, 501*
Extinction, 545, 546
Extraembryonic membranes, 513, 514
Eye:
  compound, 240, 241*, 421
  cups, 421
  development, 511
  focusing, 422
  image formation by, 422, 423
  induction, 511
  insect, 240, 241*
  simple, 240, 241*
  spots, 155, 421
  types of, 421
  vertebrate, 421
Eye-color genes, 533

Facial nerve, 410*
Factors, Mendelian, 522
Facultative symbiosis, 104
FAD, 58, 59*
  in β-oxidation, 318
  in hydrogen transport, 312
  and vitamins, 366*
Family:
  social, 20, 446
  taxonomic, 23
Fat, 52, 53*
  cells, 83
  conversion to amino acids, 334
  conversion to carbohydrate, 333
  depots, 334
Fat:
  derivatives, 53
  digestion, 297, 298
  energy content of, 318, 319
  metabolism, 334
  respiration, 317
  storage, 334
  synthesis, 53*, 333, 334*
  utilization, 334
  vacuole, 73
Fatty acid, 52, 53*
  β-oxidation, 318
  conversion to carbohydrate, 333, 334
  essential, 295
  metabolism, 334
  oxidation states, 310, 311*
  respiration, 318
  synthesis, 334
Feather, 278
Feather-duster worms, 113*, Color Figure 13
Feather stars, 261, Color Figure 22
Feces, 301
Feedback, 358
Female reproductive system, 502
Female sex hormones, 386
Femaleness, 466, 530
Fermentation, 313
Fern, 178, 194
  fossils, 554
  reproduction, 489, 490, Color Figure 26
  trees, 194
Ferredoxin, 325, 326*
Fertilization, 464
  animal, 499, 501*
  cross-, 467
  double, 495
  in heredity, 523–525
  membrane, 508
  plant, 487, 488, 491
  self-, 467
Fertilizer, soil, 124
Fetus, 515, 516
Fibers:
  angiosperm, 196
  connective tissue, 83
  sclerenchyma, 79
Fibrils, 73
Fibrin, 393
Fibrinogen, 393
Fibrocyte, 83
Fibroelastic tissue, 82, 83
Fibrous root, 179, 180*
Fighting behavior, 447
Filament, stamen, 494
Filaria worms, 222*, 223
Filicineae, 178, 194, 489, 490, Color Figure 26
Filter feeding, 226
Filtration, excretory, 402, 403
Fin, 273, 275
  clasper, 274
  ray, 274, 275
Fir, 196
Fire algae, 159
Fish, 269, 273, 274
  camouflage, Color Figure 4
  in deep sea, 113, 114*

Fish:
evolution, 561, 563
lateral-line system, 419
Fission, 459
multiple, 152, 170, 459
protozoan, 167, 170
as vegetative reproduction, 462
Flagella, 74, 75*, 152, 154*, 166
bacterial, 145
Flagellate algae, 154*
Flagellate protozoa, 167
Flagellate state, 152, 167
Flame bulbs, 217*, 218, 269
Flatworms, 216–219
Flavin adenine dinucleotide, 58, 59* (*See also* FAD)
Flavin mononucleotide, 58, 59*
Flea, 251*
Flesh-finned fishes, 274
Flies, 251*, 255
Flight:
bird, 278
insect, 252
Flint, 168
Floridean starch, 160
Florigen, 379
Flower, 494, Color Figure 28
color inheritance in, 533
Flowering, 378–380
Flowering plants, 178, 196, 494 (*See also* Angiosperm; Plant)
Flukes, 217, 219
larvae of, 109
parasitism of, 108*, 109
Fly mouth parts, 251*
Flying birds, 278
Flying insects, 252
Flying reptiles, 547*, 564
FMN, 58, 59*
Focusing in eye, 422
Folic acid, 366
Foliose lichens, 163, 164*
Foliose liverworts, 177
Follicle, ovarian, 502, 506, 507*
Follicular phase, 507
Food, 15, 49
absorption, 301, 302
in alimentary system, 295
chains, 102
crisis, 129
definition of, 49
distribution, 301
in ecosystem, 101
as energy source, 307
intake control, 296
in liver, 302, 336*
in lymph, 302
organic compounds as, 49
PGAL as, 329
photosynthesis of, 323, 328, 329
in plant, 328
pyramids, 101
respiration, 308, 315, 317, 319
storage, 329, 331
transport: animal, 300–302
plant, 293, 294
Foot:
molluscan, 228
plant embryo, 487, 488*, 490*, 493*
Foraminiferans, 168, 169*
Forebrain, 407, 409*
Forests, 116, 117, 118*
Form development, 471, 472
Formic acid, 52, 53*
Fossils, 551, 553, 559*, 560
Fovea centralis, 422
Fragmentation, reproduction by, 462
Free-energy change, 39
and activation energy, 41
in reactions, 39
in respiration, 307, 308
Fresh water, 115, 116*, 270
Frog, 269, 275
development, 510*, 511, Color Figure 14
Fructose, 51, 316*
Fruit, 495, 496*
abscission, 376, 377*
rot, 162, 164*
Fruit flies, 521, 522
Fruiting body:
fungal, 163–165, 484, 485
mushroom as, 165, 484*
in slime molds, 166, Color Figure 24
Fruticose lichen, 163, 164*
FSH, 383*, 503, 506
Fucoxanthin, 53, 158, 159
Fucus, 113, 160, 161*, 481
Functions in organisms, 15
Fungi, 162, Color Figures 9, 10
fruiting bodies, 163–165, 484, 485
reproduction in, 483–485
Fungi Imperfecti, 162, 165
Funnel, squid, 235

Gall bladder, 299*
Galls, plant, 376
Gametangium, 479
Gametes, 464
Gametic reproduction, 464
Gametogenic meiosis, 470
Gametophyte, 176, 485
algal, 479
bryophyte, 176, 486*, 487
fern, 489
generation, 470
psilopsid, 488*
seed plant, 490
tracheophyte, 488
Ganglia, 407, 411, 412
Ganoid scale, 274*
Garpike, 274*
Gases:
atmospheric, 121, 125, 400
blood transport of, 400, 401
in breathing, 400, 401
exchange of, 401
inert, 32
as nutrients, 323, 328
pressure gradients of, 401
Gastrea hypothesis, 557
Gastric juice, 297, 298
Gastric mill, 247
Gastric septa, 216*
Gastrin, 298, 299, 383*, 386
Gastrodermis, 214
Gastropoda, 229, 231
Gastrotricha, 220, 222*
Gastrozooid, 214
Gastrula, 510
Gastrulation, 510
Gavial, 278
Gel, 61
Gelidium, 161
Gemma, 486*, 487
Gemmule, 212
Gene, 60, 522
allelic, 523
in behavior, 427
and blood groups, 587
as chemical code, 339–346
cistron in, 533
in control system, 360, 361
in crossing over, 526
definitions, 528, 533
in development, 473
as DNA, 59, 60, 339–346
and dominance, 523
dosage effects, 523
duplication, 345, 346
in evolution, 539, 540
expression, 533
flow, 539
frequencies, populational, 539, 540, 584
functions, 345, 346*
homologous, 523
independent assortment of, 524
interactions, 532
linear order of, 526, 527
linkage, 526
mapping, 527
in metabolic control, 345, 361
mutation, 345, 528
muton in, 528
as nucleic acid, 59
operator, 361
in operons, 361
phenotype ratios, 523, 525, 527
pleiotropy, 587
pools, 539
in protein synthesis, 339–344
and race, 584, 587
recessiveness, 523
redundancy, 345
regulator, 361
in reproduction, 459
in reproduction control, 345, 346
reproduction errors, 345, 528
segregation, 522
selection pressure on, 541
in sex, 539
sexual recombination of, 527, 539
in steady-state control, 346, 360
structural, 361
subunits, 528, 533
systems, 59, 532, 534
and trait, 532, 533
Generations, alternation of, 470*, 471
Generative cells:
gonadal, 499, 500*, 506
in pine, 491*, 492
Generative nucleus, 494
Genetic code, 339–346
Genetic drift, 542
Genetic systems, 59, 532, 534

Genetic variations, 521, 527, 539
Genetics, 521
(*See also* Gene; Inheritance)
Genome, 532
Genotype, 522
Genus, 23, 27
Geologic time table, 551, 552*
Geology, fossil, 552*
Geotropism, 372
Germ cells, primordial, 500, 501*
Germ layers, primary, 207, 510
Germ mutations, 529
Germination, seed, 494, 496, Color Figure 27
Gestation, 515, 516
Gibberellins, 371, 372*
Gibbon, 570, 571
Gigantism, 384
Gill, 270, 271*
arthropod, 240
book, 240, 242
molluscan, 230
mushroom, 165*, 484*
pharyngeal, 266
Gill filaments, 275
Gill hearts, 236
Gill rakers, 275
Gill slits, 260, 266, 267*
Gingko, 195
Gizzard, earthworm, 239
Glaciation, 122
Glands, 351
digestive, 297
as effectors, 360*
endocrine, 352
exocrine, 352
in plants, 351
Glass sponges, 211, 212*
Globigerina, 169*
Globin, 394
Globulin, 392
Glochidia larva, 234
Gloeocapsa, 147*
Glomerulus, 270, 402
Glossopharyngeal nerve, 410*
Glottis, 300*, 399
Glucagon, 333, 386
Glucose, 51
absorption, 291
blood, 296, 333
in carbohydrate synthesis, 330*, 331
cell uptake of, 291
excretion, 403
as fat precursor, 334
in food-intake control, 296
as glycogen precursor, 332, 333
in glycolysis, 315, 316*
in hexose shunt, 317
and hormones, 296
in liver, 333
metabolism, 332
oxidation states in, 311*, 316*
phosphorylation, 291
in photosynthesis, 330*, 331
plant synthesis of, 330
in polysaccharide synthesis, 330*, 331, 333
respiration, 314, 315
UDP-, 332
Glucose-phosphate, 291, 315, 331, 332
Glutamic acid, 319
Glycerin, 317
Glycine, 53
Glycogen, 51, 52*
from glucose, 332*
granules, 73
and hormones, 333, 383*
in liver, 333
metabolism, 332
muscle, 348
in respiration, 315
as respiratory fuel, 315
synthesis, 332
Glycolysis, 315, 316*
Glyptodonts, Color Figure 34
GMP, 58
Gnetales, 195, 196
Goiter, 385
Golden-brown algae, 158
Golgi bodies, 71
Gonadotropic hormones, 382, 383*, 503
Gonads, 499, 501, 502
Gondwana, 98
Gonionemus, 214, 215*
Gonopore, 242, 246*, 502*
Gonozooid, 214
Gorillas, 570
Gradation, 123
Grade, taxonomic, 207
Gram-molecular weight, 311
Graminales, 28*
Grana, 72, 323, 324*
Granules, cellular, 72
Grasshopper, 241*, 253*
Grassland, 116, 117*
Gravity, sense of, 418
Green algae, 155, 156, 479, Color Figure 7
Green-line algae, 154
Green sulfur bacteria, 290*
Greenhouse effect, 126, 128
Ground pine, 192, Color Figure 12
Ground substance, cytoplasmic, 69
Growing point, 177
Growth, 471
and cell division, 459, 463
in development, 471
differential, 472
factors, 362–368
and form, 471
hormones: animal, 384
plant, 371, 372
movements, 372
negative, 459
of population, 99
primary, plant, 182, 185, 187
responses, plant, 372
secondary, plant, 187–189
of species, 97
of vascular plant, 182–189
GTP, 342
Guanine, 57, 58*
Guanosine, 58
Guanylic acid, 58
Guard cells, 77, 78*, 374
Guinea worms, 223
Gullet, 157
Guttation, 293
Gymnodinium, 159*, 160
Gymnosperms, 178, 194, 195
evolution of, 555*, 556
life cycle of, 491–494, Color Figure 27
wood in, 195, 196*

Habitats, 111, 115
Habituation, 415, 429
Haeckel, Ernst, 557
Haem- (*see under* Hem-)
Hagfishes, 269
Hair cell, 418, 420
Hairworms, 220, 222*
Half-reactions, 309
Haltere, 252
Halteria, 171
Hammer in ear, 420
Haploidy, 468
Haplontic life cycle, 469, 479
Haplostele, 183
Hardy-Weinberg law, 541
Hatching, 206, 512
Haversian system, 84*
Hb (*see* Hemoglobin)
Head, 205
sinuses, 399
sperm, 499, 500*
Healing, 459, 462
Hearing, 420
Heart, 205, 395, 396
muscle, 86, Color Figure 1
sounds, 396
vertebrate, 266*, 270, 271
Heart-rate center, 397
Heartwood, 191
Heat, 40, 349
from ATP, 349, 350
in breeding season, 502
and calories, 40
energy, 349
equivalents, 40
motion, 40
in ocean, 122
in reactions, 40
Hedgehog, 281*
Heidelberg man, 575
Heliozoa, 168
Helix, 233, Color Figure 18
Hematochrome, 155
Heme, 53, 54*, 394
Hemerythrin, 394
Hemicellulose, 73
Hemichordates, 260
Hemimetabola, 249, 250*
Hemiptera, 250*, 255
Hemocyanin, 394
Hemoglobin, 54*, 394
Hemophilia, 532
Henle, loop of, 402
Hepatic portal vein, 302
Hepatic vein, 302
Hepaticopsida, 176
Hepatopancreas, 230, 247
Heptose, 51
Herbaceous plants, 181, 187, 198
Herbivores, 101, 204

Heredity, 17, 345, 521
in behavior, 427
cellular, 461
(*See also* Gene; Inheritance)
Hermaphroditism, 466, 467, 530
Heteroauxin, 371
Heterocyst, 148
Heteronereis, 237, Color Figure 20
Heterospory, 489, 490
Heterotrophism, 15, 289, 290*
in ecosystem, 101
origin of, 140, 141*
Heterozygosity, 523
Hexactinellida, 211
Hexapoda, 245, 249
Hexose, 50, 51*
shunt, 317
High-energy bond, 58, 310
High-threshold substances, 403
Hindbrain, 407, 409*
Hirudin, 239
Hirudinea, 236, 239
His, bundle of, 396
Histidine, 55*
Histiocyte, 83
Holarctica, 98
Holometabola, 249, 251*
Holothuroids, 261
Holotrophism, 140, 289
Homeostasis (*see* Steady-State control)
Hominids, 570, 575–579
Hominoids, 568*, 570, 575
Homo, 27, 28*, 570, 575, 579, 584
(*See also* Man)
Homo erectus, 575, 577*
Homo sapiens, 575, 579, 584
Homoiothermy, 349
Homologous chromosome loci, 523
Homology, 27*
Homoptera, 250*, 255
Homospory, 490
Homozygosity, 523
Honey, 444
Honeypot ants, 445
Hoof, 279
Hookworms, 107*, 223
Hopeful monster hypothesis, 544
Hormogonales, 147
Hormogones, 148, 477
Hormonal transmitter substances, 413
Hormones, 352, 381, 383*
animal, 381, 503
arthropod, 247, 253
in behavior, 381, 449
in breeding cycles, 503, 506
in carbohydrate metabolism, 333, 383*
in cell division, 371
as control agents, 381, 383*
in crustacea, 247
in digestion, 299, 383*
endocrine, 352, 381
flowering, 379, 380
as growth factors, 362
as humoral agents, 381
insect, 253, 255*
invertebrate, 381
in menstrual cycle, 506, 507
in mineral metabolism, 383*, 385
in molting, 247, 253
Hormones:
in nervous system, 413
neurosecretory, 381, 413
placental, 514
plant, 371
in pregnancy, 514
in reproduction, 386, 503, 506, 507, 514
sex, 383*, 386
steroid, 386
vertebrate, 383*
Hornworts, 176, 178, 487, 488
Horny skeletons, 205
Horny sponges, 211, 212*
Horse evolution, 567*, Color Figure 33
Horseshoe crabs, 242, 243*, 244*, 246*
Horsetails, 193, 489, Color Figure 12
Host, 104
intermediate, 108
specificity, 106
and symbiont, 104, 106
Housefly mouth parts, 251*
Howler monkey, 569*
Human evolution, 575, 584
Human society, 581
Humoral agents, 381
Humus, 124
Hunger, 296
Hunting in human history, 581
Hybrids, 526
Hydathodes, 293
Hydra, 213, 214, 215*
Hydranth, 214
Hydrocarbon respiration, 308, 309*
Hydrochloric acid, gastric, 299
Hydrogen, 31
acceptors, 308
bacteria, 290*
bonds, 56
carriers, 312
donors, 312
on early earth, 137
ions, 35
in living matter, 49, 50
in nutrition, 289
in photosynthesis, 326, 328
in respiration, 308
in solar system, 137
sulfide, bacterial, 289, 290*
transfer, 311, 312
in water, 49, 121
Hydrolysis, digestive, 297
Hydrophytes, 181
Hydroponics, 124
Hydrosphere, 121
Hydroxyl ion, 35
Hydrozoa, 213–215, Color Figure 15
Hyenia, 553
Hyperparasitism, 106
Hypertonicity, 64
Hyperventilation, 400
Hypha, 162
Hypocotyl, 490, 493*
Hypoglossal nerve, 410*
Hyponasty, 373*
Hypothalamus, 382, 409*, 410, 503
Hypothesis, 6
Hypotonicity, 64
Hypoxanthine, 335*

I bands, 347*
IAA, 371
(*See also* Auxin)
Ice, polar, 122
Ice ages, 122, 556, 557
Ichthyosaurs, 546*, 547, 565, Color Figure 31
Imaginal disks, 253
Imago, 255*
Immune reactions, 392
Immunity, 392
Implantation, 513
Imprinting, 434
Impulse, nervous, 412
Incurrent siphon, 234, 267
Independent assortment, law of, 524
Indeterminate plants, 378
Index fossil, 550
Individual variations, 93, 94*, 584
Indole acetic acid, 371
Induced fit, enzymatic, 43
Induction:
chemical, 360, 362*
embryonic, 511, 512
Indusium, 489, Color Figure 26
Inert gases, 32
Information:
and brain, 414, 415
in genetic code, 342
in steady state, 16, 357
Ingestion, 295, 296
Inhalation, 400
Inheritable variations, 93, 94*, 537
Inheritance, 521
of acquired traits, 537
and behavior, 427
chromosome theory of, 521
and disease, 533
DNA in, 528, 533
and evolution, 539
of genes, 522
of genetic subunits, 528, 533
laws of, 522, 524, 526
Mendelian, 521
of mutations, 345, 528
non-Mendelian, 527
phenotype ratios of, 523, 525, 527
of sex, 529
of sex chromosomes, 530, 531
of sex-linked traits, 532
of traits, 533
Inhibition:
chemical, 361–364
of reactions, 361–364
reflex, 414
respiratory, 312
Ink sac, 235
Inner ear, 419*, 420
Inorganic compounds, 49
Insect, 245, 246*, 249
behavior, 443
camouflage, 103, Color Figure 4
development, 253, 254*
evolution, 249
eye, 240, 241*

Insect:
flight, 252
hearing, 420
hormones, 253, 255*
molting, 253, 255*
mouth parts, 250, 251*
society, 443–446
Insectivores, 281*, 567
Instinct, 427
Instrumental behavior, 431
Insulin, 55*, 56, 291, 333, 386
Integument, 88, 492
Integumentary system, 89
Intelligence, evolution of, 579, 580
Interactions:
gene, 532
of organisms (*see* Ecology)
Interbreeding, 27, 93, 543
Interglacial periods, 567, 576*
Intermediate host, 108
Intermediate threshold substances, 403
Intermedin, 384
Internal fertilization, 499, 501*
Interneurons, 407
Internodes, 186
Intersexes, 531
Interspecific competition, 98
Interspecific interactions, 99
Interspecific fertility, 93
Intertidal zone, 111, 112*
Intestinal amylase, 298
Intestinal juice, 298, 300
Intestinal lipase, 298
Intestine, 88, 89*, 297, 300
Intraspecific competition, 96
Intraspecific cooperation, 96
Intraspecific infertility, 93
Intraspecific interaction, 99
Intrathoracic space, 400
Intrauterine device, 130
Introvert, sipunculid, 229*
Invagination, 510
Inversion:
as mutation, 528
in sponge embryo, 211*
Invertebrates, 22
(*See also* specific groups)
Involuntary actions, 411
Iodine:
algal, 160
of thyroxin, 55*
Iodopsin, 421
Ionic bond, 33, 56
Ionic compound, 33
Ionization, 33, 35
by light, 325
and pH, 36
Ions, 32, 49
and dissociation, 35
Iris, 421
Irish elk, 546*
Irish moss, 161
Iron:
bacteria, 141
in blood, 54*, 394
in hemoglobin, 54*, 394
in hydrogen transport, 54*, 312, 313
in oxygen transport, 394
in respiratory pigments, 394
Iron Age, 579
Islet of Langerhans, 351*
Isoetes, 192, 193*
Isogamy, 466
Isolation:
of blastomeres, 509
in speciation, 543
Isolecithal eggs, 509
Isotonicity, 64
IUD, 130

Java man, 575
Jaw:
arthropod, 246*, 250
of snake, 278
of squid, 235
of vertebrate, 271
Jawed fishes, 273, 274
Jawless fishes, 269, 272
Jelly:
egg, 507
royal, 444
Jelly fishes, 213, 215*, 216, Color Figure 16
Jelly fungi, 165
Jelly tissues, 83, 214
Jointed-legged animals, 228, 240
Jump evolution, hypothesis of, 544
Jurassic, 552*

Kalanchoë, 463*
Kangaroo, 279
Karlingia, 163*
Karyogamy, 483*, 485
Karyokinesis, 459, 460
Kelp, 160, 161*
Keratin, 74
Keto acid, 319, 334, 335
Ketoglutaric acid, 314, 315*, 319
Ketose, 51
Kidney, 270, 402, 403
Kilocalorie, 40
Kinesis, 437
Kinetosome, 72, 73*, 75*
Kingdom, taxonomic, 23, 25*
Kinins, 371
Kinorhyncha, 220, 222*
Kiwi, 278
Koala bear, 280*
Krebs cycle, 314, 315*
Krill, 247

Labial palp, 234
Labium, 250
Labor:
division of, 21
in pregnancy, 515
Labrum, 250
Labyrinthodonts, 563
Labyrinthulae, 166
Lactase, 298
Lacteal, 302
Lactic acid, 313
Lactogenic hormone, 384, 505
Lactose, 51
Ladder-type nervous system, 217*, 218, 238*
Lagomorphs, 281*
Lakes, 115
Lamarck, J. B., 537
Lamina, leaf, 185
Laminaria, 113*, 160
Laminarin, 160
Lamp shells, 226, 227*
Lamprey, 269, 272
Lancelets, 266, 268
Land environment, 115, 122
Langerhans, islets of, 351*
Language, science as, 12
Lantern fish, 114*
Laramide revolution, 551, 556, 567
Large intestine, 299*, 300
Larva, 206, 475, 512, 513
Larvacea, 266, 268
Larynx, 297, 399, 547, 548*
Lateral-line system, 419
Latitude in ecology, 116
Laurasia, 98
Laws, natural, 8
Leaf, 179, 184*
abscission, 376, 377*
axil, 186
bud, 184*, 185
in flowering control, 378
gap, 184*, 185
growth, 184*, 185
moss, 177
movements, 374, 375
in nutrition, 292, 294
in photosynthesis, 323
phyllotaxis, 186
scars, 186
structure, 185, 186
trace, 184*, 185
transpiration, 292
types, 184*, 185, 186
veins, 186
Leaf-cutter ants, 445
Leander, 248*
Learning, 415, 428
in behavior, 428, 429
conditioning and, 430
by imprinting, 434
by trial and error, 430, 431
Lecithin, 53
Leeches, 236, 239
Lemuroids, 568, 569
Lens, 421
Lenticel, 189, 190*
Lepidodendrids, 554, Color Figure 29
Lepidoptera, 251*, 255
Leucine, 55*
Leuconoid sponges, 211, 212*
Leucosin, 158
Leukocyte, 392
Leukoplast, 71
Levels of organization, 19*, 207, 359
LH, 383*
Lichen, 104, 163, 164*, Color Figure 3
Life, 15, 18
classification, 26*
definition, 18
forms, 23
functions, 15, 16*
origin, 137
thermodynamics of, 327*, 328

Life cycles:
animal, 470, Color Figure 14
diplohaplontic, 471
diplontic, 470
haplontic, 469
meiosis in, 468
moneran, 477
plant, 471, 485, 488
protistan, 478
sex determination in, 529
Ligament, 83.
Light:
and auxin, 371, 373*
and behavior, 377, 436, 502, 503
biological, 350
energy, 323, 350
and eye, 420, 421
and flowering, 378
in nutrition, 323
and photoperiodism, 377, 436, 503
in photosynthesis, 323–325
in plant growth, 371, 377
sensory reception of, 420, 421
and stomata, 374
wavelengths of, 324
Ligia, 248*
Lignier hypothesis, 553
Lignin, 79
Ligule, 192
Lily, 495*, 496*
Lime glands, 238
Limestone, 170
Limpets, 232*
Limulus, 243*, 244*, 561
Linear order of genes, 527
Lingula, 227*, 394, 560
Linkage, genetic, 526, 532
Linnaeus, 23
Lipase, 43, 44, 297, 298
Lipid, 52
balance, 334*
β-oxidation of, 318
conversion with amino acid, 334*, 335
conversion with carbohydrate, 334*, 335
derivatives, 52, 53
digestion, 297, 298
metabolism, 334
respiration, 317
synthesis, 334
Liquid phase, colloidal, 61
Lithosphere, 121, 122
Lithotrophs, 289
Littoral zone, 111
Liver, 87, 88*, 299*, 393*
bile from, 300
in blood cell control, 394
circulation in, 302
deamination in, 319, 334
in food distribution, 302, 333, 334
food storage in, 303, 333
functions, 336*
glucose, 333
glycogen, 333
and hormones, 333
ornithine cycle in, 335
structure, 87, 88*
urea production in, 335
vitamins in, 367
Liver flukes, 108, 218*
Liverworts, 176, 177, 178*, 486*, 488, 530
Living matter, 18, 50*
Lizards, 277, 278, 564
Lobe-finned fishes, 275, 563
Lobster, 241*, 245, 246*, 247
Lobules, organ, 87
Locomotion, 203
Locust, 250*
Long-day plants, 378
Loop of Henle, 402
Lophophorates, 211, 226
Lophophore, 226, 227
Louse, 250*
Low-energy bonds, 310
Low-threshold substances, 403
LSD, 413
Luciferase and luciferin, 350
Lung, 271, 400
blood in, 395, 401
book, 240, 243
gas exchange in, 401
in vertebrate evolution, 270, 271*
Lungfishes, 275, 563
Luteal phase, 507, 514
Luteinizing hormone, (*see* LH)
Lycopodium, 192, Color Figure 12
Lycopsids, 178, 192, 489, 554, Color Figure 12
Lymph, 302, 391
circulation, 302
nodes, 393*
valves, 394*
vessels, 302, 391
Lymphocyte, 392
Lysosome, 71

Macrocystis, 160, 161*
Macromolecule, 54
Macronucleus, 171, 482*
Macrospironympha, 168*
Madreporite, 262
Magnetic ants, 440
Magnetic stimuli, 440
Maidenhair tree, 195
Malaria, 169*, 170
in racial evolution, 589, 590
and sickle-cell anemia, 588
Male reproductive system, 502
Male sex hormones, 386, 506
Maleness, 467, 530
Malpighian tubules, 242
Maltase, 298
Maltose, 51
Mammallike reptiles, 565, 566*, Color Figure 32
Mammals, 27, 270, 279
development of, 513–516
evolution in, 280, 281*, 566, 567
subgroups of, 281*
Mammary glands, 279
Mammoth, 546*
Man, 28*, 579, 584
chromosomes of, 531*
development of, 513–516
ecological niche of, 96*
environment of, 127
evolution of, 575, 579, 584
Man:
meiosis in, 469
neoteny in, 580, 581
origin of, 570, 571, 575, 579, 584
races of, 584
sex determination in, 531
social evolution of, 581–584
Mandibles, 240, 245
Mandibulata, 240, 245
Manipulative behavior, 431
Mannitol, 160
Mantle:
cavity, 230
molluscan, 228, 230
Marchantia, 177, 178*, 487, 488
gemmae, 486*, 487
Marine environment, 111
Marine plankton, 111, Color Figure 5
Marrow, 85*
Marsupials, 279, 280, 546, 547
Marsupium, 279
Mass action, 41
Mastigameoba, 168*
Mastigophora, 167
Mating, 464, 504, 505, 541
nonrandom, 541
types, 466
Maxilla, 246
Maxilliped, 246
Mayfly, 250*
Mechanism, doctrine of, 9, 10
Mechanoreceptors, 417, 418
Medulla:
adrenal, 385
gonadal, 500, 501*
oblongata, 397, 409*, 410
renal, 402
Medusa, 213, 215*, Color Figure 16
Megagametophyte, 489, 490
Megaphyll, 184*, 185
Megasporangium, 489–492, 494
Megaspore, 489, 490, 492, 494
Megasporophyll, 489*
Megastrobilus, 492
Meiosis, 468
animal, 499, 500*
chromosomes in, 468
in crossing over, 526
function of, 468
gametogenic, 470
gene shuffling by, 527
in independent assortment, 525
in life cycles, 469–471
in man, 469
meiospores in, 470
in Mendelian inheritance, 522
in ovary, animal, 499, 500*
plant, 486, 487
polar bodies in, 499, 500*
in protists, 151, 479, 481, 483
in segregation, 522
sporogenic, 470
in testis, 499, 500*
timing of, 469–471
zygotic, 469
Meiospores, 470
Meiotic divisions, 468
Meissner's corpuscles, 418*
Melanin, 335*, 337

Membrane:
active transport in, 63
basement, 84, 86*
cellular, 67
in colloid, 62
diffusion, 63
extraembryonic, 513, 514
in nerve fiber, 412, 413*
nuclear, 67, 68*, 69*
osmosis by, 63
permeability, 62
selectivity, 63
undulating, 170
Membranelle, 170*, 171
Memory, 415
Mendel, Gregor, 521
laws of, 522, 524
Mendelian inheritance, 521
Menopause, 508
Menstrual cycle, 507
Menstruation, 507
Meristem, 182, 184*
apical, 182, 184*
auxin in, 375, 376
primary, 182
secondary, 188
Merostomata, 242
Mesencephalon, 409*, 410
Mesenchyme, 82*, 83
Mesentery, 209
Mesocoel, 260, 261
Mesoderm, 207, 510
coelomate, 208*, 209
Mesogloea, 214
Mesonephros, 270
Mesophyll, 185
Mesophyte, 181
Mesosome, 260, 261
Mesozoic, 552*, 555, 564, Color Figures 31, 32
Messenger RNA, 340*, 341
Metabola, 249
Metabolism, 15, 16*, 288
acceleration of, 360, 363
amino acid, 334
anabolic, 307, 323, 331
balance in, 331
carbohydrate, 332
catabolic, 307
in cell maintenance, 351, 352
constructive, 323, 331
control of, 345, 360
deceleration of, 360, 363
destructive, 307
developmental, 473
DNA in, 345, 361
fat, 334
genetic control of, 345, 361
glucose, 332
hormonal control of, 362, 383*
lipid, 334
nutritional, 289
operon control of, 361
in parasites, 107
pathways of, 336*
physical, 346
processes of, 332
protein, 339, 360
respiratory, 307
reversibility of, 363
Metabolism:
summary, 352*
synthesis, 323, 331, 336*
Metabolites, 289
Metacoel, 260, 261
Metal, 33
Metamerism, 211, 228, 236, 266, 268, 270
Metamorphosis, 206, 512
Metanauplius, 247
Metanephridium, 226
Metanephros, 270*, 271, 402
Metaphase, 460
meiotic, 468
mitotic, 460, Color Figure, 23
plate, 460
Metaphyta, 25, 26*, 175
alternation of generations in, 470, 485, 488
embryos of, 182
evolution of, 143
life cycle of, 470
pigments in, 175, 323, 378
reproduction of, 485, 488, 490
(*See also* Plant)
Metasome, 260, 261
Metatheria, 279, 280
Metatroch, 228*
Metazoa, 25, 26*, 203
body cavities in, 209
classification of, 26*, 207
coelom in, 209
coelomate, 209
deuterostomial, 208
enterocoelomate, 210
evolution in, 143, 210*
protostomial, 208
reproduction of, 206, 499
schizocoelomate, 209
structure of, 204*
(*See also* Animal)
Metencephalon, 409*, 410
Methane, 137
oxidation, 308, 309*
Methyl alcohol, 309*
Microgametophyte, 489
Micron, 67
Micronucleus, 171, 482*
Microphyll, 184*, 185, 191–193
Micropyle, 492, 495
Microsporangium, 489, 490
Microspore, 489–494
Microsporophyll, 489*, 491
Microtubules, 72, 73*, 460
Mictic eggs, 220*
Midbrain, 407, 409*
Middle ear, 420
Middle lamella, 73
Middle piece, sperm, 499, 500*
Middle Stone Age, 576*, 579
Migrations, 438, 439
diurnal, 112
Mildews, 162, 164*
Milk, 299
Millepore corals, 215*
Millipedes, 245, 248
Mimicry, 103
Mimosa, 374, 375*
Minerals:
in blood, 391, 392
Minerals:
in body fluids, 391
in cell, 49
in control systems, 362, 364
cycles of, 122, 123
in environment, 121, 122
in excretion, 403
in fresh water, 115
as growth factors, 362, 364
as ions, 32, 49
in lithosphere, 122
in living matter, 49, 362
as nutrients, 289, 295
in ocean, 111
in soil, 123, 124
Miocene, 567*
Miracidium, 109
Mistletoe, 107*
Mites, 242, 243*
Mitochondria, 69, 70*
Mitosis, 459, 460, Color Figure 23
chromosomes in, 459
DNA in, 461
nuclear division in, 459
protistan, 151
Mitospore, 469, 470
Mitral valve, 396
Modification, reflex, 414
Modulation, developmental, 473
Modulator, 357, 362–364, 414
Mold, fungal, 162–164
Mole, chemical, 311
Molecular reproduction, 459
Molecule, 33, 359, 459
Mollusks, 26*, 228, 229, 561, 562*, Color Figure 18
eyes in, 421
Molting:
crustacean, 247
hormones, 247, 253
insect, 253, 254*
nematode, 221
Monera, 25, 26*, 143, 477
bacteria as, 144
blue-greens as, 147
reproduction in, 477
sex in, 477, 478
Monkeys, 569
Monocot, 196, 198
Monocotyledonae, 196
Monoecious plants, 490
Monoestrous animals, 506
Monogamy, 505, 582
Monokaryophase, 483*, 484
Monolinia, 164*
Monophyletism, 139
Monosaccharide, 50, 51*
Moose, 119*
Morel, 163, Color Figure 9
Morgan, T. H., 526
Morphogenesis, 471
Mosaic eggs, 508
Mosquito, 251*, 255
Moss, 176, 486–488
Irish, 161
Moss animals, 226
Moths, 251*, 255
Motility, animal, 203
Motion, 347
(*See also* Movement)

Motivation, behavioral, 427
Motor nerve, 407
Motor path, 357, 359, 360, 407
Motor unit, 87
Mountain building, 122
Mountain environment, 119, 120*
Mountain lion, 118*
Mouth, 297
  protozoan, 157
Mouth parts, insect, 250, 251*
Movement, 346
  amoeboid, 74
  ATP in, 347
  Brownian, 61
  chromosome, 347, 460
  ciliary, 75, 167, 170
  contact, 374, 375
  cyclotic, 73
  developmental, 471
  flagellary, 74, 154*, 167
  growth, 372
  guard cell, 374
  kinesis, 437
  leaf, 374, 375
  locomotor, 203
  migratory, 438, 439
  muscular, 347–349
  nastic, 372
  nutational, 372
  sense of, 418, 419
  sleep, 375
  spiral, 372
  tropistic, 372, 429
  turgor, 374
*m*RNA, 340, 341
Mucosa, intestinal, 88, 89*, 301
Mule, 93
Multicellularity, 19, 153
Multinucleate cells, 67
Multiple fission, 152, 170
Muscle, 86, 347, Color Figure 1
  action cycle, 348
  ATP, 348
  bundle, 87
  contraction, 347, 348
  as effector, 360
  electric events in, 348
  energy supply of, 348
  fatigue, 348
  fiber, 87, 347
  glycogen, 348
  motor unit, 87
  nervous control of, 348*, 349
  oxygen debt in, 313
  phosphagens, 348
  proteins, 347
  respiration, 348
  types, 86, 87, Color Figure 1
Muscular system, 89, 203
Muscularis, 88, 89*
Mushroom, 165, 484*
Muskox, 120*
Mutants, 529
Mutation, 60, 345, 528
  chromosome, 528
  in DNA, 60, 345
  effects, 529
  in evolution, 539, 542, 544
  germ, 529
  point, 528
Mutation:
  and radiation, 529
  somatic, 529
  types of, 528
Muton, 528
Mutualism, 104, Color Figure 3
Mycelium, 162
Mycophyta, 162, 483–485, Color
    Figures 3, 9, 10
Myelencephalon, 409*, 410
Myelin sheath, 407
Myofibril, 73, 347
Myosin, 347
Myriapods, 248, 249*
Myxedema, 385
Myxobacteriales, 146
Myxomyceteae, 166
Myxophyta, 166, Color Figure 24

NAA, 371
NAD, 59, 312, 315, 366*
NADP, 59, 312, 317, 326–328
Naegleria, 169*
Nasal passages, 416, 417*
Nastic movements, 372
Native protein, 56
Natural selection, 538, 540*
  Darwinian, 538
  as differential reproduction, 539,
    541
  modern meaning of, 539, 540
Nauplius, 247
Nautiloids, 560, Color Figure 30
Nautilus, chambered, 235
Navel, 514
Navigation, animal, 438–440
Neanderthal man, 576, 577, 578*
Neck, archegonial, 486*
Needle leaves, 186
Nekton, 111
Nematocyst, 213
Nematoda, 220–222
Nematomorpha, 220, 222*
Nemertina, 216
Neoteny, 558, 580, 581
Nephric capsule, 270, 402
Nephric tubule, 270, 402
Nephridia, 217*, 218, 226
  amphioxus, 269
Nephron, 270, 402
Nereis, 237, Color Figure 20
Neritic zone, 112*
Nerve, 407
  autonomic, 411, 412
  cells, 407
  centers, 407, 414
  cord, 266, 407
  cranial, 410*, 411
  ganglia, 407
  net, 407
  ring, 264
  spinal, 411
  types of, 407
Nerve fiber, 407
  action potential in, 412
  adrenergic, 413
  cholinergic, 413
  depolarization of, 412
  electric charges on, 412
Nerve fiber:
  as endocrine cell, 413
  hormones in, 413
  ions in, 412
  myelinated, 407
  nonmyelinated, 413
  postganglionic, 412
  preganglionic, 412
  semipermeability, 412, 413
  thicknesses, 413
  types, 407
Nerve impulse, 412, 413
  in muscle contraction, 348
  speeds of, 413
  summation of, 414
  in synapse, 413
Nervous system, 89, 407
  autonomic, 411
  central, 407
  development of, 407, 510*
  in gland control, 360
  ladder-type of, 217, 218, 237
  in muscle control, 348*, 349
  pathways in, 407–412
  sense organs in, 415–423
  in steady state, 407, 414
Nest:
  bird, 279
  insect, 443
Net-veined leaf, 186
Neural centers, 414, 415
Neural pathways, 407
Neural receptors, 415
Neural tube, 407, 510*
Neurofibrils, 73
Neuroglia cells, 407, 408*
Neurosecretory cells, 253, 381, 413
Neurosensory receptors, 415, 416*
Neurospora, 162*
Neurotransmitter substances, 413
Neutrality, chemical, 36
Neutron, 31
New Stone Age, 576*, 579
New World monkeys, 568, 569
Newt, 269, 275
Niacin, 59, 366
Niche, ecological, 96
Nicotinamide, 59
  (*See also* NAD; NADP)
Nicotinic acid, 59, 335*, 337, 366
Nictitating membrane, 278
Night lengths, effects of, 378
Nitrate, 127, 295
Nitrification, 127
Nitrifying bacteria, 127
Nitrite, 127
Nitrogen:
  in bacteria, 145
  cycle, 126, 127*
  in decay, 126, 127
  in environment, 121, 125, 126
  in excretion, 335
  fixation, 105, 126, 127*
  in living matter, 49, 50
  metabolism, 335
  as nutrient, 295
Nitrogen bases, 57, 58*
  degradation of, 335*
  in DNA, 60, 342
  in nucleic acid, 59

Nitrogen bases:
in RNA, 59
triplet codes of, 342, 343*
Noctiluca, 159*, 160
Node:
in heart, 396
lymph, 302, 393*
stem, 186
Noncyclic electron transfer, 326, 327
Nonelectrolyte, 35
Noninheritable variations, 93
Non-Mendelian inheritance, 521, 527
Nonmetal, 35
Noradrenalin, 386, 413
Norepinephrine, 386
Nose, 416, 417
Nostoc, 148, Color Figure 6
Notochord, 27, 260, 266
Nuclear constancy, 219, 220
Nuclear membrane, 67, 68*, 69*
Nucleic acid, 59, 60
(*See also* DNA; RNA)
Nucleocytoplasmic interactions, 69
Nucleolus, 67
Nucleoplasm, 67
Nucleoprotein, 67
Nucleotide, 57, 59
Nucleus:
atomic, 31
cellular, 67, 68*
adaptive role of, 339
chromosomes in, 67
in ciliates, 171
and cytoplasm, 69
division of, 460, 468
macro-, 171
in meiosis, 468
micro-, 171
in mitosis, 460, Color Figure 23
organelles in, 67
Nudibranchs, 33, Color Figure 18
Nursing, mammalian, 515, 516
Nutation, 372
Nutrient, 15, 289
animal, 295
in blood, 391, 392
distribution, 31, 292, 294, 301
energy, 307, 308
in environment, 101, 121, 122, 125
as food, 289
oxidation, 308, 315
in phloem, 294
plant, 292
respiration, 308, 315, 317, 319
in soil, 123, 291, 292
types, 289, 307
Nutrition, 15, 289
by absorption, 290
by active transport, 290
by alimentation, 295
animal, 204, 295
autotrophic, 289
cellular, 290, 291
crisis, 129
in development, 473, 500, 509
diffusion in, 290
embryonic, 473, 500, 509
energy sources in, 307, 308
forms of, 289
Nutrition:
heterotrophic, 289
osmosis in, 290
by photosynthesis, 323
plant, 292
protistan, 152
and soil, 291
transport in, 292, 294, 301
Nymph, 253

Obelia, 213, 214
Obligatory symbiosis, 104
Observation, scientific, 5
Ocean, 111, 112*
currents, 122
life in, 111, Color Figure 5
minerals in, 123
origin of, 138
Octopus, 229, 234, 236
Oculomotor nerve, 410*
Odonata, 250*
Odor perception, 417
Oedogonium, 156, 479
Oikopleura, 268*
Old Stone Age, 576*, 577
Old World monkeys, 568*, 569
Oleic acid, 52
Olfactory lobes, 407, 409*
Olfactory nerve, 410*
Oligocene, 567*
Oligochaeta, 236, 238, 239
Ommatidium, 241*
Omnivore, 204
Oncopoda, 228, 229*
Ontogeny, 557
Oogamy, 466
Open circulation, 230, 240
Open system, 121
Operant conditioning, 415, 431
Operator genes, 361
Operculum, 242, 274*, 275
Operon, 361
Ophiocytium, 158*
Ophiopluteus larva, 264*
Ophiothrix, 265*
Ophiuroids, 261, Color Figure 22
Opossum, 280*
Opportunism, evolutionary, 547
Opposite leaf growth, 186
Opsin, 420, 421*
Optic chiasma, 410*, 422, 423*
Optic lobes, 409*, 410
Optic nerve, 410*, 422
Orangutans, 570
Orbit, electronic, 31, 32*
Order, taxonomic, 23
Ordovician, 552*, 560, 561, Color Figure 30
Oreopithecus, 575, 576*
Organ, 19, 77
animal, 87
of Corti, 420
plant, 81
Organ-forming zones, 508
Organ-pipe corals, Color Figure 17
Organ systems, 19, 81, 89
Organelles, 19, 69
Organic carbon, 49
formation of, 323
Organic compounds, 49, 138
Organism, 15, 19
classification, 23, 25*, 26*
functions in, 15
kinds of, 26*
reproduction of, 462
structure in, 19
Organization, 19*
levels of, 19, 207
Organotrophs, 289
Orientation:
space-time, 435, 437
by sun compass, 438
Origin:
of cell, 138
of life, 137, 140
of species, 538, 540
Ornithine cycle, 335
Orthoptera, 250*, 255
Oryx, 117*
Oscillator circuits, 414
Oscillatoria, 148
Osculum, 211
Osmosis, 63
in blood, 391, 392
in cell nutrition, 290, 291*
in excretion, 403
in freshwater life, 115
in guard cells, 374
Ossicle, 265
Ossification, 85*
Osteichthyes, 269, 274
Osteoblasts, 85*
Osteoclasts, 85*
Ostia, 211
Ostracoderms, 561, 562*
Ostrich, 278
Outer ear, 420
Oval window, 420
Ovary:
angiosperm, 494, 495*, Color Figure 28
animal, 466, 502
egg production, 506, 507*
flower, 494, 495*, Color Figure 28
hormones of, 506, 507
ovulation from, 506
plant, 494, 495*, Color Figure 28
Overpopulation, 129
Oviducts, 502, 503*
Oviparity, 500, 501*
Ovipositors, 252
Ovoviviparity, 500, 501*
Ovulation, 506, 507*
Ovule, 491, 492, 494, 495*
Oxaloacetic acid, 314, 315*, 319
Oxidation, 308
in citric acid cycle, 314, 315
by dehydrogenation, 308, 309
in electron sharing, 34
electron shifts in, 308
in electron transfer, 33
energy changes in, 308
of fatty acid, 318
in glycolysis, 315, 316*
in hexose shunt, 317
levels, 31*, 33, 34
and reduction, 308
respiratory, 308
Oxidation-reduction process, 308

Oxidation states, 31*, 33, 34
of carbon groups, 308
in nutrients, 310*, 311*
Oxides, 142
Oxygen, 49, 50
atmospheric, 121, 125, 141
in blood, 401
in breathing, 401
cycle, 125, 126*
debt, 313
on early earth, 141
exchange, 401
and hemoglobin, 401
as hydrogen acceptor, 312
in photolysis, 326*, 327
in photosynthesis, 326*, 327
in plant nutrition, 293
and pollution, 128
in respiration, 312
and respiratory pigments, 401
revolution, 141
transport, 401
Oxyhemoglobin, 401
Ozone, 141*, 142

Pacemaker, 396
Pacinian corpuscle, 418*
Pain, 416, 423
Paleocene, 567*
Paleoniscoid fishes, 562*, 563
Paleontology, 551, Color Figures 29–34
Paleozoic, 552*, 553, 560, Color Figures, 29, 30
Palisade mesophyll, 185
Palmate leaf, 186*
Palmitic acid, 52
Palp, labial, 234
Pancreas, 299*, 383*
Pancreatic secretions, 298, 300, 383*
Pangea, 98
Pangolin, 281*
Pantopoda, 242
Pantothenic acid, 59, 366
Parallel evolution, 547
Paramecium, 93, 170*, 171
autogamy, 482
conjugation, 465
mating types, 466, 482*
sex in, 465, 482
syngens, 93, 483
Paramylum, 157
Paraphyses, 481*
Parapodium, 237
Parasite, 105, 108
Parasitism, 105, 106, 140, 289
Parasympathetic nervous system, 412
Parathormone, 385
Parathyroid gland, 385
Paratylenchus, 221*
Parazoa, 207, 211
Parchment worm, 238*
Parenchyma, 77, 78*, 180*
Parental behavior, 505
Parthenogenesis, 467
artificial, 467
natural, 444, 467
in rotifers, 220*, 221
in social insects, 444

Partial dominance, 524
Particles, atomic, 31, 32*
Passage cells, 77*, 79, 80*, 292
Passive transfer, parasitic, 108
Pasteur, Louis, 537
Pathogenic bacteria, 106, 145
Peacock, 504*
Peanut worms, 228, 229*
Peat moss, 177
Peck orders, 451
Pectin, 73, 147
Pectine, 242
Pectoral fin, 275
Pedal cords, 230
Pedicellariae, 262
Pedipalp, 240, 242
Peking man, 575
Pelagic zone, 111
Pelecypoda, 229, 233
Pellagra, 367
Pellicle, 74, 167, 170*
Pelomyxa, 168, 169*
Pelvic fin, 275
Pen, squid, 235
Penetrant, 213*
Penicillium, 163, 164*
Penis, 502
Pentose, 50, 51*, 57
Pepsin, 298, 299
Pepsinogen, 298, 299
Peptidases, 298
Peptide bond, 54, 55*
Perch, 274*
Perching birds, 279
Perciform fishes, 275
Perennial plants, 181
photoperiods in, 378
vernalization in, 380
Pericardial cavity, 230
Perichondrium, 85*
Pericycle, 79
Periderm, 189
Peridinium, 159*, 160
Periods, geologic, 551, 552*
Periosteum, 85*
Peripatus, 229*
Peristalsis, 297
Peristomium, 237
Peritoneal septa, 236
Peritoneum, 209
Periwinkle, 232*
Permafrost, 119
Permeability, 62
Permeases, 291
Permian, 552*, 555, 563
Permo-Triassic crisis, 555, 563
Petal, 494, Color Figure 28
Petiole, 185
Peziza, Color Figure 9
PGA, 316*, 329*
PGAL:
in Calvin cycle, 329*, 330
as carbohydrate source, 316*, 332*
conversion with glucose, 330, 332*
conversion with glycerol, 317*, 332*
in photosynthesis, 329, 330
in respiration, 316*
pH, 36
and blood, 391, 392
and enzyme, 43

Phaeophyta, 160, 161*, 481
Phaeothamnion, 158*
Phagocytosis, 74
in blood, 392
Pharyngeal air sac, 271, 275
Pharynx, 297
amphioxus, 268, 269*
chordate, 266
mammalian, 297
nematode, 221
vertebrate, 271, 275
Phase reversal, colloidal, 62
Phellem, 189, 190*
Phelloderm, 189, 190*
Phellogen, 190*
Phenotype, 522
Phenylalanine, 55*, 335*, 342
Phenylthiocarbamide, 417
Pheromones, 433
Philosophy, scientific, 9
Phloem, 79, 80*, 179
in bark, 190
in food transport, 294
primary, 79
rays, 189
secondary, 189
in stele, 80, 184*, 185
translocation in, 294
in vascular bundle, 184*, 185
Phonoreceptors, 419, 420
Phoronida, 226
Phosphagens, 348
Phosphate, 49
bond energy, 310
buffer, 36
in carbohydrates, 291, 332
in glucose metabolism, 315, 332
high-energy, 310
in nucleic acids, 59
in nucleotides, 57
organic, 49
in photosynthesis, 328, 329*
in respiration, 310
Phosphoenolpyruvic acid, 316*
Phosphoglyceraldehyde (*see* PGAL)
Phosphoglyceric acid (*see* PGA)
Phosphoric acid, 57, 315, 316*
Phosphorylation, 291, 301, 311, 325
Photic zone, 111
Photoexcitation, 325
Photoionization, 325
Photolithotrophs, 289
Photolysis, 323, 324
Photoorganotrophs, 289
Photoperiodism:
animal, 436, 503
plant, 378
Photophosphorylation, 325
Photopigments, 420
Photoreceptors, 420–423
Photosynthesis, 15, 289, 323
air in, 323
algal, 154
ATP in, 326
bacterial, 145
Calvin cycle in, 328, 329*
carbohydrates from, 329
in carbon cycle, 126
carbon dioxide in, 323, 328
carbon dioxide fixation in, 323, 328

Photosynthesis:
chlorophyll in, 141, 323, 325
dark reaction of, 323
efficiency of, 331
electron transfers in, 325, 326*
endproduct of, 329
food production by, 326, 327
hydrogen transfer in, 325, 326*
light reaction in, 323
origin of, 141
oxygen from, 323, 326
in oxygen cycle, 126
photoionization in, 325
photolysis in, 323, 324
photophosphorylation in, 325
pigments in, 154, 323, 325
raw materials for, 323, 328
thermodynamics of, 327
water in, 323, 326
Phototropism, 372
Phycocyanin, 147, 160
Phycoerythrin, 147, 160
Phycomycetes, 162, 163*
Phyllotaxis, 186
Phylogeny, animal, 210*, 557, 559*
Phylum, 23, 27
Physalia, 95*, 214, Color Figure 15
Physarum, 166
Physical metabolism, 347
Phytochromes, 378
Phytoplankton, 111
Piercing-sucking insects, 250, 251*
Pigment, 154
blood, 392, 394
cells, 82*, 83
granules, 72
in photosynthesis, 323, 324
plant, 175, 323, 378
in plastids, 71
respiratory, 394
visual, 420, 421
Pike, 274*
Pine, 491–493
leaf, 180*
seed, Color Figure 27
wood, 196*
Pineal body, 272, 278, 410
Pinnate leaf, 186
Pinocytosis, 74
Pistil, 494, Color Figure 28
Pit, 77, 79
bordered, 80
membrane, 79
Pith, 80
Pithecanthropus, 575
Pituitary gland, 382, 384, 411
Placenta, 513, 514
Placental mammals, 279
Placental phase, 514
Placoderms, 17*, 561
Planarians, 217, 218
Plankton, 111, 112, Color Figure 5
Plant, 25, 26*, 175
adaptations of, 175, 179–182
and air, 239, 323
amino acids, 334
angiosperm, 196
annual, 181
aquatic, 181
behavior, 371
Plant:
biennial, 181
bryophyte, 176
carbohydrates, 329
cells, 68*, 73, 77
classification, 26*
coniferous, 195
cuttings, 376
deciduous, 181
developmental responses of, 375, 377
embryo, 182, 485, 488, 492–495
embryo initials, 493
evolution, 143, 553, 555*
fats, 329
fern, 178, 194, 489
flower, 494
flowering, 196, 494
flowering control in, 378, 380
food production, 326, 327
fossils, 553–556, Color Figure 29
growth, 182, 185, 187, 189
gymnosperm, 195
herbaceous, 181
hormones, 371
leaf, 185
light effects on, 371, 377
mitosis, Color Figure 23
movements, 373, 374
nutrition, 292, 294
organs, 81
perennial, 181
phloem, 79, 294
photoperiodism, 378
photosynthesis, 323
pigments, 175, 323, 378
primary growth, 185
reproduction, 485, 488
root, 183
secondary growth, 187, 189
seeds, 491
and soil, 123, 124
stem, 183
stimuli in, 374, 377, 380
structure, 176, 182
tissues, 77, 182, 187
tracheophyte, 178
tumors, 376
types, 26*, 176, 178
vascular, 178
vernalization, 380
woody, 187
xylem, 79, 183, 292
Plantae, kingdom of, 25*
Planula larva, 213, 214*
Plasma, 391, 392*
carbon dioxide in, 398, 401
clotting in, 393, 394*
membrane, 67
nutrients in, 391
respiratory pigments in, 394
Plasmodesmata, 73
Plasmodium, 169*, 170, 588
Plasmodium, 166, 482*
Plasmogamy, 483*, 484
Plastids, 71, 72*
Plastron, 277
Platelets, 393
Platyhelminthes, 216–219
Platypus, duck-billed, 280*
Play behavior, 430
Pleiotropy, 587
Pleistocene, 567*, 575, Color Figure 34
Plesiosaurs, 565
Pleural ganglia, 230
Pleural membranes, 398
Pleurobrachia, 213*
Pliocene, 567*
Ploidy, 468
Pluteus larva, 264*
Pogonophora, 260
Poikilothermy, 350
Point mutation, 528
Polar bodies, 499, 500*
Polar ice, 122
Polar nuclei, 495
Polar zone, 119
Polarity, developmental, 471
Polarization, nerve, 412
Polian vesicle, 263*
Pollen, 490, 491*, 493*
basket, bee, 444
dispersal, 492, 494
tube, 491, 492, 494
Pollination, 491
angiosperm, 495
cross-, 494
and fertilization, 491
fluid, 492
gymnosperm, 492
in seed plant, 491
self-, 494
Pollutants, amplification of, 128
Pollution crisis, 127, 128
Polychaeta, 236
Polyclads, 217*
Polyestrous animals, 506
Polygamy, 505
Polymerase, 341, 345
Polymerization, 51, 52*, 53, 54, 59, 60
Polymorphism, 95
balanced, 589
Polynucleotide, 59
Polyp, 213–215, Color Figures, 15, 16
Polypeptide, 54, 55*
Polyphyletism, 139
Polyribosome, 71
Polysaccharide, 51, 52*
digestion, 298*
respiration, 315
storage, 331, 333
synthesis, 332, 333
Polysiphonia, 161, 481*
Polytoma, 155
Polyunsaturated fatty acid, 52
Pongids, 570, 575
Pons, 409*, 410
Population, 20, 99, 539
balance, 102
in community, 99
crisis, 129
in ecosystem, 99
in evolution, 539, 541
gene frequencies in, 541, 584
growth, 99, 102*
and human races, 584, 587, 589

Population:
pressure, 103
size, evolutionary, 541, 542
social, 99
Porella, 177
Porifera, 211
Porphyra, 161
Porphyridium, 161
Portuguese man-of-war, 95*
Position effect, genetic, 532
Position sense, 418, 419
Posterior decay, 486*, 487
Postganglionic fiber, 412
Potassium-argon dating, 551
Pouched mammals, 279, 280
Prawn, 248*
Praying mantis, 250*
Precambrian, 551, 552*
Precipitation, environmental, 116
Preganglionic fiber, 412
Pregnancy, 500, 512, 513
hormones in, 514, 515*
Prehensors, 248
Premonera, 140
Pressure:
blood, 398
effect on chemicals, 40
effect on reactions, 40
in ocean, 113
of respiratory gases, 401
selection, 541
sense, 417–419
Priapulids, 220, 222*
Primary cell wall, 73
Primary germ layers, 207, 510
Primary growth, 182, 185, 187
Primary meristems, 182
Primary phloem, 79, 188*
Primary structure, protein, 55
Primary xylem, 79, 188*
Primates, 281*, 567–571
Primordial germ cells, 500, 501*
Primordial root, 187
Probability in origin of life, 139
Problem, scientific, 5
Proboscis worms, 216
Proconsul, 575, 576*
Producers, ecological, 101
Progesterone, 507, 514, 515*
Proglottids, 218*, 219
Programmed behavior, 415, 429
Prolactin, 384, 505
Pronephros, 270
Prop root, 179, 180*
Prophase, 460, Color Figure 23
Proprioceptors, 418
in circulation, 397
Prorennin, 299
Prorodon, 171
Prosimians, 568*
Prostate glands, 502
Prostomium, 237
Protein, 53
amino acids in, 53
blood, 392
bonds, 54, 55*, 56*
in clotting, 393
coagulation, 56
denaturation, 56
digestion, 297, 298
Protein:
energy in, 320
as enzyme, 42
functions, 57
as genetic trait, 345, 346, 533
metabolism, 333, 334
in origin of life, 138
peptide in, 53, 55*
physical properties of, 55, 56
respiration, 319
specific dynamic action of, 320
specificity, 43, 57
structure, 55–57, 339
Protein synthesis, 339–344
control of, 360, 361
DNA in, 341
genetic code in, 341, 342
operons in, 361
RNA in, 342, 343
Proteinase, 44, 298
Proteus, 145*
Prothallial cells, 491*, 492
Prothoracic glands, 253, 255
Prothrombin, 392, 393
Protista, 25, 26*, 151
cell structure in, 152*
evolution in, 152, 153*
origin of, 143
reproduction of, 478
Protococcus, 156
Protocoel, 260, 261
Proton, 31
Protonema, 177
Protoplasm, 18, 66
Protopterus, 274*
Protosome, 260, 261
Protostele, 183
Protostomia, 208, 216, 219, 510
Prototheria, 279
Prototroch, 228*
Protozoa, 167, 172
origin of, 143, 153
parasitic, 169*, 170
as protists, 143, 153, 167
reproduction of, 482, 483
sex in, 482, 483
structure of, 167
types of, 167
Pseudocoel, 209
Pseudocoelomata, 209, 219
Pseudomonadales, 146
Pseudoplasmodium, 166, 482*
Pseudopodia, 74, 168
Pseudosporochnus, 553
Psilopsids, 178, 191
evolution of, 553
reproduction of, 488*, 489
Psilotum, 191, 192*
Psychological castration, 452
Pteropsids, 178, 194
evolution of, 554–556
reproduction of, 488–490
Pterosaurs, 547*, 564
Pterygota, 249
Puberty, 506
Puffballs, 165, Color Figure 10
Puffs, chromosome, 341, 342*
Pulmonary blood vessels, 396
Pulse, 396
Pulvinus, 374
Punnett square, 525*
Pupa, 250, 253, 254*, 255
Pupation hormones, 253, 255*
Pupil, 421
Pure science, 5
Purine, 57, 58*
degradation, 335*
in RNA synthesis, 340*, 341
Purkinje, J. E., 67
Purple bacteria, 289
Purple sulfur bacteria, 289
Pus, 393
Pycnogonida, 242
Pyloric caeca, 264
Pyrenoid, 155, 178
Pyridoxine, 366
Pyrimidine, 57, 58*
degradation, 335*
in RNA synthesis, 340*, 341
Pyrrophyta, 159
Pyruvic acid, 313, 314, 316

Quaternary, 552*, 567*
Quaternary protein structure, 56
Queen, insect, 443, 444
Quillwort, 192, 193*

Rabbits, 281*
Races, human, 584
and blood groups, 587
concept, 584–586
definition of, 584
and environment, 584, 588
evolution of, 589, 590
Radial canals, 262
Radial nerves, 264
Radial symmetry, 175, 205
Radiata, 207, 213
Radiation:
adaptive, 545
mammalian, 281*, 567
and mutation, 529
Radicle, 490, 493*
Radiocarbon dating, 550
Radiolaria, 168
Radula, 228, 230
Rain forest, 116, 118*
Ramapithecus, 575, 576*
Rana, 27
Ranks, taxonomic, 23
Ray, 269, 273, 275
vascular, in plant, 189
Ray-finned ıishes, 274*, 275
RDP, 328, 329*
Reabsorption, 402, 403
Reaction, chemical, 36
acceleration of, 360, 361, 364
activation energy in, 40, 41
competition in, 363
control of, 361, 362
deceleration of, 360, 361, 364
by electron sharing, 34
by electron transfer, 33
energy, 38
equilibrium, 41
free-energy change in, 39
ionic, 33
mass action in, 41
molecular, 34

Reaction, chemical:
and pressure, 40
properties of, 36–44
redox, 308
and temperature, 40
thermodynamics, 37
types, 36, 37
Reactive behavior, 429
Rearrangement reaction, 36
Recapitulation critique, 557–559
Recent epoch, 567*
Receptacles, 481, 494
Receptors, 357, 415–423
cutaneous, 423
neural, 415
sense organs as, 359, 360*, 415
Recessiveness, 523
Recombination, sexual, 527, 539
Rectal gland, 273
Rectum, 300
Red algae, 160, 161*, Color Figure 8
reproduction of, 481
Red corpuscles, 394
Red—far-red light effects, 378
Red-line algae, 154
Red tides, 160
Redi, Francesco, 537
Redia, 109
Redirection, behavioral, 448
Redox reaction, 308
Reduction:
chemical, 308
photosynthesis, 328, 329*
respiratory, 308
Redundancy, genetic, 345
Redwood trees, 196
Reef corals, 216, Color Figure 17
Referred pain, 416
Reflex, 360, 407, 408*, 414
conditioned, 415
Regeneration, 462, 463, 474
Regulative eggs, 508
Regulator genes, 361
Reinforcement, 415
Rejuvenation, 17
Releasers:
behavioral, 432
in imprinting, 434
Religion and science, 8, 10, 13
Remora fish, 105
Renal blood vessels, 402
Renal cortex and medulla, 402
Renal organs, 231, 402
Renin, 386
Rennin, 298, 299
Replacement, evolutionary, 546, 547
Replacement bone, 84, 85*
Repression, chemical, 360, 361*
Reproduction, 17*, 459, 462
animal, 206, 499
bacterial, 477
breeding cycles in, 502–508
by budding, 462
cellular, 459–462
colony formation by, 461
as communal factor, 102
development in, 472
differential, 539, 541
DNA in, 345, 459
Reproduction:
of DNA, 60, 345
and evolution, 539, 543
by fragmentation, 462
gametic, 464
genetic control of, 345, 346*
hormones in, 383*, 386, 503, 506, 514
molecular, 459
in monerans, 477
organs of, 486–490, 500–502
plant, 485, 488
and population growth, 102
in protists, 478
regenerative, 462
and sex, 464
by spores, 464
vegetative, 463
Reproductive barriers, 97, 543
Reproductive behavior, 502–505
Reproductive cells, 463
Reproductive systems, 89
animal, 500–502
plant, 487, 489, 491
Reproductive units, 462
Reptiles, 269, 276
eggs of, 513
evolution of, 563–566
Resin canals, 196
Respiration, 15, 307
acetyl CoA in, 316
aerobic, 142, 311, 312
amino acid, 319
anaerobic, 142, 312, 313*
ATP in, 310, 311
by β-oxidation, 318
calories from, 317, 318
carbohydrate, 315
in carbon cycle, 126
carbon dioxide in, 314
of carbon groups, 310, 311
citric acid cycle in, 314, 315*
dehydrogenation in, 308
in development, 473
on early earth, 142
energy gain in, 317*, 318, 320
energy sources in, 313*
energy transfer in, 310
by fermentation, 312, 313
of glucose, 315, 316
of glycerol, 332*
of glycogen, 315, 316
by glycolysis, 315, 316*
by hexose shunt, 317
hormones in, 320
hydrogen transfer in, 311, 312
lipid, 317
in muscle, 348
oxidation-reduction in, 308
oxidation states in, 308
oxidative events in, 309*
in oxygen cycle, 126
phosphates in, 310
process, 307
protein, 319
redox changes in, 308, 309
thermodynamics of, 307
Respiratory pigments, 394
Responses, 16, 357
behavioral, 432
Responses:
plant, 371
Resting stage, 461
Reticular tissues, 83*
Reticulum, endoplasmic, 69, 70*
Retina, 421, 422
Retinene, 420, 421*
Rh blood groups, 587, 588
Rhabdocoela, 217*, 218
Rhesus monkey, 569
Rhizoid, 175, 177
Rhizome, 179
Rhizophore, 192
Rhizoplast, 74, 75*
Rhizopodea, 168
Rhizopus, 162, 163*, 483
Rhodesia man, 576
Rhodophyta, 160, 161*, 481, Color Figure 8
Rhodopsin, 421
Rhodymenia, 161
Rhynchocoela, 216
Rhynia, 553
Rhythms:
behavioral, 435–437
breeding, 502, 503
circadian, 435
in egg production, 506, 507
reproductive, 502, 503
Rib muscles, 400
Ribbon worms, 216
Riboflavin, 58, 365*, 366
Ribonucleic acid (*see* RNA)
Ribonucleotide, 57
Ribose, 51, 57
Ribose nucleic acid (*see* RNA)
Ribosomal RNA, 341
Ribosome, 70*, 71
Ribotide, 51
Ribulose, 51, 328, 329*
diphosphate, 328, 329*
Rickets, 367
Rickettsias, 145
Ring, annual, 191
Ring canal, 262, 263*
Ritualization, behavioral, 448, 504
River environment, 115
RNA, 59
in amino acid activation, 343
in cell, 67
code transcription, 339–344
messenger, 340*, 341
in origin of life, 139
polymerase, 341
in protein synthesis, 342, 343
ribosomal, 341
structure, 59, 60
synthesis, 341
transfer, 340*, 341
triplet coding in, 342
Rock and soil, 122, 124
Rod, retinal, 421, 422
Rodents, 271, 281*
Root, 179, 183
apex, 182
auxin in, 373
branching, 186, 187*
cambium, 188
cap, 183
development, 182

Root:
geotropism, 372
growth, 183, 189
lateral, 187
nodules, 104*, 105, 127
in nutrition, 290, 292
phototropism, 372
pressure, 292
primordium, 187
steles, 80, 183
structure, 183
tip, 183
tissues, 79, 80
types, 179, 180*
water in, 291, 292
Root-hair cells, 77, 78*
Root-hair zone, 183, 291, 292
Rot, fungal, 162, 164*
Rotifera, 219*, 220, 221
Roughage, 301
Round window, 420
Roundworms, 220, 221, 223
Royal jelly, 444
*r*RNA, 341
Ruffini, organs of, 418*
Runner, stem, 179
Rust fungi, 165, 485

Sabella, Color Figure 13
Sabertooths, 546*
Sac, alimentary, 208, 213
Sac fungi, 162, 164*
Sac worms, 219–223
Saccule, 419
Sacculina, 248
Sago palms, 195
Salamander, 269, 275
Salinity, oceanic, 111
Saliva, 297, 298
Salivary amylase, 298
Salivary glands, 297, 299*
Salivary maltase, 298
Salt, 35
in blood, 391, 392
in ocean, 138
taste, 417
Sand in soil, 124
Sand dollars, 265*
Sap flow, 292, 294
Saprolegnia, 162, 163*
Saprotrophism, 101, 289
decay by, 289, 290
origin of, 140
types of, 126, 127, 289
Sapwood, 191
Sarcina, 145
Sarcodina, 167, 168, 169*
Sargasso sea, 439
Sargassum, 112*
Satiation, behavioral, 427
Satiety center, 296
Saturated fatty acid, 52
Scale:
bud, 186
fish, 275
leaf, 186
Scaphopoda, 229, 233
Schizocoel, 209, 233
Schizocoelomates, 209, 226, 228
Schizogony, 169*
Schizomeris, 156
Schizophyta, 144
Schleiden, M. K., 67
Schwann, T., 67
Schwann sheath, 407
Science, 5, 8
crisis, 130
Scientific method, 5
Sclera, 421
Sclereid, 79
Sclerenchyma, 79
Sclerotium, 482*
Scolex, 218*
Scorpions, 242, 243*, 244*, 246*
Scouring rushes, 193, Color Figure 12
Scrotum, 501
Scurvy, 367
Scyphistoma, 216
Scyphozoa, 213, 215*, 216, Color Figure 16
Sea (*see* Ocean)
Sea anemones, 213, 216, Color Figure 17
Sea cows, 281*
Sea cucumber, 261, Color Figure 22
Sea lampreys, 269, 272
Sea lettuce, 156, 479, 480*
Sea lilies, 261
Sea spiders, 242, 243*
Sea squirts, 266
Sea stars, 261, Color Figure 22
Sea urchins, 261, Color Figure 22
Sea water, 111
Sea weed, 160, 161*
Seal, 453*
tree, 554
Seasonal behavior, 435, 502, 503
Seasonal rhythms, 435
Seasons, oceanic, 112
Sebaceous glands, 88, 351*
Secondary cell wall, 73
Secondary growth, 187, 189
Secondary meristems, 188
Secondary phloem, 188*, 189
Secondary protein structure, 56
Secondary sex characteristics, 506
Secondary wood, 189
Secondary xylem, 188*, 189
Secretin, 386
Secretion, 291, 351
endocrine, 381
and excretion, 402
granules, 72
Seed, 182*, 491
angiosperm, 495, 496*, 497
coat, 491
dormancy, 491, 496
embryo in, 491, 493, 495, 496*
ferns, 554
germination, 494, 496, Color Figure 27
gymnosperm, 493, 494, Color Figure 27
hidden, 496
leaves, 493
naked, 494
wing, 491*, 493
Seed plant:
cone-bearing, 195, 491
embryo, 182, 491
evolution, 554–556
flowering, 196, 494
heterospory in, 490
life cycles, 491*
sex organs, 492, 494
spores, 490
types of, 195, 196
Seeing, sense of, 420–423
Segmentation, 211
in amphioxus, 268
in annelids, 228, 236
in arthropods, 240, 243*, 246*
in chordates, 266
superficial, 211
in vertebrates, 270
Segmented worms, 228, 236
Segregation:
genetic, 521, 522
of organ-forming zones, 508
Selaginella, 183*, 192, Color Figure 12
reproduction, 489, 490
Selection:
artificial, 544
natural, 538, 539, 541
pressure, 541
Selectivity:
of behavior, 432
of brain, 414
of kidney, 403
of membranes, 63
in steady-state control, 357, 359
Self-duplication, molecular, 345, 459
Self-fertilization, 467
Self-perpetuation, 16
DNA in, 345, 346*
genetic control of, 345, 346*
Self-pollination, 494
Semen, 502
Semicircular canals, 419
Semiherbaceous plants, 197*, 198
Seminal fluid, 502
Seminal receptacle, 502, 503*
Seminal vesicle, 502
Semipermeability, 62, 63, 412
Sense organs, 359, 360, 415–423
Sensitive plant, 374, 375*
Sensory adaptation, 416
Sensory nerves, 407
Sensory neurons, 407
Sensory paths, 357, 407
Sensory receptors, 359, 360, 415–423
Sepals, 494, Color Figure 28
Separate sexes, 466
Septa:
gastic, 216*
peritoneal, 236
Sere, 100
Serosa, 88, 89*
Serotonin, 335*, 337, 413
Serum, 393
Sessilism, 203
Setae, 237
Sex, 17, 464
as adaptive process, 466
in animals, 449, 504, 505

Sex:
attractants, 433
bacterial, 477, 478
balance theory of, 531
cells, 464
characteristic, 506
chromosomes, 530, 531
by conjugation, 464
cycles, 502, 503, 506
determination, 529
in development, 474, 475
distinctions, 466
DNA in, 345, 346*
forms of, 464, 465
genes in, 345, 530
in hermaphrodites, 466, 467
hormones, 54*, 383*, 386, 503, 506, 514
and life cycle, 468
and mating types, 466
and meiosis, 468
organs, 466
in plants, 485–496
separate, 466
and stress, 465
by syngamy, 464
water requirement in, 464
Sex-linked genes, 532
Sexual behavior, 449, 503, 504
Sexual compatibility, 467
Sexual development, 475
Sexual dimorphism, 95
Sexual process, 464, 465
Sexual recombination, 527, 539
Seymouria, 564*
Shark, 269, 273
Shark sucker, 105
Shell:
brachiopod, 227*
cellular, 74
diatom, 158, Color Figure 5
electronic, 31, 32*
glands, 502
mollusk, 230, 232*, 234*, 235*
protozoan, 167, 168
of vertebrate egg, 513
Shoot, 177, 182
apex, 182
development, 182
tip, 182
Short-day plants, 378
Shrews, 281*, 567, 568
Sickle-cell anemia, 588
and malaria, 588
in racial studies, 589, 590
Sieve tubes, 79, 80*
Sigillaria, 554, Color Figure 29
Signs, behavioral, 432
Silica, 74, 159, 168
skeletons, 205
sponges, 211
Silk, 244
Silk glands, 244
Silkworm, 254*
Silurian, 552*, 553, 561
Silverfish, 249, 250*
Simple epithelium, 84, 86*
Simple eye, 240, 241*
Simple pit, 77, 79
Simplification, parasitic, 107
Sinus, head, 399
Sinus gland, 245
Sinus node, 396
Sinusoids, 302
Siphon, 234, 267
Siphonaceous algae, 156
Siphonaptera, 250*
Siphonoglyph, 216*
Sipunculids, 228, 229*
Skates, 269, 273
Skeletal muscle, 86, Color Figure 1
Skeletal system, 89
Skeleton, 84, 85*, 205
animal, 205
human, 205*
hydraulic, 209
plant, 175
Skin, 86
breathing, 399
gills, 262
sense organs in, 423
Slater, 248*
Slave-making ants, 445
Sleep movements, 375
Sleeping sickness, 168
Slime molds, 26*, 143, 153, 166, Color Figure 24
life cycle, 166, 481, 482
Sloths, 281*, Color Figure 34
Small intestine, 297, 298
Smell sense, 416, 417
Smooth muscle, 86, Color Figure 1
Smut fungi, 165, 485
Snails, 231, 232*, 467*, 501*, Color Figure 18
Snakes, 277, 278
Social insects, 443–446
Social population, 99
Society, 20, 443
human, 581–584
insect, 443–446
vertebrate, 446–454
Soil, 123
bacteria, 124, 126, 127
formation, 124
in lithosphere, 123
minerals, 124
nutrients, 124
in nutrition, 291, 292
types, 124
Sol, 61
Sol-gel transformation, 61
Solar energy, 121, 323
Soldiers, insect, 444
Solo man, 576
Solution, chemical, 61
Somatic mutation, 529
Somite, 237
Song birds, 279
Sorus, 489, Color Figure 26
Sound:
heart, 396
reception, 420
Sour taste, 417
space orientation, 437
Spawning, 499, 501*
Specialization, 21, 95
differentiation as, 437
functional, 21
parasitic, 106
Specialization:
polymorphic, 95
structural, 95
Speciation, 97, 537, 543
Species, 20, 23, 93, 538
characteristics, 93, 94
in communities, 100
cosmopolitan, 97
definition, 93
dispersal, 97
distribution, 97
as ecological unit, 96
in ecosystem, 100
endemic, 97
evolution, 538, 540
as evolutionary unit, 93, 539, 543
formation, 97, 538, 540
gene pool in, 539
geography, 96, 97
growth, 96
life history, 97
origin of, 538, 540
population, 99
as reproductive unit, 93
subgroups in, 93, 94*, 95
as taxonomic unit, 23, 27
theories of origin of, 537, 539
Specific dynamic action, 320
Specificity:
antibody, 392
control of, 339
of DNA, 339
of enzymes, 43
in genetic code, 343
of immune reaction, 392
parasite, 106
protein, 43, 57, 339
of sensory receptors, 416
Sperm, 464, 466
animal, 499, 500*
in copulation, 499, 501*
duct, 502
in fertilization, 508
nuclei, plant, 493–495
in oogamy, 466
packets, 499, 501*
production, hormones in, 503, 506
sac, 502
in semen, 502
Spermatophore, 499, 501*
Spermatophyta, 28*
Sphaerocarpos, 530*
Sphagnum, 177
Sphenodon, 277*
Sphenophyllum, 554*, Color Figure 29
Sphenopsids, 178, 193, Color Figure 12
evolution of, 554
reproduction of, 489
Spicules, 211, 212*
Spiders, 242, 244, 246*
Spike mosses, 192
Spinal accessory nerve, 410*
Spinal canal, 407
Spinal cord, 407, 411*, 414
Spinal fluid, 407
Spinal ganglia, 411
Spinal nerves, 411
Spindle, mitotic, 460, Color Figure 23

Spinnerets, 244
Spiny-headed worms, 219
Spiny-skinned animals, 260, 261
Spiracles:
centipede, 249
insect, 246, 252
shark, 273
Spiral movements, plant, 372
Spiral valve, 273*
Spirillum, 144, 145
Spirochaetales, 146
Spirogyra, 156
life cycle, 464, 479
Spleen, 394
Sponges, 207, 211
Spongy bone, 85*
Spongy mesophyll, 185
Spontaneous generation, 537
Spoon worms, 228
Sporangiospore, 477
Sporangium:
algal, 478
bacterial, 477, 478
bryophyte, 487
fern, 489, Color Figure 26
fungal, 163, 165, 483, Color Figures 9, 10
lycopsid, 489, Color Figure 12
seed plant, 490, Color Figure 28
slime mold, 481, Color Figure 24
sphenopsid, 489, Color Figure 25
Spore, 152, 464, 469–471
as dispersal agent, 464
elaters, 488
mega-, 489, 490, 492, 494
meio-, 470
and meiosis, 470
micro, 489
mito-, 469
mother cell, 488, 490, 491
Spore-forming protozoa, 167, 169*, 170
Sporine state, 152
Sporocyst, 109
Sporogenic meiosis, 470
Sporogeny, 169*
Sporophyll, 489, 491
Sporophyte, 176
algal, 479
bryophyte, 176, 487
fern, 489
generation, 470
metaphyte, 178, 487
seed plant, 490
Selaginella, 489
tracheophyte, 488
Sporozoa, 167, 169*, 170
Springtails, 249
Spruce, 196
Squamous epithelium, 84, 86*
Squids, 114*, 229, 234, 236*, 547*
Stalk cell, 493
Stamen, 494, Color Figure 28
Staphylococcus, 145
Starch, 51
cyanophycean, 147
floridean, 160
granules, 72
in respiration, 315
storage, 331
synthesis, 331, 332
Starfish, 261, 262, 510*
Static equilibrium, 419
Statocyst, 246, 418
Statolith, 418
Statoreceptors, 418, 419
Steady-state control, 16, 345, 357
blood in, 391, 393
and disease, 17, 359, 363
in ecosystem, 100
effectors in, 357
feedback in, 358
genetic, 345
modulators in, 357
nervous, 407
pathways in, 357
receptors in, 357, 415–423
Stearic acid, 52
Stele, 79, 183
angiosperm, 184*, 185
gymnosperm, 184*, 185
root, 183
stem, 183
types, 183, 184*, 185
Stem, 79, 179
apex, 182
auxin effect on, 373, 375, 376
branch, 184*, 186
cambium, 188*, 189
conduction, 292, 294
development, 182, 183
dormant, 186, 187*
geotropism, 373
gibberellin effect on, 371, 372*
growth, 183
moss, 177
nutrients in, 292, 294
phototropism, 373
steles, 79, 80, 183, 185
tissues, 79, 80
twining, 179
types, 179
woody, 187, 188*
Stem reptiles, 563, 565
Stentor, 171, 482*
Stereoblastula, 509*
Steroid, 53, 54*
hormones, 386
vitamins, 54*
Stigma, 155
of pistil, 494, Color Figure 28
Stimulus, 16, 357
in behavior, 432
localization, 416
for nerve impulse, 416
in plant growth, 373, 375, 377, 380
in steady-state control, 357, 416
Stingray, 274
Stinkhorns, 165, Color Figure 10
Stipules, 185
Stirrup, ear, 420
Stoma, 77, 78*, 176
control of, 374
gas uptake by, 293
sunken, 180*
Stomach, 297, 298
Stone canal, 262, 263*
Stone cell, 79
Stoneworts, 157, 480
Stony corals, 213, 215*, Color Figure 17
Storage:
fats in animals, 334
fats in plants, 330*, 331
foods, 330*, 331
in plant, 179
synthesis, 331
Stratified epithelium, 86
Streptococcus, 144, 145*
Streptomycin, 146, 477
Stress, 357, 465
Stretch receptors, 418
Stretch reflexes, circulatory, 397
Striated muscle, 86, Color Figure 1
Strobilus, 489, 491, Color Figures 12, 25
Stroma, 87, 88*
Structural genes, 361
Structure, 15, 18
animal, 204
moneran, 143, 144*
plant, 175
protistan, 151, 152*
in taxonomy, 23
Style, pistil, 494, Color Figure 28
Subatomic particles, 31
Suberin, 79
Subgrades, taxonomic, 209
Submissive behavior, 447
Submucosa, 88, 89*
Subsoil, 124
Subspecies, 95*
Substrate, 43
Succession, ecologic, 100
Succinic acid, 314, 315*
Succulence, plant, 179
Sucking insects, 250, 251*
Sucrose, 51, 330*, 331
Suctoria, 172
Sugar, 50, 51*
bonds, 51*
deoxy types, 51*
formation in plant, 330*, 331
in nucleic acids, 59
in photosynthesis, 330, 331
polymers, 51, 52*
respiration, 315, 316
Sulfur, protein, 56
Sulfur bacteria, 289
Summation, nerve impulse, 414
Sun compass orientation, 438
Sunflower stem, 197*, 198
Sunlight:
in behavior, 438
in nutrition, 323
in origin of life, 138
in photolysis, 323, 325
in photosynthesis, 323
Sunstar, 263*
Superfemale, 531
Superficial segmentation, 211
Supermale, 531
Suppression, reflex, 414
Surface precipitation membrane, 62
Suspension, 61
Suspensor, 483, 488, 490
Swamp moss, 177
Swanscombe man, 576
Sweat glands, 88
Sweet taste, 417
Swim bladder, 275

Swimmerets, 247
Syconoid sponges, 211, 212*
Symbiont, 104, 289
Symbiosis, 104, 106
  in heterotrophism, 289
  parasitism as, 106
  types of, 104
Symbols, behavioral, 432
Symmetry:
  animal, 204, 205, 207
  in development, 471
  plant, 175
Sympathetic nervous system, 412
Synapse, 407, 408, 413
Syncytium, 67
  in muscle, 87
  in rotifer, 220
  in sac worms, 220
Syngamy, 464
Syngens, 93, 483
Synthesis, 16, 323
  amino acid, 334
  ATP in, 331
  carbohydrate, 323, 328, 332
  control of, 361, 362
  in development, 473
  of DNA, 345, 346
  intermediary, 331
  lipid, 334
  metabolism, 331, 336*
  in origin of life, 138
  protein, 339–344
  reaction, 37
  in reproduction, 459
  of RNA, 339–344
  of storage foods, 330
  thermodynamics of, 327, 331, 332
Synura, 153*
Syphilis, 146
Systematics, 23
  (*See also* Taxonomy)
Systems:
  animal, 89, 203–205
  plant, 81

Tadpole:
  amphibian, 276, 512, Color Figure 14
  chordate, 260
  tunicate, 267*
Taiga, 119
Tail, 266
  sperm, 499, 500*
Tapeworms, 107, 108*, 217, 218*
Taproot, 179, 180*
Tarantula, 243*
Tarsoids, 568, 569
Taste, sense of, 416, 417
Taste buds, 417*
Taxon, 23
Taxonomy, 23, 26*
  animal, 210*, 213, 216, 219, 226, 260
  comparisons in, 27
  evolutionary criteria in, 23
  of Monera, 144
  naturalness in, 23, 27
  plant, 176, 178
  of Protista, 154, 162, 166, 167
Taxonomy:
  structural criteria in, 23, 27
Tear ducts, 399
Technology, 5
  crisis in, 130
Tectorial membrane, 420
Teeth:
  epidermal, 272*
  mammalian, 280, 281
  sea urchin, 265
Telencephalon, 407, 409*
Teleology, 11, 12
Teleosts, 275
Teloblast cells, 209, 228
Telolecithal eggs, 509*
Telophase:
  meiotic, 468
  mitotic, 460, Color Figure 23
Telotroch, 228*
Telson, 242, 243, 246
Temperate zone, 116–118, 181
Temperature:
  absolute zero, 40
  and breeding, 503
  and chemicals, 40
  coefficient, 41
  and environment, 116, 119
  and enzymes, 43
  and flowering, 380
  in ocean, 113, 122
  and plants, 380
  in reaction, 40
  senses, 423
Template:
  enzyme as, 43
  in RNA synthesis, 341
Tendons, 83
Tentacles:
  annelid, 237
  coelenterate, 214, 215*
  lophophorate, 226
  squid, 235
Termites:
  flagellates in, 105
  societies of, 443, 444, 446*
Tern, arctic, 439
Terrestrial environment, 115, 122
Territoriality, 452, 453
Tertiary, 552*, 567*
Tertiary protein structure, 56
Testicular tubules, 502
Testis, 466, 501
  migration, 501, 502
  tubules, 501, 502
Testosterone, 54*, 506
Tethys sea, 98
Tetracoccus, 144, 145*
Tetrahymena, 75*
Tetrapoda, 28*
Tetrapyrrols, 53, 54*
Tetrasporophyte, 481*
Tetrose, 50
Thalamus, 409*, 410
Thalassemia, 589
Thaliacea, 266, 268
Thallophyta, 25*
Thallose liverworts, 177
Thallus, 177
Thecodonts, 564, 565*
Theory, scientific, 7
Therapsids, 565, 566*, Color Figure 32
Theria, 281*
Thermal motion, 40
Thermocline, 112
Thermodynamics, 20, 37, 38
  in levels of organization, 20
  in photosynthesis, 327
  in respiration, 307
  in synthesis, 331
Thiamine, 316
Thigmotropism, 372
Thorax, arthropod, 240, 246, 252
Threat displays, 447
Thresholds, excretory, 403
Thrombin, 393
Thrombokinase, 393
Thymidine, 58
Thymidylic acid, 58
Thymine, 57, 58*
Thyone, 264*
Thyroglobulin, 384
Thyroid gland, 384
Thyrotropic hormone, 382, 383*
Thyroxin, 55*, 382, 384
  in respiration, 320
  synthesis, 335*, 337
Thysanura, 250*
Ticks, 107*, 242
Tidal zone, 111, 112
Tiedemann bodies, 263
Tilapsis, 505*
Time orientation, 435
Time table, geologic, 551, 552*
Tinsel flagellum, 75
Tissue, 19, 77, 84
  animal, 81
  connective, 81
  culture, 462
  epithelial, 84
  plant, 77
Titanotheres, Color Figure 33
Tmesipteris, 191
TMP, 58
Toads, 269, 275
Tonus, muscular, 87
Topsoil, 124
Torsion, snail, 231, 232*
Torus, 80, 81*
Touch sense, 417, 418
Trachea, 399
Tracheal system, arthropod, 240, 253
Tracheids, 79, 81*
Tracheophyte, 178
  adaptations, 179–182
  aquatic, 181
  bark formation, 189, 190
  cambia, 188
  development, 182, 488–491
  embryo, 182, 488–491
  evolution, 553–556
  gametophyte, 488, 489
  growth, 182, 185, 187
  leaves, 185
  as metaphyte, 178
  organs, 81
  primary growth, 182, 185
  reproduction, 488, 490
  roots, 182, 183
  secondary growth, 187

Tracheophyte:
- seed formation, 490, 491
- sporophyte, 488, 489
- steles, 183, 184*, 185
- stems, 182, 183, 185
- wood, 187
- (*See also* Plant)

Transamination, 319
Transcription, genetic code, 339–346
Transduction, 528
Transfer:
- electron, 33
- parasitic, 108

Transfer RNA, 341, 343
Transformation, bacterial, 527, 528*
Transfusion, blood, 392
Translocation:
- mutational, 528
- in plant nutrition, 294

Transmitter substances, hormonal, 413
Transpiration, 292
Transport:
- active, 63
- in blood, 391, 392
- in sap, 292, 294

Trapdoor spider, 243*
Tree:
- anatomy, 187, 190
- ferns, 194
- primate adaptations to, 568–571

Tree frogs, 276*
Trematoda, 217
Treponema, 146
Trial-and-error:
- in learning, 430, 431
- in steady-state control, 358

Triceratops, 566*
Trichina worms, 222*, 223
Trichocyst, 170
Trichomonas, 168
Trichonympha, 168
Triclads, 217, 218
Tricuspid valve, 396
Tridacna, 234*
Trigeminal nerve, 410*
Trilobites, 561
Triose, 50
Triple bond, chemical, 34
Triplet codes, 342, 343*
Triploidy, 495
Tristearin, 52, 318
*t*RNA, 341
Trochlear nerve, 410*
Trochophore larva, 228, 231, 237
Tropic hormones, 382, 383*
Tropic zone, 112, 116
Tropisms:
- animal, 429
- plant, 372, 373

True-breeding traits, 521
Truffles, 162
Trypanosoma, 168
Trypsin, 298
Tryptophan, 335*
TSH, 383*
Tuatara, 277*, 278
Tube cell, 491*, 492
Tube feet, 262, 263*
Tube nucleus, 494
Tube pattern, alimentary, 208
Tube worms, 236
Tuber, 179
Tubipora, Color Figure 17
Tubulanus, 216*
Tumor, plant, 376
Tundra, 119, 120*
Tunic, 265
Tunicates, 265, 266
- tadpole of, 267*

Tunicin, 261
Turbellaria, 217
Turgidity, plant cell, 179
Turgor movements, 374
Turnover:
- ecological, 101
- metabolic, 332

Turtles, 277, 278, 564
Tusk shells, 229, 233
Twining stems, 179, 372
Twinning, 509
Tyrannosaurus, 565, 566*

UDP, 58
UDP-glucose, 332
Ulothrix, 156, 478, 479
Ulva, 156, 479, 480*
Umbilical cord, 514
UMP, 58
Undernourishment, 129
Undetermined eggs, 508
Undulating membrane, 170
Ungulate mammals, 279
Unicellularity, 19
Uniparental heredity, 527–529
Unsaturated fatty acids, 52
Uracil, 57, 58*
Urea, 319, 335*
Ureter, 402
Urethra, 402, 502
Uric acid, 319, 335
Uridine, 58, 332
Uridylic acid, 58
Urinary bladder, 402
Urine, 402, 403
Urochordates, 265
Uropod, 247
Use and disuse hypothesis, 537
Uterus, 502, 503*, 507
UTP, 58, 332, 342
- in RNA synthesis, 341

Utricle, 419

Vacuoles, 72, 73
- contractile, 170*, 171

Vagina, 502, 503*
Vagus nerve, 397, 410*
Valence, chemical, 31*
Valine, 55*
Valve:
- brachiopod, 227*
- heart, 395
- lymph vessel, 394*
- mollsucan, 230, 232*, 234*, 235*
- venous, 395

Variation:
- individual, 584
- inheritable, 93, 521, 539
- genetic sources of, 521, 527, 539
- racial, 584, 587, 589
- in species, 93, 94*

Vascular bundle, 184*, 185
Vascular cambium, 188
Vascular plants, 178
- (*See also* Plant; Tracheophyte)

Vascular tissues, 79, 80, 175
- animal, 395
- in nutrient transport, 292, 294, 391, 392
- plant, 79, 80, 175

Vasomotion, 398
Vegetative reproduction, 462, 463
Vegetative states, 152
Veins:
- blood, 394*, 395
- leaf, 186

Veliger larva, 228, 231
Vena cava, 395
Venter, archegonial, 486*, 487
Ventral glands, 221
Ventricles:
- brain, 407, 409*
- heart, 395

Venturia, 164*
Venus flower basket, 212*
Venus flytrap, 375
Vernalin, 380
Vernalization, 380
Vernation, circinate, 194*, 195
Vertebrate, 22, 27, 266, 269
- adaptations, 270
- characteristics, 270, 271
- development, 508
- evolution, 270, 561, 562*, 565*
- hormones, 383*
- societies, 446
- (*See also* Animal)

Vessels:
- circulatory, 394*, 395
- xylem, 79, 81*, 196

Vibration sense, 419
Villi, 300, 302*
Virus, 106, 146
- bacteriophage, 106
- origin, 142
- reproduction, 459
- transduction, 143, 528

Visceral cords, 230
Visceral ganglia, 230*
Visceral hump, 228, 230
Vision, 420
- acuity, 422
- brain centers of, 422
- chemistry, 420, 421
- and vitamin A, 421*

Visual purple, 421
Vital functions, 15
Vitalism, doctrine of, 9
Vitamin, 364, 365*, 366*
- as animal nutrient, 295
- in control systems, 362, 364
- functions, 364–368
- as growth factor, 362, 364
- in hydrogen transport, 312

Vitamin A, 365, 366, 421*
Vitamin B, 58, 366
- in coenzymes, 58, 59*, 316, 365

Vitamin B:
deficiency, 365*, 366
in respiration, 312, 316
Vitamin C, 367
Vitamin D, 54*, 367
Vitamin E, 367
Vitamin H, 366
Vitamin K, 368
Vitreous humor, 421
Viviparity, 500, 501*
Vocal cords, 399
Voice production, 399
Voluntary actions, 411, 412
Volvant, 213*
Volvox, 153*, 155, 479, Color Figure 7
Vorticella, 171, 712*

Waggle dance, 438
Wallace, Alfred, 538
Warmbloodedness, 349
Wasps, 251*, 255, 443, 444
Waste, excretory, 402
Water, 49
absorption, 291, 292
intestinal, 300
root, 291
atmospheric, 125
in blood, 391, 392
in citric acid cycle, 314, 315*
cohesion of, 293
cycle, 121, 126*
as decay product, 126
as digestive agent, 297
dissociation, 326
on early earth, 137
electrons of, 326, 327
environmental, 111, 115, 121
in excretion, 403
as freshwater habitat, 115
hormone control of, 383*, 384, 386
as hydrogen source, 326
in hydrosphere, 121
ions, 326
in lithosphere, 123
in living matter, 49
molds, 162, 163
as nutrient, 289, 292, 295
in ocean, 111
in organisms, 49
in photosynthesis, 323, 325, 326
Water:
plant management of, 180, 181, 292
in plant reproduction, 486–488
in respiration, 313
secretion, 352, 403
soil, 123, 291, 292
vacuoles, 72
Water fleas, 247, 248*
Water-vascular system, 262, 263*
Watson-Crick model, 60
(*See also* DNA)
Wavelengths, light, 324, 378
Wax, 53, 175
cuticle, 73
Way of life:
animal, 203–207
plant, 178–182
Weaning, 516
Weather:
effects of, 121, 122
in fresh water, 115
in ocean, 112, 113
Webs, spider, 244
Weeds, auxin control of, 377
Weismann, August, 537
Whales, 280, 281*
Wheel organ, rotifer, 220
Whelks, 231
Whey, 299
Whiplash flagellum, 75
White blood cell, 392, 393*
Whorled leaf growth, 186, 193
Wild-type traits, 521
Windpipe, 297, 399
Wing:
bird, 278, 279
homology and analogy in, 27*
insect, 252
seed, 491*, 492
Winter:
hardening, 181
plant adaptations to, 181
Wolffian duct, 270
Wood, 80, 189
angiosperm, 197*
annual rings, 191
dicot, 197*
digestion, protozoan, 105
formation, 188, 189
gymnosperm, 196*
monocot, 197*
Wood:
oak, 197*
pine, 196*
primary, 187
secondary, 187
xylem in, 80, 189
Woody stem, 189, 196*, 197*
Worker, social insect, 443, 444

X chromosome, 530
X-organ, 247
X rays, mutational, 529
Xanthine, 335*
Xanthophyceae, 158
Xanthophyll, 53, 155, 175, 323
Xerophyte, 180
Xiphosurida, 242
Xylem, 79, 80
in nutrition, 292
pits, 80
primary, 79
in primary growth, 182
rays, 189
secondary, 187
in secondary growth, 189
in stele, 79, 80, 179
in vascular bundle, 184*, 185*
vessels, 79, 81*
water conduction in, 292
as wood, 80, 189

Y chromosome, 530
Y-organ, 247
Yeast, 162, 164*, 485*
Yellow-brown algae, 158
Yellow-green algae, 158
Yews, 196
Yolk, 499, 509
glands, 502, 503*
sac, 513, 514

Zea, 28*
Zinjanthropus, 575
Zoaea, 247
Zooflagellates, 167
Zooid, 214
Zooplankton, 112
Zygospore, 465*, 479, 483*
Zygote, 464
Zygotic meiosis, 469

W77-1002

W77-1002

W77-1002